Dynamic Instructional Strategies	... present clear and comprehensive coverage of middle school science.	
	■ Each engaging chapter opener includes a *Launch Lab* and *Foldables*™.	
	■ *National Geographic Visualizing* features illustrate important concepts in middle school science.	82
A Strong Reading Strand	... encourages active reading and learning for students of all reading levels. In the *Student Edition:*	
	■ **as you read** gives students a preview of learning objectives and vocabulary for each section;	102
	■ *Reading Checks* help students check their reading comprehension; and	164
	■ *Caption questions* ask students to interpret visuals.	197
	■ *Reading Essentials, An Interactive Student Textbook* is designed to help struggling readers comprehend core content. It is written at a reading level of about two to three grades below the *Student Edition*.	
Meeting the Needs of All Students	... facilitates understanding of science concepts for students of all learning levels. In the *Teacher Wraparound Edition:*	
	■ *Differentiated Instruction* strategies help meet the needs of students with learning disabilities and physical challenges, or create opportunities to enrich and extend students' learning;	221
	■ *Daily Intervention* provides intervention strategies for struggling students; and	256
	■ *Identifying Misconceptions* helps uncover and address common science misconceptions.	280F
	■ The *English/Spanish Glossary*, also in the *Student Edition*, helps English-language learners comprehend science terms.	714–743
Extensive Standardized Test Practice	... gives students the opportunity to practice for state and national exams.	
	■ Each chapter ends with a variety of standardized test practice questions, including *Multiple Choice, Short Response/Grid In*, and *Open Ended*.	336–337
A Variety of Labs	... gets students excited about being involved in science. The *Student Edition* provides:	
	■ *MiniLABs,* traditional labs, and *Design Your Own, Model and Invent,* and *Use the Internet* labs; and	314, 355, 362
	■ *Extra Try at Home Labs* provide opportunities for students to practice their science skills at home with adult supervision using materials from the kitchen, junk drawer, or backyard.	682–692
	■ *Virtual Labs* CD-ROM contains an interactive virtual lab for each chapter.	378
	■ *Video Labs* (VHS) reinforce lab techniques and safety skills, offer troubleshooting tips, and give expected outcomes.	411
	■ The *Science Lab Manual, Probeware Lab Manual,* and *Science Inquiry Lab Manual* provide additional opportunities to practice laboratory techniques.	
Multi-Level Review	... presents multiple opportunities for all students to review and master content.	
	■ Each section ends with a review that contains a *Summary* of the section's major concepts and a *Self Check* that has questions to assess student learning and practice math or science skills.	437
	■ The *Study Guide* at the end of each chapter can preview, review, summarize, and visualize the chapter's main ideas.	483
	■ *Study Guide* and *Reinforcement* help students grasp core content.	
Teacher Resources	... provide innovative strategies to help new and experienced teachers.	
	■ *Chapter Resources Fast File* ™ contains important reproducible masters.	488B
	■ Section Focus, Assessment, and Teaching transparencies accompany each chapter.	518C
	■ *Performance Assessment in the Science Classroom* has assessment guidelines, strategies, sample rubrics, and more.	
Online Resources	... enrich the learning experience with the click of a mouse.	
	■ For prescreened Web links, standardized test practice, self-check quizzes, chapter tests, *Vocabulary PuzzleMaker,* extra math practice, science career information, current science news, and *WebQuest* interactive projects, visit **ips.msscience.com**.	
	■ The complete interactive *Student Edition* is available at The McGraw-Hill Learning Network Web site, **mhln.com**.	
Technology	... provides timesaving products to help teachers creatively engage their students.	
	■ *MindJogger Videoquizzes* (VHS & DVD) provide a game-show style interactive quiz for each chapter.	
	■ Easy to edit *Interactive Chalkboard* Microsoft® PowerPoint® presentations include step-by-step lessons, an image bank, chapter and section review questions, standardized test practice, and transparencies.	
	■ *ExamView® Pro Testmaker* CD-ROM in English or Spanish allows you to customize assessments.	
	■ *TeacherWorks* CD-ROM is your all-in-one resource center that helps you plan and organize lessons.	
	■ *StudentWorks* CD-ROM solves the heavy backpack problem.	

D1324444

SAFETY SYMBOLS

SAFETY SYMBOLS	HAZARD	EXAMPLES	PRECAUTION	REMEDY
DISPOSAL	Special disposal procedures need to be followed.	certain chemicals, living organisms	Do not dispose of these materials in the sink or trash can.	Dispose of wastes as directed by your teacher.
BIOLOGICAL	Organisms or other biological materials that might be harmful to humans	bacteria, fungi, blood, unpreserved tissues, plant materials	Avoid skin contact with these materials. Wear mask or gloves.	Notify your teacher if you suspect contact with material. Wash hands thoroughly.
EXTREME TEMPERATURE	Objects that can burn skin by being too cold or too hot	boiling liquids, hot plates, dry ice, liquid nitrogen	Use proper protection when handling.	Go to your teacher for first aid.
SHARP OBJECT	Use of tools or glassware that can easily puncture or slice skin	razor blades, pins, scalpels, pointed tools, dissecting probes, broken glass	Practice common-sense behavior and follow guidelines for use of the tool.	Go to your teacher for first aid.
FUME	Possible danger to respiratory tract from fumes	ammonia, acetone, nail polish remover, heated sulfur, moth balls	Make sure there is good ventilation. Never smell fumes directly. Wear a mask.	Leave foul area and notify your teacher immediately.
ELECTRICAL	Possible danger from electrical shock or burn	improper grounding, liquid spills, short circuits, exposed wires	Double-check setup with teacher. Check condition of wires and apparatus.	Do not attempt to fix electrical problems. Notify your teacher immediately.
IRRITANT	Substances that can irritate the skin or mucous membranes of the respiratory tract	pollen, moth balls, steel wool, fiberglass, potassium permanganate	Wear dust mask and gloves. Practice extra care when handling these materials.	Go to your teacher for first aid.
CHEMICAL	Chemicals can react with and destroy tissue and other materials	bleaches such as hydrogen peroxide; acids such as sulfuric acid, hydrochloric acid; bases such as ammonia, sodium hydroxide	Wear goggles, gloves, and an apron.	Immediately flush the affected area with water and notify your teacher.
TOXIC	Substance may be poisonous if touched, inhaled, or swallowed.	mercury, many metal compounds, iodine, poinsettia plant parts	Follow your teacher's instructions.	Always wash hands thoroughly after use. Go to your teacher for first aid.
FLAMMABLE	Flammable chemicals may be ignited by open flame, spark, or exposed heat.	alcohol, kerosene, potassium permanganate	Avoid open flames and heat when using flammable chemicals.	Notify your teacher immediately. Use fire safety equipment if applicable.
OPEN FLAME	Open flame in use, may cause fire.	hair, clothing, paper, synthetic materials	Tie back hair and loose clothing. Follow teacher's instruction on lighting and extinguishing flames.	Notify your teacher immediately. Use fire safety equipment if applicable.

 Eye Safety Proper eye protection should be worn at all times by anyone performing or observing science activities.

 Clothing Protection This symbol appears when substances could stain or burn clothing.

 Animal Safety This symbol appears when safety of animals and students must be ensured.

 Handwashing After the lab, wash hands with soap and water before removing goggles.

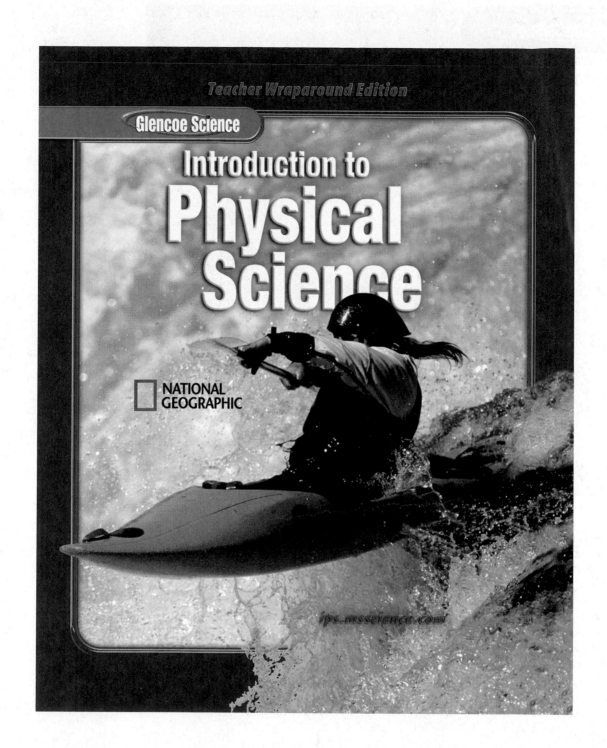

Teacher Wraparound Edition

Glencoe Science

Introduction to Physical Science

NATIONAL GEOGRAPHIC

ips.msscience.com

Glencoe

New York, New York   Columbus, Ohio   Chicago, Illinois   Peoria, Illinois   Woodland Hills, California

Glencoe Science

Introduction to Physical Science

While gravity brings this kayaker to a landing, an opposing force, buoyancy, determines how deep in the landing pool the boat will submerge. To avoid underwater rocks, larger kayaks are chosen on creeks with steep drops in order to increase buoyancy.

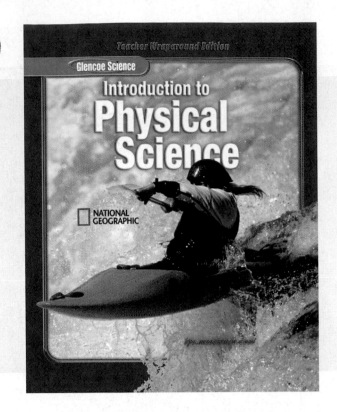

 **Glencoe**

The McGraw·Hill Companies

Send all inquiries to:
Glencoe/McGraw-Hill
8787 Orion Place
Columbus, OH 43240-4027

ISBN 0-07-861704-9 (Student Edition)
ISBN 0-07-861705-7 (Teacher Wraparound Edition)

Printed in the United States of America.

3 4 5 6 7 8 9 10 071/043 09 08 07 06

Authors

NATIONAL GEOGRAPHIC
Education Division
Washington, D.C.

Cathy Ezrailson
Science Department Head
Academy for Science and
Health Professions
Conroe, TX

Nicholas Hainen
Chemistry/Physics Teacher, Retired
Worthington City Schools
Worthington, OH

Patricia Horton
Mathematics and Science Teacher
Summit Intermediate School
Etiwanda, CA

Deborah Lillie
Math and Science Writer
Sudbury, MA

Thomas McCarthy, PhD
Science Department Chair
St. Edward's School
Vero Beach, FL

Eric Werwa, PhD
Department of Physics
and Astronomy
Otterbein College
Westerville, OH

Dinah Zike
Educational Consultant
Dinah-Might Activities, Inc.
San Antonio, TX

Margaret K. Zorn
Science Writer
Yorktown, VA

Series Consultants

CONTENT

Alton J. Banks, PhD
Director of the Faculty Center
for Teaching and Learning
North Carolina State University
Raleigh, NC

Jack Cooper
Ennis High School
Ennis, TX

Sandra K. Enger, PhD
Associate Director,
Associate Professor
UAH Institute for Science Education
Huntsville, AL

David G. Haase, PhD
North Carolina State University
Raleigh, NC

Michael A. Hoggarth, PhD
Department of Life and
Earth Sciences
Otterbein College
Westerville, OH

Jerome A. Jackson, PhD
Whitaker Eminent Scholar in Science
Program Director
Center for Science, Mathematics,
and Technology Education
Florida Gulf Coast University
Fort Meyers, FL

William C. Keel, PhD
Department of Physics
and Astronomy
University of Alabama
Tuscaloosa, AL

Linda McGaw
Science Program Coordinator
Advanced Placement Strategies, Inc.
Dallas, TX

Madelaine Meek
Physics Consultant Editor
Lebanon, OH

Robert Nierste
Science Department Head
Hendrick Middle School, Plano ISD
Plano, TX

Connie Rizzo, MD, PhD
Depatment of Science/Math
Marymount Manhattan College
New York, NY

Dominic Salinas, PhD
Middle School Science Supervisor
Caddo Parish Schools
Shreveport, LA

Cheryl Wistrom, PhD
St. Joseph's College
Rensselaer, IN

Carl Zorn, PhD
Staff Scientist
Jefferson Laboratory
Newport News, VA

MATH

Michael Hopper, DEng
Manager of Aircraft Certification
L-3 Communications
Greenville, TX

Teri Willard, EdD
Mathematics Curriculum Writer
Belgrade, MT

READING

Elizabeth Babich
Special Education Teacher
Mashpee Public Schools
Mashpee, MA

Barry Barto
Special Education Teacher
John F. Kennedy Elementary
Manistee, MI

Carol A. Senf, PhD
School of Literature,
Communication, and Culture
Georgia Institute of Technology
Atlanta, GA

Rachel Swaters-Kissinger
Science Teacher
John Boise Middle School
Warsaw, MO

SAFETY

Aileen Duc, PhD
Science 8 Teacher
Hendrick Middle School, Plano ISD
Plano, TX

Sandra West, PhD
Department of Biology
Texas State University-San Marcos
San Marcos, TX

ACTIVITY TESTERS

Nerma Coats Henderson
Pickerington Lakeview Jr. High
School
Pickerington, OH

Mary Helen Mariscal-Cholka
William D. Slider Middle School
El Paso, TX
Science Kit and Boreal Laboratories
Tonawanda, NY

Science Kit and Boreal Laboratories
Tonawanda, NY

Reviewers

Deidre Adams
West Vigo Middle School
West Terre Haute, IN

Sharla Adams
IPC Teacher
Allen High School
Allen, TX

Maureen Barrett
Thomas E. Harrington Middle School
Mt. Laurel, NJ

John Barry
Seeger Jr.-Sr. High School
West Lebanon, IN

Desiree Bishop
Environmental Studies Center
Mobile County Public Schools
Mobile, AL

William Blair
Retired Teacher
J. Marshall Middle School
Billerica, MA

Tom Bright
Concord High School
Charlotte, NC

Nora M. Prestinari Burchett
Saint Luke School
McLean, VA

Lois Burdette
Green Bank Elementary-Middle
School
Green Bank, WV

Marcia Chackan
Pine Crest School
Boca Raton, FL

Karen Curry
East Wake Middle School
Raleigh, NC

Joanne Davis
Murphy High School
Murphy, NC

Anthony J. DiSipio, Jr.
8th Grade Science
Octorana Middle School
Atglen, PA

Sueanne Esposito
Tipton High School
Tipton, IN

Sandra Everhart
Dauphin/Enterprise Jr. High Schools
Enterprise, AL

Mary Ferneau
Westview Middle School
Goose Creek, SC

Cory Fish
Burkholder Middle School
Henderson, NV

Linda V. Forsyth
Retired Teacher
Merrill Middle School
Denver, CO

Teacher Advisory Board

The Teacher Advisory Board gave the editorial staff and design team feedback on the content and design of the Student Edition. They provided valuable input in the development of the 2005 edition of *Glencoe Introduction to Physical Science.*

Student Advisory Board

The Student Advisory Board gave the editorial staff and design team feedback on the design of the Student Edition. We thank these students for their hard work and creative suggestions in making the 2005 edition of *Glencoe Introduction to Physical Science* student friendly.

Aaron Haupt

The Glencoe middle school science Student Advisory Board taking a timeout at COSI, a science museum in Columbus, Ohio.

Teacher Handbook

Table of Contents

Dynamic Instruction

The consistent instructional strategies in each chapter strengthen students' learning—from the beginning of each chapter where students see "Chapter Preview," to the end where they have a chance to test the knowledge they have acquired and prepare for the next lesson.

Dinah Zike's Foldables™ let students create interactive study guides.

Chapter Preview at the beginning of each chapter introduces the main concepts.

Launch Lab gives students an opportunity to explore new ideas at the beginning of the chapter.

Science Journal promotes writing and critical-thinking skills.

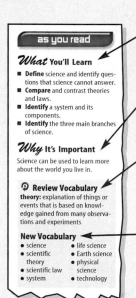

What You'll Learn at the beginning of each section introduces the main concepts.

Why It's Important provides an answer to "Why do we have to learn this?"

Review Vocabulary reviews a term that helps students better understand section content.

New Vocabulary highlights new terms students will learn in the section.

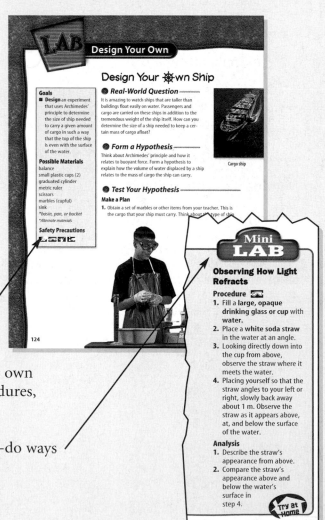

Labs Whether students are designing their own experiments or following well-tested procedures, they'll learn and practice science processes.

MiniLABS offer students quick and easy-to-do ways to clarify concepts and reinforce skills.

Multi-Level Review and Assessment

Each chapter provides five pages of review and testing to help you evaluate students' knowledge and ability to apply science concepts.

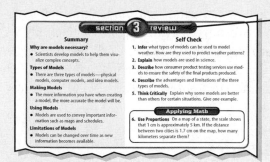

Section Review
- Summary pinpoints important concepts in the section.
- Skill-based questions promote critical thinking skills.

Study Guide
- Main idea summary of each section
- Concept mapping activity to help students visualize the main ideas

Chapter Review
- Using Vocabulary
- Checking Concepts
- Thinking Critically
- Performance Activities
- Applying Math

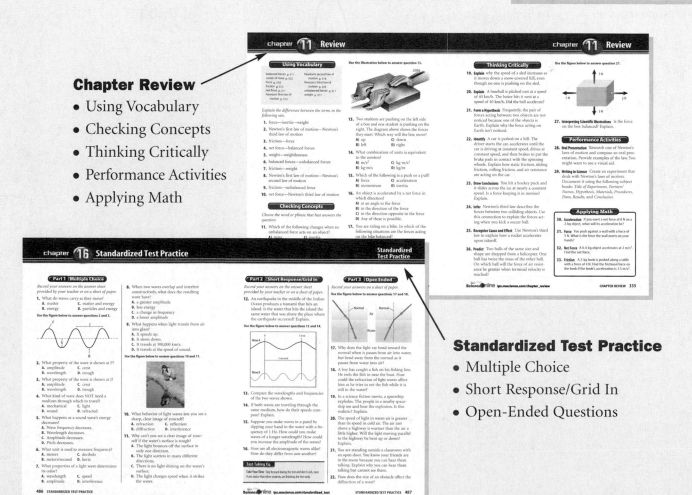

Standardized Test Practice
- Multiple Choice
- Short Response/Grid In
- Open-Ended Questions

Time-Saving Teacher Resources

Glencoe Science provides an extensive array of support materials and resources designed to help you create and customize your science course quickly and easily.

FAST FILE Chapter Resources

For each chapter, Chapter Resources contain key reproducible masters along with additional teaching strategies, teacher support, and answer keys.

Reproducible Student Resources include:

- Worksheets for all MiniLABs and Labs
- *Directed Reading for Content Mastery* (in English and Spanish), *Reinforcement* and *Enrichment* worksheets for each chapter
- *Section Focus, Teaching,* and *Assessment Transparencies* masters
- Chapter Review and Chapter Test masters

Teacher Support and Planning includes:

- Additional student preparation materials for each chapter
- Spanish Resources provide translations of all objectives, vocabulary, and main ideas
- Answer keys and teaching strategies

Teacher Wraparound Edition

The *Teacher Wraparound Edition* is your key to the teaching resources available. In addition to teaching strategies and suggestions, the *Teacher Wraparound Edition* provides a guide for all print and software materials available for each lesson.

Transparencies

- Section Focus Transparency
- Assessment Transparency
- Teaching Transparency
- Transparency masters and worksheets

ExamView® Pro Testmaker CD-ROM

- Create, edit, and customize tests
- Create multiple versions of tests
- Translate tests from English to Spanish and vice versa
- Build tests aligned with state standards

Video Labs

- Step-by-step lab procedures for selected *Student Edition* labs
- Lab safety skills
- Teacher support
- Troubleshooting advice

Technology Support

Teacher Works™

This CD-ROM is your all-in-one resource center. Personalize a lesson plan, access resources from the *Teacher Wraparound Edition*, connect to the Internet, or make a to-do list. These are only a few of the many features that can assist you in the planning and organizing of your lessons.

Includes:

- A calendar feature
- Access to all program blackline masters
- Standards correlations and more

Student Works™

This CD-ROM is a valuable resource for students to access content online and use online resources to continue learning chapter concepts.

🎧 Guided Reading Audio Program has been updated to StudentWorks Plus™.

Includes:

- Complete *Student Edition* on CD-ROM
- Links to online activities and resources
- Access to all student worksheets

PowerPoint® Presentations

This CD-ROM brings Microsoft® PowerPoint® presentations right to your door. With the large number of graphics provided, students can use a visual approach to learning chapter content.

Includes:

- A pre-made presentation for every chapter
- Image bank and interactive graphics
- Animations and audio clips
- All new section and chapter questions
- Standardized test practice
- Transparencies
- Pre-lab questions for all labs
- Foldables™ directions
- Links to **ips.msscience.com**

💿 Virtual Labs CD-ROM Program

The Virtual Labs CD-ROM contains a collection of labs that allow students to complete labs that are too expensive, take too long to complete, or might be too dangerous in a classroom laboratory.

ips.msscience.com

For students:

- Prescreened Internet sites (Web links) that correlate to text chapters
- Interactive activities that review chapter concepts
- Internet Labs where students can share data with each other
- Access to *Student Edition* online
- Interactive self-check quizzes for each chapter section as well as the entire chapter

For teachers:

- *WebQuest* activities
- Teacher Forum for teachers to share activities and ideas

McGraw Hill Learning Network
mhln.com

mhln.com is an online teaching and learning space for teachers, students, and parents.

- For students, **mhln.com** provides an interactive online textbook. This means a lighter student backpack.
- For teachers, **mhln.com** provides a customizable online learning space for posting assignments, web-based instruction, student resources, and a class calendar.
- For parents, **mhln.com** provides tools to help their child succeed in school. Parents have instant access to their child's progress and daily assignments.

Help Your Students with Reading and Writing

Glencoe Science increases science literacy, improves reading comprehension, and deepens students' understanding of ideas and concepts. The reading strategies are active, constructive, and engaging.

In the *Student Edition*

Reading Checks stimulate quick recall and keep students focused on the main idea.

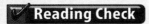

Caption Questions offer a visual approach to learning. Students are asked to recall what they have read by interpreting the visual.

> **Figure 18** Three allotropes of carbon are depicted here.
> **Identify** *the geometric shapes that make up each allotrope.*

Science Journals provide opportunities to write responses to questions that require critical thinking, to conduct research and write about it, or to practice creative writing skills.

Skill Words such as *compare and contrast, describe, explain,* and *state* are included in the Self Check at the end of each section, in the goals of each Lab, and in the chapter reviews.

Technology Support

Vocabulary PuzzleMaker allows you to create crossword puzzles, jumble puzzles, or word searches in minutes to review chapter vocabulary. The puzzles can be printed or played on the computer screen.

Guided Reading Audio Program (available on MP3-formatted CD-ROMs) provides a comprehensive overview in Spanish and English for auditory learners, students with reading difficulties, and English-language learners (ELL).

In the *Teacher Edition*

Project CRISS™ (**C**reating **R**ependence through **S**tudent-Owned **S**trategies) strategies are highlighted in the Unit Openers where an activity is supplied that relates to unit content. For more information about Project CRISS™, visit **www.projectcriss.com**.

Use Science Words features encourage students to look up biology terms. Use these as a pre-reading activity, or have students keep a vocabulary journal.

> **Use Science Words**
> **Word Usage** The distinction between distance and displacement can be confusing. Have students use each of these words correctly in a sentence. Possible response: When I go to school and then back home, my displacement is zero, even though the distance from home to school is 2 km.

Additional Science Journal writing activities promote writing and critical thinking skills and extend the *Student Edition* journaling activity.

Active Reading Strategies utilize a variety of learning styles, and encourage cooperative learning and intrapersonal reflection on chapter content.

Additional Teacher Resources

Reading Essentials provides summaries of each section of the textbook, focusing on the most important scientific concepts.

Reading and Writing in the Science Classroom provides teachers with effective strategies for building students' skills in reading and writing about science.

Reading and Writing

Making Concept Maps and Charts

Bubble Map Students brainstorm and organize words in clusters to describe concepts.

Flow Chart Students logically analyze and draw a sequence of events.

Cause-and-Effect Chart Students visually represent the causes and effects of an event or process.

Supporting-Idea Chart Students make a concept map to analyze relationships between a whole and its parts.

Network-Tree Concept Map Students show a hierarchy and use branching procedures.

Events-Chain Concept Map Students order steps or stages in a linear procedure.

Cycle Concept Map Students show how a series of events interact.

Spider Concept Map Students use for brainstorming and grouping nonrelated terms to a central idea.

Using the Science Journal

Double-Reference Journal Students read and record ideas.

Metacognition Students analyze what and how they have learned.

Learning Journal Students create notes and reflect on the content.

Problem-Solution Journal Students analyze problems and suggest workable solutions.

Speculation About Effects/Prediction Journal Students examine events and speculate about their possible long-term effects.

Synthesis Journal Students reflect on a project, a paper, or a performance task and plan how to apply what they have learned to their own lives.

Reflective Journal Students identify what they learned in an activity and record responses.

Quickwrites Students use spontaneous writing to discover what they already know.

Collaborative Learning Strategies

Pair of Pairs Partners respond to a question and compare their response to other pairs and to the class.

Write-Draw-Discuss Students write about and draw a picture of a concept, then share it with the class.

Active Reading

Learning Reading Have students divide a sheet of paper in half. Have them record research notes, lecture notes, and vocabulary terms related to the laws of motion in the left column. Tell them to use the right column to respond, interpret, question, and analyze left-column entries. L2 **Intrapersonal**

Four-Corner Discussion The class works in four groups to debate a complex issue.

Jigsaw Students work in groups to become experts on a portion of text and share what they've learned with the class.

Buddy Interviews Students interview one another to find out what strategies they use to learn the text.

Reciprocal Teaching Students take turns reading a section of text, retelling it in their own words, then asking questions about it.

News Summary Students are given several minutes to summarize, retell, or analyze an activity for a "TV" audience.

ReQuest The teacher reads aloud an article or story. Student pairs then construct discussion questions and review the content.

Foldables™

Foldables™ are easy-to-make, three-dimensional, interactive graphic organizers that students create out of simple sheets of paper. These unique hands-on tools for studying and reviewing were created exclusively for Glencoe by education specialist Dinah Zike.

Research Behind Foldables™

According to research (Bransford, 1979; Corno, 1994), study strategies help students understand, organize, remember and apply new information presented in science textbooks. Some study strategies include concept mapping, highlighting, outlining, note taking, summarizing, and underlining (Peverly, Brobst, Graham & Shaw, 2003). Glencoe Science offers Dinah Zike's Foldables™ Study Organizers as an organizational tool and study guide for students.

Build Prereading Skills

• Encourages students to prepare for what they will be learning

• Gives students an opportunity to recall what they already know about a subject

Encourage Active Reading and Writing

• Practices basic reading and writing skills

• Develops skills in finding and reporting main ideas

• Organizes information

• Reviews key vocabulary terms

Summarize Content for Review

• Creates a comprehensive, interactive snapshot of the chapter

• Provides preparation support for chapter, unit, and end-of-course exams, as well as standardized tests

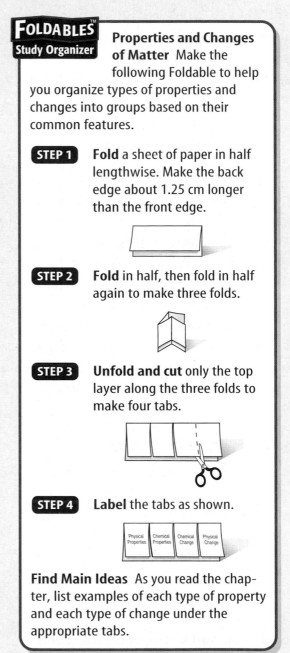

FOLDABLES™ Study Organizer

Properties and Changes of Matter Make the following Foldable to help you organize types of properties and changes into groups based on their common features.

STEP 1 **Fold** a sheet of paper in half lengthwise. Make the back edge about 1.25 cm longer than the front edge.

STEP 2 **Fold** in half, then fold in half again to make three folds.

STEP 3 **Unfold and cut** only the top layer along the three folds to make four tabs.

STEP 4 **Label** the tabs as shown.

Physical Properties | Chemical Properties | Chemical Change | Physical Change

Find Main Ideas As you read the chapter, list examples of each type of property and each type of change under the appropriate tabs.

Dinah Zike's *Teaching Science with Foldables*™

• Comprehensive presentations of Foldables™ instructions

• More ideas on how to incorporate Foldables™ into your lessons

• Easy-to-read folding instruction pages in color

Course Planning Guide

Glencoe Science programs provide a complete selection of core concepts that can be presented in a way that meets the needs of all your students. As the teacher, you are in the best position to design a science course that sets the pace at which the content is covered and determines what material should be given the most emphasis. To assist you in planning the course, the following Course Planning Guide is provided.

The chart shown below offers general suggestions for pacing your students through the book. Pacing for both standard class periods and block schedule class periods is given. The total number of days in each level of pacing is the typical 180-day school year and 90-day semester.

Chapter	Single-Class (180 days)	Block (90 days)
1	9	4.5
2	10	5.5
3	8	4
4	8	3
5	9	5
6	6	3.5
7	7	3
8	9	4.5
9	8	4
10	9	4
11	9	4.5
12	7	4
13	9	5
14	8	4
15	10	5
16	7	3.5
17	8	4
18	7	3.5
19	9	4.5
20	8	4
21	7	3
22	8	4

Assessment

Glencoe Science offers the Glencoe Assessment Advantage, a system designed to give you all the tools you need to prepare your students for success in any testing situation.

In the *Student Edition*

Section Review and **Applying Math** questions appear in every chapter.

Chapter Review questions help you evaluate students' knowledge and ability to apply science concepts.

Standardized Test Practice questions at the end of each chapter provide students with additional opportunities to practice their test-taking skills.

In the *Teacher Wraparound Edition*

Assessments located throughout the *Teacher Wraparound Edition* provide methods for assessing students' comprehension with Performance, Process, and Content exercises.

Teacher Classroom Resources

Performance Assessment in the Science Classroom
- Guidelines for assessing the performance of a task
- Reproducible activities for evaluating students
- Sample rubrics and checklists

***Fast File* Chapter Resources** provides six pages of assessement for every chapter including *Testing Concepts, Applying Concepts,* and *Writing Skills.*

Technology Support

MindJogger Videoquizzes are interactive video quizzes set in game show format. Each is designed for the full range of student learning styles.

Exam*View*® Pro Testmaker CD-ROM for Windows® and Macintosh® provides an easy way to create, edit, and customize your tests. Select your own test items by objective from two different levels of difficulty, or write and edit your own. Translate tests from English to Spanish and vice versa.

Rubrics

The following rubrics are sample scoring devices for short response and open-ended questions.

Short Response

Points	Description
2	The student demonstrates a thorough understanding of the science of the task. The response may contain minor flaws that do not detract from the demonstration of a thorough understanding.
1	The student has provided a response that is only partially correct.
0	The student has provided a completely incorrect solution or no response at all.

Open Ended

Points	Description
4	The student demonstrates a thorough understanding of the science of the task. The response may contain minor flaws that do not detract from the demonstration of a thorough understanding.
3	The student demonstrates an understanding of the science of the task. The response is essentially correct and demonstrates an essential but less than thorough understanding of the science.
2	The student demonstrates only a partial understanding of the science of the task. Although the student may have used the correct approach to a solution or may have provided a correct solution, the work lacks an essential understanding of the underlying science concepts.
1	The student demonstrates a very limited understanding of the science of the task. The response is incomplete and exhibits many flaws.
0	The student provides a completely incorrect solution or no response at all.

Assessment

Educational Partnerships

NATIONAL GEOGRAPHIC

Some topics in the chapter either require or benefit from a larger, more detailed visual explanation. The National Geographic Society has created *Visualizing* features that call out an important concept from the chapter and illustrate it in a way that will inform, excite, and motivate your students.

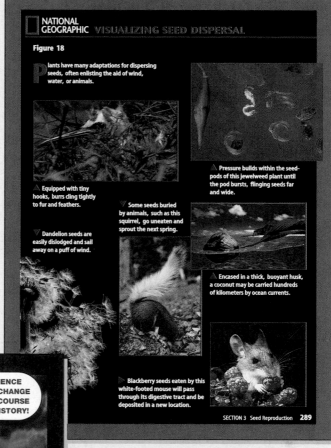

NATIONAL GEOGRAPHIC VISUALIZING SEED DISPERSAL

Figure 18

Plants have many adaptations for dispersing seeds, often enlisting the aid of wind, water, or animals.

Equipped with tiny hooks, burrs cling tightly to fur and feathers.

Dandelion seeds are easily dislodged and sail away on a puff of wind.

Pressure builds within the seed-pods of this jewelweed plant until the pod bursts, flinging seeds far and wide.

Some seeds buried by animals, such as this squirrel, go uneaten and sprout the next spring.

Encased in a thick, buoyant husk, a coconut may be carried hundreds of kilometers by ocean currents.

Blackberry seeds eaten by this white-footed mouse will pass through its digestive tract and be deposited in a new location.

SECTION 3 Seed Reproduction **289**

TIME **SCIENCE** AND **HISTORY** **SCIENCE CAN CHANGE THE COURSE OF HISTORY!**

Overcoming the Odds

Guts and determination helped one pioneering doctor to save the lives of thousands

Overcoming the odds is a challenge that many people face. Dr. Samuel Lee Kountz, Jr. had the odds stacked against him. Thanks to his determination he beat them.

Dr. Kountz was interested in kidney transplants, a process that was still brand new in the 1950s. For many patients, a kidney transplant added months or a year to one's life. But then a patient's body would reject the kidney, and the patient would die. Dr. Kountz was determined to see that kidney transplants saved lives and kept patients healthy for years.

A donated organ is on its way to save a life.

Fixing the Problem

Kountz discovered the root of the problem—why and how a patient's body rejected the transplanted kidney. He discovered that the patient's cells attacked and destroyed the small blood vessels of the transplanted kidney. So the new kidney would die from lack of blood-supplied oxygen. From this, doctors knew when to give patients the right kinds of drugs, so that their bodies could overcome the rejection process.

In 1959, Kountz performed the first successful kidney transplant. He went on to develop a procedure to keep body organs healthy for up to 60 hours after being taken from a donor. He also set up a system of organ donor cards through the National Kidney Foundation. And in his career, Dr. Kountz transplanted more than 1,000 kidneys himself—and paved the way for thousands more.

Research What kinds of medical breakthroughs has the last century brought? Locate an article that explains either a recent advance in medicine or the work that doctors and medical researchers are doing. Share your findings with your class.

Science Online

TIME

TIME magazine brings science topics and history together to further explain the chapter's main ideas and show how science relates to real life.

Differentiated Instruction

Teaching Strategies

Following each suggested assessment and activity, ability levels are supplied to accommodate all students.

- **LS** Multiple Learning Styles logos are used throughout the text to indicate strategies that address different learning styles.
- **L1** Level 1 activities should be appropriate for students with learning difficulties.
- **L2** Level 2 activities should be within the ability range of all students.
- **L3** Level 3 activities are designed for above-average students.
- **ELL** English-Language Learners activities should be within the ability range of English-Language Learners or students who speak English as a second language (ESL).
- **COOP LEARN** Cooperative Learning activities are designed for small group work.
- **PBL** Problem-Based Learning activities apply real-world situations to learning.
- **P** Portfolio strategies represent student products that can be placed into a best-work portfolio.

Identifying Misconceptions

These short, diagnostic, and perscriptive lessons target common science misconceptions.

Misconceptions

Necessary Metals Students may think it strange that metals are needed by the body. Explain that the metals calcium, potassium, and sodium, for example, help transmit electrical signals within the nervous system.

Multiple Learning Styles

Look for these italicized designations under various activities to help you target your lessons to each student's preferred learning style.

- **Kinesthetic** learners learn through touch, movement, and manipulating objects.
- **Visual-Spatial** learners think in terms of images, illustrations, and models.
- **Interpersonal** learners understand and work well with other people.
- **Intrapersonal** learners can analyze their own strengths and weaknesses and may prefer to work on their own.
- **Linguistic** learners write clearly and easily understand the written word.
- **Logical-Mathematical** learners understand numbers easily and have highly-developed reasoning skills.

Daily Interventions

Found at the end of each chapter section, this feature is designed to intercept students who are struggling and prescribe a system to help them get back on track. *Reteach* provides reinforcement of the section's concepts through visual activities.

DAILY INTERVENTION

Check for Understanding
Kinesthetic Have a student light a match and allow it to burn. Also, place an ice cube in a glass container and allow it to melt. Have students explain what type of changes took place with each item and describe the final properties of each.

Differentiated Instruction

These activities present various teaching strategies designed to help you meet the special needs of students with learning disabilities, physical challenges, visual impairment, and hearing impairment. Challenge activities provide opportunities for students who excel to engage in activities and research projects that extend the chapter's concepts. English-language learners in the classroom will also find exercises that bridge the gap between language barriers and the chapter content.

Differentiated Instruction

English-Language Learners Have students make flashcards with the name of a gland on one side and the hormone it produces on the other. Student pairs can quiz each other using the flashcards.

Cultural Diversity

These readings provide insights into the unique ways in which people of different ethnicities and cultural heritage have approached science. The intent of these features is to build awareness and appreciation for the global community in which we live.

Cultural Diversity

Tsunami! Tsunamis occur in many areas around the world and have been reported since ancient times. One of the earliest record tsunamis struck Syria around 2,000 B.C. Thera, one of the Cyclades Islands in the Mediterranean, may be the remnant of a volcano that erupted—causing tsunamis that ended the Minoan civilization on Crete. Tsunami is a Japanese word for "harbor wave." Many have struck the Japanese shore. Because Japan is an island nation, the threat of tsunamis is a national safety concer. Today, by using expected tsunami characteristics, the Japan Meteorological Agency can forecast tsunami heights for the Japanese coastline. This provides residents with the knowledge necessary to move a safe distance away from the shore.

Inquiry-Based Science

The call for more inquiry-based science by the *National Science Education Standards* has been met by Glencoe Science.

Glencoe Science recognizes the importance of conducting inquiry-based science activities in the classroom. The process of doing inquiry models actual science practice, encouraging problem-solving strategies and developing critical thinking skills. Inquiry gets students actively involved in the learning process by allowing them to determine materials, procedures, or the topics and questions they want to investigate.

Inquiry can range from a very structured activity for those students who need more guidance to a more open-ended approach where students lead the investigations. Glencoe Science recognizes that the inquiry activities suggested will not look the same in every classroom. We encourage teachers to modify the suggested activities in a manner that best supports your students.

Glencoe also provides teachers with Alternative Inquiry Labs, teaching strategies or suggestions for making existing labs more inquiry-based.

Alternative Inquiry Lab

Extend the Experience To make this Lab an Inquiry Lab, have students examine the magnetic field around the motor, using a compass or iron fillings. Test the armature and rotor before final assembly, as it will be difficult to fit the compass inside the motor. Encourage students to make various adaptations to the motor. Ask them to figure out how to make the motor spin the other way, spin faster, and spin slower. How could the motor be turned into a generator? How could they make the motor consume less power? Finally, students might research how these issues are handled by industry or other questions they find interesting.

Research-Based Learning Strategies

Glencoe Science incorporates the most current and applicable educational research on science learning and follows recommendations from the American Association for the Advancement of Science and the National Science Teachers Association. The following research-based strategies can be found throughout the text.

Learning Strategies

The following research-based strategies can be found throughout the text:

- **Using Prior Knowledge** Glencoe Science encourages students to use their prior knowledge to learn information because this adds relevance to the material. Students are referred back to other parts of the text or to their own real-life experiences.

- **Practicing Important Tasks** By offering students an opportunity to practice important tasks using a variety of labs and activities in the *Student Edition, Teacher Wraparound Edition,* ancillaries and technology, Glencoe Science makes learning fun and relevant for students.

- **Using Visuals to Communicate, Organize, and Reinforce Learning** High-quality art and photos throughout the text communicate concepts more efficiently and reinforce learning, while allowing students to organize information.

White Paper

The Glencoe Science White Paper outlines the educational strategies on which this program was based. This document provides specific examples from the *Student Edition, Teacher Wraparound Edition,* ancillary program, and technology resources, highlighting extensive use of educationally sound strategies that help students learn science.

- **Motivating Students to Achieve** Active strategies and real-world experiences motivate students to achieve. Throughout Glencoe's programs, students are encouraged to apply their knowledge in ways that will motivate them to learn.

- **Developing Decoding and Reading Comprehension Strategies** Throughout the text, students are supplied with caption questions, reading checks, and other strategies to aid in comprehension.

- **Using Study Strategies** Through the use of highlighting, outlining, note-taking, summarizing, and other such strategies, students can monitor their own progress and organize information more effectively, thereby increasing their scientific literacy. These strategies are found throughout the text and ancillaries.

The use of these strategies within Glencoe Science will help teachers to achieve the goals set forth by the *National Science Education Standards.*

Spencer Grant/PhotoEdit, Inc.

Field Research and Testing

Feedback from students, teachers, curriculum supervisors, department chairpersons, parents, learning specialists, and science content experts was invaluable in the development of this program. The following pre-publication and post-publication research was conducted.

Prior to Publication

- Detailed classroom teacher and curriculum supervisor **surveys** were conducted by independently contracted researchers.

- A **nationwide panel** of science teachers, curriculum supervisors, and department chairpersons provided countless hours of feedback and assistance throughout program development.

- A wide range of **educator and content reviewers** provided in-depth reviews of and suggestions for manuscripts and pre-publication versions of the program.

- **Face-to-face interviews** with science teachers provided insight into teachers' day-to-day challenges.

After Publication

- Field tests were conducted in which students and teachers used a pre-publication manuscript in the classroom.

- Follow-up interviews, observations, and surveys of Glencoe Science users provide ongoing opportunities for program development and verification of program success.

Field-Test Results

- Field-test research indicates that test scores increased among students using Glencoe Science programs.

- Nine out of ten students earned higher scores after using Glencoe programs.

- Scores improved among both male and female students.

- Scores improved among both minority and non-minority students.

- Overall, the gap between the average pre-test score and a perfect score closed by 33 percent. Stated differently, on average, **scores increased 77 percent after students used the Glencoe program.**

KS Studios

National Education Standards

Correlation of *Introduction to Physical Science* to the National Science Education Standards.

Content Standard	Chapter and Section
(UCP) Unifying Concepts and Processes	
1. Systems, order, and organization	1-2, 1-3, 1-4, 2-1, 2-2, 2-3, 3-1, 3-2, 3-3, 4-1, 4-2, 4-3, 5-1, 5-2, 5-3, 6-1, 6-2, 7-1, 7-2, 8-1, 8-2, 8-3, 9-1, 9-2, 9-3, 11-1, 11-2, 11-3, 12-1, 12-2, 12-3, 13-1, 13-2, 13-3, 15-1, 15-2, 15-3, 16-1, 16-2, 16-3, 17-1, 17-2, 18-1, 18-2, 18-3, 20-1, 20-2, 20-3, 21-1, 21-2, 22-1, 22-2
2. Evidence, models, and explanation	1-1, 1-2, 1-3, 1-4, 2-1, 2-2, 2-3, 3-1, 3-2, 3-3, 4-1, 4-2, 4-3, 5-1, 5-2, 5-3, 6-1, 6-2, 7-1, 7-2, 8-1, 8-2, 8-3, 9-1, 9-2, 9-3, 10-1, 10-2, 10-3, 11-1, 11-2, 11-3, 12-1, 12-2, 12-3, 13-1, 13-2, 13-3, 14-1, 14-2, 14-3, 15-1, 15-2, 15-3, 16-1, 16-2, 16-3, 17-1, 17-2, 18-1, 18-2, 18-3, 19-1, 19-2, 19-3, 19-4, 20-1, 20-2, 20-3, 21-1, 21-2, 22-1, 22-2
3. Change, constancy, and measurement	1-3, 1-4, 2-1, 2-2, 2-3, 3-1, 3-2, 3-3, 4-1, 4-2, 4-3, 5-1, 5-2, 5-3, 6-1, 6-2, 7-1, 7-2, 8-1, 8-2, 8-3, 9-1, 9-2, 9-3, 10-1, 10-2, 10-3, 11-1, 11-2, 11-3, 12-1, 12-2, 12-3, 13-1, 13-2, 13-3, 14-1, 14-2, 14-3, 15-1, 15-2, 15-3, 16-1, 16-2, 16-3, 17-1, 17-2, 18-1, 18-2, 18-3, 19-1, 19-2, 19-3, 19-4, 20-1, 20-2, 20-3, 21-1, 21-2, 22-1, 22-2
4. Evolution and equilibrium	5-3, 14-1, 14-2, 14-3
5. Form and function	3-1, 3-2, 3-3, 4-1, 4-2, 4-3, 5-1, 5-2, 5-3, 6-1, 6-2, 7-1, 7-2, 8-1, 8-2, 8-3, 9-1, 9-2, 9-3, 10-1, 10-2, 10-3, 12-1, 12-2, 12-3, 13-1, 13-2, 13-3, 15-1, 15-2, 15-3, 16-1, 16-2, 16-3, 17-1, 17-2, 18-1, 18-2, 18-3, 19-1, 19-2, 19-3, 19-4, 20-1, 20-2, 20-3, 21-1, 21-2, 22-1, 22-2
(A) Science as Inquiry	
1. Abilities necessary to do scientific inquiry	1-1, 1-2, 1-3, 1-4, 2-1, 2-2, 2-3, 3-1, 3-2, 3-3, 4-1, 4-2, 4-3, 5-1, 5-2, 5-3, 6-1, 6-2, 7-1, 7-2, 8-1, 8-2, 8-3, 9-1, 9-2, 9-3, 10-1, 10-2, 10-3, 11-1, 11-2, 11-3, 12-1, 12-2, 12-3, 13-1, 13-2, 13-3, 14-1, 14-2, 14-3, 15-1, 15-2, 15-3, 16-1, 16-2, 16-3, 17-1, 17-2, 18-1, 18-2, 18-3, 19-1, 19-2, 19-3, 19-4, 20-1, 20-2, 20-3, 21-1, 21-2, 22-1, 22-2
2. Understandings about scientific inquiry	1-1, 1-2, 1-3, 1-4, 2-1, 2-2, 2-3, 3-1, 3-2, 3-3, 4-1, 4-2, 4-3, 5-1, 5-2, 5-3, 6-1, 6-2, 7-1, 7-2, 8-1, 8-2, 8-3, 9-1, 9-2, 9-3, 10-1, 10-2, 10-3, 11-1, 11-2, 12-1, 12-2, 12-3, 13-1, 13-2, 13-3, 14-1, 14-2, 14-3, 15-1, 15-2, 15-3, 16-1, 16-2, 16-3, 17-1, 17-2, 18-1, 18-2, 18-3, 19-1, 19-2, 19-3, 19-4, 20-1, 20-2, 20-3, 21-1, 21-2, 22-1, 22-2
(B) Physical Science	
1. Properties and changes of properties in matter	1-1, 3-1, 3-2, 3-3, 4-1, 4-2, 4-3, 5-1, 5-2, 5-3, 6-1, 6-2, 7-1, 7-2, 8-1, 8-2, 8-3, 9-1, 9-2, 9-3, 10-1, 10-2, 10-3, 11-1, 11-2, 11-3, 12-1, 12-2, 12-3, 13-1, 13-2, 15-1, 15-2, 17-1, 17-2, 18-1, 18-2, 18-3, 19-1, 20-1, 20-2, 20-3, 21-1, 21-2
2. Motions and forces	4-1, 4-2, 4-3, 6-1, 6-2, 7-2, 8-2, 10-1, 10-2, 10-3, 11-2, 11-3, 12-1, 12-2, 12-3, 13-1, 13-2, 14-1, 14-2, 14-3, 15-2, 15-3, 16-1, 16-3, 17-1, 17-2, 18-1, 18-2, 18-3, 19-1, 19-2, 19-3, 19-4, 20-1, 20-2, 20-3, 21-1, 21-2
3. Transfer of energy	4-1, 4-2, 7-1, 7-2, 8-2, 11-2, 11-3, 13-1, 13-2, 13-3, 14-1, 14-2, 14-3, 15-1, 15-2, 15-3, 16-1, 16-3, 17-1, 17-2, 18-1, 18-2, 18-3, 20-1, 20-2, 20-3
(C) Life Science	
1. Structure and function in living systems	9-1, 9-2, 9-3
(D) Earth and Space Science	
1. Structure of the Earth system	16-1, 16-2, 16-3
2. Earth's history	12-1
3. Earth in the solar system	21-1, 21-2
(E) Science and Technology	
1. Abilities of technological design	4-3
2. Understandings about science and technology	4-3, 22-1, 22-2
(F) Science in Personal and Social Perspectives	
1. Personal health	9-3
2. Populations, resources, and environments	13-3, 17-2
3. Natural hazards	12-3, 20-3
4. Risks and benefits	13-3
5. Science and technology in society	1-1, 4-3, 11-3, 22-1, 22-2

National Education Standards

Content Standard	Chapter and Section
(G) History and Nature of Science	
1. Science as a human endeavor	3-1, 3-3, 9-3
2. Nature of science	1-1, 1-2, 1-3, 1-4, 3-1, 3-3, 11-1, 13-1
3. History of science	3-1, 3-2, 3-3, 4-3, 9-3, 11-1, 12-2, 13-1, 17-2, 19-4, 20-3, 22-2

How Glencoe Science Aligns with the National Science Education Standards

The correlations at the left and above show the close alignment between Glencoe Science and the grade-appropriate standards. Glencoe Science allows students to discover concepts within each of the content standards and gives students opportunities to make connections among the science disciplines. Hands-on activities and inquiry-based lessons reinforce the science processes emphasized in the standards.

How Glencoe Science Aligns with the NCTM Standards for Grades 6–8

Throughout Glencoe Science, each Applying Math activity provides students with the opportunity to practice and apply some of the mathematical concepts and applications described in the NCTM Standards. These activities serve to reinforce mathematical skills in real-life situations, thus preparing students to meet their needs in an ever-changing world.

Correlation of *Introduction to Physical Science* to NCTM Standards

Math Standard	Page
1. Number and Operations	37, 48, 65, 97, 121, 135, 155, 185, 196, 213, 245, 279, 284, 290, 294, 305, 319, 335, 341, 367, 401, 408, 409, 413, 415, 429, 455, 485, 503, 537, 545, 581, 597, 600, 609, 637, 669
2. Algebra	97, 135, 155, 196, 213, 279, 284, 290, 294, 305, 319, 335, 341, 367, 401, 408, 409, 413, 415, 429, 436, 455, 485, 537, 545, 597, 600, 609, 669
3. Geometry	135, 155, 367
4. Measurement	37, 65, 135, 155, 245, 436, 455
5. Data Analysis and Probability	17, 65, 129, 155, 185, 213, 245, 279, 305, 367, 429, 581, 609, 637, 669
6. Problem Solving	17, 121, 185, 581
7. Reasoning and Proof	121
8. Communication	287, 305
9. Connections	135, 155, 185, 196, 213, 245, 279, 284, 290, 294, 305, 319, 335, 341, 367, 401, 408, 409, 413, 415, 429, 436, 455, 485, 503, 537, 545, 581, 597, 600, 609, 669
10. Representation	129, 196, 213

Learning in the Laboratory

In the *Student Edition*

Working in the lab is perhaps the most exciting part of science. Labs and MiniLABs give your students the hands-on opportunity to create, investigate, and explore science. Students will learn new material, while having fun.

Traditional Labs provide guided inquiry as students hypothesize, plan investigations, and collect and analyze data.

Design Your Own Labs challenge students to design their own experiments that will provide answers to lab problems.

Model and Invent Labs allow students to create a model or invent a product that can demonstrate scientific concepts.

Use the Internet Labs help students share and retrieve data from others around the country and world, by posting data they have collected on **ips.msscience.com**. These activities show students the possible range of data, importance of collecting large amounts of data, and data analysis.

MiniLABs and **Applying Science** activities are a quick way for students to practice specific process skills as they learn science concepts. Many of them can be classroom demonstrations or homework assignments.

Extra Try at Home Labs reinforce chapter content while providing students more opportunities to practice laboratory techniques. They are written for performance at home, but can be used in the classroom.

In the *Teacher Wraparound Edition*

Quick Demos allow students to visualize biology concepts.

Inquiry Labs in each chapter can be used to support inquiry-based science or as alternatives to traditional labs.

Alternative Inquiry Labs offer a strategy to make many of the student labs more open-ended and inquiry-based. These labs can be used as explorations or as extensions before or after completion of the Student Edition lab.

Technology Support

Virtual Labs CD-ROM includes a collection of interactive activities involving major chapter themes that allow students to understand science concepts in a virtual setting. These labs provide a way to conduct experiments without classroom time, cost, and safety constraints.

Video Labs show students step-by-step lab procedures while emphasizing important lab safety skills. The lab videos also include teacher support, troubleshooting advice, and expected outcomes.

Additional Resources

Laboratory Activities offer a variety of traditional laboratory experiences that reinforce the science principles in the text. The *Teacher Wraparound Edition* provides full support.

Probeware Labs present activities for students to explore scientific concepts using a probeware data collection system. These hand-held systems provide a fast and simple way to collect, view, and analyze data in the classroom or during a field investigation. Integrating technology in the classroom is made simple with step-by-step instructions for setting up and using probeware.

Science Inquiry Lab Manual gives students the opportunity to become increasingly independent in stating hypotheses, designing and performing experiments, and collecting and analyzing data.

Safety in the Laboratory

All activities are designed to minimize dangers in the laboratory. Careful laboratory planning and management by both the instructor and the student are essential to a safe laboratory experience. **Local, state, and federal laboratory safety laws and regulations must be strictly followed.** The information provided here is one of the many resources to which you can refer for information about laboratory safety.

Classroom and Laboratory Preparation

1. Label and store chemicals properly and securely. See p. 20T.
2. Store equipment properly and securely and other thing.
   a. Clean and dry all equipment before storing.
   b. Protect electronic equipment and microscopes from dust, humidity, and extreme temperatures.
   c. Number, catalog, and organize equipment.
3. Ensure adequate work space for each student.
4. Ensure adequate classroom and storeroom ventilation.
5. Explain and post safety and evacuation guidelines along with expectations of conduct.
6. Ensure that all safety equipment is functioning properly and is clearly visible.
7. Provide hot plates as a heat source whenever possible. If gas burners are used, know where the central gas supply shutoff valve is located.
8. Ensure that each workstation has a GFCI-protected electrical source.
9. Provide safety goggles consistent with ANSI Standard Z87.1 for each student, including students who wear corrective lenses.

First Day of Class (with students)

1. Distribute and discuss safety rules, safety symbols, and first aid guidelines. Have students to review safety symbols and guidelines.
2. Review safe use of equipment and chemicals.
3. Review use and location of safety equipment.
4. Discuss safe disposal of materials and laboratory cleanup policy.
5. Discuss proper laboratory attitude and conduct.
6. Document students' understanding of the preceding points. Have students sign a safety contract and return it.

Before Each MiniLAB or Lab

1. Perform each investigation yourself before assigning it.
2. Arrange the lab in such a way that equipment and supplies are clearly labeled and easily accessible.
3. Have available only equipment and supplies needed to complete the assigned investigation.
4. Review the procedure with students, emphasizing any caution statements or safety symbols that appear.
5. Be sure all students know the proper procedures to follow if an accident should occur.
6. Provide containers for disposing of chemicals, waste products, and biological specimens. Disposal methods should meet local guidelines.

During the MiniLAB or Lab

1. Make sure the lab is clean and free of clutter.
2. Insist that students wear goggles and aprons.
3. Never allow a student to work alone in the lab.
4. Never allow students to use a cutting device with more than one edge.
5. Students should not point the open end of a heated test tube toward anyone.
6. Remove broken glassware or frayed cords from use. Also clean up any spills immediately. Dilute solutions with water before removing.
7. Be sure all glassware that is to be heated is of a heat-treated type that will not shatter.
8. Remind students that hot glassware looks cool.
9. Prohibit eating and drinking in the lab.

After the MiniLAB or Lab

1. Be sure that the lab is clean.
2. Be certain that students have returned all equipment and disposed of broken glassware and chemicals properly.
3. Be sure that all hot plates and electrical connections are off.
4. Insist that each student wash his or her hands when lab work is completed.

Chemical Storage and Disposal

General Guidelines

Be sure to store all chemicals properly. The following are guidelines commonly used. Your school, city, county, or state may have additional requirements for handling chemicals. It is the responsibility of each teacher to become informed of the rules or guidelines in effect in his or her area.

1. Separate chemicals by reaction type. Strong acids should be stored together. Likewise, strong bases should be stored together and should be separated from acids. Oxidants should be stored away from easily oxidized materials, and so on.

2. Be sure all chemicals are stored in labeled containers indicating contents, concentration, source, date purchased (or prepared), any precautions for handling and storage, and expiration date.

3. Dispose of any outdated or waste chemicals properly according to accepted disposal procedures.

4. Do not store chemicals above eye level.

5. Wood shelving is preferable to metal. All shelving should be firmly attached to the wall and should have anti-roll edges.

6. Store only those chemicals that you plan to use.

7. Hazardous chemicals require special storage containers and conditions. Be sure to know which chemicals those are and the accepted practices for your area. Some substances must be stored outside the building.

8. When working with chemicals or preparing solutions, observe the same general safety precautions that you would expect from students. These include wearing an apron and goggles. Wear gloves and use the fume hood when necessary. Students will want to do as you do whether they admit it or not.

9. If you are a new teacher in a particular laboratory, it is your responsibility to survey the chemicals stored there to be sure they are stored properly. If not, they should be disposed of. Consult the rules and laws in your area concerning which chemicals can be kept in your classroom. For disposal, consult up-to-date disposal information from state and federal governments.

Disposal of Chemicals

Local, state, and federal laws regulate the proper disposal of chemicals. These laws should be consulted before chemical disposal is attempted. Although many substances encountered in the science classroom can be flushed down the drain with plenty of water, it is not safe to assume that this is always true. Teachers who use chemicals should consult the following book from the National Research Council:

Prudent Practices in the Laboratory. Washington, DC: National Academy Press, 1995. This book is useful and was revised in 1995. Current laws in your area would, of course, supersede the information in this book.

DISCLAIMER

Glencoe Publishing Company makes no claims to the completeness of this discussion of laboratory safety and chemical storage. The material presented is not all-inclusive, nor does it address all of the hazards associated with handling, storing, and disposing of chemicals, or with laboratory management.

Clement Mok/PictureQuest

Preparation of Solutions

It is important to use safe laboratory techniques when handling all chemicals. Always check the MSDS (Material Safety Data Sheet) for each chemical before using it in the classroom. Many substances might appear harmless, but might be toxic, corrosive, or very reactive. Chemicals should never be ingested. Use proper techniques to smell any chemical, wear safety goggles and an apron in the laboratory, and observe the following precautions.

1. **Dilution of Acids and Bases** When diluting acids with water, always add the acids to the water. Never add water to acids. When sulfuric acid and sodium hydroxide are added to water, a large amount of thermal energy is released. Use extra care when handling these substances.

2. **Poisonous and Corrosive Liquids or Vapors** Use a fume hood if possible. Examples include hydrochloric acid, acetic acid, nitric acid, and ammonium hydroxide.

3. **Poisonous and Corrosive to Eyes, Lungs, and Skin** Examples include acids, bases, silver nitrate, iodine, and potassium permanganate.

Bromthymol blue: Add 0.5 g bromthymol blue powder to 500 mL distilled water to make a BTB stock solution. Dilute 40 mL BTB stock solution to 2 L with distilled water. Solution should be bright blue. If not, add one drop of NaOH at a time, swirling to mix. Check color.

Hydrochloric acid (HCL) solution: To make a 5% solution, add 13.6 mL concentrated HCl to 73 mL water while stirring. To make a $0.1M$ solution, add 1 mL concentrated hydrochloric acid to 100 mL water while stirring.

Iodine solution/Iodine stain: Dilute 1 part Lugol's solution with 15 parts water.

Lugol's solution: Dissolve 10 g potassium iodide in 100 mL distilled water. Then add and dissolve 5 g iodine. Store in dark bottle. Keeps indefinitely.

Phenolphthalein indicator: From a drug store, buy a package of any laxative that contains phenolphthalein. To make 1% solution, mash 4 tablets and pour the powder into 10 mL of rubbing alcohol. Let mixture soak for 15 minutes. Pour liquid into and store in a dropper bottle.

Potassium permanganate: For a $0.01M$ solution of potassium permanganate, dissolve 0.15 g $KMnO_4$ in 100 mL water.

Red cabbage concentrate: Put 5 leaves of red cabbage in a pot. Add 1 L of water, bring to a boil, and simmer until water turns a deep purple. Pour liquid through a strainer or piece of cheesecloth into a storage bottle. Keep refrigerated.

Salt solution: For a 3.5% salt (NaCl) solution that simulates the concentration of ocean water, dissolve 35 g of salt (NaCl) in 965 mL of water. For a 1% solution (weak), dissolve 1 g of salt (NaCl) in 99 mL of water. For a 6% solution, dissolve 6 g of salt (NaCl) in 94 mL of water.

Silver nitrate solution: To make a 10% solution, put 5 g of silver nitrate in 50 mL of distilled water.

Sugar solution: Add 1 tablespoon of sugar to 1 cup of warm water in a deep jar or flask. Stir to dissolve.

Sodium hydroxide (dilute): To make a 1% solution, dissolve 1 g NaOH in 99 mL of water.

Equipment and Materials List

These easy-to-use tables of equipment and consumable materials can help you prepare for your science classes for the year. Refer to the Chapter Organizer in front of each chapter for a list of equipment and materials used for each laboratory activity in the chapter.

Consumables

Material	Launch Lab (Chapter)	MiniLAB (Chapter-Section)	Lab (Chapter-Section)
alcohol, rubbing		3-3, 4-2	
alum powder			8-2
ammonia, household			8-3
antacids			5-3
bag, plastic resealable			5-3
baking soda	7	3-3, 5-3, 7-2	
baking soda (solution)			8-3
ball, clay or plastic foam	9		
balloon(s)	20	7-1, 8-2	11-3
black plastic		13-3	
borax soap (solution)			8-3
bouillon cube—ground, whole	8		
bread			9-3
calcium chloride			5-3
candy-coated chocolates			6-2
carbonated beverage bottle		8-2	
carbonated soft drink (colorless)			8-3
card, 10-cm×10-cm		19-4	
cardboard, corrugated			6-2, 19-4
cardboard tube(s)			17-1
cereal packages		7-2	
citrus fruits			9-3
clay—modeling, soft		9-1, 13-2	18-1, 19-2, 19-4
cleaners, household			5-3
clear-plastic wrap		13-3	
cola			9-3
construction paper, black	18		19-2
cornstarch			3-3
cotton string		17-1	
crackers		7-2	
cups—insulated foam, paper	19		10-3
dirt, sand, or snow		12-1	
eraser, flat		11-1	
ethanol			9-2
food coloring		1-3, 15-2	
fruit juices			5-3
grapes	9		
gumdrops	9	9-1	
hydrochloric acid, 0.1M (solution)			8-3
hydrogen peroxide solution, 3%			7-2
index cards—large, 3-in×5-in		4-3, 22-2	3-2
insulated wire			20-3
iodine solution			3-3, 9-3
iron filings		21-1	
liver, raw			7-2
mailing tubes, cardboard			1-4
meat trays, insulated foam			10-3
milk			9-3
nails			21-2
onions			9-3
orange juice			9-3
paper	20, 21	19-1, 22-2	3-2, 6-2, 21-1
paper clips	6	21-2	

Equipment and Materials List

Equipment and Materials List

Material	Launch Lab (Chapter)	MiniLAB (Chapter-Section)	Lab (Chapter-Section)
paper plate		5-3	
paper towel	3		
paper, colored		6-2	6-2
paper, graph			2-2, 5-3, 22-3
paper, unlined			19-2
pencil, grease			8-3
pencils, colored			18-2
pepper		20-2	
pH paper			5-3, 9-2
phenol red solution			5-3
potassium permanganate solution			9-2
potatoes			7-2, 9-3
powdered sugar			3-3
raisins	9		
red cabbage, concentrated			8-3
rope			1-4
rubber band		17-2	
rubber tubing			7-2
salad oil		3-3	
salt		20-2	5-3, 9-3
salt water		5-3	
sandpaper, fine			21-2
shoe box		3-1	
soap—solution, bar		11-1	8-3
soaps and detergents			5-3
sodium hydroxide solution			9-2
soft drinks—regular, diet		1-2	5-3
spoon, plastic		12-3	21-1
starch solution			9-3
steel wool, fine		5-3, 7-1	
straws, drinking—narrow, wide, white	12	16-3	10-3, 11-3
string		12-3	8-2, 11-3
sugar	7	3-3	5-3, 9-3
tape	1, 3	21-1	10-3, 11-3, 16-3, 18-1, 19-2, 21-1
tape, masking		10-1, 10-2	11-3, 19-4, 21-2
tomatoes			9-3
toothpicks	9	9-1	
vegetable oil		1-3	
vinegar			5-3, 7-2, 9-3
vinegar, white		7-1	3-3, 8-3
vitamin-C solution			9-3
water, distilled			5-3, 8-3
wire		20-3, 21-2	22-1
wire—18-gauge insulated, 22-gauge enameled			21-2
wool	20		
yarn, colored			16-2
Nonconsumables			
aluminum pan			12-2
balance			4-3, 7-2, 8-2, 14-3
baseball	10		
batteries, 1.5-V			20-3
battery		20-3	
battery holders			20-3
battery, 6-V			21-2
battery, D-cell (and holder)		21-2	22-1
beakers	8	2-1, 15-2	3-3, 4-2, 7-2, 8-2, 9-3, 12-2, 15-2, 15-3, 20-3
beverage containers			15-3
blocks, wooden			14-1, 21-2
board, wooden			21-2

Equipment and Materials List

Material	Launch Lab (Chapter)	MiniLAB (Chapter-Section)	Lab (Chapter-Section)
book	11, 13, 14		
bottles, labeled			8-3
bowl	3	17-1	
bricks			14-3
broomstick		14-3	
bulletin board, large			3-2
calculator	22		
clock with second hand			7-2
coffee cup		15-2	
coiled spring toy, long			16-2, 16-3
coins			6-2
comb—hard plastic, rubber		18-1, 20-2	
computer probe		2-1, 13-3	
container		8-2	
cork or straw	16		
cup, plastic	3	4-3	4-3
desk		16-1	
diffraction grating			18-2
diode, light-emitting			22-1
drinking glass, opaque		16-3	
dropper bottle(s)			3-3, 8-3
dropper(s)	16	4-2	2, 3
eggs, plastic			10-3
electrical motor, small			13-2
encyclopedia			3-2
eraser	14		
Erlenmeyer flask, 500-mL			7-2
evaporating dish		7-1	
eyedropper			8-3
flashlight			18-1, 19-2, 19-4
flashlight bulb		20-3	
force spring scale			14-3
funnel			12-2, 20-3
glass(es)		3-3, 15-2	
golf ball—regular, plastic	5	13-2	11-3
graduated cylinder			4-3, 5-3, 7-2, 9-2, 9-3, 12-2, 15-3
hammer			21-2
headphone jack			13-2
heater, electric		18-2	
hose clamp			20-3
hot plate		15-2	3-3, 4-2, 8-2, 15-2, 15-3
key		11-1, 17-1	
knitting needle, steel			21-2
laboratory burner	7		
lens, convex			19-4
lid, plastic			11-3
lightbulb and holder			22-1
lightbulb, clear tubular			18-2
lightbulbs, 1.5-V			20-3
magnets—bar, ceramic	6, 21	21-1	21-1, 21-2
magnetic board			6-2
magnetic strips, rubber			6-2
marble(s)	11, 13	13-2	4-3, 10-3
measuring cup, liquid, plastic or glass		2-2	
measuring tape			17-2
Merck Index			3-2
metal object			12-2
metal tongs		15-2	
microscope slides			18-1
minibulb sockets			20-3
mirror, concave		18-2	

Equipment and Materials List

Material	Launch Lab (Chapter)	MiniLAB (Chapter-Section)	Lab (Chapter-Section)
mirror, small plane			19-2
mortar and pestle	8		9-3
musical instruments			17-2
notebook, hardsided		11-1	
notebooks, thin			14-1
one-hole stopper (with glass tube)			7-2
pans	15		
petri dishes, plastic		21-1	21-1
pH color chart			5-3
pie pan, small			3-3
pins, straight			10-3
plate		20-2	
plate, clear plastic	16		
pot, large		1-2, 13-3	
power supply with variable resistor switch			18-2
prism	18		
protractor			17-1, 19-2
pulley systems			14-3
radio or CD player			13-2
ramp		14-1	
ring stand with ring			20-3
rope		14-3	
rope, nylon			14-3
ruler	14		14-1
ruler, wooden		16-1	
scale		14-1	
scoops, small			3-3
sewing needle			21-1
shoe box		17-2	
sink			4-3
socket			18-2
spring scale (in Newtons)			11-3
spring scale(s)		11-3	12-2, 14-1
steel bar			14-3
steel nail, 16-penny		21-2	
stirrer			4-2, 8-2, 9-3
stopper		19-4	9-2
stopwatch	22		2-3, 7-2, 11-3, 15-2, 15-3, 16-2, 16-3, 20-3
table-tennis ball	5		
tacks, colored			6-2
teaspoons			5-3
tennis balls	10		
test tubes	4, 7	1-3, 7-1, 19-4	3-3, 4-3, 7-2, 8-3, 9-2, 9-3
test-tube holder	7		3-3
test-tube rack	4		7-2, 9-2, 9-3
thermal gloves or mitts			8-2, 15-3
thermometers	4, 18	2-1, 13-3	7-2, 8-2, 15-2, 15-3
thermometer, Celsius			4-2
thumbtacks or pins			3-2
tongs			15-3
towel		17-1	
tub		17-1	
tubing, rubber or plastic			20-3
tuning forks			17-2
watch or clock (with second hand)		10-1	17-1
weighing dish			7-2
weights			14-3
wire cutters			21-2
wool clothing		18-1, 20-2	

Suppliers

Equipment Suppliers

American Science & Surplus
P.O. Box 1030
Skokie, IL 60076
(847) 647-0011
www.sciplus.com

Bio-Rad Laboratories
2000 Alfred Nobel Dr.
Life Science Group
Hercules, CA 94547
(800) 424-6723
www.bio-rad.com

Carolina Biological Supply Co.
2700 York Road
Burlington, NC 27215
(800) 334-5551
www.carolina.com

Chem Scientific, LLC
1250 Washington St.
Norwood, MA 02062
(888) 527-5827
www.chemscientific.com

Edmund Scientific Company
60 Pearce Ave.
Tonawanda, NY 14150
(800) 728-6999
www.edmundscientific.com

Fisher Science Education
Educational Materials Division
4500 Turnberry Dr.
Hanover Park, IL 60133
(800) 955-1177
www.fisheredu.com

Flinn Scientific
P.O. Box 219
770 N. Raddant Rd.
Batavia, IL 60510
(800) 452-1261
www.flinnsci.com

Frey Scientific, Div. of Beckley Cardy
P.O. Box 8101
Mansfield, OH 44901
(800) 225-FREY (3739)
www.freyscientific.com

Nasco Science
901 Janesville Avenue
P.O. Box 901
Fort Atkinson, WI 53538-0901
(800) 558-9595
www.enasco.com

Nebraska Scientific
3823 Leavenworth St.
Omaha, NE 68105-1180
(800) 228-7117
nebraskascientific.com

PASCO Scientific
10101 Foothills Blvd.
Roseville, CA 95747
(800) 772-8700
www.pasco.com

Sargent-Welch/VWR Scientific Products
P.O. Box 5229
Buffalo Grove, IL 60089-5229
(800) SAR-GENT 727-4368
www.SargentWelch.com

Science Kit and Boreal Laboratories
777 East Park Dr.
P.O. Box 5003
Tonawanda, NY 14150
(800) 828-7777
www.sciencekit.com

Ward's Natural Science Est.
5100 W. Henrietta Road
P.O. Box 92912
Rochester, NY 14692-9012
(800) 962-2660
www.wardsci.com

Audiovisual Distributors

Bullfrog Films
P.O. Box 149
Oley, PA 19547
(800) 543-FROG (3764)
www.bullfrogfilms.com

Coronet/MTI Film & Video
2349 Chaffee Dr.
St. Louis, MO 63146
(800) 221-1274
www.phoenixlearninggroup.com

Discovery Channel School
1 Discovery Place
Silver Springs, MD 20910
(240) 662-2000
www.discoveryschool.com

Films for the Humanities and Sciences
P.O. Box 2053
Princeton, NJ 08543
(800) 257-5126
www.films.com

Flinn Scientific
P.O. Box 219
770 N. Raddant Rd.
Batavia, IL 60510
(800) 452-1261
www.flinnsci.com

Frey Scientific, Div. of Beckley Cardy
P.O. Box 8101
Mansfield, OH 44901
(800) 225-FREY (3739)
www.freyscientific.com

Media Design Associates
1731 15th St.
Suite 220
Boulder, CO 80302
(866) 546-9151
www.indra.com

National Geographic Society Educational Services
1145 17th Street, N.W.
Washington, DC 20036-4688
(800) 647-5463
www.nationalgeographic.com

Scholastic, Inc.
557 Broadway
New York, NY 10012-3999
(800) 246-2986
www.scholastic.com

Videodiscovery Inc.
920 N. 34th St.
Seattle, WA 98103
(800) 548-3472
www.videodiscovery.com

Software Distributors

Boreal Laboratories, Ltd.
399 Vansickle Rd.
St. Catharines, Ontario,
L2S 3T4
Canada
(800) 387-9393
boreal.com

Educational Activities, Inc.
1937 Grand Ave.
P.O. Box 87
Baldwin, NY 11510
(800) 645-3739
www.edact.com

IBM Education
1133 Westchester Ave.
White Plains, NY 10604
(800) 426-4968
www.solutions.ibm.com/k12

J. Weston Walch, Publisher
40 Walch Dr.
P.O. Box 658
Portland, ME 04104-0658
(800) 341-6094
www.walch.com

Scholastic, Inc.
557 Broadway
New York, NY 10012-3999
(800) 246-2986
www.scholastic.com

Sunburst Technology, Inc.
1550 Executive Drive
Elgin, IL 60123
(888) 492-8817
www.SUNBURST.com

Suppliers

Contents In Brief

HOW TO...

Use Your Science Book

Why do I need my science book?

Have you ever been in class and not understood all of what was presented? Or, you understood everything in class, but at home, got stuck on how to answer a question? Maybe you just wondered when you were ever going to use this stuff?

These next few pages are designed to help you understand everything your science book can be used for ... besides a paperweight!

Glencoe Science

Introduction to **Physical Science**

NATIONAL GEOGRAPHIC

ips.msscience.com

Before You Read

- **Chapter Opener** Science is occurring all around you, and the opening photo of each chapter will preview the science you will be learning about. The **Chapter Preview** will give you an idea of what you will be learning about, and you can try the **Launch Lab** to help get your brain headed in the right direction. The **Foldables** exercise is a fun way to keep you organized.

- **Section Opener** Chapters are divided into two to four sections. The **As You Read** in the margin of the first page of each section will let you know what is most important in the section. It is divided into four parts. **What You'll Learn** will tell you the major topics you will be covering. **Why It's Important** will remind you why you are studying this in the first place! The **Review Vocabulary** word is a word you already know, either from your science studies or your prior knowledge. The **New Vocabulary** words are words that you need to learn to understand this section. These words will be in **boldfaced** print and highlighted in the section. Make a note to yourself to recognize these words as you are reading the section.

As You Read

- **Headings** Each section has a title in large red letters, and is further divided into blue titles and small red titles at the beginnings of some paragraphs. To help you study, make an outline of the headings and subheadings.

- **Margins** In the margins of your text, you will find many helpful resources. The **Science Online** exercises and **Integrate** activities help you explore the topics you are studying. **MiniLabs** reinforce the science concepts you have learned.

- **Building Skills** You also will find an **Applying Math** or **Applying Science** activity in each chapter. This gives you extra practice using your new knowledge, and helps prepare you for standardized tests.

- **Student Resources** At the end of the book you will find **Student Resources** to help you throughout your studies. These include **Science, Technology,** and **Math Skill Handbooks,** an **English/Spanish Glossary,** and an **Index.** Also, use your **Foldables** as a resource. It will help you organize information, and review before a test.

- **In Class** Remember, you can always ask your teacher to explain anything you don't understand.

FOLDABLES™
Study Organizer

Science Vocabulary Make the following Foldable to help you understand the vocabulary terms in this chapter.

STEP 1 **Fold** a vertical sheet of notebook paper from side to side.

STEP 2 **Cut** along every third line of only the top layer to form tabs.

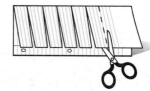

STEP 3 **Label** each tab with a vocabulary word from the chapter.

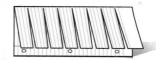

Build Vocabulary As you read the chapter, list the vocabulary words on the tabs. As you learn the definitions, write them under the tab for each vocabulary word.

Look For...

FOLDABLES™

At the beginning of every section.

In Lab

Working in the laboratory is one of the best ways to understand the concepts you are studying. Your book will be your guide through your laboratory experiences, and help you begin to think like a scientist. In it, you not only will find the steps necessary to follow the investigations, but you also will find helpful tips to make the most of your time.

- Each lab provides you with a **Real-World Question** to remind you that science is something you use every day, not just in class. This may lead to many more questions about how things happen in your world.

- Remember, experiments do not always produce the result you expect. Scientists have made many discoveries based on investigations with unexpected results. You can try the experiment again to make sure your results were accurate, or perhaps form a new hypothesis to test.

- Keeping a **Science Journal** is how scientists keep accurate records of observations and data. In your journal, you also can write any questions that may arise during your investigation. This is a great method of reminding yourself to find the answers later.

Look For...
- **Launch Labs** start every chapter.
- **MiniLabs** in the margin of each chapter.
- **Two Full-Period Labs** in every chapter.
- **EXTRA Try at Home Labs** at the end of your book.
- the **Web site** with **laboratory demonstrations.**

Before a Test

Admit it! You don't like to take tests! However, there *are* ways to review that make them less painful. Your book will help you be more successful taking tests if you use the resources provided to you.

- Review all of the **New Vocabulary** words and be sure you understand their definitions.

- Review the notes you've taken on your **Foldables,** in class, and in lab. Write down any question that you still need answered.

- Review the **Summaries** and **Self Check questions** at the end of each section.

- Study the concepts presented in the chapter by reading the **Study Guide** and answering the questions in the **Chapter Review.**

a or b?
?
T or F?

Look For...

- **Reading Checks** and **caption questions** throughout the text.

- The **Summaries** and **Self Check questions** at the end of each section.

- The **Study Guide** and **Review** at the end of each chapter.

- The **Standardized Test Practice** after each chapter.

Let's Get Started

To help you find the information you need quickly, use the Scavenger Hunt below to learn where things are located in Chapter 1.

1. What is the title of this chapter?

2. What will you learn in Section 1?

3. Sometimes you may ask, "Why am I learning this?" State a reason why the concepts from Section 2 are important.

4. What is the main topic presented in Section 2?

5. How many reading checks are in Section 1?

6. What is the Web address where you can find extra information?

7. What is the main heading above the sixth paragraph in Section 2?

8. There is an integration with another subject mentioned in one of the margins of the chapter. What subject is it?

9. List the new vocabulary words presented in Section 2.

10. List the safety symbols presented in the first Lab.

11. Where would you find a Self Check to be sure you understand the section?

12. Suppose you're doing the Self Check and you have a question about concept mapping. Where could you find help?

13. On what pages are the Chapter Study Guide and Chapter Review?

14. Look in the Table of Contents to find out on which page Section 2 of the chapter begins.

15. You complete the Chapter Review to study for your chapter test. Where could you find another quiz for more practice?

In each chapter, look for these opportunities for review and assessment:
- Reading Checks
- Caption Questions
- Section Review
- Chapter Study Guide
- Chapter Review
- Standardized Test Practice
- Online practice at ips.msscience.com

Chemistry—158

Atomic Structure and Chemical Bonds—160

Chemical Reactions—188

Substances, Mixtures, and Solubility—216

Carbon Chemistry—248

unit 4 Motion and Forces—278

In each chapter, look for these opportunities for review and assessment:
- Reading Checks
- Caption Questions
- Section Review
- Chapter Study Guide
- Chapter Review
- Standardized Test Practice
- Online practice at ips.msscience.com

unit 5
Energy—370

chapter 13
Energy and Energy Resources—372

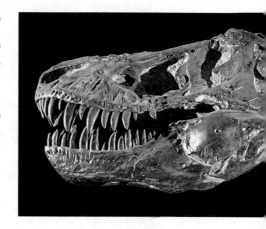

chapter 14
Work and Simple Machines—404

Contents

unit 6 Waves, Sound, and Light—458

In each chapter, look for these opportunities for review and assessment:
- **Reading Checks**
- **Caption Questions**
- **Section Review**
- **Chapter Study Guide**
- **Chapter Review**
- **Standardized Test Practice**
- **Online practice at ips.msscience.com**

In each chapter, look for these opportunities for review and assessment:
- Reading Checks
- Caption Questions
- Section Review
- Chapter Study Guide
- Chapter Review
- Standardized Test Practice
- Online practice at ips.msscience.com

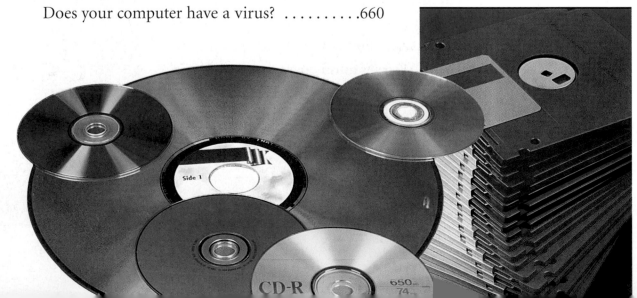

Student Resources—668

Cross-Curricular Readings

NATIONAL GEOGRAPHIC Unit Openers

NATIONAL GEOGRAPHIC VISUALIZING

Content Details

TIME SCIENCE AND Society

TIME SCIENCE AND HISTORY

Oops! Accidents in SCIENCE

Science and Language Arts

SCIENCE Stats

LABS

 available as a video lab

Launch LAB

Mini LAB

Content Details

Mini LAB Try at Home

available as a video lab

One-Page Labs

Content Details

Activities

Applying Math

Applying Science

Content Details

INTEGRATE

Astronomy: 51, 343, 496, 533, 536
Career: 13, 43, 78, 148, 165, 229, 264, 352, 448, 654
Chemistry: 593, 646
Earth Science: 91, 252, 388, 468
Environment: 221, 225, 656
Health: 9, 47, 137, 203, 470, 601, 630
History: 73, 104, 205, 317, 408, 529, 594, 629
Life Science: 90, 123, 140, 193, 236, 284, 311, 324, 361, 381, 383, 415, 419, 442, 443, 495, 530, 602, 618
Physics: 108, 171, 466, 557, 634
Social Studies: 294, 502

Science Online

18, 22, 47, 58, 76, 81, 90, 105, 111, 113, 123, 138, 146, 164, 175, 195, 201, 219, 235, 238, 256, 267, 286, 296, 313, 324, 341, 358, 380, 390, 410, 413, 446, 471, 477, 495, 507, 521, 538, 558, 588, 601, 619, 627, 645, 652, 656, 658

Standardized Test Practice

38–39, 66–67, 98–99, 130–131, 156–157, 186–187, 214–215, 246–247, 276–277, 306–307, 336–337, 368–369, 402–403, 430–431, 456–457, 486–487, 516–517, 546–547, 578–579, 610–611, 638–639, 666–667

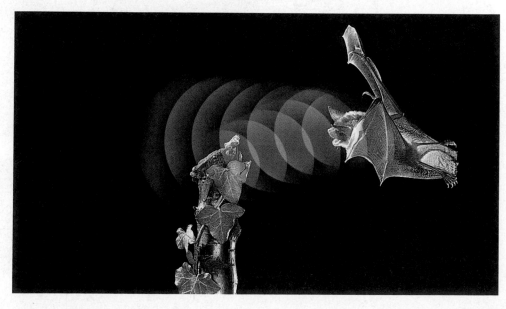

Unit Contents

 The Nature of Science: Evaluating Bias in Advertisements is an exploration of specific internet sites. Students become informed about the techniques of advertising as well as evaluating bias in advertising. They use their new evaluation skills to take a critical look at a print advertisement.

How Are Arms & Centimeters Connected?

PROJECT CRISSSM

Study Skills

Discussion The sticky-note strategy is used to stimulate discussion and to encourage students to ask questions. Provide students with sticky-notes. As they read this unit, have them use the sticky-notes to mark information they find interesting or sentences about which they have questions. Follow this activity with a class discussion.

About 5,000 years ago, the Egyptians developed one of the earliest recorded units of measurement—the cubit, which was based on the length of the arm from elbow to fingertip. The Egyptian measurement system probably influenced later systems, many of which also were based on body parts such as arms and feet. Such systems, however, could be problematic, since arms and feet vary in length from one person to another. Moreover, each country had its own system, which made it hard for people from different countries to share information. The need for a precise, universal measurement system eventually led to the adoption of the meter as the basic international unit of length. A meter is defined as the distance that light travels in a vacuum in a certain fraction of a second—a distance that never varies. Meters are divided into smaller units called centimeters, which are seen on the rulers here.

unit projects

Visit ips.msscience.com/unit_project to find project ideas and resources.
Projects include:

- **History** Brainstorm characteristics of science fields, and then design a collage with science ideas for a ceiling tile or book cover.
- **Technology** Convert a family recipe from English measurement to SI units of measurement. Enjoy a classroom bake-off!
- **Model** Create a character in an SI world. Develop a picture storybook or comic book to demonstrate your knowledge of SI measurement.

WebQuest *The Nature of Science: Evaluating Bias in Advertisements* helps students to become informed about the techniques of advertising and evaluate bias in print media.

3

unit projects

History Have students brainstorm characteristics of different branches of science. Working in small groups, ask students to design a collage to represent one branch of science. Students may paint their design on bulletin board paper which may be placed over ceiling tiles in the classroom or science hallway. It may be preferable for individuals to use their design on personal science book covers.

Technology Ask students to supply a copy of a favorite family recipe. Have students rewrite their recipe using SI units: volume, weight, length, and temperature. Some students may want to bake their food for class presentation. Discuss what makes it difficult for people to switch from one system of measurement to another for baking, building, or car repair.

Model Have students create a unique character with a simple SI measurement topic. Themes might include an octopus in water (volume), an elephant in a strong-elephant contest (mass), an inchworm in a metric world (length), or a hotheaded fire ant (temperature). Have students design a problem situation for their character, and then solve it using SI measurements. Ask students to create a small story book to illustrate their science knowledge through literature.

Additional Resources For more information, resources, and assessment rubrics, visit ips.msscience.com/unit_project

---

NATIONAL GEOGRAPHIC   How Are Arms & Centimeters Connected?

As ancient people traveled and trade began, a need for accuracy in measuring became necessary. Early weight units may have been derived from containers or calculations of what a person or animal could haul.

Early linear measurements were often based on body parts. Because of its accuracy, the Egyptian cubit was the standard of linear measurement. All cubit sticks used in Egypt were measured at regular intervals against the royal master cubit made of black granite.

There are seven basic SI units, one of which is the meter. The centimeter is a subunit of the meter.

chapter ① Organizer

Section/Objectives	Standards		Labs/Features
Chapter Opener	**National**	**State/Local**	**Launch Lab:** Observe How Gravity Accelerates Objects, p. 5 **Foldables,** p. 5
	See p. 16T–17T for a Key to Standards.		
Section 1 What is science? ⏱ 2 sessions 📦 1 block 1. **Define** science and identify questions that science cannot answer. 2. **Compare and contrast** theories and laws. 3. **Identify** a system and its components. 4. **Identify** the three branches of science.	National Content Standards: UCP.1, UCP.2, A.1, A.2, B.1, F.5, G.2		**MiniLAB:** Classify Parts of a System, p. 8 **Integrate Health,** p. 9
Section 2 Science in Action ⏱ 2 sessions 📦 1 block 5. **Identify** some skills scientists use. 6. **Define** hypothesis. 7. **Recognize** the difference between observation and inference.	National Content Standards: UCP.1, UCP.2, A.1, A.2, G.2		**Integrate Career,** p. 13 **MiniLAB:** Forming a Hypothesis, p. 14 **Applying Math:** Seasonal Temperatures, p. 17 **Science Online,** p. 18
Section 3 Models in Science ⏱ 2 sessions 📦 1 block 8. **Describe** various types of models. 9. **Discuss** limitations of models.	National Content Standards: UCP.1, UCP.2, UCP.3, A.1, A.2, G.2		**Science Online,** p. 22 **MiniLAB:** Thinking Like a Scientist, p. 23 **Visualizing the Modeling of King Tut,** p. 24
Section 4 Evaluating Scientific Explanation ⏱ 3 sessions 📦 1.5 blocks 10. **Evaluate** scientific explanations. 11. **Evaluate** promotional claims.	National Content Standards: UCP.1, UCP.2, UCP.3, A.1, A.2, G.2		**Lab:** What is the right answer?, p. 31 **Lab:** Identifying Parts of an Investigation, pp. 32–33 **Science and History:** Women in Science, p. 34

Glencoe Exclusive!
TeacherWorks™
All-In-One Planner and Resource Center

Lab Materials	Reproducible Resources	Section Assessment	Technology
Launch Lab: 3 identical unsharpened pencils, tape	**Chapter *FAST FILE* Resources** Foldables Worksheet, p. 19 Note-taking Worksheets, pp. 37–39	GLENCOE'S **ASSESSMENT** ADVANTAGE	**TeacherWorks** includes: • Interactive Teacher Edition • Lesson Planner with calendar • Access to all program blacklines • Correlations to standards • Web links
MiniLAB: paper, pencil or pen *Need materials?* Contact Science Kit at 1-800-828-7777 or www.sciencekit.com on the Internet.	**Chapter *FAST FILE* Resources** Transparency Activity, p. 48 MiniLAB, p. 3 Enrichment, p. 33 Reinforcement, p. 29 Directed Reading, p. 22 **Life Science Critical Thinking/ Problem Solving,** p.1	**Portfolio** Assessment, p. 8 **Performance** Assessment, p. 11 Applying Skills, p. 11 **Content** Section Review, p. 11	Section Focus Transparency Virtual Labs CD-ROM Guided Reading Audio Program Interactive Chalkboard CD-ROM
MiniLAB: large pot of water, unopened can of diet soda, unopened can of regular soda	**Chapter *FAST FILE* Resources** Transparency Activity, p. 49 MiniLAB, p. 4 Enrichment, p. 34 Reinforcement, p. 30 Directed Reading, p. 23 Lab Activity, pp. 11–14 Transparency Activity, pp. 53–54	**Portfolio** Active Reading, p. 16 **Performance** MiniLAB, p. 14 Applying Math, p. 17 **Content** Section Review, p. 20	Section Focus Transparency Teaching Transparency Virtual Labs CD-ROM Guided Reading Audio Program Interactive Chalkboard CD-ROM
MiniLAB: 15 mL water, test tube, 5 mL vegetable oil, 2 drops food coloring, graduated cylinder, watch or clock	**Chapter *FAST FILE* Resources** Transparency Activity, p. 50 MiniLAB, p. 5 Enrichment, p. 35 Reinforcement, p. 31 Directed Reading, p. 23 Lab Activity, pp. 15–18	**Portfolio** Curriculum Connection, p. 22 **Performance** MiniLAB, p. 23 Applying Math, p. 26 **Content** Section Review, p. 26	Section Focus Transparency Guided Reading Audio Program Interactive Chalkboard CD-ROM
Lab: cardboard mailing tubes, length of rope, scissors **Lab:** description of fertilizer experiment, data table from the fertilizer experiment	**Chapter *FAST FILE* Resources** Transparency Activity, p. 51 Enrichment, p. 36 Reinforcement, p. 32 Directed Reading, pp. 23, 24 Lab Worksheet, pp. 7–8, 9–10	**Portfolio** Assessment, p. 30 **Performance** Assessment, p. 30 Applying Skills, p. 30 **Content** Section Review, p. 30	Section Focus Transparency Virtual Labs CD-ROM Guided Reading Audio Program Interactive Chalkboard CD-ROM Video Lab

GLENCOE'S **ASSESSMENT** ADVANTAGE

End of Chapter Assessment

Blackline Masters	Technology	Professional Series
Chapter *FAST FILE* Resources Chapter Review, pp. 41–42 Chapter Tests, pp. 43–46 **Standardized Test Practice,** pp. 7–10	MindJogger Videoquiz Virtual Labs CD-ROM ExamView® Pro Testmaker TeacherWorks CD-ROM Interactive Chalkboard CD-ROM	**Performance Assessment in the Science Classroom (PASC)**

Transparencies

Section Focus

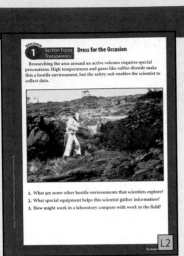

SECTION 1 Section Focus Transparency — **Dress for the Occasion**

Researching the area around an active volcano requires special precautions. High temperatures and gases like sulfur dioxide make this a hostile environment, but the safety suit enables the scientist to collect data.

1. What are some other hostile environments that scientists explore?
2. What special equipment helps this scientist gather information?
3. How might work in a laboratory compare with work in the field?

L2

SECTION 2 Section Focus Transparency — **Did we skip a step?**

These are the remains of the *Vasa*, the largest warship of its time. Due to improper testing, it sank on its maiden voyage in 1625. In 1961, the ship was salvaged and a museum built to house it.

1. Prior to the *Vasa*'s maiden voyage an admiral ordered a test for stability. The ship failed the test, but the admiral kept the result a secret. What would a scientist have done with this result?
2. How could you test a new ship design without actually building the ship?

L2

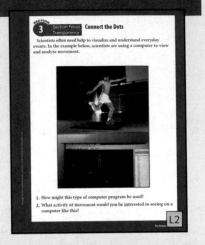

SECTION 3 Section Focus Transparency — **Connect the Dots**

Scientists often need help to visualize and understand everyday events. In the example below, scientists are using a computer to view and analyze movement.

1. How might this type of computer program be used?
2. What activity or movement would you be interested in seeing on a computer like this?

L2

This is a representation of key blackline masters available in the Teacher Classroom Resources. See Resource Manager boxes within the chapter for additional information.

Key to Teaching Strategies

The following designations will help you decide which activities are appropriate for your students.

L1 Level 1 activities should be appropriate for students with learning difficulties.

L2 Level 2 activities should be within the ability range of all students.

L3 Level 3 activities are designed for above-average students.

ELL ELL activities should be within the ability range of English Language Learners.

COOP LEARN Cooperative Learning activities are designed for small group work.

LS Multiple Learning Styles logos, as described on page 12T, are used throughout to indicate strategies that address different learning styles.

P These strategies represent student products that can be placed into a best-work portfolio.

PBL Problem-Based Learning activities apply real-world situations to learning.

Assessment

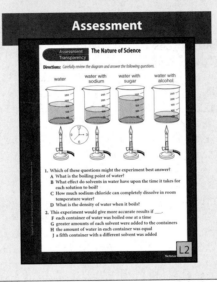

Assessment Transparency — **The Nature of Science**

Directions: Carefully review the diagram and answer the following questions.

water / water with sodium / water with sugar / water with alcohol

1. Which of these questions might the experiment best answer?
   A What is the boiling point of water?
   B What effect do solvents in water have upon the time it takes for each solution to boil?
   C How much sodium chloride can completely dissolve in room temperature water?
   D What is the density of water when it boils?
2. This experiment would give more accurate results if ___.
   F each container of water was boiled one at a time
   G greater amounts of each solvent were added to the containers
   H the amount of water in each container was equal
   J a fifth container with a different solvent was added

L2

Teaching

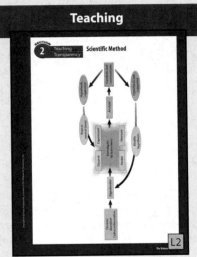

SECTION 2 Teaching Transparency — **Scientific Method**

L2

Hands-on Activities

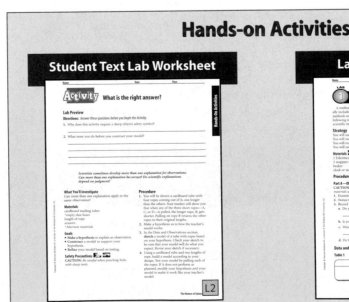

Student Text Lab Worksheet

Activity — What is the right answer?

Lab Preview
Directions: *Answer these questions before you begin the Activity.*

1. Why does this activity require a sharp objects safety symbol?

2. What must you do before you construct your model?

Scientists sometimes develop more than one explanation for observations. Can more than one explanation be correct? Do scientific explanations depend on judgment?

What You'll Investigate
Can more than one explanation apply to the same observation?

Materials
cardboard mailing tubes
*empty shoe boxes
length of rope
scissors
*Alternate materials

Goals
■ **Make** a hypothesis to explain an observation.
■ **Construct** a model to support your hypothesis.
■ **Refine** your model based on testing.

Safety Precautions 🧤⚠️
CAUTION: *Be careful when punching holes with sharp tools.*

Procedure
1. You will be shown a cardboard tube with four ropes coming out of it, one longer than the others. Your teacher will show you that when any of the three short ropes—A, C, or D—is pulled, the longer rope, B, gets shorter. Pulling on rope B returns the other ropes to their original lengths.
2. Make a hypothesis as to how the teacher's model works.
3. In the Data and Observations section, **sketch** a model of a tube with ropes based on your hypothesis. Check your sketch to be sure that your model will do what you expect. Revise your sketch if necessary.
4. Using a cardboard tube and two lengths of rope, build a model according to your design. Test your model by pulling each of the ropes. If it does not perform as planned, modify your hypothesis and your model to make it work like your teacher's model.

The Nature of Science

L2

Laboratory Activities

LAB 1 Laboratory Activity — **Solving a Problem with a Scientific Method**

A method by which a scientist solves a problem is called a scientific method. This method usually includes observation, hypothesis formation, experimentation, and interpretation. Scientific methods are often compared to the procedures a detective uses in solving a crime or mystery. The following investigation creates a scientific problem for you and asks you to solve it. You will use a scientific method in attempting to solve the problem.

Strategy
You will use a scientific method to solve whether flasks A and B contain similar liquids.
You will make careful observations.
You will record accurate experimental results.
You will use your data as a basis for deciding if the two liquids are similar or different.

Materials 🥽🧤🔬🧪⏱️
2 Erlenmeyer flasks containing liquids
2 stoppers (to fit flasks)
beaker
clock or watch with second hand

Procedure
Part A—Observation
CAUTION: *Do not dispose of these materials in the sink or trash can. Do not taste, eat, or drink any materials used in the lab. Inform your teacher if you come in contact with any chemicals.*
1. Examine the two flasks. DO NOT remove the stoppers and DO NOT shake the contents.
2. Notice that the flasks have been labeled A and B.
3. Record in Table 1 two or three similarities and differences between the two flasks.
   a. Do you think both flasks contain the same liquid? Explain.

   b. Is your hypothesis to question a based on experimentation or observation?

   c. Would scientists form a hypothesis about answers to questions, or would they experiment first?

   d. Do both flasks contain exactly the same amount of liquid?

Data and Observations
Table 1

Similarities	Differences

The Nature of Science

L2

Meeting Different Ability Levels

Content Outline

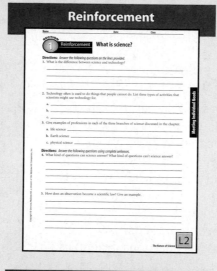

Reinforcement

Enrichment

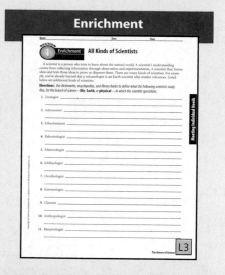

Directed Reading (English/Spanish)

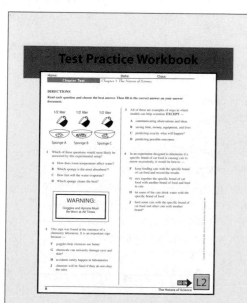

Study Guide

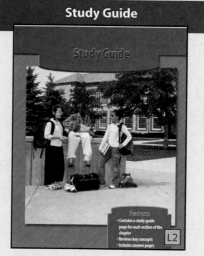

Reading Essentials

Assessment

Test Practice Workbook

Chapter Review

Chapter Tests

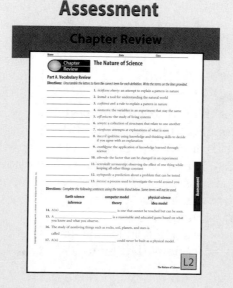

Science Content Background

section 1 What is science?
Learning About the World

Science has a dual nature. On one hand it can be thought of as an organized body of agreed upon descriptions and explanations about the natural world. On the other hand, it can be thought of as the methods that lead to the development of descriptions and explanations about the world.

When solving a problem, scientists often break it down into parts, or questions. Scientists spend a great deal of time researching and studying background information about the problem before deciding on a specific new question to investigate. They determine what research has been done already. What will need to be done first? Asking well-researched questions instead of random questions can save time and funds.

Scientists often study the interaction of components in a system. Systems in science include solar systems, ecosystems, and weather systems. Systems can be narrowly defined such as the lymphatic system or broadly defined such as in the Earth system.

The Branches of Science

Often the most fertile ground for investigation is at the periphery of two or more branches of science. Biochemistry originated at the borders of biology and chemistry and today is its own branch of science. In a similar way, biophysics is arising from biology and physics.

section 2 Science in Action
Science Skills

Science skills or science process skills are abilities used to investigate the natural world. Observations are the basis of scientific investigation, in that any hypothesis, theory, or law must be consistent with all observations. Other process skills include classifying, predicting, and communicating.

The term *The Scientific Method* is an inaccurate description of the work of scientists. The term *The*

Micheal Simpson/FPG International

makes it seem as though all scientists use one method, which is certainly not the case. There are differences between the methods of an astronomer and a medical researcher as there are between a theoretical physicist and a conservation biologist. Furthermore, science does not proceed in a linear fashion. False starts, dead ends, backtracking, and detours can occur often in the path. Thus the term *Science Methods* is preferred, because it is more inclusive of the diverse methods of science. It is, however, still useful to talk about components of methods of science, such as problems and hypotheses, because they shed light on aspects of

---

Teacher to Teacher
Diedre Adams
West Vigo Middle School
West Terre Haute, Indiana

"To help students calculate speed, I provide them with a variety of wind-up, pull-back toys. By placing these toys next to a meterstick, students can measure the time it takes the toy to reach the end of the stick. By using both fast and slow toys, students can also measure the distance that different toys stop. Advanced students can convert their measurements to m/s."

Diedre Adams

scientific endeavors and because scientific papers often use this format to report results.

The difference between observations and inferences is shown in the discovery of different solar systems. The observation of unusual movements in stars is used to infer the presence of a large planet near that star.

Experiments

Scientists usually apply the term *experiment* to situations in which they manipulate a variable to see the effect. Observing a star would not be an experiment because no variable was manipulated.

In past experiments, many sick people who believed they were receiving medicine, but in fact were given only sugar pills, actually got better. For this reason, in drug trials, the participants never know whether or not they are actually being given a drug. The treatment group is given the drug while the control group is given a placebo—something that resembles the drug but, like a sugar pill, has no effect.

section 3 Models in Science
Making Models

An important part of science is to construct models that approximate the real world. Models come in many forms such as physical, conceptual, or mathematical. In many cases, models are analogies: balls and springs, for example, can be presented as analogous to molecules and forces. Models may be similar to the real world, but they are never perfect matches. Perhaps for this reason it is common to have different models attempting to describe the same phenomenon.

section 4 Evaluating Scientific Explanation
Believe it or not?

Many of the most common fallacies of logic also afflict scientific inquiry, and even the most experienced scientist must be aware of the various errors that can invalidate an investigation. The design of an experiment can be flawed from the beginning—for instance, a variable that will affect the result is not rigorously controlled or is completely overlooked. Even in a well-designed experiment, the scientist's observations might be biased, however subtly. If the data collected from a perfectly designed and properly executed experiment are based on too small a sample, conclusions drawn from the data may not be reliable for wider application. And it is even possible that an incorrect conclusion will be drawn from completely reliable data. A successful scientific investigation is the result of careful thought and painstaking procedure.

---

chapter content resources

Internet Resources

For additional content background, visit **ips.msscience.com** to:

- access your book online
- find references to related articles in popular science magazines
- access Web links with related content background
- access current events with science journal topics

Print Resources

Resources for Teaching Middle School Science, by National Science Resources Center of the National Academy of Sciences, National Academy of Engineering, Institute of Medicine, and the Smithsonian Institution, 1998

Classroom Critters and the Scientific Method, by Sally Kneidel, Fulcrum Pub., 1999

Oh, Yuck: The Encyclopedia of Everything Nasty, by Joy Masoff and Terry Sirrell, Workman Publishing Company, 2000

Chapter Vocabulary

Science Journal Student responses may vary, but may include cooking food, heating your home, or food digestion.

INTERACTIVE CHALKBOARD
with Image Bank

PowerPoint® Presentations

This CD-ROM is an editable Microsoft® PowerPoint® presentation that includes:

- a pre-made presentation for every chapter
- interactive graphics
- animations
- audio clips
- image bank
- all new section and chapter questions
- Standardized Test Practice
- transparencies
- pre-lab questions for all labs
- Foldables directions
- links to ips.msscience.com

The Nature of Science

chapter preview

sections

1 **What is science?**
2 **Science in Action**
3 **Models in Science**
4 **Evaluating Scientific Explanation**
   Lab **What is the right answer?**
   Lab **Identifying Parts of an Investigation**
   Virtual Lab **How is a controlled experiment performed?**

How is science a part of your everyday life?

Scientists studying desert ecosystems in California wondered how such a dry environment could produce such beautiful, prolific flowers. Scientists began asking questions and performing investigations.

Science Journal Write down three examples of science in your everyday life.

Theme Connection

Systems and Interactions Science is a systematic way of studying the world to find relationships and interactions among the processes, cycles, and structures that make up the systems of the world.

About the Photo

Wonders of Nature In this photo, wildflowers are growing in the desert while very little vegetation is growing in the mountain. Ask students why they think this occurs. Giving possible explanations as to why something occurs allow scientists to share information.

Start-Up Activities

Observe How Gravity Accelerates Objects

Gravity is a familiar natural force that keeps you anchored on Earth, but how does it work? Scientists learn about gravity and other concepts by asking questions and making observations. By observing things in action scientists can study nature. Perform the lab below to see how gravity affects objects.

1. Collect three identical, unsharpened pencils.
2. Tape two of the pencils together.
3. Hold all the pencils at the same height as high as you can. Drop them together and observe what happens as they fall.
4. **Think Critically** Did the single pencil fall faster or slower than the pair? Predict in your Science Journal what would happen if you taped 30 pencils together and dropped them at the same time as you dropped a single pencil.

Preview this chapter's content and activities at ips.msscience.com

ips.msscience.com

FOLDABLES™
Study Organizer

Science Make the following Foldable to help identify what you already know, what you want to know, and what you learned about science.

STEP 1 **Fold** a vertical sheet of paper from side to side. Make the front edge about 1/2 inch shorter than the back edge.

STEP 2 **Turn** lengthwise and fold into thirds.

STEP 3 **Unfold and cut** only the top layer along both folds to make three tabs. **Label** each tab.

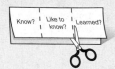
Know? | Like to know? | Learned?

Identify Questions Before you read the chapter, write what you already know about science under the left tab of your Foldable, and write questions about what you'd like to know under the center tab. After you read the chapter, list what you learned under the right tab.

Purpose Students explore how gravity affects objects of different masses. L2 IS **Kinesthetic**

Materials 3 identical, unsharpened pencils; tape

Teaching Strategy Make sure students drop the pencils from the greatest height possible.

Think Critically
The single pencil and the pair of pencils fall at the same rate. From this, students can infer that 30 pencils also should fall just as quickly as one pencil.

Assessment
Process Have students design other experiments to test how quickly objects of different sizes and weights fall. Encourage them to compare objects of different shapes and sizes. Use **Performance Assessment in the Science Classroom,** p. 95.

FOLDABLES™
Study Organizer **Dinah Zike Study Fold**

Student preparation materials for this Foldable are available in the **Chapter FAST FILE Resources.**

What is science?

Learning About the World

When you think of a scientist, do you imagine a person in a laboratory surrounded by charts, graphs, glass bottles, and bubbling test tubes? It might surprise you to learn that anyone who tries to learn something about the natural world is a scientist. **Science** is a way of learning more about the natural world. Scientists want to know why, how, or when something occurred. This learning process usually begins by keeping your eyes open and asking questions about what you see.

Asking Questions Scientists ask many questions. How do things work? What do things look like? What are they made of? Why does something take place? Science can attempt to answer many questions about the natural world, but some questions cannot be answered by science. Look at the situations in **Figure 1.** Who should you vote for? What does this poem mean? Who is your best friend? Questions about art, politics, personal preference, or morality can't be answered by science. Science can't tell you what is right, wrong, good, or bad.

as you read

What You'll Learn
- **Define** science and identify questions that science cannot answer.
- **Compare** and contrast theories and laws.
- **Identify** a system and its components.
- **Identify** the three main branches of science.

Why It's Important
Science can be used to learn more about the world you live in.

🔍 Review Vocabulary
theory: explanation of things or events that is based on knowledge gained from many observations and experiments

New Vocabulary
- science
- scientific theory
- scientific law
- system
- life science
- Earth science
- physical science
- technology

Figure 1 Questions about politics, literature, and art cannot be answered by science.

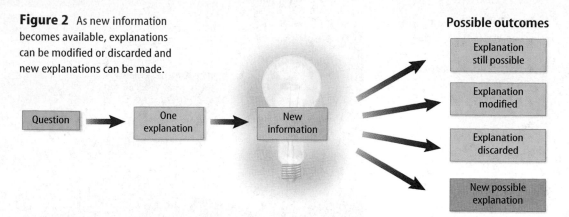

Figure 2 As new information becomes available, explanations can be modified or discarded and new explanations can be made.

Possible outcomes

Question → One explanation → New information →

Explanation still possible

Explanation modified

Explanation discarded

New possible explanation

Possible Explanations If learning about your world begins with asking questions, can science provide answers to these questions? Science can answer a question only with the information available at the time. Any answer is uncertain because people will never know everything about the world around them. With new knowledge, they might realize that some of the old explanations no longer fit the new information. As shown in **Figure 2,** some observations might force scientists to look at old ideas and think of new explanations. Science can only provide possible explanations.

✔ **Reading Check** *Why can't science answer questions with certainty?*

Scientific Theories An attempt to explain a pattern observed repeatedly in the natural world is called a **scientific theory.** Theories are not simply guesses or someone's opinions, nor are theories vague ideas. Theories in science must be supported by observations and results from many investigations. They are the best explanations that have been found so far. However, theories can change. As new data become available, scientists evaluate how the new data fit the theory. If enough new data do not support the theory, the theory can be changed to fit the new observations better.

Scientific Laws A rule that describes a pattern in nature is a **scientific law.** For an observation to become a scientific law, it must be observed repeatedly. The law then stands until someone makes observations that do not follow the law. A law helps you predict that an apple dropped from arm's length will always fall to Earth. The law, however, does not explain why gravity exists or how it works. A law, unlike a theory, does not attempt to explain why something happens. It simply describes a pattern.

Use Science Words

Word Origins The word *scientist* was first used by William Whewell who suggested this term be used for those who studied the natural world. He thought of it as a counterpart to the word *artist.* An artist is a person skilled in one of the arts. Have students look up the words *science* and *scientist* in the dictionary and suggest how the word *scientist* relates to the word *artist.* The word *science* comes from the Latin word *scire,* which means "to know." A scientist is a person learned in science like an artist is a person skilled in art. L2 LS Linguistic

✔ **Reading Check**

Answer New information is being discovered all the time. People will never know everything about the world around them.

Discussion

Theories and Laws Have students state things they know about the world and determine whether they are theories or laws. Possible statements: "The Sun rises in the east every morning" is a law because it describes an observation. "The Sun rises every day because gravity keeps Earth in orbit around the Sun" is a theory because it explains something. L2

Visual Learning

Figure 2 This flow chart demonstrates how as new information becomes available, scientific explanations can be modified and discarded. How could you use this flow chart to answer the question proposed in the Explore Activity about how gravity affects objects? Students observed that a single pencil fell at the same rate that two pencils fell. They may infer then that 30 pencils would fall at the same rate; however, new information would point out that heavier objects accelerate more rapidly.

Figure 3 Systems are a collection of structures, cycles, and processes.
Infer *What systems can you identify in this classroom?*

Mini LAB

Classifying Parts of a System

Procedure
Think about how your school's cafeteria is run. Consider the physical structure of the cafeteria. How many people run it? Where does the food come from? How is it prepared? Where does it go? What other parts of the cafeteria system are necessary?

Analysis
Classify the parts of your school cafeteria's system as structures, cycles, or processes.

Try at Home

Systems in Science

Scientists can study many different things in nature. Some might study how the human body works or how planets move around the Sun. Others might study the energy carried in a lightning bolt. What do all of these things have in common? All of them are systems. A **system** is a collection of structures, cycles, and processes that relate to and interact with each other. The structures, cycles, and processes are the parts of a system, just like your stomach is one of the structures of your digestive system.

Reading Check *What is a system?*

Systems are not found just in science. Your school is a system with structures such as the school building, the tables and chairs, you, your teacher, the school bell, your pencil, and many other things. **Figure 3** shows some of these structures. Your school day also has cycles. Your daily class schedule and the calendar of holidays are examples of cycles. Many processes are at work during the school day. When you take a test, your teacher has a process. You might be asked to put your books and papers away and get out a pencil before the test is distributed. When the time is over, you are told to put your pencil down and pass your test to the front of the room.

Parts of a System Interact In a system, structures, cycles, and processes interact. Your daily schedule influences where you go and what time you go. The clock shows the teacher when the test is complete, and you couldn't complete the test without a pencil.

Parts of a Whole All systems are made up of other systems. For example, you are part of your school. The human body is a system—within your body are other systems. Your school is part of a system—district, state, and national. You have your regional school district. Your district is part of a statewide school system. Scientists often break down problems by studying just one part of a system. A scientist might want to learn about how construction of buildings affects the ecosystem. Because an ecosystem has many parts, one scientist might study a particular animal, and another might study the effect of construction on plant life.

The Branches of Science

Science often is divided into three main categories, or branches—life science, Earth science, and physical science. Each branch asks questions about different kinds of systems.

Life Science The study of living systems and the ways in which they interact is called **life science.** Life scientists attempt to answer questions like "How do whales navigate the ocean?" and "How do vaccines prevent disease?" Life scientists can study living organisms, where they live, and how they interact. Dian Fossey, **Figure 4,** was a life scientist who studied gorillas, their habitat, and their behaviors.

People who work in the health field know a lot about the life sciences. Physicians, nurses, physical therapists, dietitians, medical researchers, and others focus on the systems of the human body. Some other examples of careers that use life science include biologists, zookeepers, botanists, farmers, and beekeepers.

INTEGRATE Health

Health Integration Systems The human body is composed of many different systems that all interact with one another to perform a function. The heart is like the control center. Even though not all systems report directly to the heart, they all interact with its function. If the heart is not working, the other systems fail as well. Research human body systems and explain how one system can affect another.

Figure 4 Over a span of 18 years, life scientist Dian Fossey spent much of her time observing mountain gorillas in Rwanda, Africa. She was able to interact with them as she learned about their behavior.

INTEGRATE Health

Health Integration Systems Body systems can fail at any time without warning. Doctors have developed different tests to try and predict health problems, but these tests are not guaranteed.

Research Have students research some of the tests that have been developed to test body systems. How can these tests lead to treatment and prevention of body system failure? What advancements have been made to adjust for the body system failure in order to keep the body working? L2

Use Science Words

Word Meaning Have students look up the names of various branches of science. Have them determine how the name came to be applied to that branch of science. Possible examples: Zoology comes from the Greek word *zoe,* which means "life." Zoology is the study of living animals. Medicine derives from the Latin word *medicina,* which means "remedy." L2 LS **Linguistic**

Discussion

Science Activities Ask students to name their favorite activities and discuss the types of science that are important to these activities. Possible responses: Reading—chemistry is involved in the processes for making the ink and the paper; physics was applied in the designing of the printing press. Sports—athletes regularly consult physicians and trainers who use their knowledge of life science to help athletes stay in good condition.

L2 LS **Logical-Mathematical**

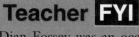

Teacher FYI

Gorillas Dian Fossey was an occupational therapist. She went to Africa to study and observe gorillas without any formal training. Her research led to a new view of these animals, once believed to be savage. She found the gorillas to be gentle vegetarians, some even sacrificing themselves in defense of the group.

Fun Fact

Ecotourists to Rwanda can visit the mountain gorillas that Dian Fossey worked so hard to study and save. Small groups are led on a remote trek to a family of gorillas. The guides warn the visitors not to look the male silverback in the eyes and, if he attacks, not to run.

10 CHAPTER 1 The Nature of Science

IDENTIFYING
Misconceptions

Branches of Science Students may think that each branch of science is isolated and that the branches never overlap. In fact, a scientist doing work in one of the branches of science often must rely on information obtained from the other branches. Have students think of investigations in which the different sciences would interact. Possible examples: To study how the Sun produces heat, an Earth scientist would need to know about physical science. To study an organism's interaction with its environment, a life scientist would have to know something about the rocks, soil, and water the organism comes into contact with. L3 LS **Logical-Mathematical**

Activity

Professional Scientists Ask professionals in Earth, life, and physical science to come to class and tell students about the things they do. L2 LS **Auditory-Musical**

Figure 5 These volcanologists are studying the temperature of the lava flowing from a volcano.

Figure 6 Physical scientists study a wide range of subjects.

Earth Science The study of Earth systems and the systems in space is **Earth science.** It includes the study of nonliving things such as rocks, soil, clouds, rivers, oceans, planets, stars, meteors, and black holes. Earth science also covers the weather and climate systems that affect Earth. Earth scientists ask questions like "How can an earthquake be detected?" or "Is water found on other planets?" They make maps and investigate how geologic features formed on land and in the oceans. They also use their knowledge to search for fuels and minerals. Meteorologists study weather and climate. Geologists study rocks and geologic features. **Figure 5** shows a volcanologist—a person who studies volcanoes—measuring the temperature of lava.

☑ **Reading Check** *What do Earth scientists study?*

Physical Science The study of matter and energy is **physical science.** Matter is anything that takes up space and has mass. The ability to cause change in matter is energy. Living and nonliving systems are made of matter. Examples include plants, animals, rocks, the atmosphere, and the water in oceans, lakes, and rivers. Physical science can be divided into two general fields—chemistry and physics. Chemistry is the study of matter and the interactions of matter. Physics is the study of energy and its ability to change matter. Figure 6 shows physical scientists at work.

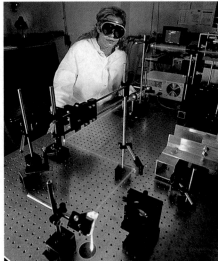

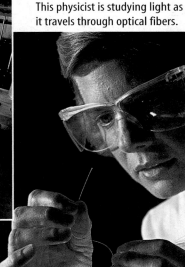

This physicist is studying light as it travels through optical fibers.

This chemist is studying the light emitted by certain compounds.

Differentiated Instruction

Challenge Have each student research careers that are of interest to him or her and then make a table showing how each career relies on the different branches of science. L3 LS **Linguistic**

Learning Disabled Have each student make three flash cards, one saying life science, one saying Earth science, and one saying physical science. Name different structures or processes, and have students raise the card naming the branch of science that studies those structures or processes. Ask students to explain their responses. L1

Careers Chemists ask questions such as "How can I make plastic stronger?" or "What can I do to make aspirin more effective?" Physicists might ask other types of questions, such as "How does light travel through glass fibers?" or "How can humans harness the energy of sunlight for their energy needs?"

Many careers are based on the physical sciences. Physicists and chemists are some obvious careers. Ultrasound and X-ray technicians working in the medical field study physical science because they study the energy in ultrasound or X rays and how it affects a living system.

Science and Technology Although learning the answers to scientific questions is important, these answers do not help people directly unless they can be applied in some way. **Technology** is the practical use of science, or applied science, as illustrated in **Figure 7**. Engineers apply science to develop technology. The study of how to use the energy of sunlight is science. Using this knowledge to create solar panels is technology. The study of the behavior of light as it travels through thin, glass, fiber-optic wires is science. The use of optical fibers to transmit information is technology. A scientist uses science to study how the skin of a shark repels water. The application of this knowledge to create a material that helps swimmers slip through the water faster is technology.

Figure 7 Solar-powered cars and the swimsuits worn in the Olympics are examples of technology—the application of science.

section 1 review

Summary

Learning About the World
- Scientists ask questions to learn how, why, or when something occurred.
- A theory is a possible explanation for observations that is supported by many investigations.
- A scientific law describes a pattern but does not explain why things happen.

Systems in Science
- A system is composed of structures, cycles, and processes that interact with each other.

The Branches of Science
- Science is divided into three branches—life science, Earth science, and physical science.
- Technology is the application of science in our everyday lives.

Self Check

1. **Compare and contrast** scientific theory and scientific law. Explain how a scientific theory can change.
2. **Explain** why science can answer some questions, but not others.
3. **Classify** the following statement as a theory or a law: Heating the air in a hot-air balloon causes the balloon to rise.
4. **Think Critically** Describe the importance of technology and how it relates to science.

Applying Skills

5. **Infer** Scientists ask questions and make observations. What types of questions and observations would you make if you were a scientist studying schools of fish in the ocean.

Science Online ips.msscience.com/self_check_quiz

section 1 review

1. A scientific theory tries to explain why something happens. A scientific law describes a regularity in nature. As new information becomes available, scientific theories can change.
2. Science can answer questions about the natural world through observa-

tions and investigation. Opinions and questions about art, books, and music cannot be answered by science.
3. scientific law
4. Science answers scientific questions, and technology applies those

answers to make products that help people.
5. Answers will vary. For example, "Why do fish swim in schools?" "Are fish swimming in schools more protected from enemies or are they more vulnerable?"

3 Assess

DAILY INTERVENTION

Check for Understanding
Logical-Mathematical Have students propose scientific laws. These do not have to be accepted laws but can be any general statement. Possible response: On the second Tuesday of each month, there is a science test. Next, have them provide theories to explain why the law holds. Possible response: There's a science test on the second Tuesday of each month, because the teacher plans it that way. Accept multiple explanations and have the class decide which makes the most sense. L3 LS

Reteach
Baseball Systems Ask students to name the different systems in a baseball game and classify them as structures, processes, or cycles. The bat, ball, bases, and field are structures; the rules and different strategies of play are processes; and the batting lineup, the nine innings, and each team's turn at bat are cycles. L2 LS
Logical-Mathematical

☑ Assessment

Performance Have students act out a play in which a group of scientists proposes a scientific law. Be sure the play includes the scientists making detailed observations to determine the exact nature of the regularity they are seeing. Use **Performance Assessment in the Science Classroom**, p. 147. L2

1 Motivate

Bellringer

Section Focus Transparencies also are available on the Interactive Chalkboard CD-ROM.

 L2 ELL

Did we skip a step?

These are the remains of the *Vasa*, the largest warship of its time. Due to improper testing, it sank on its maiden voyage in 1625. In 1961, the ship was salvaged and a museum built to house it.

1. Prior to the *Vasa's* maiden voyage an admiral ordered a test for stability. The ship failed the test, but the admiral kept the result a secret. What would a scientist have done with this result?
2. How could you test a new ship design without actually building the ship?

The Nature of Science

Tie to Prior Knowledge

Science Process Ask students whether they've ever tried to move a big piece of furniture through a doorway. Ask them to describe the process they used. They probably looked at the piece first, thought of a way to get it through the doorway, and then tried moving it. If this didn't work, they then might have put it down and rethought the problem. Explain that this is similar to the process scientists use when they try to solve a problem in science. L2

Text Question Answer

The scientific method can be applied to any investigation. Observations lead to hypotheses. Once you have developed a hypothesis, you must perform an investigation that provides you data to analyze.

---

as you read

What You'll Learn
- **Identify** some skills scientists use.
- **Define** hypothesis.
- **Recognize** the difference between observation and inference.

Why It's Important
Science can be used to learn more about the world you live in.

🔍 Review Vocabulary
observation: a record or description of an occurrence or pattern in nature

New Vocabulary
- hypothesis
- infer
- controlled experiment
- variable
- independent variable
- dependent variable
- constant

Science Skills

You know that science involves asking questions, but how does asking questions lead to learning? Because no single way to gain knowledge exists, a scientist doesn't start with step one, then go to step two, and so on. Instead, scientists have a huge collection of skills from which to choose. Some of these skills include thinking, observing, predicting, investigating, researching, modeling, measuring, analyzing, and inferring. Science also can advance with luck and creativity.

Science Methods Investigations often follow a general pattern. As illustrated in **Figure 8,** most investigations begin by seeing something and then asking a question about what was observed. Scientists often perform research by talking with other scientists. They read books and scientific magazines to learn as much as they can about what is already known about their question. Usually, scientists state a possible explanation for their observation. To collect more information, scientists almost always make more observations. They might build a model of what they study or they might perform investigations. Often, they do both. How might you combine some of these skills in an investigation?

Figure 8 Although there are different scientific methods for investigating a specific problem, most investigations follow a general pattern.

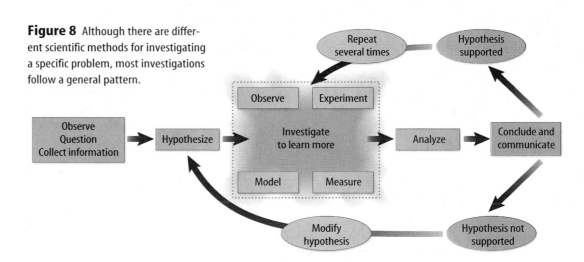

Section 2 Resource Manager

Chapter *FAST FILE* Resources
Transparency Activity, pp. 42, 49–50
Directed Reading for Content Mastery, p. 23
Enrichment, p. 34
MiniLAB, p. 4
Lab Activity, pp. 11–14
Reinforcement, p. 30

Physical Science Critical Thinking/Problem Solving, p. 2
Mathematics Skill Activities, p. 29
Reading and Writing Skill Activities, pp. 7, 41
Life Science Critical Thinking/Problem Solving, p. 7
Performance Assessment in the Science Classroom, p. 42

It's not very heavy.

What's that metal-like sound?

It sounds like a stapler.

Questioning and Observing Ms. Clark placed a sealed shoe box on the table at the front of the laboratory. Everyone in the class noticed the box. Within seconds the questions flew. "What's in the box?" "Why is it there?"

Ms. Clark said she would like the class to see how they used some science skills without even realizing it.

"I think that she wants us to find out what's in it," Isabelle said to Marcus.

"Can we touch it?" asked Marcus.

"It's up to you," Ms. Clark said.

Marcus picked up the box and turned it over a few times.

"It's not heavy," Marcus observed. "Whatever is inside slides around." He handed the box to Isabelle.

Isabelle shook the box. The class heard the object strike the sides of the box. With every few shakes, the class heard a metallic sound. The box was passed around for each student to make observations and write them in his or her Science Journal. Some observations are shown in **Figure 9.**

Taking a Guess "I think it's a pair of scissors," said Marcus.

"Aren't scissors lighter than this?" asked Isabelle, while shaking the box. "I think it's a stapler."

"What makes you think so?" asked Ms. Clark.

"Well, staplers are small enough to fit inside a shoe box, and it seems to weigh about the same," said Isabelle.

"We can hear metal when we shake it," said Enrique.

"So, you are guessing that a stapler is in the box?"

"Yes," they agreed.

"You just stated a hypothesis," exclaimed Ms. Clark.

"A what?" asked Marcus.

INTEGRATE Career

Biologist Some naturalists study the living world, using mostly their observational skills. They observe animals and plants in their natural environment, taking care not to disturb the organisms they are studying. Make observations of organisms in a nearby park or backyard. Record your observations in your Science Journal.

Visual Learning

Figure 8 Although there is no one right way to carry out a scientific investigation, most follow the pattern outlined in this flow chart. Think of a scientific investigation as trying to make a tasty pot of soup. How would the steps outlined in the figure help you do this? Possible response: You select ingredients and decide which ones should go in the soup (hypothesize). You add them and sample the soup to see how it tastes (observe and analyze). You keep adding to and taking away from the recipe until it tastes the best (experiment). You write down the recipe so others can make it in exactly the same way (conclude and communicate). L2

INTEGRATE Career

Biologist Have a local biologist come to the classroom and discuss the organisms that they study. Ask the biologist to explain what type of observations that they make. The biologist can work for a zoo, local or federal wildlife protection agency, or botanical garden.

Differentiated Instruction

Visually Impaired Glue string to a sheet of construction paper to make a three-dimensional map of **Figure 7.** Place Braille labels on the different skills. Visually impaired students can use this for later reference.

Mini LAB

Purpose Students form a hypothesis based on observations.

L2 **LS** Kinesthetic

Materials large pot, water, can of regular soda, can of diet soda

Teaching Strategy Not all regular soda cans will sink. If regular soda cans float, have students suggest possible reasons this occurs.

Safety Precautions Caution students not to shake the cans or handle them roughly.

Analysis

1. The can of regular soda did not float, but the can of diet soda did.
2. Possible answer: It led me to think that the cans behaved differently because they contained different ingredients.
3. Answers may vary. The regular soda uses a lot of sugar for sweetening. The diet soda uses only a little artificial sweetener.

Assessment

Process Have students measure the mass and volume of the soda in each can and determine the density of the soda. Ask them to suggest how the soda's density affected the behavior of the can in the water. Use **Performance Assessment in the Science Classroom**, p. 97.

Mini LAB

Forming a Hypothesis

Procedure

1. Fill a large **pot** with **water**. Place an **unopened can of diet soda** and an **unopened can of regular soda** into the pot of water and observe what each can does.
2. In your **Science Journal**, make a list of the possible explanations for your observation. Select the best explanation and write a hypothesis.
3. Read the nutritional facts on the back of each can and compare their ingredients.
4. Revise your hypothesis based on this new information.

Analysis

1. What did you observe when you placed the cans in the water?
2. How did the nutritional information on the cans change your hypothesis?
3. Infer why the two cans behaved differently in the water.

The Hypothesis "A hypothesis is a reasonable and educated possible answer based on what you know and what you observe."

"We know that a stapler is small, it can be heavy, and it is made of metal," said Isabelle.

"We observed that what is in the box is small, heavier than a pair of scissors, and made of metal," continued Marcus.

Analyzing Hypotheses "What other possible explanations fit with what you observed?" asked Ms. Clark.

"Well, it has to be a stapler," said Enrique.

"What if it isn't?" asked Ms. Clark. "Maybe you're overlooking explanations because your minds are made up. A good scientist keeps an open mind to every idea and explanation. What if you learn new information that doesn't fit with your original hypothesis? What new information could you gather to verify or disprove your hypothesis?"

"Do you mean a test or something?" asked Marcus.

"I know," said Enrique, "We could get an empty shoe box that is the same size as the mystery box and put a stapler in it. Then we could shake it and see whether it feels and sounds the same." Enrique's test is shown in **Figure 10.**

Making a Prediction "If your hypothesis is correct, what would you expect to happen?" asked Ms. Clark.

"Well, it would be about the same weight and it would slide around a little, just like the other box," said Enrique.

"It would have that same metallic sound when we shake it," said Marcus.

"So, you predict that the test box will feel and sound the same as your mystery box. Go ahead and try it," said Ms. Clark.

Figure 10 Comparing the known information with the unknown information can be valuable even though you cannot see what is inside the closed box.

LAB DEMONSTRATION

Purpose to make predictions based on sounds

Materials 5 identical glasses, spoon, water

Preparation Put a different amount of water in each glass.

Procedure Tap on the glass containing the most water, and tell students this glass contains the most water. Do the same with the glass containing the least water. Then tap on two of the other glasses and ask which has more water in it. Repeat this process until students have ranked the five glasses from the one containing the most water to the one with the least water.

Assessment

State the relationship between the amount of water in a glass and the pitch produced when the glass is hit. The more water in the glass, the higher the pitch. Is this a hypothesis, a theory, or a law? Why? It is a law—it is based on observation.

Testing the Hypothesis Ms. Clark gave the class an empty shoe box that appeared to be identical to the mystery box. Isabelle found a metal stapler. Enrique put the stapler in the box and taped the box closed. Marcus shook the box.

"The stapler does slide around but it feels just a little heavier than what's inside the mystery box," said Marcus. "What do you think?" he asked Isabelle as he handed her the box.

"It is heavier," said Isabelle "and as hard as I shake it, I can't get a metallic sound. What if we find the mass of both boxes? Then we'll know the exact mass difference between the two."

Using a balance, as shown in **Figure 11,** the class found that the test box had a mass of 410 g, and the mystery box had a mass of 270 g.

Organizing Your Findings "Okay. Now you have some new information," said Ms. Clark. "But before you draw any conclusions, let's organize what we know. Then we'll have a summary of our observations and can refer back to them when we are drawing our conclusions."

"We could make a chart of our observations in our Science Journals," said Marcus.

"We could compare the observations of the mystery box with the observations of the test box," said Isabelle. The chart that the class made is shown in **Table 1.**

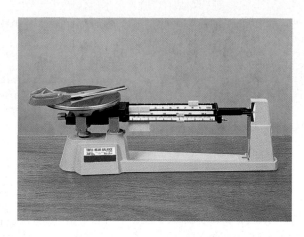

Figure 11 Laboratory balances are used to find the mass of objects.

Table 1 Observation Chart		
Questions	**Mystery Box**	**Our Box**
Does it roll or slide?	It slides and appears to be flat.	It slides and appears to be flat.
Does it make any sounds?	It makes a metallic sound when it strikes the sides of the box.	The stapler makes a thudding sound when it strikes the sides of the box.
Is the mass evenly distributed in the box?	No. The object doesn't completely fill the box.	No. The mass of the stapler is unevenly distributed.
What is the mass of the box?	270 g	410 g

Figure 12 Observations can be used to draw inferences.
Infer *Looking at both of these photos, what do you infer has taken place?*

Drawing Conclusions

"What have you learned from your investigation so far?" asked Ms. Clark.

"The first thing that we learned was that our hypothesis wasn't correct," answered Marcus.

"Would you say that your hypothesis was entirely wrong?" asked Ms. Clark.

"The boxes don't weigh the same, and the box with the stapler doesn't make the same sound as the mystery box. But there could be a difference in the kind of stapler in the box. It could be a different size or made of different materials."

"So you infer that the object in the mystery box is not exactly the same type of stapler, right?" asked Ms. Clark.

"What does *infer* mean?" asked Isabelle.

"To **infer** something means to draw a conclusion based on what you observe," answered Ms. Clark.

"So we inferred that the things in the boxes had to be different because our observations of the two boxes are different," said Marcus.

"I guess we're back to where we started," said Enrique. "We still don't know what's in the mystery box."

"Do you know more than you did before you started?" asked Ms. Clark.

"We eliminated one possibility," Isabelle added.

"Yes. We inferred that it's not a stapler, at least not like the one in the test box," said Marcus.

"So even if your observations don't support your hypothesis, you know more than you did when you started," said Ms. Clark.

Continuing to Learn "So when do we get to open the box and see what it is?" asked Marcus.

"Let me ask you this," said Ms. Clark. "Do you think scientists always get a chance to look inside to see if they are right?"

"If they are studying something too big or too small to see, I guess they can't," replied Isabelle. "What do they do in those cases?"

"As you learned, your first hypothesis might not be supported by your investigation. Instead of giving up, you continue to gather information by making more observations, making new hypotheses, and by investigating further. Some scientists have spent lifetimes researching their questions. Science takes patience and persistence," said Ms. Clark.

Communicating Your Findings It is not unusual for one scientist to continue the work of another or to try to duplicate the work of another scientist. It is important for scientists to communicate to others not only the results of the investigation, but also the methods by which the investigation was done. Scientists often publish reports in journals, books, and on the Internet to show other scientists the work that was completed. They also might attend meetings where they make speeches about their work.

Like the science-fair student in **Figure 13** demonstrates, an important part of doing science is the ability to communicate methods and results to others.

Reading Check *Why do scientists share information?*

Figure 13 Presentations are one way people in science communicate their findings.

Applying Math   Make a Data Table

SEASONAL TEMPERATURES Suppose you were given the average temperatures in a city for the four seasons over a three-year period: spring 1997 was 11°C; summer 1997 was 25°C; fall 1997 was 5°C; winter 1997 was −5°C; spring 1998 was 9°C; summer 1998 was 36°C; fall 1998 was 10°C; winter 1998 was −3°C; spring 1999 was 10°C; summer 1999 was 30°C; fall 1999 was 9°C; and winter 1999 was −2°C. How can you tell in which of the years each season had its coldest average?

Solution

1 *This is what you know:*   Temperatures were: 1997: 11°C, 25°C, 5°C, −5°C

                                            1998: 9°C, 36°C, 10°C, −3°C

                                            1999: 10°C, 30°C, 9°C, −2°C

2 *This is what you need to find out:*   Which of the years each season had its coldest temperature?

3 *This is the procedure you need to use:*
- Create a table with rows for seasons and columns for the years.
- Insert the values you were given.

4 *Check your answer:*   The four coldest seasons were spring 1998, summer 1997, fall 1997, and winter 1997.

Practice Problems

Use your table to find out which season had the greatest difference in temperatures over the three years from 1997 through 1999.

Science Online   **For more practice, visit ips.msscience.com/ math_practice**

Differentiated Instruction

Learning Disabled To help students organize the data given in the Problem-Solving Activity, suggest that before they construct their tables, they write the data as a list. `L1`

Spring 1997: 11°C   Fall 1997: 5°C
Summer 1997: 25°C   Winter 1997: −5°C
Spring 1998: 9°C , and so on.

Inquiry Lab

Understanding the Scientific Method

Purpose To understand the scientific method, have students work through the steps and design an experiment based on an observation made in the schoolyard.

Possible Materials paper, pen, magnifying glass, thermometer, rain gauge

Estimated Time 1 class session (Students may need to collect research for a few days before performing their investigation.)

Teaching Strategies
- Students can place thermometers around the schoolyard and record the temperature at each location several times throughout the day. They could hypothesize why the temperature varies from one location to another.
- Students can set rain gauges up around the schoolyard to collect rainwater. They could hypothesize which areas will receive more water than others.
- Students could compare the pH levels of the rainwater with that of a nearby lake or stream. `L2`

For additional inquiry activities, see *Science Inquiry Labs.*

Applying Math

National Math Standards

Correlation to Mathematics Objectives

5, 6

Answers to Practice Problems

1. Summer; it had a range of 11°C.

2. Possible answers: You can say that spring temperatures changed the least and that fall and spring temperatures are the closest to each other.

Experiments

Different types of questions call for different types of investigations. Ms. Clark's class made many observations about their mystery box and about their test box. They wanted to know what was inside. To answer their question, building a model—the test box—was an effective way to learn more about the mystery box. Some questions ask about the effects of one factor on another. One way to investigate these kinds of questions is by doing a controlled experiment. A **controlled experiment** involves changing one factor and observing its effect on another while keeping all other factors constant.

Variables and Constants Imagine a race in which the lengths of the lanes vary. Some lanes are 102 m long, some are 98 m long, and a few are 100 m long. When the first runner crosses the finish line, is he or she the fastest? Not necessarily. The lanes in the race have different lengths.

Variables are factors that can be changed in an experiment. Reliable experiments, like the race shown in **Figure 14,** attempt to change one variable and observe the effect of this change on another variable. The variable that is changed in an experiment is called the **independent variable.** The **dependent variable** changes as a result of a change in the independent variable. It usually is the dependent variable that is observed in an experiment. Scientists attempt to keep all other variables constant—or unchanged.

The variables that are not changed in an experiment are called **constants.** Examples of constants in the race include track material, wind speed, and distance. This way it is easier to determine exactly which variable is responsible for the runners' finish times. In this race, the runners' abilities were varied. The runners' finish times were observed.

Figure 14 The 400-m race is an example of a controlled experiment. The distance, track material, and wind speed are constants. The runners' abilities and their finish times are varied.

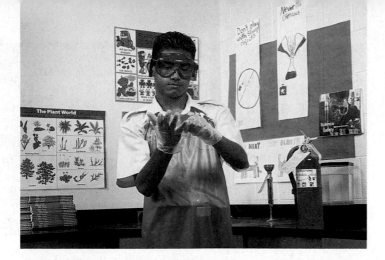

Figure 15 Safety is the most important aspect of any investigation.

Laboratory Safety

In your science class, you will perform many types of investigations. However, performing scientific investigations involves more than just following specific steps. You also must learn how to keep yourself and those around you safe by obeying the safety symbol warnings, shown in **Figure 16.**

In a Laboratory When scientists work in a laboratory, as shown in **Figure 15,** they take many safety precautions.

The most important safety advice in a science lab is to think before you act. Always check with your teacher several times in the planning stage of any investigation. Also make sure you know the location of safety equipment in the laboratory room and how to use this equipment, including the eyewashes, thermal mitts, and fire extinguisher.

Good safety habits include the following suggestions. Before conducting any investigation, find and follow all safety symbols listed in your investigation. You always should wear an apron and goggles to protect yourself from chemicals, flames, and pointed objects. Keep goggles on until activity, cleanup, and handwashing are complete. Always slant test tubes away from yourself and others when heating them. Never eat, drink, or apply makeup in the lab. Report all accidents and injuries to your teacher and always wash your hands after working with lab materials.

In the Field Investigations also take place outside the lab, in streams, farm fields, and other places. Scientists must follow safety regulations there, as well, such as wearing eye goggles and any other special safety equipment that is needed. Never reach into holes or under rocks. Always wash your hands after you've finished your field work.

Eye Safety

Clothing Protection

Disposal

Biological

Extreme Temperature

Sharp Object

Fume

Irritant

Toxic

Animal Safety

Flammable

Electrical

Chemical

Open Flame

Handwashing

Figure 16 Safety symbols are present on nearly every investigation you will do this year.
List the safety symbols that should be on the lab the student is preparing to do in **Figure 15.**

Check for Understanding

Logical-Mathematical Ask students what might be some of the variables and constants in a study of local wildlife. Variables might include the amount of daylight at the time of year and the time an animal can spend looking for food. A constant might be the physical features of the land the animal lives on. L2 LS

Reteach

Scientific Investigations Have students draw their own diagrams showing the steps in a scientific investigation. Encourage them to incorporate safety notes into their diagrams. L2 LS **Visual-Spatial**

☑ Assessment

Content Have each student write an ending to the story in this section. Have groups of students act the story out as a play, incorporating the different endings written by the students in the group. Use **Performance Assessment in the Science Classroom,** p. 147. L2

Figure 17 Accidents are not planned. Safety precautions must be followed to prevent injury.

Why have safety rules? Doing science in the class laboratory or in the field can be much more interesting than reading about it. However, safety rules must be strictly followed, so that the possibility of an accident greatly decreases. However, you can't predict when something will go wrong.

Think of a person taking a trip in a car. Most of the time when someone drives somewhere in a vehicle, an accident, like the one shown in **Figure 17,** does not occur. But to be safe, drivers and passengers always should wear safety belts. Likewise, you always should wear and use appropriate safety gear in the lab—whether you are conducting an investigation or just observing. The most important aspect of any investigation is to conduct it safely.

section ② review

Summary

Science Skills
- The scientific method was developed to help scientists investigate their questions.
- Hypotheses are possible explanations for why something occurs.

Drawing Conclusions
- Scientists communicate with one another to share important information.

Experiments
- Controlled experiments test the effect of one factor on another.

Laboratory Safety
- Safety precautions must be followed when conducting any investigation.

Self Check

1. **Explain** the difference between an inference and an observation.
2. **Explain** the differences between independent and dependent variables.
3. **Think Critically** A classroom investigation lists bleach as an ingredient. Bleach can irritate your skin, damage your eyes, and stain your clothes. What safety symbols should be listed with this investigation? Explain.

Applying Skills

4. **Describe** the different types of safety equipment found in a scientific laboratory. From your list, which equipment should you use when working with a flammable liquid in the lab?

Science Online ips.msscience.com/self_check_quiz

section ② review

1. An observation is something that comes from your senses. An inference is a conclusion your mind draws.
2. An independent variable is the variable that changes in an experiment. The dependent variable changes as a result of the changing independent variable.
3. Symbols listed: disposal alert, irritant alert, fume safety, clothing protection, eye safety, toxic alert, and chemical safety.
4. You should wear an apron, goggles, and gloves. You also should wear long, tight sleeves to protect your arms. You should make sure an eyewash and a fire extinguisher are nearby.

Models in Science

Why are models necessary?

Just as you can take many different paths in an investigation, you can test a hypothesis in many different ways. Ms. Clark's class tested their hypothesis by building a model of the mystery box. A model is one way to test a hypothesis. In science, a **model** is any representation of an object or an event used as a tool for understanding the natural world.

Models can help you visualize, or picture in your mind, something that is difficult to see or understand. Ms. Clark's class made a model because they couldn't see the item inside the box. Models can be of things that are too small or too big to see. They also can be of things that can't be seen because they don't exist anymore or they haven't been created yet. Models also can show events that occur too slowly or too quickly to see. **Figure 18** shows different kinds of models.

Figure 18 Models help scientists visualize and study complex things and things that can't be seen.

as you read

What You'll Learn
- **Describe** various types of models.
- **Discuss** limitations of models.

Why It's Important
Models can be used to help understand difficult concepts.

Review Vocabulary
scientific method: processes scientists use to collect information and answer questions

New Vocabulary
- model

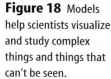

Prototype model

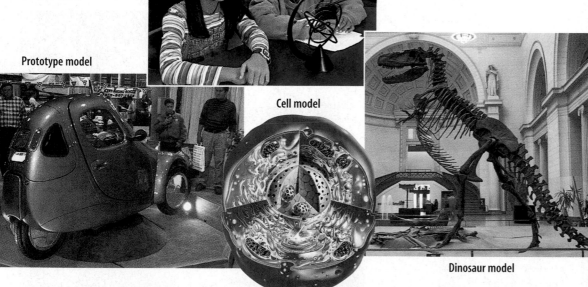

Cell model

Solar system model

Dinosaur model

1 Motivate

INTERACTIVE CHALKBOARD
PowerPoint® Presentations

Bellringer

Section Focus Transparencies also are available on the Interactive Chalkboard CD-ROM.
L2 ELL

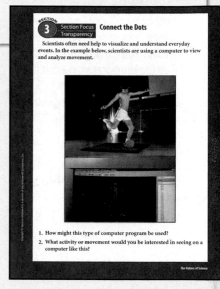

3 Section Focus Transparency — Connect the Dots

Scientists often need help to visualize and understand everyday events. In the example below, scientists are using a computer to view and analyze movement.

1. How might this type of computer program be used?
2. What activity or movement would you be interested in seeing on a computer like this?

The Nature of Science

Tie to Prior Knowledge

Modeling Events Ask students whether they've ever described an event to someone and had a hard time doing it. To make things easier, they may try to act out the event. If it was the winning shot in a basketball game, for example, they may have begun "Okay, there's the basket and you're the player guarding me. . . ." Tell them that if they did this, they made a model of the event. L1

Section 3 Resource Manager

Chapter *FAST FILE* Resources
Transparency Activity, pp. 50, 51
MiniLAB, p. 5
Enrichment, p. 35
Directed Reading for Content Mastery, pp. 23, 24

Reinforcement, p. 31
Lab Activity, pp. 15–18
Reading and Writing Skill Activities, p. 43

Use an Analogy

Sports When you practice playing a sport, you are making a model. Good coaches know the kinds of plays another team uses and will simulate those plays in practice to prepare the players. This is a type of physical model.

Fun Fact

Pilots and astronauts receive some of their most critical flight training without ever leaving the ground. They use complicated, realistic flight simulators that allow them to practice emergency procedures without risking an accident in the air.

✓ Reading Check

Answer show things that occur too slowly or too quickly to be seen and show motions and positions of things that would take hours or days to calculate by hand or using a calculator

Discussion

Topographic Maps Show students a topographic map and point out the contour lines that show changes in elevation. Explain that when the contour lines get closer together, elevation changes are much steeper. Point out the different symbols for mountains, rivers, and lakes. Have students find a topographic map of their home state and analyze the symbols and elevation gradients.

Science Online

Topic: Topographic Maps
Visit ips.msscience.com for Web links to information about topographic maps.

Activity List some of the different features found on topographic maps and explain their importance when reading and interpreting maps.

Types of Models

Most models fall into three basic types—physical models, computer models, and idea models. Depending on the reason that a model is needed, scientists can choose to use one or more than one type of model.

Physical Models Models that you can see and touch are called physical models. Examples include things such as a table-top solar system, a globe of Earth, a replica of the inside of a cell, or a gumdrop-toothpick model of a chemical compound. Models show how parts relate to one another. They also can be used to show how things appear when they change position or how they react when an outside force acts on them.

Computer Models Computer models are built using computer software. You can't touch them, but you can view them on a computer screen. Some computer models can model events that take a long time or take place too quickly to see. For example, a computer can model the movement of large plates in the Earth and might help predict earthquakes.

Computers also can model motions and positions of things that would take hours or days to calculate by hand or even using a calculator. They can also predict the effect of different systems or forces. **Figure 19** shows how computer models are used by scientists to help predict the weather based on the motion of air currents in the atmosphere.

✓ Reading Check   *What do computer models do?*

Figure 19 A weather map is a computer model showing weather patterns over large areas. Scientists can use this information to predict the weather and to alert people to potentially dangerous weather on the way.

22   CHAPTER 1 The Nature of Science

Curriculum Connection

Social Studies You may have heard that a TV program is the number-one-rated show, but what exactly does that mean? Have students find out and report on how TV viewing statistics are obtained. TV viewing statistics are obtained by selecting a scientifically identified representative sample (a model) of the entire country's population. These households' viewing habits are monitored by special boxes on their sets and the results extended to the whole country. In the United States, about 25,000 homes rate the viewing habits of the entire country.
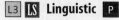 **Linguistic** P

Figure 20 Models can be created using various types of tools.

Idea Models Some models are ideas or concepts that describe how someone thinks about something in the natural world. Albert Einstein is famous for his theory of relativity, which involves the relationship between matter and energy. One of the most famous models Einstein used for this theory is the mathematical equation $E = mc^2$. This explains that mass, m, can be changed into energy, E. Einstein's idea models never could be built as physical models, because they are basically ideas.

Making Models

The process of making a model is something like a sketch artist at work, as shown in **Figure 20.** The sketch artist attempts to draw a picture from the description given by someone. The more detailed the description is, the better the picture will be. Like a scientist who studies data from many sources, the sketch artist can make a sketch based on more than one person's observation. The final sketch isn't a photograph, but if the information is accurate, the sketch should look realistic. Scientific models are made much the same way. The more information a scientist gathers, the more accurate the model will be. The process of constructing a model of King Tutankhamun, who lived more than 3,000 years ago, is shown in **Figure 21.**

 *How are sketches like specific models?*

Using Models

When you think of a model, you might think of a model airplane or a model of a building. Not all models are for scientific purposes. You use models, and you might not realize it. Drawings, maps, recipes, and globes are all examples of models.

Mini LAB

Thinking Like a Scientist

Procedure
1. Pour 15 mL of **water** into a **test tube.**
2. Slowly pour 5 mL of **vegetable oil** into the test tube.
3. Add two drops of **food coloring** and observe the liquid for 5 min.

Analysis
1. Record your observations of the test tube's contents before and after the oil and the food coloring were added to it.
2. Infer a scientific explanation for your observations.

SECTION 3   Models in Science   **23**

☑ Assessment

Process Have students suggest ways in which the observations made in this activity could be used to design an experiment that determines the identity of a substance. Use **Performance Assessment in the Science Classroom,** p. 95. L2

☑ Reading Check

Answer The more detailed the information used to make the model or the sketch, the better it will be.

Quick Demo
Star Gazing
Materials star chart
Estimated Time 10 minutes
Procedure Obtain a star chart and demonstrate how it can be used to make predictions of the night sky on different days of the year.

Purpose Students use scientific thinking as they make observations and draw inferences. L2
IS Kinesthetic
Materials water, vegetable oil, graduated cylinder, test tube, food coloring, watch or clock

Teaching Strategies
• Before they do the experiment, explain to students that some liquids do not mix with each other.
• Tell the students to remember the phrase "like dissolves like."
• Have students discuss what the wisest choice would be for disposal of the vegetable oil following the experiment.

Troubleshooting Have students keep the test tubes as still as possible.

Analysis
1. Students' records should show that the drops remained intact in the oil and sat on the oil and water border for several seconds until they pushed through the layer. Once in the water, the food dye exploded into swirls of color.
2. Food coloring does not mix with oil. Food coloring mixes with water because it is like water and "like dissolves like."

Assessment

Performance Extend the MiniLab and have students experiment what happens when you mix soap in with the oil and water. How does the use of soapy water help clean dishes?

Visualizing the Modeling of King Tut

Have students examine the pictures and read the captions. Then ask the following questions.

Why might scientists want to make a model of the face of a person from a skull? **Possible answer: to help discover the identity of victims of accidents, fires, plane crashes, war, or murder.**

How is the model of King Tut like other models used by scientists? **Like other models, it is used by scientists to describe things they cannot see directly. Models can help scientists explain data and predict outcomes.**

Activity

Models Have small groups of students make models of objects or ideas related to science. After the models are complete, have each group present and explain its model to the class. Discuss the accuracy of each model and how well it serves its purpose. L2

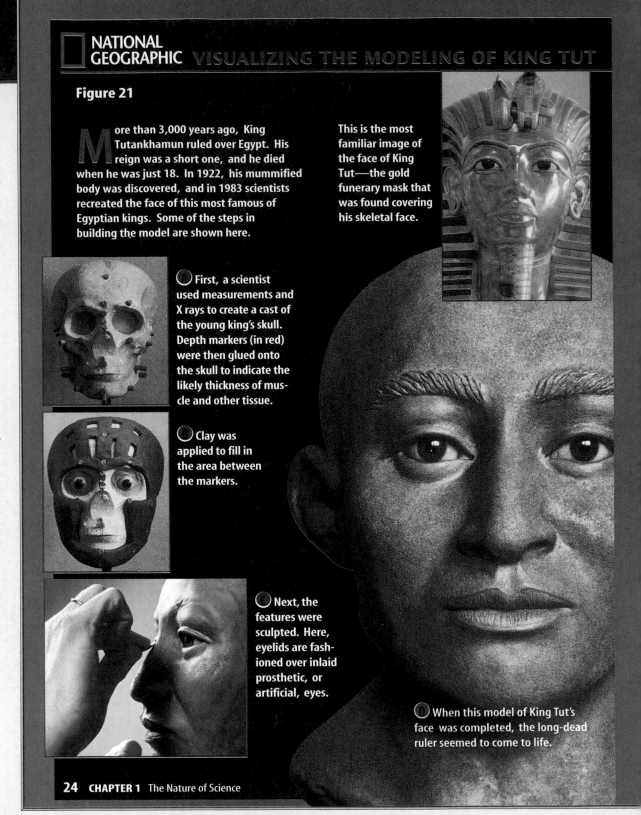

Figure 21

More than 3,000 years ago, King Tutankhamun ruled over Egypt. His reign was a short one, and he died when he was just 18. In 1922, his mummified body was discovered, and in 1983 scientists recreated the face of this most famous of Egyptian kings. Some of the steps in building the model are shown here.

This is the most familiar image of the face of King Tut—the gold funerary mask that was found covering his skeletal face.

A First, a scientist used measurements and X rays to create a cast of the young king's skull. Depth markers (in red) were then glued onto the skull to indicate the likely thickness of muscle and other tissue.

B Clay was applied to fill in the area between the markers.

C Next, the features were sculpted. Here, eyelids are fashioned over inlaid prosthetic, or artificial, eyes.

D When this model of King Tut's face was completed, the long-dead ruler seemed to come to life.

24 CHAPTER 1 The Nature of Science

Differentiated Instruction

Challenge Have students research how forensic anthropologists use the technique described in this feature to identify skeletal remains. Students could present their information in written or oral reports. L3

Visually Impaired Have students use clay to construct a simple model of something familiar to them. Ask the students to share their models with one another. Rather than viewing the model with open eyes, ask the students to close their eyes and gently feel the model. Do they recognize what the model is?

Models Communicate
Some models are used to communicate observations and ideas to other people. Often, it is easier to communicate ideas you have by making a model instead of writing your ideas in words. This way others can visualize them, too.

Models Test Predictions
Some models are used to test predictions. Ms. Clark's class predicted that a box with a stapler in it would have characteristics similar to their mystery box. To test this prediction, the class made a model. Automobile and airplane engineers use wind tunnels to test predictions about how air will interact with their products.

Models Save Time, Money, and Lives
Other models are used because working with and testing a model can be safer and less expensive than using the real thing. For example, the crash-test dummies shown in **Figure 22** are used in place of people when testing the effects of automobile crashes. To help train astronauts in the conditions they will encounter in space, NASA has built a special airplane. This airplane flies in an arc that creates the condition of freefall for 20 to 25 seconds. Making several trips in the airplane is easier, safer, and less expensive than making a trip into space.

Figure 22 Models are a safe and relatively inexpensive way to test ideas.

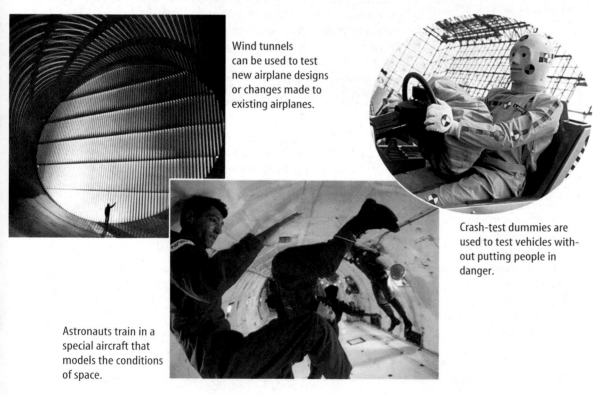

Wind tunnels can be used to test new airplane designs or changes made to existing airplanes.

Crash-test dummies are used to test vehicles without putting people in danger.

Astronauts train in a special aircraft that models the conditions of space.

Check for Understanding

Visual-Spatial Have students use a video camera to model a special effect in a motion picture. Possible effects might include someone flying, a giant river, or a tornado.
L3 LS

Reteach

Models Ask students which type of model—physical, computer, or idea—they'd use to represent the following: how a building will look when it's completed; the relationship between mass and gravity; how Earth's landscape has changed over time. physical or computer, idea, computer.
L2 LS **Logical-Mathematical**

☑ Assessment

Process Students probably had some knowledge of models before reading the section. Have them write in their Science Journals how their ideas about models have changed since reading the section. Use **Performance Assessment in the Science Classroom,** p. 157.
L2

Figure 23 The model of Earth's solar system changed as new information was gathered.

An early model of the solar system had Earth in the center with everything revolving around it.

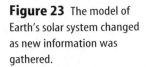

Later on, a new model had the Sun in the center with everything revolving around it.

Limitations of Models

The solar system is too large to be viewed all at once, so models are made to understand it. Many years ago, scientists thought that Earth was the center of the universe and the sky was a blanket that covered the planet.

Later, through observation, it was discovered that the objects you see in the sky are the Sun, the Moon, stars, and other planets. This new model explained the solar system differently. Earth was still the center, but everything else orbited it as shown in **Figure 23.**

Models Change Still later, through more observation, it was discovered that the Sun is the center of the solar system. Earth, along with the other planets, orbits the Sun. In addition, it was discovered that other planets also have moons that orbit them. A new model was developed to show this.

Earlier models of the solar system were not meant to be misleading. Scientists made the best models they could with the information they had. More importantly, their models gave future scientists information to build upon. Models are not necessarily perfect, but they provide a visual tool to learn from.

---

section 3 review

Summary

Why are models necessary?

- Scientists develop models to help them visualize complex concepts.

Types of Models

- There are three types of models—physical models, computer models, and idea models.

Making Models

- The more information you have when creating a model, the more accurate the model will be.

Using Models

- Models are used to convey important information such as maps and schedules.

Limitations of Models

- Models can be changed over time as new information becomes available.

Self Check

1. **Infer** what types of models can be used to model weather. How are they used to predict weather patterns?
2. **Explain** how models are used in science.
3. **Describe** how consumer product testing services use models to ensure the safety of the final products produced.
4. **Describe** the advantages and limitations of the three types of models.
5. **Think Critically** Explain why some models are better than others for certain situations. Give one example.

Applying Math

6. **Use Proportions** On a map of a state, the scale shows that 1 cm is approximately 5 km. If the distance between two cities is 1.7 cm on the map, how many kilometers separate them?

Science Online ips.msscience.com/self_check_quiz

---

section 3 review

1. Computer models and paper drawings can be used to model weather. Each can show past events but computer models can predict future events.
2. Models are used in science to study things that are too big, too small, take too long, or happen too quickly.
3. A model product is tested using a wide range of conditions in which the product is expected to operate.
4. physical model—can take a while to make and be difficult to modify; computer model—can show slow or fast changes and can be run many times but can't show spatial relations very well; idea model—can show relationships between abstract concepts but can be hard to understand
5. Possible response: It would be difficult to make a physical model of weather changes because there are too many factors to consider.

6. $1.7 \text{ cm} \times \frac{5 \text{ km}}{1 \text{ cm}} = 8.5 \text{ km}$

Evaluating Scientific Explanation

Believe it or not?

Look at the photo in **Figure 24.** Do you believe what you see? Do you believe everything you read or hear? Think of something that someone told you that you didn't believe. Why didn't you believe it? Chances are you looked at the facts you were given and decided that there wasn't enough proof to make you believe it. What you did was evaluate, or judge the reliability of what you heard. When you hear a statement, you ask the question "How do you know?" If you decide that what you are told is reliable, then you believe it. If it seems unreliable, then you don't believe it.

Critical Thinking When you evaluate something, you use critical thinking. Critical thinking means combining what you already know with the new facts that you are given to decide if you should agree with something. You can evaluate an explanation by breaking it down into two parts. First you can look at and evaluate the observations. Based upon what you know, are the observations accurate? Then you can evaluate the inferences—or conclusions made about the observations. Do the conclusions made from the observations make sense?

Figure 24 In science, observations and inferences are not always agreed upon by everyone.
Compare *Do you see the same things your classmates see in this photo?*

27

as you read

What You'll Learn
■ **Evaluate** scientific explanations.
■ **Evaluate** promotional claims.

Why It's Important
Evaluating scientific claims can help you make better decisions.

Review Vocabulary
prediction: an educated guess as to what is going to happen based on observation

New Vocabulary
● critical thinking
● data

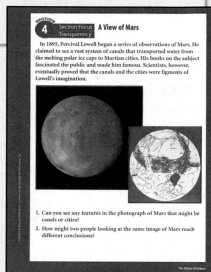

Caption Answer
Figure 24 Answers will vary.

Discussion

Evaluating Ads Have students discuss different advertisements they've heard on the radio or seen on TV. Do any of these ads use scientific evidence to back up their claims? Students may mention ads that say "Four out of five doctors prefer . . ." or "Hospitals recommend . . ." Do you trust this evidence? Answers will vary. [L2]

Activity

Percentages Ask students to express the data given in Table 2 as percentages. What percent of the people surveyed preferred pizza? $37 \div (37 + 28) \times 100\% = 57\%$ What percent preferred hamburgers? $28 \div (37 + 28) \times 100\% = 43\%$ How many people in this survey would make up 50% of the people surveyed? $x \div (37 + 28) \times 100\% = 50\%$; $x = 50\% \times (37 + 28) \div 100\% = 32.5$ Point out that the statement "More people surveyed preferred pizza than preferred hamburgers" would be true if anywhere from 33 to 65 people in the survey preferred pizza. [L2] **LS** **Logical-Mathematical**

Caption Answer

Figure 25 It will increase the reliability of their data, because they will be less likely to forget something important.

Table 2 Favorite Foods		
People's Preference	Tally	Frequency
Pepperoni pizza	卌 卌 卌 卌 卌 卌 卌 II	37
Hamburgers with ketchup	卌 卌 卌 卌 卌 III	28

Evaluating the Data

A scientific investigation always contains observations—often called **data.** Data are gathered during a scientific investigation and can be recorded in the form of descriptions, tables, graphs, or drawings. When evaluating a scientific claim, you might first look to see whether any data are given. You should be cautious about believing any claim that is not supported by data.

Are the data specific? The data given to back up a claim should be specific. That means they need to be exact. What if your friend tells you that many people like pizza more than they like hamburgers? What else do you need to know before you agree with your friend? You might want to hear about a specific number of people rather than unspecific words like *many* and *more.* You might want to know how many people like pizza more than hamburgers. How many people were asked about which kind of food they liked more? When you are given specific data, a statement is more reliable and you are more likely to believe it. An example of data in the form of a frequency table is shown in **Table 2.** A frequency table shows how many times types of data occur. Scientists must back up their scientific statements with specific data.

Take Good Notes Scientists must take thorough notes at the time of an investigation, as the scientists shown in **Figure 25** are doing. Important details can be forgotten if you wait several hours or days before you write down your observations. It is also important for you to write down every observation, including ones that you don't expect. Often, great discoveries are made when something unexpected happens in an investigation.

Figure 25 These scientists are writing down their observations during their investigation rather than waiting until they are back on land.
Draw Conclusions *Do you think this will increase or decrease the reliability of their data?*

28

Visual Learning

Figure 24 Many times it's no accident that pictures of supposed UFOs appear out of focus. Why might this make the claim more believable? Because the object is blurry, you can't say for sure that it's not a UFO. How is this similar to using words like many and most? The words *many* and *most* sometimes blur ideas like a camera's lens can blur an object. [L2] **LS**
Visual-Spatial

Differentiated Instruction

English-Language Learners Have students observe something outside for 5 min. A bird, students on the playground, traffic in front of the schoolyard. Ask them to write down their observations emphasizing that their notes should be specific. Pair students up and have them compare their notes and compose a paragraph describing what they observed.

Your Science Journal During this course, you will be keeping a science journal. You will write down what you do and see during your investigations. Your observations should be detailed enough that another person could read what you wrote and repeat the investigation exactly as you performed it. Instead of writing "the stuff changed color," you might say "the clear liquid turned to bright red when I added a drop of food coloring." Detailed observations written down during an investigation are more reliable than sketchy observations written from memory. Practice your observation skills by describing what you see in **Figure 26.**

Can the data be repeated? If your friend told you he could hit a baseball 100 m, but couldn't do it when you were around, you probably wouldn't believe him. Scientists also require repeatable evidence. When a scientist describes an investigation, as shown in **Figure 27,** other scientists should be able to do the investigation and get the same results. The results must be repeatable. When evaluating scientific data, look to see whether other scientists have repeated the data. If not, the data might not be reliable.

Evaluating the Conclusions

When you think about a conclusion that someone has made, you can ask yourself two questions. First, does the conclusion make sense? Second, are there any other possible explanations? Suppose you hear on the radio that your school will be running on a two-hour delay in the morning because of snow. You look outside. The roads are clear of snow. Does the conclusion that snow is the cause for the delay make sense? What else could cause the delay? Maybe it is too foggy or icy for the buses to run. Maybe there is a problem with the school building. The original conclusion is not reliable unless the other possible explanations are proven unlikely.

Figure 26 Detailed observations are important in order to get reliable data.
Observe *Use ten descriptive words to describe what you see happening in this photo.*

Figure 27 Working together is an important part of science. Several scientists must repeat an experiment and obtain the same results before data are considered reliable.

29

Caption Answer

Figure 26 Answers will vary. Examples include: A spiral-shaped, copper-colored metal is in a blue solution. Sparkly silver stuff is also in the blue solution. It looks like the sparkly stuff is coming from the metal.

Discussion

Multiple Trials Tell students that, when doing experiments, scientists often run multiple trials of the same test and average the results. How does this affect the way you evaluate the scientists' data? Because the results are based on the averages of repeated trials, they are more likely to be repeatable and reliable.
[L2] **IS** Logical-Mathematical

Quick Demo
Packaging Claims
Materials cereal boxes, food labels, product wrapping
Estimated Time 10 minutes
Procedure Share the products with the students and have them write down five claims made on the packaging. These can include ingredients, uses for the product, age requirements, allergic concerns, photos, etc. Which claims do they believe and which do they not believe? Why? [L2]

Differentiated Instruction

Challenge Have students research the consequences companies face when they advertise false claims. How do corporations try and cover their mistake when it becomes public knowledge? What sort of things would a corporation need to do to make the public believe their advertising after being identified as having made false claims? [L3]

MIRACLE CREAM
MAKES WRINKLES
DISAPPEAR
OVERNIGHT

With twice daily use you will see improvement almost immediately, noticeable change within 30 DAYS... significant improvement within 60 days and even greater results after 6 months.

Figure 28 All material should be read with an analytical mind. **Explain** *what this advertisement means.*

Evaluating Promotional Materials

Scientific processes are not used only in the laboratory. Suppose you saw an advertisement in the newspaper like the one in **Figure 28.** What would you think? First, you might ask, "Does this make sense?" It seems unbelievable. You would probably want to hear some of the scientific data supporting the claim before you would believe it. How was this claim tested? How is the amount of wrinkling in skin measured? You might also want to know if an independent laboratory repeated the results. An independent laboratory is one that is not related in any way to the company that is selling the product or service. It has nothing to gain from the sales of the product. Results from an independent laboratory usually are more reliable than results from a laboratory paid by the selling company. Advertising materials are designed to get you to buy a product or service. It is important that you carefully evaluate advertising claims and the data that support them before making a quick decision to spend your money.

section 4 review

Summary

Believe it or not?
- By combining what you already know with new information as it becomes available, you can decide whether something is fact or fiction.
- Explanations should be evaluated by looking at both the observations and the conclusions the explanation is based on.

Evaluating the Data
- It is important to take thorough notes during any investigation.

Evaluating the Conclusions
- In order for a conclusion to be reliable, it must make sense.

Evaluating Promotional Materials
- Independent laboratories test products in order to provide more reliable results.

Self Check

1. **Describe** why it is important that scientific experiments be repeated.
2. **List** what types of scientific claims should be verified.
3. **Explain** how vague claims in advertising can be misleading.
4. **Think Critically** An advertisement on a food package claims it contains Glistain, a safe taste enhancer. Make a list of ten questions you would ask when evaluating this claim.

Applying Skills

5. **Classify** Watch three television commercials and read three magazine advertisements. Record the claims that each advertisement made. Classify each claim as being vague, misleading, reliable, and/or scientific.

Science Online ips.msscience.com/self_check_quiz

section 4 review

1. In order for scientific evidence to be reliable, experiments need to be repeatable by other scientists.
2. All scientific claims should be verified by some kind of specific data.
3. Vague claims are misleading because they contain terms that can have more than one meaning.
4. Possible questions include: What is Glistain? Has Glistain been tested? What were the results? Has it been tested on humans? Over how long a period of time was it tested? Was it tested by an independent lab?
5. Answers will vary. Make sure students select ads from each medium.

What is the right answer?

Scientists sometimes develop more than one explanation for observations. Can more than one explanation be correct? Do scientific explanations depend on judgment?

● *Real-World Question*

Can more than one explanation apply to the same observation?

Goals
- **Make a hypothesis** to explain an observation.
- **Construct** a model to support your hypothesis.
- **Refine** your model based on testing.

Materials
cardboard mailing tubes   length of rope
*empty shoe boxes   scissors
*Alternate materials

Safety Precautions

WARNING: *Be careful when punching holes with sharp tools.*

● *Procedure*

1. You will be shown a cardboard tube with four ropes coming out of it, one longer than the others. Your teacher will show you that when any of the three short ropes—A, C, or D—are pulled, the longer rope, B, gets shorter. Pulling on rope B returns the other ropes to their original lengths.
2. Make a hypothesis as to how the teacher's model works.
3. **Sketch** a model of a tube with ropes based on your hypothesis. Using a cardboard tube and two lengths of rope, build a model

according to your design. Test your model by pulling each of the ropes. If it does not perform as planned, modify your hypothesis and your model to make it work like your teacher's model.

● *Conclude and Apply*

1. **Compare** your model with those made by others in your class.
2. Can more than one design give the same result? Can more than one explanation apply to the same observation? Explain.
3. Without opening the tube, can you tell which model is exactly like your teacher's?

𝒞ommunicating Your Data

Make a display of your working model. Include sketches of your designs. **For more help, refer to the Science Skill Handbook.**

𝒞ommunicating Your Data

Suggest that students draw different designs and show how they can act similarly. If students have access to a computer animation program, encourage them to make animated drawings of the inside of the tube. L3

● *Real-World Question*

Purpose Students show that multiple explanations sometimes can apply to the same observations. L2 IS **Kinesthetic**

Process Skills Form a hypothesis, design an experiment to test a hypothesis, control variables, observe, infer, predict, recognize cause and effect, communicate

Time Required 45 minutes

● *Procedure*

Alternate Materials Empty shoe boxes with lids can be used in place of the tube allowing easy access to the ropes inside.

Teaching Strategy Demonstrate a way in which one rope may affect another rope.

● *Conclude and Apply*

1. Have students note differences and similarities in their designs and demonstrate that all models work.
2. Yes; yes; the ropes may be configured differently but perform the same.
3. No

☑ Assessment

Content Students can show their rope trick to students in lower grades. Encourage students to present the trick, and then clearly explain how it works. Use **Performance Assessment in the Science Classroom,** p. 143. L2

Identifying Parts of an Investigation

◉ Real-World Question

Purpose Students identify the steps of a scientific investigation.
L2

Process Skills recognize cause and effect, observe, infer, make and use graphs

Time Required 45 minutes

◉ Procedure

Teaching Strategies Write the steps of the scientific method on the board for students to use as a reference as they complete this lab. Students should refer to the Science Skill Handbook.

◉ Analyze Your Data

Expected Outcome Students should see that fertilizer B gave the best results. They should also see that, after starting out more slowly, fertilizer A did produce about the same results from week to week as did fertilizer B.

Goals
- **Identify** parts of an experiment.
- **Identify** constants, variables, and controls in the experiment.
- **Graph** the results of the experiment and draw appropriate conclusions.

Materials
description of fertilizer experiment

◉ Real-World Question

Science investigations contain many parts. How can you identify the various parts of an investigation? In addition to variables and constants, many experiments contain a control. A control is one test, or trial, where everything is held constant. A scientist compares the control trial to the other trials. What are the various parts of an experiment to test which fertilizer helps a plant grow best?

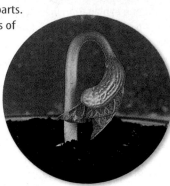

◉ Procedure

1. **Read** the description of the fertilizer experiment.
2. **List** factors that remained constant in the experiment.
3. **Identify** any variables in the experiment.
4. **Identify** the control in the experiment.
5. **Identify** one possible hypothesis that the gardener could have tested in her investigation.
6. **Describe** how the gardener went about testing her hypothesis using different types of fertilizers.

7. **Graph** the data that the gardener collected in a line graph.

A gardener was interested in helping her plants grow faster. When she went to the nursery, she found three fertilizers available for her plants. One of those fertilizers, fertilizer A, was recommended to her. However, she decided to conduct a test to determine which of the three fertilizers, if any, helped her plants grow fastest. The gardener planted four seeds, each in a separate pot. She used the same type of pot and the same type of soil in each pot. She fertilized one seed

Alternative Inquiry Lab

Real-World Connection To make this Lab an Inquiry Lab, work with a local community center or another local organization to plan landscaping to help make their grounds more attractive. The community center may want to use plants that are native to the area and that require relatively little care and maintenance. The students will need to investigate the growing and watering require-

ments of the plants. What plant suggestions could the students provide? What type of experiment could they design to verify the information they provide to the community center? Encourage students to research how landscape designers determine what plants to use in landscapes and what the variables and constants are in landscape environments. L2 PBL

with fertilizer A, one with fertilizer B, and one with fertilizer C. She did not fertilize the fourth seed. She placed the four pots near one another in her garden. She made sure to give each plant the same amount of water each day. She measured the height of the plants each week and recorded her data. After eight weeks of careful observation and record keeping, she had the following table of data.

Plant Height (cm)				
Week	Fertilizer A	Fertilizer B	Fertilizer C	No Fertilizer
1	0	0	0	0
2	2	4	1	1
3	5	8	5	4
4	9	13	8	7
5	14	18	12	10
6	20	24	15	13
7	27	31	19	16
8	35	39	22	20

Analyze Your Data

1. **Describe** the results indicated by your graph. What part of an investigation have you just done?

2. **Infer** Based on the results in the table and your graph, which fertilizer do you think the gardener should use if she wants her plants to grow the fastest? What part of an investigation have you just done?

3. **Define** Suppose the gardener told a friend who also grows these plants about her results. What is this an example of?

Conclude and Apply

1. **Interpret Data** Suppose fertilizer B is much more expensive than fertilizers A and C. Would this affect which fertilizer you think the gardener should buy? Why or why not?

2. **Explain** Does every researcher need the same hypothesis for an experiment? What is a second possible hypothesis for this experiment (different from the one you wrote in step 5 in the Procedure section)?

3. **Explain** if the gardener conducted an adequate test of her hypothesis.

Communicating Your Data

Compare your conclusions with those of other students in your class. **For more help, refer to the Science Skill Handbook.**

LAB **33**

Answers to Questions

1. The graph shows that the plant grew the most with fertilizer B, that it grew only slightly better with fertilizer C than with no fertilizer, and that with fertilizer A the plant started slowly, but then grew as fast as the plant with fertilizer B. This step is analyzing data.
2. She'd use fertilizer B. This is hypothesizing, or making a guess based on data.
3. This is communicating results.

Error Analysis Other factors might have affected the rate of plant growth. There may have been some problem with the soil in fertilizer C's pot. Maybe the seed in fertilizer A just didn't grow as much.

Conclude and Apply

1. Probably; if the gardener cannot afford the extra money she should buy fertilizer A because it helps the plant almost as much as fertilizer B.
2. No, but the procedures must be the same or you cannot compare the results. One possible hypothesis is that fertilizers stop having an effect after eight weeks.
3. She worked hard to control variables and she did her experiment over a good period of time. To confirm her results, she could try the experiment more times and for longer periods of time.

✔ Assessment

Performance Have students act out the gardener going to buy the fertilizer, the store clerk's comments to her, and her comments back to the store clerk after her investigation. Make sure each character argues using scientific evidence. Use **Performance Assessment in the Science Classroom**, p. 147. L2

Communicating Your Data

Students can use a computer graphing program to make their graphs look more professional. The programs also may allow them to predict seed growth in upcoming weeks. Using these predictions, students can argue for or against a specific fertilizer. L2

Content Background

All three women featured here made sacrifices to work in their chosen fields. Maria Goeppert Mayer often had to work "under" or "for" men in order to make her famous discovery. After earning her doctorate in 1930, Mayer worked as a lecturer and on secondary projects that helped back up the findings of men. In 1960, the University of Chicago offered her a full professorship and Mayer was finally considered for her talents as a physicist.

Politics and geography inhibited Montalcini's work. A 1936 Manifesto forbid non-Aryan Italian citizens from holding academic and professional jobs. In order to continue her work, Montalcini built a research unit in her bedroom.

Discussion

Overcoming Obstacles Each of these women had to overcome many obstacles in pursuing their careers. Discuss some obstacles that students and their families have had to overcome. Answers will vary. May include moving from a different country, new school, and special needs requirements. L2

Historical Significance

Focusing on women in science is one way of turning attention to important scientific discoveries made by women. It is also a way to inform students that women have not always been considered capable of such rigorous pursuits. Engage students in a discussion about the ways women have been excluded from many disciplines throughout history. As an example, tell them that the first woman senator, Hattie Wyatt Caraway, was not elected into office until 1932. In 2001, only 13 of the 100 U.S. Senators were women. L2

TIME

SCIENCE AND HISTORY

SCIENCE CAN CHANGE THE COURSE OF HISTORY!

Women in Science

Is your family doctor a man or a woman? To your great-grandparents, such a question would likely have seemed odd. Why? Because 100 years ago, women weren't encouraged to study science as they are today. But that does not mean that there were no female scientists back in your great-grandparents' day. Many women managed to overcome great barriers and made discoveries that changed the world.

Mayer won the Nobel Prize in Physics in 1963 for her work on the structure of an atom. Her model greatly increased human understanding of atoms, which make up all forms of matter.

Rita Levi-Montalcini

In 1986, Dr. Rita Levi-Montalcini was awarded the Nobel Prize in Medicine for her discovery of growth factors. Growth factors regulate the growth of cells and organs in the body. Because of her work, doctors are better able to understand why tumors form and wounds heal.

Rosalyn Sussman Yalow

"The world cannot afford the loss of the talents of half its people if we are to solve the many problems which beset us," Dr. Rosalyn Sussman Yalow said upon winning the Nobel Prize in Medicine in 1977 for discovering a way to measure tiny substances in the blood, such as hormones and drugs.

Her discovery made it possible for doctors to diagnose problems that they could not detect before.

Maria Goeppert Mayer

"To my surprise, winning the prize wasn't half as exciting as doing the work itself. That was the fun—seeing it work out."
Dr. Maria Goeppert

Research Visit the link to the right to research some recent female Nobel prizewinners in physics, chemistry, and medicine. Write a short biography about their lives. How did their discoveries impact their scientific fields or people in general?

Science Online

For more information, visit ips.msscience.com/time

Research Answers will vary. Marie Curie is best known for her discovery of the radioactive elements polonium and radium. Rosalind Franklin was the first to recognize the helix shape of DNA.

Resources for Teachers and Students

Nobel Prize Women in Science: Their Lives, Struggles, and Momentous Discoveries, by Sharon Bertsch McGrayne, Kensington Pub. Corp., 2001

Tech camps inspire girls but may not narrow growing gender gap, by the Associated Press, USA Today, July 2003

Nobel Prize Winners (Women in Profile Service), by Carlotta Hacker. Crabtree Publishing, 1998

Reviewing Main Ideas

Section 1 What is science?

1. Science is a way of learning more about the natural world. It can provide possible explanations for why and how things happen.

2. Systems are made up of structures, cycles, and processes that interact with one another.

Section 2 Science in Action

1. A hypothesis is a possible explanation based on what you know and what you observe.

2. It is important to always follow laboratory safety symbols and to wear and use appropriate gear during an experiment.

Section 3 Models in Science

1. Models are a graphic representation of an object or an event used to communicate ideas; test predictions; and save time, money, and lives.

Section 4 Evaluating Scientific Explanation

1. Reliable data are specific and repeatable by other scientists.

2. In order for a conclusion to be considered reliable, it must make sense and be the most likely explanation.

Visualizing Main Ideas

Copy and complete the following concept map.

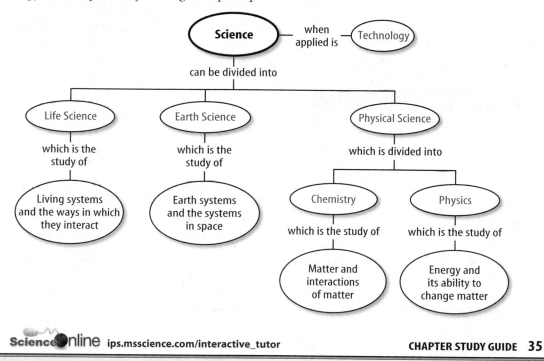

ips.msscience.com/interactive_tutor

CHAPTER STUDY GUIDE 35

Reviewing Main Ideas

Summary statements can be used by students to review the major concepts of the chapter.

Visualizing Main Ideas

See student page.

Science Online

Visit ips.msscience.com
  /self_check_quiz
  /interactive_tutor
  /vocabulary_puzzlemaker
  /chapter_review
  /standardized_test

Assessment Transparency

For additional assessment questions, use the *Assessment Transparency* located in the transparency book.

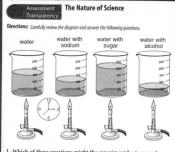

Using Vocabulary

1. A hypothesis is a guess scientists make based upon what they observe. A scientific theory is an attempt to explain a pattern seen repeatedly in the natural world.

2. Variables are the parts of an experiment that change. A constant is the one variable in an experiment that does not change.

3. Science is a way of learning about the world. Technology is the use of this knowledge.

4. Science is a way of learning about the world. A system is a collection of structures, cycles, or processes in the world that relate to one another.

5. Earth science is the study of Earth systems and the systems in space. Physical science is the study of matter and energy and their relationships.

6. Critical thinking is used to evaluate evidence. To infer is to draw a conclusion based on that evidence.

7. A scientific law is a rule that describes some pattern seen in nature. An observation can be anything you notice about the natural world.

8. A model is any representation of an object or event. A system is a collection of processes, cycles, or structures in the world.

9. A controlled experiment is an experiment in which everything but one part stays the same. Variables are the things in a controlled experiment that can change.

10. A scientific theory is an explanation of why something happens in the world. A scientific law is a statement of some regularity about something seen in the world.

Checking Concepts

11. B	14. C	17. A
12. C	15. A	18. C
13. C	16. C	19. A

Using Vocabulary

constant p.18	life science p.9
controlled experiment p.18	model p.21
critical thinking p.27	physical science p.10
data p.28	science p.6
dependent variable p.18	scientific law p.7
Earth science p.10	scientific theory p.7
hypothesis p.14	system p.8
independent variable p.18	technology p.11
infer p.16	variable p.18

Explain the relationship between the words in the following sets.

1. hypothesis—scientific theory

2. constant—variable

3. science—technology

4. science—system

5. Earth science—physical science

6. critical thinking—infer

7. scientific law—observation

8. model—system

9. controlled experiment—variable

10. scientific theory—scientific law

Checking Concepts

Choose the word or phrase that best answers the question.

11. What does it mean to make an inference?
    A) make observations
    B) draw a conclusion
    C) replace
    D) test

12. Which of the following CANNOT protect you from splashing acid?
    A) goggles   C) fire extinguisher
    B) apron   D) gloves

13. If the results from your investigation do not support your hypothesis, what should you do?
    A) Should not do anything.
    B) Repeat the investigation until it agrees with the hypothesis.
    C) Modify your hypothesis.
    D) Change your data to fit your hypothesis.

14. Which of the following is NOT an example of a scientific hypothesis?
    A) Earthquakes happen because of stresses along continental plates.
    B) Some animals can detect ultrasound frequencies caused by earthquakes.
    C) Paintings are prettier than sculptures.
    D) Lava takes different forms depending on how it cools.

15. Using a computer to make a three-dimensional picture of a building is a type of which of the following?
    A) model   C) constant
    B) hypothesis   D) variable

16. Which of the following increases the reliability of a scientific explanation?
    A) vague statements
    B) notes taken after an investigation
    C) repeatable data
    D) several likely explanations

17. Which is an example of technology?
    A) a squirt bottle   C) a cat
    B) a poem   D) physical science

18. What explains something that takes place in the natural world?
    A) scientific law   C) scientific theory
    B) technology   D) experiments

19. An airplane model is an example of what type of model?
    A) physical   C) idea
    B) computer   D) mental

Science Online ips.msscience.com/vocabulary_puzzlemaker

Use the ExamView® Pro Testmaker CD-ROM to:
- create multiple versions of tests
- create modified tests with one mouse click for inclusion students
- edit existing questions and add your own questions
- build tests aligned with state standards using built-in State Curriculum Tags
- change English tests to Spanish with one mouse click and vice versa

Thinking Critically

20. Draw Conclusions When scientists study how well new medicines work, one group of patients receives the medicine while a second group does not. Why?

21. Predict How is using a rock hammer an example of technology?

22. Compare and Contrast How are scientific theories and scientific laws similar? How are they different?

Use the table below to answer question 23.

Hardness	
Object	**Mohs Scale**
copper	3.5
diamond	10
fingernail	2.5
glass	5.5
quartz	7
steel file	6.5

23. Use Tables Mohs hardness scale measures how easily an object can be scratched. The higher the number, the harder the material is. Use the table above to identify which material is the hardest and which is the softest.

24. Make Operational Definitions How does a scientific law differ from a state law? Give some examples of both types of laws.

25. Infer Why it is important to record and measure data accurately during an experiment?

26. Predict the quickest way to get to school in the morning. List some ways you could test your prediction.

Performance Activities

27. Hypothesize Using a basketball and a tennis ball, make a hypothesis about the number of times each ball will bounce when it hits the ground. Drop each ball from shoulder height five times, recording the number of bounces in a table. Which ball bounced more? Make a hypothesis to explain why.

28. Observe Pour some water in a small dish and sprinkle some pepper on top. Notice how the pepper floats on the water. Now add a few drops of liquid soap to the water. Write down your observations as you watch what happens to the pepper.

Applying Math

Use the illustration below to answer question 29.

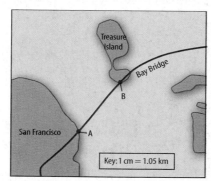

Treasure Island
Bay Bridge
B
San Francisco
A
Key: 1 cm = 1.05 km

29. Use Proportions The map above shows the distance between two points. The scale shows that 1 cm is approximately 1.05 km. What is the approximate distance between Point A and Point B?

Thinking Critically

20. By not giving the medicine to one group of patients, scientists can see the effects of that medicine on the other group.

21. The study of levers and the study of materials are applied to create a rock hammer that uses a material that will break rocks and a shape that acts as a lever.

22. Both scientific theories and scientific laws are generalizations. A scientific theory explains why something happens, but a scientific law only says that something happens.

23. Diamond is the hardest and a fingernail is the softest.

24. A state law tells you what you are forbidden to do. A scientific law just tells you that things happen. A state law could forbid a driver to turn right at a red light. A scientific law would tell the driver that the force of gravity keeps the car on the road.

25. You need to record data accurately so you can be sure of the results of your experiment when you go back later to draw your conclusions.

26. You could test the hypothesis by timing your method and comparing it to the times it takes to get to school using other methods.

Performance Activities

27. The tennis ball bounced more times than the basketball. The surface area of the tennis ball is less than the basketball and therefore retains more energy while it bounces.

28. The pepper spreads to the outer edges of the dish when soap is added to the water.

Applying Math

National Math Standards
1, 4

29. The distance between the two points is 2.1 cm. The distance is

$$2.1 \text{ cm} \cdot \frac{1.05 \text{ km}}{1 \text{ cm}} = 2.2 \text{ km}.$$

Assessment Resources

Reproducible Masters

Chapter *Fast File* Resources
Chapter Review, pp. 41–42
Chapter Tests, pp. 43–46
Assessment Transparency Activity, p. 55

Glencoe Science Web site
Chapter Review Test
Standardized Test Practice

Glencoe Technology
Assessment Transparency
Exam*View*® Pro Testmaker
MindJogger Videoquiz
Interactive Chalkboard

Answer Sheet A practice answer sheet can be found at ips.msscience.com/answer_sheet.

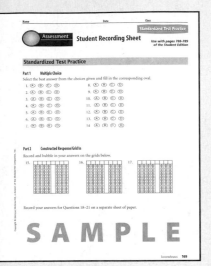

S A M P L E

Part 1 Multiple Choice

1. B	**4.** A	**7.** C
2. C	**5.** D	**8.** B
3. D	**6.** D	**9.** A

Part 2 Short Response

10. Answers will vary.

11. goggles, apron, thermal mitts, tie back hair, caution should be used around the sharp objects

12. Science answers questions with the information available at the time. As new information becomes available, explanations for why things happen can change and be modified.

13. Scientists share information with other scientists because experiments must be repeatable and the results must be the same in order for the data to be reliable.

14. An observation is when you watch something and make notes of its movements or contents. An inference means you draw a conclusion based on what you have observed.

Part 1 Multiple Choice

Record your answers on the answer sheet provided by your teacher or on a sheet of paper.

1. What is a rule describing a pattern in nature called?
A. possible explanation
B. scientific law
C. scientific theory
D. technology

Use the illustration below to answer questions 2–3.

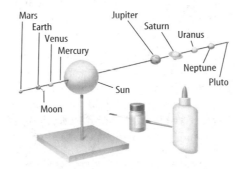

2. The model of the solar system best represents which kind of scientific model?
A. idea   C. physical
B. computer   D. realistic

3. All of the following are represented in the model EXCEPT which of the following?
A. the sun   C. planets
B. the moon   D. stars

4. Which of the following is not an example of a model?
A. CD   C. recipe
B. map   D. drawing

Test-Taking Tip

Practice Practice Remember that test taking skills can improve with practice. If possible, take at least one practice test and familiarize yourself with the test format and instructions.

5. Which of the following questions can science NOT answer?
A. Why do the leaves on trees change colors in the fall?
B. Why do bears hibernate in the winter?
C. Where do waves in the ocean form?
D. What is the most popular book?

6. What is it called when you combine what you already know with new facts?
A. estimate   C. inference
B. hypothesis   D. critical thinking

7. What are the variables that do not change in an experiment called?
A. independent variables
B. dependent variables
C. constants
D. inferences

8. An educated guess based on what you know and what you observe is called which of the following?
A. prediction.   C. conclusion.
B. hypothesis.   D. data.

Use the photo below to answer question 9.

9. What type of scientist could the person above be classified as?
A. life scientist
B. physical scientist
C. Earth scientist
D. medical doctor

15. Science studies why or how things happen in the natural world. Technology applies that information to everyday life.

16. Scientists follow the steps of the scientific method. In general, they observe, question, and collect information, then hypothesize, followed by investigations to learn more, then analyze their informa-tion, and finally conclude and communicate.

17. The three branches of science are life science, Earth science, and physical science. Life science asks questions like: "How do whales navigate the ocean?" and "How do vaccines prevent disease?" Earth science asks questions like "How can an earthquake be detected?" or "Is water found on other plan-ets?" Physical science asks ques-tions like: "How can plastic be made stronger?" or "How can humans harness the energy of sun-light for their energy needs?"

18. Models allow scientists to visualize something that is difficult to see or understand.

Record your answers on the answer sheet provided by your teacher or on a sheet of paper.

Use the photo below to answer questions 10 and 11.

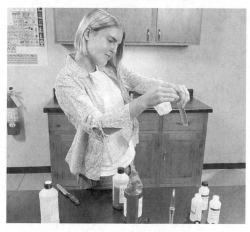

10. Look at the photo above and write down your immediate observations.

11. What safety precautions might this student want to take?

12. Explain why science can only provide possible explanations for occurrences in nature.

13. In class it is sometimes not common for students to share their answers on a test. Why is it important for scientists to share information?

14. Compare and contrast observation and inference.

15. Explain the relationship between science and technology.

16. What steps do scientists follow when investigating a problem?

17. List the three branches of science and give examples of questions that they ask.

18. What is the importance of scientific models?

Record your answers on a sheet of paper.

19. You want to know whether plants grow faster if there is music playing in their environment. How would you conduct this experiment? Be sure to identify the independent and dependent variables, and the constants.

20. Many outdoor clothing products are coated in a special waterproofing agent to protect the material from rain and snow. The manufacturers of the waterproofing agent hire independent field-testers to use their product in the field before marketing it to the public. Why would you want to know the results of the field-testers tests?

Use the illustrations below to answer questions 21–23.

21. What are the above drawings outlining?

22. Body systems interact with one another in order to function. What would happen if one system failed?

23. What is the importance of systems in science?

24. Make a frequency table from the following data. Make two observations about the data. 15 students prefer cold pizza for lunch; 10 students enjoy peanut butter with jelly; 3 students bring ham and cheese; and 5 students eat hot dogs and chips.

are not paid by the company and would not get in trouble or lose their job for being honest when testing the product. If the creators of Gore-Tex say their product is waterproof and then sell it to the public and it gets wet, they will go out of business. However, if independent testers take the product out into the field and find that the material does not get wet, the company can stand behind its claim that the material is indeed waterproof.

21. body systems

22. The body systems all interact with one another and if one was to fail or stop working, the other systems would suffer. Some systems would work harder to compensate for the failed system while others would simply stop working.

23. Scientists are usually interested in problems within a system. They must break down the parts of the system to see how one part affects another.

24. The frequency table should be two columns listing food preference in one column and frequency in the other. Possible observations include: more students prefer cold pizza than other foods. Ham and cheese is the least preferred food. Twice as many students prefer peanut butter and jelly than hot dogs and chips.

Rubrics

For more help evaluating open-ended assessment questions, see the rubric on p. 10T.

19. Experiment setup: materials: two plants, radio, watering can
The plants should be placed in the exact same environment. Light exposure needs to be the same for both plants. They need to be given the same amount of water at the

same interval. The radio is placed by one of the plants but not anywhere near the other plant. Music should be played softly at all times.
Independent variable: radio
Dependent variable: growth of the plants

Constants: amount of water provided to each plant and timing of water, lighting exposure

20. The company is trying to sell a product and could enhance the results of their tests in order to make it sell. Independent testers

Section/Objectives	Standards		Labs/Features
	National	**State/Local**	
Chapter Opener	See pp. 16T–17T for a Key to Standards.		**Launch Lab:** Measuring Accurately, p. 41 **Foldables,** p. 41 A data-collection lab using Probeware technology can be found in the **Probeware Lab Manual,** pp. 41–43
Section 1 Description and Measurement ⏱ 4 sessions 📦 2 blocks 1. **Determine** how reasonable a measurement is by estimating. 2. **Identify** and use the rules for rounding a number. 3. **Distinguish** between precision and accuracy in measurements.	National Content Standards: UCP.1, UCP.2, UCP.3, A.1, A.2		**Integrate Career,** p. 43 **MiniLAB:** Measuring Temperature, p.44 **Visualizing Precision and Accuracy,** p. 46 **Science Online,** p. 47 **Applying Math:** Rounding, p. 48
Section 2 SI Units ⏱ 4 sessions 📦 2 blocks 4. **Identify** the purpose of SI. 5. **Identify** the SI units of length, volume, mass, temperature, time, and rate.	National Content Standards: UCP.1, UCP.2, UCP.3, A.1, A.2		**Integrate Astronomy,** p. 51 **MiniLAB:** Measuring Volume, p. 52 **Lab:** Scale Drawing, p. 55
Section 3 Drawings, Tables, and Graphs ⏱ 5 sessions 📦 2.5 blocks 6. **Describe** how to use pictures and tables to give information. 7. **Identify** and use three types of graphs. 8. **Distinguish** the correct use of each type of graph.	National Content Standards: UCP.1, UCP.2, UCP.3, A.1, A.2		**Science Online,** p. 58 **Lab:** Pace Yourself, pp. 60–61 **Science Stats:** Biggest, Tallest, Loudest, p. 62

Lab Materials	Reproducible Resources	Section Assessment	Technology
Launch Lab: none	**Chapter FAST FILE Resources** Foldables Worksheet, p. 13 Directed Reading Overview, p. 15 Note-taking Worksheets, pp. 29–31	**GLENCOE'S ASSESSMENT ADVANTAGE**	**TeacherWorks** includes: • Interactive Teacher Edition • Lesson Planner with calendar • Access to all program blacklines • Correlations to standards • Web links
MiniLAB: 400-mL beaker, crushed ice, water, computer temperature probe, alcohol, thermometer, paper towel, Science Journal	**Chapter FAST FILE Resources** Transparency Activity, p. 40 MiniLAB, p. 3 Enrichment, p. 26 Reinforcement, p. 23 Directed Reading, p. 16 **Cultural Diversity,** p. 29 **Physical Science Critical Thinking/Problem Solving,** p. 11	**Portfolio** Science Journal, p. 45 Assessment, p. 49 **Performance** MiniLAB, p. 44 Applying Math, p. 48 Applying Math, p. 49 **Content** Section Review, p. 49	Section Focus Transparency Guided Reading Audio Program Interactive Chalkboard CD-ROM
MiniLAB: measuring cup, water, solid object that will fit in cup, pencil, Science Journal **Lab:** 1-cm graph paper, pencil, metric ruler, meterstick	**Chapter FAST FILE Resources** Transparency Activity, p. 41 MiniLAB, p. 4 Enrichment, p. 27 Reinforcement, p. 24 Directed Reading, pp. 16, 17 Lab Worksheet, pp. 5–6 Lab Activity, pp. 9–10, 11–12 Transparency Activity, pp. 43–44	**Portfolio** Assessment, p. 54 **Performance** MiniLAB, p. 52 Applying Math, p. 54 **Content** Section Review, p. 54	Section Focus Transparency Teaching Transparency Guided Reading Audio Program Interactive Chalkboard CD-ROM
Lab: meterstick, stopwatch or watch with a second hand *Need materials?* Contact Science Kit at 1-800-828-7777 or www.sciencekit.com on the Internet.	**Chapter FAST FILE Resources** Transparency Activity, p. 42 Enrichment, p. 28 Reinforcement, p. 25 Directed Reading, pp. 17, 18 Lab Worksheet, pp. 7–8 **Lab Management and Safety,** pp. 70, 71	**Portfolio** Activity, p. 57 **Performance** Applying Skills, p. 59 **Content** Section Review, p. 59	Section Focus Transparency Virtual Labs CD-ROM Guided Reading Audio Program Interactive Chalkboard CD-ROM Video Lab Probeware Lab

End of Chapter Assessment

GLENCOE'S ASSESSMENT ADVANTAGE

Blackline Masters	Technology	Professional Series
Chapter FAST FILE Resources Chapter Review, pp. 33–34 Chapter Tests, pp. 35–38 **Standardized Test Practice,** pp. 11–14	MindJogger Videoquiz Virtual Labs CD-ROM ExamView® Pro Testmaker TeacherWorks CD-ROM Interactive Chalkboard CD-ROM	**Performance Assessment in the Science Classroom (PASC)**

Transparencies

Section Focus

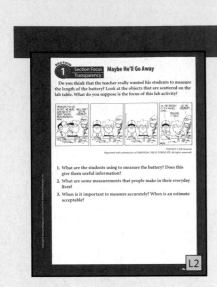

Section Focus Transparency 1 — Maybe He'll Go Away

Do you think that the teacher really wanted his students to measure the length of the battery? Look at the objects that are scattered on the lab table. What do you suppose is the focus of this lab activity?

1. What are the students using to measure the battery? Does this give them useful information?

2. What are some measurements that people make in their everyday lives?

3. When is it important to measure accurately? When is an estimate acceptable?

L2

Section Focus Transparency 2 — Fresh, not Frozen

These people are shopping in a market in Grenada. Grenada uses a unit of currency called the East Caribbean dollar. How do tourists from the United States know how many U.S. dollars to use when buying something in Grenada? They need to convert their American money into Grenadian money.

1. Would it be easier if all countries used one type of money? Explain.

2. What would happen if each country had its own way of measuring length or time?

3. What units of measurement do you know that are used everywhere?

L2

Section Focus Transparency 3 — Different Views

This house, called Fallingwater, was designed as a weekend home. Along with photograph, you also see a plan for the main floor.

1. What could you learn about a house by looking at a floor plan?

2. Could you get the same information from a photograph? Explain.

3. What sort of information do you need to build a house? What is the best way to communicate that information?

L2

This is a representation of key blackline masters available in the Teacher Classroom Resources. See Resource Manager boxes within the chapter for additional information.

Key to Teaching Strategies

The following designations will help you decide which activities are appropriate for your students.

L1 Level 1 activities should be appropriate for students with learning difficulties.

L2 Level 2 activities should be within the ability range of all students.

L3 Level 3 activities are designed for above-average students.

ELL ELL activities should be within the ability range of English Language Learners.

COOP LEARN Cooperative Learning activities are designed for small group work.

LS Multiple Learning Styles logos, as described on page 12T, are used throughout to indicate strategies that address different learning styles.

P These strategies represent student products that can be placed into a best-work portfolio.

PBL Problem-Based Learning activities apply real-world situations to learning.

Assessment

Assessment Transparency — Measurement

Directions: Carefully review the table and answer the following questions.

Edson's General Market Revenues for 1999 (January–June)	
Month	**Revenue in dollars**
January	$3,000
February	$3,500
March	$3,800
April	$4,000
May	$4,800
June	$8,000

1. According to the information in the table, which of the following would best show the changes in revenue over time?
   A word web   C line graph
   B pie chart   D circle graph

2. A reasonable hypothesis based on the data in the table is that ___.
   F Edson's is located in a winter vacation area
   G Edson's is not making a profit
   H Edson's is not open during autumn
   J Edson's is located in a summer vacation area

3. Which of the following would be the greatest benefit of placing the information in the table into a circle graph?
   A to compare revenues for each month
   B to see each month's percentage of the total
   C to see the pattern of revenue change from month to month
   D to see the total revenue for the six-month period

L2

Teaching

Teaching Transparency 2 — Kelvin Scale

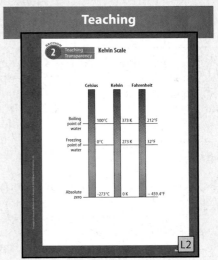

	Celsius	Kelvin	Fahrenheit
Boiling point of water	100°C	373 K	212°F
Freezing point of water	0°C	273 K	32°F
Absolute zero	–273°C	0 K	–459.4°F

L2

Hands-on Activities

Student Text Lab Worksheet

Activity — Scale Drawing

Lab Preview
Directions: Answer these questions before you begin the Activity.

1. Explain why a scale in a scale drawing provides helpful information.

2. Explain how using a scale drawing helps to compare the relative sizes of the objects in the drawing.

A scale drawing is used to represent something that is too large or too small to be drawn at its actual size. Blueprints for a house are a good example of a scale drawing.

What You'll Investigate
How can you represent your classroom accurately in a scale drawing?

Materials
1-cm graph paper
pencil
metric ruler
meterstick

Goals
• Measure using SI.
• Make a data table.
• Calculate new measurements.
• Make an accurate scale drawing.

Data and Observations

Procedure
1. Use your meterstick to measure the length and width of your classroom. Note the locations and sizes of doors and windows.
2. Record the lengths of each item in the data table below.
3. Use a scale of 2 cm = 1 m to calculate the lengths to be used in the drawing. Record them in your data table.
4. Draw the floor plan on the next page. Include the scale.

Room Dimensions		
Part of room	Distance in room (m)	Distance on drawing (cm)

L2

Laboratory Activities

Laboratory Activity 1 — Mass and Weight

Mass is the measure of the amount of matter in an object. Weight is the measure of the force with which one body is attracted toward another body. This force of attraction is called gravity. For example, the Moon is attracted toward Earth by Earth's gravitational field. Likewise, Earth is attracted toward the Moon by the Moon's gravitational field.

Strategy
You will measure the force of gravity on marbles.
You will deduce the relationship between mass and weight.

Materials
rubber band (large, wide)
plastic bottle (with handle)
balance
meterstick
12 glass marbles (large)
scissors

Procedure
1. Cut the rubber band. Attach one end to the handle of the bottle.
2. Measure the mass of the bottle and the attached rubber band in grams and record in Table 1. Lift the bottle using the rubber band. Measure the length of the rubber band in centimeters and record.
3. Place three marbles in the bottle. Measure the mass of the bottle with the three marbles in it and record. Lift the bottle and measure the length of the rubber band. Record.
4. Add three more marbles to the bottle and measure the mass of the bottle with the six marbles in it. Record in the table. Lift the bottle and measure the length of the rubber band. Record.
5. Add the remaining marbles and measure the mass of the bottle with the 12 marbles in it. Record. Lift the bottle, measure the length of the rubber band, and record.

Data and Observations

Table 1

	Mass (g)	Length of the rubber band (cm)
Plastic bottle		
Bottle + 3 marbles		
Bottle + 6 marbles		
Bottle + 12 marbles		

L2

Resource Manager

Meeting Different Ability Levels

Content Outline

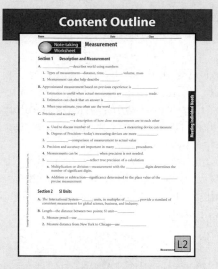

Content Outline worksheet (L2): Note-taking Worksheet — Measurement, Section 1 Description and Measurement, Section 2 SI Units

Reinforcement

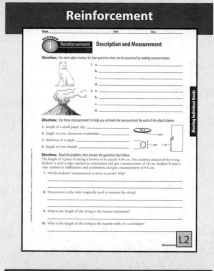

Reinforcement worksheet (L2): Description and Measurement

Enrichment

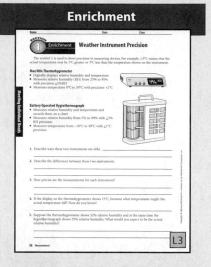

Enrichment worksheet (L3): Weather Instrument Precision

Directed Reading (English/Spanish)

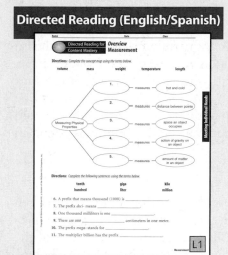

Directed Reading for Content Mastery (L1): Overview — Measurement

Study Guide

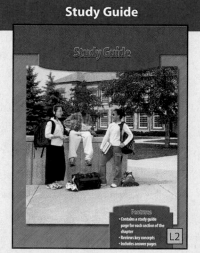

Study Guide (L2)
- Contains a study guide page for each section of the chapter
- Reviews key concepts
- Includes answer pages

Reading Essentials

Reading Essentials for Glencoe Science — An Interactive Student Workbook (L1)
- Condensed core content
- Actively involves students in reading
- Reinforces key vocabulary

Assessment

Test Practice Workbook

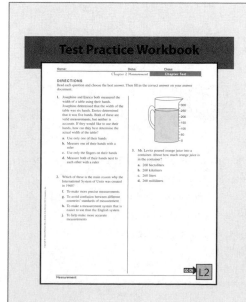

Test Practice Workbook (L2)

Chapter Review

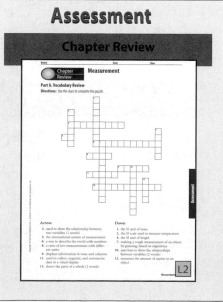

Chapter Review (L2): Measurement

Chapter Tests

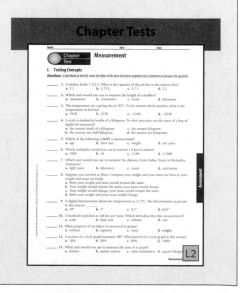

Chapter Tests (L2): Measurement

Science Content Background

Runk/Schoenberger/Grant Heilman Photography, Inc.

section 1 Description and Measurement
Degrees of Precision

Scientists use physical and chemical properties to describe matter. Measurement describes properties with numbers. It describes features such as how long, how far, and how many.

Precision and Accuracy

Precision is related to the degree of exactness that is used to measure an item. Although measurements of 4.2 and 4.20 may seem to be the same, the 4.20 measurement shows that it is a more precise measurement. When numbers are rounded off in calculations, they are rounded to show the precision of the measuring instruments.

section 2 SI Units
The International System

The initials SI stand for the International System of Units for measurement. These units are used all over the world for science, commerce, and communication.

SI standards are defined by the prefixes, of which the most commonly used measurement units are: *kilo-*, *centi-*, and *milli-*. All units differ by factors of ten, so to convert the same unit with different prefixes simply requires the sliding of the decimal point to the left or right. To convert between units, use dimensional analysis, also called unit analysis. Cancel units the same way you cancel numbers.

- 3 km × (1,000 m/1 km) = 3,000 m
- 45 cm (1 m/100 cm) = 0.45 m

Length

Old units of length students might have heard of include the cubit and the roman mile. Accurate length measurement was important for ancient engineering projects such as the Nazca lines, pyramids in Central America and Africa, and the great public buildings found in many cultures.

Mass

Mass and weight are often confused. When moving an object to different locations, the mass is constant while the weight—a measure of the amount of gravity on an object—can change. Because the force of gravity is nearly constant on Earth's surface, mass and weight are often used interchangeably. The weight on Earth is found by multiplying the mass by the acceleration due to gravity, which averages 9.8 m/s^2.

chapter content resources

Internet Resources
For additional content background, visit **ips.msscience.com** to:
- access your book online
- find references to related articles in popular science magazines
- access Web links with related content background
- access current events with science journal topics

Print Resources
Hershey's Milk Chocolate Weights and Measures, Jerry Pallota and Rob Bolster, Scholastic, Inc., 2003

Take a Guess: A Look at Estimation, Janine Scott and Mary Beth Fletcher, Compass Point Books, 2003

Weights and Measures, SparkCharts, Spark Publishing, 2002

section 3 | Drawings, Tables, and Graphs

Scientific Illustrations

Each science develops a visual language, a standard way to illustrate and communicate important information. A geologist, for example, will learn to "read," or interpret, illustrations of geological strata as part of his or her training. Meteorologists learn to interpret images captured by satellites.

Tables and Graphs

A line graph is used to show the relationship between two numerical variables. As a rule, the independent variable is on the horizontal axis and the dependent variable is on the vertical axis. For example, distance traveled depends on time. While it is common to use the left and bottom sides of a grid as axes, the top or right side can also be used. Bar graphs and circle graphs often are used to present the results of opinion polls.

Teacher to Teacher

Eva Vanliere
Waubay School
Waubay, South Dakota

"I have the students measure the basketball court in feet then convert it to inches. They then convert those to m, cm, and mm. Then I have students measure the width and do the same conversions. Then the students measure the distance to the three-point line, and to the free-throw line. Students learn conversion of English measure to metric and learn math skills."

Eva Vanliere

Warren Faidley/International Stock

Chapter Vocabulary

Science Journal Student responses will vary, but should include answers on how to calculate the distance the driver drove and calculate how much gas was used.

INTERACTIVE CHALKBOARD
with Image Bank

PowerPoint® Presentations

This CD-ROM is an editable Microsoft® PowerPoint® presentation that includes:
- a pre-made presentation for every chapter
- interactive graphics
- animations
- audio clips
- image bank
- all new section and chapter questions
- Standardized Test Practice
- transparencies
- pre-lab questions for all labs
- Foldables directions
- links to ips.msscience.com

Measurement

chapter preview

sections

1 **Description and Measurement**

2 **SI Units**
   Lab Scale Drawing

3 **Drawings, Tables, and Graphs**
   Lab Pace Yourself

Virtual Lab How are graphs used to represent data?

The Checkered Flag

Race car drivers win or lose by tenths of a second. The driver has to monitor his fuel usage, speed, and oil temperature in order to win the race. In this chapter, you will learn how scientists measure things like distance, time, volume, and temperature.

Science Journal As a member of the pit crew, how can you determine the miles per gallon the car uses? Write in your Science Journal how you would calculate this.

Theme Connection

Systems and Interactions The SI system is used throughout the world. Because it is based on powers of 10, it is easy to convert between units and do calculations.

About the Photo

Does the expression "winning by a nose" mean anything to you? If you have ever "won by a nose," that means the race was close. Sometimes car races, such as this one, are so close the winner has to be determined by a photograph. But there is more to measure than just how close the race was. How fast did the car drive? In this chapter, you will learn how scientists measure things like distance, time, volume, and temperature.

Start-Up Activities

Measuring Accurately

You make measurements every day. If you want to communicate those measurements to others, how can you be sure that they will understand exactly what you mean? Using vague words without units won't work. Do the lab below to see how confusion can result from using measurements that aren't standard.

1. As a class, choose six objects to measure in your classroom.

2. Measure each object using the width of your hand and write your measurements in your Science Journal.

3. Compare your measurements to those of your classmates.

4. **Think Critically** Describe in your Science Journal why it is better to switch from using hands to using units of measurement that are the same all the time.

Preview this chapter's content and activities at ips.msscience.com

Study Organizer

Measurement Make the following Foldable to help you organize information about measurements.

STEP 1 **Fold** a sheet of paper in half two times lengthwise. Unfold

STEP 2 **Fold** the paper widthwise in equal thirds and then in half.

STEP 3 **Unfold,** lay the paper lengthwise, and draw lines along the folds. **Label** your table as shown.

	Estimate It	Measure It	Round It
Length of			
Volume of			
Mass of			
Temperature of			
Rate of			

Estimates Before you read the chapter, select objects to measure and estimate their measurements. As you read the chapter, complete the table.

41

section

1 Description and Measurement

as you read

What You'll Learn

- **Determine** how reasonable a measurement is by estimating.
- **Identify** and use the rules for rounding a number.
- **Distinguish** between precision and accuracy in measurements.

Why It's Important

Measurement helps you communicate information and ideas.

Review Vocabulary

description: an explanation of an observation

New Vocabulary

- measurement
- estimation
- precision
- accuracy

Measurement

How would you describe what you are wearing today? You might start with the colors of your outfit and perhaps you would even describe the style. Then you might mention sizes— size 7 shoes, size 14 shirt. Every day you are surrounded by numbers. **Measurement** is a way to describe the world with numbers. It answers questions such as how much, how long, or how far. Measurement can describe the amount of milk in a carton, the cost of a new compact disc, or the distance between your home and your school. It also can describe the volume of water in a swimming pool, the mass of an atom, or how fast a penguin's heart pumps blood.

The circular device in **Figure 1** is designed to measure the performance of an automobile in a crash test. Engineers use this information to design safer vehicles. In scientific endeavors, it is important that scientists rely on measurements instead of the opinions of individuals. You would not know how safe the automobile is if this researcher turned in a report that said, "Vehicle did fairly well in head-on collision when traveling at a moderate speed." What does "fairly well" mean? What is a "moderate speed"?

Figure 1 This device measures the range of motion of a seat-belted mannequin in a simulated accident.

42 CHAPTER 2 Measurement

Figure 2 Accurate measurement of distance and time is important for competitive sports like track and field.
Infer *Why wouldn't a clock that measured in minutes be precise enough for this race?*

Describing Events Measurement also can describe events such as the one shown in **Figure 2.** In the 1956 summer Olympics, sprinter Betty Cuthbert of Australia came in first in the women's 200-m dash. She ran the race in 23.4 s. In the 2000 summer Olympics, Marion Jones of the United States won the 100-m dash in a time of 10.75 s. In this example, measurements convey information about the year of the race, its length, the finishing order, and the time. Information about who competed and in what event are not measurements but help describe the event completely.

Estimation

What happens when you want to know the size of an object but you can't measure it? Perhaps it is too large to measure or you don't have a ruler handy. **Estimation** can help you make a rough measurement of an object. When you estimate, you can use your knowledge of the size of something familiar to estimate the size of a new object. Estimation is a skill based on previous experience and is useful when you are in a hurry and exact numbers are not required. Estimation is a valuable skill that improves with experience, practice, and understanding.

 **Reading Check** *When should you not estimate a value?*

How practical is the skill of estimation? In many instances, estimation is used on a daily basis. A caterer prepares for each night's crowd based on an estimation of how many will order each entree. A chef makes her prize-winning chili. She doesn't measure the cumin; she adds "just that much." Firefighters estimate how much hose to pull off the truck when they arrive at a burning building.

INTEGRATE Career

Precision and Accuracy
A pharmacist has a very important job: making sure that patients receive the right medication at the correct dosage. Any error in dosage or type of pill could harm the patient. Explain how precision and accuracy play a role in the pharmacist's job. If a patient receives the wrong medication or an extra pill, how could that affect their health? Research some other careers that rely on precision and accuracy. How could errors in a measurement affect the professional's finished product?

Caption Answer
Figure 3 About 4.5 meters (15 feet); accept all reasonable estimates.

Mini LAB

Purpose Students will practice measurement skills with computer temperature probes and thermometers.

Materials crushed ice, cold water, 400-mL beaker, computer temperature probe, alcohol thermometer

Teaching Strategies

- Demonstrate how to make accurate temperature measurements by not letting the thermometer touch the sides or bottom of the beaker.
- Show students how to read an alcohol thermometer.
- Make sure that the beaker is mostly ice for each measurement.

Analysis

1. Review the process for calculating an average.
2. Possible answers: The most precise instrument will give the set of measurements that are closest together. The computer probe tends to be more precise. To determine the accuracy of the measurements, the actual temperature needs to be known. If the students know that the water should be 0°C, then they can determine which device is more accurate by seeing which average is closest to 0°C.

Assessment

Oral Have students work in small groups to define measurement and show how it is done. Have students demonstrate and present their results to the class. Use **Performance Assessment in the Science Classroom**, p. 143. L1 ELL
IS **Kinesthetic**

Mini LAB

Measuring Temperature

Procedure
1. Fill a **400-mL beaker** with **crushed ice**. Add enough **cold water** to fill the beaker.
2. Make three measurements of the temperature of the ice water using a **computer temperature probe**. Remove the computer probe and dry it with a **paper towel**. Record the measurement in your **Science Journal**. Allow the probe to warm to room temperature between each measurement.
3. Repeat step two using an **alcohol thermometer**.

Analysis
1. Average each set of measurements.
2. Which measuring device is more precise? Explain. Can you determine which is more accurate? How?

Figure 3 This student is about 1.5 m tall. **Estimate** the height of the tree in the photo.

Using Estimation You can use comparisons to estimate measurements. For example, the tree in **Figure 3** is too tall to measure easily, but because you know the height of the student next to the tree, you can estimate the height of the tree. When you estimate, you often use the word *about*. For example, doorknobs are about 1 m above the floor, a sack of flour has a mass of about 2 kg, and you can walk about 5 km in an hour.

Estimation also is used to check that an answer is reasonable. Suppose you calculate your friend's running speed as 47 m/s. You are familiar with how long a second is and how long a meter is. Think about it. Can your friend really run a 50-m dash in 1 s? Estimation tells you that 47 m/s is unrealistically fast and you need to check your work.

Precision and Accuracy

One way to evaluate measurements is to determine whether they are precise. **Precision** is a description of how close measurements are to each other. Suppose you measure the distance between your home and your school five times with an odometer. Each time, you determine the distance to be 2.7 km. Suppose a friend repeated the measurements and measured 2.7 km on two days, 2.8 km on two days, and 2.6 km on the fifth day. Because your measurements were closer to each other than your friend's measurements, yours were more precise. The term *precision* also is used when discussing the number of decimal places a measuring device can measure. A clock with a second hand is considered more precise than one with only an hour hand.

Differentiated Instruction

Learning Disabled Make sure that learning disabled students handle measuring equipment and make measurements, rather than just reading and observing.

Fun Fact

The earliest known calculating device is probably the abacus. It dates back to at least 1100 B.C. and it is still in use today, particularly in Asia. It consists of a rectangular frame with thin parallel rods strung with beads. Merchants trading goods not only needed a way to count goods bought and sold, but also to calculate the cost of those goods.

Degrees of Precision The timing for Olympic events has become more precise over the years. Events that were measured in tenths of a second 100 years ago are measured to the hundredth of a second today. Today's measuring devices are more precise. **Figure 4** shows an example of measurements of time with varying degrees of precision.

Accuracy When you compare a measurement to the real, actual, or accepted value, you are describing **accuracy.** A watch with a second hand is more precise than one with only an hour hand, but if it is not properly set, the readings could be off by an hour or more. Therefore, the watch is not accurate. However, measurements of 1.03 m, 1.04 m, and 1.06 m compared to an actual value of 1.05 m are accurate, but not precise. **Figure 5** illustrates the difference between precision and accuracy.

> **Reading Check** *What is the difference between precision and accuracy?*

Figure 4 Each of these clocks provides a different level of precision. **Infer** *which of the three you could use to be sure to make the 3:35 bus.*

Before the invention of clocks, as they are known today, a sundial was used. As the Sun passes through the sky, a shadow moves around the dial.

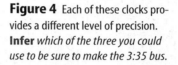

For centuries, analog clocks—the kind with a face—were the standard.

Digital clocks are now as common as analog ones.

Discussion

Timekeeping Tools Discuss with students timekeeping tools used at school and at home. These include a stopwatch, clock, kitchen timer, alarm clock, and timer on a microwave oven. What are some of the limitations of these tools for timing an event? *Possible answers: Many timers read only to the second and sometimes it is necessary to measure tenths or hundredths of seconds. The time it takes a timekeeper to start and stop a stopwatch affects its precision.* L2 **LS** **Linguistic**

> **Reading Check**

Answer Precision describes the exactness of a measure. Accuracy compares a measurement to the actual or accepted value.

Caption Answer
Figure 4 the analog or digital clock

Visual Learning

Figure 4 Have small groups discuss ways each of the clocks could be used. *Possible answers: sundial to see if it is before or after noon; analog clock to make it on time for school or for after-school activities; The digital clock could be used to determine if exactly three minutes has elapsed.* L2 **ELL** **COOP LEARN** **LS**
Interpersonal

Teacher FYI

Cesium Atomic Clock The cesium atomic clock uses the radiation generated by the transition between two states of cesium-133 atoms to operate a clock that is both precise and accurate. The clock is used for the basic unit of time in the International System of Units. It has an error of plus or minus one second in one million years.

Science Journal

Using Measurements In their Science Journals, have students describe a situation in which both accuracy and precision in measurement are necessary. Have students share examples in a small group. *Sample answers: shooting a basketball into a hoop, landing on a balance beam after doing a flip, throwing a strike in bowling* L2 **LS** **Linguistic**

Visualizing Precision and Accuracy

Have students examine the pictures and read the captions. Then ask the following questions.

How would you describe the accuracy and the precision of a basketball player who makes 97 out of 100 free throws? good accuracy and good precision

How would you describe the accuracy and precision of a basketball player who has 99 out of 100 free throws hit the front rim of the basket and bounce off? good precision, poor accuracy

How would you describe the accuracy and precision of a basketball player who makes 33 out of 100 free throws, while the others miss the basket completely? poor precision, poor accuracy

Activity

Sport Display Have small groups of students select another sport and make a similar display that illustrates precision and accuracy. Have each group present its display to the class. L2 ELL COOP LEARN LS **Visual-Spatial and Interpersonal**

Make a Model

Estimate Measurement Collect commonly used containers such as one- and two-liter bottles. Pour given amounts of water into each bottle. Use a permanent ink marker to draw a line at the water level and to mark metric amounts on the outside of the bottle. For example, pour 100 mL of water into a two-liter bottle, draw a line around the container at the water level, and write *100 mL* above the line. Have students estimate where the 200-mL mark would be on each bottle. L2 ELL LS **Visual-Spatial**

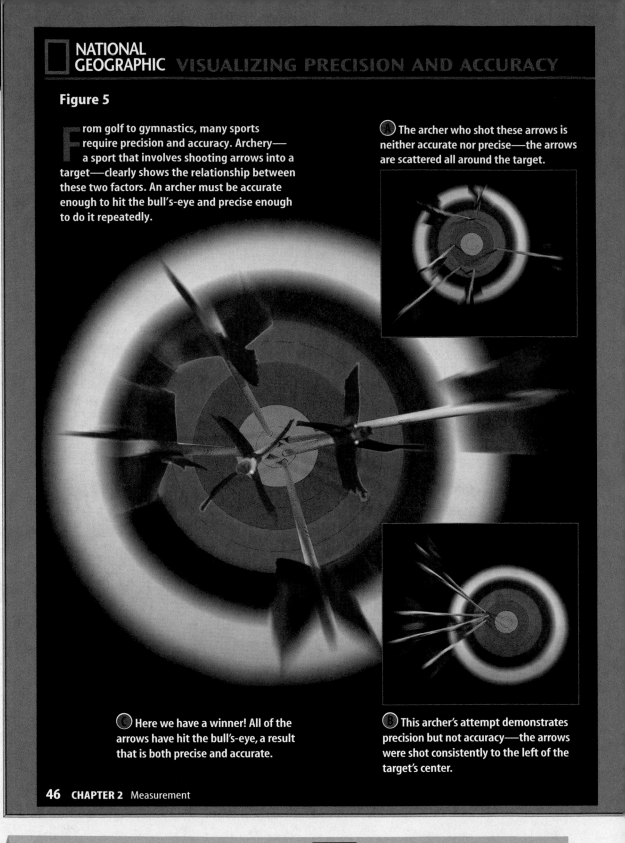

NATIONAL GEOGRAPHIC VISUALIZING PRECISION AND ACCURACY

Figure 5

From golf to gymnastics, many sports require precision and accuracy. Archery—a sport that involves shooting arrows into a target—clearly shows the relationship between these two factors. An archer must be accurate enough to hit the bull's-eye and precise enough to do it repeatedly.

Ⓐ The archer who shot these arrows is neither accurate nor precise—the arrows are scattered all around the target.

Ⓒ Here we have a winner! All of the arrows have hit the bull's-eye, a result that is both precise and accurate.

Ⓑ This archer's attempt demonstrates precision but not accuracy—the arrows were shot consistently to the left of the target's center.

46 CHAPTER 2 Measurement

Teacher FYI

GPS Satellites Twenty-four Global Positioning System (GPS) satellites orbit Earth. Each satellite measures time precisely and accurately using four atomic clocks. A coded signal telling the time, the satellite's location, and other data is continuously broadcasted toward Earth. GPS receivers pick up signals and can measure the distance from any GPS satellite based on the time it took the signal to arrive. The receiver compares data from four different satellites to calculate its own latitude, longitude, and elevation, as well as the correct time. If the receiver is moving, it also can determine its own velocity.

INTEGRATE Health

Precision and accuracy are important in many medical procedures. One of these procedures is the delivery of radiation in the treatment of cancerous tumors. Because radiation damages cells, it is important to limit the radiation to only the cancerous cells that are to be destroyed. A technique called Stereotactic Radiotherapy (SRT) allows doctors to be accurate and precise in delivering radiation to areas of the brain. The patient makes an impression of his or her teeth on a bite plate that is then attached to the radiation machine. This same bite plate is used for every treatment to position the patient precisely the same way each time. A CAT scan locates the tumor in relation to the bite plate, and the doctors can pinpoint with accuracy and precision where the radiation should go.

Rounding a Measurement Not all measurements have to be made with instruments that measure with great precision like the scale in **Figure 6.** Suppose you need to measure the length of the sidewalk outside your school. You could measure it to the nearest millimeter. However, you probably would need to know the length only to the nearest meter or tenth of a meter. So, if you found that the length was 135.841 m, you could round off that number to the nearest tenth of a meter and still be considered accurate. How would you round this number? To round a given value, follow these steps:

1. Look at the digit to the right of the place being rounded to.

   - If the digit to the right is 0, 1, 2, 3, or 4, the digit being rounded to remains the same.

   - If the digit to the right is 5, 6, 7, 8, or 9, the digit being rounded to increases by one.

2. The digits to the right of the digit being rounded to are deleted if they are also to the right of a decimal. If they are to the left of a decimal, they are changed to zeros.

Look back at the sidewalk example. If you want to round the sidewalk length of 135.841 to the tenths place, you look at the digit to the right of the 8. Because that digit is a 4, you keep the 8 and round it off to 135.8 m. If you want to round to the ones place, you look at the digit to the right of the 5. In this case you have an 8, so you round up, changing the 5 to a 6, and your answer is 136 m.

Science Online

Topic: Measurement
Visit ips.msscience.com for Web links to information about the importance of accuracy and precision in the medical field.

Activity Research a topic of interest on the Internet and present the topic and numeric data to your class. How might your classmates' understanding of the topic be affected if you presented crucial information inaccurately?

Figure 6 This laboratory scale measures to the nearest hundredth of a gram.

Quick Demo
Rounding Measurements
Materials bag of candy, laboratory scale
Estimated Time 10–15 minutes
Procedure To demonstrate rounding measurements to students, you could use a bag of M&Ms (any type of candy or popcorn) and divide the contents amongst the students. First, the M&Ms would need to be counted and then divided by the number of students in the class. If the total number of M&Ms divides into the number of students, remove some from the bag. Record the numbers on the chalkboard and have students round to the number of M&Ms they will receive. As they eat the candy, you could measure the weight of an individual piece on a laboratory scale and round to the nearest hundredth of a gram.

INTEGRATE Health

Measurement Accuracy Ask students to identify which parts of the procedure make the measurement precise and which make it accurate. Precise: the instruments and the techniques used make measurements with a high degree of exactness; also, the bite plate positions the patient exactly the same way each time. Accurate: the CAT scan locates the tumor accurately.

Curriculum Connection

History The first chemists were the alchemists of ancient Egypt, China, Greece, and Rome, and of medieval Arabia and Europe. Have students find out what alchemists did and what kinds of systems they used for measurement. Alchemists tried to change metals into gold and helped develop perfumes, cosmetics, and the gilding of metals. They did not have precise tools or a standard measuring system.

National Math Standards
Correlation to Mathematics
Objectives
1

Teaching Strategies
To round to a certain place, remember to ignore all of the numbers more than one place to the right.

Answers to Practice Problems
1. first object = 6.9 g; second object = 20.2 g
2. 26, 3.4, 5.98, 9.8

Inquiry Lab

Purpose To practice measurement, estimation, and prediction skills, and collecting data. PBL

Possible Materials tape measure, calculator, string, ruler, balance, trees, paper clip

Estimated Time 3–5 days to collect data (a few minutes at the beginning or end of class)

Teaching Strategies
• Identify opportunities within the school that give students an authentic role in an investigation. The students are...
  ● members of the School Beautification Committee. They will assist a landscape architect in determining the need for additional school landscaping materials.
  ● assisting the school custodian in measuring floor tile or carpeting for replacement.
  ● members of the Student Athletic Committee will determine the storage needed for athletic equipment.

For additional inquiry activities, see *Science Inquiry Labs.*

Precision and Number of Digits When might you need to round a number? Suppose you want to divide a 2-L bottle of soft drink equally among seven people. When you divide 2 by 7, your calculator display reads as shown in **Figure 7.** Will you measure exactly 0.285 714 285 L for each person? No. All you need to know is that each person gets about 0.3 L of soft drink.

Using Precision and Significant Digits The number of digits that truly reflect the precision of a number are called the significant digits or significant figures. They are figured as follows:

• Digits other than zero are always significant.

• Final zeros after a decimal point (6.545 600 g) are significant.

• Zeros between any other digits (507.0301 g) are significant.

• Initial zeros (0.000 2030 g) are NOT significant.

• Zeros in a whole number (1650) may or may not be significant.

• A number obtained by counting instead of measuring, such as the number of people in a room or the number of meters in a kilometer, has infinite significant figures.

Applying Math — Rounding

ROUNDED VALUES The mass of one object is 6.941 g. The mass of a second object is 20.180 g. You need to know these values only to the nearest whole number to solve a problem. What are the rounded values?

Solution
❶ *This is what you know:*
 • mass of first object = 6.941 g
 • mass of second object = 20.180 g

❷ *This is what you need to find out:*
 • the number to the right of the one's place
 • first object: 9; second object: 1

❸ *This is the procedure you need to use:*
 digits 0, 1, 2, 3, 4 remain the same
 for digits 5, 6, 7, 8, 9, round up

❹ *Check your answer:*
 • first object: 9 makes the 6 round up = 7
 • second object: 1 makes the 0 remain the same = 20

Practice Problems

1. What are the rounded masses of the objects to the nearest tenth of a unit?

2. Round the following numbers: 25.643 to the ones place, 3.429 to the tenths place, 5.982 to the hundredths place, and 9.8210 to the tenths place.

Science Online | For more practice, visit **ips.msscience.com/ math_practice**

Cultural Diversity

Social Time While time's passage can be accurately measured, its perceived importance, or social time, varies from culture to culture. In the U.S., people call and apologize if they expect to be late. In Latin American and Arab countries, people may arrive an hour late with no apology expected or given. One study of social time rated Japan highest and the U.S. second in accuracy of bank clocks and pace of life.

Differentiated Instruction

Challenge Discuss this example with your students. The mass of a substance is determined to be 0.0045 kilograms. How many significant digits are in this measurement? There are two significant digits. The zeros in 0.0045 are used to show only the place value of the decimal and are not counted as significant digits. L3

Following the Rules In the soft drink example you have an exact number, seven, for the number of people. This number has infinite significant digits. You also have the number two, for how many liters of soft drink you have. This has only one significant digit.

There are also rules to follow when deciding the number of significant digits in the answer to a calculation. They depend on what kind of calculation you are doing.

- For multiplication and division, you determine the number of significant digits in each number in your problem. The significant digits of your answer are determined by the number with fewer digits.

$$6.14 \times 5.6 = \boxed{34}.384$$

3 digits 2 digits 2 digits

- For addition and subtraction, you determine the place value of each number in your problem. The significant digits of the answer are determined by the number that is least precise.

$$\begin{array}{r} 6.14 \quad \text{to the hundredths} \\ + \ 5.6 \quad \text{to the tenths} \\ \hline \boxed{11.7}4 \quad \text{to the tenths} \end{array}$$

In the soft drink example you are dividing and the number of significant digits is determined by the amount of soft drink, 2 L. There is one significant digit there; therefore, the amount of soft drink each person gets is rounded to 0.3 L.

Figure 7 Sometimes considering the size of each digit will help you realize they are unneeded. In this calculation, the seven ten-thousandths of a liter represents just a few drops of soft drink.

section 1 review

Summary

Measurement
- Measurement is used to answer questions such as how much, how long, or how far.

Estimation
- When making an estimate, rely on previous knowledge to make an educated guess about the size of an object.

Precision and Accuracy
- Precision is the ability to remain consistent. Accuracy compares a measurement to the real value of an object.
- Significant digits affect precision when calculating an answer and are determined by rules based on calculation.

Self Check

1. **Estimate** the distance between your desk and your teacher's desk. Explain the method you used.
2. **Infer** John's puppy has chewed on his ruler. Will John's measurements be accurate or precise? Why?
3. **Think Critically** Would the sum of 5.7 cm and 6.2 cm need to be rounded? Why or why not? Would the sum of 3.28 cm and 4.1 cm need to be rounded? Why or why not?

Applying Math

4. **Calculate** Perform the following calculations and express the answer using the correct number of significant digits: 42.35 + 214; 225/12. **For more help, refer to the Math Skill Handbook.**

section 1 review

1. Possible answer: About 3 m; it looks like two students could almost lie down head to toe in this space.
2. John's measurements will not be precise in the area in which measuring lines have been destroyed by the dog. They may still be accurate, depending on what he's measuring and what the dog destroyed.
3. The sum of 5.7 and 6.2 would not need to be rounded because both are measured to the same place—the tenths place. The sum of 3.28 and 4.1 would be rounded to the place of the least precise measurement—the tenths place.
4. 256; 19

section 2
SI Units

as you read

What You'll Learn
- **Identify** the purpose of SI.
- **Identify** the SI units of length, volume, mass, temperature, time, and rate.

Why It's Important
The SI system is used throughout the world, allowing you to measure quantities in the exact same way as other students around the world.

Review Vocabulary
variable: factors that can be changed in an experiment

New Vocabulary
- ● SI
- ● meter
- ● volume
- ● mass
- ● kilogram
- ● weight
- ● kelvin
- ● rate

The International System

Can you imagine how confusing it would be if people in every country used different measuring systems? Sharing data and ideas would be complicated. To avoid confusion, scientists established the International System of Units, or **SI,** in 1960 as the accepted system for measurement. It was designed to provide a worldwide standard of physical measurement for science, industry, and commerce. SI units are shown in **Table 1.**

Reading Check *Why was SI established?*

The SI units are related by multiples of ten. Any SI unit can be converted to a smaller or larger SI unit by multiplying by a power of 10. For example, to rewrite a kilogram measurement in grams, you multiply by 1,000.

$$\text{Ex. } 5.67 \text{ kg} \times 1000 = 5670 \text{ grams}$$

The new unit is renamed by changing the prefix, as shown in **Table 2.** For example, one millionth of a meter is one *micro*meter. One thousand grams is one *kilo*gram. **Table 3** shows some common objects and their measurements in SI units.

Table 1 SI Base Units

Quantity	Unit	Symbol
length	meter	m
mass	kilogram	kg
temperature	kelvin	K
time	second	s
electric current	ampere	A
amount of substance	mole	mol
intensity of light	candela	cd

Table 2 SI Prefixes

Prefix	Multiplier
giga-	1,000,000,000
mega-	1,000,000
kilo-	1,000
hecto-	100
deka-	10
[unit]	1
deci-	0.1
centi-	0.01
milli-	0.001
micro-	0.000 001
nano-	0.000 000 001

50 CHAPTER 2

Length

Length is defined as the distance between two points. Lengths measured with different tools can describe a range of things from the distance from Earth to Mars to the thickness of a human hair. In your laboratory activities, you usually will measure length with a metric ruler or meterstick.

The **meter** (m) is the SI unit of length. One meter is about the length of a baseball bat. The size of a room or the dimensions of a building would be measured in meters. For example, the height of the Washington Monument in Washington, D.C. is 169 m.

Smaller objects can be measured in centimeters (cm) or millimeters (mm). The length of your textbook or pencil would be measured in centimeters. A twenty-dollar bill is 15.5 cm long. You would use millimeters to measure the width of the words on this page. To measure the length of small things such as blood cells, bacteria, or viruses, scientists use micrometers (millionths of a meter) and nanometers (billionths of a meter).

A Long Way Sometimes people need to measure long distances, such as the distance a migrating bird travels or the distance from Earth to the Moon. To measure such lengths, you use kilometers. Kilometers might be most familiar to you as the distance traveled in a car or the measure of a long-distance race, as shown in **Figure 8.** The course of a marathon is measured carefully so that the competitors run 42.2 km. When you drive from New York to Los Angeles, you cover 4,501 km.

Figure 8 These runners have just completed a 10-kilometer race—known as a 10K.
Estimate *how many kilometers is the distance between your home and your school.*

Measurement Accuracy
How important are accurate measurements? In 1999, the *Mars Climate Orbiter* disappeared as it was to begin orbiting Mars. NASA later discovered that a unit system error caused the flight path to be incorrect and the orbiter to be lost. Research the error and determine what systems of units were involved. How can using two systems of units cause errors?

Table 3 Common Objects in SI Measurements

Object	Type of Measurement	Measurement
can of soft drink	volume	355 mL
bag of potatoes	mass	4.5 kg
fluorescent tube	length	1.2 m
refrigerator	temperature	276 K

Caption Answer

Figure 8 Answers will vary. Have students explain how they arrived at their answers.

Use Science Words

Word Origin The prefix *centi-*, the word *percent*, and the American unit of money called *cent* all derive from the same French and Latin root, which means 100. Can you think of other ways we use the root word *cent?* centimeter, century, centigrade, centipede L2 LS **Linguistic**

Measurement Accuracy The error occurred because the common unit *pound • seconds* was used instead of the SI unit *Newton • seconds* in the computer program that determined trajectories of the orbiter.

Research Have students research other errors that resulted from using two different systems of units. Ask students to explain how these errors can be minimized and how scientists can predict the possibility of error before the error is made.

Activity

Measurement Accuracy Have students use rulers to measure the length of a small item on their desks while sitting. Then have them remeasure the item while standing. Discuss which measurement is more accurate. The measurement made while looking directly at it from above is more accurate. L2 ELL LS **Kinesthetic**

Visual Learning

Tables 1 and 2 Have students use the information in the tables to determine the meaning of the following units: kilogram—1,000 grams; centimeter—1/100 meter. Have pairs take turns using the prefixes to make their own units and identifying their meanings. Sample answer: gigagram (1 billion grams) and megameter (1 million meters) L2 ELL LS
Logical-Mathematical

Figure 9 A cubic meter equals the volume of a cube 1 m by 1 m by 1 m.
Infer *how many cubic centimeters are in a cubic meter.*

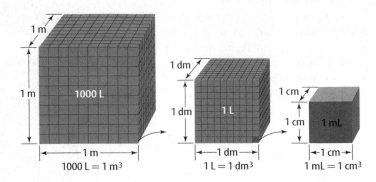

Volume

The amount of space an object occupies is its **volume.** The cubic meter (m^3), shown in **Figure 9,** is the SI unit of volume. You can measure smaller volumes with the cubic centimeter (cm^3 or cc). To find the volume of a square or rectangular object, such as a brick or your textbook, measure its length, width, and height and multiply them together. What is the volume of a compact disc case?

You are probably familiar with a 2-L bottle. A liter is a measurement of liquid volume. A cube 10 cm by 10 cm by 10 cm holds 1 L (1,000 cm^3) of water. A cube 1 cm on each side holds 1 mL (1 cm^3) of water.

Volume by Immersion Not all objects have an even, regular shape. How can you find the volume of something irregular like a rock or a piece of metal?

Have you ever added ice cubes to a nearly full glass of water only to have the water overflow? Why did the water overflow? Did you suddenly have more water? The volume of water did not increase at all, but the water was displaced when the ice cubes were added. Each ice cube takes up space or has volume. The difference in the volume of water before and after the addition of the ice cubes equals the volume of the ice cubes that are under the surface of the water.

The ice cubes took up space and caused the total volume in the glass to increase. When you measure the volume of an irregular object, you do the same thing. You start with a known volume of water and drop in, or immerse, the object. The increase in the volume of water is equal to the volume of the object.

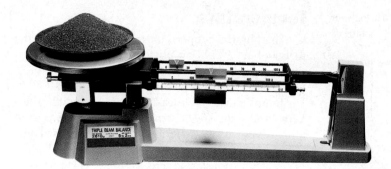

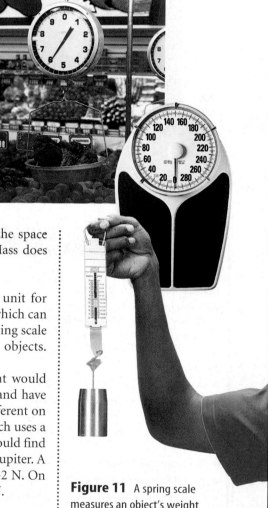

Figure 10 A triple beam balance compares an unknown mass to known masses.

Mass

The **mass** of an object measures the amount of matter in the object. The **kilogram** (kg) is the SI unit for mass. One liter of water has a mass of about 1 kg. Smaller masses are measured in grams (g). One gram is about the mass of a large paper clip.

You can determine mass with a triple-beam balance, shown in **Figure 10.** The balance compares an object to a known mass. It is balanced when the known standard mass of the slides on the balance is equal to the object on the pan.

Why use the word *mass* instead of *weight*? Weight and mass are not the same. Mass depends only on the amount of matter in an object. If you ride in an elevator in the morning and then ride in the space shuttle later that afternoon, your mass is the same. Mass does not change when only your location changes.

Weight **Weight** is a measurement of force. The SI unit for weight is the newton (N). Weight depends on gravity, which can change depending on where the object is located. A spring scale measures how a planet's gravitational force pulls on objects. Several spring scales are shown in **Figure 11.**

If you were to travel to other planets, your weight would change, even though you would still be the same size and have the same mass. This is because gravitational force is different on each planet. If you could take your bathroom scale, which uses a spring, to each of the planets in this solar system, you would find that you weigh much less on Mars and much more on Jupiter. A mass of 75 pounds, or 34 kg, on Earth is a weight of 332 N. On Mars, the same mass is 126 N, and on Jupiter it is 782 N.

> **Reading Check** *What does weight measure?*

Figure 11 A spring scale measures an object's weight by how much it stretches a spring.

---

54 CHAPTER 2 Measurement

3 Assess

DAILY INTERVENTION

Check for Understanding

Visual-Spatial Have each student make a chart to organize the information he or she learned in this section. The chart should include a title with International System in it. It should also include pictures and information about measuring length, volume, mass, temperature, and time. L2 **ELL** **LS**

Reteach

Tools Collect a set of measurement tools. Display each tool and have a student volunteer tell the class its name, what it measures, and the unit(s) it uses. L1 **ELL** **LS** Visual-Spatial

Assessment

Process Ask each student to make an illustration of a spring scale, showing how it works. Use **Performance Assessment in the Science Classroom,** p. 127. P

Figure 12 The kelvin scale starts at 0 K. In theory, 0 K is the coldest temperature possible in nature.

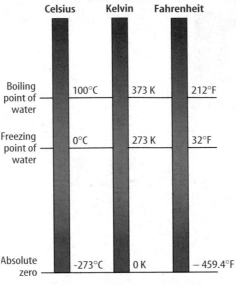

Temperature

The physical property of temperature is related to how hot or cold an object is. Temperature is a measure of the kinetic energy, or energy of motion, of the particles that make up matter.

Temperature is measured in SI with the **kelvin** (K) scale. The Fahrenheit and Celsius temperature scales are the two most common scales used on thermometers and in classroom laboratories. These two scales do not start at zero, as shown in **Figure 12.** A 1 K difference in temperature is the same as a 1°C difference in temperature.

Time and Rates

Time is the interval between two events. The SI unit of time is the second (s). Time also is measured in hours (h). Can you imagine hearing that a marathon was run in 7,620 s instead of 2 h and 7 min?

A **rate** is the amount of change of one measurement in a given amount of time. One rate you are familiar with is speed, which is the distance traveled in a given time. Speeds often are measured in kilometers per hour (km/h).

The unit that is changing does not necessarily have to be an SI unit. For example, you can measure the number of cars that pass through an intersection per hour in cars/h.

---

section 2 review

Summary

The International System

- The International System of Units, SI, was established to provide a standard of physical measurement and to reduce international confusion when comparing measurements.

Measurement

- Length is the distance between two points.
- Volume is the amount of space an object occupies.
- To calculate volume, multiply length by width by height.
- The amount of matter in an object is its mass.
- Weight is determined by gravitational pull.
- Celsius temperature scales are more common in laboratories than kelvin scales.

Self Check

1. **Describe** a situation in which different units of measure could cause confusion.
2. **Define** what type of quantity the cubic meter measures.
3. **Explain** how you would change a measurement in centimeters to kilometers.
4. **Identify** what SI unit replaces the pound. What does this measure?
5. **Think Critically** How would you find the mass of a metal cube?

Applying Math

6. **Measure** A block of wood is 0.2 m by 0.1 m by 0.5 m. Find its dimensions in centimeters. Then find its volume in cubic centimeters.

54 CHAPTER 2 Measurement

Science Online ips.msscience.com/self_check_quiz

---

section 2 review

1. Possible answer: Someone thinks a temperature is given in Fahrenheit degrees, but it is actually in Celsius degrees.
2. volume
3. divide by 100,000
4. Newton; the force of gravity on an object
5. Use a pan balance or scale. The description should provide step-by-
   step instructions for using the instrument.
6. 20 cm × 10 cm × 50 cm = 10,000 cm³

Scale Drawing

A scale drawing is used to represent something that is too large or too small to be drawn at its actual size. Blueprints for a house are a good example of a scale drawing.

● Real-World Question

How can you represent your classroom accurately in a scale drawing?

Goals
- **Measure** using SI.
- **Make** a data table.
- **Calculate** new measurements.
- **Make** an accurate scale drawing.

Materials
1-cm graph paper   metric ruler
pencil   meterstick

● Procedure

1. Use your meterstick to measure the length and width of your classroom. Note the locations and sizes of doors and windows.
2. **Record** the lengths of each item in a data table similar to the one below.
3. Use a scale of 2 cm = 1 m to calculate the lengths to be used in the drawing. Record them in your data table.
4. **Draw** the floor plan. Include the scale.

Room Dimensions		
Part of Room	Distance in Room (m)	Distance on Drawing (cm)

● Conclude and Apply

1. How did you calculate the lengths to be used on your drawing? Did you put a scale on your drawing?
2. **Infer** what your scale drawing would look like if you chose a different scale?
3. **Sketch** your room at home, estimating the distances. Compare this sketch to your scale drawing of the classroom. When would you use each type of illustration?
4. What measuring tool simplifies this task?

𝒞ommunicating
Your Data

Measure your room at home and compare it to the estimates on your sketch. Explain to someone at home what you did and how well you estimated the measurements. **For more help, refer to the Science Skill Handbook.**

LAB 55

● Real-World Question

Purpose to learn how to make and use a scale drawing [L2] [ELL] [COOP LEARN] [IS] Visual-Spatial

Process Skills compare and contrast, interpret data, make and use tables, use numbers, make models

Time Required one 45-minute period to measure the classroom, one 30-minute period to draw the room to scale (could be homework)

● Procedure

Teaching Strategy
- Demonstrate how to draw the length of a wall to scale.

● Conclude and Apply

1. Length was measured with a meterstick. The scale of 2 cm/1 m should be noted on the drawing.
2. The shape of the drawing would remain the same, but it would be larger or smaller, depending on the new scale chosen.
3. Check students' work. A rough sketch might be used to give an idea of how to design a room. A scale drawing might be used to determine if the furniture will actually fit in the space available.
4. Possible tools to use: meterstick, tape measure, retractable metal tape measure, measuring wheel

☑ Assessment

Portfolio Have students add to their work a detailed explanation of how to make and use a scale drawing. Use **Performance Assessment in the Science Classroom**, p. 177.

𝒞ommunicating
Your Data

Have students use a drawing to discuss scale and features with a small group or the class, in addition to explaining these things to someone at home.

Bellringer

Section Focus Transparencies also are available on the Interactive Chalkboard CD-ROM.

L2 ELL

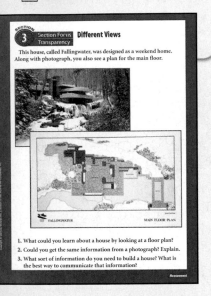

Tie to Prior Knowledge

Publication Charts Ask students to recall publications other than science books in which they have seen graphs and charts. Newspapers and news magazines are good sources of examples.

---

section 3 Drawings, Tables, and Graphs

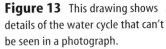
as you read

What You'll Learn

- **Describe** how to use pictures and tables to give information.
- **Identify** and use three types of graphs.
- **Distinguish** the correct use of each type of graph.

Why It's Important

Illustrations, tables, and graphs help you communicate data about the world around you in an organized and efficient way.

⊘ Review Vocabulary

model: a representation of an object or event used as a tool for understanding the natural world

New Vocabulary

- table
- graph
- line graph
- bar graph
- circle graph

Scientific Illustrations

Most science books include pictures. Photographs and drawings model and illustrate ideas and sometimes make new information clearer than written text can. For example, a drawing of an airplane engine shows how all the parts fit together much better than several pages of text could describe it.

Drawings A drawing is sometimes the best choice to show details. For example, a canyon cut through red rock reveals many rock layers. If the layers are all shades of red, a drawing can show exactly where the lines between the layers are. A drawing can emphasize only the things that are necessary to show.

A drawing also can show things you can't see. You can't see the entire solar system, but drawings show you what it looks like. Also, you can make quick sketches to help model problems. For example, you could draw the outline of two continents to show how they might have fit together at one time.

Drawings can show hidden things, as well. A drawing can show the details of the water cycle, as in **Figure 13.** Architects use drawings to show what the inside of a building will look like. Biologists use drawings to show where the nerves in your arm are found.

Figure 13 This drawing shows details of the water cycle that can't be seen in a photograph.

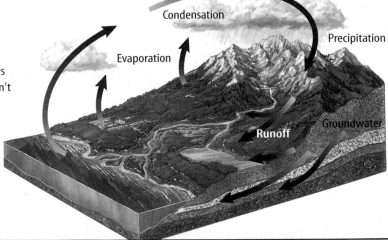

Condensation
Precipitation
Evaporation
Runoff
Groundwater

Section 3 Resource Manager

Chapter *FAST FILE* Resources

Transparency Activity, p. 42

Directed Reading for Content Mastery, pp. 17, 18

Enrichment, p. 28

Reinforcement, p. 25

Lab Worksheet, pp. 7–8

Photographs A still photograph shows an object exactly as it is at a single moment in time. Movies show how an object moves and can be slowed down or sped up to show interesting features. In your schoolwork, you might use photographs in a report. For example, you could show the different types of trees in your neighborhood for a report on ecology.

Tables and Graphs

Everyone who deals with numbers and compares measurements needs an organized way to collect and display data. A **table** displays information in rows and columns so that it is easier to read and understand, as seen in **Table 4.** The data in the table could be presented in a paragraph, but it would be harder to pick out the facts or make comparisons.

A **graph** is used to collect, organize, and summarize data in a visual way. The relationships between the data often are seen more clearly when shown in a graph. Three common types of graphs are line, bar, and circle graphs.

Line Graph A **line graph** shows the relationship between two variables. A variable is something that can change, or vary, such as the temperature of a liquid or the number of people in a race. Both variables in a line graph must be numbers. An example of a line graph is shown in **Figure 14.** One variable is shown on the horizontal axis, or *x*-axis, of the graph. The other variable is placed along the vertical axis, or *y*-axis. A line on the graph shows the relationship between the two variables.

Table 4 Endangered Animal Species in the United States

Year	Number of Endangered Animal Species
1984	192
1986	213
1988	245
1990	263
1992	284
1994	321
1996	324
1998	357
2000	379
2002	389

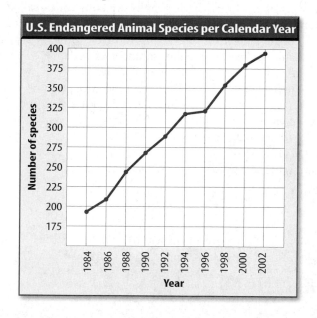

U.S. Endangered Animal Species per Calendar Year

Number of species (y-axis): 175, 200, 225, 250, 275, 300, 325, 350, 375, 400
Year (x-axis): 1984, 1986, 1988, 1990, 1992, 1994, 1996, 1998, 2000, 2002

Figure 14 To find the number of endangered animal species in 1992, find that year on the *x*-axis and see what number corresponds to it on the *y*-axis.
Interpret Data *How many species were endangered in 1998?*

Quick Demo

Materials chalk, chalkboard, some data to graph

Estimated Time five minutes

Procedure Draw two line graphs on the chalkboard having the same data but two different scales for the *y*-axis. Point out to students that one of the lines looks much steeper than the other. Have students study the units on the axes of the graphs to see that the information in both graphs is the same.

Visual Learning

Figure 15 Ask students to calculate the percent values of each endangered species.

Arachnids = 5.9%

Amphibians = 9.8%

Reptiles = 13.7%

Crustaceans = 17.7%

Snails = 19.6%

Insects = 29.4%

Clams = 59.8%

Mammals = 61.8%

Fishes = 66.7%

Discussion

Everyday Graphs Discuss how graphs play a very important role in conveying information to the public. Have students look through a newspaper and find references to graphs. Ask students where else they may find graphs. Possible answers: magazines, doctor's offices, informational brochures, textbooks, reference materials, stores Ask students how these graphs help them understand the product or information. The graphs display the data as an easy-to-understand visual reference. Sometimes the translation of data into text becomes confusing. Graphs make it easier to understand complex information or view the results of an experiment.

Reading Check

pie graph

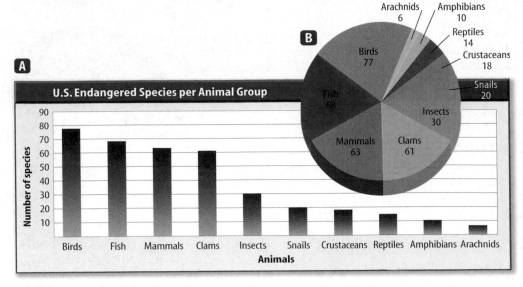

Figure 15 **A** Bar graphs allow you to picture the results easily.
B On this circle graph, you can see what part of the whole each animal represents.
Infer *Which category of animals has the most endangered species?*

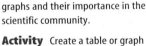
Science Online

Topic: scientific Data
Visit ips.msscience.com for Web links to information about scientific illustrations, tables, and graphs and their importance in the scientific community.

Activity Create a table or graph using data collected from a classroom observation.

Bar Graph A **bar graph** uses rectangular blocks, or bars, of varying sizes to show the relationships among variables. One variable is divided into parts. It can be numbers, such as the time of day, or a category, such as an animal. The second variable must be a number. The bars show the size of the second variable. For example, if you made a bar graph of the endangered species data from **Figure 14,** the bar for 1990 would represent 263 species. An example of a bar graph is shown in **Figure 15A.**

Circle Graph Suppose you want to show the relationship among the types of endangered species. A **circle graph** shows the parts of a whole. Circle graphs are sometimes called pie graphs. Each piece of pie visually represents a fraction of the total. Looking at the circle graph in **Figure 15B,** you see quickly which animals have the highest number of endangered species by comparing the sizes of the pieces of pie.

A circle has a total of 360°. To make a circle graph, you need to determine what fraction of 360 each part should be. First, determine the total of the parts. In **Figure 15B,** the total of the parts, or endangered species, is 367. One fraction of the total, *Mammals,* is 63 of 367 species. What fraction of 360 is this? To determine this, set up a ratio and solve for *x:*

$$\frac{63}{367} = \frac{x}{360°} \qquad x = 61.8°$$

Mammals will have an angle of 61.8° in the graph. The other angles in the circle are determined the same way.

Reading Check *What is another name for a circle graph?*

Active Reading

Metacognition Journal In this strategy, each student analyzes his or her own thought processes. Have students divide the paper in half. On the left, have them record what they have learned about a topic. On the right, have them record the reason they learned it. Have students write a Metacognition Journal about graphs.

Differentiated Instruction

English-Language Learners Have students pair up and compose quick surveys to gather information from the class. They can write their questions on a sheet of paper and either conduct them in front of the class or have students fill them out on paper. When the survey is complete, have the students choose a graph that will best display their data. **ELL**

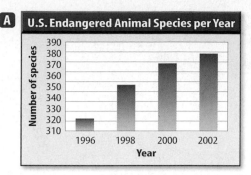

A U.S. Endangered Animal Species per Year

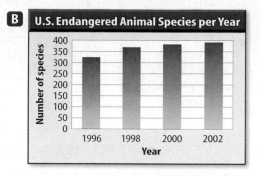

B U.S. Endangered Animal Species per Year

Reading Graphs When you are using or making graphs to display data, be careful—the scale of a graph can be misleading. The way the scale on a graph is marked can create the wrong impression, as seen in **Figure 16A.** Until you see that the *y*-axis doesn't start at zero, it appears that the number of endangered species has quadrupled in just six years.

This is called a broken scale and is used to highlight small but significant changes, just as an inset on a map draws attention to a small area of a larger map. **Figure 16B** shows the same data on a graph that does not have a broken scale. The number of species has only increased 20 percent from 1996 to 2002. Both graphs have correct data, but must be read carefully. Always analyze the measurements and graphs that you come across. If there is a surprising result, look closer at the scale.

Figure 16 Careful reading of graphs is important. **A** This graph does not start at zero, which makes it appear that the number of species has more than quadrupled from 1996–2002. **B** The actual increase is about 20 percent, as you can see from this full graph. The broken scale must be noted in order to interpret the results correctly.

DAILY INTERVENTION

Check for Understanding

Visual-Spatial Have students collect tables and graphs from newspapers or magazines. Display their information on a bulletin board with the following headings: table, line graph, bar graph, circle graph, other graphs, misleading graphs. Ask students to place their graphs in the appropriate category. Discuss placement of each or some of the graphs. L2 COOP LEARN LS

Reteach

Types of Graphs Have each student make a chart of the different types of graphs defined in the section. Then have them write the key words that define each under the type of graph. line graph: shows relationship between two number variables; bar graph: shows relationship between a number variable and a number or category variable; circle graph: shows relationship among parts of a whole L2 LS **Visual-Spatial**

---

section 3 review

Summary

Scientific Illustrations

- Drawings and illustrations can help people visualize complex concepts.
- A drawing can include details you see and those that are hidden.
- Photographs are an exact representation of an object at a single moment in time.

Tables and Graphs

- Tables display information while graphs are used to summarize data.
- A line graph shows the relationship between two variables, a bar graph shows the relationship among variables, and a circle graph shows the parts of a whole.
- It is important to pay close attention to the scale on graphs in order to analyze the information.

Self Check

1. **Explain** how to use **Figure 16** to find the number of endangered species in 1998.
2. **Infer** what type of graph you would use to display data gathered in a survey about students' after-school activities.
3. **Think Critically** Why is it Important to be careful when making or using graphs?
4. **Describe** a time when an illustration would be helpful in everyday activities.
5. **Identify** when you would use a broken scale.

Applying Skills

6. **Use a Spreadsheet** Make a spreadsheet to display how the total mass of a 500-kg elevator changes as 50-kg passengers are added one at a time.

Assessment

Performance Have students collect weather data for a week and display it in a table and a graph. Use **Performance Assessment in the Science Classroom,** p. 111.

Virtual Labs

Graphs *How are graphs used to represent data?*

Science online ips.msscience.com/self_check_quiz

SECTION 3 Drawings, Tables, and Graphs **59**

---

section 3 review

1. Possible answer: Find the bar for 1998. Use a ruler or visually align the top of the bar with the time scale. This tells you the number of endangered species for that year.
2. A bar graph or a circle graph would be appropriate. A circle graph would show the percent of students who prefer each activity. A bar graph

would show the number of students who prefer each activity.

3. It is important to be careful when making graphs because the data is displayed visually. It must be as accurate as possible. There is often a key to help understand the data displayed in the graph, but the lines and numbers must be clearly identi-

fied and labels should be used to help others understand the graph.

4. Illustrations could be used to display daily schedules, maps and directions, and confusing instructions.
5. A broken scale is used to highlight small but important changes.
6. Accept all reasonable spreadsheets

Real-World Question

Purpose to apply the concepts of precision, measurement, and graphing to a specific problem **L2** **ELL** **LS** **Kinesthetic**

Process Skills design an experiment, form a hypothesis, communicate, observe and infer, make and use tables, interpret data

Time Required 45 minutes each to plan and do the experiment

Materials meterstick, stopwatch

Alternate Materials clock with a second hand

Safety Precautions Work in an area where it is safe to run. If this is not possible, measure walking speed only. Check that students do not have health problems that could prevent them from exercising. Allow students to decline running if it is physically uncomfortable or embarrassing for them.

Form a Hypothesis

Possible Hypotheses A course on a flat, straight surface will be the most accurately measurable with the given tools. Accuracy will be better if more than one group member times each walker or runner.

Design Your Own

Goals
- **Design** an experiment that allows you to measure speed for each member of your group accurately.
- **Display** data in a table and a graph.

Possible Materials
meterstick
stopwatch
*watch with a second hand
*Alternate materials

Safety Precautions
Work in an area where it is safe to run. Participate only if you are physically able to exercise safely. As you design your plan, make a list of all the specific safety and health precautions you will take as you perform the investigation. Get your teacher's approval of the list before you begin.

PACE YOURSELF

Real-World Question

Track meets and other competitions require participants to walk, run, or wheel a distance that has been precisely measured. Officials make sure all participants begin at the same time, and each person's time is stopped at the finish line. If you are practicing for a local marathon or 10K, you need to know your speed or pace in order to compare it with those of other participants. How can your performance be measured accurately? How will you measure the speed of each person in your group? How will you display these data?

Form a Hypothesis

Think about the information you have learned about precision, measurement, and graphing. In your group, make a hypothesis about a technique that will provide you with the most precise measurement of each person's pace.

60 CHAPTER 2 Measurement

Test Your Hypothesis

Possible Procedures Measure the distance to be walked. Mark the starting and ending points for the walk. For each student, use a stopwatch to measure walking time to the nearest tenth of a second. Record each student's time on a data table. Graph the results. Repeat these steps, replacing the walk with a run.

	Time to Walk and Run 18 m			
Student	Walking Time	Running Time	Walking Speed	Running Speed
Carlos	21.3 s	10.6 s	0.845 m/s	1.70 m/s
Brianna	19.6 s	10.9 s	0.918 m/s	1.65 m/s

● Test Your Hypothesis

Make a Plan

1. As a group, decide what materials you will need.

2. How far will you travel? How will you measure that distance? How precise can you be?

3. How will you measure time? How precise can you be?

4. List the steps and materials you will use to test your hypothesis. Be specific. Will you try any part of your test more than once?

5. Before you begin, create a data table. Your group must decide on its design. Be sure to leave enough room to record the results for each person's time. If more than one trial is to be run for each measurement, include room for the additional data.

Follow Your Plan

1. Make sure that your teacher approves your plan before you start.

2. Carry out the experiment as planned and approved.

3. Be sure to record your data in the data table as you proceed with the measurements.

● Analyze Your Data

1. **Graph** your data. What type of graph would be best?

2. Are your data table and graph easy to understand? Explain.

3. How do you know that your measurements are precise?

4. Do any of your data appear to be out of line with the rest?

● Conclude and Apply

1. **Explain** how it is possible for different members of a group to find different times while measuring the same event.

2. **Infer** what tools would help you collect more precise data.

3. What other data displays could you use? What are the advantages and disadvantages of each?

*C*ommunicating Your Data

Make a larger version of your graph to display in your classroom with the graphs of other groups. **For more help, refer to the Science Skill Handbook.**

☑ Assessment

Performance Ask students to design a method to measure another speed, such as the speed of a person swimming two laps in a pool. Use **Performance Assessment in the Science Classroom,** p. 95.

*C*ommunicating Your Data

Have each group use its graph to explain its data to the class.

Teaching Strategy Demonstrate to students how to use the meterstick to measure walking/running distance and how to stop, start, and reset the stopwatch.

Expected Outcome Most results will show students moving at different speeds from each other. Often, two students recording the same event will measure different times.

● Analyze Your Data

Answers to Questions

1. bar graph
2. Check students' work. A person unfamiliar with the experiment should be able to quickly grasp the results.
3. Students should explain their efforts to measure precisely.
4. Students should use their bar graphs to answer this question.

Error Analysis Have students compare their results and their hypotheses and explain why differences occurred.

● Conclude and Apply

1. People's reaction times with the stopwatch may be different. People watching the race from different angles may see the runner pass the finish line at slightly different times. Stopwatches may vary.
2. Sample response: global positioning data, a timer that used infrared or laser light to determine start and stop times
3. Sample response: Graph with a different scale, bar graph or data table comparing average time for male students versus average time for female students; each arranges the information in different ways, so more relationships can be seen.

Stats

Content Background

The rafflesia is a parasitic plant that grows in the mountains of Malaysia. This plant has adapted to feed off of the roots of large vines that are in the grape family. The large, fleshy flower remains open for five to seven days. The flower emits a very strong, offensive odor that attracts carrion-feeding flies. It is thought that the flies are the source of pollination.

The eruption of Krakatau in 1883 was so loud that the explosion was heard 3,500 km (2,175 mi) away. A series of eruptions discharged so much ash and dust into the air that the area surrounding the volcano was plunged into darkness for days.

Discussion

Magnitude Students may not have a good grasp of the magnitude of these features. Make the conversion calculations to English units on the board as a class to give students a better idea of how large these items are. Useful conversion factors (numbers are rounded off): 1 kg = 2.2 lbs; 1 m = 3.281 ft. Converted Numbers: 11 kg = 24.2 lbs; 1 m = 39.37 in; 1,800 m = 5,900 ft; 110 m = 360 ft; 452 m = 1,480 ft; 442 m = 1,450 ft; 33.5 m = 110 ft (three significant figures); 1.65 m = 5.41 ft

Applying Math

Answer 33.5 or 34

Biggest, Tallest, Loudest

Did you know...

... The world's most massive flower belongs to a species called *Rafflesia* (ruh FLEE zhee uh) and has a mass of up to 11 kg. The diameter, or the distance across the flower's petals, can measure up to 1 m.

... The world's tallest building is the Petronus Towers in Kuala Lumpur, Malaysia. It is 452 m tall. The tallest building in the United States is Chicago's Sears Tower, shown here, which measures 442 m.

Applying Math How many of the largest rafflesia petals would you have to place side by side to equal the height of the Sears Tower?

...One of the loudest explosions on Earth was the 1883 eruption of Krakatau (krah kuh TAHEW), an Indonesian volcano. It was heard from more than 3,500 km away.

Write About It

Visit ips.msscience.com/science_stats to find facts that describe some of the shortest, smallest, or fastest things on Earth. Create a class bulletin board with the facts you and your classmates find.

Write About It

Shortest, Smallest, Fastest Have students research some of the shortest, smallest, or fastest things on Earth and record this information on a bulletin board. A good source of information for this may be *The Guinness Book of World Records*.

Differentiated Instruction

Challenge Have students research the heights of different historical features worldwide. The features should include both human-made and natural landforms. Students can graph the measurements they find and then compare the differences in height, length, and width. L3

Reviewing Main Ideas

Section 1 — Description and Measurement

1. Length, volume, mass, temperature, and rates are used to describe objects and events.

2. Estimation is used to make an educated guess at a measurement.

3. Accuracy describes how close a measurement is to the true value. Precision describes how close measurements are to each other.

Section 2 — SI Units

1. The international system of measurement is called SI. It is used throughout the world for communicating data.

2. The SI unit of length is the meter. Volume— the amount of space an object occupies— can be measured in cubic meters. The mass of an object is measured in kilograms.

Section 3 — Drawings, Tables, and Graphs

1. Tables, photographs, drawings, and graphs are tools used to collect, organize, summarize, and display data in a way that is easy to use and understand.

2. Line graphs show the relationship between two variables that are numbers on an x-axis and a y-axis. Bar graphs divide a variable into parts to show a relationship. Circle graphs show the parts of a whole like pieces of a pie.

Visualizing Main Ideas

Copy and complete the following concept map.

SI Measurements

quantities measured — quantities measured

Length · Mass · Time · Volume · Temperature · Weight

SI units used to describe measurements — SI units used to describe measurements

Meter · Kilogram · Second · Cubic meter · Kelvin · Newton

---

chapter Study Guide ②

Reviewing Main Ideas

Summary statements can be used by students to review the major concepts of the chapter.

Visualizing Main Ideas

See student page.

Science Online

Visit ips.msscience.com
/self_check_quiz
/interactive_tutor
/vocabulary_puzzlemaker
/chapter_review
/standardized_test

Assessment Transparency

For additional assessment questions, use the *Assessment Transparency* located in the transparency book.

Assessment

Assessment Transparency — **Earthquakes**

Directions: *Carefully review the table and answer the following questions.*

Worldwide Earthquakes, 1990–1994

Magnitude	1990	1991	1992	1993	1994
8.0–9.9	0	0	0	1	2
7.0–7.9	12	11	23	15	13
6.0–6.9	115	105	104	141	161
5.0–5.9	1,635	1,469	1,541	1,449	1,542
4.0–4.9	4,493	4,372	5,196	5,034	4,544
3.0–3.9	3,457	2,952	4,643	4,263	5,000
2.0–2.9	2,364	2,927	3,068	5,390	5,369
1.0–1.9	474	801	887	1,177	779
0.1–0.9	0	1	2	9	17
No Magnitude	5,062	3,878	4,084	3,997	1944
Total	16,612	16,516	19,548	21,476	19,371
Estimated Deaths	51,916	2,326	3,814	10,036	1,038

1. According to this information, which magnitude earthquakes were the most common between 1990 and 1994?
   A No magnitude C 4.0–4.9
   B 3.0–3.9 D 5.0–5.9

2. According to the information in the table, the year that experienced the most deadly earthquake activity was___.
   F 1992 H 1993
   G 1994 J 1990

3. According to the table, the year that had the greatest number of earthquakes was___.
   A 1992 C 1993
   B 1991 D 1990

Using Vocabulary

1. meter
2. measurement
3. estimation
4. mass
5. circle graph
6. precision
7. Kelvin
8. SI
9. volume

Checking Concepts

10. D	15. C
11. D	16. A
12. C	17. C
13. A	18. B
14. D	

Using Vocabulary

accuracy p. 45	measurement p. 42
bar graph p. 58	meter p. 51
circle graph p. 58	precision p. 44
estimation p. 43	rate p. 54
graph p. 57	SI p. 50
kelvin p. 54	table p. 57
kilogram p. 53	volume p. 52
line graph p. 57	weight p. 53
mass p. 53	

Each phrase below describes a vocabulary word. Write the word that matches the phrase describing it.

1. the SI unit for length
2. a description with numbers
3. a method of making a rough measurement
4. the amount of matter in an object
5. a graph that shows parts of a whole
6. a description of how close measurements are to each other
7. the SI unit for temperature
8. an international system of units
9. the amount of space an object occupies

Checking Concepts

Choose the word or phrase that best answers the question.

10. The measurement 25.81 g is precise to the nearest
    A) gram.
    B) kilogram.
    C) tenth of a gram.
    D) hundredth of a gram.

11. What is the SI unit of mass?
    A) kilometer   C) liter
    B) meter   D) kilogram

12. What would you use to measure length?
    A) graduated cylinder
    B) balance
    C) meterstick
    D) spring scale

13. The cubic meter is the SI unit of what?
    A) volume   C) mass
    B) weight   D) distance

14. Which term describes how close measurements are to each other?
    A) significant digits
    B) estimation
    C) accuracy
    D) precision

15. Which of the following is a temperature scale?
    A) volume   C) Celsius
    B) mass   D) Mercury

16. Which of the following is used to organize data?
    A) table   C) precision
    B) rate   D) meterstick

17. To show the number of wins for each football team in your district, which of the following would you use?
    A) photograph   C) bar graph
    B) line graph   D) SI

18. To show 25 percent on a circle graph, the section must measure what angle?
    A) 25°   C) 180°
    B) 90°   D) 360°

Science Online ips.msscience.com/vocabulary_puzzlemaker

Use the ExamView® Pro Testmaker CD-ROM to:
- create multiple versions of tests
- create modified tests with one mouse click for inclusion students
- edit existing questions and add your own questions
- build tests aligned with state standards using built-in State Curriculum Tags
- change English tests to Spanish with one mouse click and vice versa

Thinking Critically

19. Infer How would you estimate the volume your backpack could hold?

20. Explain Why do scientists in the United States use SI rather than the English system (feet, pounds, pints, etc.) of measurement?

21. List the following in order from smallest to largest: 1 m, 1 mm, 10 km, 100 mm.

22. Describe Give an example of an instance when you would use a line graph. Could you use a bar graph for the same purpose?

23. Compare and contrast volume, length, and mass. How are they similar? Different? Give several examples of units that are used to measure each quantity. Which units are SI?

24. Infer Computer graphics artists can specify the color of a point on a monitor by using characters for the intensities of three colors of light. Why was this method of describing color invented?

Use the photo below to answer question 25.

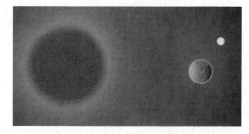

25. Interpreting Scientific Illustrations What does the figure show? How has this drawing been simplified?

Performance Activities

26. Newspaper Search Look through a week's worth of newspapers and evaluate any graphs or tables that you find.

Applying Math

Use the table below to answer question 27.

Areas of Bodies of Water	
Body of Water	**Area (km²)**
Currituck Sound (North Carolina)	301
Pocomoke Sound (Maryland/Virginia)	286
Chincoteague Bay (Maryland/Virginia)	272
Core Sound (North Carolina)	229

27. Make and Use Graphs The table shows the area of several bodies of water. Make a bar graph of the data.

Use the illustration below to answer question 28.

Distance = 2,859.85 km

New York

Denver

28. Travel Distances The map above shows the driving distance from New York City to Denver, Colorado in kilometers. Convert the distance to meters and then find out how many meters are in a mile and convert the distance to miles.

29. Round Digits Round the following numbers to the correct number of significant digits.

$$42.86 \text{ kg} \times 38.703 \text{ kg}$$
$$10 \text{ g} \times 25.05 \text{ g}$$
$$5.8972 \text{ nm} \times 34.15731 \text{ nm}$$

Thinking Critically

19. Multiply its length times its width times its height.

20. The SI system of measurement is understood internationally, while the English system is understood in only a limited number of countries.

21. 1 mm, 100 mm, 1 m, 10 km

22. Accept any reasonable answer. Sample answer: To show distance traveled versus time of travel; no, you cannot use a bar graph for this.

23. Volume, length, and mass are all properties that can be measured. Volume is the amount of space an object occupies; length is the distance between two points; mass is the amount of matter in an object. Sample units: cubic meter (volume); meter (length); kilogram (mass). These are all SI units.

24. Sample response: to allow for precision and reproducibility in design and printing; for example, ads for a given product all use exactly the same colors.

25. It shows Earth, the Moon, and the Sun. Size and distance are not to scale, and the inner planets are missing.

Performance Activities

26. Use **Performance Assessment in the Science Classroom,** p.99.

Applying Math

National Math Standards
1, 4, 5

27. Check students' graphs.

28. 1000 m = 1 km; 0.62 miles = 1 km; 2,859.85 km × 1000 m/1 km = 2,859,850 m

2,859.85 km × 0.62 miles/1 km = 1773.11 miles

29. 1,658.81; 250; 201.4325; traveled versus time of travel; no, you cannot use a bar graph for this.

✓ **Assessment** Resources

📁 **Reproducible Masters**
Chapter *Fast File* Resources
Chapter Review, pp. 33–34
Chapter Tests, pp. 35–38
Assessment Transparency Activity, p. 45
Glencoe Science Web site
Chapter Review Test
Standardized Test Practice

Glencoe Technology
🖱 Assessment Transparency
Ⓔ Exam*View*® Pro Testmaker
📼 MindJogger Videoquiz
Ⓘ Interactive Chalkboard

Answer Sheet A practice answer sheet can be found at ips.msscience.com/answer_sheet.

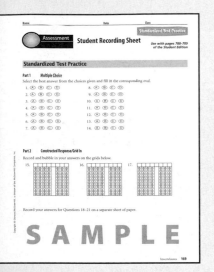

SAMPLE

Part 1 | Multiple Choice

1. A	**5.** B
2. C	**6.** C
3. B	**7.** A
4. D	**8.** D

Part 2 | Short Response

9. 95.3, with three significant digits, is less precise than 35.77, with four significant digits. The answer is only significant to the tenths place, so it must be rounded from 131.07 g to 131.1 g.

10. From least to most precise: sundial, wall clock, stopwatch, atomic clock.

11. Volume is the amount of space occupied by an object. The volume of the cube is 4 cm x 4 cm x 4 cm, or 64 cm^3. 64 cm^3 = 64 mL.

12. Measure and record a volume of water. Immerse the cube in the water, and record the new volume. Subtract the initial volume from the new volume to find the volume of the cube.

Part 1 | Multiple Choice

Record your answers on the answer sheet provided by your teacher or on a sheet of paper.

1. Which best describes measurements that are accurate?
- **A.** They are very close to an accepted value.
- **B.** They are based on an estimate.
- **C.** They are very close to each other.
- **D.** They are not based on numbers.

2. The mass of a sample of calcium chloride is 33.755 grams. Round to the nearest hundredth of a gram.
- **A.** 33.8 g
- **B.** 34 g
- **C.** 33.76 g
- **D.** 33.75 g

Use the illustration below to answer questions 3 and 4.

3. Which quantity is measured using this tool?
- **A.** weight
- **B.** mass
- **C.** volume
- **D.** length

4. Which measurement does this balance show?
- **A.** about 315 g
- **B.** about 326 g
- **C.** about 325 g
- **D.** about 215 g

Test-Taking Tip

Take Your Time Read carefully and make notes of the units used in any measurement.

Phase Changes of H$_2$O

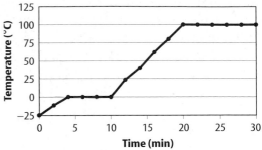

5. The graph shows data from an experiment in which ice was heated until it melted, then became steam. In what phase is the H$_2$O at 16 minutes?
- **A.** solid
- **B.** liquid
- **C.** gas
- **D.** plasma

6. Which statement describes the trend evident in the data?
- **A.** Temperature continually increased as time increased.
- **B.** Temperature did not change as time increased.
- **C.** Temperature increases were divided by plateaus as time increased.
- **D.** Temperature continually decreased as time increased.

7. Which of these represents 1/1000th of a meter?
- **A.** mm
- **B.** km
- **C.** ms
- **D.** dm

8. Which is NOT a unit of volume?
- **A.** milliliter
- **B.** cubic centimeter
- **C.** deciliter
- **D.** kelvin

13.

Mass	Weight
Measures the amount of matter in an object	A measurement of force
Does not change with location	Can change with location
Is not affected by gravitational changes	Depends on gravity
Measured using a balance	Measured using a scale

14. Relationships between data are often more clear when the data is shown on a graph.

15. Drawings can be used to communicate ideas and information, sometimes more clearly than written text. Many times, it is easier to visualize how all the parts of an item fit together than reading about it. Drawings can show things that are too large to see at once, as well as the details of objects, which are very small. Drawings can show things which are usually hidden.

Part 2 | Short Response/Grid In

Record your answers on the answer sheet provided by your teacher or on a sheet of paper.

9. 35.77 g of Solid A are mixed with 95.3 g of Solid B. Write the mass of the mixture with the correct number of significant digits. Explain your answer.

10. Arrange these measuring tools in order from least to most precise: stopwatch measuring to 1/100ths of a second, atomic clock, sundial, wall clock with 2 hands.

Use the illustration below to answer questions 11 and 12.

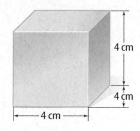

4 cm

4 cm

4 cm

11. Define the term volume. Calculate the volume of the cube shown above. Give your answer in cm^3 and mL.

12. Describe how you would find the volume of the cube using the immersion method.

13. Create a table which shows the differences between mass and weight.

14. How do graphs make it easier to analyze data?

15. Why are drawings an effective way to communicate information?

16. Explain the difference between precision and accuracy.

Part 3 | Open Ended

Record your answers on a sheet of paper.

17. A recipe calls for 1 cup sugar, 1 cup flour, and 1 cup milk. Define the term precision, and explain how to measure these ingredients precisely using kitchen tools.

18. While shopping, you find a rug for your room. Without a ruler, you must estimate the rug's size to determine if it will fit in your room. How will you proceed?

19. Identify the most appropriate SI length unit to measure the following: your height, the distance between two cities, the width of a computer screen, the radius of a coin, the length of a muscle cell. How are units converted in the SI system?

Use the figure below to answer questions 20 and 21.

Composition of Earth's Atmosphere

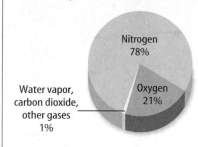

Nitrogen 78%

Oxygen 21%

Water vapor, carbon dioxide, other gases 1%

20. Calculate the angle of each section in this circle graph.

21. Create a bar graph using this data.

22. Measurement is a part of everyday life. Describe measurements someone might make as part of his or her normal activities.

23. You must decide what items to pack for a hiking trip. Space is limited, and you must carry all items during hikes. What measurements are important in your preparation?

19. Height: meter; distance between 2 cities: kilometer; width of computer screen: centimeter or decimeter; radius of a coin: millimeter or centimeter; length of a muscle cell: micrometer or nanometer. SI units are converted by multiplying by the appropriate power of 10.

20. Nitrogen: $\frac{78}{100} = \frac{x}{360°}; x = 280.8°$

Oxygen: $\frac{21}{100} = \frac{x}{360°}; x = 75.6°$

Other: $\frac{1}{100} = \frac{x}{360°}; x = 3.6°$

21. check student's work

22. Student responses will vary but may include examples such as cooking, buying paint, clothes, or carpet. Accept all reasonable answers.

23. The length, width, and height, or total amount of volume in the duffel bag should determine which items would fit. Mass is important, as massive objects, which must be carried on hikes will be difficult to manage.

Rubrics

For more help evaluating open-ended assessment questions, see the rubric on p. 10T.

16. Precision is how close measurements are to each other. Accuracy is a comparison of a measurement to the actual or accepted value.

Part 3 | Open Ended

17. Precision is a description of how close measurements are to each other. To measure the ingredients precisely, use the same measuring cup each time, pouring each ingredient to the exact same height in the cup.

18. Possible techniques: estimate the length of a hand, arm, or foot, and use this body part to mark and add increments along the rug; estimate the length of an object like a book or piece of string, and use this object to mark and add increments along the rug.

Unit Contents

Web*Quest*   ***Art of Neon*** is a motivating and challenging investigation of the chemistry of noble gases and how they are used in colorful neon signs and glowing sculptures. Students will research how the noble gases are inserted into bent tubing and made to glow. As a culminating activity, students will design a "blueprint" of their own neon sign, its components, colors, shape, size, and use.

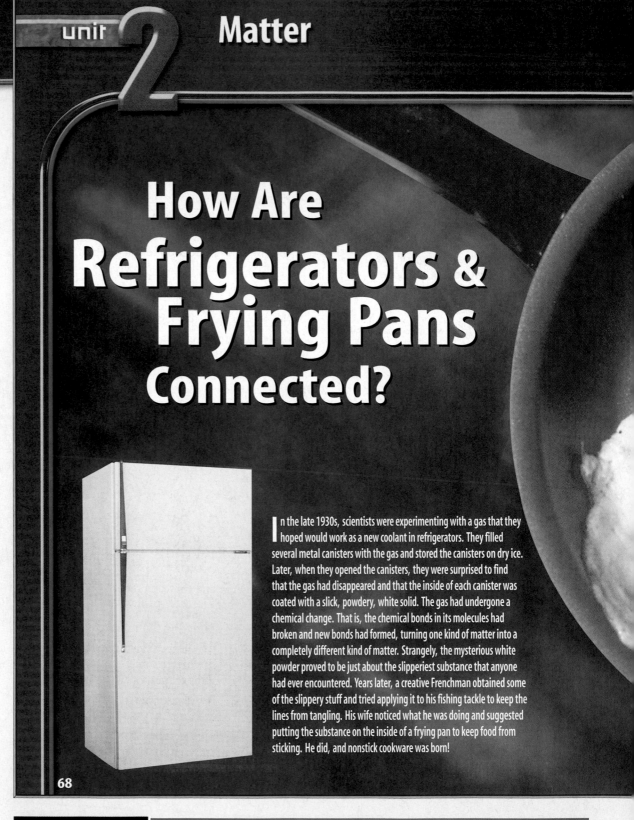

How Are Refrigerators & Frying Pans Connected?

In the late 1930s, scientists were experimenting with a gas that they hoped would work as a new coolant in refrigerators. They filled several metal canisters with the gas and stored the canisters on dry ice. Later, when they opened the canisters, they were surprised to find that the gas had disappeared and that the inside of each canister was coated with a slick, powdery, white solid. The gas had undergone a chemical change. That is, the chemical bonds in its molecules had broken and new bonds had formed, turning one kind of matter into a completely different kind of matter. Strangely, the mysterious white powder proved to be just about the slipperiest substance that anyone had ever encountered. Years later, a creative Frenchman obtained some of the slippery stuff and tried applying it to his fishing tackle to keep the lines from tangling. His wife noticed what he was doing and suggested putting the substance on the inside of a frying pan to keep food from sticking. He did, and nonstick cookware was born!

68

unit ⚡ projects

History Have students research the life and career of Antoine-Laurent Lavoisier, a French chemist. Ask students to design a time line with brief descriptions of 20 events to represent Lavoisier's biography and his contributions to the field of chemistry.

Technology Have students research an assigned element from the periodic table. Have them present its symbol, atomic number, atomic mass, and name on a 1-inch by 2-inch card. On a second card, have students write the electron configuration, state of matter at room temperature, and synthetic or man-made. The class may display their cards in a wall mural, or class sets may be distributed for a periodic review game.

Model Ask students to demonstrate their knowledge of physical and chemical changes in the kitchen. Ask pairs of students to prepare a simple food that focuses on either a physical or chemical change. Students may then present their snack along with an explanation of the characteristics of the change they are demonstrating.

Additional Resources For more information, resources, and assessment rubrics, visit ips.msscience.com/unit_project

unit ⚡ projects

Visit ips.msscience.com/unit_project to find project ideas and resources. Projects include:

- **History** Research the French chemist Antoine-Laurent Lavoisier. Design a time line with 20 of his contributions to chemistry.
- **Technology** Design a classroom periodic table wall mural. Use the information as a learning tool and review game.
- **Model** Demonstrate your knowledge of the characteristics of physical and chemical change by preparing a simple snack to share.

Web*Quest* *Art of Neon* is an investigation of the noble gases and how they are inserted into glass tubes to be used in art and signage.

NATIONAL GEOGRAPHIC   How Are Refrigerators & Frying Pans Connected?

It was Roy Plunkett who first discovered phytetrafluoroethylene (PTFE) in 1938. It was used to protect metal equipment from corrosion during World War II. It was 1960 when the first nonstick cookware was released. PTFE is an organic polymer known for its strength, toughness, and slippery surface. It is almost completely indifferent to attack, by all chemicals, and retains its physical properties at high temperatures. These qualities make it ideal for use in gaskets, bearings, cooking utensils, and numerous other products.

Section/Objectives	Standards		Labs/Features
	National	**State/Local**	
Chapter Opener	See p. 31T for a Key to Standards.		**Launch Lab:** Observe Matter, p. 71 **Foldables,** p. 71
Section 1 Structure of Matter ⏱ 2 sessions 📦 1 block 1. **Describe** the characteristics of matter. 2. **Identify** what makes up matter. 3. **Identify** the parts of an atom. 4. **Compare** the models that are used for atoms.	National Content Standards: UCP.1, UCP.2, UCP.3, UCP.5, A.1, A.2, B.1, G.1, G.2, G.3		**Integrate History,** p. 73 **MiniLAB:** Investigating the Unseen, p. 74 **Science Online,** p. 76 **Integrate Career,** p. 78
Section 2 The Simplest Matter ⏱ 2 sessions 📦 1 block 5. **Describe** the relationship between elements and the periodic table. 6. **Explain** the meaning of atomic mass and atomic number. 7. **Identify** what makes an isotope. 8. **Contrast** metals, metalloids, and nonmetals.	National Content Standards: UCP.1, UCP.2, UCP.3, UCP.5, A.1, A.2, B.1, G.3		**Science Online,** p. 81 **Visualizing the Periodic Table,** p. 82 **Lab:** Elements and the Periodic Table, p. 86
Section 3 Compounds and Mixtures ⏱ 4 sessions 📦 2 blocks 9. **Identify** the characteristics of a compound. 10. **Compare and contrast** different types of mixtures.	National Content Standards: UCP.1, UCP.2, UCP.3, UCP.5, A.1, A.2, B.1, G.1, G.2, G.3		**MiniLAB:** Comparing Compounds, p. 88 **Applying Science:** What's the best way to desalt ocean water?, p. 89 **Science Online,** p. 90 **Integrate Earth Science,** p. 91 **Lab:** Mystery Mixture, p. 92 **Science and History:** Ancient Views of Matter, p. 94

Lab Materials	Reproducible Resources	Section Assessment	Technology
Launch Lab: dry paper towel or tissue, tape, plastic cup, bowl, or sink water	**Chapter FAST FILE Resources** Foldables Worksheet, p. 13 Note-taking Worksheets, pp. 29–31	GLENCOE'S ASSESSMENT ADVANTAGE	**TeacherWorks** includes: • Interactive Teacher Edition • Lesson Planner with calendar • Access to all program blacklines • Correlations to standards • Web links
MiniLAB: sealed shoe box, one or more items *Need materials?* **Contact Science Kit at 1-800-828-7777 or www.sciencekit.com on the Internet.**	**Chapter FAST FILE Resources** Transparency Activity, p. 40 MiniLAB, p. 3 Enrichment, p. 26 Reinforcement, p. 23 Directed Reading, p. 16 Transparency Activity, pp. 43–44 **Reading and Writing Skill Activities,** p. 41 **Mathematics Skill Activities,** p. 39	**Portfolio** Activity, p. 76 **Performance** MiniLAB, p. 74 Applying Skills, p. 79 **Content** Section Review, p. 79	Section Focus Transparency Teaching Transparency Virtual Labs CD-ROM Guided Reading Audio Program Interactive Chalkboard CD-ROM
Lab: colored markers, large index cards, Merck index, encyclopedia, large bulletin board, 8 1/2- × 14-inch paper, thumbtacks	**Chapter FAST FILE Resources** Transparency Activity, p. 41 Enrichment, p. 27 Reinforcement, p. 24 Directed Reading, p. 17 Activity Worksheet, pp. 5–6 **Science Inquiry Labs,** pp. 49–50	**Portfolio** Science Journal, p. 84 Assessment, p. 86 **Performance** Applying Math, p. 85 **Content** Section Review, p. 85	Section Focus Transparency Guided Reading Audio Program Interactive Chalkboard CD-ROM
MiniLAB: sugar, rubbing alcohol, salad oil, spoon, glasses, hot water **Lab:** test tubes and holder, cornstarch, sugar, baking soda, mystery mixture, small scoops, dropper bottles, iodine solution, white vinegar, hot plate, 250-mL beaker, water, small pie pan, matches	**Chapter FAST FILE Resources** Transparency Activity, p. 42 MiniLAB, p. 4 Enrichment, p. 28 Reinforcement, p. 25 Directed Reading, pp. 17, 18 Lab Worksheet, pp. 7–8 Lab Activity, pp. 9–10, 11–12 **Lab Management and Safety,** p. 44	**Portfolio** MiniLAB Assessment, p. 88 **Performance** MiniLAB, p. 88 Applying Science, p. 89 Applying Skills, p. 91 **Content** Section Review, p. 91	Section Focus Transparency Guided Reading Audio Program Interactive Chalkboard CD-ROM Video Lab

End of Chapter Assessment

GLENCOE'S ASSESSMENT ADVANTAGE

Blackline Masters	Technology	Professional Series
Chapter FAST FILE Resources Chapter Review, pp. 33–34 Chapter Tests, pp. 35–38 **Standardized Test Practice,** pp. 15–18	MindJogger Videoquiz Virtual Labs CD-ROM ExamView® Pro Testmaker TeacherWorks CD-ROM Interactive Chalkboard CD-ROM	**Performance Assessment in the Science Classroom (PASC)**

Transparencies

Section Focus

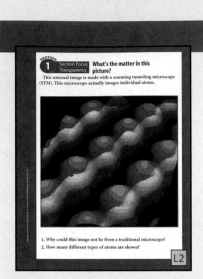

SECTION 1 · Section Focus Transparency · What's the matter in this picture?
This unusual image is made with a scanning tunneling microscope (STM). This microscope actually images individual atoms.

1. Why could this image not be from a traditional microscope?
2. How many different types of atoms are shown?

L2

SECTION 2 · Section Focus Transparency · Some Call It Quicksilver
This element is a liquid at room temperature. It is probably best known as the liquid in traditional thermometers; however, it is so toxic that people often choose digital thermometers that do not contain this element.

1. Describe what you see in the picture. What characteristics does this element have?
2. Which element do you think this is? Do you know of any other uses for it?

L2

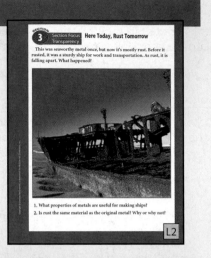

SECTION 3 · Section Focus Transparency · Here Today, Rust Tomorrow
This was seaworthy metal once, but now it's mostly rust. Before it rusted, it was a sturdy ship for work and transportation. As rust, it is falling apart. What happened?

1. What properties of metals are useful for making ships?
2. Is rust the same material as the original metal? Why or why not?

L2

This is a representation of key blackline masters available in the Teacher Classroom Resources. See Resource Manager boxes within the chapter for additional information.

Key to Teaching Strategies

The following designations will help you decide which activities are appropriate for your students.

L1 Level 1 activities should be appropriate for students with learning difficulties.

L2 Level 2 activities should be within the ability range of all students.

L3 Level 3 activities are designed for above-average students.

ELL ELL activities should be within the ability range of English Language Learners.

COOP LEARN Cooperative Learning activities are designed for small group work.

LS Multiple Learning Styles logos, as described on page 12T, are used throughout to indicate strategies that address different learning styles.

P These strategies represent student products that can be placed into a best-work portfolio.

PBL Problem-Based Learning activities apply real-world situations to learning.

Assessment

Assessment Transparency · Matter

Directions: Carefully review the table and answer the following questions.

Characteristics of Some Elements

Element	Atomic number	Mass number	Number of protons	Number of electrons	Number of neutrons
Boron	5	11	5	5	6
Carbon	6	12	6	6	6
Nitrogen	7	14	7	7	7
Oxygen	8	16	8	8	8
Fluorine	9	19	9	9	10

1. According to the table, which element has an atomic number of 7?
   A Boron
   B Carbon
   C Nitrogen
   D Oxygen
2. According to the table, which element has a mass number less than 12?
   F Boron
   G Carbon
   H Oxygen
   J Fluorine
3. According to the table, an atom with 9 protons in its nucleus is ___.
   A carbon
   B nitrogen
   C oxygen
   D fluorine

L2

Teaching

SECTION 1 · Teaching Transparency · Fire and Ash

L2

Hands-on Activities

Student Text Lab Worksheet

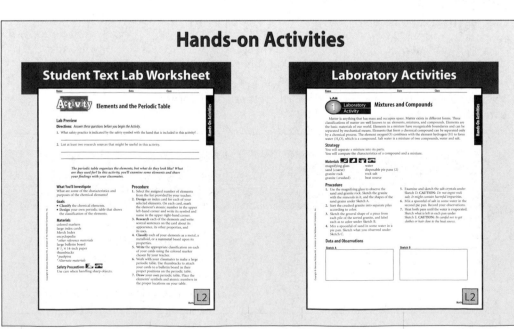

Activity · Elements and the Periodic Table

Lab Preview
Directions: Answer these questions before you begin the Activity.

1. What safety practice is indicated by the safety symbol with the hand that is included in this activity?

2. List at least two research sources that might be useful in this activity.

The periodic table organizes the elements, but what do they look like? What are they used for? In this activity, you'll examine some elements and share your findings with your classmates.

What You'll Investigate
What are some of the characteristics and purposes of the chemical elements?

Goals
• **Classify** the chemical elements.
• **Design** your own periodic table that shows the classification of the elements.

Materials
colored markers
large index cards
Merck Index
encyclopedia
*other reference materials
large bulletin board
8 ½ × 14-inch paper
thumbtacks
*pushpins
*Alternate materials

Safety Precautions
Use care when handling sharp objects.

Procedure
1. Select the assigned number of elements from the list provided by your teacher.
2. **Design** an index card for each of your selected elements. On each card, mark the element's atomic number in the upper left-hand corner and write its symbol and name in the upper right-hand corner.
3. **Research** each of the elements and write several sentences on the card about its appearance, its other properties, and its uses.
4. **Classify** each of your elements as a metal, a nonmetal, or a metalloid based upon its properties.
5. **Write** the appropriate classification on each of your cards using the colored marker chosen by your teacher.
6. Work with your classmates to make a large periodic table. Use thumbtacks to attach your cards to a bulletin board in their proper positions on the periodic table.
7. **Draw** your own periodic table. Place the elements' symbols and atomic numbers in the proper locations on your table.

L2

Laboratory Activities

LAB 1 · Laboratory Activity · Mixtures and Compounds

Matter is anything that has mass and occupies space. Matter exists in different forms. Three classifications of matter are well known to us: elements, mixtures, and compounds. Elements are the basic materials of our world. Elements in a mixture have recognizable boundaries and can be separated by mechanical means. Elements that form a chemical compound can be separated only by a chemical process. The element oxygen (O) combines with the element hydrogen (H) to form water (H_2O), which is a compound. Salt water is a mixture of two compounds, water and salt.

Strategy
You will separate a mixture into its parts.
You will compare the characteristics of a compound and a mixture.

Materials
magnifying glass
sand (coarse)
granite rock
granite (crushed)
water
disposable pie pans (2)
rock salt
heat source

Procedure
1. Use the magnifying glass to observe the sand and granite rock. Sketch the granite with the minerals in it, and the shapes of the sand grains under Sketch A.
2. Sort the crushed granite into separate piles according to color.
3. Sketch the general shape of a piece from each pile of the sorted granite, and label each as to color under Sketch B.
4. Mix a spoonful of sand in some water in a pie pan. Sketch what you observed under Sketch C.
5. Examine and sketch the salt crystals under Sketch D. CAUTION: *Do not ingest rock salt. It might contain harmful impurities.*
6. Mix a spoonful of salt in some water in the second pie pan. Record your observations.
7. Heat both pans until the water is evaporated. Sketch what is left in each pan under Sketch E. CAUTION: *Be careful not to get clothes or hair close to the heat source.*

Data and Observations

Sketch A | Sketch B

L2

Meeting Different Ability Levels

Content Outline

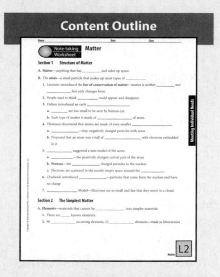

Reinforcement

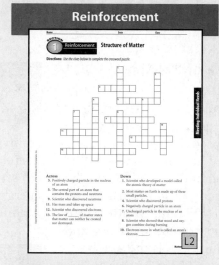

Enrichment

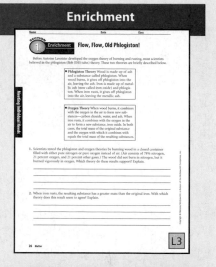

Directed Reading (English/Spanish)

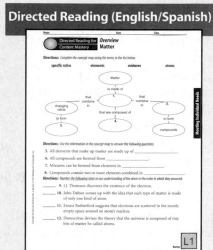

Study Guide

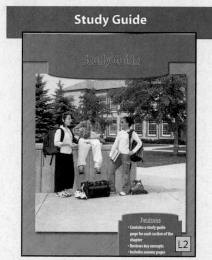

Reading Essentials

Assessment

Test Practice Workbook

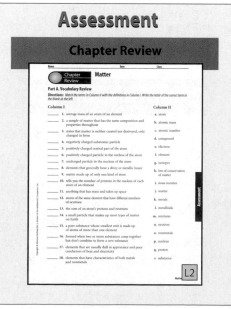

Chapter Review

Chapter Tests

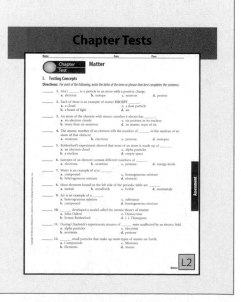

Science Content Background

section 1 Structure of Matter
Matter Basics

Solids, liquids, and gases are matter—they take up space and have mass. The amount of space an object occupies is its volume. The mass of an object refers to the amount of matter it contains. On Earth the amount of mass is directly proportional to the weight of the object. Dividing matter into smaller pieces reduces its volume and mass, and because the mass is reduced, so is the weight.

Ions

Many substances are ionic. That is, they are made up of charged particles called ions rather than neutral atoms. For example, sodium chloride is made up of sodium ions that have 1+ charges and chloride ions that have 1− charges. A sodium ion is formed when a sodium atom loses one of its 11 electrons. A chloride ion is formed when a chlorine atom gains an additional electron to go with the 17 it had as an atom.

Plasma

Plasma, another fluid state of matter, is a gaslike state of negatively charged electrons and positively charged ions. Most matter in the universe is plasma. Stars are mostly plasma, and the hydrogen ions that occur in interstellar space exist in the plasma state.

section 2 The Simplest Matter
Elements

The arrangement of electrons in the energy levels and sublevels in the atoms of an element determines the properties of that element. Elements whose atoms have identical arrangements of electrons in their highest energy levels have similar properties and make up a family of elements on the periodic table.

section 3 Compounds and Mixtures
Compounds

Electron sharing is called covalent bonding. Covalent bonding between atoms of different elements produces molecular compounds. The molecules of molecular compounds attract each other to varying degrees. In the solid state, these attractions sometimes lead to an orderly arrangement of molecules called a molecular crystal.

When atoms react by losing or gaining electrons, called ionic bonding, ions are formed. The formula for an ionic compound such as sodium chloride (NaCl) is called an empirical formula and gives the simplest ratio of ions in the compound, not the formula for a molecule.

Mixtures

Solid solutions, made up of uniform mixtures of metals and sometimes nonmetals, are called alloys. Brass and stainless steel are common alloys.

chapter content resources

Internet Resources
For additional content background, visit
ips.msscience.com to:
- access your book online
- find references to related articles in popular science magazines
- access Web links with related content background
- access current events with science journal topics

Print Resources
Chemistry, Steve S. Zumdahl, Susan A. Zumdahl, Houghton Mifflin Company, 2003
Chemistry, Raymond Chang, McGraw-Hill College, 2001
General Chemistry, Ralph Petrucci, William Harwood, Prentice Hall, 1997

IDENTIFYING ▸ Misconceptions

Find Out What Students Think

Students may think that . . .

Objects have mass only if you can feel them.

If you keep dividing matter, you will eventually get small pieces with no mass.

Students may have these misconceptions because they are relying on their senses. In this case they are relying on their sense of touch. They may think that if an object does not press down on their hands and feel heavy, it has no mass.

Demonstration

Hold up a plastic foam cup, and ask students if the cup has mass. Establish that it does. Break a chunk off the cup, and ask how the mass of this part of the cup compares with the mass of the original cup. Establish that it has less mass. Give pieces of the cup to four different students sitting in different parts of the classroom. Ask students to break their pieces and hold up the biggest piece of cup that has no mass. When they hold these up ask other students if they agree that the pieces have no mass.

Promote Understanding

Activity

Divide the class into groups. Give a foam cup to each group. Have them discuss whether the cup is matter. Establish that it is because it has mass and takes up space. Explain that on Earth, the mass of a cup is directly proportional to its weight. This means that if a cup has a large mass, it has a large weight, and if it has a small mass, it has a small weight. Perform the following:

- Using a balance that can measure mass to at least 0.1 g, measure the mass of the cup.

- Draw a picture of the cup, and write its mass.

- Use scissors to cut the cup exactly in half.

- Draw a picture of the half cup, calculate its mass (original mass divided by two), and write the new mass by the picture.

- Take one half of the cup and cut it into two equal parts.

- Draw a picture of one of the new pieces, and write its mass next to it.

- Repeat this procedure four more times, each time cutting the piece in half, drawing it, and calculating its mass.

- Make a graph of the data. The x-axis should be labeled *Mass (g)*. It should start with zero and have a range that includes the mass of the whole cup. The y-axis should be labeled *Fraction of cup*. It should begin with 1/64th of a cup and go up in the following increments: 1/32, 1/16, 1/8, 1/4, 1/2, and 1.

Instruct students to examine their data and discuss whether they will ever get a piece of cup that has absolutely no mass. Make sure students understand that as pieces get smaller and smaller, their masses and their weights get smaller and smaller, but the pieces always have some mass.

Assess

After completing the chapter, see *Identifying Misconceptions* in the Study Guide at the end of the chapter.

Chapter Vocabulary

matter, p. 72
atom, p. 73
law of conservation of matter, p. 74
electron, p. 76
nucleus, p. 77
proton, p. 77
neutron, p. 78
element, p. 80
atomic number, p. 83
isotope, p. 83
mass number, p. 83
atomic mass, p. 84
metal, p. 84
nonmetal, p. 85
metalloid, p. 85
substance, p. 87
compound, p. 87
mixture, p. 89

Science Journal Student responses will vary but may include questions about flight, balloons, and how matter is involved with flight.

INTERACTIVE CHALKBOARD
with Image Bank

PowerPoint® Presentations

This CD-ROM is an editable Microsoft® PowerPoint® presentation that includes:
- a pre-made presentation for every chapter
- interactive graphics
- animations
- audio clips
- image bank
- all new section and chapter questions
- Standardized Test Practice
- transparencies
- pre-lab questions for all labs
- Foldables directions
- links to ips.msscience.com

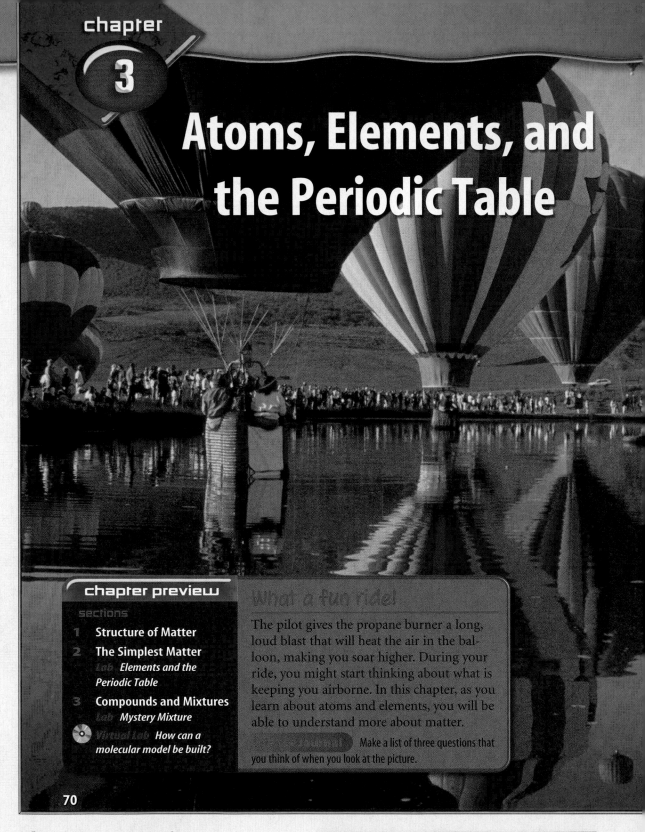

Atoms, Elements, and the Periodic Table

chapter preview

sections

1 Structure of Matter

2 The Simplest Matter
Lab Elements and the Periodic Table

3 Compounds and Mixtures
Lab Mystery Mixture

Virtual Lab How can a molecular model be built?

What a fun ride!

The pilot gives the propane burner a long, loud blast that will heat the air in the balloon, making you soar higher. During your ride, you might start thinking about what is keeping you airborne. In this chapter, as you learn about atoms and elements, you will be able to understand more about matter.

Science Journal Make a list of three questions that you think of when you look at the picture.

70

Theme Connection

Scale and Structure Tiny particles called atoms make up elements. Elements are the building blocks of all matter.

About the Photo

Rise and Sink What keeps a hot air balloon flying? It is the same principle that keeps food frozen in the open chest freezers at the grocery store. The principle is that hot air rises and cold air sinks. While the super-cooled air in a open chest freezer settles down around the food, the hot air in a hot air balloon pushes up, keeping the balloon afloat.

Start-Up Activities

Observe Matter

You've just finished playing basketball. You're hot and thirsty. You reach for your bottle of water and take a drink. Releasing your grip, you notice that the bottle is nearly empty. Is the bottle really almost empty? According to the dictionary, *empty* means "containing nothing." When you have finished all the water in the bottle, will it be empty or full?

1. Wad up a dry paper towel or tissue and tape it to the inside of a plastic cup as shown.

2. Fill a bowl or sink with water. Turn the cup upside down and slowly push the cup straight down into the water as far as you can.

3. Slowly raise the cup straight up and out of the water. Remove the paper towel or tissue paper and examine it.

4. **Think Critically** In your Science Journal, describe the lab and its results. Explain what you think happened. Was anything in the cup besides the paper? If so, what was it?

FOLDABLES™
Study Organizer

Atoms, Elements, and the Periodic Table Make the following Foldable to help you identify the main ideas about atoms, elements, compounds, and mixtures.

STEP 1 **Draw** a mark at the midpoint of a sheet of paper along the side edge. Then **fold** the top and bottom edges in to touch the midpoint.

STEP 2 **Fold** in half from side to side.

STEP 3 **Open and cut** along the inside fold lines to form four tabs.

STEP 4 **Label** each tab as shown.

Read and Write As you read the chapter, list several everyday examples of atoms, elements, compounds, and mixtures on the back of the appropriate tab.

Science Online **Preview this chapter's content and activities at** ips.msscience.com

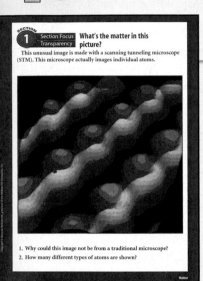
Structure of Matter

as you read

What You'll Learn

- **Describe** characteristics of matter.
- **Identify** what makes up matter.
- **Identify** the parts of an atom.
- **Compare** the models that are used for atoms.

Why It's Important

Matter makes up almost everything we see—and much of what we can't see.

⊙ Review Vocabulary
density: the mass of an object divided by its volume

New Vocabulary
- matter
- atom
- law of conservation of matter
- electron
- nucleus
- proton
- neutron

What is matter?

Is a glass with some water in it half empty or half full? Actually, neither is correct. The glass is completely full—half full of water and half full of air. What is air? Air is a mixture of several gases, including nitrogen and oxygen, which are kinds of matter. **Matter** is anything that has mass and takes up space. So, even though you can't see it or hold it in your hand, air is matter. What about all the things you can see, taste, smell, and touch? Most are made of matter, too. Look at the things pictured in **Figure 1** and determine which of them are matter.

What isn't matter?

You can see the words on this page because of the light from the Sun or from a fixture in the room. Does light have mass or take up space? What about the warmth from the Sun or the heat from the heater in your classroom? Light and heat do not take up space, and they have no mass. Therefore, they are not forms of matter. Emotions, thoughts, and ideas are not matter either. Does this information change your mind about the items in **Figure 1**?

Reading Check *Why is air matter, but light is not?*

Figure 1 A rainbow is formed when light filters through the raindrops, a plant grows from a seed in the ground, and a statue is sculpted from bronze.
Identify *which are matter.*

72 CHAPTER 3 Atoms, Elements, and the Periodic Table

Section 1 Resource Manager

Figure 2 Early Beliefs About the Composition of Matter

Many Indian Philosophers (1,000 B.C.)	Kashyapa, an Indian Philosopher (1,000 B.C.)	Many Greek Philosophers (500–300 B.C.)	Democritus (380 B.C.)	Aristotle (330 B.C.)	Chinese Philosophers (300 B.C.)
• Ether—an invisible substance that filled the heavens • Earth • Water • Air • Fire	• Five elements broken down into smaller units called parmanu • Parmanu of earth elements are heavier than air elements	• Earth • Water • Air • Fire	• Tiny individual particles he called *atomos* • Empty space through which atoms move • Each substance composed of one type of *atomos*	• Empty space could not exist • Earth • Water • Air • Fire	• Metal • Earth • Water • Air • Fire

What makes up matter?

Suppose you cut a chunk of wood into smaller and smaller pieces. Do the pieces seem to be made of the same matter as the large chunk you started with? If you could cut a small enough piece, would it still have the same properties as the first chunk? Would you reach a point where the last cut resulted in a piece that no longer resembled the first chunk? Is there a limit to how small a piece can be? For centuries, people have asked questions like these and wondered what matter is made of.

An Early Idea Democritus, who lived from about 460 B.C. to 370 B.C., was a Greek philosopher who thought the universe was made of empty space and tiny bits of stuff. He believed that the bits of stuff were so small they could no longer be divided into smaller pieces. He called these tiny pieces atoms. The term *atom* comes from a Greek word that means "cannot be divided." Today an **atom** is defined as a small particle that makes up most types of matter. **Figure 2** shows the difference between Democritus's ideas and those of other early scientists and philosophers. Democritus thought that different types of atoms existed for every type of matter and that the atom's identity explained the characteristics of each type of matter. Democritus's ideas about atoms were a first step toward understanding matter. However, his ideas were not accepted for over 2,000 years. It wasn't until the early 1800s that scientists built upon the concept of atoms to form the current atomic theory of matter.

Atomism Historians note that Leucippus developed the idea of the atom around 440 B.C. He and his student, Democritus, refined the idea of the atom years later. Their concept of the atom was based on five major points: (1) all matter is made of atoms, (2) there are empty spaces between atoms, (3) atoms are complete solids, (4) atoms do not have internal structure, and (5) atoms are different in size, shape, and weight.

Curriculum Connection

Physics Ancient astronomers had no understanding of what stars were. This is because they lacked a framework of physics in which to understand how stars worked and what they constituted. The study of modern physics includes a wide variety of fields that are used to understand the origin and evolution of stars, matter, energy and the forces of nature.

2 Teach

IDENTIFYING Misconceptions

Weight/Mass Students may think that objects have weight only if you can feel them. Refer to the F page at the beginning of the chapter for teaching strategies that address this misconception.

Activity

Classifying Matter Take students outside to make a list of all the things they observe. Return to the classroom and have them classify the items as "Matter" and "Not Matter." What is matter? Possible answers: Matter is anything that has mass and takes up space and includes things that we see, taste, smell, and touch. What isn't matter? Possible answers: Emotions, thoughts, ideas, and light are not matter because they do not have mass and do not take up space. L2

Atomism Democritus (460–370 B.C.) was born into a noble and wealthy family. The Magi instructed him in astronomy and theology. After the death of his father, Democritus traveled to search for wisdom. It was said that he visited many countries, such as Egypt and Ethiopia. Democritus was known as "The Laughing Philosopher" because he expressed disapproval for human foolishness while laughing. He lived for more than one hundred years.

Mini LAB

Purpose Students infer the number and types of objects in a sealed box to model how scientists study atoms. L2 LS
Logical-Mathematical

Materials sealed shoe box containing various items (eraser, coin, paper clip, ruler)

Teaching Strategy Emphasize that students should not open the box.

Analysis

1. Answers will vary depending on items in the box.
2. Scientists perform experiments on matter to make models of the atom, but they cannot actually see inside an atom to verify that their models are correct.

Assessment

Process Have students open the box and examine the items contained inside. Ask them to infer why some objects were easier to identify than others. Use **Performance Assessment in the Science Classroom,** p. 89.

Teacher FYI

Creating Matter According to the law of conservation of matter, matter can neither be created nor destroyed. But experimental data indicate that a high energy X ray can collide with the nucleus of an atom to create an electron and a positron in its place. Also, an electron and positron can collide with and annihilate each other to produce X rays. Although matter is created and destroyed in these instances, the amount of total energy stays the same, but the energy can change its form from electromagnetic radiation to matter.

Figure 3 When wood burns, matter is not lost. The total mass of the wood and the oxygen it combines with during a fire equals the total mass of the ash, water vapor, carbon dioxide, and other gases produced.
Infer *When you burn wood in a fireplace, what is the source of oxygen?*

wood + oxygen = ash + gases + water vapor

Mini LAB

Investigating the Unseen

Procedure

1. Your teacher will give you a **sealed shoe box** that contains **one or more items.**
2. Try to find out how many and what kinds of items are inside the box. You cannot look inside the box. The only observations you can make are by handling the box.

Analysis

1. How many items do you infer are in the box? Sketch the apparent shapes of the items and identify them if you can.
2. Compare your procedure with how scientists perform experiments and make models to find out more about the atom.

Lavoisier's Contribution Lavoisier (la VWAH see ay), a French chemist who lived about 2,000 years after Democritus, also was curious about matter—especially when it changed form. Before Lavoisier, people thought matter could appear and disappear because of the changes they saw as matter burned or rusted. You might have thought that matter can disappear if you've ever watched wood burn in a fireplace or at a bonfire. Lavoisier showed that wood and the oxygen it combines with during burning have the same mass as the ash, water, carbon dioxide, and other gases that are produced, as shown in **Figure 3.** In a similar way, an iron bar, oxygen, and water have the same mass as the rust that forms when they interact. From Lavoisier's work came the **law of conservation of matter,** which states that matter is not created or destroyed—it only changes form.

Models of the Atom

Models are often used for things that are too small or too large to be observed or that are too difficult to be understood easily. One way to make a model is to make a smaller version of something large. If you wanted to design a new sailboat, would you build a full-sized boat and hope it would float? It would be more efficient, less expensive, and safer to build and test a smaller version first. Then, if it didn't float, you could change your design and build another model. You could keep trying until the model worked.

In the case of atoms, scientists use large models to explain something that is too small to be looked at. These models of the atom were used to explain data or facts that were gathered experimentally. As a result, these models are also theories.

Visual Learning

Figure 3 Why could being in a closed space with a fire be hazardous, even if you are in no danger of being burned? As the fuel burns, it consumes oxygen and produces smoke. Thus, being confined with a fire can lead to suffocation, not only from lack of oxygen, but also from smoke inhalation.

Dalton's Atomic Model In the early 1800s, an English schoolteacher and chemist named John Dalton studied the experiments of Lavoisier and others. Dalton thought he could design an atomic model that explained the results of those experiments. Dalton's atomic model was a set of ideas—not a physical object. Dalton believed that matter was made of atoms that were too small to be seen by the human eye. He also thought that each type of matter was made of only one kind of atom. For example, gold atoms make up a gold nugget and give a gold ring its shiny appearance. Likewise, iron atoms make up an iron bar and give it unique properties, and so on. Because predictions using Dalton's model were supported by data, the model became known as the atomic theory of matter.

Sizes of Atoms Atoms are so small it would take about 1 million of them lined up in a row to equal the thickness of a human hair. For another example of how small atoms are, look at **Figure 4.** Imagine you are holding an orange in your hand. If you wanted to be able to see the individual atoms on the orange's surface, the size of the orange would have to be increased to the size of Earth. Then, imagine the Earth-sized orange covered with billions and billions of marbles. Each marble would represent one of the atoms on the skin of the orange. No matter what kind of model you use to picture it, the result is the same—an atom is an extremely small particle of matter.

Fun Fact

Our knowledge of Democritus' atomic theory comes from a poem written by the Roman Lucretius, who lived about 300 years after Democritus.

Virtual Labs

Atomic Structure *How can a molecular model be built?*

Figure 4 If this orange were as large as Earth, each of its atoms would be marble-sized.

LAB DEMONSTRATION

Purpose to demonstrate that matter is neither created nor destroyed
Materials fine steel wool, heat-proof mitt, safety goggles, crucible tongs, burner, pan balance
Preparation Wear goggles and heat-proof mitt while performing this activity.

Procedure Obtain the mass of a piece of steel wool. Hold the steel wool in a burner flame using tongs. After a few fibers burn, ask question 1. After students have responded, obtain the mass of the burned steel wool and then ask question 2.
Expected Outcome Mass increases.

Assessment

1. Will what's left have a mass greater or less than the original? Most students will likely think the mass has decreased. 2. Why is there a gain in mass? The iron in the steel wool reacted with O_2 in the air to form iron oxide, so the mass of the O_2 has been added to the original mass.

Caption Answers

Figure 5 The rays would straighten.

Figure 6 Because matter is neutral, if it contains particles with negative charges, it must also contain particles with positive charges.

Figure 7 in the nucleus

Quick Demo

Magnetic Field

Materials iron filings, overhead projector, transparency sheet, bar magnet

Estimated Time five minutes

Procedure Demonstrate the presence and shape of a magnet field by placing the iron filings on a transparency sheet and placing the sheet over a bar magnet on an overhead projector.

Use Science Words

Word Usage Have students use the word *electron* in a sentence describing its characteristics. Sentences should include that an electron has a small mass, a negative charge, and is found outside the atomic nucleus. L2

Reading Check

Answer The particles in the rays were charged, and thus were affected by the magnet's magnetic field.

Activity

Parts of an Atom Have students fold a piece of paper into four sections. Instruct them to write one of the following terms in each box: electron, nucleus, proton, neutron. As you read and discuss this section, have students illustrate and write key facts for each part of the atom. Illustrations will vary. Key facts should include: electron—negatively charged particles scattered outside the nucleus; nucleus—positively charged central part of the atom; proton—positively charged particle located in the nucleus; neutron—a particle with no charge found in the nucleus of the atom. P

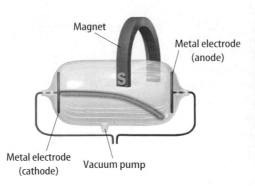

Magnet

Metal electrode (anode)

Metal electrode (cathode) Vacuum pump

Figure 5 In Thomson's experiment, the magnet caused the cathode rays inside the tube to bend. **Describe** *what you think would happen to the cathode rays if the magnet were removed.*

Science Online

Topic: Subatomic Particles

Visit ips.msscience.com for Web links to information about particles that make up atoms.

Activity Can any of the particles be divided further? Display your data in a table.

Discovering the Electron One of the many pioneers in the development of today's atomic model was J.J. Thomson, an English scientist. He conducted experiments using a cathode ray tube, which is a glass tube sealed at both ends out of which most of the air has been pumped. Thomson's tube had a metal plate at each end. The plates were connected to a high-voltage electrical source that gave one of the plates—the anode—a positive charge and the other plate—the cathode—a negative charge. During his experiments, Thomson observed rays that traveled from the cathode to the anode. These cathode rays were bent by a magnet, as seen in **Figure 5,** showing that they were made up of particles that had mass and charge. Thomson knew that like charges repel each other and opposite charges attract each other. When he saw that the rays traveled toward a positively charged plate, he concluded that the cathode rays were made up of negatively charged particles. These invisible, negatively charged particles are called **electrons**.

Reading Check

Why were the cathode rays in Thomson's cathode ray tube bent by a magnet?

Try to imagine Thomson's excitement at this discovery. He had shown that atoms are not too tiny to divide after all. Rather, they are made up of even smaller subatomic particles. Other scientists soon built upon Thomson's results and found that the electron had a small mass. In fact, an electron is 1/1,837 the mass of the lightest atom, the hydrogen atom. In 1906, Thomson received the Nobel Prize in Physics for his work on the discovery of the electron.

Matter that has an equal amount of positive and negative charge is said to be neutral—it has no net charge. Because most matter is neutral, Thomson pictured the atom as a ball of positive charge with electrons embedded in it. It was later determined that neutral atoms contained an equal number of positive and negative charges.

76 CHAPTER 3 Atoms, Elements, and the Periodic Table

Differentiated Instruction

Learning Disabled Have students make up new lyrics to a familiar tune using the vocabulary and definitions from the chapter. The song can focus on one concept, such as the parts of an atom, or cover the entire chapter's content. Some examples for the familiar tune are "Row, Row, Row Your Boat," "Old McDonald," and "Itsy Bitsy Spider." LS **Auditory-Musical**

Active Reading

Reflective Journal Have students write reflective journals about their experiences in this activity. Have students divide sheets of paper into several columns and record their thoughts under headings such as *What I Did, What I Learned, What Questions I Have, What Surprises I Experienced,* and *Overall Response.* Suggest that volunteers share their reflections with the class.

Thomson's Model Thomson's model, shown in **Figure 6,** can be compared to chocolate chips spread throughout a ball of cookie dough. However, the model did not provide all the answers to the questions that puzzled scientists about atoms.

Rutherford—The Nucleus Scientists still had questions about how the atom was arranged and about the presence of positively charged particles. In about 1910, a team of scientists led by Ernest Rutherford worked on these questions. In their experiment, they bombarded an extremely thin piece of gold foil with alpha particles. Alpha particles are tiny, high-energy, positively charged particles that he predicted would pass through the foil. Most of the particles passed straight through the foil as if it were not there at all. However, other particles changed direction, and some even bounced back. Rutherford thought the result was so remarkable that he later said, "It was almost as incredible as if you had fired a 15-inch shell at a piece of tissue paper, and it came back and hit you."

Positive Center Rutherford concluded that because so many of the alpha particles passed straight through the gold foil, the atoms must be made of mostly empty space. However, because some of the positively charged alpha particles bounced off something, the gold atoms must contain some positively charged object concentrated in the midst of this empty space. Rutherford called the positively charged, central part of the atom the **nucleus** (NEW klee us). He named the positively charged particles in the nucleus **protons**. He also suggested that electrons were scattered in the mostly empty space around the nucleus, as shown in **Figure 7.**

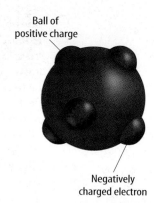

Ball of positive charge

Negatively charged electron

Figure 6 Thomson's model shows the atom as electrons embedded in a ball of positive charge.
Explain *how Thomson knew atoms contained positive and negative charges.*

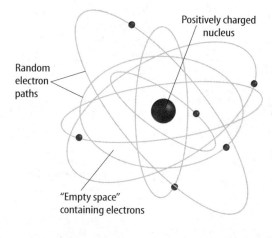

Positively charged nucleus

Random electron paths

"Empty space" containing electrons

Figure 7 Rutherford concluded that the atom must be mostly empty space in which electrons travel in random paths around the nucleus. He also thought the nucleus of the atom must be small and positively charged.
Identify *where most of the mass of an atom is concentrated.*

SECTION 1 Structure of Matter **77**

Visual Learning

Figures 6 and 7 Have students compare Thomson's model with Rutherford's model. How are they the same? Both are spherical and contain particles. How are they different? Thomson's model is like a solid ball, while Rutherford's is mostly empty space, like a cloud.

Discussion
Protons and Neutrons How are protons and neutrons similar and how are they different? Protons and neutrons are both found in atomic nuclei. Both particles are small but massive, and their masses are nearly equal. The proton is positively charged, while the neutron has no charge.

Inquiry Lab

Touching Atoms
Purpose Students will work with models of atoms to gain a better understanding of their structure and properties.

Possible Materials nuts or bolts in two different sizes, long-distance measuring tape, ground stake

Estimated Time one or two class sessions

Teaching Strategies
• Size: Have students calculate where the first electron would be if the nucleus of an atom was the size of the head of a pin (1mm diameter). The average atom is of the order of 10^{-10} m, while the average nucleus is of the order of 10^{-15} m. It will be about 100 m away.

• Isotopes: Gather a handful of small and large bolts. Tell students it is the element 'bolt' and you want to find its average mass, just like atoms have average masses for all of their real isotopes. Have students weigh a large bolt and a small bolt and record the mass. Then, multiply the mass of the object by the number of objects, add it to the mass of the other size object times the number of objects, and divide by the total number of objects. This is the same method for calculating isotopic mass of elements. You could add a medium-sized bolt to the calculation, too.

• Have students brainstorm other ways to represent this information.

For additional inquiry activities, see *Science Inquiry Labs.*

Make a Model

Atomic Model Students may find this abstract information difficult to understand unless models and visual examples are used during reading and discussion. Have students construct a teaching model by using a standard paper plate as the electron cloud. Have them use different colors for electrons (negative symbols) and protons (positive symbols).

IDENTIFYING Misconceptions

Three-Dimensional Students may think that atoms and their structures are two-dimensional or flat because the models and illustrations are flat. In fact, an atom is a three-dimensional object in which the electrons travel in a random pattern within a given distance around the nucleus.

INTEGRATE Career

Physicists and Chemists Science is a team effort. Even though physicists and chemists may study different subjects, often they are working on a joint project. One of the newest areas of study is nanotechnology. This is one field where physicists and chemists can work jointly to develop new products.

Research Have students investigate the various places where physicists and chemists can work.

INTEGRATE Career

Physicists and Chemists Physicists generally study the physical atom. The physical atom includes the inner components of an atom such as protons and neutrons, the forces that hold or change their positions in space and the bulk properties of elements such as melting point. Chemists, on the other hand, study the chemical atom. The chemical atom refers to the manner in which different elements relate to each other and the new substances formed by their union.

Figure 8 This simplified Bohr model shows a nucleus of protons and neutrons and electron paths based on energy levels.

Discovering the Neutron Rutherford had been puzzled by one observation from his experiments with nuclei. After the collisions, the nuclei seemed to be heavier. Where did this extra mass come from? James Chadwick, a student of Rutherford's, answered this question. The alpha particles themselves were not heavier. The atoms that had been bombarded had given off new particles. Chadwick experimented with these new particles and found that, unlike electrons, the paths of these particles were not affected by an electric field. To explain his observations, he said that these particles came from the nucleus and had no charge. Chadwick called these uncharged particles **neutrons** (NEW trahnz). His proton-neutron model of the atomic nucleus is still accepted today.

Improving the Atomic Model

Early in the twentieth century, a scientist named Niels Bohr found evidence that electrons in atoms are arranged according to energy levels. The lowest energy level is closest to the nucleus and can hold only two electrons. Higher energy levels are farther from the nucleus and can contain more electrons. To explain these energy levels, some scientists thought that the electrons might orbit an atom's nucleus in paths that are specific distances from the nucleus, as shown in **Figure 8.** This is similar to how the planets orbit the Sun.

The Modern Atomic Model As a result of continuing research, scientists now realize that because electrons have characteristics that are similar to waves and particles, their energy levels are not defined, planet-like orbits around the nucleus. Rather, it seems most likely that electrons move in what is called the atom's electron cloud, as shown in **Figure 9.**

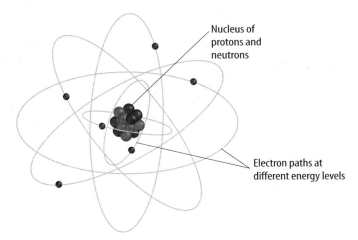

Nucleus of protons and neutrons

Electron paths at different energy levels

Differentiated Instruction

Challenge Have students find out more about the people involved in the discovery of the parts of the atom—where they lived and worked, when they made their discoveries, how the discoveries were made, and other scientists they worked with. Have them combine their reports to make a class newspaper called "Great Moments in Atomic History." L3 COOP LEARN LS Linguistic

Teacher FYI

Alpha Particles An alpha particle consists of two protons and two neutrons and is identical to the nucleus of a helium atom. Alpha particles are emitted by many radioactive nuclei, such as the ones that Rutherford used in his experiment.

The Electron Cloud The electron cloud is a spherical cloud of varying density surrounding the nucleus. The varying density shows where an electron is more or less likely to be. Atoms with electrons in higher energy levels have electron clouds of different shapes that also show where those electrons are likely to be. Generally, the electron cloud has a radius 10,000 times that of the nucleus.

Further Research By the 1930s, it was recognized that matter was made up of atoms, which were, in turn, made up of protons, neutrons, and electrons. But scientists, called physicists, continued to study the basic parts of this atom. Today, they have succeeded in breaking down protons and neutrons into even smaller particles called quarks. These particles can combine to make other kinds of tiny particles, too. The six types of quarks are *up, down, strange, charmed, top,* and *bottom.* Quarks have fractional electric charges of $+2/3$ or $-1/3$, unlike the $+1$ charge of a proton or the -1 charge of an electron. Research will continue as new discoveries are made about the structure of matter.

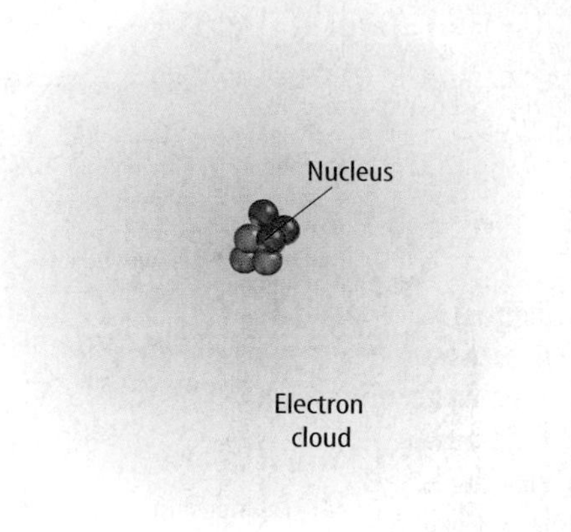

Nucleus

Electron cloud

Figure 9 This model of the atom shows the electrons moving around the nucleus in a region called an electron cloud. The dark cloud of color represents the area where the electron is more likely to be found.
Infer *What does the intensity of color near the nucleus suggest?*

Caption Answer
Figure 9 The intensity of color near the nucleus suggests that the electrons are more likely to be found here.

3 Assess

DAILY INTERVENTION

Check for Understanding
Kinesthetic Have students use common materials to make models that correspond to today's model of the atom. Have a contest and award prizes to the models that are judged the most accurate or creative. L2 ELL COOP LEARN LS

Reteach
Diagram an Atom Have students make a labeled diagram of an atom. Diagrams should include the nucleus, protons, neutrons, and electrons. Labels should include brief definitions. L1 LS
Visual-Spatial

Assessment

Performance Have students work in small groups to create presentations that illustrate the basic structure of matter. Use **Performance Assessment in the Science Classroom,** p. 143.

section 1 review

Summary

What is matter?
- Matter is anything that has mass and takes up space.
- Matter is composed of atoms.

Models of the Atom
- Democritus introduced the idea of an atom. Lavoisier showed matter is neither created nor destroyed, just changed.
- Dalton's ideas led to the atomic theory of matter.
- Thomson discovered the electron.
- Rutherford discovered protons exist in the nucleus.
- Chadwick discovered the neutron.

Improving the Atomic Model
- Niels Bohr suggested electrons move in energy levels.
- More recent physicists introduced the idea of the electron cloud and were able to break down protons and neutrons into smaller particles called quarks.

Self Check

1. **List** five examples of matter and five examples that are not matter. Explain your answers.
2. **Describe** and name the parts of the atom.
3. **Explain** why the word *atom* was an appropriate term for Democritus's idea.
4. **Think Critically** When neutrons were discovered, were these neutrons created in the experiment? How does Lavoisier's work help answer this question?
5. **Explain** the law of conservation of matter using your own examples.
6. **Think Critically** How is the electron cloud model different from Bohr's atomic model?

Applying Skills

7. **Classify** each scientist and his contribution according to the type of discovery each person made. Explain why you grouped certain scientists together.
8. **Evaluate Others' Data and Conclusions** Analyze, review, and critique the strengths and weaknesses of Thomson's "cookie dough" theory using the results of Rutherford's gold foil experiment.

section 1 review

1. Possible answers: matter: things that have mass and occupy space; not matter: ideas, emotions
2. A nucleus consists of positively charged protons and neutral neutrons; negatively charged electrons move outside the nucleus.
3. *Atom* means cannot be divided.

4. No; According to the law of the conservation of matter, matter cannot be created or destroyed.
5. Possible answer: wood burning in a fireplace is an example of the law of conservation of mass. The wood and oxygen from the air have the same mass as the ash, water, and gases

that are produced.
6. The electron cloud model, unlike Bohr's model, does not have the electrons moving around the nucleus in a planet-like orbit.
7. Classification schemes will vary.
8. Thomson: atom is a ball of positive charge with electrons embedded in

it. Rutherford: atom is mostly empty space with electrons scattered around small nucleus. Strength: shows atom is divisible and composed of charged particles. Weakness: does not show atom is mostly space and has "structure".

as you read

What **You'll Learn**

- **Describe** the relationship between elements and the periodic table.
- **Explain** the meaning of atomic mass and atomic number.
- **Identify** what makes an isotope.
- **Contrast** metals, metalloids, and nonmetals.

Why **It's Important**

Everything on Earth is made of the elements that are listed on the periodic table.

⊙ **Review Vocabulary**

mass: a measure of the amount of matter an object has

New Vocabulary

- element
- atomic number
- isotope
- mass number
- atomic mass
- metal
- nonmetal
- metalloid

The Elements

Have you watched television today? TV sets are common, yet each one is a complex system. The outer case is made mostly of plastic, and the screen is made of glass. Many of the parts that conduct electricity are metals or combinations of metals. Other parts in the interior of the set contain materials that barely conduct electricity. All of the different materials have one thing in common: they are made up of even simpler materials. In fact, if you had the proper equipment, you could separate the plastics, glass, and metals into these simpler materials.

One Kind of Atom Eventually, though, you would separate the materials into groups of atoms. At that point, you would have a collection of elements. An **element** is matter made of only one kind of atom. At least 115 elements are known and about 90 of them occur naturally on Earth. These elements make up gases in the air, minerals in rocks, and liquids such as water. Examples of naturally occurring elements include the oxygen and nitrogen in the air you breathe and the metals gold, silver, aluminum, and iron. The other elements are known as synthetic elements. These elements have been made in nuclear reactions by scientists with machines called particle accelerators, like the one shown in **Figure 10.** Some synthetic elements have important uses in medical testing and are found in smoke detectors and heart pacemaker batteries.

Figure 10 The Tevatron has a circumference of 6.3 km—a distance that allows particles to accelerate to high speeds. These high-speed collisions can create synthetic elements.

80

Figure 11 When you look for information in the library, a system of organization called the Dewey Decimal Classification System helps you find a book quickly and efficiently.

The Periodic Table

Suppose you go to a library, like the one shown in **Figure 11,** to look up information for a school assignment. How would you find the information? You could look randomly on shelves as you walk up and down rows of books, but the chances of finding your book would be slim. To avoid such haphazard searching, some libraries use the Dewey Decimal Classification System to categorize and organize their volumes and to help you find books quickly and efficiently.

Charting the Elements Chemists have created a chart called the periodic table of the elements to help them organize and display the elements. **Figure 12** shows how scientists changed their model of the periodic table over time.

On the inside back cover of this book, you will find a modern version of the periodic table. Each element is represented by a chemical symbol that contains one to three letters. The symbols are a form of chemical shorthand that chemists use to save time and space—on the periodic table as well as in written formulas. The symbols are an important part of an international system that is understood by scientists everywhere.

The elements are organized on the periodic table by their properties. There are rows and columns that represent relationships between the elements. The rows in the table are called periods. The elements in a row have the same number of energy levels. The columns are called groups. The elements in each group have similar properties related to their structure. They also tend to form similar bonds.

Dewey Decimal Classification System

000	Computers, information and general reference
100	Philosophy and psychology
200	Religion
300	Social sciences
400	Languages
500	Science
600	Technology
700	Arts and recreation
800	Literature
900	History and geography

Science Online

Topic: New Elements
Visit ips.msscience.com for Web links to information about new elements.

Activity Research physical properties of two synthetic elements.

Activity
Familiar Elements Have students skim the periodic table for symbols and names of familiar elements. Have them share with the class the things that these elements with similar properties are found in. Example: Ca—calcium is found in milk and other food products.
L2 **LS Interpersonal**

Use an Analogy
Calendar Describe a month's calendar as being like the periodic table. The days are arranged from left to right, as periods of elements are arranged from left to right. Days with the same name are arranged in columns, as groups of elements are arranged in the table.

Teacher FYI

Ancient Elements Elements such as gold, silver, tin, copper, lead, and mercury have been known since ancient times. As more elements were discovered, people began to recognize patterns in their properties. Later, scientists used the patterns to classify the elements.

Fun Fact

The Fermilab, which is home to the Tevatron particle accelerator, is about 20,000 times longer than Thompson's cathode-ray tube.

Differentiated Instruction

English-Language Learners Ask the students to pick 8–10 elements and share with the class both the English and native pronunciation of each element.

Visualizing the Periodic Table

Have students examine the pictures and read the captions. Then ask the following questions.

Why do you think the periodic table is so useful to scientists? It helps them organize and understand the chemical properties of the elements.

One difference between Mendeleev's table and the one used today is that his table lacks the column containing the elements helium through radon. Why do you think this is? None of the elements in that column had been discovered in Mendeleev's time. This is because they are not common and they don't readily undergo chemical reactions.

Activity

Periodic Groups Divide the class into eighteen groups. Assign each group a different group of elements from the periodic table. Have them research the similarities and differences among the elements in their respective groups and make a poster illustrating the properties of these elements. [L2]

COOP LEARN [LS] **Interpersonal**

Fun Fact

Mendeleev left gaps in his periodic table to locate the next element in its proper family and predicted properties of undiscovered elements that would fit these spaces. His predictions were confirmed when three predicted elements, gallium, germanium, and scandium were discovered.

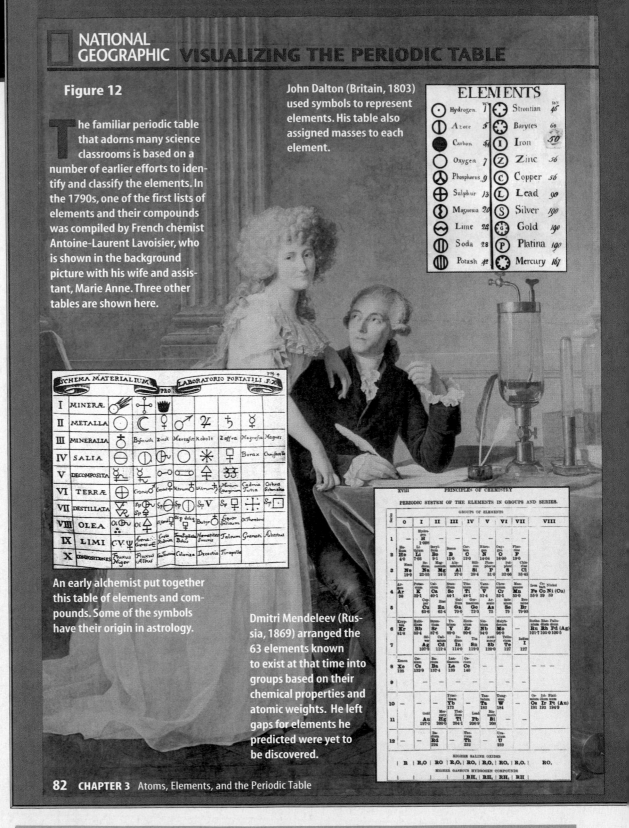

Figure 12

The familiar periodic table that adorns many science classrooms is based on a number of earlier efforts to identify and classify the elements. In the 1790s, one of the first lists of elements and their compounds was compiled by French chemist Antoine-Laurent Lavoisier, who is shown in the background picture with his wife and assistant, Marie Anne. Three other tables are shown here.

John Dalton (Britain, 1803) used symbols to represent elements. His table also assigned masses to each element.

An early alchemist put together this table of elements and compounds. Some of the symbols have their origin in astrology.

Dmitri Mendeleev (Russia, 1869) arranged the 63 elements known to exist at that time into groups based on their chemical properties and atomic weights. He left gaps for elements he predicted were yet to be discovered.

82 CHAPTER 3 Atoms, Elements, and the Periodic Table

Teacher FYI

Mendeleev's Periodic Table In 1869, Dmitri Mendeleev published a periodic table based on properties and atomic masses of 60 known elements. He made a card for each element. Each card contained the element's symbol, atomic mass, and its characteristic chemical and physical properties. By arranging the cards on a table, in order of increasing atomic mass, and by grouping elements of similar properties together, the resultant "periodic table" showed vertical, horizontal, and diagonal relationships. Mendeleev left gaps in his table for future discovery of some of the then unknown elements.

Identifying Characteristics

Each element is different and has unique properties. These differences can be described in part by looking at the relationships between the atomic particles in each element. The periodic table contains numbers that describe these relationships.

Number of Protons and Neutrons Look up the element chlorine on the periodic table found on the inside back cover of your book. Cl is the symbol for chlorine, as shown in **Figure 13,** but what are the two numbers? The top number is the element's **atomic number.** It tells you the number of protons in the nucleus of each atom of that element. Every atom of chlorine, for example, has 17 protons in its nucleus.

 **Reading Check** *What are the atomic numbers for Cs, Ne, Pb, and U?*

Isotopes Although the number of protons changes from element to element, every atom of the same element has the same number of protons. However, the number of neutrons can vary even for one element. For example, some chlorine atoms have 18 neutrons in their nucleus while others have 20. These two types of chlorine atoms are chlorine-35 and chlorine-37. They are called **isotopes** (I suh tohps), which are atoms of the same element that have different numbers of neutrons.

You can tell someone exactly which isotope you are referring to by using its mass number. An atom's **mass number** is the number of protons plus the number of neutrons it contains. The numbers 35 and 37, which were used to refer to chlorine, are mass numbers. Hydrogen has three isotopes with mass numbers of 1, 2, and 3. They are shown in **Figure 14.** Each hydrogen atom always has one proton, but in each isotope the number of neutrons is different.

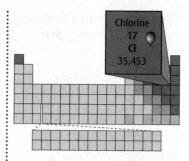

Figure 13 The periodic table block for chlorine shows its symbol, atomic number, and atomic mass.
Determine *if chlorine atoms are more or less massive than carbon atoms.*

Figure 14 Three isotopes of hydrogen are known to exist. They have zero, one, and two neutrons in addition to their one proton. Protium, with only the one proton, is the most abundant isotope.

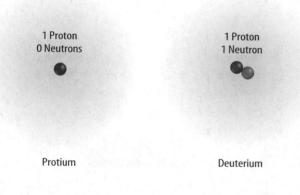

1 Proton
0 Neutrons

Protium

1 Proton
1 Neutron

Deuterium

1 Proton
2 Neutrons

Tritium

SECTION 2 The Simplest Matter **83**

Caption Answer
Figure 13 more massive

Fun Fact

To get an idea of how small the mass of an atom is, consider that there are roughly 560 quintillion (560,000,000,000,000,000,000) atoms of hydrogen and oxygen combined in one drop of water.

Reading Check

Answer Cs—55; Ne—10; Pb—82; U—92

Visual Learning

Figure 14 Have students identify the differences among the three isotopes of hydrogen. Then explain that almost all elements have some isotopes. As an extension, have students research the isotopes of some elements and draw the different nuclei. Carbon is an example: C-12: 6 p, 6 n; C-13: 6 p, 7 n; C-14: 6 p, 8 n. Remind students that all of the isotopes of one element have the same number of protons.

Science Journal

Heavy Water Have students write a summary about what heavy water is. Have them explain how it differs from normal water. Normal water is made of two hydrogen atoms and an oxygen atom covalently bonded together. This gives the famous H_2O formula. Heavy water has exactly the same structure, except the hydrogen atoms are isotopes of hydrogen called deuterium. Standard hydrogen has one proton in its nucleus while deuterium has one proton and one neutron in it nucleus; hence it is 'heavier' than normal hydrogen. This leads to the water being heavier. L2

Discussion

Cobalt and Nickel Have students use the information on these pages to explain how cobalt and nickel got their current positions on the periodic table. Position on the current periodic table is based on the atomic number of an element. L2

Differentiated Instruction

Learning Disabled While presenting information about the atom and its structure, use colored markers to illustrate the parts of the atom and their location on an overhead projector. For example, protons are orange and neutrons are blue in **Figure 14.** Remind students that these parts are not really colored. L1

Activity

Classifying by Atomic Mass
Mendeleev grouped elements based on their atomic masses. Have students find three pairs of elements on the periodic table at the back of the book that would have been switched in Mendeleev's table based on atomic masses. Cobalt is element 9 and has an atomic mass of 58.933; nickel is element 10 and has an atomic mass of 58.693. Other pairs of elements that would have been switched on Mendeleev's table are iodine and tellurium, and argon and potassium. L2
LS Logical-Mathematical

Quick Demo

Testing for Metals

Materials copper wire; 1.5-V mini lightbulb, D-size battery, electrical tape, wire cutter, different metallic and nonmetallic objects or materials to test

Estimated Time 15 minutes

Procedure Cut a piece of copper wire and tape one end to the positive end of the battery and wrap the other end around the bottom of the lightbulb. Cut another piece of copper wire and tape that end to the negative end of the battery. Cut another piece of copper wire and tape one end to the bottom of the lightbulb. Take one of the objects you are testing and place the wire that is connected to the negative side of the battery to one end of the object and place the wire that is connected to the bottom of the lightbulb to the other end of the object. Repeat the last step until you have tested all the objects. Observe whether the lightbulb lights up or not for each object that is tested. A property of metals is that they conduct electricity. This experiment is based on that property. Make students notice that metallic materials made the lightbulb light up while other nonmetals didn't.

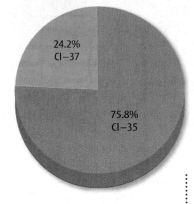

Circle Graph Showing Abundance of Chlorine Isotopes

Average atomic mass = 35.45 u

24.2% Cl–37

75.8% Cl–35

Figure 15 If you have 1,000 atoms of chlorine, about 758 will be chlorine-35 and have a mass of 34.97 u each. About 242 will be chlorine-37 and have a mass of 36.97 u each. The total mass of the 1,000 atoms is 35,454 u, so the average mass of one chlorine atom is about 35.45 u.

Figure 16 The artisan is chasing, or chiseling, the malleable metal into the desired form.

Atomic Mass The atomic mass is the weighted average mass of the isotopes of an element. The atomic mass is the number found below the element symbol in **Figure 13.** The unit that scientists use for atomic mass is called the atomic mass unit, which is given the symbol u. It is defined as 1/12 the mass of a carbon-12 atom.

The calculation of atomic mass takes into account the different isotopes of the element. Chlorine's atomic mass of 35.45 u could be confusing because there aren't any chlorine atoms that have that exact mass. About 76 percent of chlorine atoms are chlorine-35 and about 24 percent are chlorine-37, as shown in **Figure 15.** The weighted average mass of all chlorine atoms is 35.45 u.

Classification of Elements

Elements fall into three general categories—metals, metalloids (ME tuh loydz), and nonmetals. The elements in each category have similar properties.

Metals generally have a shiny or metallic luster and are good conductors of heat and electricity. All metals, except mercury, are solids at room temperature. Metals are malleable (MAL yuh bul), which means they can be bent and pounded into various shapes. The beautiful form of the shell-shaped basin in **Figure 16** is a result of this characteristic. Metals are also ductile, which means they can be drawn into wires without breaking. If you look at the periodic table, you can see that most of the elements are metals.

Science Journal

Medical Uses of Isotopes Have students research and write essays on isotopes that are used to diagnose and treat diseases. Some isotopes students might research include ^{67}Cu, ^{111}In, ^{186}Re, ^{82}Sr, ^{68}Ge, ^{153}Sm, and ^{103}Pd. L3 P

Differentiated Instruction

Challenge Have students research the following questions: How were alchemists' ideas about matter different from modern ideas? How is this reflected in their version of the periodic table? How did modern chemistry develop from the methods of alchemy? Ask students to share their findings with the class. L3 **LS** Linguistic

Other Elements Nonmetals are elements that are usually dull in appearance. Most are poor conductors of heat and electricity. Many are gases at room temperature, and bromine is a liquid. The solid nonmetals are generally brittle, meaning they cannot change shape easily without breaking. The nonmetals are essential to the chemicals of life. More than 97 percent of your body is made up of various nonmetals, as shown in **Figure 17.** You can see that, except for hydrogen, the nonmetals are found on the right side of the periodic table.

Metalloids are elements that have characteristics of metals and nonmetals. On the periodic table, metalloids are found between the metals and nonmetals. All metalloids are solids at room temperature. Some metalloids are shiny and many are conductors, but they are not as good at conducting heat and electricity as metals are. Some metalloids, such as silicon, are used to make the electronic circuits in computers, televisions, and other electronic devices.

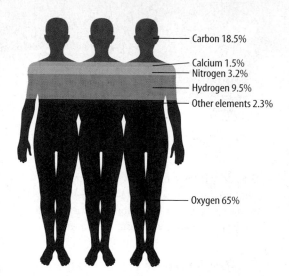

Carbon 18.5%
Calcium 1.5%
Nitrogen 3.2%
Hydrogen 9.5%
Other elements 2.3%
Oxygen 65%

Figure 17 You are made up of mostly nonmetals.

✓ **Reading Check** *What is a metalloid?*

Science Online ips.msscience.com/self_check_quiz

---

section 2 review

Summary

The Elements
- An element is matter made of only one type of atom.
- Some elements occur naturally on Earth. Synthetic elements are made in nuclear reactions in particle accelerators.
- Elements are divided into three categories based on certain properties.

The Periodic Table
- The periodic table arranges and displays all known elements in an orderly way.
- Each element has a chemical symbol.

Identifying Characteristics
- Each element has a unique number of protons, called the atomic mass number.
- Isotopes of an element are important when determining the atomic mass of an element.

Self Check

1. **Explain** some of the uses of metals based on their properties.
2. **Describe** the difference between atomic number and atomic mass.
3. **Define** the term *isotope*. Explain how two isotopes of an element are different.
4. **Identify** the isotopes of hydrogen.
5. **Think Critically** Describe how to find the atomic number for the element oxygen. Explain what this information tells you about oxygen.

Applying Math

6. **Simple Equation** An atom of niobium has a mass number of 93. How many neutrons are in the nucleus of this atom? An atom of phosphorus has 15 protons and 15 neutrons in the nucleus. What is the mass number of this isotope?

✓ **Reading Check**

Answer an element with characteristics of both metals and nonmetals

3 Assess

DAILY INTERVENTION

Check for Understanding

Linguistic Have small groups of students classify classroom objects as being made mostly of metals or nonmetals and record their answers on a chart. Then have students write a statement that can be used to determine if their chart is correct.

Possible Answers:

Metal	Nonmetal
File cabinet	Carpet
Chair legs	Plastic seat

Metal items are shiny, solid at room temperature, conduct heat and electricity, and can be pounded into different shapes without breaking. Nonmetals do not have those properties.

Reteach

Periodic Table Write all the information found on the periodic table for one element on the board. Have students tell what each symbol or number represents. L2 **IS** **Visual-Spatial**

✓ **Assessment**

Oral Name elements on the periodic table at random. Ask students to tell whether each selected element is a metal, a metalloid, or a nonmetal.

---

section 2 review

1. good conductors of heat and electricity (electrical circuits and cookware), malleable (formed into tools), ductile (drawn into wires)
2. atomic number: the number of protons in the nucleus of each atom of an element; mass number: the sum of an atom's protons and neutrons
3. Isotopes are atoms of the same element that contain different numbers of neutrons.
4. The isotopes of hydrogen are protium, deuterium, and tritium.
5. Locate oxygen on the periodic table. Oxygen's atomic number (8) is the large number in the element's box and means that every atom of oxygen contains eight protons in its nucleus.
6. $93 - 41 = 52$ n; 15 p $+ 15$ n $= 30$

Elements and the Periodic Table

Real-World Question

Purpose Students classify elements and build a periodic table that shows their classifications.
L2 **LS** Visual-Spatial

Process Skills classify, compare and contrast, make and use tables, interpret data, predict

Time Required two to three class periods

Procedure

Teaching Strategy Because a large amount of information is available for most elements, advise students to focus their efforts and collect only key information.

Conclude and Apply

1. The table students make will look like the periodic table, but only certain elements will be present.
2. This element should be shiny in the solid state, have such metallic characteristics as high electrical and thermal conductivities, and be reactive with nonmetals to form compounds.

✔ Assessment

Portfolio Take a photograph of the class periodic table and have a copy made for each student. Have students include the index cards for their elements and the photograph of the class periodic table in their portfolios. Use **Performance Assessment in the Science Classroom,** pp. 135; 169. **P**

The periodic table organizes the elements, but what do they look like? What are they used for? In this lab, you'll examine some elements and share your findings with your classmates.

Real-World Question
What are some of the characteristics and purposes of the chemical elements?

Goals
■ **Classify** the chemical elements.
■ **Organize** the elements into the groups and periods of the periodic table.

Materials
colored markers	large bulletin board
large index cards	8½-in × 14-in paper
Merck Index	thumbtacks
encyclopedia	*pushpins
*other reference	
materials	*Alternate materials

Safety Precaution

WARNING: *Use care when handling sharp objects.*

Procedure
1. **Select** the assigned number of elements from the list provided by your teacher.
2. **Design** an index card for each of your selected elements. On each card, mark the element's atomic number in the upper left-hand corner and write its symbol and name in the upper right-hand corner.

3. **Research** each of the elements and write several sentences on the card about its appearance, its other properties, and its uses.
4. **Classify** each of your elements as a metal, a metalloid, or a nonmetal based upon its properties.
5. **Write** the appropriate classification on each of your cards using the colored marker chosen by your teacher.
6. Work with your classmates to make a large periodic table. Use thumbtacks to attach your cards to a bulletin board in their proper positions on the periodic table.
7. **Draw** your own periodic table. Place the elements' symbols and atomic numbers in the proper locations on your table.

Conclude and Apply
1. **Interpret** the class data and classify the elements into the categories metal, metalloid, and nonmetal. Highlight each category in a different color on your periodic table.
2. **Predict** the properties of a yet-undiscovered element located directly under francium on the periodic table.

86 CHAPTER 3 Atoms, Elements, and the Periodic Table

Communicating Your Data

Have students use a database program to display their results. The printed database can be shared with a small group or with the class.

Using Science Words

Word Meaning Have students use the dictionary to determine the meaning of the word *element.* Ask them why chemical particles are referred to as elements. In chemistry, the basic chemical particles are called elements because elements are fundamental components of matter. L2

Compounds and Mixtures

Substances

Scientists classify matter in several ways that depend on what it is made of and how it behaves. For example, matter that has the same composition and properties throughout is called a **substance.** Elements, such as a bar of gold or a sheet of aluminum, are substances. When different elements combine, other substances are formed.

Compounds What do you call the colorless liquid that flows from the kitchen faucet? You probably call it water, but maybe you've seen it written H_2O. The elements hydrogen and oxygen exist as separate, colorless gases. However, these two elements can combine, as shown in **Figure 18,** to form the compound water, which is different from the elements that make it up. A **compound** is a substance whose smallest unit is made up of atoms of more than one element bonded together.

Compounds often have properties that are different from the elements that make them up. Water is distinctly different from the elements that make it up. It is also different from another compound made from the same elements. Have you ever used hydrogen peroxide (H_2O_2) to disinfect a cut? This compound is a different combination of hydrogen and oxygen and has different properties from those of water.

Water is a nonirritating liquid that is used for bathing, drinking, cooking, and much more. In contrast, hydrogen peroxide carries warnings on its labels such as *Keep Hydrogen Peroxide Out of the Eyes.* Although it is useful in solutions for cleaning contact lenses, it is not safe for your eyes as it comes from the bottle.

as you read

What You'll Learn
■ **Identify** the characteristics of a compound.
■ **Compare and contrast** different types of mixtures.

Why It's Important
The food you eat, the materials you use, and all matter can be classified by compounds or mixtures.

Review Vocabulary
formula: shows which elements and how many atoms of each make up a compound

New Vocabulary
● substance   ● mixture
● compound

Bellringer

Section Focus Transparencies also are available on the Interactive Chalkboard CD-ROM.
L2 ELL

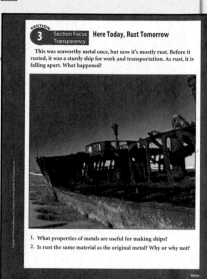

3 Section Focus Transparency | **Here Today, Rust Tomorrow**

This was seaworthy metal once, but now it's mostly rust. Before it rusted, it was a sturdy ship for work and transportation. As rust, it is falling apart. What happened?

1. What properties of metals are useful for making ships?
2. Is rust the same material as the original metal? Why or why not?

Figure 18 A space shuttle is powered by the reaction between liquid hydrogen and liquid oxygen. The reaction produces a large amount of energy and the compound water.
Explain *why a car that burns hydrogen rather than gasoline would be friendly to the environment.*

Tie to Prior Knowledge

Combining Elements Have students recall chemical formulas for substances such as water or salt. H_2O and NaCl Show a periodic table and point out that these substances represent a combination of elements from the periodic table.

Caption Answer

Figure 18 It would release water as a by-product rather than pollution.

Section 3 Resource Manager

Chapter FAST FILE Resources
Transparency Activity, p. 42
Directed Reading for Content Mastery, pp. 17, 18
MiniLAB, p. 4
Enrichment, p. 28

Lab Worksheet, pp. 7–8
Lab Activity, pp. 9–10, 11–12

Make a Model

H_2O_2 and H_2O While discussing the law of definite proportions, have students make models of the compounds in **Figure 19** using materials such as gumdrops and toothpicks. Have them share their models with the class. L1 ELL LS **Kinesthetic**

Mini LAB

Purpose Students observe and compare the properties of three compounds. L2 ELL LS **Visual-Spatial**

Materials sugar, rubbing alcohol, salad oil, glasses (3), hot water

Teaching Strategy Warn students to use hot tap water, not boiling water, in Step 3.

Analysis
1. rubbing alcohol—colorless liquid, strong chemical smell, dissolves in water; salad oil—golden liquid, more viscous than rubbing alcohol, little or no odor, floats on water; sugar—white granular solid, little or no odor, dissolves easily in water
2. The number of atoms of each type of element and their arrangement account for the different properties.

Assessment

Content Have students draw pictures showing how the substances mix with each other in the MiniLAB. Use **Performance Assessment in the Science Classroom**, p. 127. P

Try at Home

Reading Check

Answer C_3H_8

Figure 19 The elements hydrogen and oxygen can form two compounds—water and hydrogen peroxide. Note the differences in their structure.

H_2O_2

H_2O

Mini LAB

Comparing Compounds

Procedure

1. Collect the following substances—**granular sugar, rubbing alcohol,** and **salad oil.**
2. Observe the color, appearance, and state of each substance. Note the thickness or texture of each substance.
3. Stir a spoonful of each substance into separate **glasses** of **hot tap water** and observe.

Analysis
1. Compare the different properties of the substances.
2. The formulas of the three substances are made of only carbon, hydrogen, and oxygen. Infer how they can have different properties.

Try at Home

88 CHAPTER 3 Atoms, Elements, and the Periodic Table

Compounds Have Formulas What's the difference between water and hydrogen peroxide? H_2O is the chemical formula for water, and H_2O_2 is the formula for hydrogen peroxide. The formula tells you which elements make up a compound as well as how many atoms of each element are present. Look at **Figure 19.** The subscript number written below and to the right of each element's symbol tells you how many atoms of that element exist in one unit of that compound. For example, hydrogen peroxide has two atoms of hydrogen and two atoms of oxygen. Water is made up of two atoms of hydrogen and one atom of oxygen.

Carbon dioxide, CO_2, is another common compound. Carbon dioxide is made up of one atom of carbon and two atoms of oxygen. Carbon and oxygen also can form the compound carbon monoxide, CO, which is a gas that is poisonous to all warm-blooded animals. As you can see, no subscript is used when only one atom of an element is present. A given compound always is made of the same elements in the same proportion. For example, water always has two hydrogen atoms for every oxygen atom, no matter what the source of the water is. No matter what quantity of the compound you have, the formula of the compound always remains the same. If you have 12 atoms of hydrogen and six atoms of oxygen, the compound is still written H_2O (6 H_2O), not $H_{12}O_6$. The formula of a compound communicates its identity and makeup to any scientist in the world.

Reading Check

Propane has three carbon and eight hydrogen atoms. What is its chemical formula?

Visual Learning

Figure 19 Ask students to write the formula for hydrogen peroxide. (H_2O_2) Point out how much easier it is to write the chemical formulas than it is to write out all of the words.

Teacher FYI

Chemical Formulas Structural formulas show the bonding relationship (e.g. H-O-O-H); molecular formulas show how many atoms of each element are present (e.g. H_2O_2); empirical formulas show kinds of atoms are present, and gives the simplest whole number ratio of atoms in the compound (e.g. HO).

Mixtures

When two or more substances (elements or compounds) come together but don't combine to make a new substance, a **mixture** results. Unlike compounds, the proportions of the substances in a mixture can be changed without changing the identity of the mixture. For example, if you put some sand into a bucket of water, you have a mixture of sand and water. If you add more sand or more water, it's still a mixture of sand and water. Its identity has not changed. Air is another mixture. Air is a mixture of nitrogen, oxygen, and other gases, which can vary at different times and places. Whatever the proportion of gases, it is still air. Even your blood is a mixture that can be separated, as shown in **Figure 20,** by a machine called a centrifuge.

 **Reading Check** *How do the proportions of a mixture relate to its identity?*

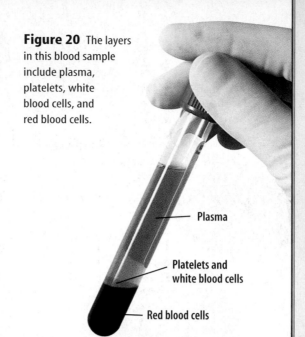

Figure 20 The layers in this blood sample include plasma, platelets, white blood cells, and red blood cells.

Plasma

Platelets and white blood cells

Red blood cells

Applying Science

What's the best way to desalt ocean water?

You can't drink ocean water because it contains salt and other suspended materials. Or can you? In many areas of the world where drinking water is in short supply, methods for getting the salt out of salt water are being used to meet the demand for fresh water. Use your problem-solving skills to find the best method to use in a particular area.

Methods for Desalting Ocean Water			
Process	Amount of Water a Unit Can Desalt in a Day (m^3)	Special Needs	Number of People Needed to Operate
Distillation	1,000 to 200,000	lots of energy to boil the water	many
Electrodialysis	10 to 4,000	stable source of electricity	1 to 2 persons

Identifying the Problem

The table above compares desalting methods. In distillation, the ocean water is heated. Pure water boils off and is collected, and the salt is left behind. Electrodialysis uses an electric current to pull salt particles out of water.

Solving the Problem

1. What method(s) might you use to desalt the water for a large population where energy is plentiful?
2. What method(s) would you choose to use in a single home?

SECTION 3 Compounds and Mixtures **89**

Cultural Diversity

Ocher Ocher, a naturally occurring iron oxide (Fe_2O_3), is formed by the weathering of rocks. Historically, ocher has been used to produce rock paintings and continues to be used for artwork today. It comes in a variety of colors, depending on the percentage of iron oxide present. Hematite ore is one source of ocher that can be ground to produce a bright red color. Ocher also has been found in burial plots of several different cultures. Have students find out the other colors produced by iron oxide ores. Other colors produced include black (magnetite), brown to dark yellow (limonite), and brown (siderite and pyrite).

Figure 21 Mixtures are part of your everyday life.

Your blood is a mixture made up of elements and compounds. It contains white blood cells, red blood cells, water, and a number of dissolved substances. The different parts of blood can be separated and used by doctors in different ways. The proportions of the substances in your blood change daily, but the mixture does not change its identity.

Separating Mixtures Sometimes you can use a liquid to separate a mixture of solids. For example, if you add water to a mixture of sugar and sand, only the sugar dissolves in the water. The sand then can be separated from the sugar and water by pouring the mixture through a filter. Heating the remaining solution will separate the water from the sugar.

At other times, separating a mixture of solids of different sizes might be as easy as pouring them through successively smaller sieves or filters. A mixture of marbles, pebbles, and sand could be separated in this way.

Science Online

Topic: Mixtures
Visit ips.msscience.com for Web links to information about separating mixtures.

Activity Describe the difference between mixtures and compounds.

90 CHAPTER 3 Atoms, Elements, and the Periodic Table

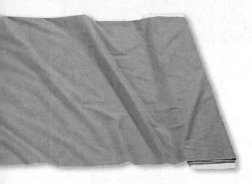

Homogeneous or Heterogeneous Mixtures, such as the ones shown in **Figure 21,** can be classified as homogeneous or heterogeneous. *Homogeneous* means "the same throughout." You can't see the different parts in this type of mixture. In fact, you might not always know that homogeneous mixtures are mixtures because you can't tell by looking. Which mixtures in **Figure 21** are homogeneous? No matter how closely you look, you can't see the individual parts that make up air or the parts of the mixture called brass in the lamp shown. Homogeneous mixtures can be solids, liquids, or gases.

A heterogeneous mixture has larger parts that are different from each other. You can see the different parts of a heterogeneous mixture, such as sand and water. How many heterogeneous mixtures are in **Figure 21?** A pepperoni and mushroom pizza is a tasty kind of heterogeneous mixture. Other examples of this kind of mixture include tacos, vegetable soup, a toy box full of toys, or a toolbox full of nuts and bolts.

INTEGRATE Earth Science

Rocks and Minerals Scientists called geologists study rocks and minerals. A mineral is composed of a pure substance. Rocks are mixtures and can be described as being homogeneous or heterogeneous. Research to learn more about rocks and minerals and note some examples of homogeneous and heterogeneous rocks in your Science Journal.

INTEGRATE Earth Science

Rocks and Minerals Strictly speaking, the term *rocks* applies to the solid materials that make up Earth's crust. These materials are not homogeneous and have no definite chemical composition. *Minerals,* on the other hand, have more or less definite chemical compositions, crystal structures, and properties.

3 Assess

DAILY INTERVENTION

Check for Understanding

Visual-Spatial Have students develop a demonstration that differentiates between homogeneous and heterogeneous mixtures. Possible answer: Homogeneous mixtures can include substances such as apple juice or non-carbonated soft drinks. Heterogeneous mixtures can include substances such as a tossed salad, or fruit salad.

Reteach

Blood Ask a medical technologist to make a class presentation explaining the different parts of the mixture known as human blood and describing how these parts can be separated by physical means. L1

✓ Assessment

Process Have students design an experimental procedure that they could use to separate a mixture of white sand and sugar. Use **Performance Assessment in the Science Classroom,** p. 95.

---

section 3 review

Summary

Substances
- A substance can be either an element or a compound.
- A compound contains more than one kind of element bonded together.
- A chemical formula shows which elements and how many atoms of each make up a compound.

Mixtures
- A mixture contains substances that are not chemically bonded together.
- There are many ways to separate mixtures, based on their physical properties.
- Homogeneous mixtures are those that are the same throughout. These types of mixtures can be solids, liquids, or gases.
- Heterogeneous mixtures have larger parts that are different from each other.

Self Check

1. **List** three examples of compounds and three examples of mixtures. Explain your choices.
2. **Determine** A container contains a mixture of sand, salt, and pebbles. How can each substance be separated from the others?
3. **Think Critically** Explain whether your breakfast was a compound, a homogeneous mixture, or a heterogeneous mixture.

Applying Skills

4. **Compare and contrast** compounds and mixtures based on what you have learned from this section.
5. **Use a Database** Use a computerized card catalog or database to find information about one element from the periodic table. Include information about the properties and uses of the mixtures and/or compounds in which the element is frequently found.

Science Online ips.msscience.com/self_check_quiz

SECTION 3 Compounds and Mixtures **91**

---

section 3 review

1. Possible answers: compounds— water, carbon dioxide, table salt; mixtures— air, ocean water, brass; mixtures can be separated by physical means; compounds can't.
2. The pebbles can be separated by using a sieve that allows the sand and salt to fall through. The salt can be separated from the sand by dissolving the salt in water. The sand can be separated from the salt water.
3. Answers will vary, but most breakfasts, such as orange juice and cold cereal with milk, will be heterogeneous mixtures.
4. Possible answer: Compounds are pure substances whose properties vary from the original elements that they are made from. Mixtures are made from different parts and can be separated.
5. Sample answer: Carbon is found in the Sun, stars, comets, and atmospheres of most planets. It is present as carbon dioxide in the atmosphere and dissolved in water. It is a component of rocks as carbonates of calcium (limestone), magnesium, and iron.

Real-World Question

Purpose Students test for certain compounds and decide which are present in a mystery mixture. L2 ELL IS Logical-Mathematical

Process Skills form a hypothesis, communicate, observe and infer, recognize cause and effect, separate and control variables, interpret data

Time Required 45 minutes

Procedure

Materials Compounds used are cornstarch, powdered sugar, and baking soda. Combine any two of these compounds to make the mystery mixture. Prepare iodine test solution by adding 7 g of iodine and 5 g of potassium iodide to 5 mL of water, then diluting to 100 mL with denatured alcohol.

Safety Precautions

- Students must wear goggles and aprons. Remind students that while heating the test tube, the opening of the tube should never be pointed at themselves or others.
- Iodine is poisonous and will stain clothing.
- Remind students that test tubes should not be touched while they are hot.

Mystery Mixture

Real-World Question

You will encounter many compounds that look alike. For example, a laboratory stockroom is filled with white powders. It is important to know what each is. In a kitchen, cornstarch, baking powder, and powdered sugar are compounds that look alike. To avoid mistaking one for another, you can learn how to identify them. Different compounds can be identified by using chemical tests. For example, some compounds react with certain liquids to produce gases. Other combinations produce distinctive colors. Some compounds have high melting points. Others have low melting points. How can the compounds in an unknown mixture be identified by experimentation?

Goals

- **Test** for the presence of certain compounds.
- **Decide** which of these compounds are present in an unknown mixture.

Materials

test tubes (4)
cornstarch
powdered sugar
baking soda
mystery mixture
small scoops (3)
dropper bottles (2)
iodine solution
white vinegar
hot plate
250-mL beaker
water (125 mL)
test-tube holder
small pie pan

Safety Precautions

WARNING: *Use caution when handling hot objects. Substances could stain or burn clothing. Be sure to point the test tube away from your face and your classmates while heating.*

Alternative Inquiry Lab

Separating Compounds To extend this Lab into an Inquiry Lab, have students brainstorm and/or research the difference between mixtures and compounds. Chemical reactions are required to separate compounds. You may have students try reducing copper oxide ore by combining it with carbon powder and heating it in a crucible—they should get pure shiny copper metal as a result (keep the lid on and heat it as hot as possible for at least fifteen minutes). Special instruments (such as magnetic resonance imaging and infrared spectrometers) are available to find out what elements are in compounds, but tell students that these machines involve complex processes. Some students may want to research the MRI and IR processes.

Procedure

1. Copy the data table into your Science Journal. Record your results carefully for each of the following steps.

2. Place a small scoopful of cornstarch on the pie pan. Do the same for the sugar and baking soda making separate piles. Add a drop of vinegar to each. Wash and dry the pan after you record your observations.

3. Again, place a small scoopful of cornstarch, sugar, and baking soda on the pie pan. Add a drop of iodine solution to each one. Wash and dry the pan after you record your observations.

4. Again place a small scoopful of each compound in a separate test tube. Hold the test tube with the test-tube holder and with an oven mitt. Gently heat the test tube in a beaker of boiling water on a hot plate.

5. Follow steps 2 through 4 to test your mystery mixture for each compound.

Identifying Presence of Compounds

Substance to Be Tested	Fizzes with Vinegar	Turns Blue with Iodine	Melts When Heated
Cornstarch	no	yes	no
Sugar	no	no	yes
Baking soda	yes	no	no
Mystery mix	yes	yes	yes

Analyze Your Data

Identify from your data table which compound(s) you have.

Conclude and Apply

1. **Describe** how you decided which substances were in your unknown mixture.

2. **Explain** how you would be able to tell if all three compounds were not in your mystery substance.

3. **Draw a Conclusion** What would you conclude if you tested baking powder from your kitchen and found that it fizzed with vinegar, turned blue with iodine, and did not melt when heated?

Communicating Your Data

Make a different data table to display your results in a new way. **For more help, refer to the Science Skill Handbook.**

LAB **93**

Teaching Strategies

- In Steps 2 and 3, have students use only sufficient amounts of the solids to produce satisfactory test results. Test your scoops to determine how much to use.

- In Step 4, have students use only enough solid to fill the bottom, rounded portion of the test tubes.

Analyze Your Data

Expected Outcome Cornstarch will react with iodine to make a blue color. Sugar will melt when heated. Baking soda will fizz in the presence of vinegar.

Error Analysis If students let their experiments run together or do not clean their equipment, they may get erroneous results. Have students compare their results to the results of other groups. If results differ, discuss errors that could have caused the differences.

Conclude and Apply

1. Answers will vary depending on the two compounds used for the mystery mixture. In describing their conclusions, students should include the data they gathered.

2. If all three compounds were absent from the mystery mixture, the mixture would not turn blue in the presence of iodine, it would not melt when heated, and it would not fizz with vinegar.

3. It contained baking soda and cornstarch.

Assessment

Performance After students have determined the two compounds that were present in the mystery mixture, have them determine other possible two-material combinations and explain how the combinations would react when tested. Use **Performance Assessment in the Science Classroom,** p. 89.

Communicating Your Data

Students could use illustrations, chemical symbols, or color to revise their data table.

Content Background

Kashyapa lived during the 6th century B.C., and was the first to use the word *parmanu;* derived from the two Sanskrit words *param*, meaning "beyond", and *anu*, meaning "atom." Among other things, he proposed that two different classes of parmanu could combine to form what he called *dwinuka*, or binary molecules, of new substances.

The Chinese term for the five material agents of matter, as they called the five elements, is *wu hsing.* The Chinese believed that these material agents took part in cyclical patterns of change that resulted in the opposites, yin and yang.

Discussion

Atomic Theory Do you think Kashyapa's ideas were known to Democritus when he developed his theory of the atom? Why or why not? Accept all well-supported answers. Point out to students on a globe the relative locations of Greece and India and remind them of the means of transportation and communication available at the time these two men lived.

Historical Significance

Both the Chinese and Indian philosophies have roots in ancient history. Encourage students to choose a current scientific theory and use a variety of research tools to trace the idea back to its earliest origins. Make sure students understand that one theory may have origins in ideas that arose independently in different cultures. This activity will help students become aware that our modern theories have had a long history of development.

Ancient Views of Matter

air

water

metal

Two cultures observed the world around them differently

The world's earliest scientists were people who were curious about the world around them and who tried to develop explanations for the things they observed. This type of observation and inquiry flourished in ancient cultures such as those found in India and China. Read on to see how the ancient Indians and Chinese defined matter.

Indian Ideas

To Indians living about 3,000 years ago, the world was made up of five elements: fire, air, earth, water, and ether, which they thought of as an unseen substance that filled the heavens. Building upon this concept, the early Indian philosopher Kashyapa (kah SHI ah pah) proposed that the five elements could be broken down into smaller units called parmanu (par MAH new). Parmanu were similar to atoms in that they were too small to be seen but still retained the properties of the original element. Kashyapa also believed that each type of parmanu had unique physical and chemical properties.

Parmanu of earth elements, for instance, were heavier than parmanu of air elements. The different properties of the parmanu determined the characteristics of a substance. Kashyapa's ideas about matter are similar to those of the Greek philosopher Democritus, who lived centuries after Kashyapa.

Chinese Ideas

The ancient Chinese also broke matter down into five elements: fire, wood, metal, earth, and water. Unlike the early Indians, however, the Chinese believed that the elements constantly changed form. For example, wood can be burned and thus changes to fire. Fire eventually dies down and becomes ashes, or earth. Earth gives forth metals from the ground. Dew or water collects on these metals, and the water then nurtures plants that grow into trees, or wood.

This cycle of constant change was explained in the fourth century B.C. by the philosopher Tsou Yen. Yen, who is known as the founder of Chinese scientific thought, wrote that all changes that took place in nature were linked to changes in the five elements.

fire

earth

Research Write a brief paragraph that compares and contrasts the ancient Indian and Chinese views of matter. How are they different? Similar? Which is closer to the modern view of matter? Explain.

Science Online

For more information, visit ips.msscience.com/time

Resources for Teachers and Students

Chemistry in Action, by Nina Morgan, Oxford University Press, 1995

The Periodic Kingdom, by P.W. Atkins, Basic Books, 1995

Research Students will need to research their information by using the school's media center, the library, or visiting the link on the student page.

Reviewing Main Ideas

Section 1 Structure of Matter

1. Matter is anything that occupies space and has mass.

2. Matter is made up of atoms.

3. Atoms are made of smaller parts called protons, neutrons, and electrons.

4. Many models of atoms have been created as scientists try to discover and define the atom's internal structure. Today's model has a central nucleus with the protons and neutrons, and an electron cloud surrounding it.

Section 2 The Simplest Matter

1. Elements are the building blocks of matter.

2. An element's atomic number tells how many protons its atoms contain, and its atomic mass tells the average mass of its atoms.

3. Isotopes are two or more atoms of the same element that have different numbers of neutrons.

Section 3 Compounds and Mixtures

1. Compounds are substances that are produced when elements combine. Compounds contain specific proportions of the elements that make them up.

2. Mixtures are combinations of compounds and elements that have not formed new substances. Their proportions can change.

Visualizing Main Ideas

Copy and complete the following concept map.

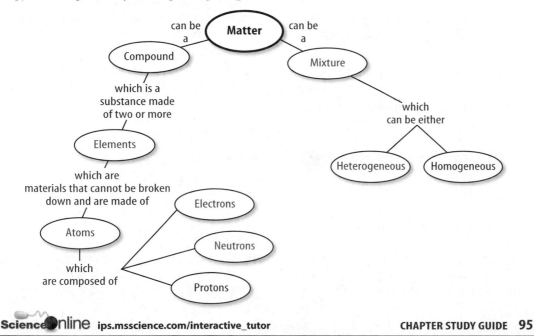

Reviewing Main Ideas

Summary statements can be used by students to review the major concepts of the chapter.

Visualizing Main Ideas

See student page.

Science❍nline

Visit ips.msscience.com
/self_check_quiz
/interactive_tutor
/vocabulary_puzzlemaker
/chapter_review
/standardized_test

Assessment Transparency

For additional assessment questions, use the *Assessment Transparency* located in the transparency book.

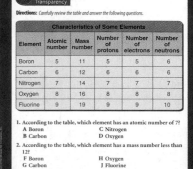

Identifying Misconceptions

Assess

Use the assessment as follow-up to page F at the beginning of the chapter after students have completed the chapter.

Materials 50-mL graduated cylinder, beaker, water, droppers, pan balance

Procedure Find the mass of the empty graduated cylinder, then pour 50 mL of water into it and find the mass again. Use the dropper to decrease the volume of water by one half and calculate the mass of the water. Repeat this process three more times to obtain volumes of 50 mL, 25 mL, 12.5 mL, 6.25 mL, and 3.125 mL. Will you ever get a drop of water that has no mass?

Expected Outcome No matter how small the volume, the water has mass and therefore weight.

Using Vocabulary

Using Vocabulary

1. proton
2. compound
3. matter
4. neutrons
5. metals

Checking Concepts

6. D   11. B
7. C   12. C
8. B   13. C
9. C   14. B
10. D   15. D

Thinking Critically

16. one sulfur atom to two oxygen atoms
17. An atom with seven protons is nitrogen.
18. C, 6; Na, ll; Ni, 28
19. Cobalt-60 and cobalt-59 are isotopes because they both have 27 protons in their nuclei.
20. Rutherford's gold foil experiment told scientists that the atom contains a small, dense, positively charged structure.
21. Because the nuclei in all atoms are composed of densely packed positive charge (protons), the positive alpha particle would have been deflected by the aluminum foil. Students also may add that the angle of deflection would not be as great because an aluminum nucleus is less dense than a gold nucleus.

Using Vocabulary

atom p.73	matter p.72
atomic mass p.84	metal p.84
atomic number p.83	metalloid p.85
compound p.87	mixture p.89
electron p.76	neutron p.78
element p.80	nonmetal p.85
isotope p.83	nucleus p.77
law of conservation of matter p.74	proton p.77
mass number p.83	substance p.87

Fill in the blanks with the correct vocabulary word or words.

1. The _____ is the particle in the nucleus of the atom that carries a positive charge and is counted to identify the atomic number.

2. The new substance formed when elements combine chemically is a(n) _____.

3. Anything that has mass and takes up space is _____.

4. The particles in the atom that account for most of the mass of the atom are protons and _____.

5. Elements that are shiny, malleable, ductile, good conductors of heat and electricity, and make up most of the periodic table are _____.

Checking Concepts

Choose the word or phrase that best answers the question.

6. What is a solution an example of?
   A) element
   B) heterogeneous mixture
   C) compound
   D) homogeneous mixture

7. The nucleus of one atom contains 12 protons and 12 neutrons, while the nucleus of another atom contains 12 protons and 16 neutrons. What are the atoms?
   A) chromium atoms
   B) two different elements
   C) two isotopes of an element
   D) negatively charged

8. What is a compound?
   A) a mixture of chemicals and elements
   B) a combination of two or more elements
   C) anything that has mass and occupies space
   D) the building block of matter

9. What does the atom consist of?
   A) electrons, protons, and alpha particles
   B) neutrons and protons
   C) electrons, protons, and neutrons
   D) elements, protons, and electrons

10. In an atom, where is an electron located?
    A) in the nucleus with the proton
    B) on the periodic table of the elements
    C) with the neutron
    D) in a cloudlike formation surrounding the nucleus

11. How is matter defined?
    A) the negative charge in an atom
    B) anything that has mass and occupies space
    C) the mass of the nucleus
    D) sound, light, and energy

12. What are two atoms that have the same number of protons called?
    A) metals
    B) nonmetals
    C) isotopes
    D) metalloids

13. Which is a heterogeneous mixture?
    A) air   C) a salad
    B) brass   D) apple juice

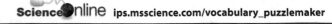
Science Online ips.msscience.com/vocabulary_puzzlemaker

Use the ExamView® Pro Testmaker CD-ROM to:
- create multiple versions of tests
- create modified tests with one mouse click for inclusion students
- edit existing questions and add your own questions
- build tests aligned with state standards using built-in State Curriculum Tags
- change English tests to Spanish with one mouse click and vice versa

Use the illustration below to answer questions 14 and 15.

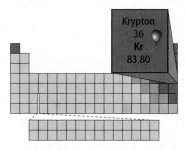

Krypton
36
Kr
83.80

14. Using the figure above, krypton has
A) an atomic number of 84.
B) an atomic number of 36.
C) an atomic mass of 36.
D) an atomic mass of 72.

15. From the figure, the element krypton is
A) a solid.
C) a mixture.
B) a liquid.
D) a gas.

Thinking Critically

16. Analyze Information A chemical formula is written to indicate the makeup of a compound. What is the ratio of sulfur atoms to oxygen atoms in SO_2?

17. Determine which element contains seven protons.

18. Describe Using the periodic table, what are the atomic numbers for carbon, sodium, and nickel?

19. Explain how cobalt-60 and cobalt-59 can be the same element but have different mass numbers.

20. Analyze Information What did Rutherford's gold foil experiment tell scientists about atomic structure?

21. Predict Suppose Rutherford had bombarded aluminum foil with alpha particles instead of the gold foil he used in his

experiment. What observations do you predict Rutherford would have made? Explain your prediction.

22. Draw Conclusions You are shown a liquid that looks the same throughout. You're told that it contains more than one type of element and that the proportion of each varies throughout the liquid. Is this an element, a compound, or a mixture?

Use the illustrations below to answer question 23.

23. Interpret Scientific Illustrations Look at the two carbon atoms above. Explain whether or not the atoms are isotopes.

24. Explain how the atomic mass of an element is determined.

Performance Activities

25. Newspaper Article As a newspaper reporter in the year 1896, you have heard about the discovery of the electron. Research and write an article about the scientist and the discovery.

Applying Math

26. Atomic Mass Krypton has six naturally occurring isotopes with atomic masses of 78, 80, 82, 83, 84, and 86. Make a table of the number of protons, electrons, and neutrons in each isotope.

27. Atomic Ratio A researcher is analyzing two different compounds, sulfuric acid (H_2SO_4) and hydrogen peroxide (H_2O_2). What is the ratio of hydrogen to oxygen in sulfuric acid? What is the ratio of hydrogen to oxygen in hydrogen peroxide?

 Science Online ips.msscience.com/chapter_review

CHAPTER REVIEW **97**

22. The liquid is a mixture. Students also might add that it is homogeneous.

23. The atoms are isotopes because they differ in their number of neutrons. The atom on the left has 6 p and 6 n whereas the one on the right has 6 p and 8 n.

24. The atomic mass of an element is determined by using the weighted average of the isotopes of an element.

Performance Activities

25. Student's article should contain information about J.J. Thomson and his cathode ray tube experiment. **Performance Assessment in the Science Classroom,** p. 141.

Applying Math

National Math Standards
7.6.1, 7.7.1
26.

Isotope/Atomic Mass	P	E	N
Kr_{78}	36	36	42
Kr_{80}	36	36	44
Kr_{82}	36	36	46
Kr_{83}	36	36	47
Kr_{84}	36	36	48
Kr_{86}	36	36	50

27. 2:1; 1:1.

✓ Assessment   Resources

📁 **Reproducible Masters**
Chapter *Fast File* Resources
Chapter Review, pp. 33–34
Chapter Tests, pp. 35–38
Assessment Transparency Activity, p. 45
Glencoe Science Web site
Chapter Review Test
Standardized Test Practice

Glencoe Technology
🎤 Assessment Transparency
⬤ Exam*View*® Pro Testmaker
💽 MindJogger Videoquiz
⬤ Interactive Chalkboard

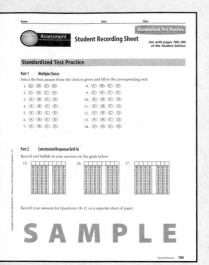

SAMPLE

Part 1 | Multiple Choice

1. D	5. D
2. D	6. D
3. A	7. C
4. C	8. B

Part 2 | Short Response

9. They are more likely to be close to the nucleus because they are attracted to the positive charges of the protons.

10. 90

11. nonmetals

12. $6 H_2O_2$

13. electrons

14. mixture

15. substance

Record your answers on the answer sheet provided by your teacher or on a sheet of paper.

1. Which of the scientists below introduced the idea that matter is made up of tiny, individual bits called atoms?
- **A.** Arrhenius
- **C.** Chadwick
- **B.** Avogadro
- **D.** Democritus

Use the illustration below to answer questions 2 and 3.

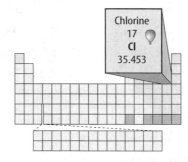

Chlorine
17
Cl
35.453

2. The periodic table block shown above lists properties of the element chlorine. What does the number 35.453 mean?
- **A.** the number of neutrons and in every chlorine atom
- **B.** the number of neutrons and protons in every chlorine atom
- **C.** the average number of neutrons in a chlorine atom
- **D.** the average number of neutrons and protons in a chlorine atom

3. According to the periodic table block, how many electrons does an uncharged atom of chlorine have?
- **A.** 17
- **C.** 35
- **B.** 18
- **D.** 36

> **Test-Taking Tip**
>
> **Full Understanding** Read each question carefully for full understanding.

---

4. Which of the following scientists envisioned the atom as a ball of positive charge with electrons embedded in it, much like chocolate chips spread through cookie dough?
- **A.** Crookes
- **C.** Thomson
- **B.** Dalton
- **D.** Rutherford

Use the illustration below to answer questions 5 and 6.

1 Proton	1 Proton	1 Proton
0 Neutrons	1 Neutron	2 Neutrons

5. Which of the following correctly identifies the three atoms shown in the illustration above?
- **A.** hydrogen, lithium, sodium
- **B.** hydrogen, helium, lithium
- **C.** hydrogen, helium, helium
- **D.** hydrogen, hydrogen, hydrogen

6. What is the mass number for each of the atoms shown in the illustration?
- **A.** 0, 1, 2
- **B.** 1, 1, 1
- **C.** 1, 2, 2
- **D.** 1, 2, 3

7. Which of the following are found close to the right side of the periodic table?
- **A.** metals
- **C.** nonmetals
- **B.** lanthanides
- **D.** metalloids

8. Which of the following is a characteristic that is typical of a solid, nonmetal element?
- **A.** shiny
- **B.** brittle
- **C.** good heat conductor
- **D.** good electrical conductor

Part 3 | Open Ended

16. Dalton thought that matter was made up of atoms, and the atoms could not be divided into smaller pieces. He proposed that all atoms of an element are exactly alike. Different elements, he said, are made of different kinds of atoms. Dalton pictured the atom as a hard sphere that was the same throughout.

17. A source of alpha particles was aimed at a thin sheet of gold foil. The foil was surrounded by a fluorescent screen that emitted a flash of light each time it was hit by a charged particle. Rutherford thought most of the alpha particles would pass straight through the foil. He didn't think the foil contained enough matter to stop or deflect the particles. He thought the positive charge in the gold might cause a few small changes in the paths of the alpha particles.

18. The particles that reflected at large angles showed that Thomson's model of the atom was incorrect. The positive charge in the gold was

Part 2 | Short Response/Grid In

Record your answers on the answer sheet provided by your teacher or on a sheet of paper.

9. Are electrons more likely to be in an energy level close to the nucleus or far away from the nucleus? Why?

10. How many naturally-occurring elements are listed on the periodic table?

11. Is the human body made of mostly metal, nonmetals, or metalloids?

12. A molecule of hydrogen peroxide is composed of two atoms of hydrogen and two atoms of oxygen. What is the formula for six molecules of hydrogen peroxide?

13. What is the modern-day name for cathode rays?

Use the illustration below to answer questions 14 and 15.

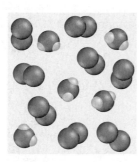

14. The illustration above shows atoms of an element and molecules of a compound that are combined without making a new compound. What term describes a combination such as this?

15. If the illustration showed only the element or only the compound, what term would describe it?

Part 3 | Open Ended

Record your answers on a sheet of paper.

16. Describe Dalton's ideas about the composition of matter, including the relationship between atoms and elements.

Use the illustration below to answer questions 17 and 18.

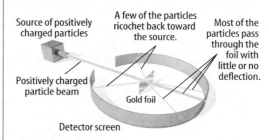

Source of positively charged particles

A few of the particles ricochet back toward the source.

Most of the particles pass through the foil with little or no deflection.

Positively charged particle beam

Gold foil

Detector screen

17. The illustration above shows Rutherford's gold foil experiment. Describe the setup shown. What result did Rutherford expect from his experiment?

18. What is the significance of the particles that reflected back from the gold foil? How did Rutherford explain his results?

19. Describe three possible methods for separating mixtures. Give an example for each method.

20. What are the rows and columns on the periodic table called? How are elements in the rows similar, and how are elements in the columns similar?

21. Describe how Thomson was able to show that cathode rays were streams of particles, not light.

22. Describe how the mass numbers, or atomic masses, listed on the periodic table for the elements are calculated.

were deflected. Since light is not deflected by a magnet, Thomson deduced that the rays must be made of charged particles.

22. Each atom's mass number is the number of protons plus the number of neutrons. Each isotope has an integer mass number. The mass number for the element is calculated by calculating a weighted average. The weighted average is the sum of each isotope's mass number multiplied by the percentage of isotopes of that kind.

Rubrics

For more help evaluating open-ended assessment questions, see the rubric on p. 10T.

reflecting the particles. Rutherford proposed that almost all the mass of the atom and all of its positive charge was contained in a small nucleus of the atom.

19. A mixture of sugar and sand can be separated by adding water. The sugar dissolves in the water and the sand can then be filtered out. A mixture of water and sugar can be separated by heating the water so that the water evaporates, leaving the sugar. Mixtures of different-sized solids, such as pebbles and sand, can be separated by filtering out the larger solid.

20. The rows are called periods. Elements in a row have the same number of energy levels. The columns are called groups.

Elements in each group have similar properties related to their structure. They also tend to form similar bonds.

21. Thomson repeated Crookes' experiment so that cathode rays moved from the negative electrode to the positive electrode. However, when Thomson placed a magnet near the cathode ray tube, the cathode rays

Section/Objectives	Standards		Labs/Features
	National	**State/Local**	
Chapter Opener	See pp. 16T–17T for a Key to Standards.		**Launch Lab:** Experiment with a Freezing Liquid, p. 101 **Foldables,** p. 101
Section 1 Matter ⏱ 2 sessions 📦 1 block 1. **Recognize** that matter is made of particles in constant motion. 2. **Relate** the three states of matter to the arrangement of particles within them.	National Content Standards: UCP.1, UCP.2, UCP.3, UCP.5, A.1, A.2, B.1, B.2, B.3		**Integrate History,** p. 104 **Science Online,** p. 105
Section 2 Changes of State ⏱ 3 sessions 📦 1.5 blocks 3. **Define and compare** thermal energy and temperature. 4. **Relate** changes in thermal energy to changes of state. 5. **Explain** how atoms have greater energy of motion when temperature increases.	National Content Standards: UCP.1, UCP.2, UCP.3, UCP.5, A.1, A.2, B.1, B.2, B.3		**Integrate Physics,** p. 108 **Visualizing States of Matter,** p. 110 **Science Online,** p. 111 **Applying Science:** How can ice save oranges?, p. 111 **MiniLAB:** Observing Vaporization, p. 112 **Science Online,** p. 113 **Lab:** The Water Cycle, p. 115
Section 3 Behavior of Fluids ⏱ 3 sessions 📦 1.5 blocks 6. **Explain** why some things float but others sink. 7. **Describe** how pressure is transmitted through fluids.	National Content Standards: UCP.1, UCP.2, UCP.3, UCP.5, A.1, A.2, B.1, B.2, E.1, E.2, F.5, G.3		**MiniLAB:** Predicting a Waterfall, p. 119 **Applying Math:** Calculating Density, p. 121 **Science Online,** p. 123 **Lab:** Design Your Own Ship, p. 124 **Oops! Accidents in Science:** The Incredible Stretching Goo, p. 126

Lab Materials	Reproducible Resources	Section Assessment	Technology
Launch Lab: test tubes, laboratory-grade stearic acid, test-tube rack, thermometer	**Chapter FAST FILE Resources** Foldables Worksheet, p. 15 Directed Reading Overview, p. 17 Note-taking Worksheets, pp. 31–32	**GLENCOE'S ASSESSMENT ADVANTAGE**	**TeacherWorks** includes: • Interactive Teacher Edition • Lesson Planner with calendar • Access to all program blacklines • Correlations to standards • Web links
Need materials? Contact Science Kit at 1-800-828-7777 or www.sciencekit.com on the Internet.	**Chapter FAST FILE Resources** Transparency Activity, p. 42 Enrichment, p. 28 Reinforcement, p. 25 Directed Reading, p. 18 Transparency Activity, pp. 45–46 Lab Activity, pp. 9–10	**Portfolio** Assessment, p. 106 **Performance** Applying Skills, p. 106 **Content** Section Review, p. 106	⬗ Section Focus Transparency ⬗ Teaching Transparency ◉ Virtual Labs CD-ROM 🎧 Guided Reading Audio Program ◉ Interactive Chalkboard CD-ROM
MiniLAB: dropper, rubbing alcohol **Lab:** hot plate, ice cubes, thermometer or electronic temperature probe, wall clock or watch with second hand, stirring rod, 250-mL beaker	**Chapter FAST FILE Resources** Transparency Activity, p. 43 MiniLAB, p. 3 Enrichment, p. 29 Reinforcement, p. 26 Directed Reading, p. 19 Lab Worksheet, pp. 5–6 Lab Activity, pp. 11–13 **Physical Science Critical Thinking/Problem Solving,** p. 10 **Reading and Writing Skill Activities,** p. 17	**Portfolio** Activity, p. 109 **Performance** Applying Science, p. 111 MiniLAB, p. 112 Applying Math, p. 114 **Content** Section Review, p. 114	⬗ Section Focus Transparency ◉ Virtual Labs CD-ROM 🎧 Guided Reading Audio Program ◉ Interactive Chalkboard CD-ROM
MiniLAB: plastic cup, water, index card **Lab:** balance, 2 small plastic cups, graduated cylinder, metric ruler, scissors, cupful of marbles, sink or basin	**Chapter FAST FILE Resources** Transparency Activity, p. 44 MiniLAB, p. 4 Enrichment, p. 30 Reinforcement, p. 27 Directed Reading, pp. 19–20 Lab Worksheet, pp. 7–8 **Mathematics Skill Activities,** p. 31	**Portfolio** Science Journal, p. 117 **Performance** MiniLAB, p. 119 Applying Math, p. 121 Applying Math, p. 123 **Content** Section Review, p. 123	⬗ Section Focus Transparency ◉ Virtual Labs CD-ROM 🎧 Guided Reading Audio Program ◉ Interactive Chalkboard CD-ROM 📼 Video Lab

End of Chapter Assessment

GLENCOE'S ASSESSMENT ADVANTAGE

Blackline Masters	Technology	Professional Series
Chapter FAST FILE Resources Chapter Review, pp. 35–36 Chapter Tests, pp. 37–40 **Standardized Test Practice,** pp. 19–22	📼 MindJogger Videoquiz ◉ Virtual Labs CD-ROM ◉ ExamView® Pro Testmaker ◉ TeacherWorks CD-ROM ◉ Interactive Chalkboard CD-ROM	**Performance Assessment in the Science Classroom (PASC)**

Transparencies

Section Focus

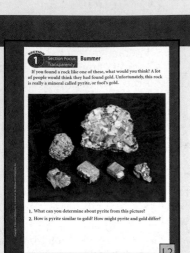

1 Section Focus Transparency **Bummer**

If you found a rock like one of these, what would you think? A lot of people would think they had found gold. Unfortunately, this rock is really a mineral called pyrite, or fool's gold.

1. What can you determine about pyrite from this picture?
2. How is pyrite similar to gold? How might pyrite and gold differ?

L2

2 Section Focus Transparency **Looking forward to some ice water, are you?**

Be sure not to forget about any water you put in the freezer to cool quickly. You might come back to a big ice cube.

1. What state of matter was the water in before it was put into the freezer? What happened in the freezer?
2. Compared to liquid water, how much space does solid water take up?
3. What are some examples of the effects of water expanding as it freezes?

L2

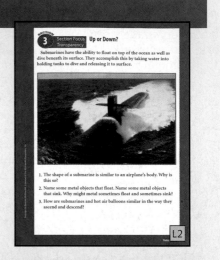

3 Section Focus Transparency **Up or Down?**

Submarines have the ability to float on top of the ocean as well as dive beneath its surface. They accomplish this by taking water into holding tanks to dive and releasing it to surface.

1. The shape of a submarine is similar to an airplane's body. Why is this so?
2. Name some metal objects that float. Name some metal objects that sink. Why might metal sometimes float and sometimes sink?
3. How are submarines and hot air balloons similar in the way they ascend and descend?

L2

This is a representation of key blackline masters available in the Teacher Classroom Resources. See Resource Manager boxes within the chapter for additional information.

Assessment

Assessment Transparency **States of Matter**

Directions: *Carefully review the diagram and answer the following questions.*

Archimedes' Principle

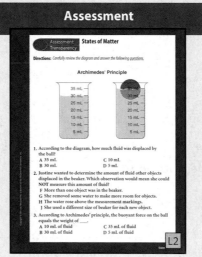

1. According to the diagram, how much fluid was displaced by the ball?
   A 35 mL.   C 10 mL.
   B 30 mL.   D 5 mL.
2. Justine wanted to determine the amount of fluid other objects displaced in the beaker. Which observation would mean she could **NOT** measure this amount of fluid?
   F More than one object was in the beaker.
   G She removed some water to make more room for objects.
   H The water rose above the measurement markings.
   J She used a different size of beaker for each new object.
3. According to Archimedes' principle, the buoyant force on the ball equals the weight of ____.
   A 10 mL. of fluid   C 35 mL of fluid
   B 30 mL. of fluid   D 5 mL of fluid

L2

Teaching

1 Teaching Transparency **Solid, Liquid, Gas**

Solid

Liquid

Gas

L2

Key to Teaching Strategies

The following designations will help you decide which activities are appropriate for your students.

L1 Level 1 activities should be appropriate for students with learning difficulties.

L2 Level 2 activities should be within the ability range of all students.

L3 Level 3 activities are designed for above-average students.

ELL ELL activities should be within the ability range of English-Language Learners.

COOP LEARN Cooperative Learning activities are designed for small group work.

LS Multiple Learning Styles logos, as described on page 12T, are used throughout to indicate strategies that address different learning styles.

P These strategies represent student products that can be placed into a best-work portfolio.

PBL Problem-Based Learning activities apply real-world situations to learning.

Hands-on Activities

Student Text Lab Worksheet

Name _____ Date _____ Class _____

Activity A Spin Around the Water Cycle

Lab Preview
Directions: *Answer these questions before you begin the Activity.*

1. Why do you need the stirring rod in this activity?

2. By increasing the temperature of water, how are you changing the energy of the water molecules?

Some of the water in the puddle you stepped in this morning could have rolled down a dinosaur's back millions of years ago because water moves through the environment in a never-ending cycle. Changes in water's physical state enable living things on Earth to use this invaluable resource.

What You'll Investigate
How does the temperature of water change as it is heated from a solid to a gas?

Materials
hot plate
ice cubes (100 mL.)
Celsius thermometer
*electronic temperature probe
wall clock
*watch with a second hand
stirring rod
250-mL beaker
*Alternate materials

Goals
- **Measure** the temperature of water as it heats.
- **Observe** what happens as the water changes from one state to another.
- **Graph** the temperature and time data.

Safety Precautions

Procedure
1. Put 150 mL. of water and 100 mL. of ice into the beaker and place the beaker on the hot plate. Do not touch the hot plate.
2. Put the thermometer into the ice/water mixture. Do not stir with the thermometer or allow it to rest on the bottom of the beaker. After 30 s, read the temperature and record it in Table 1.
3. Plug in the hot plate and turn the temperature knob to the medium setting.
4. Every 30 s, read and record the temperature in the data table. Also observe and record the physical state of the ice and/or water in the beaker. Use the stirring rod to stir the contents of the beaker before making each temperature measurement.
5. Use your data to make a graph plotting time on the x-axis and temperature on the y-axis. Draw a smooth curve through the data points.

L2
States of Matter

Laboratory Activities

Name _____ Date _____ Class _____

LAB 1 Laboratory Activity **States of Matter**

Three common states of matter are solid, liquid, and gas. A fourth state of matter, the plasma state, exists only at extremely high temperatures. Differences among the physical states depend on the attractions between the atoms or molecules and on the rate of movement of the atoms or molecules. Pressure and temperature control these two factors.

Strategy
You will observe the characteristics of a solid.
You will change a gas to a liquid.
You will compare the characteristics of a solid, a liquid, and a gas.

Materials
marker   ice cube tray
beaker (1,000 mL.)   plastic drinking glass (cold or add an ice cube)
ice cubes (frozen from 500 mL. of water)   water

Procedure
1. Mark the level of the top of the ice cube into the beaker and place the beaker on the ice cubes and place them in the beaker. Record the characteristics of ice in Table 1.
2. Let the ice cubes melt. Record the characteristics of the resulting water in Table 1.
3. Pour the water back into the tray. Mark the level of the top of the water on the tray.
4. Place the cold glass in a warm area. After a few minutes, record your observations of the surface of the glass in Table 1.
5. Place an ice cube in the beaker of water. Observe whether or not it floats. Record your observations in Table 1.

Under "Other characteristics" in Table 1, record whether this level is higher or lower than that of the ice.

Data and Observations

Table 1

Material	State of matter	Takes shape of container (yes or no)	Other characteristics
Ice cube			floats: yes or no
Water			higher or lower in tray than ice

Material	Observations
Glass	
Beaker with ice	

L2
States of Matter

Meeting Different Ability Levels

Content Outline

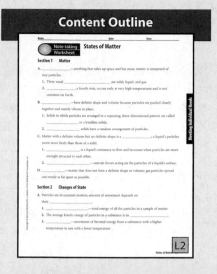

L2

Reinforcement

L2

Enrichment

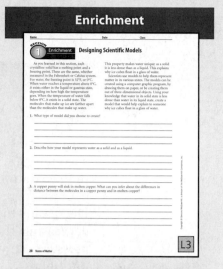

L3

Directed Reading (English/Spanish)

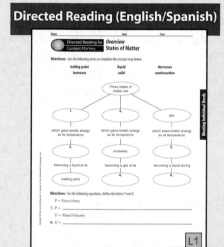

L1

Study Guide

L2

Reading Essentials

L1

Assessment

Test Practice Workbook

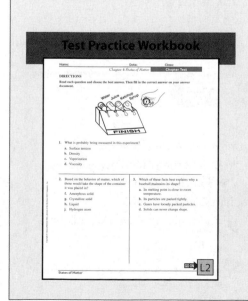

L2

Chapter Review

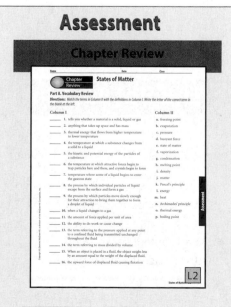

L2

Chapter Tests

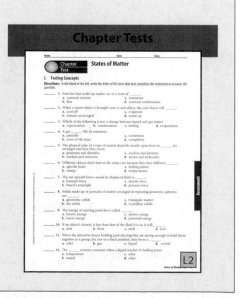

L2

Science Content Background

 Matter

section 1

Understanding Matter

Matter is made of tiny moving particles separated by space. The three states of matter that people mainly encounter are gases, liquids, and solids. In gases, the separation of the particles is the greatest because these particles are moving the fastest. Decreasing the spaces between gas molecules by decreasing the temperature or increasing the pressure can turn gases into liquids and liquids into solids.

section 2

Changes of State

Forces Between Molecules

When a liquid is poured into a container such as a glass test tube, the liquid's surface is called the meniscus. The shape of the meniscus depends on the relative strength of the cohesive forces between liquid particles and the adhesive forces between particles of the liquid and the container. If the adhesive forces are greater, the meniscus is concave. Water in a glass tube has a concave meniscus. If the cohesive forces are greater, the meniscus is convex. Mercury in a glass tube has a convex meniscus.

Temperature

The Kelvin temperature scale is an absolute scale. It begins at absolute zero, or 0 K. Each degree on the Kelvin scale is the same magnitude as a degree on the Celsius temperature scale. The freezing point of water on the Celsius scale is 0°C; the freezing point of water on the Kelvin scale is 273 K. The average kinetic energy of the particles that make up a substance is directly proportional to its Kelvin temperature. Although particles should not be moving at absolute zero, they have a small amount of motion called the zero point energy.

Heat

Heat is energy transferred from matter at a higher temperature to matter at a lower temperature. Objects do not contain heat; they contain internal energy, which is the sum of the kinetic and potential energies of their particles. Heat can be transferred three ways: radiation is the emission of electromagnetic waves, conduction is the transfer of heat by direct contact, and convection is heat transfer by warmer matter flowing into regions of colder matter.

 Behavior of Fluids

section 3

Atmospheric Pressure

Air pressure decreases rapidly with altitude. At the top of Mount Everest, 8.85 km above sea level, the pressure is only 33% of atmospheric pressure at sea level. This difference in pressure demonstrates how effectively gravity contains Earth's atmosphere.

chapter content resources

Internet Resources

For additional content background, visit
ips.msscience.com to:
- access your book online
- find references to related articles in popular science magazines
- access Web links with related content background
- access current events with science journal topics

Print Resources

Chemistry; The Molecular Nature of Matter and Change, Martin S. Silberberg, McGraw-Hill, 2003

Chemistry, Steve S. Zumdahl, Susan A. Zumdahl, Houghton Mifflin Company, 2003

Chemistry, Raymond Chang, McGraw-Hill College, 2001

IDENTIFYING ▶ Misconceptions

Find Out What Students Think

Students may think that . . .

Matter does not include liquids or gases.

Forms of energy such as heat and light are matter.

Since solids are easy to see and feel, students usually understand easily that these materials are matter. Most gases are not directly observed, either through vision or other senses, so students may have difficulty categorizing gases as matter. Some students, however, may have too inclusive a view of matter. They fail to realize that energy may affect particles but is not composed of particles. These misunderstandings about matter can interfere with acquisition of new concepts.

Discussion

Ask students to divide a page in their Science Journals into two columns, one headed *Matter* and the other headed *Not Matter*. Read the following terms, and have students write each one in the appropriate column: *oxygen gas, orange juice, science book, pencil, electricity, carbon dioxide gas, water, heat, and light.* L2

Superstock

Promote Understanding

Demonstration

Explain that matter is composed of molecules.

• Hold up an ice cube, and establish that it is matter and is made of H_2O molecules.

• Allow the ice cube to melt. Point to the water. Is this matter? Establish that it is matter and that it is still made of H_2O molecules.

• Boil the water on a hot plate to produce steam. Is the steam matter? Establish that it is and that it is still made of H_2O molecules. Matter includes solids, liquids, and gases.

• Move your hand over the hot plate, and say that it feels warm. Is heat matter? Let students discuss this.

• Does heat have particles? Make sure students realize that heat affects particles but is not composed of particles. Heat is a form of energy, just as light and X rays are forms of energy. Energy is not matter.

Have students go back to their charts and move any terms that are not in the proper columns. L2

Assess

After completing the chapter, see *Identifying Misconceptions* in the Study Guide at the end of the chapter.

Chapter Vocabulary

Science Journal The students may have questions about the source of the water, why the water is warm, why the snow hasn't melted, and how they would feel in the spring.

INTERACTIVE CHALKBOARD with Image Bank

PowerPoint® Presentations

This CD-ROM is an editable Microsoft® PowerPoint® presentation that includes:

- a pre-made presentation for every chapter
- interactive graphics
- animations
- audio clips
- image bank
- all new section and chapter questions
- Standardized Test Practice
- transparencies
- pre-lab questions for all labs
- Foldables directions
- links to ips.msscience.com

States of Matter

chapter preview

sections

1 **Matter**

2 **Changes of State**
   Lab **The Water Cycle**

3 **Behavior of Fluids**
   Lab **Design Your Own Ship**

Virtual Lab **How does thermal energy affect the state of a substance?**

A long, hot soak on a snowy day! This Asian monkey called a macaque is experiencing the effects of heat—the transfer of thermal energy from a warmer object to a colder object. In this chapter, you will learn about heat and the three common states of matter on Earth.

Science Journal Write about what you think is the source of the warm water.

Theme Connection

Systems and Interactions The structure and motion of particles of matter can be analyzed to explain many properties of systems containing huge numbers of particles. Powerful changes can be caused when energy is absorbed or released by these systems. Earth's weather offers many examples of changes involving the absorption or release of energy.

About the Photo

Heat Transfer The photo may help the students think about "the why" of every day events, such as putting ice cubes in a liquid or taking aluminum foil from a hot oven. While we observe the properties of matter daily, the students may have many misconceptions about the properties and characteristics that define matter.

Start-Up Activities

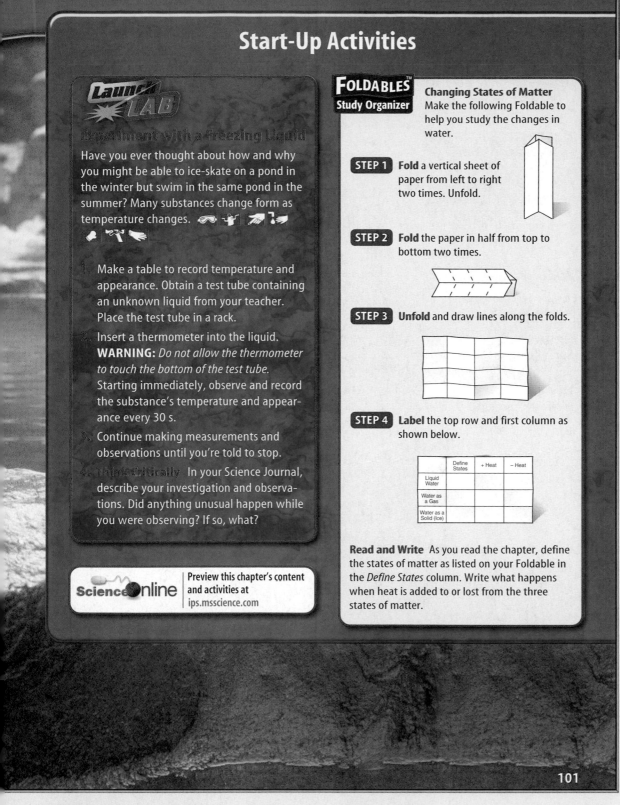

Experiment with a Freezing Liquid

Have you ever thought about how and why you might be able to ice-skate on a pond in the winter but swim in the same pond in the summer? Many substances change form as temperature changes.

1. Make a table to record temperature and appearance. Obtain a test tube containing an unknown liquid from your teacher. Place the test tube in a rack.

2. Insert a thermometer into the liquid. **WARNING:** *Do not allow the thermometer to touch the bottom of the test tube.* Starting immediately, observe and record the substance's temperature and appearance every 30 s.

3. Continue making measurements and observations until you're told to stop.

4. **Think Critically** In your Science Journal, describe your investigation and observations. Did anything unusual happen while you were observing? If so, what?

Science**Online**
Preview this chapter's content and activities at
ips.msscience.com

FOLDABLES Study Organizer

Changing States of Matter
Make the following Foldable to help you study the changes in water.

STEP 1 Fold a vertical sheet of paper from left to right two times. Unfold.

STEP 2 Fold the paper in half from top to bottom two times.

STEP 3 Unfold and draw lines along the folds.

STEP 4 Label the top row and first column as shown below.

	Define States	+ Heat	− Heat
Liquid Water			
Water as a Gas			
Water as a Solid (Ice)			

Read and Write As you read the chapter, define the states of matter as listed on your Foldable in the *Define States* column. Write what happens when heat is added to or lost from the three states of matter.

101

FOLDABLES Study Organizer **Dinah Zike Study Fold**

Student preparation materials for this Foldable are available in the Chapter *FAST FILE* Resources.

Assessment

Performance Have students predict what would happen if they were given twice as much of the unknown liquid. Use **Performance Assessment in the Science Classroom,** p. 89.

Launch LAB

Purpose Use the Launch Lab to help students discover that temperature remains constant as a substance freezes. L2
COOP LEARN **LS** **Kinesthetic**

Preparation When students arrive, have test tubes half-filled with molten stearic acid sitting in a hot water bath in a hood at a temperature of approximately 75°C. Keep test tubes in hood until needed.

Materials laboratory-grade stearic acid, glass test tube, Celsius thermometer, watch or clock with a second hand, test-tube rack or jar

Teaching Strategy Suggest that student groups divide the responsibilities of tracking time, taking temperature readings, and recording data. Students then can graph and analyze the data individually.

Safety Precautions
• Caution students to be careful with the thermometer and wear safety glasses while working with the liquid.
• Do NOT let students remove thermometers from solid stearic acid. Breaking can occur. At the end of lab, have students return all materials to you. Reheat test tubes to remove thermometers.

Think Critically

The liquid's temperature fell gradually, remained the same as the liquid formed a white solid, then fell again. Heat was given off by the freezing liquid.

Sample Data

Time(s)	Temperature (°C)
0	74.0
30	72.5
60	70.0
90	69.5
120	69.5
150	69.5
180	69.5
210	69.0
240	68.5

section 1 Matter

as you read

What **You'll Learn**
- **Recognize** that matter is made of particles in constant motion.
- **Relate** the three states of matter to the arrangement of particles within them.

Why **It's Important**
Everything you can see, taste, and touch is matter.

② Review Vocabulary
atom: a small particle that makes up most types of matter

New Vocabulary
- matter
- viscosity
- solid
- surface tension
- liquid
- gas

What is matter?

Take a look at the beautiful scene in **Figure 1.** What do you see? Perhaps you notice the water and ice. Maybe you are struck by the Sun in the background. All of these images show examples of matter. **Matter** is anything that takes up space and has mass. Matter doesn't have to be visible—even air is matter.

States of Matter All matter is made up of tiny particles, such as atoms, molecules, or ions. Each particle attracts other particles. In other words, each particle pulls other particles toward itself. These particles also are constantly moving. The motion of the particles and the strength of attraction between the particles determine a material's state of matter.

✔ Reading Check *What determines a material's state of matter?*

There are three familiar states of matter—solid, liquid, and gas. A fourth state of matter known as plasma occurs at extremely high temperatures. Plasma is found in stars, lightning, and neon lights. Although plasma is common in the universe, it is not common on Earth. For that reason, this chapter will focus only on the three states of matter that are common on Earth.

Figure 1 Matter exists in all four states in this scene.
Identify *the solid, liquid, gas, and plasma in this photograph.*

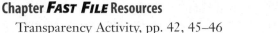

Section 1 Resource Manager

Chapter FAST FILE Resources
Transparency Activity, pp. 42, 45–46
Directed Reading for Content Mastery, pp. 17, 18
Note-taking Worksheets, pp. 31–33
Enrichment, p. 28
Reinforcement, p. 25

Lab Activity, pp. 9–10

Solids

What makes a substance a solid? Think about some familiar solids. Chairs, floors, rocks, and ice cubes are a few examples of matter in the solid state. What properties do all solids share? A **solid** is matter with a definite shape and volume. For example, when you pick up a rock from the ground and place it in a bucket, it doesn't change shape or size. A solid does not take the shape of a container in which it is placed. This is because the particles of a solid are packed closely together, as shown in **Figure 2**.

Particles in Motion The particles that make up all types of matter are in constant motion. Does this mean that the particles in a solid are moving too? Although you can't see them, a solid's particles are vibrating in place. The particles do not have enough energy to move out of their fixed positions.

Reading Check *What motion do solid particles have?*

Crystalline Solids In some solids, the particles are arranged in a repeating, three-dimensional pattern called a crystal. These solids are called crystalline solids. In **Figure 3** you can see the arrangement of particles in a crystal of sodium chloride, which is table salt. The particles in the crystal are arranged in the shape of a cube. Diamond, another crystalline solid, is made entirely of carbon atoms that form crystals that look more like pyramids. Sugar, sand, and snow are other crystalline solids.

Solid

Figure 2 The particles in a solid vibrate in place while maintaining a constant shape and volume.

Figure 3 The particles in a crystal of sodium chloride (NaCl) are arranged in an orderly pattern.

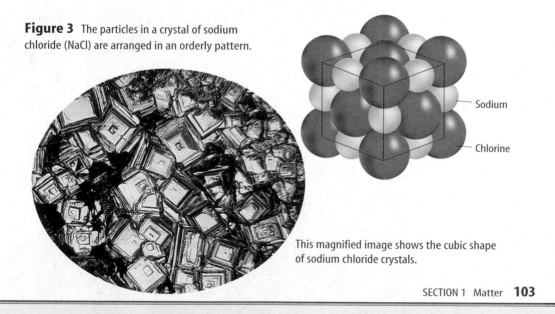

Sodium

Chlorine

This magnified image shows the cubic shape of sodium chloride crystals.

SECTION 1 Matter **103**

Use an Analogy

Different Solids The particles in a crystalline solid occupy defined spaces, like eggs in an egg carton. In an amorphous solid the particles are in a random arrangement, more like lemons in a bowl.

Reading Check

Answer The particles in amorphous solids have a random arrangement instead of an ordered arrangement.

Fresh Water What waterways, if any, are near your home and school? Are the waterways still being used? Are they natural or man-made, like canals? Find out how the waterways were used by the early settlers of your town.

Activity

States of Matter Have students create a Venn diagram of the properties of water as a solid, a liquid, and a gas. The diagrams should include characteristics such as shape, volume, and particle motion. L2

Fresh Water Early settlers have always decided to build their homes near water. The rivers provided ways for people to travel, drinking water for themselves and their animals, and irrigation for farming. Over time, small communities became larger communities with industry building along the same water.

Amorphous Solids Some solids come together without forming crystal structures. These solids often consist of large particles that are not arranged in a repeating pattern. Instead, the particles are found in a random arrangement. These solids are called amorphous (uh MOR fuhs) solids. Rubber, plastic, and glass are examples of amorphous solids.

Reading Check *How is a crystalline solid different from an amorphous solid?*

Liquids

From the orange juice you drink with breakfast to the water you use to brush your teeth at night, matter in the liquid state is familiar to you. How would you describe the characteristics of a liquid? Is it hard like a solid? Does it keep its shape? A **liquid** is matter that has a definite volume but no definite shape. When you pour a liquid from one container to another, the liquid takes the shape of the container. The volume of a liquid, however, is the same no matter what the shape of the container. If you pour 50 mL of juice from a carton into a pitcher, the pitcher will contain 50 mL of juice. If you then pour that same juice into a glass, its shape will change again but its volume will not.

Free to Move The reason that a liquid can have different shapes is because the particles in a liquid move more freely, as shown in **Figure 4,** than the particles in a solid. The particles in a liquid have enough energy to move out of their fixed positions but not enough energy to move far apart.

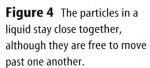

Figure 4 The particles in a liquid stay close together, although they are free to move past one another.

Liquid

Differentiated Instruction

English-Language Learners Have English-Language Learners create the Venn diagram in the activity on this page in their native language. Ask them to translate the diagram into English. Then have the students share the translated version with a classmate. L2 ELL

Viscosity Do all liquids flow the way water flows? You know that honey flows more slowly than water and you've probably heard the phrase "slow as molasses." Some liquids flow more easily than others. A liquid's resistance to flow is known as the liquid's **viscosity.** Honey has a high viscosity. Water has a lower viscosity. The slower a liquid flows, the higher its viscosity is. The viscosity results from the strength of the attraction between the particles of the liquid. For many liquids, viscosity increases as the liquid becomes colder.

Surface Tension If you're careful, you can float a needle on the surface of water. This is because attractive forces cause the particles on the surface of a liquid to pull themselves together and resist being pushed apart. You can see in **Figure 5** that particles beneath the surface of a liquid are pulled in all directions. Particles at the surface of a liquid are pulled toward the center of the liquid and sideways along the surface. No liquid particles are located above to pull on them. The uneven forces acting on the particles on the surface of a liquid are called **surface tension.** Surface tension causes the liquid to act as if a thin film were stretched across its surface. As a result you can float a needle on the surface of water. For the same reason, the water strider can move around on the surface of a pond or lake. When a liquid is present in small amounts, surface tension causes the liquid to form small droplets.

Science Online

Topic: Plasma
Visit ips.msscience.com for Web links to information about the states of matter.

Activity List four ways that plasma differs from the other three states of matter

Figure 5 Surface tension exists because the particles at the surface experience different forces than those at the center of the liquid.

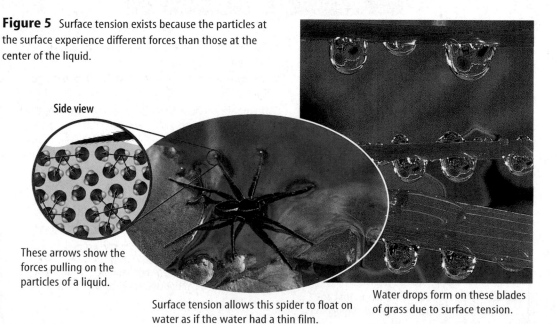

Side view

These arrows show the forces pulling on the particles of a liquid.

Surface tension allows this spider to float on water as if the water had a thin film.

Water drops form on these blades of grass due to surface tension.

Visual Learning

Figure 5 Explain the forces that are in effect in each photo and ask why surface tension is not a property of solids. The particles in solids are rigidly held in place and are not free to move. L2 **LS** **Logical-Mathematical**

Use an Analogy

Cohesion One force of attraction that causes particles to pull toward each other is called cohesion. Cohesion between particles is similar to the force of gravity that pulls inward to produce the spherical shape of the planets and sun.

Fun Fact

The physics department of the University of Queensland, Australia, has a funnel of pitch—the black, sticky material used in blacktopping roads and waterproofing basements—that is so viscous it takes about ten years for a drop to drip.

Discussion

Plasma In conjunction with the online resources, discuss the information about plasma the students found. Plasma consists of ions, electrons, and atomic nuclei that have lost all their electrons. It forms at temperatures higher than 5000°C. Information about new and practical uses of plasma can be found at www.plasma.org. L2

LAB DEMONSTRATION

Purpose to show how temperature affects the viscosity of a liquid

Materials 2 jars, syrup or molasses, refrigerator, 2 small beakers, stopwatch

Preparation Add 10 mL of syrup to each jar. Place one jar in a refrigerator overnight, and allow the other to stand at room temperature.

Procedure Have one student pour all the cold syrup into one beaker while another student pours all the room-temperature syrup into the other beaker. Have remaining students record the time it takes to empty each jar.

Expected Outcome The cold syrup takes longer to pour.

Assessment

Why does the cold syrup have higher viscosity than the warmer syrup? The particles in the cold syrup are closer together and exert a stronger force upon each other than do the warmer particles.

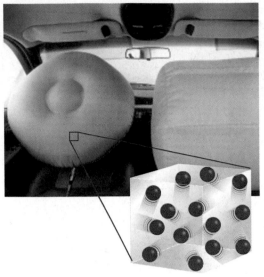

Figure 6 The particles in gas move at high speeds in all directions. The gas inside these air bags spreads out to fill the entire volume of the bag.

Gases

Unlike solids and liquids, most gases are invisible. The air you breathe is a mixture of gases. The gas in the air bags in **Figure 6** and the helium in some balloons are examples of gases. **Gas** is matter that does not have a definite shape or volume. The particles in gas are much farther apart than those in a liquid or solid. Gas particles move at high speeds in all directions. They will spread out evenly, as far apart as possible. If you poured a small volume of a liquid into a container, the liquid would stay in the bottom of the container. However, if you poured the same volume of a gas into a container, the gas would fill the container completely. A gas can expand or be compressed. Decreasing the volume of the container squeezes the gas particles closer together.

Vapor Matter that exists in the gas state but is generally a liquid or solid at room temperature is called vapor. Water, for example, is a liquid at room temperature. Thus, water vapor is the term for the gas state of water.

section 1 review

Summary

What is matter?

● Matter is anything that takes up space and has mass. Solid, liquid, and gas are the three common states of matter.

Solids

● Solids have a definite volume and shape.

● Solids with particles arranged in order are called crystalline solids. The particles in amorphous solids are not in any order.

Liquids

● Liquids have definite volume but no defined shape.

● Viscosity is a measure of how easily liquids flow.

Gases

● Gases have no definite volume or shape.

● Vapor refers to gaseous substances that are normally liquids or solids at room temperature.

Self Check

1. **Define** the two properties of matter that determine its state.

2. **Describe** the movement of particles within solids, liquids, and gases.

3. **Name** the property that liquids and solids share. What property do liquids and gases share?

4. **Infer** A scientist places 25 mL of a yellow substance into a 50-mL container. The substance quickly fills the entire container. Is it a solid, liquid, or gas?

5. **Think Critically** The particles in liquid A have a stronger attraction to each other than the particles in liquid B. If both liquids are at the same temperature, which liquid has a higher viscosity? Explain.

Applying Skills

6. **Concept Map** Draw a Venn diagram in your Science Journal and fill in the characteristics of the states of matter.

Science Online ips.msscience.com/self_check_quiz

section 1 review

1. motion of particles and strength of attraction between particles

2. solids: particles are very close together and vibrate back and forth; liquids: particles are farther apart and individual particles can flow past each other; gases: particles are very far apart and move quickly

3. solid — liquid — constant volume liquid — gas — take on shape of container

4. Gas state, the particles take the shape and volume of their container.

5. Liquid A — greater attraction among molecules, the greater the viscosity

6. Check students' work for characteristics that are shared and not shared by states of matter.

Changes of State

Thermal Energy and Heat

Shards of ice fly from the sculptor's chisel. As the crowd looks on, a swan slowly emerges from a massive block of ice. As the day wears on, however, drops of water begin to fall from the sculpture. Drip by drip, the sculpture is transformed into a puddle of liquid water. What makes matter change from one state to another? To answer this question, you need to think about the particles that make up matter.

Energy Simply stated, energy is the ability to do work or cause change. The energy of motion is called kinetic energy. Particles within matter are in constant motion. The amount of motion of these particles depends on the kinetic energy they possess. Particles with more kinetic energy move faster and farther apart. Particles with less energy move more slowly and stay closer together.

The total kinetic and potential energy of all the particles in a sample of matter is called **thermal energy.** Thermal energy, an extensive property, depends on the number of particles in a substance as well as the amount of energy each particle has. If either the number of particles or the amount of energy in each particle changes, the thermal energy of the sample changes. With identically sized samples, the warmer substance has the greater thermal energy. In **Figure 7,** the particles of hot water from the hot spring have more thermal energy than the particles of snow on the surrounding ground.

as you read

What You'll Learn
- **Define and compare** thermal energy and temperature.
- **Relate** changes in thermal energy to changes of state.
- **Explore** energy and temperature changes on a graph.

Why It's Important
Matter changes state as it heats up or cools down.

Review Vocabulary
energy: the ability to do work or cause change

New Vocabulary
- thermal energy
- temperature
- heat
- melting
- freezing
- vaporization
- condensation

Figure 7 These girls are enjoying the water from the hot spring. **Infer** *why the girls appear to be comfortable in the hot spring while there is snow on the ground.*

1 Motivate

Bellringer

Section Focus Transparencies also are available on the Interactive Chalkboard CD-ROM.
L2 ELL

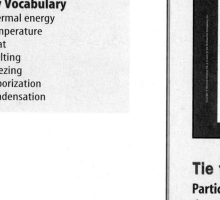

Tie to Prior Knowledge

Particle Arrangement Remind students of the differences in particle arrangement and movement in solids, liquids, and gases.

Caption Answer

Figure 7 The water in the hot spring has more thermal energy than the surrounding snow.

Section 2 Resource Manager

Chapter FAST FILE Resources
- Transparency Activity, p. 43
- Directed Reading for Content Mastery, p. 19
- Lab Activity, pp. 11–13
- Enrichment, p. 29
- MiniLab, p. 3

- Reinforcement, p. 26
- Lab Worksheets, pp. 5–6

Reading and Writing Skill Activities, p. 17

Earth Science Critical Thinking/Problem Solving, p. 10

Physical Science Critical Thinking/Problem Solving, p. 10

Caption Answer

Figure 8 the hot tea

INTEGRATE
Physics

Types of Energy All types of energy can cause change. What changes can each of the forms of energy listed in the Integrate Physics cause? thermal energy—make particles move faster; chemical energy—make and break chemical bonds; electrical energy—illuminate light bulbs, turn motors; electromagnetic energy of light—stimulate cells so we can see; nuclear energy—change mass to energy. L2 [LS] **Logical-Mathematical**

Research Have students research geothermal energy. Topics that should be included are a definition of the term, how geothermal energy is being used for household applications and how geothermal energy is being used to generate electricity. L2

Reading Check

Answer When a substance is heated, it gains thermal energy; therefore, its particles move faster and its temperature rises.

IDENTIFYING
Misconceptions

Thermal Energy Students may not realize that two systems at the same temperature can have different amounts of thermal energy. For example, a cup of boiling water and a pot of boiling water may have the same temperature, but the pot of water has more thermal energy and can transfer more heat.

Figure 8 The particles in hot tea move faster than those in iced tea. The temperature of hot tea is higher than the temperature of iced tea.
Identify which tea has the higher kinetic energy.

INTEGRATE
Physics

Types of Energy Thermal energy is one of several different forms of energy. Other forms include the chemical energy in chemical compounds, the electrical energy used in appliances, the electromagnetic energy of light, and the nuclear energy stored in the nucleus of an atom. Make a list of examples of energy that you are familiar with.

Temperature Not all of the particles in a sample of matter have the same amount of energy. Some have more energy than others. The average kinetic energy of the individual particles is the **temperature**, an intensive property, of the substance. You can find an average by adding up a group of numbers and dividing the total by the number of items in the group. For example, the average of the numbers 2, 4, 8, and 10 is $(2 + 4 + 8 + 10) \div 4 = 6$. Temperature is different from thermal energy because thermal energy is a total and temperature is an average.

You know that the iced tea is colder than the hot tea, as shown in **Figure 8.** Stated differently, the temperature of iced tea is lower than the temperature of hot tea. You also could say that the average kinetic energy of the particles in the iced tea is less than the average kinetic energy of the particles in the hot tea.

Heat When a warm object is brought near a cooler object, thermal energy will be transferred from the warmer object to the cooler one. The movement of thermal energy from a substance at a higher temperature to one at a lower temperature is called **heat**. When a substance is heated, it gains thermal energy. Therefore, its particles move faster and its temperature rises. When a substance is cooled, it loses thermal energy, which causes its particles to move more slowly and its temperature to drop.

Reading Check How is heat related to temperature?

108 CHAPTER 4 States of Matter

Science Journal

Thermal Energy on the Move Ask students to pay attention to the transfer of thermal energy around them and record all the examples they observe in one 24-hour period. Have them write their observations in their Science Journals. They should include for each example where the thermal energy came from and where it went. L2 [LS] **Naturalist**

Specific Heat

As you study more science, you will discover that water has many unique properties. One of those is the amount of heat required to increase the temperature of water as compared to most other substances. The specific heat of a substance is the amount of heat required to raise the temperature of 1 g of a substance 1°C.

Substances that have a low specific heat, such as most metals and the sand in **Figure 9,** heat up and cool down quickly because they require only small amounts of heat to cause their temperatures to rise. A substance with a high specific heat, such as the water in **Figure 9,** heats up and cools down slowly because a much larger quantity of heat is required to cause its temperature to rise or fall by the same amount.

Figure 9 The specific heat of water is greater than that of sand. The energy provided by the Sun raises the temperature of the sand much faster than the water.

Changes Between the Solid and Liquid States

Matter can change from one state to another when thermal energy is absorbed or released. This change is known as change of state. The graph in **Figure 11** shows the changes in temperature as thermal energy is gradually added to a container of ice.

Figure 10 Rather than melting into a liquid, glass gradually softens. Glass blowers use this characteristic to shape glass into beautiful vases while it is hot.

Melting As the ice in **Figure 11** is heated, it absorbs thermal energy and its temperature rises. At some point, the temperature stops rising and the ice begins to change into liquid water. The change from the solid state to the liquid state is called **melting.** The temperature at which a substance changes from a solid to a liquid is called the melting point. The melting point of water is 0°C.

Amorphous solids, such as rubber and glass, don't melt in the same way as crystalline solids. Because they don't have crystal structures to break down, these solids get softer and softer as they are heated, as you can see in **Figure 10.**

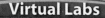
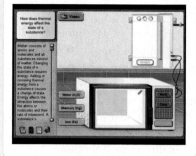
Activity

Specific Heat Between 0°C and 100°C the specific heat of water is about 4.18 J/g°C. Ask students to find the specific heats of several metals and compare them with the specific heat of water. Have them make a table from their findings. The specific heat of silver between these temperatures is 0.235 J/g°C. Between 20°C and 100°C the specific heat of aluminum is 0.903 J/g°C, the specific heat of copper is 0.385 J/g°C, and the specific heat of iron is 0.449 J/g°C. These range from about one-twentieth that of water to about one-fifth that of water.

L3 **LS** **Logical-Mathematical** **P**

IDENTIFYING Misconceptions

Changing States Students may think particles of a substance can change state only at the melting point or boiling point of the substance. In fact, at any temperature different particles of a substance have different amounts of kinetic energy and may have enough energy to change state. Melting and boiling occur when the number of particles with enough energy to change state is great enough that the average kinetic energy of the particles is at the melting point or the boiling point of the substance.

Active Reading

Quickwrites This strategy will help students identify what they already know about thermal energy, temperature, and changes in state. Have students list ideas about these topics, and then share their ideas with the class. Students can then write those ideas freely in a paragraph and share them with the class during or after a learning experience on the states of matter.

L1

Curriculum Connection

Geography Earth's temperature has increased during the past few decades. Have students research how this increase could cause changes in the state of water and the effects these changes could have on a specific geographic region. For example, melting of the polar ice caps is causing erosion along coastlines.

L3 **LS** **Linguistic**

Visualizing States of Matter

Have students examine the pictures and read the captions. Then ask the following questions.

During the melting and vaporization process the temperature remains constant. Look at the graph and identify which factor continues to increase. **thermal energy**

What changes in molecular attraction occur as water goes from a solid to a liquid to a gas? **As a solid, the molecules have the most attraction for each other. As a liquid, the molecular attraction has decreased. As a gas, there is no longer any molecular attraction between the molecules.**

During condensation, what must be removed from the gas in order for the gas to become a liquid? **thermal energy**

Activity

Water Molecule Have the students write a letter about the life of a water molecule as it goes from a solid to a gas. How free and what will it see as a molecule that's part of a solid, liquid, or vapor? L2 LS **Linguistic**

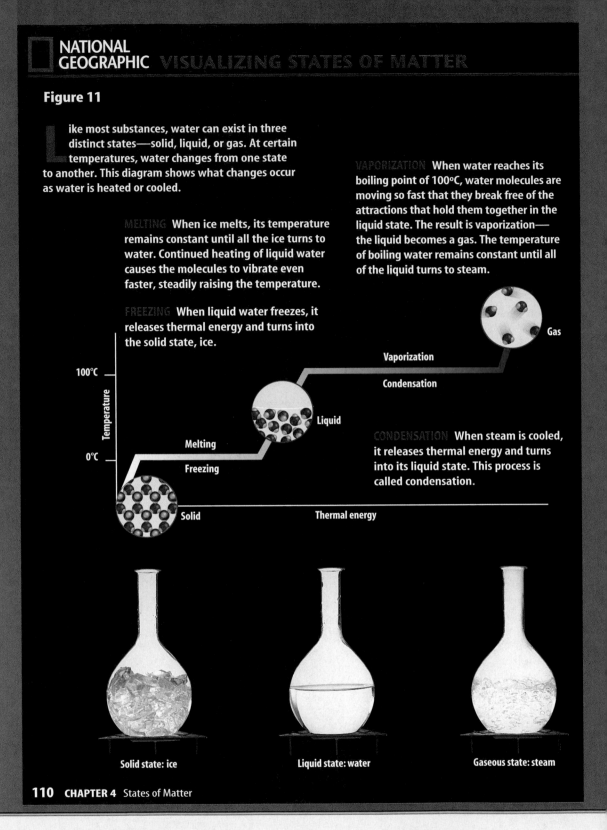

Figure 11

Like most substances, water can exist in three distinct states—solid, liquid, or gas. At certain temperatures, water changes from one state to another. This diagram shows what changes occur as water is heated or cooled.

MELTING When ice melts, its temperature remains constant until all the ice turns to water. Continued heating of liquid water causes the molecules to vibrate even faster, steadily raising the temperature.

FREEZING When liquid water freezes, it releases thermal energy and turns into the solid state, ice.

VAPORIZATION When water reaches its boiling point of 100°C, water molecules are moving so fast that they break free of the attractions that hold them together in the liquid state. The result is vaporization—the liquid becomes a gas. The temperature of boiling water remains constant until all of the liquid turns to steam.

CONDENSATION When steam is cooled, it releases thermal energy and turns into its liquid state. This process is called condensation.

Gas

Vaporization

Condensation

Liquid

100°C

Temperature

Melting

0°C

Freezing

Solid

Thermal energy

Solid state: ice

Liquid state: water

Gaseous state: steam

110 CHAPTER 4 States of Matter

Differentiated Instruction

Challenge Have students find out the energy changes that occur during the refrigeration cycle. Have them also find the properties of environmentally safe refrigerants and share the information with the class. L3

Freezing The process of melting a crystalline solid can be reversed if the liquid is cooled. The change from the liquid state to the solid state is called freezing. As the liquid cools, it loses thermal energy. As a result, its particles slow down and come closer together. Attractive forces begin to trap particles, and the crystals of a solid begin to form. As you can see in **Figure 11,** freezing and melting are opposite processes.

The temperature at which a substance changes from the liquid state to the solid state is called the freezing point. The freezing point of the liquid state of a substance is the same temperature as the melting point of the solid state. For example, solid water melts at 0°C and liquid water freezes at 0°C.

During freezing, the temperature of a substance remains constant while the particles in the liquid form a crystalline solid. Because particles in a liquid have more energy than particles in a solid, energy is released during freezing. This energy is released into the surroundings. After all of the liquid has become a solid, the temperature begins to decrease again.

Science Online

Topic: Freezing Point Study
Visit ips.msscience.com for Web links to information about freezing.

Activity Make a list of several substances and the temperatures at which they freeze. Find out how the freezing point affects how the substance is used.

Applying Science

How can ice save oranges?

During the spring, Florida citrus farmers carefully watch the fruit when temperatures drop close to freezing. When the temperatures fall below 0°C, the liquid in the cells of oranges can freeze and expand. This causes the cells to break, making the oranges mushy and the crop useless for sale. To prevent this, farmers spray the oranges with water just before the temperature reaches 0°C. How does spraying oranges with water protect them?

Identifying the Problem

Using the diagram in **Figure 11,** consider what is happening to the water at 0°C. Two things occur. What are they?

Solving the Problem

1. What change of state and what energy changes occur when water freezes?
2. How does the formation of ice on the orange help the orange?

Discussion

Energy Since temperature doesn't change as a substance is freezing, the kinetic energy of its particles doesn't change. But the substance is losing energy. What kind of energy is the substance losing? It is losing the potential energy of the attraction between the particles. [L3] [LS]
Logical-Mathematical

Applying Science

Teaching Strategies

Show students the difference between an orange that has been frozen below 0°C (-2.2°C) and one that has not been frozen. The layer of ice on top protects the orange from the colder air temperatures. Point out that this is also what occurs when a lake freezes over. The ice on top protects the water beneath, so fish can survive.

Answers

1. The two changes that occur are the phase change from water to ice and the loss of energy (exothermic) when the phase change occurs.
2. The ice forms at 0°C forming a coating on the orange that acts as insulation against the colder air temperature. Some of the energy that is released when the ice forms goes into the orange.

Differentiated Instruction

Learning Disabled Help students analyze the questions posed in Applying Science by breaking down the process that occurs as the water sprayed on the oranges freezes. Draw diagrams and use arrows to show the energy transfers involved and relate them to the graphs on the previous page.
[L2] [LS] **Logical-Mathematical**

Mini LAB

Purpose Students observe that a liquid absorbs heat from its surroundings as it evaporates. L1 **LS** **Kinesthetic**

Materials dropper, rubbing alcohol

Teaching Strategy Prevent waste by providing students with small amounts of alcohol.

Safety Precautions Students should wear goggles when performing this MiniLAB. Alcohol is flammable. There should be no open flames in the lab.

Analysis

1. The alcohol evaporated.
2. The hand felt cool where the alcohol was located. The alcohol removed heat from the skin as it evaporated, and then the hand warmed up again.
3. Sweating alone will not cool the body. The sweat has to evaporate for the body to feel cooler.

Assessment

Content Explain how the body is cooled by perspiration. Heat from the body is absorbed as perspiration evaporates from the skin. Use **Performance Assessment in the Science Classroom,** p. 89.

Caption Answer

Figure 12 Vaporization describes a liquid changing to a gas.

Visual Learning

Figure 12 Discuss with students the difference between evaporation and boiling. Could both occur at the same time? Yes; while some particles are becoming gas inside the liquid, other liquid particles can become gas at the surface. L2 **LS** **Logical-Mathematical**

Mini LAB

Observing Vaporization

Procedure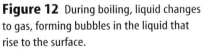

1. Use a **dropper** to place one drop of **rubbing alcohol** on the back of your hand.
2. Describe how your hand feels during the next 2 min.
3. Wash your hands.

Analysis

1. What changes in the appearance of the rubbing alcohol did you notice?
2. What sensation did you feel during the 2 min? How can you explain this sensation?
3. Infer how sweating cools the body.

Changes Between the Liquid and Gas States

After an early morning rain, you and your friends enjoy stomping through the puddles left behind. But later that afternoon when you head out to run through the puddles once more, the puddles are gone. The liquid water in the puddles changed into a gas. Matter changes between the liquid and gas states through vaporization and condensation.

Vaporization As liquid water is heated, its temperature rises until it reaches 100°C. At this point, liquid water changes into water vapor. The change from a liquid to a gas is known as **vaporization** (vay puh ruh ZAY shun). You can see in **Figure 11** that the temperature of the substance does not change during vaporization. However, the substance absorbs thermal energy. The additional energy causes the particles to move faster until they have enough energy to escape the liquid as gas particles.

Two forms of vaporization exist. Vaporization that takes place below the surface of a liquid is called boiling. When a liquid boils, bubbles form within the liquid and rise to the surface, as shown in **Figure 12.** The temperature at which a liquid boils is called the boiling point. The boiling point of water is 100°C.

Vaporization that takes place at the surface of a liquid is called evaporation. Evaporation, which occurs at temperatures below the boiling point, explains how puddles dry up. Imagine that you could watch individual water molecules in a puddle. You would notice that the molecules move at different speeds. Although the temperature of the water is constant, remember that temperature is a measure of the average kinetic energy of the molecules. Some of the fastest-moving molecules overcome the attractive forces of other molecules and escape from the surface of the water.

Figure 12 During boiling, liquid changes to gas, forming bubbles in the liquid that rise to the surface.
Define *the word that describes a liquid changing to the gas.*

Teacher FYI

Maxwell-Boltzmann Distribution At a given temperature, the motions of the particles in a substance vary according to a well-defined distribution of particle speeds called the Maxwell-Boltzmann distribution. This distribution looks similar to a bell curve but is not as symmetrical. The limit on the fastest speeds is the speed of light, while zero is the lowest speed a particle can have.

Figure 13 The drops of water on these glasses and pitcher of lemonade were formed when water vapor in the air lost enough energy to return to the liquid state. This process is called condensation.

Location of Molecules It takes more than speed for water molecules to escape the liquid state. During evaporation, these faster molecules also must be near the surface, heading in the right direction, and they must avoid hitting other water molecules as they leave. With the faster particles evaporating from the surface of a liquid, the particles that remain are the slower, cooler ones. Evaporation cools the liquid and anything near the liquid. You experience this cooling effect when perspiration evaporates from your skin.

Condensation Pour a nice, cold glass of lemonade and place it on the table for a half hour on a warm day. When you come back to take a drink, the outside of the glass will be covered by drops of water, as shown in **Figure 13.** What happened? As a gas cools, its particles slow down. When particles move slowly enough for their attractions to bring them together, droplets of liquid form. This process, which is the opposite of vaporization, is called **condensation.** As a gas condenses to a liquid, it releases the thermal energy it absorbed to become a gas. During this process, the temperature of the substance does not change. The decrease in energy changes the arrangement of particles. After the change of state is complete, the temperature continues to drop, as you saw in **Figure 11.**

✓ **Reading Check** *What energy change occurs during condensation?*

Condensation formed the droplets of water on the outside of your glass of lemonade. In the same way, water vapor in the atmosphere condenses to form the liquid water droplets in clouds. When the droplets become large enough, they can fall to the ground as rain.

Science Online

Topic: Condensation
Visit ips.msscience.com for Web links to information about how condensation is involved in weather.

Activity Find out how condensation is affected by the temperature as well as the amount of water in the air.

Teacher FYI

Refrigerant Cycle Refrigerators take advantage of temperature changes caused by the condensation and evaporation of refrigerant, which is carried through a series of pipes in the refrigerator. Refrigerant absorbs heat from inside the refrigerator and vaporizes. This process cools food. The refrigerant is then piped to the back of the refrigerator where it releases its heat to the surrounding air and condenses back into a liquid. The cycle then repeats.

✓ **Reading Check**

Answer During condensation, a gas releases energy as its particles become more ordered.

Visual Learning

Figure 13 Have students describe the various places that heat transfer is occurring in **Figure 13.** L2
IS Visual-Spatial

Quick Demo

Condensation
Materials hot plate, beaker, water, small mirror, thermal mitt
Estimated Time 10 minutes
Procedure Place a beaker half to three-quarters full of water on a hot plate. Have the water heating on a high temperature, but not boiling before the students arrive. Increase the temperature so that the water boils. While wearing the thermal mitt, hold the mirror over the boiling beaker. Hold this position until there is condensation on the mirror. Have the students explain condensation in terms of energy loss and gain.

Curriculum Connection

Geography Have students research how changes of state contribute to the formation of deserts near the Tropic of Cancer. Ask students to make posters with diagrams illustrating their findings. Warm moist air from the equator rises and flows northward and southward. As this moist air cools it loses its moisture. This dry air then descends over the Tropics of Capricorn and Cancer pulling moisture out of the ground by evaporation and drying out the land. This pattern has produced a belt of deserts along the Tropics of Capricorn and Cancer. L2 **IS** Linguistic

DAILY INTERVENTION

Check for Understanding

Logical-Mathematical If you have an automatic ice-cube maker in your freezer, you may have noticed that the older ice cubes at the bottom of the tray are much smaller than the newer cubes at the top. Use what you have learned to explain why. The faster molecules on the surface of an ice cube can escape from the cube and become a gas. Over time, the ice cube will completely sublimate away. L2 LS

Reteach

Evaporation and Boiling Have students explain the difference between evaporation and boiling. Boiling occurs when particles below the surface of a liquid change from liquid to gas. Evaporation occurs when particles at the surface of a liquid change from liquid to gas. L2 LS **Logical-Mathematical**

☑ Assessment

Oral Have students hypothesize what would happen if the unknown substance from the Launch Lab were reheated. The substance would melt at the same temperature at which it froze. The temperature would remain constant while the substance was melting, then increase gradually. Use **Performance Assessment in the Science Classroom,** p. 93.

Figure 14 The solid carbon dioxide (dry ice) at the bottom of this beaker of water is changing directly into gaseous carbon dioxide. This process is called sublimation.

Changes Between the Solid and Gas States

Some substances can change from the solid state to the gas state without ever becoming a liquid. During this process, known as sublimation, the surface particles of the solid gain enough energy to become a gas. One example of a substance that undergoes sublimation is dry ice. Dry ice is the solid form of carbon dioxide. It often is used to keep materials cold and dry. At room temperature and pressure, carbon dioxide does not exist as a liquid. Therefore, as dry ice absorbs thermal energy from the objects around it, it changes directly into a gas. When dry ice becomes a gas, it absorbs thermal energy from water vapor in the air. As a result, the water vapor cools and condenses into liquid water droplets, forming the fog you see in **Figure 14.**

section 2 review

Summary

Thermal Energy and Heat
- Thermal energy depends on the amount of the substance and the kinetic energy of particles in the substance.
- Heat is the movement of thermal energy from a warmer substance to a cooler one.

Specific Heat
- Specific heat is a measure of the amount of energy required to raise 1 g of a substance 1°C.

Changes Between Solid and Liquid States
- During all changes of state, the temperature of a substance stays the same.

Changes Between Liquid and Gas States
- Vaporization is the change from the liquid state to a gaseous state.
- Condensation is the change from the gaseous state to the liquid state.

Changes Between Solid and Gas States
- Sublimation is the process of a substance going from the solid state to the gas state without ever being in the liquid state.

Self Check

1. **Describe** how thermal energy and temperature are similar. How are they different?
2. **Explain** how a change in thermal energy causes matter to change from one state to another. Give two examples.
3. **List** the three changes of state during which energy is absorbed.
4. **Describe** the two types of vaporization.
5. **Think Critically** How can the temperature of a substance remain the same even if the substance is absorbing thermal energy?
6. **Write** a paragraph in your Science Journal that explains why you can step out of the shower into a warm bathroom and begin to shiver.

Applying Math

7. **Make and Use Graphs** Use the data you collected in the Launch Lab to plot a temperature-time graph. Describe your graph. At what temperature does the graph level off? What was the liquid doing during this time period?
8. **Use Numbers** If sample A requires 10 calories to raise the temperature of a 1-g sample 1°C, how many calories does it take to raise a 5-g sample 10°C?

Science Online ips.msscience.com/self_check_quiz

section 2 review

1. Thermal energy is the total amount of energy contained in a body whereas temperature measures the average kinetic energy of the particles in the body. Both deal with quantities of energy.
2. As thermal energy changes, the kinetic energy of the particles changes. If their kinetic energy increases, particles can overcome the attractive forces holding them together. If their kinetic energy decreases, particles can become subject to the forces pulling them together. Examples will vary.
3. melting, vaporization, and sublimation
4. Boiling occurs when particles below the surface of a liquid change from liquid to gas. Evaporation occurs when particles at the surface of a liquid change from liquid to gas.
5. The temperature remains the same because the absorbed energy is being used to break attractive forces between the particles of a substance as it changes state.
6. The water on your skin absorbs heat from your body and evaporates.
7. Check students' work. Sample data can be found in the teacher margin of the Launch Lab. Answers may vary, but should be near 69.5°C. The liquid was freezing during this time period.
8. specific heat = cal/(g × °C); 10 cal/(1 g × 1°C) = x cal/(5 g × 10°C), therefore x = 500 cal

The Water Cycle

Water is all around us and you've used water in all three of its common states. This lab will give you the opportunity to observe the three states of matter and to discover for yourself if ice really melts at 0°C and if water boils at 100°C.

● Real-World Question

How does the temperature of water change as it is heated from a solid to a gas?

Goals

■ **Measure** the temperature of water as it heats.
■ **Observe** what happens as the water changes from one state to another.
■ **Graph** the temperature and time data.

Materials

hot plate
ice cubes (100 mL)
Celsius thermometer
*electronic
    temperature probe
wall clock

*watch with
    second hand
stirring rod
250-mL beaker
*Alternate materials

Safety Precautions

● Procedure

1. Make a data table similar to the table shown.
2. Put 150 mL of water and 100 mL of ice into the beaker and place the beaker on the hot plate. Do not touch the hot plate.
3. Put the thermometer into the ice/water mixture. Do not stir with the thermometer or allow it to rest on the bottom of the beaker. After 30 s, read and record the temperature in your data table.

Characteristics of Water Sample		
Time (min)	Temperature (°C)	Physical State
	Answers will vary.	

4. Plug in the hot plate and turn the temperature knob to the medium setting.
5. Every 30 s, read and record the temperature and physical state of the water until it begins to boil. Use the stirring rod to stir the contents of the beaker before making each temperature measurement. Stop recording. Allow the water to cool.

● Analyze Your Data

Use your data to make a graph plotting time on the x-axis and temperature on the y-axis. Draw a smooth curve through the data points.

● Conclude and Apply

1. **Describe** how the temperature of the ice/water mixture changed as you heated the beaker.
2. **Describe** the shape of the graph during any changes of state.

Communicating
Your Data

Add labels to your graph. Use the detailed graph to explain to your class how water changes state. **For more help, refer to the Science Skill Handbook.**

LAB **115**

● Real-World Question

Purpose Students observe the solid and liquid states of water.
L1 LS **Kinesthetic**

Process Skills measure, observe, make and use tables, use numbers, make and use graphs, infer

Time 30 minutes

● Procedure

Alternate Materials electronic temperature probe

Safety Precautions Caution students not to use the thermometer as a stirrer or allow it to rest on the bottom of the beaker during heating.

Teaching Strategy Crushed ice or small pieces will give quicker results.

● Analyze Your Data

Expected Outcome Students' graphs should show increasing temperature until a change of state occurs and then be level until the next change of state.

● Conclude and Apply

1. The temperature increased, stayed the same for a period of time, then increased again.
2. During changes of state, the graph leveled off.

☑ Assessment

Content How would the graphs change if twice as much ice were used? The temperature would rise more slowly and the plateau would be longer. Use **Performance Assessment in the Science Classroom,** p. 101. LS **Logical-Mathematical**

Communicating
Your Data

Encourage students to compare graphs with other students and discuss possible reasons for inconsistent data.

as you read

What You'll Learn

- **Explain** why some things float but others sink.
- **Describe** how pressure is transmitted through fluids.

Why It's Important

Pressure enables you to squeeze toothpaste from a tube, and buoyant force helps you float in water.

Review Vocabulary

force: a push or pull

New Vocabulary

- pressure
- buoyant force
- Archimedes' principle
- density
- Pascal's principle

Pressure

It's a beautiful summer day when you and your friends go outside to play volleyball, much like the kids in **Figure 15.** There's only one problem—the ball is flat. You pump air into the ball until it is firm. The firmness of the ball is the result of the motion of the air particles in the ball. As the air particles in the ball move, they collide with one another and with the inside walls of the ball. As each particle collides with the inside walls, it exerts a force, pushing the surface of the ball outward. A force is a push or a pull. The forces of all the individual particles add together to make up the pressure of the air.

Pressure is equal to the force exerted on a surface divided by the total area over which the force is exerted.

$$\text{pressure} = \frac{\text{force}}{\text{area}}$$

When force is measured in newtons (N) and area is measured in square meters (m^2), pressure is measured in newtons per square meter (N/m^2). This unit of pressure is called a pascal (Pa). A more useful unit when discussing atmospheric pressure is the kilopascal (kPa), which is 1,000 pascals.

Figure 15 Without the pressure of air inside this volleyball, the ball would be flat.

Figure 16 The force of the dancer's weight on pointed toes results in a higher pressure than the same force on flat feet. **Explain** *why the pressure is higher.*

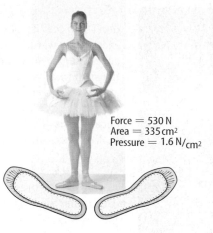

Force = 530 N
Area = 335 cm²
Pressure = 1.6 N/cm²

Force = 530 N
Area = 37 cm²
Pressure = 14 N/cm²

Force and Area You can see from the equation on the opposite page that pressure depends on the quantity of force exerted and the area over which the force is exerted. As the force increases over a given area, pressure increases. If the force decreases, the pressure will decrease. However, if the area changes, the same amount of force can result in different pressure. **Figure 16** shows that if the force of the ballerina's weight is exerted over a smaller area, the pressure increases. If that same force is exerted over a larger area, the pressure will decrease.

☑ **Reading Check** *What variables does pressure depend on?*

Atmospheric Pressure You can't see it and you usually can't feel it, but the air around you presses on you with tremendous force. The pressure of air also is known as atmospheric pressure because air makes up the atmosphere around Earth. Atmospheric pressure is 101.3 kPa at sea level. This means that air exerts a force of about 101,000 N on every square meter it touches. This is approximately equal to the weight of a large truck.

It might be difficult to think of air as having pressure when you don't notice it. However, you often take advantage of air pressure without even realizing it. Air pressure, for example, enables you to drink from a straw. When you first suck on a straw, you remove the air from it. As you can see in **Figure 17,** air pressure pushes down on the liquid in your glass then forces liquid up into the straw. If you tried to drink through a straw inserted into a sealed, airtight container, you would not have any success because the air would not be able to push down on the surface of the drink.

Figure 17 The downward pressure of air pushes the juice up into the straw.

Air pressure

SECTION 3 Behavior of Fluids **117**

Caption Answer
Figure 16 The area is different.

☑ **Reading Check**

Answer force and area

Visual Learning

Figure 17 Have students explain how a drinking straw works. Sucking on the straw creates a difference between the air pressure on the liquid in the cup and the air pressure on the liquid in the straw. The higher pressure outside the straw pushes the liquid up the straw. L2 IS **Visual-Spatial**

Discussion

Snow Skis and Snowshoes How does using snow skis or snowshoes enable a person to ski or walk on soft snow? The skis or snowshoes distribute the force of the person's weight over a larger area, decreasing the pressure exerted on the surface of the snow. L2 IS **Logical-Mathematical**

Science Journal

Pressure Applied Have each student make a drawing of a balloon in his or her Science Journal and show the molecular forces that are keeping the balloon inflated. Ask students to include captions that explain why the balloon stays inflated. After completing the section, have students compare their drawings and explanations with **Figure 19.** L2 IS **Visual-Spatial** P

Figure 18 Atmospheric pressure exerts a force on all surfaces of this dancer's body.
Explain *why she can't feel this pressure.*

Balanced Pressure If air is so forceful, why don't you feel it? The reason is that the pressure exerted outward by the fluids in your body balances the pressure exerted by the atmosphere on the surface of your body. Look at **Figure 18.** The atmosphere exerts a pressure on all surfaces of the dancer's body. She is not crushed by this pressure because the fluids in her body exert a pressure that balances atmospheric pressure.

Variations in Atmospheric Pressure

Atmospheric pressure changes with altitude. Altitude is the height above sea level. As altitude increases atmospheric pressure decreases. This is because fewer air particles are found in a given volume. Fewer particles have fewer collisions, and therefore exert less pressure. This idea was tested in the seventeenth century by a French physician named Blaise Pascal. He designed an experiment in which he filled a balloon only partially with air. He then had the balloon carried to the top of a mountain. **Figure 19** shows that as Pascal predicted, the balloon expanded while being carried up the mountain. Although the amount of air inside the balloon stayed the same, the air pressure pushing in on it from the outside decreased. Consequently, the particles of air inside the balloon were able to spread out further.

Figure 19 Notice how the balloon expands as it is carried up the mountain. The reason is that atmospheric pressure decreases with altitude. With less pressure pushing in on the balloon, the gas particles within the balloon are free to expand.

118 CHAPTER 4 States of Matter

Air Travel If you travel to higher altitudes, perhaps flying in an airplane or driving up a mountain, you might feel a popping sensation in your ears. As the air pressure drops, the air pressure in your ears becomes greater than the air pressure outside your body. The release of some of the air trapped inside your ears is heard as a pop. Airplanes are pressurized so that the air pressure within the cabin does not change dramatically throughout the course of a flight.

Changes in Gas Pressure

In the same way that atmospheric pressure can vary as conditions change, the pressure of gases in confined containers also can change. The pressure of a gas in a closed container changes with volume and temperature.

Pressure and Volume If you squeeze a portion of a filled balloon, the remaining portion of the balloon becomes more firm. By squeezing it, you decrease the volume of the balloon, forcing the same number of gas particles into a smaller space. As a result, the particles collide with the walls more often, thereby producing greater pressure. This is true as long as the temperature of the gas remains the same. You can see the change in the motion of the particles in **Figure 20.** What will happen if the volume of a gas increases? If you make a container larger without changing its temperature, the gas particles will collide less often and thereby produce a lower pressure.

Figure 20 As volume decreases, pressure increases.

As the piston is moved down, the gas particles have less space and collide more often. The pressure increases.

Mini LAB

Predicting a Waterfall

Procedure
1. Fill a **plastic cup** to the brim with **water.**
2. Cover the top of the cup with an **index card.**
3. Predict what will happen if you turn the cup upside down.
4. While holding the index card in place, turn the cup upside down over a sink. Then let go of the card.

Analysis
1. What happened to the water when you turned the cup?
2. How can you explain your observation in terms of the concept of fluid pressure?

Try at Home

Mini LAB

Purpose to observe how air pressure produces enough force to hold water in a cup [L2] **ELL** **COOP LEARN** **IS** **Kinesthetic**

Materials plastic cup, water, index card

Teaching Strategy Tell students to try not to let any water out of the cup as they turn it over.

Troubleshooting The card must be able to make a tight seal with the cup in order for this experiment to work. Any cup used should have a continuously smooth rim.

Analysis
1. The water remained in the cup.
2. The pressure of the molecules in the air pushing up on the card was greater than the pressure of the water pushing down on the card.

Assessment

Process Ask students to form a hypothesis concerning what will happen if some air is included in the cup. Have them try the experiment. As long as the cup contains enough water to make a seal between the rim and the card, the card will remain in place. Use **Performance Assessment in the Science Classroom,** p. 93.

Try at Home

Fun Fact

Relationships between temperature, pressure, and volume in a gas sample were defined by Jacques Charles and Robert Boyle. Charles's law relates temperature and volume. Boyle's law relates pressure and volume.

Warming Gas Provide students with balloons. Have them blow up the balloons and tie them shut. Ask each student to measure the circumference of his or her balloon at its widest point, then hold it over a lit lightbulb for a few minutes and measure the circumference again. What happened to the balloon as it was warmed by the lightbulb? The gas particles inside it started moving faster, pushing out on the balloon and causing it to expand. Extend the activity by placing one or two balloons in the freezer for a short while. L2

LS **Kinesthetic**

Caption Answer

Figure 21 The container will explode.

✔ Reading Check

Answer As temperature decreases, pressure decreases. This makes the pressure inside the container lower than the pressure outside the container. The external pressure pushes the container inward.

Discussion

Buoyant Force What do you think will happen if the buoyant force in a fluid is equal to the weight of an object in it? The object will remain suspended in the fluid, neither rising nor falling. L3 **LS** **Logical-Mathematical**

Quick Demo

Cartesian Diver

Materials beaker, squeeze condiment packet such as ketchup or soy sauce, empty 2-L bottle with cap, water

Estimated Time 15 minutes

Procedure Fill a beaker with water. Place several types of unopened condiment packets in the water. The one that barely floats will be used for the next step. Fill the 2-L bottle with water to the very top of the bottle. Insert the unopened condiment packet from the first step. Replace the cap on the bottle. Squeezing the bottle will make the condiment packet sink to the bottom. Release the bottle and the packet rises.

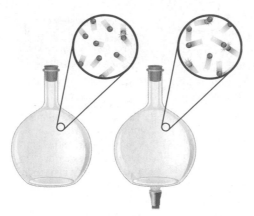

Figure 21 Even though the volume of this container does not change, the pressure increases as the substance is heated.
Describe *what will happen if the substance is heated too much.*

Figure 22 The pressure pushing up on an immersed object is greater than the pressure pushing down on it. This difference results in the buoyant force.

Pressure and Temperature When the volume of a confined gas remains the same, the pressure can change as the temperature of the gas changes. You have learned that temperature rises as the kinetic energy of the particles in a substance increases. The greater the kinetic energy is, the faster the particles move. The faster the speed of the particles is, the more they collide and the greater the pressure is. If the temperature of a confined gas increases, the pressure of the gas will increase, as shown in **Figure 21.**

✔ Reading Check
Why would a sealed container of air be crushed after being frozen?

Float or Sink

You may have noticed that you feel lighter in water than you do when you climb out of it. While you are under water, you experience water pressure pushing on you in all directions. Just as air pressure increases as you walk down a mountain, water pressure increases as you swim deeper in water. Water pressure increases with depth. As a result, the pressure pushing up on the bottom of an object is greater than the pressure pushing down on it because the bottom of the object is deeper than the top.

The difference in pressure results in an upward force on an object immersed in a fluid, as shown in **Figure 22.** This force is known as the **buoyant force.** If the buoyant force is equal to the weight of an object, the object will float. If the buoyant force is less than the weight of an object, the object will sink.

Pressure pushing down

Pressure pushing up

Weight

Buoyant force

Weight is a force in the downward direction. The buoyant force is in the upward direction. An object will float if the upward force is equal to the downward force.

Differentiated Instruction

Challenge Have students construct a neutrally buoyant helium balloon and gondola—one that has the same density as air. When you test the balloon, make sure there are no drafts in the room. Students will have succeeded if the balloon and gondola remain stationary between the ceiling and floor of a room for several minutes or if they ascend or descend slowly. L3 **LS** **Kinesthetic**

Archimedes' Principle What determines the buoyant force? According to **Archimedes'** (ar kuh MEE deez) **principle**, the buoyant force on an object is equal to the weight of the fluid displaced by the object. In other words, if you place an object in a beaker that already is filled to the brim with water, some water will spill out of the beaker, as in **Figure 23**. If you weigh the spilled water, you will find the buoyant force on the object.

Density Understanding density can help you predict whether an object will float or sink. **Density** is mass divided by volume.

$$\text{density} = \frac{\text{mass}}{\text{volume}}$$

An object will float in a fluid that is more dense than itself and sink in a fluid that is less dense than itself. If an object has the same density, the object will neither sink nor float but instead stay at the same level in the fluid.

Figure 23 When the golf ball was dropped in the large beaker, it displaced some of the water, which was collected and placed into the smaller beaker. **Communicate** *what you know about the weight and the volume of the displaced water.*

Applying Math   Find an Unknown

CALCULATING DENSITY You are given a sample of a solid that has a mass of 10.0 g and a volume of 4.60 cm³. Will it float in liquid water, which has a density of 1.00 g/cm³?

Solution

1 *This is what you know:*
- mass = 10.0 g
- volume = 4.60 cm³
- density of water = 1.00 g/cm³

2 *This is what you need to find:* the density of the sample

3 *This is the procedure you need to use:*
- density = mass/volume
- density = 10.0 g/4.60 cm³ = 2.17 g/cm³
- The density of the sample is greater than the density of water. The sample will sink.

4 *Check your answer:*
- Find the mass of your sample by multiplying the density and the volume.

Practice Problems

1. A 7.40-cm³ sample of mercury has a mass of 102 g. Will it float in water?
2. A 5.0-cm³ sample of aluminum has a mass of 13.5 g. Will it float in water?

Science Online   For more practice, visit ips.msscience.com/ math_practice

Activity

Soft-Drink Mass Obtain unopened aluminum cans of regular and diet versions of a soft drink. Show the class that the volumes of the cans are equal. Have students predict what will happen when the cans are placed in a sink or aquarium filled with water. Place the cans into the water and observe. The can of diet drink floats, while the can of regular drink sinks. Divide the class in half and have each group measure the masses of the cans with a balance. Ask how the masses compare. The regular drink is heavier. Discuss with students the idea that equal volumes of different substances can have different masses. Explain that the difference in mass is due to sugar. L2 ELL LS Kinesthetic

Applying Math

National Math Standards
Correlation to Mathematics Objectives
1, 6, 7

Teaching Strategy

This is what you know: mass = 102 g, volume = 7.40 cm³, density of water = 1.00 g/cm³

This is what you need to find: density of the sample.

This is the equation you need to use: density = mass/volume

Substitute in the known values: density = 102 g/7.40 cm³ = 13.78 g/cm³

Answers to Practice Problems

1. No; the density of mercury, which is 13.8 g/cm³, is greater than the density of water.
2. No; density of aluminum, which is 2.7 g/cm³, is greater than the density of water.

Curriculum Connection

History Archimedes was one of history's most gifted mathematicians. He very nearly invented calculus, but did not have the notation to describe his ideas. According to legend, he came to an unfortunate end when he yelled at an invading Roman soldier for ruining calculations he was writing in the dirt. The unappreciative soldier killed him with his sword. Have students find out when Archimedes lived. 287–212 B.C. L2

Differentiated Instruction

Learning Disabled Demonstrate to students how density affects the buoyant force. Have two beakers full of the same amount of water. In one beaker add pieces of styrofoam. In the other add several pennies. Ask students to explain why the styrofoam floated, but the pennies sank.

Purpose to explore and observe density by making miniature lava lamps

Possible Materials glass jar or clear drinking glass, vegetable oil, salt, water, food coloring

Estimated Time 20 minutes

Teaching Strategies

• Students make simple lava lamps by pouring about 7.5 cm of water in the bottom of the jar. Then have them pour about 78 mL of vegetable oil into the jar. Add food coloring.

• Students should shake salt on top of oil while slowly counting to 5.

Observe

What happened when salt is added to the oil? Salt is more dense than water. When salt is poured on the oil, it sinks to the bottom of the mixture, carrying some of the oil with it. In the water layer, the salt starts to dissolve. As it dissolves, the oil is released and floats back up to the top of the water.

For additional inquiry activities, see
Science Inquiry Labs.

Discussion

Ear Pressure Challenge students to use Pascal's principle to explain why their ears may hurt when they swim to the bottom of the deepest part of a swimming pool. The weight of the water above makes the pressure at the bottom of the pool greater than that at the surface. L2

Figure 24 A hydraulic lift utilizes Pascal's principle to help lift this car and this dentist's chair.

Pascal's Principle

What happens if you squeeze a plastic container filled with water? If the container is closed, the water has nowhere to go. As a result, the pressure in the water increases by the same amount everywhere in the container—not just where you squeeze or near the top of the container. When a force is applied to a confined fluid, an increase in pressure is transmitted equally to all parts of the fluid. This relationship is known as **Pascal's principle**.

Hydraulic Systems You witness Pascal's principle when a car is lifted up to have its oil changed or if you are in a dentist's chair as it is raised or lowered, as shown in **Figure 24.** These devices, known as hydraulic (hi DRAW lihk) systems, use Pascal's principle to increase force. Look at the tube in **Figure 25.** The force applied to the piston on the left increases the pressure within the fluid. That increase in pressure is transmitted to the piston on the right. Recall that pressure is equal to force divided by area. You can solve for force by multiplying pressure by area.

$$\text{pressure} = \frac{\text{force}}{\text{area}} \quad \text{or} \quad \text{force} = \text{pressure} \times \text{area}$$

If the two pistons on the tube have the same area, the force will be the same on both pistons. If, however, the piston on the right has a greater surface area than the piston on the left, the resulting force will be greater. The same pressure multiplied by a larger area equals a greater force. Hydraulic systems enable people to lift heavy objects using relatively small forces.

Figure 25 By increasing the area of the piston on the right side of the tube, you can increase the force exerted on the piston. In this way a small force pushing down on the left piston can result in a large force pushing up on the right piston. The force can be great enough to lift a car.

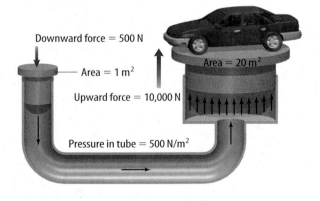

Downward force = 500 N

Area = 1 m²

Upward force = 10,000 N

Area = 20 m²

Pressure in tube = 500 N/m²

Cultural Diversity

Force Pumps Simple piston-type force pumps were known throughout the ancient world. The more efficient double-acting piston bellows were developed by the Chinese, and did not reach Europe until the 1500s. In this device, fluid is pulled in through intake valves on either side and pushed out through a nozzle on both strokes of the piston.

Visual Learning

Figure 25 Review with students the process shown in this figure. Remind students that work equals force times distance. In a hydraulic lift, the force applied to the smaller piston is small, but it is applied over a long distance, so the work done on each side of the lift is the same. L2 **LS** **Visual-Spatial**

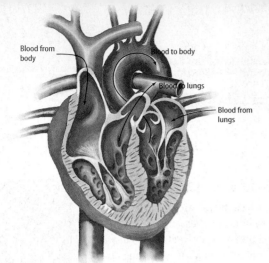

Figure 26 The heart is responsible for moving blood throughout the body. Two force pumps work together to move blood to and from the lungs and to the rest of the body.

Force Pumps If an otherwise closed container has a hole in it, any fluid in the container will be pushed out the opening when you squeeze it. This arrangement, known as a force pump, makes it possible for you to squeeze toothpaste out of a tube or mustard from a plastic container.

 Your heart has two force pumps. One pump pushes blood to the lungs, where it picks up oxygen. The other force pump pushes the oxygen-rich blood to the rest of your body. These pumps are shown in **Figure 26.**

Science Online

Topic: Blood Pressure
Visit ips.msscience.com for Web links to information about blood pressure. Find out what the term means, how it changes throughout the human body, and why it is unhealthy to have high blood pressure.

Activity Write a paragraph in your Science Journal that explains why high blood pressure is dangerous.

---

section 3 review

Summary

Pressure
- Pressure depends on force and area.
- The air around you exerts a pressure.
- The pressure inside your body matches the pressure exerted by air.

Changes in Gas Pressure
- The pressure exerted by a gas depends on its volume and its temperature.

Float or Sink
- Whether an object floats or sinks depends on its density relative to the density of the fluid it's in.

Pascal's Principle
- This principle relates pressure and area to force.

Self Check

1. **Describe** what happens to pressure as the force exerted on a given area increases.
2. **Describe** how atmospheric pressure changes as altitude increases.
3. **State** Pascal's principle in your own words.
4. **Infer** An object floats in a fluid. What can you say about the buoyant force on the object?
5. **Think Critically** All the air is removed from a sealed metal can. After the air has been removed, the can looks as if it were crushed. Why?

Applying Math

6. **Simple Equations** What pressure is created when 5.0 N of force are applied to an area of 2.0 m²? How does the pressure change if the force is increased to 10.0 N? What about if instead the area is decreased to 1.0 m²?

DAILY INTERVENTION

Check for Understanding

Logical-Mathematical Have students predict what would happen if a rock punched a small hole in the bottom of an airtight compartment in a ship. As long as no air escaped, the pressure of the air in the compartment would allow little water into the compartment. L3 LS

Reteach

Fluids Organize the class into four groups. Assign each group pressure, density, Archimedes' principle, or Pascal's principle. Have each group present to the class its understanding of the assigned term. Each group should be able to define the term and give examples illustrating it. L2 COOP LEARN LS **Interpersonal**

Assessment

Process Place a beaker of water, a beaker of alcohol, and a beaker of ethylene glycol in front of the class. Challenge students to use buoyancy to put the liquids in order from lowest density to highest density. Students may immerse objects in the liquids to determine the relative densities of the liquids. Use **Performance Assessment in the Science Classroom,** p. 97.

---

section 3 review

1. Pressure increases.
2. Atmospheric pressure decreases.
3. When a force is applied to a confined fluid, an increase in pressure is transmitted equally to all parts of the fluid.
4. The buoyant force is greater than the weight of the object.
5. After the air is removed, the atmospheric pressure on the outside of the can is greater than the pressure on the inside of the can, so the can collapses.
6. 2.5 Pa; the pressure increases to 5 Pa. If the force is 5.0 N and the area is decreased to 1.0 m², the pressure increases to 5 Pa.

Design Your Own

● Real-World Question

Purpose Students apply Archimedes' principle to shipbuilding.

IS Logical-Mathematical

Process Skills observe and infer, design an experiment to test a hypothesis, interpret data, separate and control variables, predict, use numbers

Time Required 90 minutes

Materials balance, 2 small plastic cups, graduated cylinder, metric ruler, scissors, marbles, sink

Alternate Materials basin, pan, or bucket

● Form a Hypothesis

Possible Hypothesis Students might hypothesize that a boat floats when the displaced water weighs the same as or more than the boat and its cargo.

● Test Your Hypothesis

Possible Procedure Find the mass of the cup and the marbles. Use the density of water (1.00 g/mL) to calculate the volume of water that has the same mass as the cup and marbles, which is the volume of water the boat must displace. Fill the cup with the amount of water that has the same mass as the cup and marbles. Draw a line around the cup at the water line, empty the water, trim the cup to size, and dry the cup. Put the cup into the water in the sink or basin and carefully load the marbles and the trimmed pieces of cup into the floating cup.

Design Your ⚓wn Ship

● Real-World Question

It is amazing to watch ships that are taller than buildings float easily on water. Passengers and cargo are carried on these ships in addition to the tremendous weight of the ship itself. How can you determine the size of a ship needed to keep a certain mass of cargo afloat?

● Form a Hypothesis

Think about Archimedes' principle and how it relates to buoyant force. Form a hypothesis to explain how the volume of water displaced by a ship relates to the mass of cargo the ship can carry.

● Test Your Hypothesis

Make a Plan

1. Obtain a set of marbles or other items from your teacher. This is the cargo that your ship must carry. Think about the type of ship

Cargo ship

Goals

■ **Design** an experiment that uses Archimedes' principle to determine the size of ship needed to carry a given amount of cargo in such a way that the top of the ship is even with the surface of the water.

Possible Materials

balance
small plastic cups (2)
graduated cylinder
metric ruler
scissors
marbles (cupful)
sink
*basin, pan, or bucket
*Alternate materials

Safety Precautions

Alternative Inquiry Lab

Explore Further To extend this Lab into an Inquiry Lab, have students think of similarities and differences between designing a water boat and an airship. What would an airship be filled with? lighter-than-air gases or hot air, like a hot air balloon What shape, material, and design differences are there?

Students may enjoy tracing the history of airships, including their role in World War II, researching the different kinds of airships and technologies used in their engineering and construction, and/or experimenting with commercial helium-filled balloons to see how much weight they can carry.

you will design. Consider the types of materials you will use. Decide how your group is going to test your hypothesis.

2. **List** the steps you need to follow to test your hypothesis. Include in your plan how you will measure the mass of your ship and cargo, calculate the volume of water your ship must displace in order to float with its cargo, and measure the volume and mass of the displaced water. Also, explain how you will design your ship so that it will float with the top of the ship even with the surface of the water. Make the ship.

3. **Prepare** a data table in your Science Journal to use as your group collects data. Think about what data you need to collect.

Follow Your Plan

1. Make sure your teacher approves your plan before you start.

2. Perform your experiment as planned. Be sure to follow all proper safety procedures. In particular, clean up any spilled water immediately.

3. Record your observations carefully and complete the data table in your Science Journal.

◑ *Analyze Your Data*

1. **Write** your calculations showing how you determined the volume of displaced water needed to make your ship and cargo float.

2. Did your ship float at the water's surface, sink, or float above the water's surface? Draw a diagram of your ship in the water.

3. **Explain** how your experimental results agreed or failed to agree with your hypothesis.

◑ *Conclude and Apply*

1. If your ship sank, how would you change your experiment or calculations to correct the problem? What changes would you make if your ship floated too high in the water?

2. What does the density of a ship's cargo have to do with the volume of cargo the ship can carry? What about the density of the water?

Communicating Your Data

Compare your results with other students' data. Prepare a combined data table or summary showing how the calculations affect the success of the ship. **For more help, refer to the** Science Skill Handbook.

LAB 125

☑ Assessment

Oral Have students explain why ships are designed to be taller than their anticipated cargo requires. If the ship has no excess height, waves could wash over the ship's side easily or excess cargo could be loaded onto the ship, sinking the ship. Use **Performance Assessment in the Science Classroom,** p. 89.

Communicating Your Data

Suggest students use a spreadsheet program for preparing combined data tables.

Teaching Strategies

- Before conducting the experiment, review density and its relationship to buoyancy.

- Students should not put the marbles into the boats until they are ready to test their boats.

Expected Outcome Students' data tables should include spaces for the mass of the cup and marbles, the volume of water the cup must displace, measurements of the cup, any calculations of the cup's volume, and the results of the experiment.

◑ *Analyze Your Data*

Answers to Questions

1. Typical calculations will involve relating the mass of the cargo and boat to the volume of the water displaced.

2. Results will vary.

3. Answers will vary, but should include the problems or successes that resulted when using their hypothesis.

Error Analysis

Students should explain why the boat sank or floated too high in the water and identify the problems.

◑ *Conclude and Apply*

1. Answers will vary. Either way, students should check their measurements and calculations.

2. A ship can carry only a certain mass of cargo safely. Therefore, the ship can carry less high-density cargo than low-density cargo. If the water density is greater than 1 g/mL, then the volume that the ship can carry will be less. If the water density is less, then the ship can carry more volume.

Content Background

Silicon is the second most abundant element in Earth's crust. Rubber is a natural carbon-based polymer that comes from trees. Polymers are large molecules made from many small molecules linked together. During World War II, scientists were trying to replace carbon in organic molecules such as rubber with silicon. Silicones are polymers made up of silicon atoms linked to oxygen atoms. Various organic compounds are often attached to the polymer to control and change its physical properties. Some silicones form rubbery elastic compounds, while others are designed to act as lubricants.

Activity

Make Your Own "Goo" Allow small groups of students to investigate how the addition of a compound can change the properties of a polymer. Dissolve 2 mL of borax in 125 mL of water in a beaker. Have students pour 15 mL of white glue (a polymer) into a paper cup. Then have them add 15 mL of the borax solution to the glue and stir it with a craft stick. The borax cross-links the glue polymers, making the resulting compound thicker and more rubbery. Tell students to remove the polymer from the cup and knead it for a few minutes. As a class, discuss the properties of the new polymer. **L2** **LS** **Kinesthetic**

Analyze the Event

Why do this? Ask students to brainstorm possible reasons scientists tried unusual experiments when working to come up with an inexpensive alternative to synthetic rubber.

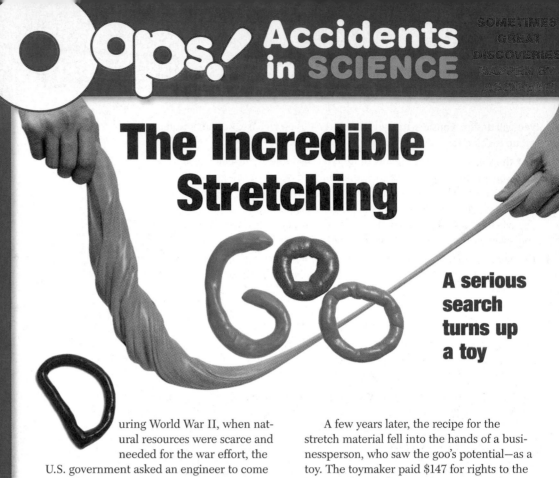

Oops! Accidents in SCIENCE

 SOMETIMES GREAT DISCOVERIES HAPPEN BY ACCIDENT!

The Incredible Stretching Goo

A serious search turns up a toy

During World War II, when natural resources were scarce and needed for the war effort, the U.S. government asked an engineer to come up with an inexpensive alternative to synthetic rubber. While researching the problem and looking for solutions, the engineer dropped boric acid into silicone oil. The result of these two substances mixing together was—a goo!

Because of its molecular structure, the goo could bounce and stretch in all directions. The engineer also discovered the goo could break into pieces. When strong pressure is applied to the substance, it reacts like a solid and breaks apart. Even though the combination was versatile—and quite amusing, the U.S. government decided the new substance wasn't a good substitute for synthetic rubber.

A few years later, the recipe for the stretch material fell into the hands of a businessperson, who saw the goo's potential—as a toy. The toymaker paid $147 for rights to the boric acid and silicone oil mixture. And in 1949 it was sold at toy stores for the first time. The material was packaged in a plastic egg and it took the U.S. by storm. Today, the acid and oil mixture comes in a multitude of colors and almost every child has played with it at some time.

The substance can be used for more than child's play. Its sticky consistency makes it good for cleaning computer keyboards and removing small specks of lint from fabrics.

People use it to make impressions of newspaper print or comics. Athletes strengthen their grips by grasping it over and over. Astronauts use it to anchor tools on spacecraft in zero gravity. All in all, a most *eggs-cellent* idea!

Research As a group, examine a sample of the colorful, sticky, stretch toy made of boric acid and silicone oil. Then brainstorm some practical—and impractical—uses for the substance.

Science nline

For more information, visit
ips.msscience.com/oops

Research Ask students in each group to describe the list of uses they came up with for the goo. Ask students in other groups to comment on whether or not they think the proposed uses would actually work. If possible, allow students to demonstrate some of the uses they brainstormed. **L2**

Resources for Teachers and Students

Super Science Concoctions, by Jill Frankel Hauser, Williamson Publishing, 1997

They All Laughed . . . From Light Bulbs to Lasers: The Fascinating Stories Behind Great Inventions That Have Changed Our Lives, by Ira Flatow, Harper Perennial, 1992

Reviewing Main Ideas

Section 1 Matter

1. All matter is composed of tiny particles that are in constant motion.

2. In the solid state, the attractive force between particles holds them in place to vibrate.

3. Particles in the liquid state have defined volumes and are free to move about within the liquid.

Section 2 Changes of State

1. Thermal energy is the total energy of the particles in a sample of matter. Temperature is the average kinetic energy of the particles in a sample.

2. An object gains thermal energy when it changes from a solid to a liquid, or when it changes from a liquid to a gas.

3. An object loses thermal energy when it changes from a gas to a liquid, or when it changes from a liquid to a solid.

Section 3 Behavior of Fluids

1. Pressure is force divided by area.

2. Fluids exert a buoyant force in the upward direction on objects immersed in them.

3. An object will float in a fluid that is more dense than itself.

4. Pascal's principle states that pressure applied to a liquid is transmitted evenly throughout the liquid.

Visualizing Main Ideas

Copy and complete the following concept map on matter.

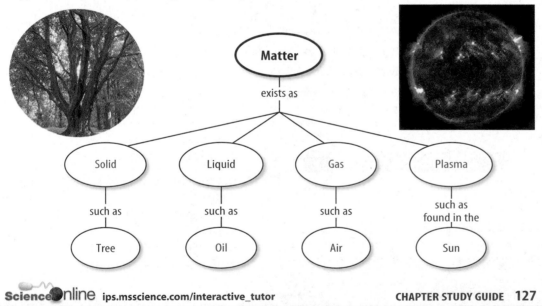

Matter exists as
- Solid — such as — Tree
- Liquid — such as — Oil
- Gas — such as — Air
- Plasma — such as found in the — Sun

Science Online ips.msscience.com/interactive_tutor

Reviewing Main Ideas

Summary statements can be used by students to review the major concepts of the chapter.

Visualizing Main Ideas

See student page.

Visit ips.msscience.com
/self_check_quiz
/interactive_tutor
/vocabulary_puzzlemaker
/chapter_review
/standardized_test

Assessment Transparency

For additional assessment questions, use the *Assessment Transparency* located in the transparency book.

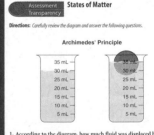

Assessment

States of Matter

Archimedes' Principle

1. According to the diagram, how much fluid was displaced by the ball?
   A 35 mL   C 10 mL
   B 30 mL   D 5 mL

2. Justine wanted to determine the amount of fluid other objects displaced in the beaker. Which observation would mean she could NOT measure this amount of fluid?
   F More than one object was in the beaker.
   G She removed some water to make more room for objects.
   H The water rose above the measurement markings.
   J She used a different size of beaker for each new object.

3. According to Archimedes' principle, the buoyant force on the ball equals the weight of ___.
   A 10 mL of fluid   C 35 mL of fluid
   B 30 mL of fluid   D 5 mL of fluid

◆ Identifying Misconceptions

Assess

Use the assessment as follow-up to page F at the beginning of the chapter after students have completed the chapter.

Materials paper, pencil

Procedure Have students work in groups to make cartoon posters of sporting events in which the Matter Team plays the Non-Matter Team. Students should choose a team sport and create each team. For instance in a baseball game there can be an Iron Infielder and Plastic Pitcher on the Matter Team and Light Left fielder and Kinetic Energy Catcher on the Non-Matter Team. L2

Expected Outcome Students should realize that matter includes solids, liquids, and gases and does not include types of energy.

Using Vocabulary

1. gas
2. liquid
3. Heat
4. Temperature
5. condensation
6. vaporization
7. Density
8. Pressure
9. Pascal's Principle

Checking Concepts

10. B	16. D
11. A	17. B
12. C	18. C
13. D	19. C
14. B	20. B
15. C	

Using Vocabulary

Archimedes' principle p. 121
buoyant force p. 120
condensation p. 113
density p. 121
freezing p. 111
gas p. 106
heat p. 108
liquid p. 104
matter p. 102

melting p. 109
Pascal's principle p. 122
pressure p. 116
solid p. 103
surface tension p. 105
temperature p. 108
thermal energy p. 107
vaporization p. 112
viscosity p. 105

Fill in the blanks with the correct vocabulary word.

1. A(n) _____ can change shape and volume.

2. A(n) _____ has a different shape but the same volume in any container.

3. _____ is thermal energy moving from one substance to another.

4. _____ is a measure of the average kinetic energy of the particles of a substance.

5. A substance changes from a gas to a liquid during the process of _____.

6. A liquid becomes a gas during _____.

7. _____ is mass divided by volume.

8. _____ is force divided by area.

9. _____ explains what happens when force is applied to a confined fluid.

Checking Concepts

Choose the word or phrase that best answers the question.

10. Which of these is a crystalline solid?
    A) glass
    C) rubber
    B) sugar
    D) plastic

11. Which description best describes a solid?
    A) It has a definite shape and volume.
    B) It has a definite shape but not a definite volume.
    C) It adjusts to the shape of its container.
    D) It can flow.

12. What property enables you to float a needle on water?
    A) viscosity
    C) surface tension
    B) temperature
    D) crystal structure

13. What happens to an object as its kinetic energy increases?
    A) It holds more tightly to nearby objects.
    B) Its mass increases.
    C) Its particles move more slowly.
    D) Its particles move faster.

14. During which process do particles of matter release energy?
    A) melting
    C) sublimation
    B) freezing
    D) boiling

15. How does water vapor in air form clouds?
    A) melting
    C) condensation
    B) evaporation
    D) sublimation

16. Which is a unit of pressure?
    A) N
    C) g/cm^3
    B) kg
    D) N/m^2

17. Which change results in an increase in gas pressure in a balloon?
    A) decrease in temperature
    B) decrease in volume
    C) increase in volume
    D) increase in altitude

18. In which case will an object float on a fluid?
    A) Buoyant force is greater than weight.
    B) Buoyant force is less than weight.
    C) Buoyant force equals weight.
    D) Buoyant force equals zero.

 Science online ips.msscience.com/vocabulary_puzzlemaker

Use the Exam*View*® Pro Testmaker CD-ROM to:
- create multiple versions of tests
- create modified tests with one mouse click for inclusion students
- edit existing questions and add your own questions
- build tests aligned with state standards using built-in State Curriculum Tags
- change English tests to Spanish with one mouse click and vice versa

Use the photo below to answer question 19.

19. In the photo above, the water in the small beaker was displaced when the golf ball was added to the large beaker. What principle does this show?
    A) Pascal's principle
    B) the principle of surface tension
    C) Archimedes' principle
    D) the principle of viscosity

20. Which is equal to the buoyant force on an object?
    A) volume of the object
    B) weight of the displaced fluid
    C) weight of object
    D) volume of fluid

Thinking Critically

21. **Explain** why steam causes more severe burns than boiling water.

22. **Explain** why a bathroom mirror becomes fogged while you take a shower.

23. **Form Operational Definitions** Write operational definitions that explain the properties of and differences among solids, liquids, and gases.

24. **Determine** A king's crown has a volume of 110 cm^3 and a mass of 1,800 g. The density of gold is 19.3 g/cm^3. Is the crown pure gold?

25. **Infer** Why do some balloons pop when they are left in sunlight for too long?

Science**Online** ips.msscience.com/chapter_review

Performance Activities

26. **Storyboard** Create a visual-aid storyboard to show ice changing to steam. There should be a minimum of five frames.

Applying Math

Use the graph below to answer question 27.

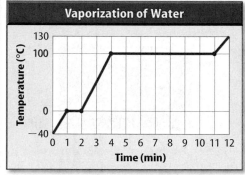

Vaporization of Water

27. **Explain** how this graph would change if a greater volume of water were heated. How would it stay the same?

Use the table below to answer question 28.

Water Pressure			
Depth (m)	Pressure (atm)	Depth (m)	Pressure (atm)
0	1.0	100	11.0
25	3.5	125	13.5
50	6.0	150	16.0
75	8.5	175	18.5

28. **Make and Use Graphs** In July of 2001, Yasemin Dalkilic of Turkey dove to a depth of 105 m without any scuba equipment. Make a depth-pressure graph for the data above. Based on your graph, how does water pressure vary with depth? Note: The pressure at sea level, 101.3 kPa, is called one atmosphere (atm).

CHAPTER REVIEW **129**

Thinking Critically

21. Steam contains more thermal energy than boiling water.

22. Some of the hot water from the shower evaporates into the air. It condenses on the mirror because the mirror is cooler than the air.

23. Solids are materials with particles that are very close together. Solids have a definite shape and volume and can be crystalline or amorphous. Liquids are materials in which particles are farther apart than in solids. The individual particles in liquids can flow past each other and have an attraction to each other that gives liquids viscosity and surface tension. Liquids have a definite volume and take the shape of their containers. Gases have particles that are very far apart, move quickly, and lack an attraction to each other. Gases have no definite shape or volume.

24. The density of the king's crown is 16.4 g/cm^3. The crown is not pure gold because its density is less than 19.3 g/cm^3.

25. The pressure of the gas inside the balloon increases as the air in the balloon heats up.

Performance Activities

26. Ice should change first to liquid water, then to steam as heat is added to the system and the water molecules move faster. Use **PASC,** p. 135.

Applying Math

National Math Standards
5, 10

27. The melting and boiling points would remain the same. However, the temperature would rise more slowly and the time required for melting and boiling would increase. Therefore, the slopes during the temperature increases would be less.

28. Water pressure increases as the depth increases.

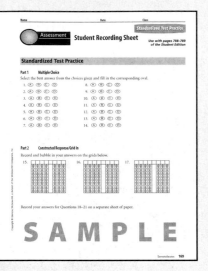

Answer Sheet A practice answer sheet can be found at ips.msscience.com/answer_sheet.

S A M P L E

Part 1 Multiple Choice

1. D
2. A
3. D
4. A
5. C
6. B
7. C
8. B
9. B

Part 2 Short Response

10. The helium will expand to occupy the volume and shape of the room.

11. The pressure she exerts is 1.52 N/cm² on the left and 13 N/cm² on the right.

12. Large clown shoes would increase the area over which she exerts force, so the force would be divided by a larger area, which would mean the pressure she exerted would be less.

Part 1 Multiple Choice

Record your answers on the answer sheet provided by your teacher or on a sheet of paper.

1. In which state of matter do particles stay close together, yet are able to move past one another?
   A. solid
   B. gas
   C. liquid
   D. plasma

Use the illustration below to answer questions 2 and 3.

2. Which statement is true about the volume of the water displaced when the golf ball was dropped into the large beaker?
   A. It is equal to the volume of the golf ball.
   B. It is greater than the volume of the golf ball.
   C. It is less than the volume of the golf ball.
   D. It is twice the volume of a golf ball.

3. What do you know about the buoyant force on the golf ball?
   A. It is equal to the density of the water displaced.
   B. It is equal to the volume of the water displaced.
   C. It is less than the weight of the water displaced.
   D. It is equal to the weight of the water displaced.

4. What is the process called when a gas cools to form a liquid?
   A. condensation
   B. sublimation
   C. boiling
   D. freezing

5. Which of the following is an amorphous solid?
   A. diamond
   B. sugar
   C. glass
   D. sand

6. Which description best describes a liquid?
   A. It has a definite shape and volume.
   B. It has a definite volume but not a definite shape.
   C. It expands to fill the shape and volume of its container.
   D. It cannot flow.

7. During which processes do particles of matter absorb energy?
   A. freezing and boiling
   B. condensation and melting
   C. melting and vaporization
   D. sublimation and freezing

Use the illustration below to answer questions 8 and 9.

8. What happens as the piston moves down?
   A. The volume of the gas increases.
   B. The volume of the gas decreases.
   C. The gas particles collide less often.
   D. The pressure of the gas decreases.

9. What relationship between the volume and pressure of a gas does this illustrate?
   A. As volume decreases, pressure decreases.
   B. As volume decreases, pressure increases.
   C. As volume decreases, pressure remains the same.
   D. As the volume increases, pressure remains the same.

130 STANDARDIZED TEST PRACTICE

13. The gas in the balloon will expand. As the temperature is increased, the particles of air in the balloon have more kinetic energy. They collide with one another more frequently and increase the pressure on the inside of the balloon.

14. Thermal energy is the total kinetic energy of all the particles in a sam-

ple of matter. Heat is the movement of thermal energy from a substance of higher energy to one of lower energy.

15. Attractive forces cause the particles on the surface of a liquid to pull themselves together and resist being pushed apart. This surface tension causes the water to act as

if a thin film were stretched across it surface. The insects are able to move around on this "film."

16. The upward buoyant force is equal to the downward force of the object's weight.

17. 12 g

Part 2 | Short Response/Grid In

Record your answers on the answer sheet provided by your teacher or on a sheet of paper.

10. A balloon filled with helium bursts in a closed room. What space will the helium occupy?

Use the illustration below to answer questions 11 and 12.

11. If the force exerted by the dancer is 510 N, what is the pressure she exerts if the area is 335 cm^2 on the left and 37 cm^2 on the right?

12. Compare the pressure the dancer would exert on the floor if she were wearing large clown shoes to the photo on the left.

13. If a balloon is blown up and tied closed, air is held inside it. What will happen to the balloon if it is then pushed into hot water or held over a heater? Why does this happen?

14. What is the relationship of heat and thermal energy?

15. Why are some insects able to move around on the surface of a lake or pond?

16. How does the weight of a floating object compare with the buoyant force acting on the object?

17. What is the mass of an object that has a density of 0.23 g/cm^3 and whose volume is 52 cm^3?

Part 3 | Open Ended

Record your answer on a sheet of paper.

18. Compare and contrast evaporation and boiling.

Use the illustration below to answer questions 19 and 20.

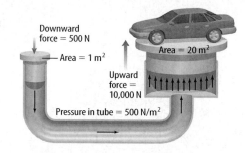

Downward force = 500 N
Area = 1 m^2
Area = 20 m^2
Upward force = 10,000 N
Pressure in tube = 500 N/m^2

19. Name and explain the principle that is used in lifting the car.

20. Explain what would happen if you doubled the area of the piston on the right side of the hydraulic system.

21. Explain why a woman might put dents in a wood floor when walking across it in high-heeled shoes, but not when wearing flat sandals.

22. Explain why the tires on a car might become flattened on the bottom after sitting outside in very cold weather.

23. Compare the arrangement and movement of the particles in a solid, a liquid, and a gas.

24. Explain why the water in a lake is much cooler than the sand on beach around it on a sunny summer day.

Test-Taking Tip

Show Your Work For open-ended questions, show all of your work and any calculations on your answer sheet.

Hint: In question 20, the pressure in the tube does not change.

21. High-heeled shoes have a smaller area than sandals do. The force the woman exerts on the floor would be greater when she is wearing high-heeled shoes than when she is wearing sandals. This greater force might be enough to put dents in the wood floor.

22. When the temperature of a confined gas decreases, the speed of the gas particles slow down and the less kinetic energy they have. The particles collide less, so they exert less pressure on the inside of the tire making the tire look flat instead of round.

23. Solid particles are very close together and vibrate in place. Liquid particles move more freely than solid particles and have enough energy to move from their fixed positions. Gas particles are much further apart than solid or liquid particles and spread out evenly as far apart as possible.

24. Water has a higher specific heat than sand does. It takes a much larger quantity of heat to make the temperature of the water rise as much as the sand. So the water heats up more slowly than the sand.

Rubrics

For more help evaluating open-ended assessment questions, see the rubric on p. 10T.

Part 3 | Open Ended

18. Both are forms of vaporization where a liquid changes to a gas. Evaporation is vaporization that takes place at the surface of a liquid and occurs at temperatures below the boiling point. Boiling is vaporization that takes place below the surface of a liquid. During boiling, bubbles form within the liquid and rise to the surface. Boiling takes place at a particular temperature called the boiling point of the liquid.

19. Pascal's principle is used in lifting the car. Pascal's principle says that when a force is applied to a confined fluid, an increase in pressure is transmitted equally to all parts of the fluid.

20. By doubling the area of the piston on the right side, the force exerted on the piston would also be doubled. This is because the pressure on the piston would still be 500 N/m^2, but the piston would have an area of 40 m^2. This means the force on the piston would be 500 N/m$^2 \times$ 40 m^2 or 20,000 N.

Section/Objectives	Standards		Labs/Features
Chapter Opener	**National**	**State/Local**	**Launch Lab:** Classifying different types of matter, p. 133 **Foldables,** p. 133
	See pp. 16T–17T for a Key to Standards.		
Section 1 Physical Properties • 3 sessions • 1.5 blocks 1. **Describe** the common physical properties of matter. 2. **Explain** how to find the density of a substance. 3. **Compare and contrast** the properties of acids and bases.	National Content Standards: UCP.1, UCP.2, UCP.3, UCP.5, A.1, A.2, B.1		**Applying Math:** Determining Density, p. 135 **MiniLAB:** Classifying Properties, p. 136 **Integrate Health,** p. 137 **Science Online,** p. 138
Section 2 Chemical Properties • 1 session • 1 block 4. **Describe** chemical properties of matter. 5. **Explain** the chemical properties of acids and bases. 6. **Explain** how a salt is formed.	National Content Standards: UCP.1, UCP.2, UCP.3, UCP.5, A.1, A.2, B.1		**Integrate Life Science,** p. 140
Section 3 Physical and Chemical Changes • 5 sessions • 2.5 blocks 7. **Identify** physical and chemical changes. 8. **Exemplify** how physical and chemical changes affect the world you live in.	National Content Standards: UCP.1, UCP.2, UCP.3, UCP.5, A.1, A.2, B.1		**MiniLAB:** Comparing Chemical Changes, p. 145 **Science Online,** p. 146 **Integrate Career,** p. 148 **Lab:** Sunset in a Bag, p. 149 **Lab:** Homemade pH Scale, p. 150 **Science and History:** Crumbling Monuments, p. 152

Lab Materials	Reproducible Resources	Section Assessment	Technology
Launch Lab: table-tennis ball, golf ball, bowl, water	**Chapter *Fast File* Resources** Foldables Worksheet, p. 15 Directed Reading Overview, p. 17 Note-taking Worksheets, pp. 31–33	**ASSESSMENT ADVANTAGE**	**Teacher**Works includes: • Interactive Teacher Edition • Lesson Planner with calendar • Access to all program blacklines • Correlations to standards • Web links
MiniLAB: 3 different sized blocks of the same type of wood, metric ruler, balance	**Chapter *Fast File* Resources** Transparency Activity, p. 42 MiniLAB, p. 3 Lab Activity, pp. 9–10 Enrichment, p. 28 Reinforcement, p. 25 Directed Reading, p. 18 **Physical Science Critical Thinking/Problem Solving,** p. 15	**Portfolio** Science Journal, p. 136 **Performance** Applying Math, p. 135 MiniLAB, p. 136 Applying Math, p. 138 **Content** Section Review, p. 138	• Section Focus Transparency • Guided Reading Audio Program • Interactive Chalkboard CD-ROM
Need materials? Contact Science Kit at 1-800-828-7777 or www.sciencekit.com on the Internet.	**Chapter *Fast File* Resources** Transparency Activity, p. 43 Enrichment, p. 29 Reinforcement, p. 26 Directed Reading, p. 18 Transparency Activity, pp. 45–46	**Portfolio** Differentiated Instruction, p. 140 Assessment, p. 142 **Performance** Applying Skills, p. 142 **Content** Section Review, p. 142	• Section Focus Transparency • Teaching Transparency • Guided Reading Audio Program • Interactive Chalkboard CD-ROM
MiniLAB: fine steel wool, tap water, salt water, paper plate **Lab:** baking soda, calcium chloride, phenol red solution, water, 2 teaspoons, resealable plastic bag, graduated cylinder **Lab:** vials of pH paper (1–14), pH color chart, distilled water, fruit juices, vinegar, salt, sugar, soft drinks, household cleaners, soaps and detergents, antacids	**Chapter *Fast File* Resources** Transparency Activity, p. 44 MiniLAB, p. 4 Lab Activity, pp. 11–13 Enrichment, p. 30 Reinforcement, p. 27 Directed Reading, pp. 19, 20 Lab Worksheets, pp. 5–6, 7–8 **Reading and Writing Skill Activities,** p. 17 **Lab Management and Safety,** p. 38	**Portfolio** Activity, p. 147 **Performance** MiniLAB, p. 145 Applying Skills, p. 148 **Content** Section Review, p. 148	• Section Focus Transparency • Guided Reading Audio Program • Interactive Chalkboard CD-ROM • Video Lab

End of Chapter Assessment

ASSESSMENT ADVANTAGE Blackline Masters	Technology	Professional Series
Chapter *Fast File* Resources Chapter Review, pp. 35–36 Chapter Tests, pp. 37–40 **Standardized Test Practice,** pp. 23–26	MindJogger Videoquiz Virtual Labs CD-ROM Exam*View*® Pro Testmaker TeacherWorks CD-ROM Interactive Chalkboard CD-ROM	**Performance Assessment in the Science Classroom (PASC)**

Transparencies

Section Focus

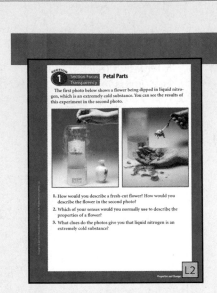

① Section Focus Transparency — Petal Parts

The first photo below shows a flower being dipped in liquid nitrogen, which is an extremely cold substance. You can see the results of this experiment in the second photo.

1. How would you describe a fresh-cut flower? How would you describe the flower in the second photo?
2. Which of your senses would you normally use to describe the properties of a flower?
3. What clues do the photos give you that liquid nitrogen is an extremely cold substance?

L2

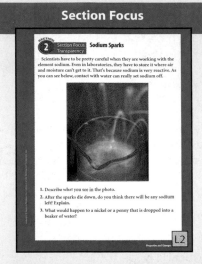

② Section Focus Transparency — Sodium Sparks

Scientists have to be pretty careful when they are working with the element sodium. Even in laboratories, they have to store it where air and moisture can't get to it. That's because sodium is very reactive. As you can see below, contact with water can really set sodium off.

1. Describe what you see in the photo.
2. After the sparks die down, do you think there will be any sodium left? Explain.
3. What would happen to a nickel or a penny that is dropped into a beaker of water?

L2

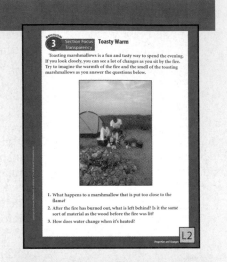

③ Section Focus Transparency — Toasty Warm

Toasting marshmallows is a fun and tasty way to spend the evening. If you look closely, you can see a lot of changes as you sit by the fire. Try to imagine the warmth of the fire and the smell of the toasting marshmallows as you answer the questions below.

1. What happens to a marshmallow that is put too close to the flame?
2. After the fire has burned out, what is left behind? Is it the same sort of material as the wood before the fire was lit?
3. How does water change when it's heated?

L2

This is a representation of key blackline masters available in the Teacher Classroom Resources. See Resource Manager boxes within the chapter for additional information.

Key to Teaching Strategies

The following designations will help you decide which activities are appropriate for your students.

L1 Level 1 activities should be appropriate for students with learning difficulties.

L2 Level 2 activities should be within the ability range of all students.

L3 Level 3 activities are designed for above-average students.

ELL ELL activities should be within the ability range of English-Language Learners.

COOP LEARN Cooperative Learning activities are designed for small group work.

LS Multiple Learning Styles logos, as described on page 12T, are used throughout to indicate strategies that address different learning styles.

P These strategies represent student products that can be placed into a best-work portfolio.

PBL Problem-Based Learning activities apply real-world situations to learning.

Assessment

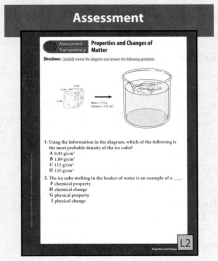

⊙ Assessment Transparency — Properties and Changes of Matter

Directions: Carefully review the diagram and answer the following questions.

Mass = 115 g
Volume = 125 cm³

1. Using the information in the diagram, which of the following is the most probable density of the ice cube?
   A 0.92 g/cm³
   B 1.09 g/cm³
   C 115 g/cm³
   D 125 g/cm³
2. The ice cube melting in the beaker of water is an example of a ___.
   F chemical property
   H chemical change
   G physical property
   J physical change

L2

Teaching

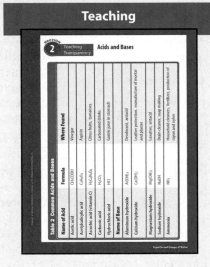

② Teaching Transparency — Acids and Bases

Table 2 Common Acids and Bases		
Name of Acid	**Formula**	**Where Found**
Acetic acid	CH₃COOH	Vinegar
Acetylsalicylic acid	C₉H₈O₄	Aspirin
Ascorbic acid (vitamin C)	H₆C₆H₆O₆	Citrus fruits, tomatoes
Carbonic acid	H₂CO₃	Carbonated drinks
Hydrochloric acid	HCl	Gastric juice in stomach
Name of Base		
Aluminum hydroxide	Al(OH)₃	Deodorant, antacid
Calcium hydroxide	Ca(OH)₂	Leather protection, manufacture of mortar and plaster
Magnesium hydroxide	Mg(OH)₂	Laxative, antacid
Sodium hydroxide	NaOH	Drain cleaner, soap making
Ammonia	NH₃	Household cleaners, fertilizers, production of rayon and nylon

Hands-on Activities

Student Text Lab Worksheet

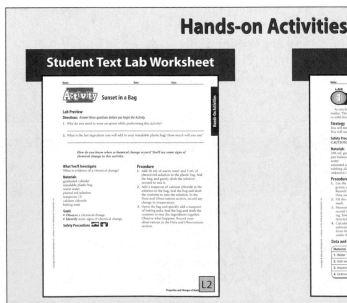

Activity — Sunset in a Bag

Lab Preview
Directions: Answer these questions before you begin the Activity.
1. Why do you need to wear an apron while performing this activity?

2. What is the last ingredient you will add to your resealable plastic bag? How much will you use?

How do you know when a chemical change occurs? You'll see some signs of chemical change in this activity.

What You'll Investigate
What is evidence of a chemical change?

Materials
graduated cylinder
resealable plastic bag
warm water
phenol red solution
teaspoons (2)
calcium chloride
baking soda

Goals
• Observe a chemical change.
• Identify some signs of chemical change.

Safety Precautions

Procedure
1. Add 20 mL of warm water and 5 mL of phenol red solution to the plastic bag. Seal the bag, and gently slosh the solution around to mix it.
2. Add a teaspoon of calcium chloride to the solution in the bag. Seal the bag and slosh the contents to mix the solution. In the Data and Observations section, record any change in temperature.
3. Open the bag and quickly add a teaspoon of baking soda. Seal the bag and slosh the contents to mix the ingredients together. Observe what happens. Record your observations in the Data and Observations section.

L2

Lab Activities

① Laboratory Activity — States of Matter

As you have learned, density is a function of mass divided by volume for a particular sample of matter. The same formula is used to calculate density, regardless of whether the matter is in liquid or solid form.

Strategy
You will find the density of three materials.
You will use density data to identify an unknown material.

Safety Precautions
CAUTION: Avoid open flames

Materials
100-mL graduated cylinder
pan balance and set of masses
water
saturated saltwater mixture
rubbing alcohol
unknown (liquid) substance

Procedure
1. Use the balance to measure the mass, in grams, of a clean, dry graduated cylinder. Record the mass in the data table in the Data and Observations section.
2. Fill the cylinder with water to the 50-mL mark.
3. Measure the mass of the filled cylinder and record it in the data table under the heading Total Mass. Then discard the water as directed by your teacher.
4. Calculate the mass of the water by subtracting the mass of the empty cylinder from the total mass. Record the result under the heading Actual Mass.
5. Repeat steps 2–4, first using the salt water, then the rubbing alcohol, and finally the unknown material. **CAUTION:** Alcohol burns readily, and it fumes can be irritating. Wear goggles. Be sure that the room is well-ventilated, and there are no open flames.
6. Record the data for each material.
7. Calculate the density for each material by dividing its actual mass by its volume. Round to two decimal places and record the values in the table.

Data and Observations

Material	Mass of cylinder	Total mass	Actual Mass	Volume	Density (g/ml)
1. Water				50 mL	
2. Salt water				50 mL	
3. Alcohol				50 mL	
4. Unknown				50 mL	

L2

Meeting Different Ability Levels

Content Outline

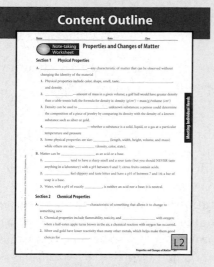

Note-taking Worksheet — **Properties and Changes of Matter**

Section 1 Physical Properties

L2

Reinforcement

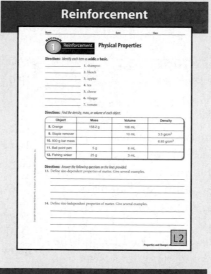

Reinforcement 1 — **Physical Properties**

L2

Enrichment

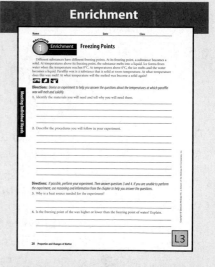

Enrichment 1 — **Freezing Points**

L3

Directed Reading (English/Spanish)

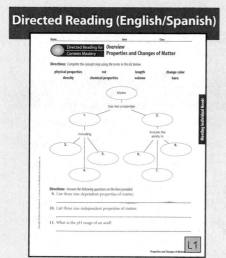

Directed Reading for Content Mastery — *Overview* **Properties and Changes of Matter**

L1

Study Guide

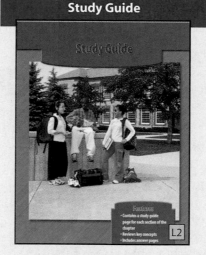

Study Guide

Features
- Contains a study guide page for each section of the chapter
- Reviews key concepts
- Includes answer pages

L2

Reading Essentials

Reading Essentials for Glencoe Science
An Interactive Student Workbook

Features
- Condensed core content
- Actively involves students in reading
- Reinforces key vocabulary

L1

Assessment

Test Practice Workbook

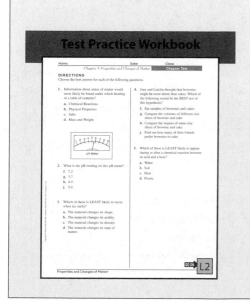

Chapter 5 Properties and Change of Matter — **Chapter Test**

L2

Chapter Review

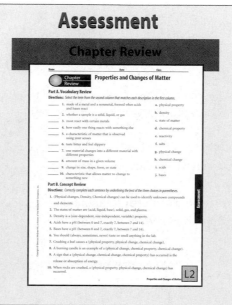

Chapter Review — **Properties and Changes of Matter**

Part A. Vocabulary Review

Part B. Concept Review

L2

Chapter Tests

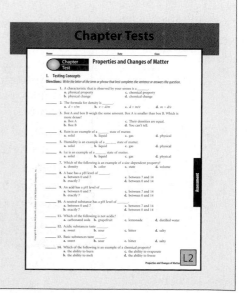

Chapter Test — **Properties and Changes of Matter**

I. Testing Concepts

L2

Science Content Background

section 1

Physical Properties

Physical Properties

The physical properties of substances are primarily collected using the senses. For instance, a physical property of table salt is it is a white, crystalline solid. Both of these properties can be observed. The freezing point, boiling point, and density are physical properties too, and they require simple measurements to obtain.

Geometric formulas can be used to find the volume for regularly shaped solid objects such as those shaped like cubes or rectangular prisms. The volume of an irregularly shaped, insoluble object can be measured by finding the volume of water the object will displace. The mass of the object is found by using a laboratory balance. Once the volume and mass are known density is found by dividing mass by volume.

section 2

Chemical Properties

A Complete Description

Unlike physical properties, the chemical properties of a substance cannot be found by observation of the substance alone. The chemical properties of a substance describe its chemical behavior with other substances. For instance, the fact that sodium will react with chlorine to form a salt is a chemical property of sodium.

Acids and Bases

Classes of substances such as acids and bases have chemical properties too. For example, acids react with bases in a neutralization reaction that forms water and a salt.

The definition of an acid and base varies slightly depending upon which theory is used. This table summarizes the Arrhenius, Bronsted-Lowry, and Lewis definitions of acids and bases. These theories are not discussed in this chapter but they may be helpful in making some explanations.

Summary of Acid-Base Theories		
Theory	**Acid Definition**	**Base Definition**
Arrhenius	Any substance that releases H^+ ion in water solution	Any substance that releases OH^- ions in water solution
Bronsted-Lowry	Any substance that donates a proton	Any substance that accepts a proton
Lewis	Any substance that can accept an electron pair	Any substance that can donate an electron pair

chapter content resources

Internet Resources
For additional content background, visit
ips.msscience.com to:
- access your book online
- find references to related articles in popular science magazines
- access Web links with related content background
- access current events with science journal topics

Print Resources
Understanding the Properties of Matter, by Michael DePodesta, Routledge 2nd ed., 2002
Investigating Solids, Liquids and Gases with Toys, by Jerry L. Sarquis, et. al., McGraw-Hill Trade, Teacher Ed., 1997
Exploring Matter with Toys: Using and Understanding the Senses, by Mickey Sarquis, McGraw-Hill Trade, 1996

Rudi Von Briel/PhotoEdit

section 3 Physical and Chemical Changes

Chemical Changes

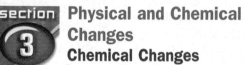
In physical changes, the original materials can be easily recovered by ordinary means because a chemical reaction has not taken place. After a chemical change, the original materials can only be recovered by another chemical reaction because new materials have been formed.

Chemical and Physical Changes in Nature

The plant pigments that are responsible for the yellow, brown, and orange colors of leaves are called carotenoids. Chlorophyll and carotenoids are present in green leaves throughout the growing season. The pigments responsible for red and purple colors, called anthocyanins, are not present in green leaves. Anthocyanins are made in autumn. Anthocyanins change color depending on the acidity of the cell sap in the plant. The brightest colors usually occur when there is a succession of sunny days and cool nights.

Teacher to Teacher
John E. Burns, Teacher
Ramona Junior High School
Chino, CA

"Introduce students to the concept of chemical change by having them heat sugar in an aluminum foil scoop over a candle. This decomposition reaction illustrates that, in chemical changes, a substance's chemical properties change and new products are formed."

John E. Burns

Chapter 5

Chapter Vocabulary

Science Journal Possible answers: becomes cloudy, algae can grow, water color can change

INTERACTIVE CHALKBOARD with Image Bank

PowerPoint® Presentations

This CD-ROM is an editable Microsoft® PowerPoint® presentation that includes:

- a pre-made presentation for every chapter
- interactive graphics
- animations
- audio clips
- image bank
- all new section and chapter questions
- Standardized Test Practice
- transparencies
- pre-lab questions for all labs
- Foldables directions
- links to ips.msscience.com

Matter— Properties and Changes

chapter preview

sections

1 **Physical Properties**
2 **Chemical Properties**
3 **Physical and Chemical Changes**
    Lab **Sunset in a Bag**
    Lab **Homemade pH Scale**
    Virtual Lab **Properties and Changes of Matter**

Why do icebergs float?

This iceberg once was part of an Antarctic ice shelf. Density is a physical property. Ice floats in water because it is less dense than water. It underwent a physical change when it became an iceberg. In this chapter you'll learn about other physical and chemical properties and the changes associated with them.

Science Journal What happens to a swimming pool when the correct chemicals are not added to the water?

132

Theme Connection

Stability and Change Matter can be described by its physical and chemical properties. Matter is capable of undergoing physical and chemical changes based upon these properties.

About the Photo

Icebergs Water expands upon freezing, lowering the density and as a result ice floats on water. Large masses of moving ice are called glaciers and they are common in both the Arctic and Antarctic regions. Portions of these glaciers can break off to form icebergs. Although they are often spectacular, these ice formations pose a large problem for navigation since the actual size of the iceberg cannot be determined by what is seen above the water.

Start-Up Activities

Classifying Different Types of Matter

Using your senses to observe characteristics of matter will help you classify, or categorize, it. This will help you understand what the types of matter are and can help you identify unknown types of matter. In this lab, you will observe and compare the characteristics of two items that you might be familiar with.

1. Obtain a table-tennis ball and a golf ball from your teacher.
2. How are the two balls similar?
3. Which ball is heavier?
4. Compare the surfaces of the table-tennis ball and the golf ball. How are their surfaces different?
5. Place each ball in water and observe.
6. **Think Critically** Create a classification system to classify different kinds of balls. Which characteristics might you use? Describe your classification system in your Science Journal.

Science Online Preview this chapter's content and activities at ips.msscience.com

Properties and Changes of Matter Make the following Foldable to help you organize types of properties and changes into groups based on their common features.

STEP 1 Fold a sheet of paper in half lengthwise. Make the back edge about 1.25 cm longer than the front edge.

STEP 2 Fold in half, then fold in half again to make three folds.

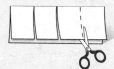

STEP 3 Unfold and cut only the top layer along the three folds to make four tabs.

STEP 4 Label the tabs as shown.

| Physical Properties | Chemical Properties | Chemical Change | Physical Change |

Find Main Ideas As you read the chapter, list examples of each type of property and each type of change under the appropriate tabs.

Purpose Use the Launch Lab to help students begin to observe and record physical properties of objects. L2 **LS Kinesthetic**

Preparation Obtain enough table-tennis balls and golf balls to allow each student to have a set. These balls may be borrowed from the athletic department at your school.

Materials golf ball, table-tennis ball, large container or beaker, water

Teaching Strategy Remind students to observe characteristics such as color, texture, and coverings.

Think Critically

Answers will vary. Possible characteristics include mass, surface, ability to bounce, and color. Check students' classification systems.

Assessment

Oral Ask students to write paragraphs comparing and contrasting the physical characteristics of the golf ball and the table-tennis ball. Use **Performance Assessment in the Science Classroom,** p. 159.

FOLDABLES Study Organizer **Dinah Zike Study Fold**

Student preparation materials for this Foldable are available in the Chapter **FAST FILE** Resources.

section 1 Physical Properties

Physical Properties

Have you ever been asked by a teacher to describe something that you saw on a field trip? How would you describe the elephant in the exhibit shown in **Figure 1?** What features can you use in your description—color, shape, size, and texture? These features are all properties, or characteristics, of the elephant. Scientists use the term *physical property* to describe a characteristic of matter that you can detect with your senses. A **physical property** is any characteristic of matter that can be observed without changing the identity of the material. All matter, such as the elephant, has physical properties.

Common Physical Properties You probably are familiar with some physical properties, such as color, shape, smell, and taste. You might not be as familiar with others, such as mass, volume, and density. Mass (m) is the amount of matter in an object. A golf ball has more mass than a table-tennis ball. Volume (V) is the amount of space that matter takes up. A swimming pool holds a larger volume of water than a paper cup does. **Density** (D) is the amount of mass in a given volume. A golf ball is more dense than a table-tennis ball. Density is determined by finding the mass of a sample of matter and dividing this mass by the volume of the sample.

Formula for Density
$$\text{Density} = \text{mass/volume} \quad \text{or} \quad D = \frac{m}{V}$$

Figure 1 This large gray African elephant is displayed on the main floor of the National Museum of Natural History in Washington, D.C.

134

Density A table-tennis ball and a golf ball are about the same volume. When you decided which had a higher density, you compared their masses. Because they are about the same volume, the one with more mass had the higher density. Suppose you were asked if all the bowling balls in **Figure 2** were identical. They appear to be the same size, shape, and color, but do they all have the same mass? If you could pick up these bowling balls, you would discover that their masses differ. You also might notice that the heavier balls strike the pins harder. Although the volumes of the balls are nearly identical, the densities of the bowling balls are different because their masses are different.

Identifying Unknown Substances In some cases, density also can be used to identify unknown compounds and elements. The element silver, for example, has a density of 10.5 g/cm³ at 20°C. Suppose you want to know whether or not a ring is pure silver. You can find the ring's density by dividing the mass of the ring by its volume. If the density of the ring is determined to be 11.3 g/cm³, then the ring is not pure silver.

Figure 2 These bowling balls look the same but have different densities.
Identify *the types of matter you think you would see, hear, taste, touch, and smell at a bowling alley.*

Applying Math   Solve a One-Step Equation

DETERMINING DENSITY An antique dealer decided to use density to help determine the material used to make a statue. The volume of the statue is 1,000 cm³ and the mass is 8,470 g. What is its density?

Solution

1 *This is what you know:*
- density = mass/volume = m/V
- m = 8,470 g, V = 1,000 cm³

2 *This is what you need to find out:*   Find the density (D)

3 *This is the procedure you need to use:*
- $D = m/V$
- $D = m/V$ = 8,470 g/1,000 cm³
    = 8.470 g/cm³

4 *Check your answer:*   Substitute the density and one of the knowns back into the main equation. Did you calculate the other known?

Practice Problems

1. If a candlestick has a mass of 8.5 g and a volume of 0.96 cm³, what is its density?

2. If the density of a plastic ball is 5.4 g/cm³ and the volume is 7.5 cm³, what is the mass of the plastic ball?

 Science Online
For more practice, visit ips.msscience.com/math_practice

SECTION 1 Physical Properties **135**

Differentiated Instruction

English-Language Learners Help these students by assigning each one a partner who can assist them with unfamiliar vocabulary. Have the student pairs look at objects in the classroom and discuss the physical changes that took place as they were made.

Visually Impaired Ask these students to describe nonvisual physical properties that can be used to identify objects. Possible answers: solid—shape, size, texture, weight, smell; liquid—thickness, slipperiness, smell; gas—smell L2 LS **Kinesthetic**

Mini LAB

Purpose Students measure wooden blocks and calculate their density. `L2` `ELL` `LS`

Kinesthetic

Materials 3 different-sized wooden blocks, ruler, balance

Teaching Strategies Make sure the blocks are made from the same type of wood.

Analysis

1. length, width, height, mass, and volume
2. density

Assessment

Process Have students find the density of a block of balsa wood using the same methods used in the Minilab. Students should compare the results. The density of balsa wood is approximately 0.11 g/cm³. Use **Performance Assessment in the Science Classroom,** p. 97.

Try at Home

Activity

Unit Analysis Unit analysis is a good way to check that a problem has been set up correctly. Explain that when doing unit analysis, you set up a problem using only the units, cancel appropriately, and see whether the answer is in the desired units. Have students do a unit analysis using mass and volume to find density. If mass is in grams and volume is in milliliters, unit analysis says mass/volume = g/mL = density, whose units are g/mL. `L2` `LS`

Logical-Mathematical

Figure 3 All three states of water are present here—solid, liquid, and gas—but you can only see the solid and liquid states. The water vapor in the air is not visible.

State of Matter State of matter is another physical property. The **state of matter** tells you whether a sample of matter is a solid, a liquid, or a gas. This property depends on the temperature and pressure of the matter. The ice in **Figure 3** is water in the solid state. Water in the liquid state can be seen in the ocean and in the clouds. Gaseous water cannot be seen but exists as vapor in the air. In each case, each molecule of water is the same—two hydrogen atoms and one oxygen atom. But water appears to be different because it exists in different states, as shown in **Figure 3**.

Size-Dependent and Size-Independent Properties

Some physical properties change when the size of an object changes. These properties are called **size-dependent properties**. For example, a wooden block might have a volume of 30 cm³ and a mass of 20 g. A larger block might have a volume of 60 cm³ and a mass of 40 g. The volume and mass of the block change when the size of the block changes. However, the density of both blocks is 0.67 g/cm³. Some physical properties do not change when an object changes size. Density is an example of a **size-independent property**. Other examples of size-dependent and size-independent properties are shown in **Table 1**.

Table 1 Physical Properties	
Type of Property	**Property**
Size-dependent properties	length, width, height, volume, mass
Size-independent properties	density, color, state

Mini LAB

Classifying Properties

Procedure

1. Obtain three different-sized **blocks** of the same type of wood.
2. Write all your observations of each block in your **Science Journal** as you make your measurements.
3. Measure the length, width, height, and mass of each block. Calculate the volume and density of each block.

Analysis

1. Which properties were size-dependent?
2. Which properties were size-independent?

Try at Home

Science Journal

A fourth state of matter is called plasma. Have students research the plasma state and record their findings in their Science Journals. Plasma is made up of electrons, and positively charged atomic nuclei completely stripped of electrons. Examples of plasma include lightning, aurora borealis, flourescent lighting, and the Sun's atmosphere. `L3` `LS` **Linguistic** `P`

Physical Properties of Acids and Bases

One way to describe matter is to classify it as either an acid or a base. The concentration of an acid or base can be determined by finding the pH of the sample. The pH scale has a range of 0 to 14. Acids have a pH below 7. Bases have a pH above 7. A sample with a pH of exactly 7 is neutral—neither acidic nor basic. Pure water is a substance with a pH of exactly 7.

Properties of Acids What do you think of when you hear the word *acid*? Do you picture a dangerous chemical that can burn your skin, make holes in your clothes, and even destroy metal? Some acids, such as concentrated hydrochloric acid, are like that. But some acids are edible. One example is shown in **Figure 4.** Carbonated soft drinks contain acids. Every time you eat a citrus fruit such as an orange or a grapefruit, you eat citric and ascorbic (uh SOR bihk) acids. What properties do these and other acids have in common?

Imagine the sharp smell of a freshly sliced lemon. That scent comes from the citric acid in the fruit. Take a big bite out of the fruit shown in **Figure 5** and you would immediately notice a sour taste. If you then rubbed your molars back and forth, your teeth would squeak. All of these physical properties are common in acids.

Reading Check *What are two uses of an acid?*

Figure 5 All citrus fruits contain citric and ascorbic acids, which is why these fruits taste sour.

Figure 4 When you sip a carbonated soft drink, you drink carbonic and phosphoric (faws FOR ihk) acids.
Identify *an area of your body where acids are found.*

INTEGRATE Health

Aging Vitamin C and alpha-hydroxy acids are found in fruits and are the active ingredient in some anti-aging skin creams. It is believed that these ingredients slow down the aging process. Researchers examine safety issues regarding these products as well as their components.

Reading Check

Answer Possible answers: vinegar for tie dyeing, acid washed jeans, digestion in the stomach, antacids, car batteries

Caption Answer
Figure 4 stomach

Discussion

Word Origins Explain to students that a base is also called an alkali. *Alkali* comes from the Arabic term for "the ashes of the plant saltwort" *(al qili). Acid* comes from the Latin word for "sour" *(acidus).* How do these word origins relate to the physical properties of acids and bases? Bases are slippery like ashes. Acids taste sour. L2 **LS** **Logical-Mathematical**

INTEGRATE Health

Aging The safety and benefits of alphahydroxy acids and vitamin C are still under debate. Some scientists believe alphahydroxy acids can actually cause skin to age more rapidly. The FDA recommends that consumers use adequate sun protection while using alphahydroxy acids because it is suspected that they cause the skin to be more sensitive to UV radiation.

Career Investigate the qualifications and training of dermatologists. Working in small groups, design a news interview to present this information to the class. L2

Visual Learning

Figure 4 Ask students what states of matter are present in the glass of soft drink. Answers should include: solid (ice cubes), liquid (soft drink), and gas (bubbles). L2 **LS** **Visual-Spatial**

Teacher FYI

Dissociation Acids and bases dissociate in water to form ions. Strong acids and bases dissociate more than weak acids and bases. In a solution of strong acid, nearly all of the acid molecules have dissociated into H^+ and negative ions. In a solution of weak acid, only a few molecules have dissociated.

Differentiated Instruction

Challenge Have students investigate the particles that make up matter. These particles will move differently in solids, liquids and gases. Have students find out how the motion differs and draw diagrams illustrating their findings. Share the diagrams with the class. L3

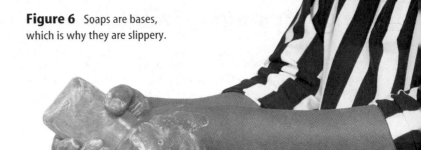

Figure 6 Soaps are bases, which is why they are slippery.

Physical Properties of Bases Bases have physical properties that are different from acids. A familiar example of a base is ammonia (uh MOH nyuh), often used for household cleaning. If you got a household cleaner that contained ammonia on your fingers and then rubbed your fingers together, they would feel slippery. Another familiar base is soap, shown in **Figure 6,** which also has a slippery feel. You shouldn't taste soap, but if you accidentally did, you'd notice a bitter taste. A bitter taste and a slippery feel are physical properties of bases.

Reading Check *What are two examples of products that contain bases?*

It is important to note that you should never taste, touch, or smell anything in a lab unless your teacher tells you to do so.

section 1 review

Summary

Physical Properties

- Characteristics that can be observed without changing the identity of the object.
- Color, shape, smell, taste, mass, volume, and density are all physical properties.
- Mass and volume are size-dependent properties of an object.

Density

- density = mass/volume

Properties of Acids and Bases

- Acids smell sharp, taste sour, and have a pH below 7.
- Bases are slippery, taste bitter, and have a pH above 7.

Self Check

1. **Describe** the physical properties of a baseball.
2. **Explain** why density is a size-independent property. How does it differ from a size-dependent property?
3. **Describe** Give an example of an acid and a base. How do they differ from a neutral substance?
4. **Think Critically** How could you identify a pure metal if you have a balance, a graduated cylinder, and a table of densities for metals? (1 mL = 1 cm^3)

Applying Math

5. **Solve One-Step Equations** What is the density of a substance with a mass of 65.7 g and a volume of 3.40 cm^3?

Science Online ips.msscience.com/self_check_quiz

section 1 review

1. Possible answers: state (solid), shape (spherical), texture, color, mass, volume, density
2. Density is a ratio of two size-dependent properties. As one property increases, so does the other. The ratio doesn't change.

Size-dependent properties are directly related to the object's size.
3. Possible answers: Acids: hydrochloric, sulfuric, citric; Bases: ammonia, soap. A neutral substance has a pH of 7.

4. Find its mass using the balance and its volume using a graduated cylinder. Divide the mass by the volume to calculate density. Compare it to the densities in the table.
5. Density equals: 65.7g/3.40cm^3 = 19.3g/cm^3

Chemical Properties

A Complete Description

You've observed that the density of a table-tennis ball is less than the density of a golf ball. You also have noticed the state of water in an ice cube and in a lake. You've noticed the taste of acid in a lemon and the slippery feel of a base such as soap. However, a description of something using only physical properties is not complete. What type of property describes how matter behaves?

Common Chemical Properties If you strike a match on a hard, rough surface, the match probably will start to burn. Phosphorus (FAWS for us) compounds on the match head and the wood in the match combine with oxygen to form new materials. Why does that happen? The phosphorus compounds and the wood have the ability to burn. The ability to burn is a chemical property. A **chemical property** is a characteristic of matter that allows it to change to a different type of matter.

Reading Check *What is a chemical property?*

You see an example of a chemical property when you leave a half-eaten apple on your desk, and the exposed part turns brown. The property you observe is the ability to react with oxygen. Two other chemical properties are shown in **Figure 7.**

as you read

What You'll Learn

- **Describe** chemical properties of matter.
- **Explain** the chemical properties of acids and bases.
- **Explain** how a salt is formed.

Why It's Important

Chemical properties can help you predict how matter will change.

Review Vocabulary
solubility: the amount of a substance that will dissolve in a given amount of another substance

New Vocabulary
- chemical property
- reactivity
- salts

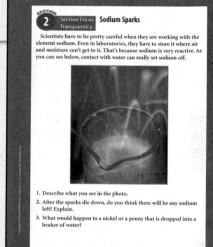

Figure 7 The chemical properties of a material often require a warning about its careful use. Gas pumps warn customers not to get near them with anything that might start the gasoline burning. Workers who use toxic chemicals have to wear protective clothing.

SECTION 2 Chemical Properties **139**

Section 2 Resource Manager

Chapter *FAST FILE* Resources
Transparency Activity, pp. 43, 45–46
Directed Reading for Content Mastery, p. 18
Enrichment, p. 29
Reinforcement, p. 26

---

1 Motivate

INTERACTIVE CHALKBOARD
PowerPoint® Presentations

Bellringer

Section Focus Transparencies also are available on the Interactive Chalkboard CD-ROM.
L2 **ELL**

SECTION 2
Section Focus Transparency   **Sodium Sparks**

Scientists have to be pretty careful when they are working with the element sodium. Even in laboratories, they have to store it where air and moisture can't get to it. That's because sodium is very reactive. As you can see below, contact with water can really set sodium off.

1. Describe what you see in the photo.
2. After the sparks die down, do you think there will be any sodium left? Explain.
3. What would happen to a nickel or a penny that is dropped into a beaker of water?

Properties and Changes of Matter

Tie to Prior Knowledge

Sour Milk Ask students if they have ever seen soured milk. Soured milk is a result of a chemical reaction that occurs in fresh milk. Point out that the properties of the milk before the chemical reaction are different from the properties of the milk after the chemical reaction. L2

Quick Demo

Corrosion

Materials clear, carbonated soft drink, cup, iron nails

Estimated Time 10 minutes

Procedure Pour colorless, carbonated soft drink into a cup and drop in an iron nail. Have students observe the results the next day.

✓ **Reading Check**

Answer a chemical property that describes how easily one thing reacts with something else (p. 7)

Caption Answer

Figure 9 A physical property can be observed without changing the composition of a substance, whereas, chemical properties cannot be observed without altering a substance.

Activity

Model Molecules The chemical properties of a substance depend on the ways the molecules of the substance interact with molecules of other substances. Tell students that a water molecule contains two hydrogen atoms and one oxygen atom. Explain that two water molecules can decompose to form two molecules of hydrogen gas and one molecule of oxygen gas. A molecule of hydrogen gas contains two hydrogen atoms, and a molecule of oxygen gas contains two oxygen atoms. Have students use gumdrops and toothpicks to make models of several water molecules and then use the models to simulate the decomposition of water. L3 COOP LEARN ELL LS Visual-Spatial

Discussion

Types of Water What chemical property makes hard water different from soft water? Hard water contains minerals that react chemically with soap to form solids. Soft water does not contain these compounds. L2

✓ **Reading Check**

Answer A metal boat will rust over time whereas a fiberglass one will not.

Gold

Iron

Figure 8 Gold and iron have different chemical properties that make them suitable for uses in a wide variety of jewelry and tools.

Figure 9 Pool water must be tested to keep the water safe for swimmers.
Determine *How do physical and chemical properties differ?*

Choosing Materials Look at **Figure 8**. Would you rather wear a bracelet made of gold or one made of iron? Why? Iron is less attractive and less valuable than gold. It also has an important chemical property that makes it unsuitable for jewelry. Think about what happens to iron when it is left out in moist air. Iron rusts easily because of its high reactivity (ree ak TIH vuh tee) with oxygen and moisture in the air. **Reactivity** is how easily one thing reacts with something else. The low reactivity of silver and gold, in addition to their desirable physical properties, makes those metals good choices for jewelry.

✓ **Reading Check** *Why is a fiberglass boat hull better than one made of a metal?*

INTEGRATE
Life Science

Chemical Properties and Pools The "chlorine" added to swimming pools is actually a compound called hypochlorous acid, which forms when chlorine reacts with water. This acid kills bacteria, insects, algae, and plants. The person in **Figure 9** is testing the pool water to see whether it has the correct amount of chlorine.

Any time you have standing water, mosquitoes and other insects can lay eggs in it. Various plants and algae can turn a sparkling blue pool into a slimy green mess. Bacteria are another problem. When you go swimming, you bring along millions of uninvited guests—the normal bacteria that live on your skin. The chlorine compounds kill the bacteria—as well as insects, algae, and plants that might be in the pool.

Hypochlorous acid can cause problems as well. It combines with nitrogen in the pool to form chloramines. Have your eyes ever burned after swimming in a pool? Chloramines can irritate the skin and eyes of swimmers.

Differentiated Instruction

Learning Disabled Have students gather pictures from magazines and newspapers that show items containing acids or bases. Have them use the pictures to create one mobile or collage for acids and one for bases. They also can use labels containing the properties of acids and bases in their mobiles and collages. L2 LS P

Challenge Ask students to find out what types of crops grow well in acidic or basic soils. Then ask them to find information from the local horticulturist or lawn and garden store about plants that grow well in your area. Ask students to use this information to infer whether the soil in your area is acidic or basic. These results should be explained in the form of a graph. L3

Chemical Properties of Acids and Bases You have learned that acids and bases have physical properties that make acids taste sour and bases taste bitter and feel slippery. The chemical properties of acids and bases are what make them both useful but sometimes harmful. Several acids and bases are shown in **Table 2.**

Acids Many acids react with, or corrode, certain metals. Have you ever used aluminum foil to cover leftover spaghetti or tomato sauce? **Figure 10** shows what you might see the next day. You might see small holes in the foil where it has come into contact with the tomatoes in the sauce. The acids in tomato sauce, oranges, carbonated soft drinks, and other foods are edible. However, many acids can damage plant and animal tissue. Small amounts of nitric (NI trihk) acid and sulfuric (sul FYOOR ihk) acid are found in rain. This rain, called acid rain, harms plant and animal life in areas where acid rain falls. Sulfuric acid that has no water mixed with it is useful in many industries because it removes water from certain materials. However, that same property causes burns on skin that touches sulfuric acid.

Figure 10 Aluminum reacts easily with acids, which is why acidic food, such as tomatoes, should not be cooked or stored in aluminum.

Table 2 Common Acids and Bases

Name of Acid	Formula	Where It's Found
Acetic acid	CH_3COOH	Vinegar
Acetylsalicylic acid	$C_9H_8O_4$	Aspirin
Ascorbic acid (vitamin C)	$C_6H_8O_6$	Citrus fruits, tomatoes
Carbonic acid	H_2CO_3	Carbonated drinks
Hyrdrochloric acid	HCl	Gastric juice in stomach
Name of Base		
Aluminum hydroxide	$Al(OH)_3$	Deodorant, antacid
Calcium hydroxide	$Ca(OH)_2$	Leather tanning, manufacture of mortar and plaster
Magnesium hydroxide	$Mg(OH)_2$	Laxative, antacid
Sodium hydroxide	NaOH	Drain cleaner, soap making
Ammonia	NH_3	Household cleaners, fertilizer, production of rayon and nylon

Cultural Diversity

Tasty Properties The ability to taste varies from person to person. Some of the variation is genetic. A dominant gene controls a person's ability to taste PTC (phenylthiocarbamide). To people who can taste it, PTC is bitter. PTC-like substances are found in foods such as buttermilk, spinach, and turnips, so tasters and nontasters have different responses to these foods. Some poisonous plants also contain PTCs, so being a taster would be useful to a food gatherer living where these plants grow. The ability to taste PTC varies from population to population. In sub-Saharan Africa, only 5 percent of the population can taste PTC; in Denmark, 57 percent can taste PTC.

Check for Understanding

Auditory-Musical Have students work in groups to compose simple songs to help them remember examples of chemical properties. Creating a repetitive rhythm may also aid in song development. Share the songs with the class. L2

Reteach

Naming Properties Ask each student to write the name of something on a slip of paper. Collect the slips of paper and put them into a container. Draw them one at a time and have students name a physical and chemical property for each item. L2

☑ Assessment

Portfolio Choose an item or material in the classroom. Ask students to write a fiction story about it, describing all the chemical and physical properties of it that they can. Examples of items or materials include water, fabric, wood, plastic, and lab chemicals. Use **Performance Assessment in the Science Classroom,** p. 155. L2 P

Teacher FYI

Hydronium Ions The term *pH* means "power of hydrogen." In water, hydrogen ions combine with water to form hydronium ions (H_3O^+). pH is a measure of the concentration of hydronium ions in a solution. The pH scale is logarithmic, not linear. A solution with a pH of 8 has ten times as many hydronium ions as a solution with a pH of 9.

Figure 11 These everyday items contain salts.

Bases A concentrated base is as dangerous as a concentrated acid. A base, such as sodium hydroxide (hi DRAHK side) can damage living tissue. It is not uncommon for someone who smells strong ammonia to get a bloody nose or to get a burn if a strong base is touched. Ammonia feels slippery to the touch because the base reacts with the proteins in the tissues on your fingertips, which results in damaged tissue.

Salts What happens in reactions between acids and bases? Acids and bases often are studied together because they react with each other to form water and other useful compounds called salts. **Salts** are compounds made of a metal and nonmetal that are formed when acids and bases react. Look at **Figure 11.** That white solid in your salt shaker—table salt—is the most common salt. Table salt, sodium chloride, can be formed by the reaction between the base sodium hydroxide and hydrochloric acid. Other useful salts are calcium carbonate, which is chalk, and ammonium chloride, which is used in some types of batteries.

section 2 review

Summary

Chemical Properties
- These properties have characteristics that cannot be observed without altering the identity of the substance.

Chemical Properties of Acids and Bases
- Strong acids and bases can be equally dangerous.
- Strong acids react with and corrode metals.
- Ammonia and sodium hydroxide are examples of bases.

Salts
- A salt is composed of a metal and a nonmetal.
- An acid and a base combine to form a salt and water.

Self Check

1. **Compare and Contrast** How do chemical and physical properties differ?
2. **Describe** three chemical properties of an acid.
3. **Identify** two different salts and their uses.
4. **Think Critically** Think about safety precautions you take around your home. Which ones are based on physical properties and which ones are based on chemical properties? Explain.

Applying Skills

5. **Classify** each of the following properties as being physical or chemical: iron rusting, gasoline burning, solid sulfur shattering, and lye feeling slippery.

142 CHAPTER 5 Matter—Properties and Changes

Science Online ips.msscience.com/self_check_quiz

section 2 review

1. A physical property can be observed without changing the composition of the substance. A chemical property cannot be observed without altering the composition of the sample.
2. Acids can kill bacteria, insects, algae, and plants; acids react with bases to form salts; acids can cause severe burns.
3. Table salt—salting foods; ammonium chloride—in batteries; calcium carbonate—chalk.
4. Physical properties—Use a safe ladder when placing items on high shelves. Wet floors are slippery. Chemical properties—Store all chemicals and cleaners away from small children. Store all flammable liquids away from an open flame such as a pilot light.
5. **a.** chemical; **b.** chemical; **c.** physical; **d.** physical

Physical and Chemical Changes

Physical Change

The crowd gathers at a safe distance and the cameras from the news media are rolling. A sense of excitement, fear, and anticipation fills the air. The demolition experts are making their final inspections. Then, in just a few seconds, the old stadium becomes a pile of rubble. The appearance of the stadium changed.

What is physical change? Most matter can undergo physical change. A **physical change** is any change in size, shape, form, or state where the identity of the matter stays the same. Only the physical properties change. The stadium in **Figure 12** underwent a physical change from its original form to a pile of steel and concrete. The materials are the same; they just look different.

> **Reading Check** *What is a physical change?*

Figure 12 This stadium underwent a physical change—its form changed.

as you read

What You'll Learn
- **Identify** physical and chemical changes.
- **Exemplify** how physical and chemical changes affect the world you live in.

Why It's Important
Chemical changes are all around us, from the leaves changing color in the fall to the baking of bread.

⊘ Review Vocabulary
weathering: the action of the elements in altering the color, texture, composition or form of exposed objects

New Vocabulary
- physical change
- chemical change

---

1 Motivate

Bellringer

Section Focus Transparencies also are available on the Interactive Chalkboard CD-ROM.
L2 ELL

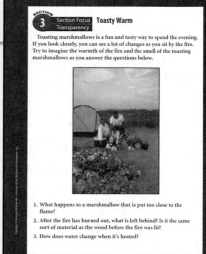

Tie to Prior Knowledge
Changing Matter Review with students some of the physical and chemical properties of matter about which they have learned. Explain that these properties can change when matter undergoes physical and chemical changes.
L2

Section 3 Resource Manager

Chapter FAST FILE Resources
Transparency Activity, p. 44
Directed Reading for Content Mastery, pp. 19, 20
MiniLAB, p. 4
Reinforcement, p. 27

Enrichment, p. 30
Lab Worksheet, pp. 5–6, 7–8
Lab Activity, pp. 11–13

Answer any change in size, shape, form, or state in which the identity of the matter stays the same

Discussion

Fruit Ripening What evidence do you have that chemical changes occur as fruit and vegetables ripen? Possible answers: apples and tomatoes turn red, pears and bananas become yellow, oranges turn from green to orange

Caption Answer

Figure 13 Yes; the substance is the same, it just looks different.

IDENTIFYING Misconceptions

Substance Change When students see a substance such as water change state, they may think there has been a chemical change, creating a different substance. Point out that ice, liquid water, and steam (gaseous water) all have the same chemical makeup and formula, H_2O.

Visual Learning

Figure 13 Mention to students that all the changes of state shown have specific names. The four changes shown are melting, freezing, condensation, and evaporation, respectively. L2 ELL LS **Visual-Spatial**

Examples of Physical Changes How can you recognize a physical change? Just look to see whether or not the matter has changed size, shape, form, or state. If you cut a watermelon into chunks, the watermelon has changed size and shape. That's a physical change. If you pop one of those chunks into your mouth and bite it, you have changed the watermelon's size and shape again.

Change of State Matter can undergo a physical change in another way, too. It can change from one state to another. Suppose it's a hot day. You and your friends decide to make snow cones. A snow cone is a mixture of water, sugar, food coloring, and flavoring. The water in the snow cone is solid, but in the hot sunshine, it begins to warm. When the temperature of the water reaches its melting point, the solid water begins to melt. The chemical composition of the water—two hydrogens and one oxygen—does not change. However, its form changes. This is an example of a physical change. The solid water becomes a liquid and drips onto the sidewalk. As the drops of liquid sit in the sunshine, the water changes state again, evaporating to become a gas. Water also can change from a solid to liquid by melting. Other examples of change of state are shown in **Figure 13.**

Figure 13 The four most common changes of state are shown here.
Explain *if physical changes can be reversed.*

A solid will melt, becoming a liquid.

As it cools, this liquid metal will become solid steel.

Water vapor in the air changes to liquid water when dew forms.

Liquid water in perspiration changes to a gas when it evaporates from your skin.

144

Differentiated Instruction

Learning Disabled The Grand Canyon was formed over time by physical changes to the rock, as were the stone pillars in Bryce National Park. Have students look through several magazines that show remarkable landscapes. Have them explain how physical weathering could have formed some of these structures. L2 LS **Visual-Spatial**

Teacher FYI

Sublimation Another change of state is sublimation. Sublimation is a change of a solid directly to a gas or a gas directly to a solid, without going through the liquid state. Sublimation is used to make freeze-dried food products. The element iodine is a solid that sublimes at room temperature, as is dry ice (solid carbon dioxide).

Figure 14 Chemical changes occur all around you.

This unprotected car fender was exposed to salt and water which caused it to rust.

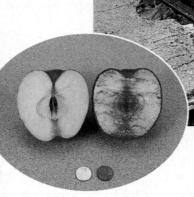

Apples and pennies darken due to chemical changes.

This bridge support will have to be repaired or replaced because of the rust damage.

Answer One type of material changes into another type of material with different properties.

Chemical Changes

Unprotected cars driven on salted roads and steel structures like the one shown in **Figure 14** can begin to rust after only a few winters. A shiny copper penny becomes dull and dark. An apple left out too long begins to turn brown. What do all these changes have in common? Each of these changes is a chemical change. A chemical change occurs when one type of matter changes into a different type of matter with different properties.

Reading Check *What happens during a chemical change?*

Examples of Chemical Change Chemical changes are going on around you—and inside you—every day. Plants use photosynthesis to produce food—the product of chemical changes. When you eat fruits and vegetables produced by photosynthesis, these products must be chemically changed again so that the cells in your body can use them as food. There are many chemical changes occurring outside of your body, too. Silver tarnishing, copper forming a green coating, iron rusting, and petroleum products combusting are all examples of chemical changes that are occurring around you. Although these reactions may be occurring at different rates and producing different products, they are still examples of chemical changes.

Mini LAB

Comparing Chemical Changes

Procedure

1. Separate a piece of **fine steel wool** into two halves.
2. Dip one half in **tap water** and the other half in the same amount of **salt water**.
3. Place both pieces of steel wool on a **paper plate** and label them. Observe every day for five days.

Analysis

1. What happened to the steel wool that was dipped in the salt water?
2. What might be a common problem with machinery that is operated near an ocean?

Mini LAB

Purpose Students observe the effect of salt on the reaction of steel wool with air [L2] (ELL) [IS] **Visual-Spatial**

Materials piece of fine steel wool, water, saltwater, paper plate, pencil

Teaching Strategy Some steel wool is lightly coated with oil. Use steel wool that has neither soap nor oil. Have students write *saltwater* or *tap water* on the paper plate next to the corresponding piece of steel wool.

Analysis

1. It rusted more than the other piece.
2. If not properly protected, salt from the ocean would speed rusting of the steel in the machinery.

Assessment

Performance Ask students to infer the benefits and problems of using plastic for car bodies. Be sure they include whether problems are caused by physical properties or chemical properties. Have each student write a paragraph describing his or her conclusions. Use **Performance Assessment in the Science Classroom,** p. 157.

SECTION 3 Physical and Chemical Changes **145**

LAB DEMONSTRATION

Purpose to deomonstrate chemical and physical changes

Materials 2 pennies, rough surface, beaker, 1*M* hydrochloric acid, burner, tongs

Preparation CAUTION: *Wear a laboratory apron, gloves, and safety goggles.* Use the rough surface to scratch the edge of each penny, exposing the zinc center.

Procedure Place one penny in a small amount of dilute HCl in a beaker. Observe the reaction. Using tongs, grip the other penny and place it near a flame.

Expected Outcome The zinc reacted with the acid while the copper did not. In the flame, the zinc melted and the copper did not.

Assessment

Which change was a physical change and which was a chemical change? The reaction in hydrochloric acid was a chemical change and the melting of the zinc was a physical change. [L2]

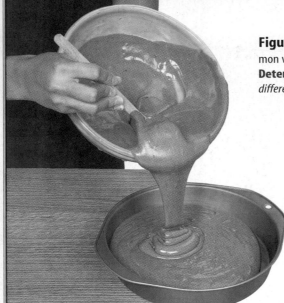

Figure 15 Chemical changes are common when food, such as cake, is cooked.
Determine *How is a chemical change different from a physical change?*

New Materials Are Formed Ice melts, paper is cut, metal is hammered into sheets, and clay is molded into a vase. Seeing signs of these physical changes is easy—something changes shape, size, form, or state.

The only sure way to know whether a chemical change has occurred is if a new type of matter is formed that is chemically different from the starting matter. A chemical change cannot be reversed easily. For example, when wood burns, you see it change to ash and gases that have properties that are different from the wood and oxygen that burned. You can't put the ash and gases back together to make wood. When the cake shown in **Figure 15** is baked, changes occur that make the cake batter become solid. The chemical change that occurs when baking powder mixes with water results in bubbles that make the cake rise. Raw egg in the batter undergoes changes that make the egg solid. These changes cannot be reversed.

Reading Check
How can you be sure that a chemical change has occurred?

Signs of Chemical Change In these examples, you know that a chemical change occurred because you can see that a new substance forms. It's not always easy to tell when new substances are formed. What are other signs of chemical change?

One sign of a chemical change is the release or absorption of energy in the form of light, heat, or sound. Release of energy is obvious when something burns—light and heat are given off. Sometimes an energy change is so small or slow that it is difficult to notice, like when something rusts. Another sign that indicates a chemical change is the formation of a gas or a solid that is not the result of a change of state.

146 **CHAPTER 5** Matter—Properties and Changes

Curriculum Connection

Art Leonardo da Vinci was one of the world's great artists, but only a few of his artworks remain. He experimented with using oil paint instead of watercolors to paint frescoes. Because of chemical changes caused by the interaction of the oil, paint, air, and plaster, *The Last Supper* faded almost completely before it was restored.

Differentiated Instruction

Challenge Have students choose a photograph of a scenic landscape and write a poem about the chemical and/or physical changes that have created the landscape. Students should colorfully illustrate the changes that are occurring on a poster. The poems and posters should be shared with the class. L2

Chemical and Physical Changes in Nature

Often, a color is evidence of a chemical change, an example of which is shown in **Figure 16.** Year round, leaves contain yellow, red, and orange pigments that are masked, or hidden, by large amounts of green chlorophyll. In autumn, changes in temperature and rainfall amounts cause trees to stop producing chlorophyll. When chlorophyll production stops, the masked pigments become visible.

Physical Weathering Some physical changes occur quickly. Others take place over a long time. Physical weathering is a physical change that is responsible for much of the shape of Earth's surface. Examples are shown in **Figure 17.** Examples also can be found in your own school yard. All of the soil that you see comes from physical weathering. Wind and water erode rocks, breaking them into small bits. Water fills cracks in rocks. When it freezes and thaws several times, the rock splits into smaller pieces. No matter how small the pieces of rock are, they are made up of the same things that made up the bigger pieces of rock. The rock simply has undergone a physical change. Gravity, plants, animals, and the movement of land during earthquakes also help cause physical changes on Earth.

Figure 16 Chemical changes that occur in the fall bring about the color changes in these leaves.

Figure 17 You can see dramatic examples of physical weathering caused by water and wind on rocky coastlines.

Visual Learning

Figure 17 What has caused the physical weathering along this coastline? The waves crashing against the rocks. L2 **LS** **Visual-Spatial**

Make a Model

Nature Change Using simple materials, make a model of a physical change that occurs in nature. Possible models: volcano eruption and island formation, land or shoreline erosion, or glacier movement. L2 **LS** **Kinesthetic**

Activity

Burning Wood Have students investigate what must occur to change the ashes left after a piece of wood has been burned into new wood. Students should illustrate a drawing and identify each step as a chemical or a physical change. L2 **P**

Active Reading

Double Entry Journal In this strategy, the student takes notes and adds his or her own reflections while reading the student text. Students are encouraged to explore ideas, make responses, and take risks in giving opinions about the reading. Have them divide the paper in half. On the left, identify a particular passage or quotation of significance in the reading. The reader records anything enlightening, enigmatic, stimulating, or disturbing. On the right, the reader responds, questions, elaborates, makes personal connections, evaluates, reflects, analyzes, or interprets. Have students make a Double Entry Journal for the discussion of physical and chemical changes in this section. L2

Cave Formation Other cave formations that can be found in Carlsbad Caverns include soda straws, drapery, flowstone, shelfstone, cave pearls, popcorn, helictites, and totem poles. All are products of the dissolution and subsequent deposition of minerals, mostly calcite. Temperature and whether water enters the cave by dripping, seeping, or splashing affect the types of cave formations formed.

3 Assess

DAILY INTERVENTION

Check for Understanding

Logical-Mathematical Using a large, two-column chart, brainstorm with the class and list physical and chemical changes observed on a daily basis. Discuss why the changes are physical or chemical. L2

Reteach

Signs of Change Have students work in groups to name signs to indicate that a chemical change has occurred. Ask each group then to identify one situation in which one of these signs is present but in which no chemical change has occurred. L2

✔ Assessment

Content Have students work in groups and use both physical and chemical changes to create works of art. Explain what each change is and how it contributes to the artwork. Use **Performance Assessment in the Science Classroom,** p. 169. L2

Figure 18 Over many years, acidic rainwater slowly reacts with layers of limestone rock. It forms caves and collects minerals that it later deposits as cave formations.

**INTEGRATE
Career**

Geologists Carlsbad Caverns in New Mexico contain cave formations similar to the ones shown here. Geologists study the history of the Earth as recorded in rocks and often investigate deep within Earth's caves. Stalagmites are cave formations that form on the floor of the cave and grow upward. Inside Carlsbad Caverns you will find a stalagmite called the Giant Dome that is 19 m tall. Research and find out more information about geologists and this huge cave.

Chemical Weathering Cave formations like the one in **Figure 18** form by chemical weathering. As drops of water drip through the rocks above this cavern room, minerals become dissolved in the water. These icicle shapes, or stalactites, are formed when the water evaporates leaving the mineral deposits. There are instances of unnatural chemical weathering. The acid in acid rain can chemically weather marble buildings and statues, and other outdoor objects.

section 3 review

Summary

Physical Changes

- Physical changes are changes in the size, shape, form, or state of an object where its identity remains the same.

Chemical Changes

- A chemical change occurs when one type of matter changes into another type of matter with different properties.
- Energy, in the form of light, heat, or sound can be released or absorbed.
- A gas or a solid, not resulting from a change of state, can be formed.
- Physical and chemical weathering also occur in nature.

Self Check

1. **List** five physical changes that you can observe in your home.
2. **Describe** how physical changes can alter Earth's surface.
3. **Explain** what happens when carbon burns. List the signs that a chemical change has occurred.
4. **Think Critically** Which of the following involves a chemical change: combining an acid and a base, dew forming, or souring milk.

Applying Skills

5. **Draw Conclusions** A log is reduced to a small pile of ash when it burns. Explain the difference in mass between the log and the ash.

148 CHAPTER 5 Matter—Properties and Changes

Science Online ips.msscience.com/self_check_quiz

section 3 review

1. Possible answers: shredding cheese, chopping onions, slicing apples, boiling water, and making ice cream.
2. Possible answers: erosion of soil by wind and water, drought or floods, freezing and thawing.
3. A chemical change occurs as carbon burns because new substances with new properties are formed; energy change, color change, formation of a gas or solid
4. combining an acid and base, souring milk
5. The difference in mass is a result of the mass of gas that was formed in the reaction and escaped.

Sunset in a Bag

● Real-World Question

How do you know when a chemical change occurs? You'll see some signs of chemical change in this lab.

Goals
- **Observe** a chemical change.
- **Identify** some signs of chemical change.

Materials
baking soda
calcium chloride
phenol red solution
warm water
teaspoons (2)
resealable plastic bag
graduated cylinder

Safety Precautions
[icons]

● Procedure

1. Add 20 mL of warm water to the plastic bag. Add a teaspoon of calcium chloride to the water, seal the bag, and slosh the contents to mix the solution. Record your observations.

2. Add 5 mL of phenol red solution to the same bag. Seal the bag, slosh the contents, and record your observations.

3. Open the bag and quickly add a teaspoon of baking soda. Seal the bag and slosh the contents to mix the ingredients together. Observe what happens.

● Conclude and Apply

1. **Identify** in which step a physical change occurred. In which step did a chemical change occur? How do you know?

2. **Predict** if a change in energy always indicates a chemical change. Why or why not?

Communicating Your Data

Compare your conclusions with those of other students in your class. **For more help, refer to the Science Skill Handbook.**

LAB   149

Differentiated Instruction

Visually Impaired Help these students by assigning each one a partner who can describe the changes that they are observing during the lab. Encourage helpers to provide each visually impaired student with just enough assistance to accomplish the task. L2

Communicating Your Data

Ask students to draw illustrations showing the changes that occurred in each step of this activity. Students can then compare their illustrations.

● Real-World Question

Purpose Students observe a physical and chemical change. L2 LS **Kinesthetic**

Process Skills observe, infer, recognize cause and effect, measure, record observations, draw conclusions

Time Required 45 minutes

● Procedure

Alternate Materials Many products sold to spread on icy pavement contain calcium chloride, however, the percentages vary. If you choose to use one of these products, try the activity ahead of time to make sure the energy change can be noticed. If phenol red is not available, a purple solution made from cooked red cabbage leaves can be used, but the color change is less dramatic.

Teaching Strategy Caution students to seal the bags before they are shaken and to open bags away from their face.

● Conclude and Apply

1. Step 1 involved $CaCl_2$ dissolving in water, a physical process. Step 2 involved making a mixture, also a physical process. Step 3 involved both a color change and the formation of bubbles, a chemical change.

2. No; step 1 was a physical change but it still involved the production of heat.

✓ Assessment

Process Ask each student to write a lab report summarizing the procedures used and results obtained. Use **PASC**, p. 119.

LAB   149

Real-World Question

Purpose Students will determine the pH of various solutions and classify the solutions as acidic, basic, or neutral. L2 LS **Kinesthetic**

Process Skills observe, classify, use numbers, communicate, measure, predict, interpret data, experiment

Time Required 45 minutes

Possible Materials Clear fruit juices with little color, such as apple juice or white grape juice, work best. Use colorless soft drinks.

Safety Precautions Do not use household cleaners that are dangerous to inhale or can irritate skin, such as strong ammonia solutions and drain and oven cleaners. Be sure to read and follow all caution statements on the labels. Be sure no cleaners are mixed together.

Form a Hypothesis

Possible Hypothesis Clear liquids have a lower pH. Fruit juices, vinegar and soft drinks are acidic. Chalky or cloudy solutions have a higher pH. Soaps and antacids are basic.

Test Your Hypothesis

Possible Procedures Dip a strip of pH paper into one solution. Compare the color of the test strip to the chart. Record the pH and whether the solution is acidic, basic, or neutral. Then test the remaining solutions.

LAB
Design Your Own

Homemade pH Scale

Real-World Question

The more concentrated an acid or base is, the more likely it is to be harmful to living organisms. A pH scale is used to measure the concentration of acids and bases. A solution with a pH below 7 is acidic, a pH of 7 is neutral, and a pH above 7 is basic. In this lab, you will measure the pH of some things using treated paper. When it is dipped into a solution, this paper changes color. Check the color against the chart below to find the pH of the solution. How acidic or basic are some common household items?

Goals

- **Design** an experiment that allows you to test solutions to find the pH of each.
- **Classify** a solution as an acid or a base according to its pH.

Possible Materials

vial of pH paper
1–14 pH color chart
distilled water
fruit juices
vinegar
salt
sugar
soft drinks
household cleaners
soaps and detergents
antacids

Safety Precautions

WARNING: *Never eat, taste, smell, or touch any chemical during a lab.*

Form a Hypothesis

Form a hypothesis to explain which kinds of solutions you are testing are acids and which kinds are bases. Copy and complete the table below.

pH of Solutions

Solution To Be Tested	pH	Acid, Base, or Neutral
dish-washing detergent	8	base
distilled water	7	neutral
apple juice	5	acid

pH	Color	pH	Color
1		8	
2		9	
3		10	
4		11	
5		12	
6		13	
7		14	

Alternative Inquiry Lab

Real-World Connection To extend this Lab into an Inquiry Lab, have students research pH in industry and the marketplace. Some possible topics include the following.

Why are some companies proud to have 'pH-balanced' shampoo? What effect does pH have on hair and skin? What is the purpose of antacids?

How do they achieve this purpose? What are the effects of pH in different foods? What pH standards do various food processors use, and why? What is the effect of soil pH on growing food and flowers? How do herbicides, pesticides, and fertilizers take pH into account?

● Test Your Hypothesis

Make a Plan

1. As a group, decide which materials you will test. If a material is not a liquid, dissolve it in water so you can test the solution.

2. List the steps and materials that you need to test your hypothesis. Be specific. What parts of the experiment will you repeat, if any?

3. Before you begin, copy a data table like the one shown into your Science Journal. Be sure to leave room to record results for each solution tested. If there is to be more than one trial for each solution, include room for the additional trials.

4. Reread the entire experiment to make sure that all the steps are in logical order.

Follow Your Plan

1. Make sure your teacher approves your plan and data table. Be sure that you have included any suggested changes.

2. Carry out the experiment as planned and approved. Wash your hands when you are done.

3. **Record** the pH value of each solution in the data table as you complete each test. Determine whether each solution is acidic, basic, or neutral.

● Analyze Your Data

1. **Infer** Were any materials neither acids nor bases? How do you know?

2. **Interpret Data** Using your data table, conclude which types of materials are usually acidic and which are usually basic.

3. **Draw Conclusions** At what pH do you think acids become too dangerous to touch? Bases? Explain your answers.

4. **Analyze Results** What is the pH range of the foods that you tested?

● Conclude and Apply

Determine Perhaps you have been told that you can use vinegar to dissolve hard-water deposits because vinegar is an acid. If you run out of vinegar, which of the items you tested could you most likely use instead of vinegar for this purpose?

*C*ommunicating Your Data

Compare your findings with those of other student groups. Discuss why any differences in the data might have occurred.

LAB 151

*C*ommunicating Your Data

Suggest students use a spreadsheet program to make tables of their data.

Teaching Strategy Demonstrate how to use the pH paper, following directions on the box.

Troubleshooting If students need to dissolve a substance in water, they should make sure the resulting solutions are fairly concentrated. This will help them get definite readings with the pH paper. Different substance-to-water ratios might give different results.

Expected Outcome Fruit juices, vinegar, soft drinks, and some cleaners will be acidic. Water, salt, and sugar will be neutral. Soaps, some household cleaners, and antacids will be basic.

● Analyze Your Data

Answers to Questions

1. Distilled water as well as solutions of salt and sugar were neutral because they gave pH readings of 7.

2. Fruit juices, vinegar, soft drinks, and some cleaners will be acidic. Water, salt, and sugar will be neutral. Soaps, some household cleaners, and antacids will be basic.

3. Answers will vary, but students can use their pH readings to support their answer.

4. See student results from lab to determine answer.

Error Analysis Discuss with students things that might cause errors in their data. Ask how they could reduce the errors.

● Conclude and Apply

lemon juice

Content Background

When sulfur dioxide (SO_2) and various nitrogen oxides (NO_x) contact water in the atmosphere, they form acids of varying strengths. The strength of an acid is determined by its degree of ionization in solution. Ionized acids increase the H^+ concentration resulting in a lower pH. Bases are H^+ receptors and will lower the H^+ concentration and raise the pH.

When acids are flushed from the atmosphere by rain and fall on materials that contain calcium carbonate, such as limestone, marble, and some sandstones, the reaction forms gypsum, CO_2, and water. The gypsum and water are easily washed away.

Discussion

Preservation Do we need to preserve historical monuments in order to learn about the past they represent? Why or why not? Some students may say that pictures in textbooks are sufficient for learning about a particular monument or the culture and events it represents. Other students may say that without the actual monument, people will learn less about the cultures and events the monument represents. L2

IS Logical-Mathematical

Historical Significance

As old or ancient structures deteriorate or disappear, the past tends to disappear with them. Students should understand that ancient buildings like the Parthenon and the Coliseum are tangible links to history that lead people to consider the events that occurred in and around them. The carvings on old temples and the images in ancient statues are indicators of the worldview of their creators. The more these images deteriorate, the more information is lost.

TIME > SCIENCE AND HISTORY

SCIENCE CAN CHANGE THE COURSE OF HISTORY!

CRUMBLING MONUMENTS

Acid rain is eroding some of the world's most famous monuments

The Taj Mahal in India, the Acropolis in Greece, and the Colosseum in Italy, have stood for centuries. They've survived wars, souvenir-hunters, and natural weathering from wind and rain. But now, something far worse threatens their existence—acid rain. Over the last few decades, this form of pollution has eaten away at some of history's greatest monuments.

Acid rain leads to health and environmental risks. It also harms human-made structures. Most of these structures are made of sandstone, limestone, and marble. Acid rain causes the calcium in these stones to form calcium sulfate, or gypsum. Gypsum's powdery little blotches are sometimes called "marble cancer." When it rains, the gypsum washes away, along with some of the surface of the monument. In many cases, acidic soot falls into the cracks of monuments. When rainwater seeps into the cracks, acidic water is formed, which further damages the structure.

In London, acid rain has forced workers to repair and replace so much of Westminster Abbey that the structure is becoming a mere copy of the original. Because of pollution, many corroding statues displayed outdoors have been brought inside museums.

Throughout the world, acid rain has weathered many structures more in the last 20 years than in the prior 2,000 years. This is one reason some steps have been taken in Europe and the United States to reduce emissions from the burning of fossil fuels.

Identify Which monuments and buildings represent the United States? Brainstorm a list with your class. Then choose a monument, and using your school's media center, learn more about it. Is acid rain affecting it in any way?

Science Online

For more information, visit ips.msscience.com/time

Preservation Suggest students also try to obtain information about the state of local monuments and how their community is dealing with acid rain damage if it is occurring. L3

Resources for Teachers and Students

Acid Rain, by Peter Tyson, Chelsea House Publishers, 1992

Markets for Clean Air: The U.S. Acid Rain Program, by Denny A. Ellerman et. al., Cambridge University Press, 2002

Reviewing Main Ideas

Section 1 Physical Properties

1. A physical property can be observed without changing the makeup of the material.

2. Acids and bases have physical properties. Acids have a sharp smell and a sour taste. Bases have a bitter taste and feel slippery.

3. Mass, volume, state of matter, and density are examples of physical properties.

Section 2 Chemical Properties

1. A chemical property is a characteristic of matter that allows it to change to a different type of matter.

2. Acids and bases are in many household products.

3. Acids and bases react with each other to produce water and a salt.

Section 3 Physical and Chemical Changes

1. A physical change is a change in the size, shape, form, or state of matter. The chemical makeup of the matter stays the same.

2. Water undergoes a change of state when it changes from a solid to a liquid or a liquid to a gas.

3. In chemical changes, new matter is changed to a different type of matter.

4. Evidence that a chemical change might have occurred includes a color or energy change or the formation of a gas or solid.

Visualizing Main Ideas

Copy and complete the following concept map about matter.

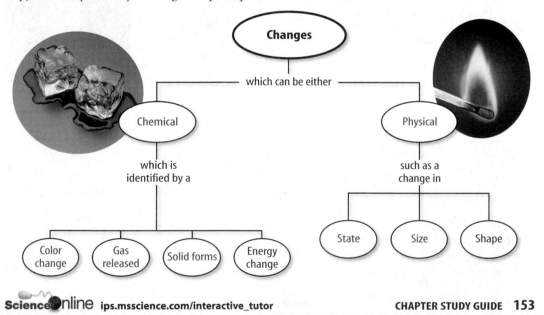

Reviewing Main Ideas

Summary statements can be used by students to review the major concepts of the chapter.

Visualizing Main Ideas

See student page.

Science **Online**

Visit ips.msscience.com
/self_check_quiz
/interactive_tutor
/vocabulary_puzzlemaker
/chapter_review
/standardized_test

Assessment Transparency

For additional assessment questions, use the *Assessment Transparency* located in the transparency book.

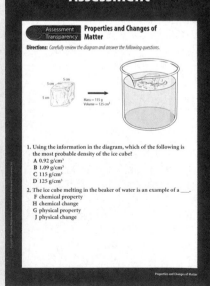

Using Vocabulary

1. Mass divided by volume is the formula for density.

2. Color, shape, size, and state are physical properties.

3. Snow melting is a physical change.

4. Acid rain damaging marble statues is an example of a chemical change.

5. Iron rusting in moist air is an example of the reactivity of iron.

Checking Concepts

6. D 10. C
7. B 11. D
8. A 12. D
9. B

Thinking Critically

13. Density Is the result of dividing a sample's mass by its volume. No; feathers are much less dense than rocks.

14. a. physical; b. chemical; c. physical; d. chemical

15. physical; a solution is made. Evaporate the water and the antacid is retained.

16. more dense; The antacid has a high mass but a low volume, therefore its density is higher than water and it will sink.

Using Vocabulary

chemical change p. 145	salt p. 142
chemical property p. 139	size-dependent property
density p. 134	p. 136
physical change p. 143	size-independent property
physical property p. 134	p. 136
reactivity p. 140	state of matter p. 136

Answer the following questions using complete sentences.

1. Mass divided by volume is the formula for which physical property?

2. Which type of properties include color, shape, size, and state?

3. Snow melting in sunshine is an example of which type of change?

4. Acid rain damaging marble statues is an example of which type of change?

5. Iron rusts in moist air. Which chemical property is this?

Checking Concepts

Choose the word or phrase that best answers the question.

6. Which of the following is a chemical property of a substance?
   A) density   C) mass
   B) white powder   D) reacts with HCl

7. Which item below is a sign of a chemical change?
   A) change of water vapor to liquid
   B) release of energy
   C) change from a liquid to a solid
   D) change in shape

8. Which type of change listed below results in new compounds being formed?
   A) chemical   C) seasonal
   B) physical   D) state

9. Salts are formed when which of the following react?
   A) solids and gases
   B) acids and bases
   C) bases and gases
   D) acids and solids

10. Which of the following physical properties does a base have?
    A) cold to touch
    B) gives off gas
    C) slippery and bitter taste
    D) sharp smell and sour taste

11. Which of the following changes when water evaporates?
    A) the physical properties of the water
    B) the chemical properties of the water
    C) the color of the water
    D) the mass of the water

Use the illustrations below to answer question 12.

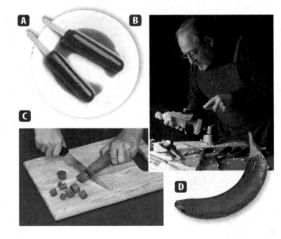

12. Which figure above clearly identifies a chemical change?
    A) A
    B) B
    C) C
    D) D

Science**online** ips.msscience.com/vocabulary_puzzlemaker

Use the Exam*View*® Pro Testmaker CD-ROM to:
- create multiple versions of tests
- create modified tests with one mouse click for inclusion students
- edit existing questions and add your own questions
- build tests aligned with state standards using built-in State Curriculum Tags
- change English tests to Spanish with one mouse click and vice versa

Thinking Critically

13. Explain Think about what you know about density. Could a bag of feathers have more mass than the same size bag of rocks? Explain.

14. Classify each of the following as either a physical property or a chemical property.
  a. Sulfur shatters when hit.
  b. Copper statues turn green.
  c. Baking soda is a white powder.
  d. Newspaper turns brown when it is exposed to air and light.

Use the photo below to answer questions 15 and 16.

15. Identify The antacid dissolves in water. Is this a physical or a chemical property of the antacid? Explain.

16. Draw Conclusions Think about what you know about density. Is the antacid tablet more or less dense than water. Explain.

17. Determine A jeweler bends gold into a beautiful ring. What type of change is this? Explain.

18. Compare and Contrast Relate such human characteristics as hair and eye color, height, and weight to physical properties of matter. Relate human behavior to chemical properties. Think about how you observe these properties.

19. Identify Sugar dissolves in water. Is this a physical property or a chemical property of sugar?

20. Evaluate When butane burns, it combines with oxygen in the air to form carbon dioxide and water. Which two elements must be present in butane?

21. Identify each of the following as a physical change or a chemical change.
  a. Metal is drawn out into a wire.
  b. Sulfur in eggs tarnishes silver.
  c. Baking powder bubbles when water is added to it.

Performance Activities

22. Display Create a display that demonstrates the characteristics of a chemical change. Be sure your display shows release of energy, change of color, and the formation of a solid.

Applying Math

Use the table below to answer questions 23–25.

Using the Density Formula

Sample	Mass (g)	Volume (cm³)	Density (g/cm³)
A	5.4	3.8	
B	6.8		0.65
C		8.6	2.18

23. Determine Density Knowing the mass and volume of Sample A, calculate its density.

24. Determine the mass of Sample C from its density and volume.

25. Determine the volume of Sample B from its mass and density.

Science Online ips.msscience.com/chapter_review

CHAPTER REVIEW 155

Thinking Critically

17. Bending is a physical change because it does not change the composition of the gold.

18. Human characteristics can be observed without interacting with a person. For example, you can observe hair and eye color from a distance. Human behavior can be observed only by observing that person's interactions.

19. It is a physical property because the compounds water and sugar remain unchanged in the solution.

20. carbon and hydrogen

21. a. physical; b. chemical; c. chemical

Performance Activities

22. Displays should make it clear that all of these characteristics do not happen with each chemical change. If students make displays that actually involve chemical reactions, check the pan for safety before students build the displays. **PASC,** p. X

Applying Math

National Math Standards
1, 2, 3, 4, 5, 9
23. 1.4 g/cm^3
24. 18.7 g
25. 10.5 cm^3

Answer Sheet A practice answer sheet can be found at ips.msscience.com/answer_sheet.

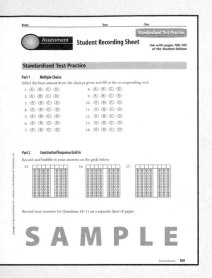

S A M P L E

Part 1 | Multiple Choice

Record your answers on the answer sheet provided by your teacher or on a sheet of paper.

1. Which of the following properties is a size-independent property?
   - **A.** state
   - **B.** length
   - **C.** mass
   - **D.** volume

Use the table below to answer questions 2, 3 and 4.

Density of Some Pure Metals	
Metal	**Density (g/cm³)**
Copper	8.96
Iron	7.87
Lead	11.3
Magnesium	1.74
Silver	10.5
Zinc	7.14

2. According to the table above, what is the mass of a 6.37-cm³ sample of iron?
   - **A.** 0.809 g
   - **B.** 1.24 g
   - **C.** 7.87 g
   - **D.** 50.1 g

3. According to the table above, what is the volume of a 25.1 g piece of silver?
   - **A.** 8.25 cm³
   - **B.** 2.39 cm³
   - **C.** 5.73 cm³
   - **D.** 3.46 cm³

4. During an experiment, you measure the mass of an unknown substance as 28.4 g and its volume as 2.5 cm³. Use the table above to determine the most likely identity of the unknown substance.
   - **A.** zinc
   - **B.** magnesium
   - **C.** lead
   - **D.** iron

5. Which of the following terms describes a substance with a pH of 7?
   - **A.** acidic
   - **B.** neutral
   - **C.** basic
   - **D.** bitter

Use the photograph below to answer questions 6 and 7.

6. Which of the following statements best explains why the nails in the photograph above rusted?
   - **A.** The nails drew rust from the air.
   - **B.** Iron in the nails changed into other elements.
   - **C.** The rust formed when iron mixed with oxygen and moisture in the air.
   - **D.** A temperature change drew rust out of the nails.

7. Which of the following best describes rust?
   - **A.** reversible physical change
   - **B.** irreversible physical change
   - **C.** reversible chemical change
   - **D.** irreversible chemical change

8. Which of the following describes a chemical change?
   - **A.** water freezing into ice
   - **B.** a match burning
   - **C.** dew forming on a leaf
   - **D.** magnetization of an iron nail

9. The density of a 30-g sample of gold is 19.3 g/cm³. What is the density of a 90-g sample?
   - **A.** 6.43 g
   - **B.** 19.3 g
   - **C.** 57.9 g
   - **D.** 79.3 g

156 STANDARDIZED TEST PRACTICE

Part 2 | Short Response/Grid In

10. An acid is sour. A base is bitter and slippery.

11. 2.65 g/cm³

12. No, many harmless substances you encounter ever day are acids and bases. For example, carbonic acid and phosphoric acid are in soft drinks. Hand soap is a base.

13. A physical change occurs as your teeth break the food into smaller pieces. A chemical change occurs as saliva reacts with the food.

14. 1.15 cm³

15. As the temperature of the water rises, the water experiences a physical change. The chemical composition of the water does not change.

16. The logs, when burning, give off light and heat, which are signs of a chemical change. The burning wood changes to ash and gas, which is also another sign of a chemical change.

Part 2 | Short Response/Grid In

Record your answers on the answer sheet provided by your teacher or on a sheet of paper.

10. Tell whether each of the following words describes an acid or a base: bitter, slippery, sour.

11. What is the density of a 25.3-g sample of quartz that has a volume of 9.55 cm³?

12. Are all acids and bases dangerous? Explain why or why not, and give examples to support your answer.

13. Describe a chemical and a physical change that occurs in food as you chew it.

14. The density of stainless steel is 8.02 g/cm³. What is the volume of a 9.25 g piece of stainless steel?

Use the photograph below to answer questions 15 and 16.

15. The photograph above shows a campfire with water heating in a cooking pot. Does the water experience a chemical or physical change as its temperature rises? Explain.

16. Are the logs on the campfire experiencing a chemical or physical change? How can you tell?

Science Online ips.msscience.com/standardized_test

Part 3 | Open Ended

Record your answers on a sheet of paper.

Use the photograph below to answer questions 17 and 18.

17. What would happen if you left the glass of cold water shown in the photograph above in sunlight for several hours? Describe how some physical properties of the water would change.

18. What properties of the water would not change? Explain why the density of the water would or would not change.

19. Suppose you have three different-sized balls, each having a different mass. Can you tell which has the greatest density simply by feeling which is heavier? Explain why or why not.

20. Describe the pH scale. What is its use?

21. What are some things you might observe during an experiment that would indicate a chemical change may be occurring? Explain which of these may, instead, be the result of a physical change.

Test-Taking Tip

Answer Every Part Make sure each part of the question is answered when listing discussion points. For example, if the question asks you to compare and contrast, make sure you list both similarities and differences.

20. The pH of a sample tells the strength of an acid or base. The pH scale has a range of 0 to 14. Acids have a pH below 7. Bases have a pH above 7. A sample with a pH of exactly 7 is neither acidic nor basic.

21. Some indications of a chemical change are formation of light, heat, or sound. Formation of a gas or solid may occur during a chemical change, but they may also result from a physical change during a change of state. Color change often results from a chemical change. However, a color change may be the result of one color masking another during a physical change.

Rubrics

For more help evaluating open-ended assessment questions, see the rubric on p. 10T.

Part 3 | Open Ended

17. The temperature of the water would increase. Part of the water would evaporate, changing from a liquid to a gas. This would decrease the mass and volume of the water in the glass.

18. The melting point, boiling point, and solubility of the water are independent of sample size and will not change. Density, also, is independent of sample size. The density of the water remaining in the glass will not change. However, the water that evaporates to a gaseous state will have a lower density.

19. No; knowing which is heavier won't tell you which has the greatest density. Density equals mass divided by volume. An object can have a high density either by having a high mass or by having a low volume.

unit 3

Chemistry

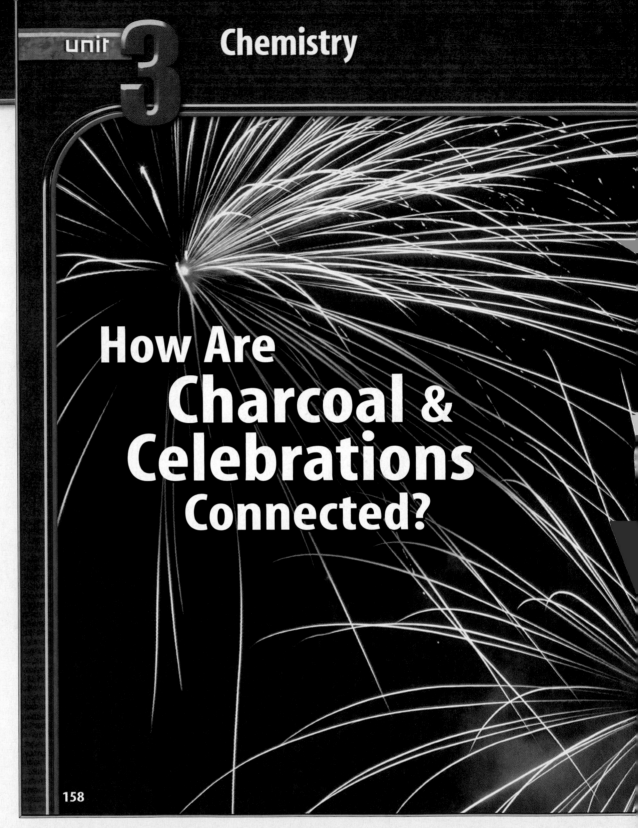

How Are Charcoal & Celebrations Connected?

158

Unit Contents

WebQuest *Chemistry of Fireworks* is designed to engage students in researching the chemical components of fireworks, how chemicals are used to produce different colors, the history of fireworks, and how firework displays are created. Students will answer a set of questions following their Web research to demonstrate the knowledge they have gained.

PROJECT *Study Skills*

CRISS™

Discussion The Think-Pair-Share strategy is effective in ensuring involvement of every student and clarifying misconceptions. After finishing the unit, pair the class members and give them specific topics regarding chemical bonds and chemical reactions. Have them individually write down what they have learned about the topic, share, clarify, and generate new ideas with their partners. Conclude with whole class discussion.

NATIONAL GEOGRAPHIC

According to one report, one day in the tenth century in China, a cook combined charcoal with two other ingredients that were common in Chinese kitchens. The result was a spectacular explosion of sparks. Whether or not that story is true, most experts agree that fireworks originated in China. The Chinese discovered that if the ingredients were put into a bamboo tube, the force of the reaction would send the tube zooming into the sky. The spectacular light and noise were perfect for celebrations. Traders carried the art of firework making westward to Europe. The Europeans added new colors to the bursts by mixing various chemicals into the explosive powder. Today, people all over the world use colorful fireworks to celebrate special occasions.

unit → projects

Visit blue.msscience.com/unit_project to find project ideas and resources. Projects include:

- **Career** Discover polymers and their uses. Brainstorm a list of questions for a polymer chemist about these new materials.
- **Technology** Investigate the chemical makeup of your breakfast cereal or snack food. Design a circle graph showing the percentages of each chemical ingredient in your food sample.
- **Model** Demonstrate to the class a common chemical reaction. Compile a class collection of these simple chemical reactions to share with others.

WebQuest *Chemistry of Fireworks* explores the chemical compounds of fireworks, what chemicals are used, and how firework displays are created.

unit → projects

Career Have students explore the world of chemical polymers. Then as a class, have students brainstorm a list of questions they might ask a chemist or chemical engineer. If possible, have students contact a person in a chemistry related field or arrange a guest speaker.

Technology Have students investigate the chemical components in their breakfast cereal, snack food, toiletries, cleaning supplies, or insecticide. After exploring the chemical make up and purpose of each ingredient, have students design a circle graph representing the correct percentages of each component. Remind students to use the proper labels on all parts of their graph, including the key.

Model Have students research and design a simple and safe chemical reaction demonstration. Using their newly acquired knowledge of states of matter, chemical bonds, mixtures, and chemical reactions, have students present their mini-chemical experiment to the class with a verbal explanation of the chemical and physical changes taking place. Each student's reaction recipe may be compiled for a take-home chemistry collection.

Additional Resources For more information, resources, and assessment rubrics, visit ips.msscience.com/unit_project

NATIONAL GEOGRAPHIC How Are Charcoal & Celebrations Connected?

The mixture of sulfur, potassium nitrate, and charcoal is called black powder and is very flammable. The Chinese perfected the recipe for black powder for entertainment and celebrations, but found it could be used to fuel rocket-powered arrows in their defense against the Mongol invaders.

The knowledge of making fireworks spread west from China, to Europe. Europeans advanced this technology to make gunpowder. Skilled tradesmen called firemakers, who made fireworks for peace or victory celebrations, also made guns. The introduction of magnesium and aluminum added brilliant color to the fireworks displays.

Section/Objectives	Standards		Labs/Features
Chapter Opener	**National**	**State/Local**	**Launch Lab:** Model the Energy of Electrons, p. 161 **Foldables,** p. 161
	See pp. 16T–17T for a Key to Standards.		
Section 1 Why do atoms combine? ● 2 sessions 🖳 1 block 1. **Identify** how electrons are arranged in an atom. 2. **Compare** the relative amounts of energy of electrons in an atom. 3. **Compare** how the arrangement of electrons in an atom is related to its place in the periodic table.	National Content Standards: UCP.1, UCP.2, UCP.3, UCP.5, A.1, A.2, B.1, B.2		**Science Online,** p. 164 **Integrate Career,** p. 165 **Applying Science:** How does the periodic table help you identify properties of elements?, p. 167 **MiniLAB:** Drawing Electron Dot Diagrams, p. 168
Section 2 How Elements Bond ● 5 sessions 🖳 2.5 blocks 4. **Compare and contrast** ionic and covalent bonds. 5. **Distinguish** between compounds and molecules. 6. **Identify** the difference between polar and nonpolar covalent bonds. 7. **Interpret** chemical shorthand.	National Content Standards: UCP.1, UCP.2, UCP.3, UCP.5, A.1, A.2, B.1, B.2		**Integrate Physics,** p. 171 **MiniLAB:** Constructing a Model of Methane, p. 173 **Science Online,** p. 175 **Visualizing Crystal Structure,** p. 176 **Lab:** Ionic Compounds, p. 179 **Lab:** Atomic Structure, p. 180 **Science and Language Arts:** Baring the Atom's Mother Heart, p. 182

Lab Materials	Reproducible Resources	Section Assessment	Technology
Launch Lab: paper clips (6), magnet	**Chapters FAST FILE Resources** Foldables Worksheet, p. 17 Directed Reading Overview, p. 19 Note-taking Worksheets, pp. 31–32	**GLENCOE'S ASSESSMENT ADVANTAGE**	**TeacherWorks** includes: • Interactive Teacher Edition • Lesson Planner with calendar • Access to all program blacklines • Correlations to standards • Web links
MiniLAB: periodic table, pencil, paper *Need materials?* Contact Science Kit at 1-800-828-7777 or www.sciencekit.com on the Internet.	**Chapter FAST FILE Resources** Transparency Activity, p. 42 MiniLAB, p. 3 Enrichment, p. 29 Reinforcement, p. 27 Directed Reading, p. 20 Transparency Activity, pp. 45–46 Lab Activity, pp. 9–12 **Cultural Diversity,** pp. 55, 59	**Portfolio** Differentiated Instruction, p. 168 **Performance** Applying Science, p. 167 MiniLAB, p. 168 Applying Math, p. 169 **Content** Section Review, p. 169	🔦 Section Focus Transparency 🔦 Teaching Transparency 💿 Virtual Labs CD-ROM 🎧 Guided Reading Audio Program 💿 Interactive Chalkboard CD-ROM
MiniLAB: construction paper (3 different colors), scissors **Lab:** 8 different colors of paper, 2 different colors of tacks, corrugated cardboard, scissors **Lab:** magnetic board, rubber magnetic strips, candy-coated chocolates, scissors, paper, marker, coins	**Chapter FAST FILE Resources** Transparency Activity, p. 43 MiniLAB, p. 4 Enrichment, p. 30 Reinforcement, p. 28 Directed Reading, pp. 21, 22 Lab Activity, pp. 13–16 Lab Worksheets, pp. 5–6, pp. 7–8 **Lab Management and Safety,** p. 79	**Portfolio** Cultural Diversity, p. 171 Assessment, p. 178 **Performance** MiniLAB, p. 173 Applying Skills, p. 178 **Content** Section Review, p. 178	🔦 Section Focus Transparency 🎧 Guided Reading Audio Program 💿 Interactive Chalkboard CD-ROM 📼 Video Lab

End of Chapter Assessment

GLENCOE'S ASSESSMENT ADVANTAGE

Blackline Masters	Technology	Professional Series
Chapter FAST FILE Resources Chapter Review, pp. 35–36 Chapter Tests, pp. 37–40 **Standardized Test Practice,** pp. 27–30	📼 MindJogger Videoquiz 💿 Virtual Labs CD-ROM 💿 ExamView® Pro Testmaker 💿 TeacherWorks CD-ROM 💿 Interactive Chalkboard CD-ROM	**Performance Assessment in the Science Classroom (PASC)**

Transparencies

Section Focus

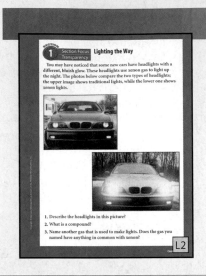

SECTION 1 Section Focus Transparency — **Lighting the Way**

You may have noticed that some new cars have headlights with a different, bluish glow. These headlights use xenon gas to light up the night. The photos below compare the two types of headlights; the upper image shows traditional lights, while the lower one shows xenon lights.

1. Describe the headlights in this picture?
2. What is a compound?
3. Name another gas that is used to make lights. Does the gas you named have anything in common with xenon?

L2

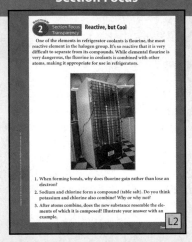

SECTION 2 Section Focus Transparency — **Reactive, but Cool**

One of the elements in refrigerator coolants is flourine, the most reactive element in the halogen group. It's so reactive that it is very difficult to separate from its compounds. While elemental flourine is very dangerous, the fluorine in coolants is combined with other atoms, making it appropriate for use in refrigerators.

1. When forming bonds, why does fluorine gain rather than lose an electron?
2. Sodium and chlorine form a compound (table salt). Do you think potassium and chlorine also combine? Why or why not?
3. After atoms combine, does the new substance resemble the elements of which it is composed? Illustrate your answer with an example.

L2

This is a representation of key blackline masters available in the Teacher Classroom Resources. See Resource Manager boxes within the chapter for additional information.

Key to Teaching Strategies

The following designations will help you decide which activities are appropriate for your students.

L1 Level 1 activities should be appropriate for students with learning difficulties.

L2 Level 2 activities should be within the ability range of all students.

L3 Level 3 activities are designed for above-average students.

ELL ELL activities should be within the ability range of English Language Learners.

COOP LEARN Cooperative Learning activities are designed for small group work.

LS Multiple Learning Styles logos, as described on page 12T, are used throughout to indicate strategies that address different learning styles.

P These strategies represent student products that can be placed into a best-work portfolio.

PBL Problem-Based Learning activities apply real-world situations to learning.

Assessment

Assessment Transparency — **Chemical Bonds**

Directions: *Carefully review the table and answer the following questions.*

Dot Diagrams for Some Atoms

Element	Periodic group	Dot diagram
Lithium	Group 1	Li·
Aluminum	Group 13	A̤l̇·
Carbon	Group 14	·C̤·
Chlorine	Group 17	:C̤l:

1. Most elements strive to become stable having eight electrons in their outer energy level. According to this information, how many more electrons would chlorine need to become stable?
   A 7   C 3
   B 5   D 1
2. Elements in the same group have a similar dot diagram. Given that potassium is a Group 1 element, its dot diagram most likely ____.
   F has three electron dots   H has one electron dot
   G has seven electron dots   J has four electron dots
3. According to the table, which element has the greatest number of electrons in its dot diagram?
   A Lithium   C Aluminum
   B Chlorine   D Carbon

L2

Teaching

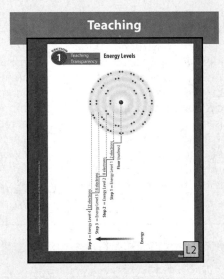

SECTION 1 Teaching Transparency — **Energy Levels**

L2

Hands-on Activities

Student Text Lab Worksheet

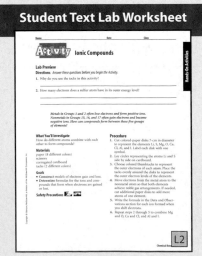

Activity — **Ionic Compounds**

Lab Preview
Directions: *Answer these questions before you begin the Activity.*
1. Why do you use the tacks in this activity?

2. How many electrons does a sulfur atom have in its outer energy level?

Metals in Groups 1 and 2 often lose electrons and form positive ions. Nonmetals in Groups 15, 16, and 17 often gain electrons and become negative ions. How can compounds form between these five groups of elements?

What You'll Investigate
How do different atoms combine with each other to form compounds?

Materials
paper (8 different colors)
scissors
corrugated cardboard
tacks (2 different colors)

Goals
• **Construct** models of electron gain and loss.
• **Determine** formulas for the ions and compounds that form when electrons are gained or lost.

Safety Precautions

Procedure
1. Cut colored-paper disks 7-cm in diameter to represent the elements Li, S, Mg, O, Ca, Cl, Al, and I. Label each disk with one symbol.
2. Lay circles representing the atoms Li and S side by side on cardboard.
3. Choose colored thumbtacks to represent the outer electrons of each atom. Place the tacks evenly around the disks to represent the outer electron levels of the elements.
4. Move electrons from the metal atom to the nonmetal atom so that both elements achieve noble gas arrangements. If needed, cut additional paper disks to add more paper tacks of one element.
5. Write the formula in the Data and Observations section for each ion formed when ions shift electrons.
6. Repeat steps 2 through 5 to combine Mg and O, Ca and Cl, and Al and I.

L2

Laboratory Activities

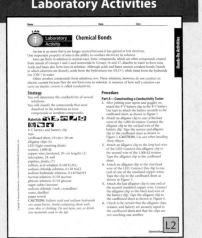

LAB 1 Laboratory Activity — **Chemical Bonds**

An ion is an atom that is no longer neutral because it has gained or lost electrons. One important property of ions is the ability to conduct electricity in solution.

Ions can form in solution in several ways. Ionic compounds, which are often compounds created from metals of Groups 1 and 2 and nonmetals in Groups 16 and 17, dissolve in water to form ions. Acids and bases also form ions in solution. Although acids and bases contain covalent bonds (bonds in which electrons are shared), acids form the hydronium ion (H₃O⁺), while bases form the hydroxide ion (OH⁻) in water.

Other covalent compounds form solutions, too. These solutions, however, do not conduct an electric current because they do not form ions in solution. A measure of how well a solution can carry an electric current is called conductivity.

Strategy
You will determine the conductivity of several solutions.
You will classify the compounds that were dissolved in the solutions as ionic compounds or covalent compounds.

Materials
9-V battery and battery clip
tape
cardboard sheet, 10 cm x 10 cm
alligator clips (4)
LED (light-emitting diode)
resistor, 1,000-Ω
copper wire, insulated, 20-cm lengths (2)
microplate, 24-well
pipettes, plastic (7)
sulfuric acid solution, 0.1M H₂SO₄
sodium chloride solution, 0.1M NaCl
sodium hydroxide solution, 0.1M NaOH
sucrose solution, 0.1M sucrose
glucose solution, 0.1M glucose
sugar cubes (sucrose)
sodium chloride (rock, crystalline)
water, distilled
paper towels
CAUTION: *Sulfuric acid and sodium hydroxide can cause burns. Avoid contacting them with your skin or clothing. Do not taste, eat, or drink any materials used in the lab.*

Procedure
Part A—Constructing a Conductivity Tester
1. After putting your apron and goggles on, attach the 9-V battery clip to the 9-V battery. Use tape to attach the battery securely to the cardboard sheet, as shown in Figure 1.
2. Attach an alligator clip to one of the lead wires of the 1,000-Ω resistor. Connect the alligator clip to the red lead wire of the battery clip. Tape the resistor and alligator clip to the cardboard sheet as shown in Figure 2. CAUTION: *Use care when handling sharp objects.*
3. Attach an alligator clip to the long lead wire of the LED. Connect this alligator clip to the second wire of the 1,000-Ω resistor. Tape the alligator clip to the cardboard sheet.
4. Attach an alligator clip to the short lead wire of the LED. Connect this clip to one end of one of the insulated copper wires. Tape the alligator clip to the cardboard sheet as shown in Figure 3.
5. Attach the last alligator clip to one end of the second insulated wire. Connect the alligator clip to the black lead wire of the battery clip. Tape the alligator clip to the cardboard sheet as shown in Figure 4.
6. Check to be certain that the alligator clips, resistor, and battery are securely taped to the cardboard sheet and that the clips are not touching one another.

L2

Meeting Different Ability Levels

Content Outline

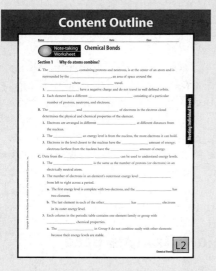

L2

Reinforcement

L2

Enrichment

L3

Directed Reading (English/Spanish)

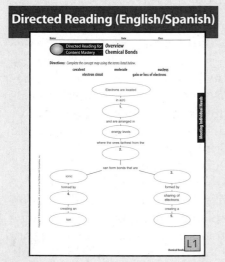

L1

Study Guide

L2

Reading Essentials

L1

Assessment

Test Practice Workbook

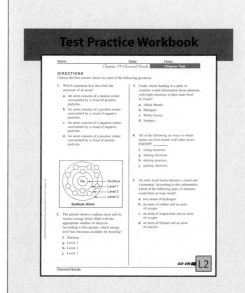

L2

Chapter Review

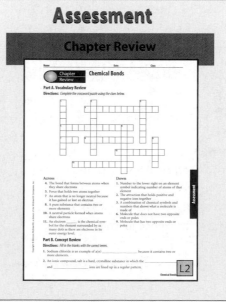

L2

Chapter Tests

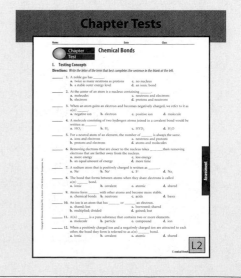

L2

Science Content Background

section 1

Why do atoms combine?
Electron Arrangement

Each electron in an atom has a set of four quantum numbers, and no sets are identical. The energy level occupied by an electron is determined by its principal quantum number, n, which can have integral values beginning with 1. The values of n correspond to the energy levels shown in **Figure 4** of the chapter. The maximum number of electrons an energy level can hold can be calculated from the expression $2n^2$. If 1, 2, 3, and 4 are substituted, in turn, into the expression $2n^2$, the results correspond to the numbers of electrons shown at each of the four steps, or energy levels. A second quantum number describes the type of orbital an electron is in and is denoted using the letters s, p, d, f, g, and so on. Different orbital types have different shapes, energies, and hold different numbers of electrons. The last two quantum numbers describe an orbital's orientation and the spin of an electron.

The Periodic Table

The number of electrons in an atom increases by one from left to right across the periodic table. These electrons fill energy levels and orbitals from lowest energy to highest energy. The order of electron filling is as follows: 1s, 2s, 2p, 3s, 3p, 4s, 3d, 4p, 5s, 4d, 5p, 6s, 4f, 5d, 6p, 7s, 5f, 6d, 7p. As you can see, electrons do not necessarily fill in the order of the principal quantum number. This is because both the principal quantum number and the orbital type determine the total energy of an electron. An energy level ($n = 2$ or higher) will only contain eight electrons before the next energy level begins filling. Therefore, an outer energy level can contain a maximum of eight electrons.

section 2

How Elements Bond
Chemical Bonds

Students can use electron dot diagrams to help them predict the ions that some of the lighter representative elements will form or the number of covalent bonds others will form. However, such predictions are not as clear-cut for the transition elements and for the heavier representative elements because many of these elements are capable of forming more than one ion. For example, iron can lose either two or three electrons to form the common ions Fe^{2+} or Fe^{3+}.

It's important to recognize the distinction between a compound and a molecule. A compound is a substance that contains two or more elements. The elements may be joined by ionic or covalent bonds. Covalently bonded compounds are called molecular compounds. Molecules may contain one or more elements.

chapter content resources

Internet Resources
For additional content background, visit
ips.msscience.com to:
- access your book online
- find references to related articles in popular science magazines
- access Web links with related content background
- access current events with science journal topics

Print Resources
Chemistry; The Molecular Nature of Matter and Change, by Martin S. Silberberg, McGraw-Hill, 2003
Structure and Bonding, by Jack Barrett and Eddie Abel, John Wiley & Sons, Incorporated, 2002
Chemical Bonding and Molecular Geometry: From Lewis to Election Densities, by Ronald J. Gillespie and Paul L. A. Popelier, Oxford University Press, 2001

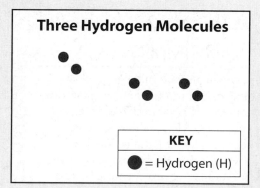

IDENTIFYING Misconceptions

Find Out What Students Think

Students may think that . . .

Formulas and coefficients in an equation tell how many atoms there are but don't tell how the atoms are bonded together.

Several misconception studies show that when students are asked to draw representations of molecules such as $3H_2$ (three hydrogen molecules), a large percentage draw six circles evenly spaced apart, rather than three sets of two circles that are close together, as shown below. This is true even for advanced students who can balance chemical equations. They simply apply the multiplication skills they know but have not grasped the concept of what a molecule is and what coefficients and subscripts are.

Demonstration

Ask each student to draw a diagram of $3H_2$, using a blue circle to represent each hydrogen atom. Explain that the number 3 means there are three molecules present.

Promote Understanding

Activity

Three Hydrogen Molecules

KEY
● = Hydrogen (H)

Ask each student to cut two circles that are each about the size of a half-dollar, from a piece of blue construction paper. Tell students that each one of these is a very, very, large model of a hydrogen atom. Ask students to make one hydrogen molecule from these two circles.

Students should determine that the two circles should be attached. Provide students with tape or glue. If they don't come to this conclusion, ask them how they would make a cheese sandwich out of two slices of bread and a slice of cheese. If students attach one piece of paper directly on top of the other, remind them that atoms are three-dimensional. Ask them how they would attach two table-tennis balls.

Once students have created a model of H_2, ask students to make a model of three hydrogen molecules from blue construction paper. Check students' models.

Finally, ask students to make representations of the following molecules using different colored circles to represent different elements: $2CO_2$, $4N_2$, and $3NH_3$. L2 **IS** **Visual-Spatial**

Assess

After completing the chapter, see *Identifying Misconceptions* in the Study Guide at the end of the chapter.

Chapter Vocabulary

electron cloud, p. 162
energy level, p. 163
electron dot diagram, p. 168
chemical bond, p. 169
ion, p. 171
ionic bond, p. 171
compound, p. 171
metallic bond, p. 172
covalent bond, p. 173
molecule, p. 173
polar bond, p. 174
chemical formula, p. 178

Science Journal Answers will vary. Look for depth and quality of information.

INTERACTIVE CHALKBOARD with Image Bank

PowerPoint® Presentations

This CD-ROM is an editable Microsoft® PowerPoint® presentation that includes:
- a pre-made presentation for every chapter
- interactive graphics
- animations
- audio clips
- image bank
- all new section and chapter questions
- Standardized Test Practice
- transparencies
- pre-lab questions for all labs
- Foldables directions
- links to ips.msscience.com

Atomic Structure and Chemical Bonds

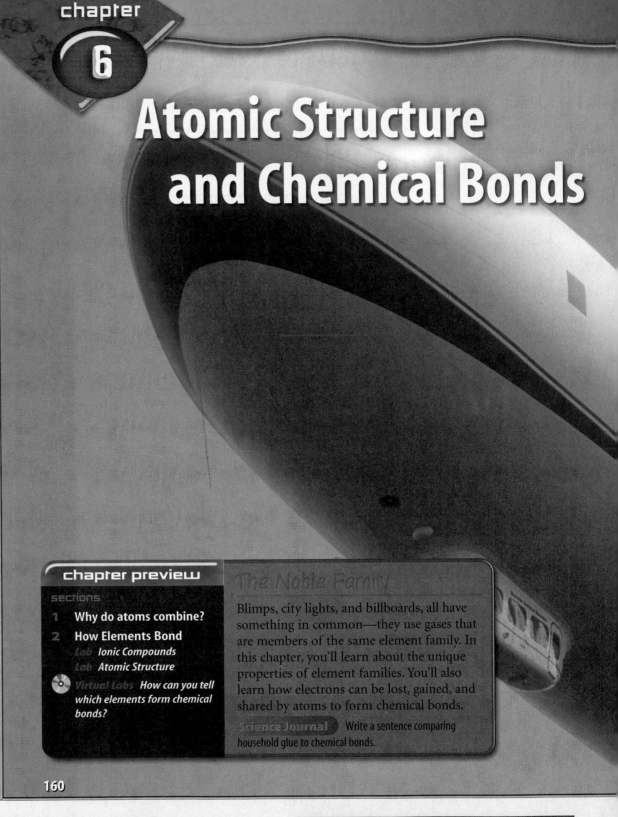

chapter preview

sections

1 **Why do atoms combine?**

2 **How Elements Bond**
   Lab Ionic Compounds
   Lab Atomic Structure
   Virtual Labs How can you tell which elements form chemical bonds?

The Noble Family

Blimps, city lights, and billboards, all have something in common—they use gases that are members of the same element family. In this chapter, you'll learn about the unique properties of element families. You'll also learn how electrons can be lost, gained, and shared by atoms to form chemical bonds.

Science Journal Write a sentence comparing household glue to chemical bonds.

160

Theme Connection

Stability and Change Atoms often will change by gaining or losing electrons to become more stable.

About the Photo

Combining Elements Blimps are filled with helium. Helium is a member of the noble gases group of the periodic table. Neon and argon, elements used to make signs, are part of this group also. The electron configurations of these three elements are the same. In this chapter, students will learn how electron configurations relate to chemical bonding.

Start-Up Activities

Model the Energy of Electrons

It's time to clean out your room—again. Where do all these things come from? Some are made of cloth and some of wood. The books are made of paper and an endless array of things are made of plastic. Fewer than 100 different kinds of naturally occurring elements are found on Earth. They combine to make all these different substances. What makes elements form chemical bonds with other elements? The answer is in their electrons.

1. Pick up a paper clip with a magnet. Touch that paper clip to another paper clip and pick it up.

2. Continue picking up paper clips this way until you have a strand of them and no more will attach.

3. Then, gently pull off the paper clips one by one.

4. **Think Critically** In your Science Journal, discuss which paper clip was easiest to remove and which was hardest. Was the clip that was easiest to remove closer to or farther from the magnet?

Chemical Bonds Make the following Foldable to help you classify information by diagramming ideas about chemical bonds.

STEP 1 Fold a vertical sheet of paper in half from top to bottom.

STEP 2 Fold in half from side to side with the fold at the top.

STEP 3 **Unfold** the paper once. **Cut** only the fold of the top flap to make two tabs.

STEP 4 **Turn** the paper vertically and **label** the tabs as shown.

Ionic
Bonds

Covalent
Bonds

Summarize As you read the chapter, identify the main ideas of bonding under the appropriate tabs. After you have read the chapter, explain the difference between polar covalent bonds and covalent bonds on the inside portion of your Foldable.

Preview this chapter's content and activities at
ips.msscience.com

Purpose Students discover that attractive forces decrease as distance increases. [L1] [ELL] [LS]
Kinesthetic

Materials magnet, 6 paper clips
Teaching Strategies

• Use small, light paper clips and magnets that are strong enough to hold at least five paper clips.
• Do not use plastic-coated paper clips.

Thinking Critically

The last paper clip attached was easiest to remove. The one attached to the magnet was the most difficult to remove.

Assessment

Content Have students think of the magnet as if it were the nucleus of an atom and the paper clips as if they were electrons. Sketch a cross section of a nitrogen atom, showing two electrons close to the nucleus and five more at a distance from the nucleus, and have them identify the electrons that are easier to remove. Use **Performance Assessment in the Science Classroom,** p. 127.

 **Dinah Zike Study Fold**

Student preparation materials for this Foldable are available in the Chapter *FAST FILE* Resources.

Why do atoms combine?

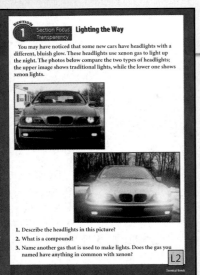
Tie to Prior Knowledge

Typical Materials Have students identify materials one might find in a typical household, such as glass, steel, wood, rubber, carpet and vinyl. Explain that the materials are made up of different kinds of atoms that have combined in particular ways. Explain that the chemical properties of an atom are based on the location and arrangement of its electrons.

as you read

What You'll Learn

- **Identify** how electrons are arranged in an atom.
- **Compare** the relative amounts of energy of electrons in an atom.
- **Compare** how the arrangement of electrons in an atom is related to its place in the periodic table.

Why It's Important

Chemical reactions take place all around you.

Review Vocabulary

atom: the smallest part of an element that keeps all the properties of that element

New Vocabulary

- electron cloud
- energy level
- electron dot diagram
- chemical bond

Figure 1 You can compare and contrast electrons with planets.

Planets travel in well-defined paths.

Atomic Structure

When you look at your desk, you probably see it as something solid. You might be surprised to learn that all matter, even solids like wood and metal contain mostly empty space. How can this be? The answer is that although there might be little or no space between atoms, a lot of empty space lies within each atom.

At the center of every atom is a nucleus containing protons and neutrons. This nucleus represents most of the atom's mass. The rest of the atom is empty except for the atom's electrons, which are extremely small compared with the nucleus. Although the exact location of any one electron cannot be determined, the atom's electrons travel in an area of space around the nucleus called the **electron cloud**.

To visualize an atom, picture the nucleus as the size of a penny. In this case, electrons would be smaller than grains of dust and the electron cloud would extend outward as far as 20 football fields.

Electrons You might think that electrons resemble planets circling the Sun, but they are very different, as you can see in **Figure 1.** First, planets have no charges, but the nucleus of an atom has a positive charge and electrons have negative charges.

Second, planets travel in predictable orbits—you can calculate exactly where one will be at any time. This is not true for electrons. Although electrons do travel in predictable areas, it is impossible to calculate the exact position of any one electron. Instead scientists use a mathmatical model that predicts where an electron is most likely to be.

Electrons travel around the nucleus. However, their paths are not well-defined.

Element Structure Each element has a different atomic structure consisting of a specific number of protons, neutrons, and electrons. The number of protons and electrons is always the same for a neutral atom of a given element. **Figure 2** shows a two-dimensional model of the electron structure of a lithium atom, which has three protons and four neutrons in its nucleus, and three electrons moving around its nucleus.

Electron Arrangement

The number and arrangement of electrons in the electron cloud of an atom are responsible for many of the physical and chemical properties of that element.

Electron Energy Although all the electrons in an atom are somewhere in the electron cloud, some electrons are closer to the nucleus than others. The different areas for an electron in an atom are called energy levels. **Figure 3** shows a model of what these energy levels might look like. Each level represents a different amount of energy.

Number of Electrons Each energy level can hold a maximum number of electrons. The farther an energy level is from the nucleus, the more electrons it can hold. The first energy level, energy level 1, can hold one or two electrons, the second, energy level 2, can hold up to eight, the third can hold up to 18, and the fourth energy level can hold a maximum of 32 electrons.

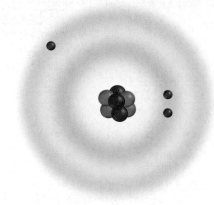

Figure 2 This neutral lithium atom has three positively charged protons, three negatively charged electrons, and four neutral neutrons.

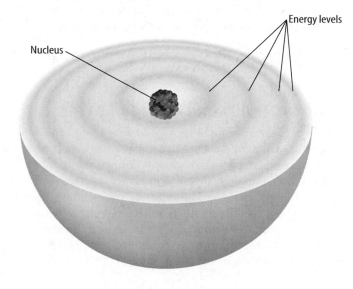

Nucleus

Energy levels

Figure 3 Electrons travel in three dimensions around the nucleus of an atom. The dark bands in this diagram show the energy levels where electrons are most likely to be found.
Identify *the energy level that can hold the most electrons.*

SECTION 1 Why do atoms combine? **163**

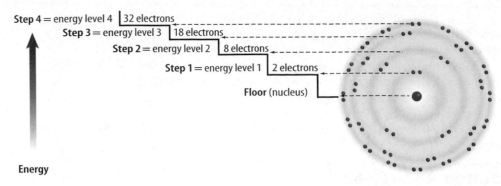

Step 4 = energy level 4 | 32 electrons
Step 3 = energy level 3 | 18 electrons
Step 2 = energy level 2 | 8 electrons
Step 1 = energy level 1 | 2 electrons
Floor (nucleus)

Energy

Caption Answer

Figure 4 Energy level 1 has the least energy and energy level 4 has the most energy for the levels shown in this figure.

Visual Learning

Figure 4 Explain to students that this model is not intended to represent relative sizes of the electrons, atom, or nucleus. L2
LS Visual-Spatial

Quick Demo
Positive Charges

Materials glass rod, piece of silk, small pieces of paper

Estimated Time 10 minutes

Procedure Vigorously rub the glass rod with the silk. Have students pick up the small pieces of paper with the rod. What type of particles in the glass rod's atoms has been removed? Electrons were removed Were the electrons removed from the highest or lowest energy step? highest

☑ Reading Check

Answer The energy level it occupies; electrons in the lowest levels have the lowest energy, and electrons in the highest levels have the most energy.

Figure 4 The farther an energy level is from the nucleus, the more electrons it can hold.
Identify *the energy level with the least energy and the energy level with the most energy.*

Topic: Electrons

Visit ips.msscience.com for Web links to information about electrons and their history.

Activity Research why scientists cannot locate the exact positions of an electron.

Energy Steps The stairway, shown in **Figure 4,** is a model that shows the maximum number of electrons each energy level can hold in the electron cloud. Think of the nucleus as being at floor level. Electrons within an atom have different amounts of energy, represented by energy levels. These energy levels are represented by the stairsteps in **Figure 4.** Electrons in the level closest to the nucleus have the lowest amount of energy and are said to be in energy level one. Electrons farthest from the nucleus have the highest amount of energy and are the easiest to remove. To determine the maximum number of electrons that can occupy an energy level, use the formula, $2n^2$, where n equals the number of the energy level.

Recall the Launch Lab at the beginning of the chapter. It took more energy to remove the paper clip that was closest to the magnet than it took to remove the one that was farthest away. That's because the closer a paper clip was to the magnet, the stronger the magnet's attractive force was on the clip. Similarly, the closer a negatively charged electron is to the positively charged nucleus, the more strongly it is attracted to the nucleus. Therefore, removing electrons that are close to the nucleus takes more energy than removing those that are farther away from the nucleus.

☑ Reading Check
What determines the amount of energy an electron has?

Periodic Table and Energy Levels

The periodic table includes a lot of data about the elements and can be used to understand the energy levels also. Look at the horizontal rows, or periods, in the portion of the table shown in **Figure 5.** Recall that the atomic number for each element is the same as the number of protons in that element and that the number of protons equals the number of electrons because an atom is electrically neutral. Therefore, you can determine the number of electrons in an atom by looking at the atomic number written above each element symbol.

164 **CHAPTER 6** Atomic Structure and Chemical Bonds

🔬 LAB DEMONSTRATION

Purpose to display energy level changes
Materials barium chloride solution, calcium chloride solution, Bunsen burner, goggles, paper clip, cork
Procedure Push one end of the paper clip into the cork. Bend the other end into a small loop. **WARNING:** *Wear safety goggles.*

Heat the wire loop in the burner's blue flame for ten seconds. Dip the wire into one solution and then put it in the tip of the flame's inner cone. Observe the flame's color. Clean the wire and test the other solution.

Expected Outcome barium chloride—green flame; calcium chloride—orange flame

Assessment

When metal ions are heated in a flame, do electrons move to higher or lower energy states? higher As they leave the flame, where do the electrons move? lower As electrons fall to a lower energy level, they release energy as light.

Electron Configurations

If you look at the periodic table shown in **Figure 5,** you can see that the elements are arranged in a specific order. The number of electrons in a neutral atom of the element increases by one from left to right across a period. For example, the first period consists of hydrogen with one electron and helium with two electrons in energy level one. Recall from **Figure 4** that energy level one can hold up to two electrons. Therefore, helium's outer energy level is complete. Atoms with a complete outer energy level are stable. Therefore, helium is stable.

Reading Check *What term is given to the rows of the periodic table?*

The second period begins with lithium, which has three electrons—two in energy level one and one in energy level two. Lithium has one electron in its outer energy level. To the right of lithium is beryllium with two outer-level electrons, boron with three, and so on until you reach neon with eight.

Look again at **Figure 4.** You'll see that energy level two can hold up to eight electrons. Not only does neon have a complete outer energy level, but also this configuration of exactly eight electrons in an outer energy level is stable. Therefore, neon is stable. The third period elements fill their outer energy levels in the same manner, ending with argon. Although energy level three can hold up to 18 electrons, argon has eight electrons in its outer energy level—a stable configuration. Each period in the periodic table ends with a stable element.

Figure 5 This portion of the periodic table shows the electron configurations of some elements. Count the electrons in each element and notice how the number increases across a period.

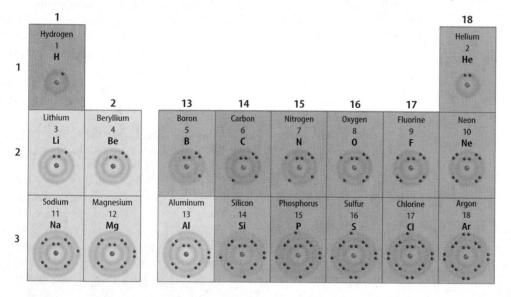

SECTION 1 Why do atoms combine? **165**

Differentiated Instruction

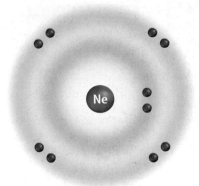

Figure 6 The noble gases are stable elements because their outer energy levels are complete or have a stable configuration of eight electrons like neon shown here.

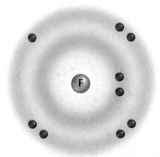

Figure 7 The halogen element fluorine has seven electrons in its outer energy level.
Determine *how many electrons the halogen family member bromine has in its outer energy level.*

Element Families

Elements can be divided into groups, or families. Each column of the periodic table in **Figure 5** contains one element family. Hydrogen is usually considered separately, so the first element family begins with lithium and sodium in the first column. The second family starts with beryllium and magnesium in the second column, and so on. Just as human family members often have similar looks and traits, members of element families have similar chemical properties because they have the same number of electrons in their outer energy levels.

It was the repeating pattern of properties that gave Russian chemist Dmitri Mendeleev the idea for his first periodic table in 1869. While listening to his family play music, he noticed how the melody repeated with increasing complexity. He saw a similar repeating pattern in the elements and immediately wrote down a version of the periodic table that looks much as it does today.

Noble Gases Look at the structure of neon in **Figure 6.** Neon and the elements below it in Group 18 have eight electrons in their outer energy levels. Their energy levels are stable, so they do not combine easily with other elements. Helium, with two electrons in its lone energy level, is also stable. At one time these elements were thought to be completely unreactive, and therefore became known as the inert gases. When chemists learned that some of these gases can react, their name was changed to noble gases. They are still the most stable element group.

This stability makes possible one widespread use of the noble gases—to protect filaments in lightbulbs. Another use of noble gases is to produce colored light in signs. If an electric current is passed through them they emit light of various colors—orange-red from neon, lavender from argon, and yellowish-white from helium.

Halogens The elements in Group 17 are called the halogens. A model of the element fluorine in period 2 is shown in **Figure 7.** Like all members of this family, fluorine needs one electron to obtain a stable outer energy level. The easier it is for a halogen to gain this electron to form a bond, the more reactive it is. Fluorine is the most reactive of the halogens because its outer energy level is closest to the nucleus. The reactivity of the halogens decreases down the group as the outer energy levels of each element's atoms get farther from the nucleus. Therefore, bromine in period 4 is less reactive than fluorine in period 2.

Alkali Metals Look at the element family in Group 1 on the periodic table at the back of this book, called the alkali metals. The first members of this family, lithium and sodium, have one electron in their outer energy levels. You can see in **Figure 8** that potassium also has one electron in its outer level. Therefore, you can predict that the next family member, rubidium, does also. These electron arrangements are what determines how these metals react.

Reading Check *How many electrons do the alkali metals have in their outer energy levels?*

The alkali metals form compounds that are similar to each other. Alkali metals each have one outer energy level electron. It is this electron that is removed when alkali metals react. The easier it is to remove an electron, the more reactive the atom is. Unlike halogens, the reactivities of alkali metals increase down the group; that is, elements in the higher numbered periods are more reactive than elements in the lower numbered periods. This is because their outer energy levels are farther from the nucleus. Less energy is needed to remove an electron from an energy level that is farther from the nucleus than to remove one from an energy level that is closer to the nucleus. For this reason, cesium in period 6 loses an electron more readily and is more reactive than sodium in period 3.

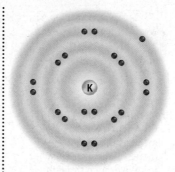

Figure 8 Potassium, like lithium and sodium, has only one electron in its outer level.

Reading Check

Answer one

Fun Fact

Atoms are extremely small. One hydrogen atom, for example, is approximately 5×10^{-8} mm in diameter. To put that in perspective, this mark - is approximately 1 mm in length. It would take almost 20 million hydrogen atoms to make a line as long as the mark.

Applying Science

Answers
1. magnesium
2. oxygen
3. group 14
4. Any of the following: sulfur, selenium, tellurium, polonium

Applying Science

How does the periodic table help you identify properties of elements?

The periodic table displays information about the atomic structure of the elements. This information includes the properties, such as the energy level, of the elements. Can you identify an element if you are given information about its energy level? Use your ability to interpret the periodic table to find out.

Identifying the Problem

Recall that elements in a group in the periodic table contain the same number of electrons in their outer levels. The number of electrons increases by one from left to right across a period. Refer to **Figure 5.** Can you identify an unknown element or the group a known element belongs to?

Solving the Problem

1. An unknown element in Group 2 has a total number of 12 electrons and two electrons in its outer level. What is it?
2. Name the element that has eight electrons, six of which are in its outer level.
3. Silicon has a total of 14 electrons, four electrons in its outer level, and three energy levels. What group does silicon belong to?
4. Three elements have the same number of electrons in their outer energy levels. One is oxygen. Using the periodic table, what might the other two be?

Teacher FYI

Relabeling the Table At one time groups of elements in the periodic table were labeled with a Roman numeral and the capital letter A or B. Today, groups are labeled 1 through 18.

Science Journal

Alkali Metals Have students research characteristics alkali metals share and write their findings in their Science Journals. All six alkali metals have low densities and are soft enough to cut with a knife. They have relatively low melting points. Alkali metals are the most reactive of all the metals and must be stored in kerosene or nitrogen to keep them from reacting with oxygen or water vapor in the air. L2 **LS Linguistic**

Mini LAB

Purpose Students observe patterns exhibited by electron dot diagrams. **L2** **ELL** **LS** **Visual-Spatial**

Materials paper, periodic table, pencil

Teaching Strategy Have students compare their diagrams with the periodic table to make sure no elements are skipped.

Troubleshooting Be sure dots are dark enough to be seen.

Analysis

1. The number of outer electrons is the same.
2. Each element has one more electron than the element that precedes it.

Assessment

Performance Have students use a thin layer of modeling clay and short pieces of drinking straws to model the above activity. Use **Performance Assessment in the Science Classroom**, p. 123.

Virtual Labs

Chemical Bonds *How can you tell which elements form chemical bonds?*

Mini LAB

Drawing Electron Dot Diagrams

Procedure

1. Draw a periodic table that includes the first 18 elements—the elements from hydrogen through argon. Make each block a 3-cm square.
2. Fill in each block with the electron dot diagram of the element.

Analysis

1. What do you observe about the electron dot diagram of the elements in the same group?
2. Describe any changes you observe in the electron dot diagrams across a period.

Figure 9 Electron dot diagrams show only the electrons in the outer energy level.
Explain *why only the outer energy level electrons are shown.*

Electron Dot Diagrams

You have read that the number of electrons in the outer energy level of an atom determines many of the chemical properties of the atom. Because these electrons are so important in determining the chemical properties of atoms, it can be helpful to make a model of an atom that shows only the outer electrons. A model like this can be used to show what happens to these electrons during reactions.

Drawing pictures of the energy levels and electrons in them takes time, especially when a large number of electrons are present. If you want to see how atoms of one element will react, it is handy to have an easier way to represent the atoms and the electrons in their outer energy levels. You can do this with electron dot diagrams. An **electron dot diagram** is the symbol for the element surrounded by as many dots as there are electrons in its outer energy level. Only the outer energy level electrons are shown because these are what determine how an element can react.

How to Write Them How do you know how many dots to make? For Groups 1 and 2, and 13–18, you can use the periodic table or the portion of it shown in **Figure 5.** Group 1 has one outer electron. Group 2 has two. Group 13 has three, Group 14, four, and so on to Group 18. All members of Group 18 have stable outer energy levels. From neon down, they have eight electrons. Helium has only two electrons, because that is all that its single energy level can hold.

The dots are written in pairs on four sides of the element symbol. Start by writing one dot on the top of the element symbol, then work your way around, adding dots to the right, bottom, and left. Add a fifth dot to the top to make a pair. Continue in this manner until you reach eight dots to complete the level.

The process can be demonstrated by writing the electron dot diagram for the element nitrogen. First, write N—the element symbol for nitrogen. Then, find nitrogen in the periodic table and see what group it is in. It's in Group 15, so it has five electrons in its outer energy level. The completed electron dot diagram for nitrogen can be seen in **Figure 9.**

The electron dot diagram for iodine can be drawn the same way. The completed diagram is shown on the right in **Figure 9.**

Nitrogen contains five electrons in its outer energy level.

Iodine contains seven electrons in its outer energy level.

Caption Answer

Figure 9 because these electrons determine how the element can react

Curriculum Connection

History Ask students to find out when and by whom electron dot diagrams were developed. In 1916, the American chemist G. N. Lewis invented the electron dot diagram, and so these diagrams are often called Lewis electron dot symbols. **L2** **LS** **Linguistic**

Differentiated Instruction

Challenge The energy levels of electrons are named *s, p, d,* and *f* atomic orbitals. Have students research the shapes of these orbitals and make drawings for each one. The shapes of orbitals define probabilities determined by quantum mechanics. The *s* orbitals are spherical, each *p* orbital is shaped like a dumbbell. Four of the *d* orbitals are shaped like pairs of crossed dumbbells and the fifth is shaped like a single dumbell with a doughnut around the middle. The *f* orbitals are complicated and can hold up to two electrons. **L3** **LS** **Visual-Spatial** **P**

Figure 10 Some models are made by gluing pieces together. The glue that holds elements together in a chemical compound is the chemical bond.

Using Dot Diagrams Now that you know how to write electron dot diagrams for elements, you can use them to show how atoms bond with each other. A **chemical bond** is the force that holds two atoms together. Chemical bonds unite atoms in a compound much as glue unites the pieces of the model in **Figure 10**. Atoms bond with other atoms in such a way that each atom becomes more stable. That is, their outer energy levels will resemble those of the noble gases.

☑ **Reading Check** *What is a chemical bond?*

3 Assess

DAILY INTERVENTION

Check for Understanding
Visual-Spatial Have students draw both electron configurations and electron dot diagrams for one element from each of groups 1, 2, and 13 through 18. L2 LS

Reteach
Electrons Obtain a large, round balloon and pour a small scoopful of rice inside it. Inflate the balloon and tie it closed. Shake the rice grains inside the balloon to simulate electrons moving around the nucleus. Have students write short paragraphs comparing and contrasting the rice to the electron cloud of an atom. The rice is small compared to the balloon, just as electrons are small when compared with the atom. Both the rice and electrons are constantly moving, and their locations are difficult to predict. The balloon has a specific boundary beyond which the rice cannot move, but electrons can move away from atoms. L2 LS **Linguistic**

section 1 review

Summary

Atom Structure
- At the center of the atom is the nucleus.
- Electrons exist in an area called the electron cloud.
- Electrons have a negative charge.

Electron Arrangement
- The different regions for an electron in an atom are called energy levels.
- Each energy level can hold a maximum number of electrons.

The Periodic Table
- The number of electrons is equal to the atomic number.
- The number of electrons in a neutral atom increases by one from left to right across a period.

Self Check

1. **Determine** how many electrons nitrogen has in its outer energy level. How many does bromine have?
2. **Solve** for the number of electrons that oxygen has in its first energy level. Second energy level?
3. **Identify** which electrons in oxygen have more energy, those in the first energy level or those in the second.
4. **Think Critically** Atoms in a group of elements increase in size as you move down the columns in the periodic table. Explain why this is so.

Applying Math

5. **Solve One-Step Equations** You can calculate the maximum number of electrons each energy level can hold using the formula $2n^2$. Calculate the number of electrons in the first five energy levels where n equals the number of energy levels.

Science online ips.msscience.com/self_check_quiz

SECTION 1 Why do atoms combine? **169**

section 1 review

1. nitrogen—5, bromine—7
2. first energy level—2; second energy level—6
3. those in the second energy level
4. A level of electrons is added to each period as you go down the periodic table.
5. The first energy level holds 2 electrons, the second holds 8 electrons, the third holds 18 electrons, the fourth holds 32 electrons, and the fifth holds 50 electrons.

☑ **Assessment**

Content Have students write short paragraphs explaining why hydrogen belongs in Group 1 of the periodic table and why it does not. Hydrogen belongs there because, like the other elements in that group, it has one electron in its outer shell, which it can lose in chemical reactions. It doesn't belong there because it can also gain one electron to complete its outer shell. Use **Performance Assessment in the Science Classroom**, p. 159. L2

1 Motivate

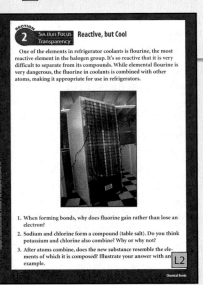

SECTION 2 Section Focus Transparency   **Reactive, but Cool**

One of the elements in refrigerator coolants is flourine, the most reactive element in the halogen group. It's so reactive that it is very difficult to separate from its compounds. While elemental flourine is very dangerous, the fluorine in coolants is combined with other atoms, making it appropriate for use in refrigerators.

1. When forming bonds, why does fluorine gain rather than lose an electron?
2. Sodium and chlorine form a compound (table salt). Do you think potassium and chlorine also combine? Why or why not?
3. After atoms combine, does the new substance resemble the elements of which it is composed? Illustrate your answer with an example.   L2

Chemical Bonds

Tie to Prior Knowledge

Chemical Changes With students, brainstorm examples of chemical changes and list them on the board. Explain that chemical changes are the result of chemical bonds breaking and forming.

SECTION 2
How Elements Bond

as you read

What **You'll Learn**

- **Compare and contrast** ionic and covalent bonds.
- **Distinguish** between compounds and molecules.
- **Identify** the difference between polar and nonpolar covalent bonds.
- **Interpret** chemical shorthand.

Why **It's Important**

Chemical bonds join the atoms in the materials you use every day.

Review Vocabulary

electron: a negatively charged particle that exists in an electron cloud around an atom's nucleus

New Vocabulary

- ion
- ionic bond
- compound
- metallic bond
- covalent bond
- molecule
- polar bond
- chemical formula

Ionic Bonds—Loss and Gain

When you put together the pieces of a jigsaw puzzle, they stay together only as long as you wish. When you pick up the completed puzzle, it falls apart. When elements are joined by chemical bonds, they do not readily fall apart. What would happen if suddenly the salt you were shaking on your fries separated into sodium and chlorine? Atoms form bonds with other atoms using the electrons in their outer energy levels. They have four ways to do this—by losing electrons, by gaining electrons, by pooling electrons, or by sharing electrons with another element.

Sodium is a soft, silvery metal as shown in **Figure 11.** It can react violently when added to water or to chlorine. What makes sodium so reactive? If you look at a diagram of its energy levels below, you will see that sodium has only one electron in its outer level. Removing this electron empties this level and leaves the completed level below. By removing one electron, sodium's electron configuration becomes the same as that of the stable noble gas neon.

Chlorine forms bonds in a way that is the opposite of sodium—it gains an electron. When chlorine accepts an electron, its electron configuration becomes the same as that of the noble gas argon.

Figure 11 Sodium and chlorine react, forming white crystalline sodium chloride.

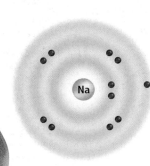

Sodium

Chlorine

Sodium is a silvery metal that can be cut with a knife. Chlorine is a greenish, poisonous gas.

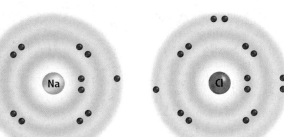

Na   Cl

Their electronic structures show why they react.

Section 2 Resource Manager

Chapter *FAST FILE* Resources
Transparency Activity, p. 43
Directed Reading for Content Mastery, pp. 21, 22
MiniLAB, p. 4
Enrichment, p. 30
Reinforcement, p. 28

Lab Activity, pp. 13–16
Lab Worksheets, pp. 5–6, 7–8
Lab Management and Safety, p. 79
Life Science Critical Thinking/Problem Solving, p. 15
Home and Community Involvement, p. 42

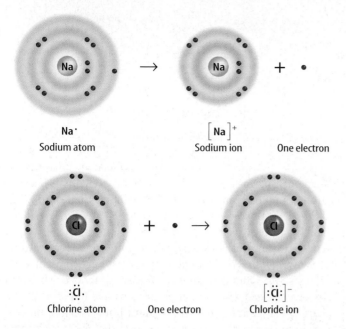

Na·
Sodium atom

[Na]⁺
Sodium ion

One electron

:Cl̈·
Chlorine atom

One electron

[:C̈l:]⁻
Chloride ion

Figure 12 Ions form when elements lose or gain electrons. When sodium comes into contact with chlorine, an electron is transferred from the sodium atom to the chlorine atom. Na becomes a Na⁺ ion. Cl becomes a Cl⁻ ion.

Ions—A Question of Balance

As you just learned, a sodium atom loses an electron and becomes more stable. But something else happens also. By losing an electron, the balance of electric charges changes. Sodium becomes a positively charged ion because there is now one fewer electron than there are protons in the nucleus. In contrast, chlorine becomes an ion by gaining an electron. It becomes negatively charged because there is one more electron than there are protons in the nucleus.

An atom that is no longer neutral because it has lost or gained an electron is called an **ion** (I ahn). A sodium ion is represented by the symbol Na⁺ and a chloride ion is represented by the symbol Cl⁻. **Figure 12** shows how each atom becomes an ion.

Bond Formation

The positive sodium ion and the negative chloride ion are strongly attracted to each other. This attraction, which holds the ions close together, is a type of chemical bond called an **ionic bond**. In **Figure 13,** sodium and chloride ions form an ionic bond. The compound sodium chloride, or table salt, is formed. A **compound** is a pure substance containing two or more elements that are chemically bonded.

Na· + ·C̈l: → [Na]⁺[:C̈l:]⁻

Ions When ions dissolve in water, they separate. Because of their positive and negative charges, the ions can conduct an electric current. If wires are placed in such a solution and the ends of the wires are connected to a battery, the positive ions move toward the negative terminal and the negative ions move toward the positive terminal. This flow of ions completes the circuit.

Figure 13 An ionic bond forms between atoms of opposite charges. **Describe** how an atom becomes positive or negative.

INTEGRATE Physics

Ions A compound whose water solution conducts electricity is called an electrolyte. Demonstrate to the class that sodium chloride is a strong electrolyte. Set up a simple conductivity apparatus using a large beaker filled with salt water, a small flashlight bulb with socket, a dry-cell battery, and three connecting wires. Attach the end of one of the wires to the lightbulb socket and place the free end in the beaker of salt water. Use another wire to connect the lightbulb socket to the positive battery terminal. Attach the third wire to the negative terminal and place the free end in the beaker. The bulb should light if the circuit is complete. If not, check the wires to make sure you have a complete circuit. If it still does not work, try dissolving another teaspoon of salt into the water to make a more concentrated solution.

Caption Answer

Figure 13 An atom becomes positively charged by losing electrons. An atom becomes negatively charged by gaining electrons.

Cultural Diversity

Salt of the Earth Long ago, Egyptians used salt to prepare bodies for the afterlife. In Arabia, people who ate salt together were pledging their loyalty to one another. Salt has been one of the most important minerals throughout human history. Have students use reference books or visit the Glencoe Science Web site to find out other historical uses for salt and make brochures summarizing their findings. Possible findings include: People of the Far East often rubbed newborn babies with salt to ensure good health. They hung small bags of salt around older children's necks to protect them from harm. Roman soldiers who built the famous Roman roads were often paid in salt, leading to the English word *salary*. L2 **LS Linguistic** P

Caption Answer

Figure 14 The electron arrangements for magnesium sulfide and calcium oxide are the same as magnesium oxide. Both magnesium and calcium can lose two electrons to be stable. Both oxygen and sulfur need to gain two electrons to be stable.

Discussion

Calcium Carbonate Limestone, a rock composed primarily of the ionic compound calcium carbonate ($CaCO_3$), is the most widely used building stone in the United States. Why is an ionic compound like calcium carbonate an appropriate choice for a building material? Limestone is strong because of the arrangement of its ions in its crystal structure. L2 LS **Logical-Mathematical**

Use Science Words

Word Usage Ask students to identify uses of the word *pool*. Possible answers: car pool, swimming pool, pool table Explain that in terms of metallic bonding, the word *pool* means "to combine in a common fund or effort." In metallic bonds, what is combined in a common fund? electrons L2 ELL **Linguistic**

Figure 14 Magnesium has two electrons in its outer energy level.

If one electron is lost to each of two chlorine atoms, magnesium chloride forms.

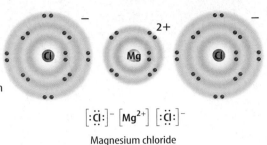

$$\left[:\overset{..}{\underset{..}{Cl}}:\right]^- \quad \left[Mg^{2+}\right] \quad \left[:\overset{..}{\underset{..}{Cl}}:\right]^-$$

Magnesium chloride

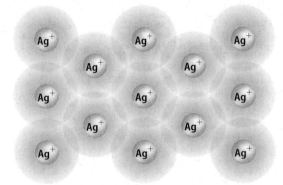

$$\left[Mg^{2+}\right] \quad \left[O^{2-}\right]$$

Magnesium oxide

If both electrons are lost to one oxygen atom, magnesium oxide forms.

Determine *the electron arrangement for magnesium sulfide and calcium oxide.*

Figure 15 In metallic bonding, the outer electrons of the silver atoms are not attached to any one silver atom. This allows them to move and conduct electricity.

More Gains and Losses You have seen what happens when elements gain or lose one electron, but can elements lose or gain more than one electron? The element magnesium, Mg, in Group 2 has two electrons in its outer energy level. Magnesium can lose these two electrons and achieve a completed energy level. These two electrons can be gained by two chlorine atoms. As shown in **Figure 14,** a single magnesium ion represented by the symbol Mg^{2+} and two chloride ions are generated. The two negatively charged chloride ions are attracted to the positively charged magnesium ion forming ionic bonds. As a result of these bonds, the compound magnesium chloride ($MgCl_2$) is produced.

Some atoms, such as oxygen, need to gain two electrons to achieve stability. The two electrons released by one magnesium atom could be gained by a single atom of oxygen. When this happens, magnesium oxide (MgO) is formed, as shown in **Figure 14.** Oxygen can form similar compounds with any positive ion from Group 2.

Metallic Bonding—Pooling

You have just seen how metal atoms form ionic bonds with atoms of nonmetals. Metals can form bonds with other metal atoms, but in a different way. In a metal, the electrons in the outer energy levels of the atoms are not held tightly to individual atoms. Instead, they move freely among all the ions in the metal, forming a shared pool of electrons, as shown in **Figure 15.** **Metallic bonds** form when metal atoms share their pooled electrons. This bonding affects the properties of metals. For example, when a metal is hammered into sheets or drawn into a wire, it does not break. Instead, layers of atoms slide over one another. The pooled electrons tend to hold the atoms together. Metallic bonding also is the reason that metals conduct electricity well. The outer electrons in metal atoms readily move from one atom to the next to transmit current.

Science Journal

Salt Crystals Have students use magnifying lenses to observe crystals of table salt. Ask them to draw in their Science Journals pictures of what they see. L2 LS **Visual-Spatial**

Differentiated Instruction

Learning Disabled Give each student between one and seven marbles. Explain that the number of marbles they have corresponds to the number of electrons in the highest energy levels of an element. Ask them to find another student that has the correct number of marbles that would enable them both to complete their energy levels and form ionic bonds. L1 ELL LS **Visual-Spatial**

Covalent Bonds—Sharing

Some atoms are unlikely to lose or gain electrons because the number of electrons in their outer levels makes this difficult. For example, carbon has six protons and six electrons. Four of the six electrons are in its outer energy level. To obtain a more stable structure, carbon would either have to gain or lose four electrons. This is difficult because gaining and losing so many electrons takes so much energy. The alternative is sharing electrons.

The Covalent Bond Atoms of many elements become more stable by sharing electrons. The chemical bond that forms between nonmetal atoms when they share electrons is called a covalent (koh VAY luhnt) bond. Shared electrons are attracted to the nuclei of both atoms. They move back and forth between the outer energy levels of each atom in the covalent bond. So, each atom has a stable outer energy level some of the time. Covalently bonded compounds are called molecular compounds.

Reading Check *How do atoms form covalent bonds?*

The atoms in a covalent bond form a neutral particle, which contains the same numbers of positive and negative charges. The neutral particle formed when atoms share electrons is called a molecule (MAH lih kyewl). A molecule is the basic unit of a molecular compound. You can see how molecules form by sharing electrons in **Figure 16.** Notice that no ions are involved because no electrons are gained or lost. Crystalline solids, such as sodium chloride, are not referred to as molecules, because their basic units are ions, not molecules.

Figure 16 Covalent bonding is another way that atoms become more stable. Sharing electrons allows each atom to have a stable outer energy level. These atoms form a single covalent bond.

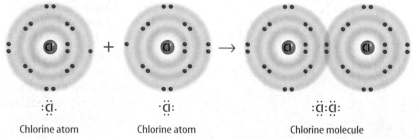

H·   ·H   H:H
Hydrogen atom   Hydrogen atom   Hydrogen molecule

Chlorine atom   Chlorine atom   Chlorine molecule

Mini LAB

Constructing a Model of Methane

Procedure

1. Using **circles of colored paper** to represent protons, neutrons, and electrons, build paper models of one carbon atom and four hydrogen atoms.
2. Use your models of atoms to construct a molecule of methane by forming covalent bonds. The methane molecule has four hydrogen atoms chemically bonded to one carbon atom.

Analysis

1. In the methane molecule, do the carbon and hydrogen atoms have the same arrangement of electrons as two noble gas elements? Explain your answer.
2. Does the methane molecule have a charge?

Try at Home

Mini LAB

Purpose Students construct a paper model of a methane molecule. L2 ELL IS **Kinesthetic**

Materials construction paper (three different colors), scissors

Teaching Strategies

• Students should make the protons and neutrons the same size. The electrons should be much smaller.

• Be sure students understand that this model is two-dimensional and does not accurately represent the size and shape of a three-dimensional molecule.

Analysis

1. Yes; each hydrogen atom shares two electrons and thus has the same electron arrangement as helium. The carbon atom shares eight electrons and has the same electron arrangement as neon.
2. No; an equal number of electrons and protons are present.

Assessment

Performance For additional practice, have students revise their carbon atoms to represent nitrogen atoms and make models of ammonia, NH_3. Use **Performance Assessment in the Science Classroom,** p. 123.

Try at Home

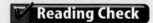
Reading Check

Answer by sharing electrons

Teacher FYI

Hydrogen Hydrogen does not exhibit all properties shown by other Group 1 elements. For example, hydrogen is a gas at room temperature, while the others are solids. Hydrogen can form covalent bonds with other elements. For these reasons, some periodic tables place hydrogen apart from Group 1 to indicate its uniqueness.

Active Reading

Metacognition Journal In this strategy, each student analyzes his or her own thought processes. Have students divide a sheet of paper in half down the center. On the left, have them record things they have learned about chemical bonds. On the right, have them record the reasons they learned these things. L2 IS **Intrapersonal**

Tug of War A covalent bond can be compared to a tug of war. The rope is analogous to a shared pair of electrons, and the people represent the nuclei. If the people pulling the rope exert an equal pull on each end of the rope, an equal amount of rope stays on both sides, as in a non-polar bond. If one side has a stronger pull, more of the rope will be on that side, as in a polar bond.

Answer two pairs

Inquiry Lab

Identifying Ionic and Molecular Compounds

Purpose To identify compounds as ionic or molecular based on physical properties. L2

Possible Materials paraffin wax, methanol, glycerin, sugar, salt, $CuSO_4$, $CaSO_4$

Estimated Time 1 class session

Teaching Strategies

• Students should develop procedures and data tables. They should record the appearance of the compounds. Can a compound's nature be determined by appearance? Generally; except for sugar, the ones that are not solid crystals are not ionic.

• Tests for solubility and conductivity in water will give more concrete answers to the compound's identity.

For additional inquiry activities, see *Science Inquiry Labs.*

Figure 17 An atom can also form a covalent bond by sharing two or three electrons.

$$\cdot\overset{\cdot}{\underset{\cdot}{C}}\cdot \quad + \quad \cdot\overset{\cdot\cdot}{\underset{\cdot\cdot}{O}}{:} \quad + \quad \cdot\overset{\cdot\cdot}{\underset{\cdot\cdot}{O}}{:} \quad \rightarrow \quad {:}\overset{\cdot\cdot}{\underset{\cdot\cdot}{O}}{::}C{::}\overset{\cdot\cdot}{\underset{\cdot\cdot}{O}}{:}$$

Carbon atom   Oxygen atoms   Carbon dioxide molecule

In carbon dioxide, carbon shares two electrons with each of two oxygen atoms forming two double bonds. Each oxygen atom shares two electrons with the carbon atom.

$${:}\overset{\cdot}{N}{\cdot} \quad + \quad \cdot\overset{\cdot}{\underset{\cdot}{N}}{:} \quad \rightarrow \quad {:}N{:}{:}{:}N{:}$$

Nitrogen atoms   Nitrogen molecule

Each nitrogen atom shares three electrons in forming a triple bond.

Double and Triple Bonds Sometimes an atom shares more than one electron with another atom. In the molecule carbon dioxide, shown in **Figure 17,** each of the oxygen atoms shares two electrons with the carbon atom. The carbon atom shares two of its electrons with each oxygen atom. When two pairs of electrons are involved in a covalent bond, the bond is called a double bond. **Figure 17** also shows the sharing of three pairs of electrons between two nitrogen atoms in the nitrogen molecule. When three pairs of electrons are shared by two atoms, the bond is called a triple bond.

 *How many pairs of electrons are shared in a double bond?*

Polar and Nonpolar Molecules

You have seen how atoms can share electrons and that they become more stable by doing so, but do they always share electrons equally? The answer is no. Some atoms have a greater attraction for electrons than others do. Chlorine, for example, attracts electrons more strongly than hydrogen does. When a covalent bond forms between hydrogen and chlorine, the shared pair of electrons tends to spend more time near the chlorine atom than the hydrogen atom.

This unequal sharing makes one side of the bond more negative than the other, like poles on a battery. This is shown in **Figure 18.** Such bonds are called polar bonds. A **polar bond** is a bond in which electrons are shared unevenly. The bonds between the oxygen atom and hydrogen atoms in the water molecule are another example of polar bonds.

Figure 18 Hydrogen chloride is a polar covalent molecule.

Partial positive charge   H   Cl   Partial negative charge

LAB DEMONSTRATION

Purpose to show the differences between ionic and covalent bonds

Materials table salt, rubbing alcohol, pan balance, two beakers

Procedure Place a beaker containing a small amount of salt on one side of a pan balance and an identical empty beaker on the other. Pour rubbing alcohol into the empty beaker until the scale is balanced. Note the quantity. Observe how long it takes to become unbalanced and measure the remaining amount of rubbing alcohol.

Expected Outcome Some of the alcohol evaporates.

Assessment

Do you think rubbing alcohol has ionic bonds or covalent bonds? Why? Covalent bonds; alcohol molecules are not as strongly attracted to each other as are sodium and chloride ions, so alcohol is a liquid and evaporates easily at room temperature.

The Polar Water Molecule Water molecules form when hydrogen and oxygen share electrons. **Figure 19** shows how this sharing is unequal. The oxygen atom has a greater share of the electrons in each bond—the oxygen end of a water molecule has a slight negative charge and the hydrogen end has a slight positive charge. Because of this, water is said to be polar—having two opposite ends or poles like a magnet.

When they are exposed to a negative charge, the water molecules line up like magnets with their positive ends facing the negative charge. You can see how they are drawn to the negative charge on the balloon in **Figure 19.** Water molecules also are attracted to each other. This attraction between water molecules accounts for many of the physical properties of water.

Molecules that do not have these uneven charges are called nonpolar molecules. Because each element differs slightly in its ability to attract electrons, the only completely nonpolar bonds are bonds between atoms of the same element. One example of a nonpolar bond is the triple bond in the nitrogen molecule.

Like ionic compounds, some molecular compounds can form crystals, in which the basic unit is a molecule. Often you can see the pattern of the units in the shape of ionic and molecular crystals, as shown in **Figure 20.**

Science Online

Topic: Polar Molecules
Visit ips.msscience.com for Web links to information about soaps and detergents.

Activity Oil and water are not soluble in one another. However, if you add a few grams of a liquid dish detergent, the oil will become soluble in the water. Instead of two layers, there will be only one. Explain why soap can help the oil become soluble in water.

Figure 19 Two hydrogen atoms share electrons with one oxygen atom, but the sharing is unequal. The electrons are more likely to be closer to the oxygen than the hydrogens. The space-saving model shows how the charges are separated or polarized. **Define** *the term* polar.

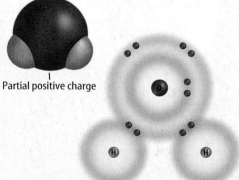

Partial negative charge

Partial positive charge

The positive ends of the water molecules are attracted to the negatively charged balloon, causing the stream of water to bend.

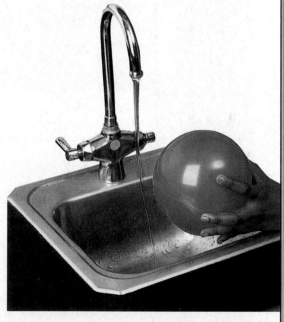

SECTION 2   How Elements Bond   **175**

Discussion

Compound States Why are ionic compounds usually solids at room temperature, whereas covalent compounds, although they may be solids, are frequently gases or liquids? The electrostatic attraction between ions is stronger than the attractions among the molecules. L2
LS Logical-Mathematical

Quick Demo

Polar Water Molecules

Materials candle, lighter, cool glass surface

Estimated Time 10 minutes

Procedure Light the candle and hold it under a cool glass surface. Observe the water droplets that condense on the glass. Explain that water vapor and carbon dioxide are released when the candle burns. Carbon dioxide is a nonpolar molecule. The water molecule however, is polar. The water molecules attract each other and easily condense to a liquid.

Activity

Balloon Attraction Provide students with balloons, and have them demonstrate how a negatively charged balloon can bend a thin stream of water, as shown in **Figure 19.** Tell students to blow up the balloons and rub them with a cloth to give them a charge. Have them place the balloons close to, but not touching, a thin stream of water. Have students explain the effect in terms of polar molecules. L2 **LS Kinesthetic**

Caption Answer

Figure 19 having two opposite ends or poles like a magnet

Differentiated Instruction

English-Language Learners Have students write a paragraph comparing and contrasting ionic and polar bonds in their native language. Then have the students translate that paragraph into English and read it aloud. L2 **ELL LS Linguistic**

Visualizing Crystal Structure

Have students examine the pictures and read the captions. Then ask the following questions.

How are the particles arranged in a crystal? in a regular repeating pattern

Do liquids exist as crystals? No; when a solid changes to a liquid, the ordered arrangement is lost. Liquid crystals are an exception to this rule and maintain their order in one or two dimensions.

Perfect crystals are rare. Infer where the imperfections may occur in the crystalline structure. Possible answer: There are two basic types of defects in the crystal structure. The first is within the unit cell structure. The second is in the joining of the unit cells.

Make a Model

Unit Cells Have students define the term *unit cells*. Then have students use easily obtainable materials to make models of the types of unit cells shown in **Figure 20**. Have them study the unit cells to see where possible defects may occur. L2 LS **Kinesthetic**

Figure 20

Many solids exist as crystals. Whether tiny grains of table salt or big, chunky blocks of quartz you might find rock hunting, a crystal's shape is often a reflection of the arrangement of its particles. Knowing a solid's crystal structure helps researchers understand its physical properties. Some crystals with cubic and hexagonal shapes are shown here.

Water

O
Si

HEXAGONAL Quartz crystals, above, are six sided, just as a snowflake, above right, has six points. This is because the molecules that make up both quartz and snowflakes arrange themselves into hexagonal patterns.

Ca^{2+}
F^-

Na^+
Cl^-

CUBIC Salt, left, and fluorite, above, form cube-shaped crystals. This shape is a reflection of the cube-shaped arrangement of the ions in the crystal.

176 CHAPTER 6 Atomic Structure and Chemical Bonds

Differentiated Instruction

Challenge Have students find out how scientists intentionally cause defects to form within crystals to make semiconductors for use in the computer industry. Have students make posters or other visual aids as an accompaniment to a class presentation about semiconductors. L3 LS **Visual-Spatial**

Chemical Shorthand

In medieval times, alchemists (AL kuh mists) were the first to explore the world of chemistry. Although many of them believed in magic and mystical transformations, alchemists did learn much about the properties of some elements. They even used symbols to represent them in chemical processes, some of which are shown in **Figure 21.**

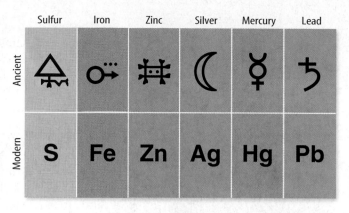

Sulfur | Iron | Zinc | Silver | Mercury | Lead
Ancient / Modern
S | Fe | Zn | Ag | Hg | Pb

Figure 21 Alchemists used elaborate symbols to describe elements and processes. Modern chemical symbols are letters that can be understood all over the world.

Symbols for Atoms Modern chemists use symbols to represent elements, too. These symbols can be understood by chemists everywhere. Each element is represented by a one letter-, two letter-, or three-letter symbol. Many symbols are the first letters of the element's name, such as H for hydrogen and C for carbon. Others are the first letters of the element's name in another language, such as K for potassium, which stands for kalium, the Latin word for potassium.

Symbols for Compounds Compounds can be described using element symbols and numbers. For example, **Figure 22** shows how two hydrogen atoms join together in a covalent bond. The resulting hydrogen molecule is represented by the symbol H_2. The small 2 after the H in the formula is called a subscript. *Sub* means "below" and *script* means "write," so a subscript is a number that is written a little below a line of text. The subscript 2 means that two atoms of hydrogen are in the molecule.

Figure 22 Chemical formulas show you the kind and number of atoms in a molecule. **Describe** the term subscript.

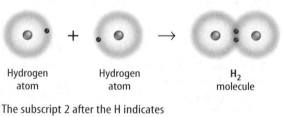

Hydrogen atom + Hydrogen atom → H_2 molecule

The subscript 2 after the H indicates that the hydrogen molecule contains two atoms of hydrogen.

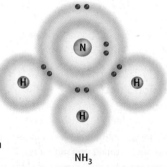

The formula for ammonia, NH_3, tells you that the ratio is one nitrogen atom to three hydrogen atoms.

NH_3

Visual Learning

Figure 21 Point out that the ancient symbols used by alchemists are complicated and might vary from alchemist to alchemist.

Discussion
Capitalizing Symbols Have students look at the periodic table, and note that capital letters are used for the first letter in a symbol. The second letter, if any, is lowercase. What confusion could result if capital letters and lowercase letters were used incorrectly? Elements could be mistaken for compounds. For example, CO is carbon monoxide, but Co is an atom of cobalt. L2 ⎗ **Logical-Mathematical**

Use Science Words
Word Origin Have students use reference books to learn about the origins of various element names. Ask students to write each element's symbol, name, and the source of its name. Many elements were named after countries or people. For example, polonium was named for Poland, the native land of its discoverer Marie Curie. L2 ⎗ **Linguistic**

Caption Answer
Figure 22 A subscript is a number written below a line of text.

Visual Learning

Figure 22 Tell students that molecules that consist of only two atoms of the same element are said to be *diatomic*. All of the gaseous elements except the noble gases exist as diatomic molecules. Have students write the formulas for other diatomic molecules. nitrogen (N_2), oxygen (O_2), chlorine (Cl_2), fluorine (F_2), bromine (Br_2), iodine (I_2) L1 ⎗ **Visual-Spatial**

Curriculum Connection

Language Arts It is no accident that many symbols for elements come from Latin words. For centuries, almost all European scholarly works were written in Latin. Have students look up and report on some scientific words of Latin origin. Computer comes from the word *computare*. Tyrannosaurus rex means "tyrant-lizard king." L2 ⎗ **Linguistic**

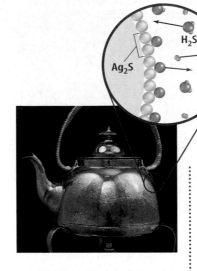

Figure 23 Silver tarnish is the compound silver sulfide, Ag_2S. The formula shows that two silver atoms are combined with one sulfur atom.

Chemical Formulas A **chemical formula** is a combination of chemical symbols and numbers that shows which elements are present in a compound and how many atoms of each element are present. When no subscript is shown, the number of atoms is understood to be one.

Reading Check
What is a chemical formula and what does it tell you about a compound?

Now that you know a few of the rules for writing chemical formulas, you can look back at other chemical compounds shown earlier in this chapter and begin to predict their chemical formulas. A water molecule contains one oxygen atom and two hydrogen atoms, so its formula is H_2O. Ammonia, shown in **Figure 22,** is a covalent compound that contains one nitrogen atom and three hydrogen atoms. Its chemical formula is NH_3.

The black tarnish that forms on silver, shown in **Figure 23,** is a compound made up of the elements silver and sulfur in the proportion of two atoms of silver to one atom of sulfur. If alchemists knew the composition of silver tarnish, how might they have written a formula for the compound? The modern formula for silver tarnish is Ag_2S. The formula tells you that it is a compound that contains two silver atoms and one sulfur atom.

section 2 review

Summary

Four Types of Bonds
- Ionic bond is the attraction that holds ions close together.
- Metallic bonds form when metal atoms pool their electrons.
- Covalent bonds form when atoms share electrons.
- A polar covalent bond is a bond in which electrons are shared unevenly.

Chemical Shorthand
- Compounds can be described by using element symbols and numbers.
- A chemical formula is a combination of element symbols and numbers.

Self Check

1. **Determine** Use the periodic table to decide whether lithium forms a positive or negative ion. Does fluorine form a positive or negative ion? Write the formula for the compound formed from these two elements.

2. **Compare and contrast** polar and nonpolar bonds.

3. **Explain** how a chemical formula indicates the ratio of elements in a compound.

4. **Think Critically** Silicon has four electrons in its outer energy level. What type of bond is silicon most likely to form with other elements? Explain.

Applying Skills

5. **Predict** what type of bonds that will form between the following pairs of atoms: carbon and oxygen, potassium and bromine, fluorine and fluorine.

Science Online ips.msscience.com/self_check_quiz

IONIC COMPOUNDS

Metals in Groups 1 and 2 often lose electrons and form positive ions. Nonmetals in Groups 16 and 17 often gain electrons and become negative ions. How can compounds form between these four groups of elements?

● Real-World Question

How do different atoms combine with each other to form compounds?

Goals
■ **Construct** models of electron gain and loss.
■ **Determine** formulas for the ions and compounds that form when electrons are gained or lost.

Materials
paper (8 different colors)
tacks (2 different colors)
corrugated cardboard
scissors

Safety Precautions

● Procedure

1. Cut colored-paper disks 7 cm in diameter to represent the elements Li, S, Mg, O, Ca, Cl, Na, and I. Label each disk with one symbol.
2. Lay circles representing the atoms Li and S side by side on cardboard.
3. Choose colored thumbtacks to represent the outer electrons of each atom. Place the tacks evenly around the disks to represent the outer electron levels of the elements.
4. Move electrons from the metal atom to the nonmetal atom so that both elements

achieve noble gas arrangements of eight outer electrons. If needed, cut additional paper disks to add more atoms of one element.

5. Write the formula for each ion and the compound formed when you shift electrons.
6. Repeat steps 2 through 6 to combine Mg and O, Ca and Cl, and Na and I.

● Conclude and Apply

1. **Draw** electron dot diagrams for all of the ions produced.
2. **Identify** the noble gas elements having the same electron arrangements as the ions you made in this lab.
3. **Analyze Results** Why did you have to use more than one atom in some cases? Why couldn't you take more electrons from one metal atom or add extra ones to a nonmetal atom?

Communicating Your Data

Compare your compounds and dot diagrams with those of other students in your class. **For more help, refer to the Science Skill Handbook.**

● Real-World Question

Purpose Students model ionic compounds and the process that forms them. L2 **ELL** **LS** Visual-Spatial

Process Skills observe and infer, recognize cause and effect, make models, use numbers

Time Required 30 minutes

● Procedure

Alternate Materials Different colors of paper are not essential if disks are clearly labeled with the symbols of the elements represented.

Safety Precautions Be sure students use caution when handling scissors and thumbtacks.

Teaching Strategies
• Suggest that students visualize the chemical symbol on each disk surrounded by a square, each side of which can contain two electrons.
• Provide templates for circles to help students make the disks.

● Conclude and Apply

1. Diagrams should show each symbol surrounded by eight dots. Ions should have the following charges: Li^+, S^{2-}, Mg^{2+}, O^{2-}, Ca^{2+}, Cl^-, N^{3-}, Na^+, and I^-.
2. Li^+: helium; S^{2-}, Ca^{2+}, Cl^-: argon; Mg^{2+}, O^{2-}, Na^+: neon; I^-: xenon
3. In some cases, a one-to-one ratio does not give the atoms a stable 8 outer energy level electrons. Atoms will not easily gain or lose electrons if they have eight electrons in their outer energy level.

☑ Assessment

Content For each pair of elements in a compound, have students show that the overall charge is zero. For Li_2S, $2(1^+) + 1(2^-) = 0$.

Communicating Your Data

Mount student models on stiff cardboard so they may be displayed around the classroom.

Model and Invent

At⚛mic Structure

● Real-World Question

● Real-World Question

Purpose
Students make a model showing how protons, neutrons, and electrons are arranged in an atom. L2

ELL **COOP LEARN** **LS**
Visual-Spatial

Process Skills Predict, communicate, make a model, evaluate others' data and conclusions

Time Required 45 minutes

Possible Materials Any small, round objects can be used to represent subatomic particles. Magnetic tape is sold at most craft and hobby stores.

Safety Precautions Be sure students use care when handling scissors.

Goals
- **Design** a model of a chosen element.
- **Observe** the models made by others in the class and identify the elements they represent.

Possible Materials
magnetic board
rubber magnetic strips
candy-coated chocolates
scissors
paper
marker
coins

Safety Precautions
🔥👁️🧪🔥

WARNING: *Never eat any food in the laboratory. Wash hands thoroughly.*

As more information has become known about the structure of the atom, scientists have developed new models. Making your own model and studying the models of others will help you learn how protons, neutrons, and electrons are arranged in an atom. Can an element be identified based on a model that shows the arrangement of the protons, neutrons, and electrons of an atom? How will your group construct a model of an element that others will be able to identify?

● Make A Model

1. Choose an element from periods 2 or 3 of the periodic table. How can you determine the number of protons, neutrons, and electrons in an atom given the atom's mass number?

2. How can you show the difference between protons and neutrons? What materials will you use to represent the electrons of the atom? How will you represent the nucleus?

● Plan the Model

Possible Procedures Use the periodic table and the atom's mass number to determine the number of each type of particle in an atom of the chosen element. Choose objects to represent electrons, protons, and neutrons. Attach a small magnetic strip to each object. On the magnetic board, cluster the protons and neutrons together. Place the appropriate number of electrons in each level around the nucleus.

Teaching Strategies
- Give students the mass number of the most common isotope of their selected element.
- Be sure students understand that the models represent the arrangement of particles in the atom only and that the models are not to scale.

Differentiated Instruction

Visually Impaired Be sure that materials used in the models can be distinguished by touch. Allow the students to manipulate the models. Have peers work with visually-impaired students to assist in identifying the parts of the model. L2

ELL **COOP LEARN** **LS** **Kinesthetic**

3. How will you model the arrangement of electrons in the atom? Will the atom have a charge? Is it possible to identify an atom by the number of protons it has?

4. Make sure your teacher approves your plan before you proceed.

● *Test Your Model*

1. Construct your model. Then record your observations in your Science Journal and include a sketch.

2. Construct another model of a different element.

3. Observe the models made by your classmates. Identify the elements they represent.

● *Analyze Your Data*

1. State what elements you identified using your classmates' models.

2. Identify which particles always are present in equal numbers in a neutral atom.

3. Predict what would happen to the charge of an atom if one of the electrons were removed.

4. Describe what happens to the charge of an atom if two electrons are added. What happens to the charge of an atom if one proton and one electron are removed?

5. Compare and contrast your model with the electron cloud model of the atom. How is your model similar? How is it different?

● *Conclude and Apply*

1. Define the minimum amount of information that you need to know in order to identify an atom of an element.

2. Explain If you made models of the isotopes boron-10 and boron-11, how would these models be different?

𝒞ommunicating
Your Data

Compare your models with those of other students. Discuss any differences you find among the models.

● *Test Your Model* —

Expected Outcome Students will determine that for a neutral atom, the number of either protons or electrons can identify an element.

● *Analyze Your Data*

1. Answers will vary. The number of protons determines the identity.
2. protons and electrons
3. The charge would become positive.
4. The charge becomes negative; the identity of the atoms changes.
5. This model is two-dimensional; the electron cloud model is three-dimensional. This model shows the electrons in definite positions, but in the electron cloud model, the positions of the electrons are not determined.

● *Conclude and Apply*

1. Either the number of protons or the number of electrons.
2. Boron-11 would contain one more neutron. Both atoms would contain the same numbers of electrons and protons.

☑ Assessment

Performance Have students trade models and check to make sure the number of electrons and protons is the same for each atom. Use **Performance Assessment in the Science Classroom,** p. 123.

𝒞ommunicating
Your Data

You may wish to display the models around the classroom so students can compare their atoms with the atoms modeled by other students.

Science and Language Arts

"Baring the Atom's Mother Heart"
from Selu: Seeking the Corn-Mother's Wisdom
by Marilou Awiakta

Understanding Literature

Refrain Repetition of the child's concerns makes the reader understand the girl's fears about nuclear technology and the girl's need to comprehend the complexity of the atom.

Respond to the Reading

1. The author's mother told her it was a basic form of matter that is in her hand and in the milk she is drinking.
2. A positive explanation; she compared it to a spiritual connection among all things.
3. **Linking Science and Writing** Students could skim the chapter for descriptive phrases to use in their poems.

INTEGRATE Physics **Nuclear Fission** Nuclear energy is produced from changes in nuclei. Nuclear fission, one method of producing nuclear energy, is the practical application of Albert Einstein's theory of relativity. Einstein explained that a small amount of mass could be converted into an enormous amount of energy. Nuclear fission generates heat. One use of this energy is to heat water to form steam, which drives turbines to generate electricity. One advantage of nuclear energy is that it produces a large amount of energy from a small amount of fuel. It does have the disadvantage of generating nuclear waste, which is difficult and expensive to store safely. It may take years to decay.

Author Marilou Awiakta was raised near Oak Ridge National Laboratory, a nuclear research laboratory in Tennessee where her father worked. She is of Cherokee and Irish descent. This essay resulted from conversations the author had with writer Alice Walker. It details the author's concern with nuclear technology.

"What is the atom, Mother? Will it hurt us?"

I was nine years old. It was December 1945. Four months earlier, in the heat of an August morning—Hiroshima. Destruction. Death. Power beyond belief, released from something invisible[1]. Without knowing its name, I'd already felt the atoms' power in another form…

"What is the atom, Mother? Will it hurt us?"

"It can be used to hurt everybody, Marilou. It killed thousands[2] of people in Hiroshima and Nagasaki. But the atom itself. . . ? It's invisible, the smallest bit of matter. And it's in everything. Your hand, my dress, the milk you're drinking—. . .

. . . Mother already had taught me that beyond surface differences, everything is [connected]. It seemed natural for the atom to be part of this connection. At school, when I was introduced to Einstein's theory of relativity—that energy and matter are one—I accepted the concept easily.

1 can't see

2 10,500

Understanding Literature

Refrain Refrains are emotionally charged words or phrases that are repeated throughout a literary work and can serve a number of purposes. In this work, the refrain is when the author asks, "What is the atom, Mother? Will it hurt us?" Do you think the refrain helps the reader understand the importance of the atom?

Respond to the Reading

1. How did the author's mother explain the atom to her?
2. Is this a positive or negative explanation of the atom?
3. **Linking Science and Writing** Write a short poem about some element you learned about in this chapter.

INTEGRATE Physics Nuclear fission, or splitting atoms, is the breakdown of an atom's nucleus. It occurs when a particle, such as a neutron, strikes the nucleus of a uranium atom, splitting the nucleus into two fragments, called fission fragments, and releasing two or three neutrons. These released neutrons ultimately cause a chain reaction by splitting more nuclei and releasing more neutrons. When it is uncontrolled, this chain reaction results in a devastating explosion.

182 CHAPTER 6 Atomic Structure and Chemical Bonds

Resources for Teachers and Students

Anything We Love Can Be Saved: A Writer's Activism, by Alice Walker, Ballantine Books, 1998

"Fallout: Nuclear Energy and Destruction," by People's Century/WGBH Boston Video, 1998

Phoenix Rising, by Karen Hesse, Puffin, 1995

Reviewing Main Ideas

Section 1 **Why do atoms combine?**

1. The electrons in the electron cloud of an atom are arranged in energy levels.

2. Each energy level can hold a specific number of electrons.

3. The periodic table supplies a great deal of information about the elements.

4. The number of electrons in an atom increases across each period of the periodic table.

5. The noble gas elements are stable because their outer energy levels are stable.

6. Electron dot diagrams show the electrons in the outer energy level of an atom.

Section 2 **How Elements Bond**

1. An atom can become stable by gaining, losing, or sharing electrons so that its outer energy level is full.

2. Ionic bonds form when a metal atom loses one or more electrons and a nonmetal atom gains one or more electrons.

3. Covalent bonds are created when two or more nonmetal atoms share electrons.

4. The unequal sharing of electrons results in a polar covalent bond.

5. A chemical formula indicates the kind and number of atoms in a compound.

Visualizing Main Ideas

Copy and complete the following concept map on types of bonds.

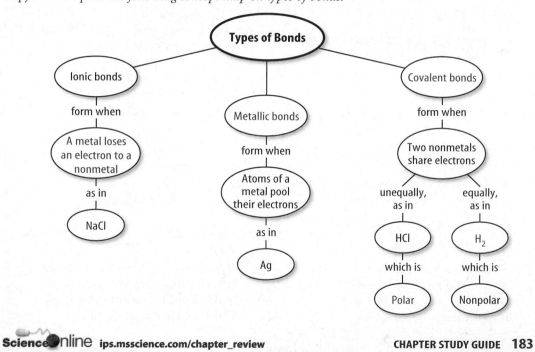

Reviewing Main Ideas

Summary statements can be used by students to review the major concepts of the chapter.

Visualizing Main Ideas

See student page.

Science Online

Visit ips.msscience.com
/self_check_quiz
/interactive_tutor
/vocabulary_puzzlemaker
/chapter_review
/standardized_test

Assessment Transparency

For additional assessment questions, use the *Assessment Transparency* located in the transparency book.

Identifying Misconceptions

Assess

Use the assessment as follow-up to page F at the beginning of this chapter.

Procedure Provide students with the figure shown here, and ask them to give the formula for each molecule and the number of molecules shown in (A) and (B).

Expected Outcome (A) $6CO_2$; (B) $3H_2O$

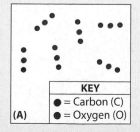

(A)

KEY
● = Carbon (C)
● = Oxygen (O)

(B)

KEY
● = Hydrogen (H)
● = Oxygen (O)

Using Vocabulary

1. An ion is a charged atom, whereas a molecule is two or more atoms covalently bonded with each other.

2. A molecule contains atoms joined by covalent bonds whereas a compound contains two or more elements, whether joined by covalent or ionic bonds.

3. An electron dot diagram indicates the number of electrons in an atom's outer energy level. If one or more of those electrons are lost or gained, an ion is formed.

4. A molecule is composed of covalently bonded atoms. Its composition may be expressed by a chemical formula.

5. An ionic bond forms when positively and negatively charged ions are attracted to each other. A covalent bond occurs when two or more atoms share electrons.

6. An electron cloud shows the areas probably occupied by electrons moving around a nucleus. An electron dot diagram indicates the number of electrons in the outer energy level of an atom.

7. A polar bond is a type of covalent bond in which electrons are shared unequally.

8. A compound is a pure substance made up of two or more elements. Its formula shows what those elements are and in what proportion they occur.

9. Metallic bonds form between metal atoms when they pool electrons. Ionic bonds form between ions that are attracted by opposing charges.

Using Vocabulary

chemical bond p. 169	energy level p. 163
chemical formula p. 178	ion p. 171
compound p. 171	ionic bond p. 171
covalent bond p. 173	metallic bond p. 172
electron cloud p. 162	molecule p. 173
electron dot diagram p. 168	polar bond p. 174

Distinguish between the terms in each of the following pairs.

1. ion—molecule

2. molecule—compound

3. electron dot diagram—ion

4. chemical formula—molecule

5. ionic bond—covalent bond

6. electron cloud—electron dot diagram

7. covalent bond—polar bond

8. compound—formula

9. metallic bond—ionic bond

Checking Concepts

Choose the word or phrase that best answers the question.

10. Which of the following is a covalently bonded molecule?
    A) Cl_2 **C)** Ne
    B) air   **D)** salt

11. What is the number of the group in which the elements have a stable outer energy level?
    A) 1   **C)** 16
    B) 13   **D)** 18

12. Which term describes the units that make up substances formed by ionic bonding?
    A) ions   **C)** acids
    B) molecules   **D)** atoms

Science Online ips.msscience.com/vocabulary_puzzlemaker

13. Which of the following describes what is represented by the symbol Cl^-?
    A) an ionic compound
    B) a polar molecule
    C) a negative ion
    D) a positive ion

14. What happens to electrons in the formation of a polar covalent bond?
    A) They are lost.
    B) They are gained.
    C) They are shared equally.
    D) They are shared unequally.

15. Which of the following compounds is unlikely to contain ionic bonds?
    A) NaF   **C)** LiCl
    B) CO   **D)** $MgBr_2$

16. Which term describes the units that make up compounds with covalent bonds?
    A) ions   **C)** salts
    B) molecules   **D)** acids

17. In the chemical formula CO_2, the subscript 2 shows which of the following?
    A) There are two oxygen ions.
    B) There are two oxygen atoms.
    C) There are two CO_2 molecules.
    D) There are two CO_2 compounds.

Use the figure below to answer question 18.

18. Which is NOT true about the molecule H_2O?
    A) It contains two hydrogen atoms.
    B) It contains one oxygen atom.
    C) It is a polar covalent compound.
    D) It is an ionic compound.

Checking Concepts

10. A	15. B
11. D	16. B
12. A	17. B
13. C	18. D
14. D	

Thinking Critically

19. Elements in Groups 1 and 2 lose one or two electrons easily. Elements in Groups 16 and 17 gain one or two electrons easily.

20. a covalent bond; The picture shows a pair of electrons that is shared between the hydrogen and the fluorine.

Use the Exam*View*® Pro Testmaker CD-ROM to:
- customize tests
- create multiple versions of tests
- generate tests in Spanish
- build tests aligned with state standards

Thinking Critically

19. Explain why Groups 1 and 2 form many compounds with Groups 16 and 17.

Use the illustration below to answer questions 20 and 21.

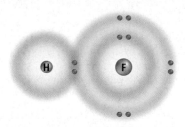

20. Explain what type of bond is shown here.

21. Predict In the HF molecule above, predict if the electrons are shared equally or unequally between the two atoms. Where do the electrons spend more of their time?

22. Analyze When salt dissolves in water, the sodium and chloride ions separate. Explain why this might occur.

23. Interpret Data Both cesium, in period 6, and lithium, in period 2, are in the alkali metals family. Cesium is more reactive. Explain this using the energy step diagram in **Figure 4**.

24. Explain Use the fact that water is a polar molecule to explain why water has a much higher boiling point than other molecules of its size.

25. Predict If equal masses of CuCl and $CuCl_2$ decompose into their components—copper and chlorine—predict which compound will yield more copper. Explain.

26. Concept Map Draw a concept map starting with the term *Chemical Bond* and use all the vocabulary words.

27. Recognize Cause and Effect A helium atom has only two electrons. Why does helium behave as a noble gas?

 Science Online ips.msscience.com/chapter_review

28. Draw a Conclusion A sample of an element can be drawn easily into wire and conducts electricity well. What kind of bonds can you conclude are present?

Performance Activities

29. Display Make a display featuring one of the element families described in this chapter. Include electronic structures, electron dot diagrams, and some compounds they form.

Applying Math

Use the table below to answer question 30.

Formulas of Compounds		
Compound	Number of Metal Atoms	Number of Nonmetal Atoms
Cu_2O	2	1
Al_2S_3	2	3
NaF	1	1
$PbCl_4$	1	4

30. Make and Use Tables Fill in the second column of the table with the number of metal atoms in one unit of the compound. Fill in the third column with the number of atoms of the nonmetal in one unit.

31. Molecules What are the percentages of each atom for this molecule, K_2CO_3?

32. Ionic Compounds Lithium, as a positive ion, is written as Li^{1+}. Nitrogen, as a negative ion, is written as N^{3-}. In order for the molecule to be neutral, the plus and minus charges have to equal zero. How many lithium atoms are needed to make the charges equal to zero?

33. Energy Levels Calculate the maximum number of electrons in energy level 6.

CHAPTER REVIEW **185**

21. The electrons are shared unequally. The electrons spend more time near the fluorine atom than the hydrogen atom.

22. The positive ends of a polar water molecule are attracted to the chloride ions and pull them out of the solid. The negative ends of the polar water molecules are attracted to the sodium ions and pull them out of the solid.

23. The outer electron in cesium is farther from the nucleus and is therefore more easily removed from the atom making cesium more reactive.

24. The negative parts of water molecules are attracted to the positive parts of other water molecules. Because of these attractions, more energy is required to separate the molecules.

25. CuCl will yield more copper because it contains a higher proportion of copper than does $CuCl_2$.

26. Check students' work.

27. The lowest energy level can contain only two electrons. Since this energy level is helium's outer level, it is full with two electrons.

28. metallic bonds

Performance Activities

29. Check displays for accuracy. Use **PASC,** p. 135.

Applying Math

National Math Standards
1, 5, 6, 9

30. See student page.

31. K, 33%; C, 17%; O, 50%

32. Three lithium atoms are needed to make the charges equal to zero.

33. 72

Assessment Resources

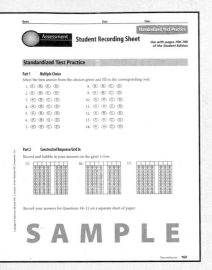

Answer Sheet A practice answer sheet can be found at ips.msscience.com/answer_sheet.

S A M P L E

Part 1 | Multiple Choice

1. A   5. B
2. C   6. A
3. B   7. C
4. D

Part 2 | Short Response

8. An electron cloud is the area of space around an atom's nucleus in which the atom's electrons travel.

9. The statement doesn't consider the case of covalent bonds between two identical atoms. For example, the covalent bond between atoms in an N_2 molecular is not polar because each nitrogen atom has the same ability to attract electrons.

10. Chlorine attracts electrons more strongly than hydrogen does.

11. $\left[H \right]^{+} \left[:\overset{..}{\underset{..}{Cl}} : \right]^{-}$

12. halogens

13. Planets have no charges, but the nucleus of an atom has a positive charge and electrons have negative

---

Part 1 | Multiple Choice

Record your answers on the answer sheet provided by your teacher or on a sheet of paper.

1. Sodium combines with fluorine to produce sodium fluoride (NaF), an active ingredient in toothpaste. In this form, sodium has the electron configuration of which other element?
   A. neon
   B. magnesium
   C. lithium
   D. chlorine

Use the illustration below to answer questions 2 and 3.

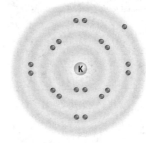

2. The illustration above shows the electron configuration for potassium. How many electrons does potassium need to gain or lose to become stable?
   A. gain 1
   B. gain 2
   C. lose 1
   D. lose 2

3. Potassium belongs to the Group 1 family of elements on the periodic table. What is the name of this group?
   A. halogens
   B. alkali metals
   C. noble gases
   D. alkaline metals

4. What type of bond connects the atoms in a molecule of nitrogen gas (N_2)?
   A. ionic
   B. single
   C. double
   D. triple

Use the illustration below to answer questions 5 and 6.

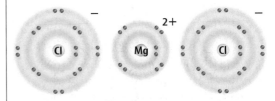

Magnesium chloride

5. The illustration above shows the electron distribution for magnesium chloride. Which of the following is the correct way to write the formula for magnesium chloride?
   A. Mg_2Cl
   B. $MgCl_2$
   C. $MgCl$
   D. Mg_2Cl_2

6. Which of the following terms best describes the type of bonding in magnesium chloride?
   A. ionic
   B. pooling
   C. metallic
   D. covalent

7. What is the maximum number of electrons in the third energy level?
   A. 8
   B. 16
   C. 18
   D. 24

186 STANDARDIZED TEST PRACTICE

Part 3 | Open Ended

charges. Planets travel in predictable orbits, but it is impossible to calculate the exact position of any one electron.

14. Noble gases used to be called inert gases. The name was changed when scientists realized some of the gases can react.

15. Argon has 18 electrons, with 8 electrons in its outer energy level. Atoms with a complete outer energy level are stable. This means that argon will not likely react with its environment, making it a good choice for use in experiments.

16. Group 17 elements are called the halogens. These elements have

seven electrons in their outer energy level. They need one more electron to be stable. Halogens easily combine with Group 1 elements which easily give up one electron. Halogen elements are fluorine, chlorine, bromine, iodine, and astatine.

Part 2 | Short Response/Grid In

Record your answers on the answer sheet provided by your teacher or on a sheet of paper.

8. What is an electron cloud?

9. Explain what is wrong with the following statement: All covalent bonds between atoms are polar to some degree because each element differs slightly in its ability to attract electrons. Give an example to support your answer.

Use the illustration below to answer questions 10 and 11.

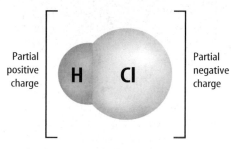

Partial positive charge | H | Cl | Partial negative charge

10. The illustration above shows how hydrogen and chlorine combine to form a polar molecule. Explain why the bond is polar.

11. What is the electron dot diagram for the molecule in the illustration?

12. What is the name of the family of elements in Group 17 of the periodic table?

13. Name two ways that electrons around a nucleus are different from planets circling the Sun.

14. Which family of elements used to be known as inert gases? Why was the name changed?

Test-Taking Tip

Take Your Time Stay focused during the test and don't rush, even if you notice that other students are finishing the test early.

Part 3 | Open Ended

Record your answers on a sheet of paper.

15. Scientific experiments frequently require an oxygen-free environment. Such experiments often are performed in containers flooded with argon gas. Describe the arrangement of electrons in an argon atom. Why is argon often a good choice for these experiments?

16. Which group of elements is called the halogen elements? Describe their electron configurations and discuss their reactivity. Name two elements that belong to this group.

17. What is an ionic bond? Describe how sodium chloride forms an ionic bond.

18. Explain metallic bonding. What are some ways this affects the properties of metals?

19. Explain why polar molecules exist, but polar ionic compounds do not exist.

Use the illustration below to answer questions 20 and 21.

20. Explain what is happening in the photograph above. What would happen if the balloon briefly touched the water?

21. Draw a model showing the electron distribution for a water molecule. Explain how the position of the electrons causes the effect shown in your illustration.

covalently bonded, meaning they share electrons. A compound is polar if the electrons are shared unequally. However, because ionic compounds don't share electrons, they can't be polar.

20. The illustration shows a stream of water deflected toward a balloon. This occurs because water molecules are polar. The positive ends of the water molecules are attracted to the negatively charged balloon. If the balloon briefly touched the water, the balloon would lose its charge. The water would no longer be deflected.

21.

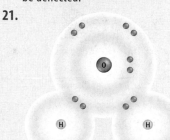

The hydrogen atoms share electrons with the oxygen atom. The electrons are more likely to be closer to the oxygen atom than the hydrogen atoms. This causes the water molecule to be polar. The partial positive charge of the water attracts it to the negatively charged balloon.

Rubrics

For more help evaluating open-ended assessment questions, see the rubric on p. 10T.

17. An ionic bond is an attraction between a positive ion (charged particle) and a negative ion that holds the ions together. When sodium and chlorine combine to form sodium chloride, a sodium atom loses an electron, becoming a positive ion. A chlorine atom gains an electron, becoming a negative ion. The attraction between these ions is an ionic bond.

18. Electrons in the outer energy levels of metal atoms are not held tightly to individual atoms. They move freely among all the ions in the metal. Attractions known as metal-lic bonds form among the atoms of these pooled electrons. This type of bonding allows layers of atoms to slide over one another. As a result, metals are often very malleable, and they conduct electricity well.

19. The term *molecule* refers to groups of two or more atoms that are

Section/Objectives	Standards		Labs/Features
Chapter Opener	**National**	**State/Local**	**Launch Lab:** Identify a Chemical Reaction, p. 189 **Foldables,** p. 189
	See pp. 16T–17T for a Key to Standards.		
Section 1 Chemical Formulas and Equations ⏰ 3 sessions 🎞 1.5 blocks 1. **Determine** whether or not a chemical reaction is occurring. 2. **Determine** how to read and understand a balanced chemical equation. 3. **Examine** some reactions that release energy and others that absorb energy. 4. **Explain** the law of conservation of mass.	National Content Standards: UCP.1, UCP.2, UCP.3, UCP.5, A.1, A.2, B.1, B.3		**Visualizing Chemical Reactions,** p. 191 **Integrate Life Science,** p. 193 **MiniLAB:** Observing the Law of Conservation of Mass, p. 194 **Science Online,** p. 195 **Applying Math: Conserving Mass,** p. 196
Section 2 Rates of Chemical Reactions ⏰ 4 sessions 🎞 2 blocks 5. **Determine** how to describe and measure the speed of a chemical reaction. 6. **Identify** how chemical reactions can be speeded up or slowed down.	National Content Standards: UCP.1, UCP.2, UCP.3, UCP.5, A.1, A.2, B.1, B.2, B.3		**Science Online,** p. 201 **MiniLAB:** Identifying Inhibitors, p. 204 **Integrate History,** p. 205 **Lab:** Physical or Chemical Change?, p. 207 **Lab:** Exothermic or Endothermic?, p. 208 **Science and History:** Synthetic Diamonds, p. 210

Lab Materials	Reproducible Resources	Section Assessment	Technology
Launch Lab: sugar, large test tube, laboratory burner, test-tube holder, test-tube rack	**Chapter FAST FILE Resources** Foldables Worksheet, p. 17 Note-taking Worksheets, pp. 31–32 Directed Reading Overview, p. 19	GLENCOE'S **ASSESSMENT** ADVANTAGE	**TeacherWorks** includes: • Interactive Teacher Edition • Lesson Planner with calendar • Access to all program blacklines • Correlations to standards • Web links
MiniLAB: steel wool, medium test tube, balloon, test-tube holder, hot water bath, test-tube rack *Need materials?* Contact Science Kit at 1-800-828-7777 or www.sciencekit.com on the Internet.	**Chapter FAST FILE Resources** Transparency Activity, p. 42 MiniLAB, p. 3 Enrichment, p. 29 Reinforcement, p. 27 Lab Activity, pp. 9–12 Directed Reading, p. 20 Transparency Activity, pp. 45–46 **Mathematics Skill Activities,** p. 9 **Science Inquiry Labs,** pp. 45–46	**Portfolio** Curriculum Connection, p. 194 **Performance** Applying Math, p. 196 Applying Math, p. 199 **Content** Section Review, p. 199	Section Focus Transparency Teaching Transparency Virtual Labs CD-ROM Guided Reading Audio Program Interactive Chalkboard CD-ROM
MiniLAB: packages of cereals and crackers **Lab:** 500-mL Erlenmeyer flask, 1,000-mL graduated cylinder, one-hole stopper with 15-cm length of glass tube inserted, 1,000-mL beaker, 45-cm length of rubber tubing, balance, stopwatch or clock with second hand, weighing dish, baking soda, vinegar **Lab:** 8 test tubes, test-tube rack, 3% hydrogen peroxide solution, raw liver, raw potato, thermometer, stopwatch or clock with second hand, 25-mL graduated cylinder	**Chapter FAST FILE Resources** Transparency Activity, p. 43 MiniLAB, p. 4 Enrichment, p. 30 Reinforcement, p. 28 Directed Reading, pp. 21, 22 Lab Worksheets, pp. 5–6, 7–8 Lab Activity, pp. 13–16 **Reading and Writing Skill Activities,** p. 1 **Physical Science Critical Thinking/Problem Solving,** p. 10 **Cultural Diversity,** p. 5 **Lab Management and Safety,** p. 50	**Portfolio** Active Reading, p. 202 **Performance** Applying Math, p. 206 **Content** Section Review, p. 206	Section Focus Transparency Virtual Labs CD-ROM Guided Reading Audio Program Interactive Chalkboard CD-ROM Video Lab

End of Chapter Assessment

GLENCOE'S ASSESSMENT ADVANTAGE Blackline Masters	Technology	Professional Series
Chapter FAST FILE Resources Chapter Review, pp. 35–36 Chapter Tests, pp. 37–40 **Standardized Test Practice,** pp. 31–34	MindJogger Videoquiz Virtual Labs CD-ROM ExamView® Pro Testmaker TeacherWorks CD-ROM Interactive Chalkboard CD-ROM	**Performance Assessment in the Science Classroom (PASC)**

Transparencies

Section Focus

SECTION 1 Section Focus Transparency I Needed That Penny

This copper penny is immersed in nitric acid. Nitric acid is made of nitrogen, oxygen, and hydrogen. Most of the bubbles consist of nitrogen and oxygen.

1. Describe what is happening in the picture. Would the same reaction occur if you put the penny in water?
2. What clues do you have that a chemical change is taking place?

L2

SECTION 2 Section Focus Transparency Preserved Mammoth

In 1997, a local man in Siberia discovered part of a mammoth sticking out of the ice. In fact, some of it was encased in ground that never thaws. Portions of the mammoth's skin, hair, and organs were preserved, enabling scientists to study soft parts of the creature that ordinarily disappear quickly after death.

1. Compare food stored in the freezer to food that is left on the counter.
2. What advantages does the ice-bound mammoth offer to scientists?
3. Do you think such finds are common? Why or why not?

L2

This is a representation of key blackline masters available in the Teacher Classroom Resources. See Resource Manager boxes within the chapter for additional information.

Key to Teaching Strategies

The following designations will help you decide which activities are appropriate for your students.

L1 Level 1 activities should be appropriate for students with learning difficulties.

L2 Level 2 activities should be within the ability range of all students.

L3 Level 3 activities are designed for above-average students.

ELL ELL activities should be within the ability range of English Language Learners.

COOP LEARN Cooperative Learning activities are designed for small group work.

LS Multiple Learning Styles logos, as described on page 12T, are used throughout to indicate strategies that address different learning styles.

P These strategies represent student products that can be placed into a best-work portfolio.

PBL Problem-Based Learning activities apply real-world situations to learning.

Assessment

Assessment Transparency Chemical Reactions

Directions: Carefully review the table and answer the following questions.

Reactants	Products	Type of reaction
1. $4K + O_2$	$2K_2O + heat$	Exothermic
2. $2CO + O_2$	$2CO_2 + heat$	Exothermic
3. $2H_2O + heat$	$2H_2 + O_2$	Endothermic
4. $CaCO_3 + heat$	$CaO + CO_2$	Endothermic

1. According to the table, which is the only equation that does not contain the molecular form of oxygen (O_2)?
   A 1
   B 2
   C 3
   D 4

2. This table shows the equations as being exothermic or endothermic. Based on the information given, a reasonable description of exothermic reactions would be ____.
   F reactions that make new compounds
   G reactions that need energy to start
   H reactions that release heat
   J reactions that decompose into smaller parts

3. Calcium carbonate has one atom of calcium, one atom of carbon, and three atoms of oxygen. According to the table, which formula represents calcium carbonate?
   A CaO
   B CO_3
   C $CaCO_3$
   D CO

L2

Teaching

SECTION 1 Teaching Transparency Reactions Around the Home

Table 1 Reactions Around the Home

Reactants		Products
Baking soda + Vinegar	→	Gas + White solid
Charcoal + Air	→	Ash + Gas + Heat
Iron + Air	→	Rust
Silver + Air	→	Black tarnish
Gas (kitchen range) + Air	→	Gas + Heat
Tea + Lemon juice	→	Lighter-colored tea

L2

Hands-on Activities

Student Text Lab Worksheet

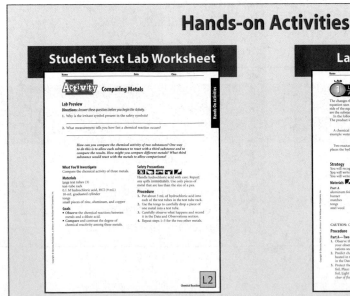

Activity Comparing Metals

Lab Preview
Directions: Answer these questions before you begin the Activity.

1. Why is the irritant symbol present in the safety symbol?

2. What measurement tells you how fast a chemical reaction occurs?

How can you compare the chemical activity of two substances? One way to do this is to allow each substance to react with a third substance and to compare the results. How might you compare different metals? What third substance would react with the metals to allow comparisons?

What You'll Investigate
Compare the chemical activity of three metals.

Materials
large test tubes (3)
test-tube rack
0.1 M hydrochloric acid, HCl (9 mL)
10-mL graduated cylinder
tongs
small pieces of zinc, aluminum, and copper

Goals
• **Observe** the chemical reactions between metals and a dilute acid.
• **Compare** and contrast the degree of chemical reactivity among these metals.

Safety Precautions
Handle hydrochloric acid with care. Report any spills immediately. Use only pieces of metal that are less than the size of a pea.

Procedure
1. Put about 3 mL of hydrochloric acid into each of the test tubes in the test tube rack.
2. Use the tongs to carefully drop a piece of one metal into a test tube.
3. Carefully observe what happens and record it in the Data and Observations section.
4. Repeat steps 1–3 for the two other metals.

L2

Laboratory Activities

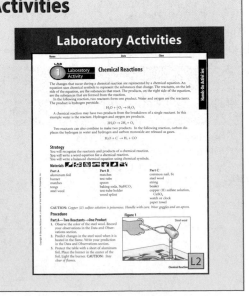

LAB 1 Laboratory Activity Chemical Reactions

The changes that occur during a chemical reaction are represented by a chemical equation. An equation uses chemical symbols to represent the substances that change. The reactants, on the left side of the equation, are the substances that react. The products, on the right side of the equation, are the substances that are formed from the reaction.

In the following reaction, two reactants form one product. Water and oxygen are the reactants. The product is hydrogen peroxide.

$$H_2O + \tfrac{1}{2}O_2 \rightarrow H_2O_2$$

A chemical reaction may have two products from the breakdown of a single reactant. In this example water is the reactant. Hydrogen and oxygen are products.

$$2H_2O \rightarrow 2H_2 + O_2$$

Two reactants can also combine to make new products. In the following reaction, carbon displaces the hydrogen in water and hydrogen and carbon monoxide are released as gases.

$$H_2O + C \rightarrow H_2 + CO$$

Strategy
You will recognize the reactants and products of a chemical reaction.
You will write a word equation for a chemical reaction.
You will write a balanced chemical equation using chemical symbols.

Materials

Part A
aluminum foil
burner
matches
tongs
steel wool

Part B
matches
test tube
spoon
baking soda, NaHCO₃
test-tube holder
wood splint

Part C
common nail, Fe
steel wool
string
beaker
copper (II) sulfate solution, CuSO₄
watch or clock
paper towel

CAUTION: Copper (II) sulfate solution is poisonous. Handle with care. Wear goggles and an apron.

Procedure

Part A—Two Reactants—One Product
1. Observe the color of the steel wool. Record your observations in the Data and Observations section.
2. Predict changes in the steel wool when it is heated in the flame. Write your prediction in the Data and Observations section.
3. Protect the table with a sheet of aluminum foil. Place the burner in the center of the foil. Light the burner. CAUTION: Stay clear of flames.

Figure 1

L2

Meeting Different Ability Levels

Content Outline

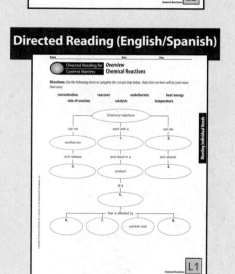

Note-taking Worksheet — **Chemical Reactions**

Section 1 Chemical Formulas and Equations

A. Matter can change physically or chemically; a process that produces a chemical change is a chemical _____.

B. A chemical _____ is a shorthand form of what **reactants** are used and what **products** are formed in a chemical reaction.
  1. Some equations use _____ or chemical _____ to identify reactants and products.
  2. Chemical _____ represent chemical names of substances in a chemical equation.

C. The mass of reactants and mass of products in a chemical reaction is always the same due to the law of _____.

D. Chemical equations are _____ when the number of atoms is the same on each side of the equation.

E. _____ is released or absorbed during a chemical reaction.
  1. When reactions release energy (_____ reactions), the products have bonds with less energy than those of the reactants.
  2. When reactions absorb energy (_____ reactions), the reactants are more stable and their bonds have less energy than those of the products.
  3. _____ energy may be absorbed or released; the rate of heat release can be rapid or slow.
  4. The word energy can be written in a _____ equation as a reactant or a product.

Section 2 Rates of Chemical Reactions

A. Different chemical reactions take different amounts of _____.

B. _____ energy—the amount of energy needed to start a chemical reaction.

C. The rate of _____ measures how quickly a reactant is disappearing or how quickly a product is appearing.
  1. Tells how quickly the amount of a _____ changes per unit of time
  2. Importance in industry: the faster a product can be made, the lower its _____.

L2

Reinforcement

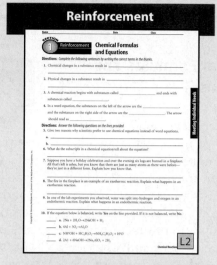

Reinforcement — **Chemical Formulas and Equations**

Directions: Complete the following sentences by writing the correct terms in the blanks.

1. Chemical changes in a substance result in _____

2. Physical changes in a substance result in _____

3. A chemical reaction begins with substances called _____ and ends with substances called _____

4. In a word equation, the substances on the left of the arrow are the _____ and the substances on the right side of the arrow are the _____. The arrow should read as _____

Directions: Answer the following questions on the lines provided.

5. Give two reasons why scientists prefer to use chemical equations instead of word equations.
  a. _____
  b. _____

6. What do the subscripts in a chemical equation tell about the equation?

7. Suppose you have a holiday celebration and over the evening six logs are burned in a fireplace. All that's left is ashes, but you know that there are just as many atoms as there were before—they're just in a different form. Explain how you know that.

8. The fire in the fireplace is an example of an exothermic reaction. Explain what happens in an exothermic reaction.

9. In one of the lab experiments you observed, water was split into hydrogen and oxygen in an endothermic reaction. Explain what happens in an endothermic reaction.

10. If the equation below is balanced, write **Yes** on the line provided. If it is not balanced, write **No.**
  a. $2Na + 2H_2O \rightarrow 2NaOH + H_2$
  b. $4Al + 3O_2 \rightarrow Al_2O$
  c. $NH_2OH + HC_2H_3O_2 \rightarrow NH_4C_2H_3O_2 + H_2O$
  d. $2Al + 6NaOH \rightarrow 2Na_3AlO_3 + 2H_2$

L2

Enrichment

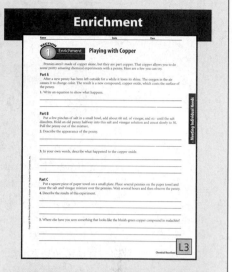

Enrichment — **Playing with Copper**

Pennies aren't made of copper alone, but they are part copper. That copper allows you to do some pretty amazing chemical experiments with a penny. Here are a few you can try.

Part A

After a new penny has been left outside for a while it loses its shine. The oxygen in the air causes it to change color. The result is a new compound, copper oxide, which coats the surface of the penny.

1. Write an equation to show what happens.

Part B

Put a few pinches of salt in a small bowl, add about 60 mL of vinegar, and stir until the salt dissolves. Hold an old penny halfway into this salt and vinegar solution and count slowly to 30. Pull the penny out of the mixture.

2. Describe the appearance of the penny.

3. In your own words, describe what happened to the copper oxide.

Part C

Put a square piece of paper towel on a small plate. Place several pennies on the paper towel and pour the salt and vinegar mixture over the pennies. Wait several hours and then observe the penny.

4. Describe the results of this experiment.

5. Where else have you seen something that looks like the bluish-green copper compound in malachite?

L3

Directed Reading (English/Spanish)

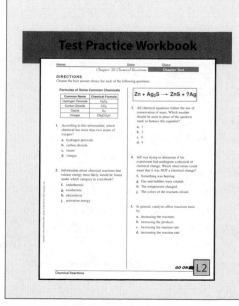

Directed Reading for Content Mastery — *Overview* **Chemical Reactions**

Directions: Use the following terms to complete the concept map below. Note that one term will be used more than once.

concentration   reactant   endothermic   heat energy
rate of reaction   catalysts   temperature

L1

Study Guide

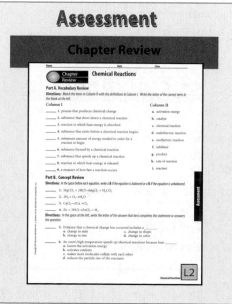

Study Guide

Features
- Contains a study guide page for each section of the chapter
- Reviews key concepts
- Includes answer pages

L1

Reading Essentials

Reading Essentials for Glencoe Science

An Interactive Student Workbook

Features
- Condensed core content
- Actively involves students in reading
- Reinforces key vocabulary

L1

Assessment

Test Practice Workbook

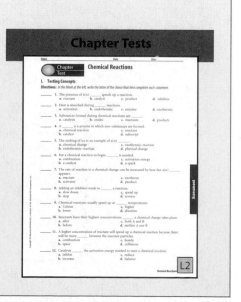

Chapter 20 Chemical Reactions — **Chapter Test**

DIRECTIONS
Choose the best answer choice for each of the following questions.

Formulas of Some Common Chemicals

Common Name	Chemical Formula
Hydrogen Peroxide	H_2O_2
Carbon Dioxide	CO_2
Ozone	O_3
Vinegar	CH_3CO_2H

$$Zn + Ag_2S \rightarrow ZnS + ?Ag$$

1. According to this information, which chemical has more than two atoms of oxygen?
  a. hydrogen peroxide
  b. carbon dioxide
  c. ozone
  d. vinegar

2. Information about chemical reactions that release energy most likely would be found under which category in a textbook?
  f. endothermic
  g. exothermic
  h. electrolysis
  j. activation energy

3. All chemical equations follow the law of conservation of mass. Which number should be used in place of the question mark to balance this equation?
  a. 1
  b. 2
  c. 0
  d. 4

4. Jeff was trying to determine if his experiment had undergone a physical or chemical change. Which observation could mean that it was NOT a chemical change?
  f. Something was burning.
  g. Gas and bubbles were created.
  h. The temperature changed.
  j. The colors of the reactants mixed.

5. In general, catalysts affect reactions most by
  a. decreasing the reactants
  b. increasing the products
  c. increasing the reaction rate
  d. decreasing the reaction rate

GO ON **L2**

Chapter Review

Chapter Review — **Chemical Reactions**

Part A. Vocabulary Review

Directions: Match the items in Column II with the definitions in Column I. Write the letter of the correct term on the blank at the left.

Column I	Column II
1. process that produces chemical change	a. activation energy
2. substance that slows down a chemical reaction	b. catalyst
3. reaction in which heat energy is absorbed	c. chemical reaction
4. substance that exists before a chemical reaction begins	d. endothermic reaction
5. minimum amount of energy needed in order for a reaction to begin	e. exothermic reaction
6. substance formed by a chemical reaction	f. inhibitor
7. substance that speeds up a chemical reaction	g. product
8. reaction in which heat energy is released	h. rate of reaction
9. a measure of how fast a reaction occurs	i. reactant

Part B. Concept Review

Directions: In the space before each equation, write a **B** if the equation is balanced or a **U** if the equation is unbalanced.

1. $MgCO_3 + 2HCl \rightarrow MgCl_2 + H_2CO_3$
2. $H_2O + O_2 \rightarrow H_2O_2$
3. $CaCl_2 \rightarrow 2Ca + Cl_2$
4. $Zn + 2HCl \rightarrow ZnCl_2 + H_2$

Directions: In the space at the left, write the letter of the answer that best completes the statement or answers the question.

5. Evidence that a chemical change has occurred includes a _____.
  a. change in state   c. change in shape
  b. change in size   d. change in color

6. An oven's high temperature speeds up chemical reactions because heat _____.
  a. lowers the activation energy
  b. activates catalysts
  c. makes more molecules collide with each other
  d. reduces the particle size of the reactants

L2

Chapter Tests

Chapter Test — **Chemical Reactions**

I. Testing Concepts

Directions: In the blank at the left, write the letter of the choice that best completes each statement.

1. The presence of a(n) _____ speeds up a reaction.
  a. reactant   b. catalyst   c. product   d. inhibitor

2. Heat is absorbed during _____ reactions.
  a. activation   b. endothermic   c. enzyme   d. exothermic

3. Substances formed during chemical reactions are _____.
  a. catalysts   b. oxides   c. reactants   d. products

4. A _____ is a process in which new substances are formed.
  a. chemical reaction   c. reactant
  b. catalyst   d. subscript

5. The melting of ice is an example of a(n) _____.
  a. chemical change   c. exothermic reaction
  b. endothermic reaction   d. physical change

6. For a chemical reaction to begin, _____ is needed.
  a. combustion   c. activation energy
  b. a catalyst   d. a spark

7. The rate of reaction in a chemical change can be measured by how fast _____ appears.
  a. reactant   b. catalyst   c. exothermic   d. product

8. Adding an inhibitor tends to _____ a reaction.
  a. slow down   b. stop   c. speed up   d. reverse

9. Chemical reactions usually speed up at _____ temperatures.
  a. Celsius   b. lower   c. higher   d. absolute

10. Reactants have their highest concentrations _____ a chemical change takes place.
  a. after   b. before   c. both A and B d. neither A nor B

11. A higher concentration of reactant will speed up a chemical reaction because there will be more _____ between the reactant particles.
  a. combustion   b. space   c. bonds   d. collisions

12. Catalysts _____ the activation energy needed to start a chemical reaction.
  a. inhibit   b. increase   c. reduce   d. balance

L2

Science Content Background

section 1 Chemical Formulas and Equations

Chemical Equations

A chemical change takes place when atoms from one or more materials interact to produce one or more different materials.

A chemical equation must show the identities and relative amounts of the reactants and products. However, it can also indicate the physical states of the reactants and products, whether energy is released or absorbed, and whether a catalyst is used. A chemical equation is not accurate unless the formulas are correct and the equation is balanced.

Energy in Chemical Reactions

The first step in a chemical reaction involves breaking bonds. This step always uses energy. When atoms or other particles recombine to form new substances, they form chemical bonds. This step always releases energy. A reaction is exergonic, releases energy, if the energy released in the formation of new bonds is greater than the energy used to break the original bonds. If the energy is released as heat, the reaction is said to be exothermic. A reaction in which the energy used to break the old bonds is greater than the energy released to form the new bonds is endergonic, that is, it absorbs energy. If the energy absorbed is in the form of heat, the reaction is said to be endothermic.

section 2 Rates of Chemical Reactions

Reaction Rate

In addition to temperature, concentration, particle size, and catalysts, reaction rate is determined by the nature of the reactants. Reactions that involve electron transfer or bond rearrangement generally take longer than reactions that do not involve these changes. The rate of a reaction is not constant throughout the course of the reaction because the rate is proportional to reactant concentration and the concentration of reactants decreases as reactants are converted to products.

Charles D. Winters/Photo Researchers, Inc.

chapter content resources

Internet Resources
For additional content background, visit
ips.msscience.com to:
- access your book online
- find references to related articles in popular science magazines
- access Web links with related content background
- access current events with science journal topics

Print Resources
Chemistry; The Molecular Nature of Matter and Change, by Martin S. Silberberg, McGraw-Hill, 2003
The Basics of Chemistry, by Richard Meyers, Greenwood Publishing Group, Incorporated, 2003
Why Chemical Reactions Happen, by James J. Keeler, Peter Wothers, and James Keeler, Oxford University Press, 2003

IDENTIFYING Misconceptions

Find Out What Students Think

Students may think that . . .

Chemical changes are separate changes in substances rather than interactions between molecules of the substances.

Students may have this misconception because they can see one material that changes in a reaction but not the others. For example, students can see iron and rust but they cannot see the oxygen that also participates in the reaction. Language may also contribute to the misconception. We say that iron rusts, rather than saying that iron interacts with oxygen to produce rust.

Discussion

Hold up two iron bolts or nails, one rusty and the other not. Explain that both are made out of iron.

- **How are the bolts different?** One is rusty; the other is not.

- **What is the rust made out of?** Have students discuss whether rust is made entirely out of iron or if it contains other things as well.

Jeff Greenberg/PhotoEdit

Promote Understanding

Activity [L2] [ELL] [COOP LEARN] [IS] Kinesthetic

Safety Precautions 🥽 ♨ 🧤 ✋

Give each group a piece of steel wool (without oil or soap), three plastic foam bowls, water, and scissors. Have students label the bowls A, B, and C. Tell students to

- Cut the steel wool into three pieces. Put one piece in each bowl.

- Expose the steel wool in bowl A to air only.

- Cover the steel wool in bowl B with water. This piece is exposed to water only.

- Fill bowl C halfway so that part of the steel wool is covered with water. This piece is exposed to both water and air.

- Leave the bowls for one week, adding water to bowls B and C as needed. Then have students examine the steel wool for rust. Only the steel wool in bowl C should have rusted.

- **Why did only the steel wool in bowl C develop rust?** Help students realize that something in the air in the presence of water interacted with the iron to form a new material called rust. Write the formula for rust on the board $(Fe_2O_3) \cdot H_2O$.

Assess

After completing the chapter, see *Identifying Misconceptions* in the Study Guide at the end of the chapter.

Chapter Vocabulary

Science Journal Answers will vary. Look for depth and quality of information.

INTERACTIVE CHALKBOARD with Image Bank

PowerPoint® Presentations

This CD-ROM is an editable Microsoft® PowerPoint® presentation that includes:
- a pre-made presentation for every chapter
- interactive graphics
- animations
- audio clips
- image bank
- all new section and chapter questions
- Standardized Test Practice
- transparencies
- pre-lab questions for all labs
- Foldables directions
- links to ips.msscience.com

Chemical Reactions

chapter preview

sections

1 Chemical Formulas and Equations

2 Rates of Chemical Reactions
Lab Physical or Chemical Change?
Lab Exothermic or Endothermic?
Virtual Lab What properties do elements have?

What chemical reactions happen at chemical plants?

Chemical plants like this one provide the starting materials for thousands of chemical reactions. The compact discs you listen to, personal items, such as shampoo and body lotion, and medicines all have their beginnings in a chemical plant.

Science Journal What additional types of products do you think are manufactured in a chemical plant?

188

Theme Connection

Systems and Interactions The reactants that interact in a chemical reaction and the products they form make up a system whose behavior depends on the energy entering and leaving the system.

About the Photo

Chemical Plants From the photo it's impossible to tell what is produced at this chemical plant. However, it is possible to tell that a chemical reaction is taking place. The by-products of the reaction are cleansed in the stacks shown in the center and released harmlessly into the environment.

Start-Up Activities

Identify a Chemical Reaction

You can see substances changing every day. Fuels burn, giving energy to cars and trucks. Green plants convert carbon dioxide and water into oxygen and sugar. Cooking an egg or baking bread causes changes too. These changes are called chemical reactions. In this lab you will observe a common chemical change.

WARNING: *Do not touch the test tube. It will be hot. Use extreme caution around an open flame. Point test tubes away from you and others.*

1. Place 3 g of sugar into a large test tube.
2. Carefully light a laboratory burner.
3. Using a test-tube holder, hold the bottom of the test tube just above the flame for 45 s or until something happens with the sugar.
4. Observe any change that occurs.
5. **Think Critically** Describe in your Science Journal the changes that took place in the test tube. What do you think happened to the sugar? Was the substance that remained in the test tube after heating the same as the substance you started with?

FOLDABLES Study Organizer

Chemical Reaction Make the following Foldable to help you understand chemical reactions.

STEP 1 Fold a vertical sheet of notebook paper in half lengthwise.

STEP 2 Cut along every third line of only the top layer to form tabs.

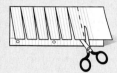

STEP 3 Label each tab.

Research Information Before you read the chapter, write several questions you have about chemical reactions on the front of the tabs. As you read, add more questions. Under the tabs of your Foldable, write answers to the questions you recorded on the tabs.

Science✺**Online** Preview this chapter's content and activities at ips.msscience.com

Purpose Use this Launch Lab to introduce students to chemical reactions. Explain that in this chapter they will be studying how chemical reactions occur and how chemists identify chemical reactions. **L2** **ELL** **LS**

Kinesthetic

Preparation Be sure to use only table sugar and not confectionery or brown sugar.

Materials table sugar, large test tube, laboratory burner, test-tube holder, test-tube rack

Teaching Strategies

• Make sure students hold the test tube just above the flame.

• Instruct students to remove the sugar from the flame every few seconds to observe the different phases of this chemical reaction.

Safety Precautions Instruct students to wear safety goggles and always use caution around an open flame.

Think Critically

The sugar will bubble and turn yellow at first. Soon, a white gas will form in the test tube, and the sugar will turn brown as the heat breaks it down to form caramel.

Assessment

Process Have each student write a paragraph relating the results of the lab to what happens when you bake a cake or make cookies. Sugar is also heated in the oven to make a sweet liquid. Use **Performance Assessment in the Science Classroom,** p. 159.

FOLDABLES Study Organizer

Dinah Zike Study Fold

Student preparation materials for this Foldable are available in the **Chapter FAST FILE Resources.**

189

Chemical Formulas and Equations

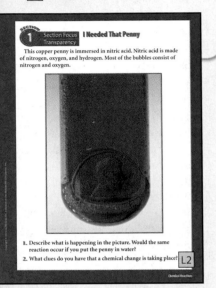
as you read

What You'll Learn

- **Determine** whether or not a chemical reaction is occurring.
- **Determine** how to read and understand a balanced chemical equation.
- **Examine** some reactions that release energy and others that absorb energy.
- **Explain** the law of conservation of mass.

Why It's Important

Chemical reactions warm your home, cook your meals, digest your food, and power cars and trucks.

⊙ Review Vocabulary

atom: the smallest piece of matter that still retains the property of the element

New Vocabulary

- chemical reaction
- reactant
- product
- chemical equation
- endothermic reaction
- exothermic reaction

Physical or Chemical Change?

You can smell a rotten egg and see the smoke from a campfire. Signs like these tell you that a chemical reaction is taking place. Other evidence might be less obvious, but clues are always present to announce that a reaction is under way.

Matter can undergo two kinds of changes—physical and chemical. Physical changes in a substance affect only physical properties, such as its size and shape, or whether it is a solid, liquid, or gas. For example, when water freezes, its physical state changes from liquid to solid, but it's still water.

In contrast, chemical changes produce new substances that have properties different from those of the original substances. The rust on a bike's handlebars, for example, has properties different from those of the metal around it. Another example is the combination of two liquids that produce a precipitate, which is a solid, and a liquid. The reaction of silver nitrate and sodium chloride forms solid silver chloride and liquid sodium nitrate. A process that produces chemical change is a **chemical reaction.**

To compare physical and chemical changes, look at the newspaper shown in **Figure 1.** If you fold it, you change its size and shape, but it is still newspaper. Folding is a physical change. If you use it to start a fire, it will burn. Burning is a chemical change because new substances result. How can you recognize a chemical change? **Figure 2** shows what to look for.

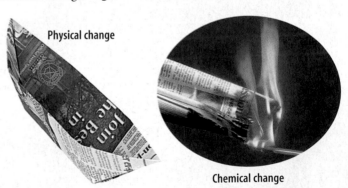

Physical change

Chemical change

Figure 1 Newspaper can undergo both physical and chemical changes.

Figure 2

Chemical reactions take place when chemicals combine to form new substances. Your senses—sight, taste, hearing, smell, and touch—can help you detect chemical reactions in your environment.

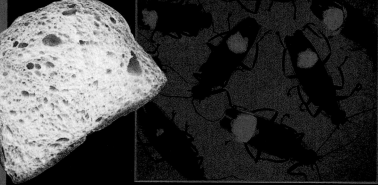

▼ TASTE A boy grimaces after sipping milk that has gone sour due to a chemical reaction.

▲ SIGHT When you spot a firefly's bright glow, you are seeing a chemical reaction in progress—two chemicals are combining in the firefly's abdomen and releasing light in the process. The holes in a slice of bread are visible clues that sugar molecules were broken down by yeast cells in a chemical reaction that produces carbon dioxide gas. The gas caused the bread dough to rise.

▲ HEARING A Russian cosmonaut hoists a flare into the air after landing in the ocean during a training exercise. The hissing sound of the burning flare is the result of a chemical reaction.

▲ SMELL AND TOUCH Billowing clouds of acrid smoke and waves of intense heat indicate that chemical reactions are taking place in this burning forest.

Visualizing Chemical Reactions

Have students examine the pictures and read the captions. Then ask the following questions.

How does temperature affect the speed of the chemical reaction that causes milk to sour? How do you know? The reaction is faster at higher temperatures because milk will sour more quickly if it is not refrigerated.

What are some other examples of chemical changes that you can detect by using your senses? Possible answers: A cut apple turns brown when it is exposed to air; a light stick glows when the chemicals inside it react; a burning candle gives off light and heat; baking soda fizzes when it is added to vinegar.

Activity

Observe Have small groups of students pour about 10 mL of 3% hydrogen peroxide into a small beaker. Then have them stir in a pinch of quick-rising dry yeast. Have students use their senses of sight and touch to describe what happens. Ask what clues told them that a chemical reaction was occurring. Bubbles of gas were produced and heat was released. L2 COOP LEARN LS **Visual-Spatial Kinesthetic**

Answer the reactants, products, and the proportions of each substance present in a chemical reaction

Caption Answer

Figure 3 Possible answer: Add vinegar to the residue to see if it foams like the original substance did.

Chemical Equations

To describe a chemical reaction, you must know which substances react and which substances are formed in the reaction. The substances that react are called the reactants (ree AK tunts). **Reactants** are the substances that exist before the reaction begins. The substances that form as a result of the reaction are called the **products.**

When you mix baking soda and vinegar, a vigorous chemical reaction occurs. The mixture bubbles and foams up inside the container, as you can see in **Figure 3.**

Baking soda and vinegar are the common names for the reactants in this reaction, but they also have chemical names. Baking soda is the compound sodium hydrogen carbonate (often called sodium bicarbonate), and vinegar is a solution of acetic (uh SEE tihk) acid in water. What are the products? You saw bubbles form when the reaction occurred, but is that enough of a description?

Describing What Happens Bubbles tell you that a gas has been produced, but they don't tell you what kind of gas. Are bubbles of gas the only product, or do some atoms from the vinegar and baking soda form something else? What goes on in the chemical reaction can be more than what you see with your eyes. Chemists try to find out which reactants are used and which products are formed in a chemical reaction. Then, they can write it in a shorthand form called a chemical equation. A **chemical equation** tells chemists at a glance the reactants, products, physical state, and the proportions of each substance present. This is very important as you will see later.

✓ Reading Check   *What does a chemical equation tell chemists?*

Figure 3 The bubbles tell you that a chemical reaction has taken place.
Predict *how you might find out whether a new substance has formed.*

Differentiated Instruction

Visually Impaired Place about 1 g of baking soda in an evaporating dish. Add 2 mL of white vinegar. When the vinegar and baking soda start reacting, allow the students to touch the foam with their fingers. After the reaction, put some baking soda in water and allow these students to feel it and compare it with the sodium acetate in water formed by the reaction of vinegar and baking soda. Have them dictate their observations into a tape recorder. Make sure they wash their hands after handling materials. L1 LS **Kinesthetic**

Table 1 Reactions Around the Home

Reactants		Products
Baking soda + Vinegar	→	Gas + White solid
Charcoal + Oxygen	→	Ash + Gas + Heat
Iron + Oxygen + Water	→	Rust
Silver + Hydrogen sulfide	→	Black tarnish + Gas
Gas (kitchen range) + Oxygen	→	Gas + Heat
Sliced apple + Oxygen	→	Apple turns brown

Using Words One way you can describe a chemical reaction is with an equation that uses words to name the reactants and products. The reactants are listed on the left side of an arrow, separated from each other by plus signs. The products are placed on the right side of the arrow, also separated by plus signs. The arrow between the reactants and products represents the changes that occur during the chemical reaction. When reading the equation, the arrow is read as *produces*.

You can begin to think of processes as chemical reactions even if you do not know the names of all the substances involved. **Table 1** can help you begin to think like a chemist. It shows the word equations for chemical reactions you might see around your home. See how many other reactions you can find. Look for the signs you have learned that indicate a reaction might be taking place. Then, try to write them in the form shown in the table.

Using Chemical Names Many chemicals used around the home have common names. For example, acetic acid dissolved in water is called vinegar. Some chemicals, such as baking soda, have two common names—it also is known as sodium bicarbonate. However, chemical names are usually used in word equations instead of common names. In the baking soda and vinegar reaction, you already know the chemical names of the reactants—sodium hydrogen carbonate and acetic acid. The names of the products are sodium acetate, water, and carbon dioxide. The word equation for the reaction is as follows.

Acetic acid + Sodium hydrogen carbonate →
      Sodium acetate + Water + Carbon dioxide

Autumn Leaves A color change can indicate a chemical reaction. When leaves change colors in autumn, the reaction may not be what you expect. The bright yellow and orange are always in the leaves, but masked by green chlorophyll. When the growth season ends, more chlorophyll is broken down than produced. The orange and yellow colors become visible.

Figure 4 The law of conservation of mass states that the number and kind of atoms must be equal for products and reactants.

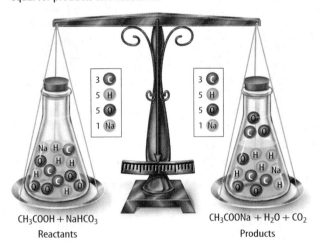

$CH_3COOH + NaHCO_3$
Reactants

$CH_3COONa + H_2O + CO_2$
Products

Using Formulas The word equation for the reaction of baking soda and vinegar is long. That's why chemists use chemical formulas to represent the chemical names of substances in the equation. You can convert a word equation into a chemical equation by substituting chemical formulas for the chemical names. For example, the chemical equation for the reaction between baking soda and vinegar can be written as follows:

$$CH_3COOH + NaHCO_3 \rightarrow CH_3COONa + H_2O + CO_2$$

| Acetic acid (vinegar) | Sodium hydrogen carbonate (baking soda) | Sodium acetate | Water | Carbon dioxide |

Subscripts When you look at chemical formulas, notice the small numbers written to the right of the atoms. These numbers, called subscripts, tell you the number of atoms of each element in that compound. For example, the subscript 2 in CO_2 means that each molecule of carbon dioxide has two oxygen atoms. If an atom has no subscript, it means that only one atom of that element is in the compound, so carbon dioxide has only one carbon atom.

Conservation of Mass

What happens to the atoms in the reactants when they are converted into products? According to the law of conservation of mass, the mass of the products must be the same as the mass of the reactants in that chemical reaction. This principle was first stated by the French chemist Antoine Lavoisier (1743–1794), who is considered the first modern chemist. Lavoisier used logic and scientific methods to study chemical reactions. He proved by his experiments that nothing is lost or created in chemical reactions.

He showed that chemical reactions are much like mathematical equations. In math equations, the right and left sides of the equation are numerically equal. Chemical equations are similar, but it is the number and kind of atoms that are equal on the two sides. Every atom that appears on the reactant side of the equation also appears on the product side, as shown in **Figure 4.** Atoms are never lost or created in a chemical reaction; however, they do change partners.

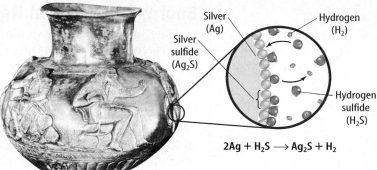

Figure 5 Keeping silver bright takes frequent polishing, especially in homes heated by gas. Sulfur compounds found in small concentrations in natural gas react with silver, forming black silver sulfide, Ag_2S.

Silver (Ag)

Hydrogen (H_2)

Silver sulfide (Ag_2S)

Hydrogen sulfide (H_2S)

$$2Ag + H_2S \longrightarrow Ag_2S + H_2$$

Balancing Chemical Equations

When you write the chemical equation for a reaction, you must observe the law of conservation of mass. Look back at **Figure 4.** It shows that when you count the number of carbon, hydrogen, oxygen, and sodium atoms on each side of the arrow in the equation, you find equal numbers of each kind of atom. This means the equation is balanced and the law of conservation of mass is observed.

Not all chemical equations are balanced so easily. For example, silver tarnishes, as in **Figure 5,** when it reacts with sulfur compounds in the air, such as hydrogen sulfide. The following unbalanced equation shows what happens when silver tarnishes.

$$\underset{\text{Silver}}{Ag} \quad + \quad \underset{\substack{\text{Hydrogen}\\\text{sulfide}}}{H_2S} \quad \rightarrow \quad \underset{\substack{\text{Silver}\\\text{sulfide}}}{Ag_2S} \quad + \quad \underset{\text{Hydrogen}}{H_2}$$

Count the Atoms Count the number of atoms of each type in the reactants and in the products. The same numbers of hydrogen and sulfur atoms are on each side, but one silver atom is on the reactant side and two silver atoms are on the product side. This cannot be true. A chemical reaction cannot create a silver atom, so this equation does not represent the reaction correctly. Place a 2 in front of the reactant Ag and check to see if the equation is balanced. Recount the number of atoms of each type.

$$2Ag + H_2S \rightarrow Ag_2S + H_2$$

The equation is now balanced. There are an equal number of silver atoms in the reactants and the products. When balancing chemical equations, numbers are placed before the formulas as you did for Ag. These are called coefficients. However, never change the subscripts written to the right of the atoms in a formula. Changing these numbers changes the identity of the compound.

ScienceOnline

Topic: Chemical Equations
Visit ips.msscience.com for Web links to information about chemical equations and balancing them.

Activity Find a chemical reaction that takes place around your home or school. Write a chemical equation describing it.

Activity
Balancing Equations Have students balance the following equations:
a. $Na + AlCl_3 \rightarrow NaCl + Al$;
  $3Na + AlCl_3 \rightarrow 3NaCl + Al$
b. $KBr + Cl_2 \rightarrow KCl + Br_2$;
  $2KBr + Cl_2 \rightarrow 2KCl + Br_2$
c. $H_2O_2 \rightarrow H_2O + O_2$;
  $2H_2O_2 \rightarrow 2H_2O + O_2$

L2 LS **Logical-Mathematical**

Virtual Labs

Elements *What properties do elements have?*

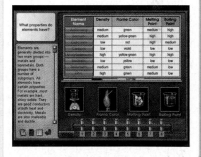

Differentiated Instruction

Learning Disabled Provide items such as paper clips, coins, and washers to represent different atoms. Have students use a double pan balance and the materials provided to balance equations. To bring the scales into balance, the same number and kind of atom must be on each side of the balance just as in a balanced equation. Start with a simple balanced equation such as $C + O_2 \rightarrow CO_2$. Then give them $H_2 + O_2 \rightarrow H_2O$ and $H_2O_2 \rightarrow H_2O + O_2$. Remind students of the law of conservation of mass, and have them use the balance to find the coefficients for the equations. The balanced equations are: $2H_2 + O_2 \rightarrow 2H_2O$ and $2H_2O_2 \rightarrow 2H_2O + O_2$. L3 ELL LS **Logical-Mathematical**

Energy in Chemical Reactions

Often, energy is released or absorbed during a chemical reaction. The energy for the welding torch in **Figure 6** is released when hydrogen and oxygen combine to form water.

$$2H_2 + O_2 \rightarrow 2H_2O + energy$$

Energy Released Where does this energy come from? To answer this question, think about the chemical bonds that break and form when atoms gain, lose, or share electrons. When such a reaction takes place, bonds break in the reactants and new bonds form in the products. In reactions that release energy, the products are more stable, and their bonds have less energy than those of the reactants. The extra energy is released in various forms—light, sound, and heat.

Applying Math   Balancing Equations

CONSERVING MASS Methane and oxygen react to form carbon dioxide, water, and heat. You can see how mass is conserved by balancing the equation: $CH_4 + O_2 \rightarrow CO_2 + H_2O$.

Solution

1 *This is what you know:*

The number of atoms of C, H, and O in reactants and products.

2 *This is what you need to do:*

Make sure that the reactants and products have equal numbers of atoms of each element. Start with the reactant having the greatest number of atoms.

Reactants	Products	Action
$CH_4 + O_2$ have 4 H atoms	$CO_2 + H_2O$ have 2 H atoms	Need 2 more H atoms in Products Multiply H_2O by 2 to give 4 H atoms
$CH_4 + O_2$ have 2 O atoms	$CO_2 + H_2O$ have 4 O atoms	Need 2 more O atoms in Reactants Multiply O_2 by 2 to give 4 O atoms

The balanced equation is $CH_4 + 2O_2 \rightarrow CO_2 + 2H_2O$.

3 *Check your answer:*

Count the carbons, hydrogens, and oxygens on each side.

Practice Problems

1. Balance the equation $Fe_2O_3 + CO \rightarrow Fe_3O_4 + CO_2$.
2. Balance the equation $Al + I_2 \rightarrow AlI_3$.

Science Online | For more practice, visit ips.msscience.com/ math_practice

Science Journal

Burning Coal By heating water to produce steam, coal-burning power plants generate much of today's electricity. This steam turns turbines whose motion is converted to electrical energy. Have students write in their Science Journals the reason these plants burn coal instead of wood. The chemical bonds in coal contain more energy than do the bonds of wood, so burning coal releases more energy than burning wood. [L2] [IS] **Logical-Mathematical**

Figure 6 This welding torch burns hydrogen and oxygen to produce temperatures above 3,000°C. It can even be used underwater.
Identify *the products of this chemical reaction.*

Energy Absorbed What happens when the reverse situation occurs? In reactions that absorb energy, the reactants are more stable, and their bonds have less energy than those of the products.

$$2H_2O + energy \rightarrow 2H_2 + O_2$$

Water · · · · · · · · · · · · · · Hydrogen · · · Oxygen

In this reaction the extra energy needed to form the products can be supplied in the form of electricity, as shown in **Figure 7.**

As you have seen, reactions can release or absorb energy of several kinds, including electricity, light, sound, and heat. When heat energy is gained or lost in reactions, special terms are used. **Endothermic** (en doh THUR mihk) **reactions** absorb heat energy. **Exothermic** (ek soh THUR mihk) **reactions** release heat energy. You may notice that the root word *therm* refers to heat, as it does in thermos bottles and thermometers.

Heat Released You might already be familiar with several types of reactions that release heat. Burning is an exothermic chemical reaction in which a substance combines with oxygen to produce heat along with light, carbon dioxide, and water.

✔ **Reading Check** *What type of chemical reaction is burning?*

Rapid Release Sometimes energy is released rapidly. For example, charcoal lighter fluid combines with oxygen in the air and produces enough heat to ignite a charcoal fire within a few minutes.

Figure 7 Electrical energy is needed to break water into its components. This is the reverse of the reaction that takes place in the welding torch shown in **Figure 6.**

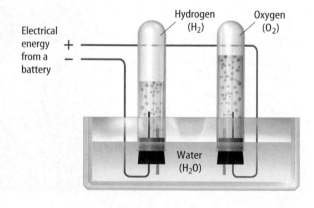

Hydrogen (H₂)   Oxygen (O₂)

Electrical energy from a battery   +   −

Water (H₂O)

Caption Answer
Figure 6 water, heat, and light

Use Science Words
Word Meaning Point out to students that in the words *endothermic* and *exothermic*, the prefix *en-* means "in" and the prefix *ex-* means "out." Ask students to identify other pairs of words with these prefixes. Possible answers: entrance and exit, endoskeleton and exoskeleton [L2] **LS** **Linguistic**

Discussion
Solar Energy Almost all energy on Earth comes in some way from the Sun, which is a mass of nuclear reactions. Are the reactions that occur inside the Sun endothermic or exothermic? The heat and light that radiate from the Sun indicate that the reactions that occur inside it are exothermic. [L2] **LS** **Logical-Mathematical**

✔ **Reading Check**

Answer exothermic

Teacher FYI

Endothermic v. Exothermic Breaking chemical bonds always requires energy. Forming chemical bonds releases energy. A reaction is classified as endothermic or exothermic by comparing the amount of energy needed to break the chemical bonds of the reactants to the amount of energy released when the chemical bonds of the products are formed. If less energy is needed to break the chemical bonds in the reactants than is released by forming the bonds in the products, the reaction is exothermic.

Curriculum Connection

History The Nobel prize is named after a man who developed a material that reacts to release energy rapidly. Have students write short reports about this man and the material he exploited. Alfred Nobel (1833–1896) developed dynamite, a mixture of nitroglycerin and filler materials that decomposes explosively when heated or jarred. [L2] **LS** **Logical-Mathematical**

Figure 8 Two exothermic reactions are shown. The charcoal fire to cook the food was started when lighter fluid combined rapidly with oxygen in air. The iron in the wheelbarrow combined slowly with oxygen in the air to form rust.

Fast reaction

Slow reaction

Slow Release Other materials also combine with oxygen but release heat so slowly that you cannot see or feel it happen. This is the case when iron combines with oxygen in the air to form rust. The slow heat release from a reaction also is used in heat packs that can keep your hands warm for several hours. Fast and slow energy release are compared in **Figure 8.**

Heat Absorbed Some chemical reactions and physical processes need to have heat energy added before they can proceed. An example of an endothermic physical process that absorbs heat energy is the cold pack shown in **Figure 9.**

The heavy plastic cold pack holds ammonium nitrate and water. The two substances are separated by a plastic divider. When you squeeze the bag, you break the divider so that the ammonium nitrate dissolves in the water. The dissolving process absorbs heat energy, which must come from the surrounding environment—the surrounding air or your skin after you place the pack on the injury.

Figure 9 The heat energy needed to dissolve the ammonium nitrate in this cold pack comes from the surrounding environment.

Energy in the Equation The word *energy* often is written in equations as either a reactant or a product. Energy written as a reactant helps you think of energy as a necessary ingredient for the reaction to take place. For example, electrical energy is needed to break up water into hydrogen and oxygen. It is important to know that energy must be added to make this reaction occur.

Similarly, in the equation for an exothermic reaction, the word *energy* often is written along with the products. This tells you that energy is released. You include energy when writing the reaction that takes place between oxygen and methane in natural gas when you cook on a gas range, as shown in **Figure 10.** This heat energy cooks your food.

Figure 10 Energy from a chemical reaction is used to cook.
Determine *if energy is used as a reactant or a product in this reaction.*

$$CH_4 \ + \ 2O_2 \ \rightarrow \ CO_2 \ + \ 2H_2O \ + \ energy$$
Methane Oxygen Carbon Water
                 dioxide

Although it is not necessary, writing the word *energy* can draw attention to an important aspect of the equation.

---

section 1 review

Summary

Physical or Chemical Change?
- Matter can undergo physical and chemical changes.
- A chemical reaction produces chemical changes.

Chemical Equations
- A chemical equation describes a chemical reaction.
- Chemical formulas represent chemical names for substances.
- A balanced chemical equation has the same number of atoms of each kind on both sides of the equation.

Energy in Chemical Reactions
- Endothermic reactions absorb heat energy.
- Exothermic reactions release heat energy.

Self Check

1. **Determine** if each of these equations is balanced. Why or why not?
   a. $Ca + Cl_2 \rightarrow CaCl_2$
   b. $Zn + Ag_2S \rightarrow ZnS + Ag$
2. **Describe** what evidence might tell you that a chemical reaction has occurred.
3. **Think Critically** After a fire, the ashes have less mass and take up less space than the trees and vegetation before the fire. How can this be explained in terms of the Law of Conservation of Mass?

Applying Math

4. **Calculate** The equation for the decomposition of silver oxide is $2Ag_2O \rightarrow 4Ag + O_2$. Set up a ratio to calculate the number of oxygen molecules released when 1 g of silver oxide is broken down. There are 2.6×10^{21} molecules in 1 g of silver oxide.

Science online ips.msscience.com/self_check_quiz

SECTION 1 Chemical Formulas and Equations **199**

---

section 1 review

1. The first equation is balanced. It has an equal number of each type of atom present on each side of the equation. The second equation is unbalanced. It has an unequal number of silver atoms on each side.

2. color change, the formation of bubbles, the formation of precipitate, an energy change, a change in the identity of a substance

3. The difference in mass is accounted for by gases that were produced.

4. Using the coefficients in the balanced equation, half as many, or 1.3×10^{21}, oxygen molecules are produced.

Caption Answer
Figure 10 Energy is a product in this reaction.

3 Assess

DAILY INTERVENTION

Check for Understanding

Logical-Mathematical Ask students which of the following equations for the formation of iron(III) chloride, $FeCl_3$, is correctly written and balanced and explain what is wrong with each of the other two.

a. $Fe + 3Cl_2 \rightarrow Fe_2Cl_3$
   The formula for iron(III) chloride is $FeCl_3$ and cannot be changed. Changing the subscript changes the compound.

b. $2Fe + 3Cl_2 \rightarrow 2FeCl_3$
   correct as written

c. $Fe + Cl_3 \rightarrow FeCl_3$
   The formula for chlorine is Cl_2. Changing the subscript changes the compound.

L3

Reteach

Balancing Equations Have students use coins or other objects to model balancing the chemical equations in the Section Review, Question 1. L1 ELL
Kinesthetic

☑ Assessment

Process Tell students that many chemical reactions are written with a double arrow ($\rightleftarrows$). Ask them what the double arrow means. The double arrow indicates that the reaction can move in either direction. Use **Performance Assessment in the Science Classroom,** p. 89.

1 Motivate

INTERACTIVE CHALKBOARD
PowerPoint® Presentations

Bellringer

Section Focus Transparencies also are available on the Interactive Chalkboard CD-ROM. L2 ELL

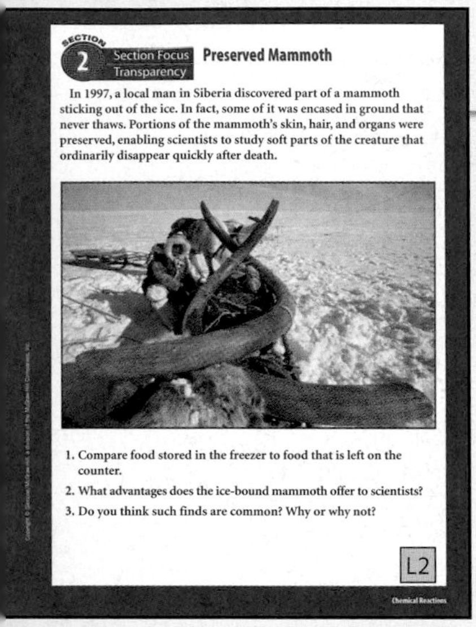
SECTION 2 Section Focus Transparency **Preserved Mammoth**

In 1997, a local man in Siberia discovered part of a mammoth sticking out of the ice. In fact, some of it was encased in ground that never thaws. Portions of the mammoth's skin, hair, and organs were preserved, enabling scientists to study soft parts of the creature that ordinarily disappear quickly after death.

1. Compare food stored in the freezer to food that is left on the counter.
2. What advantages does the ice-bound mammoth offer to scientists?
3. Do you think such finds are common? Why or why not?

L2

Chemical Reactions

Tie to Prior Knowledge

Chemical Reaction Rates Ask students whether they are aware that changing temperature can affect the rate of a chemical reaction. Remind them that putting food in the refrigerator, for example, doesn't stop the food from spoiling but slows the chemical reactions involved in spoiling. Tell students that in this section they will learn more about the factors that affect the rates of chemical reactions.

section 2

Rates of Chemical Reactions

as you read

***What* You'll Learn**

- **Determine** how to describe and measure the speed of a chemical reaction.
- **Identify** how chemical reactions can be speeded up or slowed down.

***Why* It's Important**

Speeding up useful reactions and slowing down destructive ones can be helpful.

Review Vocabulary
state of matter: physical property that is dependent on temperature and pressure and occurs in four forms—solid, liquid, gas, or plasma

New Vocabulary
- activation energy
- rate of reaction
- concentration
- inhibitor
- catalyst
- enzyme

How Fast?

Fireworks explode in rapid succession on a summer night. Old copper pennies darken slowly while they lie forgotten in a drawer. Cooking an egg for two minutes instead of five minutes makes a difference in the firmness of the yolk. The amount of time you leave coloring solution on your hair must be timed accurately to give the color you want. Chemical reactions are common in your life. However, notice from these examples that time has something to do with many of them. As you can see in **Figure 11,** not all chemical reactions take place at the same rate.

Some reactions, such as fireworks or lighting a campfire, need help to get going. You may also notice that others seem to start on their own. In this section, you will also learn about factors that make reactions speed up or slow down once they get going.

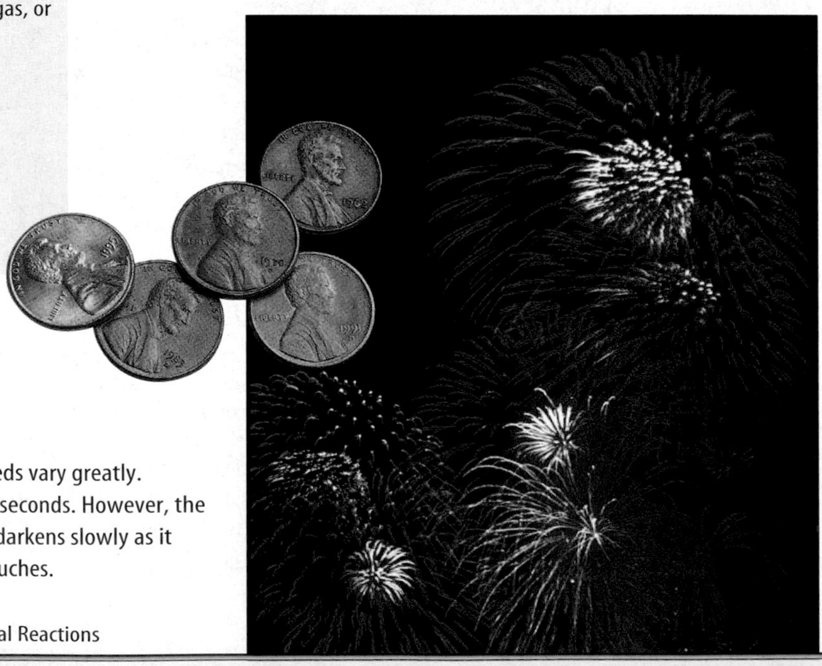

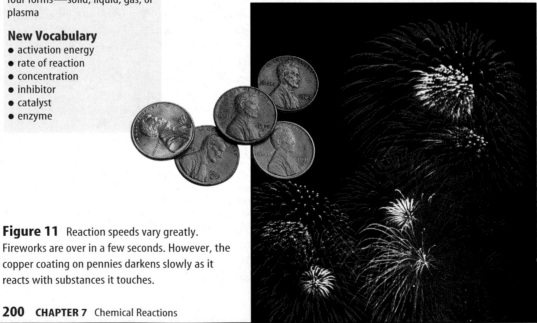

Figure 11 Reaction speeds vary greatly. Fireworks are over in a few seconds. However, the copper coating on pennies darkens slowly as it reacts with substances it touches.

Section 2 Resource Manager

Chapter *FAST FILE* Resources
Transparency Activity, p. 43
Directed Reading for Content Mastery, pp. 21, 22
Enrichment, p. 30
Lab Activity, pp. 13–16
MiniLAB, p. 4
Reinforcement, p. 28
Lab Worksheets, pp. 5–6, 7–8

Reading and Writing Skill Activities, p. 1
Physical Science Critical Thinking/Problem Solving, p. 10
Cultural Diversity, p. 5

Activation Energy—Starting a Reaction

Before a reaction can start, molecules of the reactants have to bump into each other, or collide. This makes sense because to form new chemical bonds, atoms have to be close together. But, not just any collision will do. The collision must be strong enough. This means the reactants must smash into each other with a certain amount of energy. Anything less, and the reaction will not occur. Why is this true?

To form new bonds in the product, old bonds must break in the reactants, and breaking bonds takes energy. To start any chemical reaction, a minimum amount of energy is needed. This energy is called the **activation energy** of the reaction.

Reading Check *What term describes the minimum amount of energy needed to start a reaction?*

What about reactions that release energy? Is there an activation energy for these reactions too? Yes, even though they release energy later, these reactions also need enough energy to start.

One example of a reaction that needs energy to start is the burning of gasoline. You have probably seen movies in which a car plunges over a cliff, lands on the rocks below, and suddenly bursts into flames. But if some gasoline is spilled accidentally while filling a gas tank, it probably will evaporate harmlessly in a short time.

Why doesn't this spilled gasoline explode as it does in the movies? The reason is that gasoline needs energy to start burning. That is why there are signs at filling stations warning you not to smoke. Other signs advise you to turn off the ignition, not to use mobile phones, and not to reenter the car until fueling is complete.

This is similar to the lighting of the Olympic Cauldron, as shown in **Figure 12.** Cauldrons designed for each Olympics contain highly flammable materials that cannot be extinguished by high winds or rain. However, they do not ignite until the opening ceremonies when a runner lights the cauldron using a flame that was kindled in Olympia, Greece, the site of the original Olympic Games.

Science Online

Topic: Olympic Torch
Visit ips.msscience.com for Web links to information about the Olympic Torch.

Activity With each new Olympics, the host city devises a new Olympic Torch. Research the process that goes into developing the torch and the fuel it uses.

Figure 12 Most fuels need energy to ignite. The Olympic Torch, held by Cathy Freeman in the 2000 Olympics, provided the activation energy required to light the fuel in the cauldron.

SECTION 2 Rates of Chemical Reactions **201**

2 Teach

Visual Learning

Figure 11 Have students compare pennies and the dates they were made. Ask whether anyone has an older penny that is shinier than a newer one. Ask why this might happen. The shiny penny might have been stored in a place where it wasn't in contact with people or with air, so it didn't react and corrode. L2 LS **Visual-Spatial**

Reading Check

Answer activation energy

Use an Analogy

Activation Energy Help students understand activation energy by relating it to starting a business. No matter how much money the business will eventually make, an initial investment must be made. Similarly, even exothermic reactions require some energy to get them started.

Differentiated Instruction

Challenge Draw an energy–reaction pathway diagram on the board. It should consist of a short horizontal line, a hump to indicate activation energy, and a drop (exothermic) or rise (endothermic) to indicate whether the products are of lower or higher energy than the reactants. Challenge students to identify the different parts of the diagram and whether the reaction is exothermic or endothermic. L3 LS **Logical-Mathematical**

Reading Check

Answer how quickly one reactant disappears or how quickly one product appears

Reaction Rate

Many physical processes are measured in terms of a rate. A rate tells you how much something changes over a given period of time. For example, the rate or speed at which you run or ride your bike is the distance you move divided by the time it took you to move that distance. You may jog at a rate of 8 km/h.

Chemical reactions have rates, too. The **rate of reaction** tells how fast a reaction occurs after it has started. To find the rate of a reaction, you can measure either how quickly one of the reactants is consumed or how quickly one of the products is created, as in **Figure 13.** Both measurements tell how the amount of a substance changes per unit of time.

Figure 13 The diminishing amount of wax in this candle as it burns indicates the rate of the reaction.

Reading Check

What can you measure to determine the rate of a reaction?

Reaction rate is important in industry because the faster the product can be made, the less it usually costs. However, sometimes fast rates of reaction are undesirable such as the rates of reactions that cause food spoilage. In this case, the slower the reaction rate, the longer the food will stay edible. What conditions control the reaction rate, and how can the rate be changed?

Temperature Changes Rate You can keep the food you buy at the store from spoiling so quickly by putting it in the refrigerator or freezer, as in **Figure 14.** Food spoiling is a chemical reaction. Lowering the temperature of the food slows the rate of this reaction.

Figure 14 Refrigerated foods must be kept below a certain temperature to slow spoilage. These grapes prove that spoilage, a chemical reaction, has occurred.

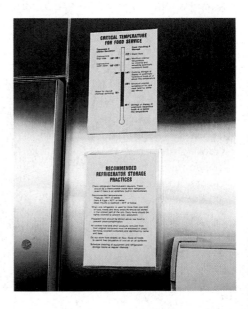

Meat and fish decompose faster at higher temperatures, producing toxins that can make you sick. Keeping these foods chilled slows the decomposition process. Bacteria grow faster at higher temperatures, too, so they reach dangerous levels sooner. Eggs may contain such bacteria, but the heat required to cook eggs also kills bacteria, so hard-cooked eggs are safer to eat than soft-cooked or raw eggs.

Temperature Affects Rate Most chemical reactions speed up when temperature increases. This is because atoms and molecules are always in motion, and they move faster at higher temperatures, as shown in **Figure 15.** Faster molecules collide with each other more often and with greater energy than slower molecules do, so collisions are more likely to provide enough energy to break the old bonds. This is the activation energy.

The high temperature inside an oven speeds up the chemical reactions that turn a liquid cake batter into a more solid, spongy cake. This works the other way, too. Lowering the temperature slows down most reactions. If you set the oven temperature too low, your cake will not bake properly.

Concentration Affects Rate The closer reactant atoms and molecules are to each other, the greater the chance of collisions between them and the faster the reaction rate. It's like the situation shown in **Figure 16.** When you try to walk through a crowded train station, you're more likely to bump into other people than if the station were not so crowded. The amount of substance present in a certain volume is called the **concentration** of that substance. If you increase the concentration, you increase the number of particles of a substance per unit of volume.

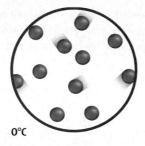

0°C

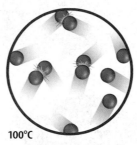

100°C

Figure 15 Molecules collide more frequently at higher temperatures than at lower temperatures. This means they are more likely to react.

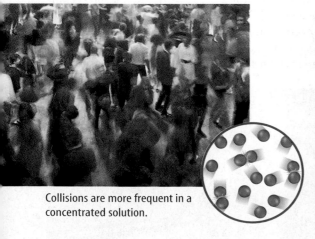

Collisions are more frequent in a concentrated solution.

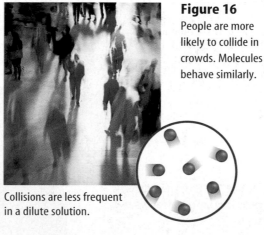

Collisions are less frequent in a dilute solution.

Figure 16 People are more likely to collide in crowds. Molecules behave similarly.

Fun Fact

Collisions by themselves are not enough to achieve a reaction. The atoms or molecules must have correct orientation and sufficient energy to complete the chemical reaction.

Differentiated Instruction

Visually Impaired To demonstrate how concentration affects the rate of molecular collisions, place some pennies in a box and have students shake the box quickly and then slowly. Increase and decrease the number of pennies in the box and have students note the changes in the sound made. L2 **ELL** **LS** **Auditory-Musical**

Inquiry Lab

Factors Affecting Reaction Rate

Purpose Students observe sugar dissolving and explain observations in terms of reaction rate. L1 **ELL** **LS** **Kinesthetic**

Possible Materials granulated table sugar, sugar cubes, rock sugar, beakers, water, hot plate, stirring rod, spatula

Estimated Time 1 class session

Teaching Strategies

• Have students design an experiment about reaction rates. Variables could include stirring/no stirring and water temperature.

• Have them explain how dissolving sugar relates to reaction rates in its reliance on particle size, stirring, and temperature.

• Try caramelizing the sugar. Contrast granulated sugar with uncrushed sugar cubes or rock sugar. Heat the sugar, watching carefully. Once it starts to caramelize, it will burn quickly. The rate for this reaction will be slower for the sugar cubes than the granulated sugar.

For additional inquiry activities, see *Science Inquiry Labs.*

Quick Demo

Effects of Concentration

Materials jar candle with a lid, matches

Estimated Time 10 minutes

Procedure Light the candle and describe to students the need for oxygen in order for the candle to burn. The candle burns brightly because of the high concentration of oxygen. Place the lid loosely on the candle. Do not extinguish the candle. Show how the concentration of oxygen is lowered, but the candle still burns.

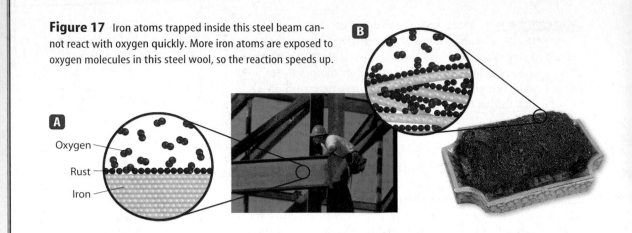

Figure 17 Iron atoms trapped inside this steel beam cannot react with oxygen quickly. More iron atoms are exposed to oxygen molecules in this steel wool, so the reaction speeds up.

Oxygen
Rust
Iron

Identifying Inhibitors

Procedure

1. Look at the ingredients listed on **packages of cereals** and **crackers** in your kitchen.

2. Note the preservatives listed. These are chemical inhibitors.

3. Compare the date on the box with the approximate date the box was purchased to estimate shelf life.

Analysis

1. What is the average shelf life of these products?

2. Why is increased shelf life of such products important?

Try at Home

Surface Area Affects Rate The exposed surface area of reactant particles also affects how fast the reaction can occur. You can quickly start a campfire with small twigs, but starting a fire with only large logs would probably not work.

Only the atoms or molecules in the outer layer of the reactant material can touch the other reactants and react. **Figure 17A** shows that when particles are large, most of the iron atoms are stuck inside and can't react. In **Figure 17B,** more of the reactant atoms are exposed to the oxygen and can react.

Slowing Down Reactions

Sometimes reactions occur too quickly. For example, food and medications can undergo chemical reactions that cause them to spoil or lose their effectiveness too rapidly. Luckily, these reactions can be slowed down.

A substance that slows down a chemical reaction is called an **inhibitor.** An inhibitor makes the formation of a certain amount of product take longer. Some inhibitors completely stop reactions. Many cereals and cereal boxes contain the compound butylated hydroxytoluene, or BHT. The BHT slows the spoiling of the cereal and increases its shelf life.

Figure 18 BHT, an inhibitor, is found in many cereals and cereal boxes.

204 CHAPTER 7 Chemical Reactions

Differentiated Instruction

English-Language Learners Have students copy the list of ingredients off packages of cereal and crackers. Have them define the words that they know. Encourage them to use a dictionary to define the words that they do not know. L2

ELL LS Linguistic

Cultural Diversity

Ozone Punta Arenas, Chile is located under an ozone hole for part of the year. Ozone protects Earth from the Sun's high-energy radiation. In Punta Arenas, plants are turning yellow, apparently burned by high levels of ultraviolet radiation. Ask students to find out what people are doing to slow down the reaction that is depleting Earth's ozone layer. Scientists are researching ways to put less chlorine into Earth's atmosphere. L3

Speeding Up Reactions

Is it possible to speed up a chemical reaction? Yes, you can add a catalyst (KAT uh lihst). A **catalyst** is a substance that speeds up a chemical reaction. Catalysts do not appear in chemical equations, because they are not changed permanently or used up. A reaction using a catalyst will not produce more product than a reaction without a catalyst, but it will produce the same amount of product faster.

 Reading Check *What does a catalyst do in a chemical reaction?*

How does a catalyst work? Many catalysts speed up reaction rates by providing a surface for the reaction to take place. Sometimes the reacting molecules are held in a particular position that favors reaction. Other catalysts reduce the activation energy needed to start the reaction. When the activation energy is reduced, the reaction rate increases.

Catalytic Converters Catalysts are used in the exhaust systems of cars and trucks to aid fuel combustion. The exhaust passes through the catalyst, often in the form of beads coated with metals such as platinum or rhodium. Catalysts speed the reactions that change incompletely burned substances that are harmful, such as carbon monoxide, into less harmful substances, such as carbon dioxide. Similarly, hydrocarbons are changed into carbon dioxide and water. The result of these reactions is cleaner air. These reactions are shown in **Figure 19.**

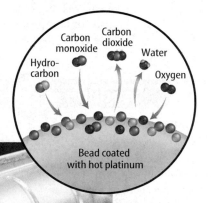

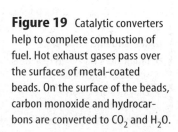

Figure 19 Catalytic converters help to complete combustion of fuel. Hot exhaust gases pass over the surfaces of metal-coated beads. On the surface of the beads, carbon monoxide and hydrocarbons are converted to CO_2 and H_2O.

Breathe Easy The Clean Air Act of 1970 required the reduction of 90 percent of automobile tailpipe emissions. The reduction of emissions included the amount of hydrocarbons and carbon monoxide released. Automakers did not have the technology to meet this new standard. After much hard work, the result of this legislation was the introduction of the catalytic converter in 1975.

Reading Check

Answer It speeds up the reaction.

 **INTEGRATE History**

Breathe Easy The introduction of the Clean Air Act of 1970 not only affected domestic automakers, but foreign as well. If foreign cars were to be imported to the United States and did not have emissions controlling equipment, the cars had to be fitted before being allowed into the country. Car companies are currently releasing prototype cars where the only emission is water vapor.

Use Science Words

Word Usage The word *catalyst* has become part of our general vocabulary. Have students use the word in a sentence describing a situation that is not a chemical reaction. Possible sentence: Sarah's home run was the catalyst for a nine-run third inning. L2 LS **Linguistic**

SECTION 2 Rates of Chemical Reactions **205**

LAB DEMONSTRATION

Purpose to show how surface area affects reaction rate

Materials cornstarch, Bunsen burner, spatula, poster board, goggles, gloves

Preparation Practice this demo before class. If possible, do it under a hood.

Procedure Place a lit match on a pile of cornstarch. The cornstarch will not ignite. Then place about 25 g of cornstarch onto the poster board and roll it into a cone. Hold the small end of the cone near the Bunsen burner and blow the cornstarch toward the flame.

Expected Outcome The flame will burn very brightly.

Assessment

Why did blowing the cornstarch over the flame cause such an intense reaction? It increased the surface area of the cornstarch, making it easier for it to react with oxygen. It was also easier for the flame to transfer enough energy to each particle to reach the activation energy.

DAILY INTERVENTION

Check for Understanding

Visual-Spatial Have each student choose a chemical reaction and make a miniposter showing the activation energy for the reaction and ways the reaction can be speeded up or slowed down. L3

Reteach

Inhibitors Have students design an experiment to determine the rate of spoilage of two pieces of bread, one containing an inhibitor, such as BHT, and the other containing no inhibitor. Be sure to check students' procedures before they carry them out. L2 **LS** **Logical-Mathematical**

✓ Assessment

Content Have students work alone or in groups to brainstorm all the times in a typical day that they either speed up or slow down chemical reactions. Possible answers: cooking, freezing, washing contact lenses Use **Performance Assessment in the Science Classroom**, p. 89.

Figure 20 The enzymes in meat tenderizer break down protein in meat, making it more tender.

Enzymes Are Specialists Some of the most effective catalysts are at work in thousands of reactions that take place in your body. These catalysts, called **enzymes,** are large protein molecules that speed up reactions needed for your cells to work properly. They help your body convert food to fuel, build bone and muscle tissue, convert extra energy to fat, and even produce other enzymes.

These are complex reactions. Without enzymes, they would occur at rates that are too slow to be useful or they would not occur at all. Enzymes make it possible for your body to function. Like other catalysts, enzymes function by positioning the reacting molecules so that their structures fit together properly. Enzymes are a kind of chemical specialist—enzymes exist to carry out each type of reaction in your body.

Other Uses Enzymes work outside your body, too. One class of enzymes, called proteases (PROH tee ay ses), specializes in protein reactions. They work within cells to break down large, complex molecules called proteins. The meat tenderizer shown in **Figure 20** contains proteases that break down protein in meat, making it more tender. Contact lens cleaning solutions also contain proteases that break down proteins from your eyes that can collect on your lenses and cloud your view.

---

section ② review

Summary

Chemical Reactions

- To form new bonds in the product, old bonds must break in the reactants. This takes energy.
- Activation energy is the minimum quantity of energy needed to start a reaction.

Reaction Rate

- The rate of reaction tells you how fast a reaction occurs.
- Temperature, concentration, and surface area affect the rate of reaction.

Inhibitors and Catalysts

- Inhibitors slow down reactions. Catalysts speed up reactions.
- Enzymes are catalysts that speed up or slow down reactions for your cells.

Self Check

1. **Describe** how you can measure reaction rates.
2. **Explain** in the general reaction A + B + energy → C, how the following will affect the reaction rate.
   a. increasing the temperature
   b. decreasing the reactant concentration
3. **Describe** how catalysts work to speed up chemical reactions.
4. **Think Critically** Explain why a jar of spaghetti sauce can be stored for weeks on the shelf in the market but must be placed in the refrigerator after it is opened.

> **Applying Math**
>
> 5. **Solve One-Step Equations** A chemical reaction is proceeding at a rate of 2 g of product every 45 s. How long will it take to obtain 50 g of product?

Science online  ips.msscience.com/self_check_quiz

---

section ② review

1. by examining how fast a product forms or how fast a reactant is used up
2. **a.** increases the rate **b.** decreases the rate
3. Catalysts reduce the activation energy, thus increasing the reaction rate.
4. On the shelf the jar is air tight. Air may even have been removed when the sauce was packaged, causing the lid to bend in slightly. If a lid bulges outward, it could mean dangerous reactions have taken place. Opening the jar exposes the spaghetti sauce to oxygen and other substances in the air that might react with the sauce and cause it to spoil. Refrigeration slows down these reactions.
5. 2 g/45 s = 50 g/x, therefore x = 1,125 s

Physical or Chemical Change?

● Real-World Question

Matter can undergo two kinds of changes—physical and chemical. A physical change affects the physical properties. When a chemical change takes place, a new product is produced. How can a scientist tell if a chemical change took place?

Goals
■ **Determine** if a physical or chemical change took place.

Materials
500-mL Erlenmeyer flask
1,000-mL graduated cylinder
one-hole stopper with 15-cm length of glass
    tube inserted
1,000-mL beaker
45-cm length of rubber (or plastic) tubing
stopwatch or clock with second hand
weighing dish   balance
baking soda   vinegar

Safety Precautions

WARNING: *Vinegar (acetic acid) may cause skin and eye irritation.*

● Procedure

1. Measure 300 mL of water. Pour water into 500-mL Erlenmeyer flask.

2. Weigh 5 g of baking soda. Carefully pour the baking soda into the flask. Swirl the flask until the solution is clear.

3. Insert the rubber stopper with the glass tubing into the flask.

4. Measure 600 mL of water and pour into the 1,000-mL beaker.

5. Attach one end of the rubber tubing to the top of the glass tubing. Place the other end of the rubber tubing in the beaker. Be sure the rubber tubing remains under the water.

6. Remove the stopper from the flask. Carefully add 80 mL of vinegar to the flask. Replace the stopper.

7. Count the number of bubbles coming into the beaker for 20 s. Repeat this two more times.

8. Record your data in your Science Journal.

● Conclude and Apply

1. **Describe** what you observed in the flask after the acid was added to the baking soda solution.

2. **Classify** Was this a physical or chemical change? How do you know?

3. **Analyze Results** Was this process endothermic or exothermic?

4. **Calculate** the average reaction rate based on the number of bubbles per second.

*C*ommunicating
Your Data

Compare your results with those of other students in your class.

☑ Assessment

Oral Have students explain why the experiment was carried out three times. Use **Performance Assessment in the Science Classroom,** p. 89.

*C*ommunicating
Your Data

Have students make a bar graph of the average number of bubbles that each student (or team) saw during the experiment.

● Real-World Question

Purpose Students will create a reaction and determine if it is a physical change or a chemical change. L2 ELL COOP LEARN LS Kinesthetic

Process Skills observe, record data, interpret data, identify

Time Required 45 minutes

● Procedure

Safety Precautions Avoid contact of vinegar with skin. Wash thoroughly if this does occur. Do not touch eyes especially if vinegar has come in contact with skin. Rinse eyes thoroughly if this does occur.

Teaching Strategies

- Consider having students work in pairs. One student can ensure that the rubber tubing stays in the beaker of water while the other student counts the bubbles.

- An infrared bubble counter with LED display may be used.

Troubleshooting All connections between flasks, stoppers, and tubing must be secure.

● Conclude and Apply

1. It was foamy. Bubbles started to form, then gas was released.
2. It was a chemical change. You know because gas was produced from the reaction of vinegar and baking soda.
3. exothermic
4. Results will vary.

Design Your Own

● Real-World Question

Purpose Students will design an experiment to determine whether a reaction is exothermic or endothermic. **L2** **ELL**

COOP LEARN **LS** **Kinesthetic**

Process Skills design an experiment, classify, make and use tables, observe and infer, form a hypothesis, interpret data, measure, use numbers

Time Required 40 minutes

Materials To dispose of the potato and liver, wrap in paper and put into the trash. The hydrogen peroxide can be flushed down the drain.

● Form a Hypothesis

Possible Hypothesis Students might hypothesize that you can tell whether a reaction is exothermic or endothermic by whether the temperature rises or falls during the reaction.

● Test Your Hypothesis

Possible Procedures Pour hydrogen peroxide into each test tube while in test-tube rack until it is about half full. Drop small pieces of liver into half of the tubes and small pieces of potato into the other half. Immediately after adding the liver and potato, measure and record the temperature of the liquid in each tube. After a certain number of minutes, again measure and record each temperature. Average each group of temperatures.

Goals
■ **Design** an experiment to test whether a reaction is exothermic or endothermic.
■ **Measure** the temperature change caused by a chemical reaction.

Possible Materials
test tubes (8)
test-tube rack
3% hydrogen peroxide solution
raw liver
raw potato
thermometer
stopwatch
clock with second hand
25-mL graduated cylinder

Safety Precautions

🚫 🧤 🥽 ⚗️ 🥼

WARNING: *Hydrogen peroxide can irritate skin and eyes and damage clothing.* Be careful when handling glass thermometers. Test tubes containing hydrogen peroxide should be placed and kept in racks. Dispose of materials as directed by your teacher. Wash your hands when you complete this lab.

Exothermic or Endothermic?

● Real-World Question

Energy is always a part of a chemical reaction. Some reactions need energy to start. Other reactions release energy into the environment. What evidence can you find to show that a reaction between hydrogen peroxide and liver or potato is exothermic or endothermic? Think about the difference between these two types of reactions.

● Form a Hypothesis

Make a hypothesis that describes how you can use the reactions between hydrogen peroxide and liver or potato to determine whether a reaction is exothermic or endothermic.

● Test Your Hypothesis

Make a Plan

1. As a group, look at the list of materials. Decide which procedure you will use to test your hypothesis, and which measurements you will make.

2. **Decide** how you will detect the heat released to the environment during the reaction. Determine how many measurements you will need to make during a reaction.

3. You will get more accurate data if you repeat each experiment several times. Each repeated experiment is called a trial. Use the average of all the trials as your data for supporting your hypothesis.

4. **Decide** what the variables are and what your control will be.

5. **Copy** the data table in your Science Journal before you begin to carry out your experiment.

Follow Your Plan

1. Make sure your teacher approves your plan before you start.

2. Carry out your plan.

3. **Record** your measurements immediately in your data table.

4. **Calculate** the averages of your trial results and record them in your Science Journal.

Alternative Inquiry Lab

Continue Learning Make this Lab an Inquiry Lab by building on the experience. Encourage your students to use what they have learned to brainstorm questions about exothermic and endothermic reactions. Have student groups each choose one question to explore. Ask them to list the materials they need to explore their question. Unsafe or impractical questions should be eliminated. Students should have their plans for their additional experiments approved before continuing. Conduct the experiments after all of the necessary materials have been gathered.

● Analyze Your Data

1. Can you infer that a chemical reaction took place? What evidence did you observe to support this?

2. **Identify** what the variables were in this experiment.

3. **Identify** the control.

Temperature After Adding Liver/Potato

Trial	Temperature After Adding Liver (°C)		Temperature After Adding Potato (°C)	
	Starting	After____min	Starting	After____min
1				
2				
3	Student data for both liver and potato should show an			
4	increase in temperature. The reaction is exothermic.			

● Conclude and Apply

1. Do your observations allow you to distinguish between an exothermic reaction and an endothermic reaction? Use your data to explain your answer.

2. Where do you think that the energy involved in this experiment came from? Explain your answer.

Communicating Your Data

Compare the results obtained by your group with those obtained by other groups. Are there differences? **Explain** how these might have occurred.

LAB 209

☑ Assessment

Performance Have students repeat the lab using a slurry of carrots instead of liver or potato. Have each student write a short paragraph analyzing his or her data. Use **Performance Assessment in the Science Classroom**, p. 99.

Communicating Your Data

Have students use bar graphs to present and compare their data. The graphs should show temperature on the y-axis and trial number on the x-axis. Have them graph data for both the potato and the liver on the same graph. Students can use a computer graphing program.

Teaching Strategies

• Interested students may ask what is happening during the reaction. Tell them that enzymes in the potato and liver are breaking down the hydrogen peroxide into water and oxygen.

• Students may want to use tongs to handle the liver.

Expected Outcome Temperature will rise after the liver and potato are added, showing that the reactions are exothermic. The rise in temperature will be more pronounced for the liver.

● Analyze Your Data

Answers to Questions

1. Yes, energy in the form of heat and gas were released.
2. liver and potato
3. The control is the hydrogen peroxide and its starting temperature (assuming all tubes had the same starting temperature).

Error Analysis If a trial using potatoes does not show an increase in temperature, the piece of potato was probably too small. Have pairs of students read the thermometers to avoid human error in the readings.

● Conclude and Apply

1. Possible answer: Yes, the temperature increased in each case, so exothermic reactions must have taken place.
2. The energy came from the following chemical reaction:
$2H_2O_2 \rightarrow 2H_2O + O_2$.

TIME

Content Background

Diamonds and graphite are two naturally occurring forms of carbon. Their differences in appearance and physical properties arise from the way the individual carbon atoms are arranged. In diamonds, the atoms are tightly packed in a symmetrical array. Each atom is bonded to four others. In graphite, the atoms are arranged in hexagonal sheets. Each atom is bonded to three others in each layer. Each layer is loosely bonded to the other.

There is little difference between naturally occurring diamonds and synthetic diamonds. They share the same physical properties, down to the carat (a unit of weight). Because synthetic diamonds are produced in a controlled environment, they are more uniform in size and shape.

Discussion

Diamond Applications Ask students to brainstorm commercial or industrial applications that make use of diamonds' unique physical properties. Possible answers: cutting tools, drill bits, wear-resistant coating, infrared windows, and electronic devices
L2 **LS Logical-Mathematical**

Historical Significance

Chemists tried without success in the 1800s to convert carbon to diamonds. The General Electric Company produced the first artificial diamonds in 1954. By the mid-1960s artificial diamonds were produced on a commercial scale using High Pressure High Temperature synthesis (HPHT). Technologies developed by the 1990s lead to the Chemical Vapor Deposition (CVD) process. This new process makes diamonds that are superior to natural diamonds for uses in technology.

TIME SCIENCE AND HISTORY

SCIENCE CAN CHANGE THE COURSE OF HISTORY!

Synthetic Diamonds

Natural Diamond **Almost the Real Thing** Synthetic Diamond

Diamonds are the most dazzling, most dramatic, most valuable natural objects on Earth. Strangely, these beautiful objects are made of carbon, the same material graphite—the stuff found in pencils—is made of. So why is a diamond hard and clear and graphite soft and black? A diamond's hardness is a result of how strongly its atoms are linked. What makes a diamond transparent is the way its crystals are arranged. The carbon in a diamond is almost completely pure, with trace amounts of boron and nitrogen in it. These elements account for the many shades of color found in diamonds.

A diamond is the hardest naturally occurring substance on Earth. It's so hard, only a diamond can scratch another diamond. Diamonds are impervious to heat and household chemicals. Their crystal structure allows them to be split (or crushed) along particular lines.

Diamonds are made when carbon is squeezed at high pressures and temperatures in Earth's upper mantle, about 150 km beneath the surface. At that depth, the temperature is about 1,400°C, and the pressure is about 55,000 atmospheres greater than the pressure at sea level.

As early as the 1850s, scientists tried to convert graphite into diamonds. It wasn't until 1954 that researchers produced the first synthetic diamonds by compressing carbon under extremely high pressure and heat. Scientists converted graphite powder into tiny diamond crystals using pressure of more than 68,000 atm, and a temperature of about 1,700°C for about 16 hours.

Synthetic diamonds are human-made, but they're not fake. They have all the properties of natural diamonds, from hardness to excellent heat conductivity. Experts claim to be able to detect synthetics because they contain tiny amounts of metal (used in their manufacturing process) and have a different luminescence than natural diamonds. In fact, most synthetics are made for industrial use. One major reason is that making small synthetic diamonds is cheaper than finding small natural ones. The other reason is that synthetics can be made to a required size and shape. Still, if new techniques bring down the cost of producing large, gem-quality synthetic diamonds, they may one day compete with natural diamonds as jewelry.

Research Investigate the history of diamonds—natural and synthetic. Explain the differences between them and their uses. Share your findings with the class.

Science online

For more information, visit
ips.msscience.com/time

Research Have students use a T-diagram (a large block letter T) to compare and contrast natural and synthetic diamonds. Students should record the similarities between natural and synthetic diamonds in the leg of the T, and the differences between the two types of diamonds on the opposite sides of the top of the T. Make sure they include the differences in how the diamonds are formed and how they are used. L2

Resources for Teachers and Students

Diamond Formula: Diamond Synthesis: A gemmological perspective, by Amanda Barnard and A.S. Barnard, Elsevier Science & Technology, 2000

Synthetic Diamond: Emerging CVD Science and Technology, by Karl E. Spear and John P. Dismukes, John Wiley & Sons Inc., New York, 1994

Reviewing Main Ideas

Reviewing Main Ideas

Summary statements can be used by students to review the major concepts of the chapter.

Section 1 — Formulas and Chemical Equations

1. Chemical reactions often cause observable changes, such as a change in color or odor, a release or absorption of heat or light, or a release of gas.

2. A chemical equation is a shorthand method of writing what happens in a chemical reaction. Chemical equations use symbols to represent the reactants and products of a reaction, and sometimes show whether energy is produced or absorbed.

3. The law of conservation of mass requires that the same number of atoms of each element be in the products as in the reactants of a chemical equation. This is true in every balanced chemical equation.

Section 2 — Rates of Chemical Reactions

1. The rate of reaction is a measure of how quickly a reaction occurs.

2. All reactions have an activation energy—a certain minimum amount of energy required to start the reaction.

3. The rate of a chemical reaction can be influenced by the temperature, the concentration of the reactants, and the exposed surface area of the reactant particles.

4. Catalysts can speed up a reaction without being used up. Inhibitors slow down the rate of reaction.

5. Enzymes are protein molecules that act as catalysts in your body's cells.

Visualizing Main Ideas

Visualizing Main Ideas

See student page.

Copy and complete the following concept map on chemical reactions.

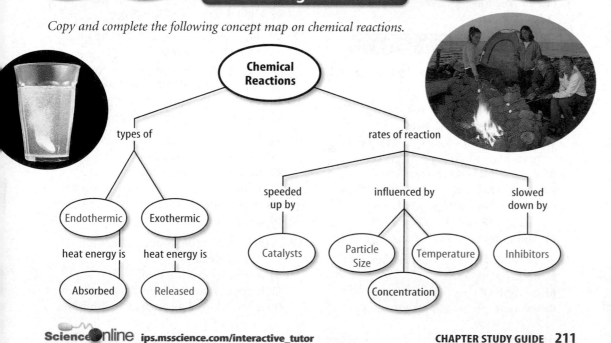

Chemical Reactions

types of — Endothermic (heat energy is Absorbed), Exothermic (heat energy is Released)

rates of reaction — speeded up by Catalysts; influenced by Particle Size, Concentration, Temperature; slowed down by Inhibitors

Science Online ips.msscience.com/interactive_tutor

CHAPTER STUDY GUIDE 211

Assessment Transparency

For additional assessment questions, use the *Assessment Transparency* located in the transparency book.

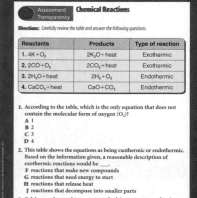

Assessment

Assessment Transparency — **Chemical Reactions**

Directions: Carefully review the table and answer the following questions.

Reactants	Products	Type of reaction
1. $4K + O_2$	$2K_2O + heat$	Exothermic
2. $2CO + O_2$	$2CO_2 + heat$	Exothermic
3. $2H_2O + heat$	$2H_2 + O_2$	Endothermic
4. $CaCO_3 + heat$	$CaO + CO_2$	Endothermic

1. According to the table, which is the only equation that does not contain the molecular form of oxygen (O_2)?
   A 1
   B 2
   C 3
   D 4

2. This table shows the equations as being exothermic or endothermic. Based on the information given, a reasonable description of exothermic reactions would be ___.
   F reactions that make new compounds
   G reactions that need energy to start
   H reactions that release heat
   J reactions that decompose into smaller parts

3. Calcium carbonate has one atom of calcium, one atom of carbon, and three atoms of oxygen. According to the table, which formula represents calcium carbonate?
   A CaO
   B CO_2
   C $CaCO_3$
   D CO

Identifying Misconceptions

Assess

After students have done the activity on page F at the beginning of this chapter, have them perform this activity.

Procedure Explain that two hydrogen atoms and one oxygen atom make a water molecule. Have students draw a large circle on a sheet of paper. This represents a drop of water that has been magnified. Have them draw six molecules of water in the circle. Make sure they include the hydrogen and oxygen atoms. [L2]

Expected Outcome Students should understand that chemical change involves the formation of new materials from the interaction of one or more atoms.

chapter 7 Review

Using Vocabulary

1. An exothermic reaction releases energy. An endothermic reaction absorbs energy.

2. Activation energy is the amount of energy necessary to start a chemical reaction. The rate of reaction is a measure of how fast a chemical reaction takes place.

3. The reactants are the materials present at the beginning of a chemical reaction and the products are the materials that are present when the reaction is over.

4. Both affect the rate of a reaction. A catalyst makes a reaction go faster. An inhibitor makes a reaction go slower.

5. The concentration is the amount of material in a given volume. The rate of reaction is a measure of how fast a chemical reaction takes place.

6. A chemical equation shows all the substances that react and are produced by a chemical reaction. A reactant is a substance that exists before a chemical reaction.

7. An inhibitor slows down a chemical reaction. A product is a material that results from a chemical reaction.

8. A catalyst speeds up a chemical reaction. A chemical equation shows all the substances that react in and result from a chemical reaction.

9. The rate of reaction is a measure of how fast a chemical reaction takes place. An enzyme is a protein that speeds up reactions in cells.

Checking Concepts

10. C	15. A
11. C	16. D
12. D	17. B
13. C	18. B
14. A	19. B

Using Vocabulary

activation energy p. 201	enzyme p. 206
catalyst p. 205	exothermic reaction p. 197
chemical equation p. 192	inhibitor p. 204
chemical reaction p. 190	product p. 192
concentration p. 203	rate of reaction p. 202
endothermic reaction p. 197	reactant p. 192

Explain the differences between the vocabulary terms in each of the following sets.

1. exothermic reaction—endothermic reaction
2. activation energy—rate of reaction
3. reactant—product
4. catalyst—inhibitor
5. concentration—rate of reaction
6. chemical equation—reactant
7. inhibitor—product
8. catalyst—chemical equation
9. rate of reaction—enzyme

Checking Concepts

Choose the word or phrase that best answers the question.

10. Which statement about the law of conservation of mass is NOT true?
    A) The mass of reactants must equal the mass of products.
    B) All the atoms on the reactant side of an equation are also on the product side.
    C) The reaction creates new types of atoms.
    D) Atoms are not lost, but are rearranged.

11. To slow down a chemical reaction, what should you add?
    A) catalyst   C) inhibitor
    B) reactant   D) enzyme

12. Which of these is a chemical change?
    A) Paper is shredded.
    B) Liquid wax turns solid.
    C) A raw egg is broken.
    D) Soap scum forms.

13. Which of these reactions releases heat energy?
    A) unbalanced   C) exothermic
    B) balanced   D) endothermic

14. A balanced chemical equation must have the same number of which of these on both sides of the equation?
    A) atoms   C) molecules
    B) reactants   D) compounds

15. What does NOT affect reaction rate?
    A) balancing   C) surface area
    B) temperature   D) concentration

16. Which is NOT a balanced equation?
    A) $CuCl_2 + H_2S \rightarrow CuS + 2HCl$
    B) $AgNO_3 + NaI \rightarrow AgI + NaNO_3$
    C) $2C_2H_6 + 7O_2 \rightarrow 4CO_2 + 6H_2O$
    D) $MgO + Fe \rightarrow Fe_2O_3 + Mg$

17. Which is NOT evidence that a chemical reaction has occurred?
    A) Milk tastes sour.
    B) Steam condenses on a cold window.
    C) A strong odor comes from a broken egg.
    D) A slice of raw potato darkens.

18. Which of the following would decrease the rate of a chemical reaction?
    A) increase the temperature
    B) reduce the concentration of a reactant
    C) increase the concentration of a reactant
    D) add a catalyst

19. Which of these describes a catalyst?
    A) It is a reactant.
    B) It speeds up a reaction.
    C) It appears in the chemical equation.
    D) It can be used in place of an inhibitor.

Science Online ips.msscience.com/vocabulary_puzzlemaker

Use the ExamView® Pro Testmaker CD-ROM to:
- create multiple versions of tests
- create modified tests with one mouse click for inclusion students
- edit existing questions and add your own questions
- build tests aligned with state standards using built-in State Curriculum Tags
- change English tests to Spanish with one mouse click and vice versa

Thinking Critically

20. Cause and Effect Pickled cucumbers remain edible much longer than fresh cucumbers do. Explain.

21. Analyze A beaker of water in sunlight becomes warm. Has a chemical reaction occurred? Explain.

22. Distinguish if $2Ag + S$ is the same as Ag_2S. Explain.

23. Infer Apple slices can be kept from browning by brushing them with lemon juice. Infer what role lemon juice plays in this case.

24. Draw a Conclusion Chili can be made using ground meat or chunks of meat. Which would you choose, if you were in a hurry? Explain.

Use the graph below to answer question 25.

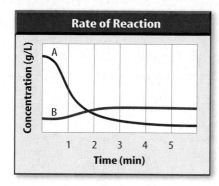

Rate of Reaction

Concentration (g/L)

A

B

1 2 3 4 5
Time (min)

25. Interpret Scientific Illustrations The two curves on the graph represent the concentrations of compounds A (blue) and B (red) during a chemical reaction.
   a. Which compound is a reactant?
   b. Which compound is a product?
   c. During which time period is the concentration of the reactant changing most rapidly?

Science Online ips.msscience.com/chapter_review

26. Form a Hypothesis You are cleaning out a cabinet beneath the kitchen sink and find an unused steel wool scrub pad that has rusted completely. Will the remains of this pad weigh more or less than when it was new? Explain.

Performance Activities

27. Poster Make a list of the preservatives in the food you eat in one day. Present your findings to your class in a poster.

Applying Math

Use the graph below to answer question 28.

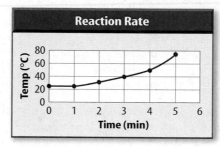

Reaction Rate

Temp (°C)

80
60
40
20
0
  0   1   2   3   4   5   6
Time (min)

28. Reaction Rates In the reaction graph above, how long does it take the reaction to reach 50°C?

29. Chemical Equation In the following chemical equation, $3Na + AlCl_3 \longrightarrow 3NaCl + Al$, how many aluminum molecules will be produced if you have 30 molecules of sodium?

30. Catalysis A zinc catalyst is used to reduce the reaction time by 30%. If the normal time for the reaction to finish is 3 h, how long will it take with the catalyst?

31. Molecules Silver has 6.023×10^{23} molecules per 107.9 g. How many molecules are there if you have
   a. 53.95 g?
   b. 323.7 g?
   c. 10.79 g?

CHAPTER REVIEW 213

Thinking Critically

20. The pickling compounds inhibit spoilage of the pickles.

21. No; a chemical reaction did not occur because there is no change in the identity of the water.

22. No; both representations show one sulfur atom and two silver atoms, but in the second one, the atoms are combined in the compound silver sulfide. In the first one, they are individual atoms.

23. Lemon juice acts as an inhibitor.

24. You would use ground meat. It has a greater surface area and so would cook faster.

25. (a) A is the reactant. (b) B is the product. (c) the first minute

26. The iron in the steel wool has reacted with oxygen and water vapor in the air, therefore the mass should increase.

Performance Activities

27. Encourage students to use a computer spreadsheet program to organize the data they collect. Use **PASC,** p. 145 to assess students' posters.

Applying Math

National Math Standards
1, 2, 5, 9, 10

28. four minutes

29. $\frac{1\ Al}{3\ Na} \times \frac{30\ Na}{1} = 10$ Al molecules

30. 3 hours $\times$ 0.30 = 0.9 hours which is the time the catalyst will reduce the reaction.

3 hours $-$ 0.9 hours = 2.1 hours which is the new reaction time with the catalyst.

31. a. (53.95 / 107.9) $\times$ (6.023 $\times$ 10^{23}) = 3.012 $\times$ 10^{23}
   b. (323.7 / 107.9) $\times$ (6.023 $\times$ 10^{23}) = 1.807 $\times$ 10^{24}
   c. (10.79 / 107.9) $\times$ (6.023 $\times$ 10^{23}) = 6.023 $\times$ 10^{22}

✓ Assessment   Resources

Reproducible Masters
Chapter *Fast File* Resources
Chapter Review, pp. 35–36
Chapter Tests, pp. 37–40
Assessment Transparency Activity, p. 47

Glencoe Science Web site
Chapter Review Test
Standardized Test Practice

Glencoe Technology
🔊 Assessment Transparency
🔘 Exam*View*® Pro Testmaker
📺 MindJogger Videoquiz
🔘 Interactive Chalkboard

CHAPTER REVIEW 213

Part 1 | Multiple Choice

1. B   **5. C**
2. A   **6. A**
3. C   **7. C**
4. B

Part 2 | Short Response

8. A change in volume is a physical change because the chemical makeup of the material is the same before and after the change.

9. The precipitate is silver chloride, AgCl.

10. The speed of the molecules would decrease, but the molecules would never stop moving entirely.

11. The speed of most chemical reactions increases when temperature increases. The faster movement of atoms and molecules at higher temperatures means the particles are more likely to collide with each other.

12. Yes, even though the reactions release energy later, they need a minimum amount of energy to start.

Part 1 | Multiple Choice

Record your answers on the answer sheet provided by your teacher or on a sheet of paper.

Use the photo below to answer questions 1 and 2.

1. The photograph shows the reaction of copper (Cu) with silver nitrate ($AgNO_3$) to produce copper nitrate ($Cu(NO_3)_2$) and silver (Ag). The chemical equation that describes this reaction is the following:

$$2AgNO_3 + Cu \rightarrow Cu(NO_3)_2 + 2Ag$$

What term describes what is happening in the reaction?
   A. catalyst
   B. chemical change
   C. inhibitor
   D. physical change

2. Which of the following terms describes the copper on the left side of the equation?
   A. reactant   **C.** enzyme
   B. catalyst   **D.** product

3. Which of the following terms best describes a chemical reaction that absorbs heat energy?
   A. catalytic   **C.** endothermic
   B. exothermic   **D.** acidic

4. What should be balanced in a chemical equation?
   A. electrons   **C.** molecules
   B. atoms   **D.** molecules and atoms

Test-Taking Tip

Read All Questions Never skip a question. If you are unsure of an answer, mark your best guess on another sheet of paper and mark the question in your test booklet to remind you to come back to it at the end of the test.

Use the photo below to answer questions 5 and 6.

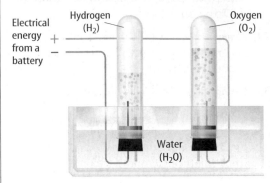

5. The photograph above shows a demonstration of electrolysis, in which water is broken down into hydrogen and oxygen. Which of the following is the best way to write the chemical equation for this process?
   A. $H_2O + energy \rightarrow H_2 + O_2$
   B. $H_2O + energy \rightarrow 2H_2 + O_2$
   C. $2H_2O + energy \rightarrow 2H_2 + O_2$
   D. $2H_2O + energy \rightarrow 2H_2 + 2O_2$

6. For each atom of hydrogen that is present before the reaction begins, how many atoms of hydrogen are present after the reaction?
   A. 1   **C.** 4
   B. 2   **D.** 8

7. What is the purpose of an inhibitor in a chemical reaction?
   A. decrease the shelf life of food
   B. increase the surface area
   C. decrease the speed of a chemical reaction
   D. increase the speed of a chemical reaction

Part 3 | Open Ended

13. Substances in the wood combine with oxygen to produce heat along with light, carbon dioxide, and water. Burning is an exothermic reaction. Exothermic reactions release heat energy. In the case of a forest fire, the released heat energy causes nearby trees to ignite and the fire spreads.

14. Before a chemical reaction can begin, the reactant compounds must collide with enough energy to break chemical bonds. This minimum energy is called the activation energy for the reaction. Lightning can provide the activation energy necessary to cause trees in a forest to burn.

15. A reaction can only occur if the reactants are in contact. Only the atoms or molecules in the outer layer of a reactant material can touch the other reactants and react. Materials with a large surface area have more atoms or molecules that can contact other reactants. One example of this

Part 2 | Short Response/Grid In

Record your answers on the answer sheet provided by your teacher or on a sheet of paper.

8. Is a change in the volume of a substance a physical or a chemical change? Explain.

Use the equation below to answer question 9.

$$CaCl_2 + 2AgNO_3 \rightarrow 2 \boxed{} + Ca(NO_3)_2$$

9. When solutions of calcium chloride ($CaCl_2$) and silver nitrate ($AgNO_3$) are mixed, calcium nitrate ($Ca(NO_3)_2$) and a white precipitate, or residue, form. Determine the chemical formula of the precipitate.

Use the illustration below to answer questions 10 and 11.

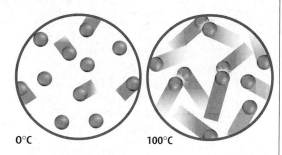

0°C   100°C

10. The figure above demonstrates the movement of water molecules at temperatures of 0°C and 100°C. What would happen to the movement of the molecules if the temperature dropped far below 0°C?

11. Describe how the difference in the movement of the molecules at two different temperatures affects the rate of most chemical reactions.

12. Is activation energy needed for reactions that release energy? Explain why or why not.

Part 3 | Open Ended

Record your answers on a sheet of paper.

Use the illustration below to answer questions 13 and 14.

13. The photograph above shows a forest fire that began when lightning struck a tree. Describe the chemical reaction that occurs when trees burn. Is the reaction endothermic or exothermic? What does this mean? Why does this cause a forest fire to spread?

14. The burning of logs in a forest fire is a chemical reaction. What prevents this chemical reaction from occurring when there is no lightning to start a fire?

15. Explain how the surface area of a material can affect the rate at which the material reacts with other substances. Give an example to support your answer.

16. One of the chemical reactions that occurs in the formation of glass is the combining of calcium carbonate ($CaCO_3$) and silica (SiO_2) to form calcium silicate ($CaSiO_3$) and carbon dioxide (CO_2):

$$CaCO_3 + SiO_2 \rightarrow CaSiO_3 + CO_2$$

Describe this reaction using the names of the chemicals. Discuss which bonds are broken and how atoms are rearranged to form new bonds.

Rubrics

The following rubrics are sample scoring devices for short response and open-ended questions.

Short Response

Points	Description
2	The student demonstrates a thorough understanding of the science of the task. The response may contain minor flaws that do not detract from the demonstration of a thorough understanding.
1	The student has provided a response that is only partially correct.
0	The student has provided a completely incorrect solution or no response at all.

Open Ended

Points	Description
4	The student demonstrates a thorough understanding of the science of the task. The response may contain minor flaws that do not detract from the demonstration of a thorough understanding.
3	The student demonstrates an understanding of the science of the task. The response is essentially correct and demonstrates an essential but less than thorough understanding of the science.
2	The student demonstrates only a partial understanding of the science of the task. Although the student may have used the correct approach to a solution or may have provided a correct solution, the work lacks an essential understanding of the underlying science concepts.
1	The student demonstrates a very limited understanding of the science of the task. The response is incomplete and exhibits many flaws.
0	The student provides a completely incorrect solution or no response at all.

is the difference in reaction rate between steel wool and steel construction beams. The reaction rate of steel wool is greater because the thin strands of steel have greater surface area for oxygen to make contact with.

16. Calcium carbonate is one atom of calcium bonded to an atom of carbon and three atoms of oxygen. Silica is one silicon atom bonded to two oxygen atoms. During the reaction, these bonds are broken and new bonds are formed. One carbon and two oxygen atoms

break from the calcium carbonate to form carbon dioxide. The remaining calcium atom and oxygen atom combine with the silica to form calcium silicate.

Section/Objectives	Standards		Labs/Features
	National	State/Local	
Chapter Opener	See pp. 16T–17T for a Key to Standards.		**Launch Lab:** Particle Size and Dissolving Rates, p. 217 **Foldables,** p. 217
Section 1 What is a solution? ● 2 sessions ▣ 1 block 1. **Distinguish** between substances and mixtures. 2. **Describe** two different types of mixtures. 3. **Explain** how solutions form. 4. **Describe** different types of solutions.	National Content Standards: UCP.1, UCP.2, UCP.3, UCP.5, A.1, A.2, B.1		**Science Online,** p. 219
Section 2 Solubility ● 2 sessions ▣ 1.5 blocks 5. **Explain** why water is a good general solvent. 6. **Describe** how the structure of a compound affects which solvents it dissolves in. 7. **Identify** factors that affect how much of a substance will dissolve in a solvent. 8. **Describe** how temperature affects reaction rate. 9. **Explain** how solute particles affect physical properties of water.	National Content Standards: UCP.1, UCP.2, UCP.3, UCP.5, A.1, A.2, B.1, B.2, B.3		**Integrate Environment,** p. 225 **MiniLAB:** Observing Chemical Processes, p. 228 **Integrate Career,** p. 229 **Applying Science:** How can you compare concentrations?, p. 229 **Lab:** Observing Gas Solubility, p. 231
Section 3 Acidic and Basic Solutions ● 4 sessions ▣ 2 blocks 10. **Compare** acids and bases and their properties. 11. **Describe** practical uses of acids and bases. 12. **Explain** how pH is used to describe the strength of an acid or base. 13. **Describe** how acids and bases react when they are brought together.	National Content Standards: UCP.1, UCP.2, UCP.3, UCP.5, A.1, A.2, B.1		**MiniLAB:** Observing a Nail in a Carbonated Drink, p. 233 **Visualizing Acid Precipitation,** p. 234 **Science Online,** p. 235 **Integrate Life Science,** p. 236 **Science Online,** p. 238 **Lab:** Testing pH Using Natural Indicators, p. 240 **Science Stats:** Salty Solutions, p. 242

Lab Materials	Reproducible Resources	Section Assessment	Technology
Launch Lab: 2 bouillon cubes, mortar and pestle, 2 large beakers, water, stirring rod, timer	**Chapter *FAST FILE* Resources** Foldables Worksheet, p. 17 Directed Reading Overview, p. 19 Note-taking Worksheets, pp. 33–35	**GLENCOE'S ASSESSMENT ADVANTAGE**	**TeacherWorks** includes: • Interactive Teacher Edition • Lesson Planner with calendar • Access to all program blacklines • Correlations to standards • Web links
Need materials? Contact Science Kit at 1-800-828-7777 or www.sciencekit.com on the Internet.	**Chapter *FAST FILE* Resources** Transparency Activity, p. 44 Lab Activity, pp. 9–12 Enrichment, p. 30 Reinforcement, p. 27 Directed Reading, p. 20 **Physical Science Critical Thinking/Problem Solving,** pp. 10, 13	**Portfolio** Differentiated Instruction, p. 223 **Performance** Applying Skills, p. 223 **Content** Section Review, p. 223	🔊 Section Focus Transparency 💿 Virtual Labs CD-ROM 🎧 Guided Reading Audio Program 💿 Interactive Chalkboard CD-ROM
MiniLAB: 2 small beverage glasses, milk, refrigerator **Lab:** 2 chilled carbonated beverages, tape, 2 balloons, fabric tape measure, container, hot water, clock	**Chapter *FAST FILE* Resources** Transparency Activity, p. 45 MiniLAB, p. 3 Lab Activity, pp. 13–16 Enrichment, p. 31 Reinforcement, p. 28 Directed Reading, p. 20 Lab Worksheet, pp. 5–6 **Science Inquiry Labs,** pp. 43–44	**Portfolio** Assessment, p. 230 Assessment, p. 231 **Performance** Applying Science, p. 229 Applying Skills, p. 230 **Content** Section Review, p. 230	🔊 Section Focus Transparency 💿 Virtual Labs CD-ROM 🎧 Guided Reading Audio Program 💿 Interactive Chalkboard CD-ROM
MiniLAB: iron nail, carbonated soft drink, cup **Lab:** test tubes and rack; concentrated red cabbage juice; bottles of ammonia, soap solution, baking soda solution, white vinegar, hydrochloric acid solution, borax soap solution, colorless carbonated soft drink, and distilled water; grease pencil; droppers (9)	**Chapter *FAST FILE* Resources** Transparency Activity, p. 46 MiniLAB, p. 4 Enrichment, p. 32 Reinforcement, p. 29 Transparency Activity, pp. 47–48 Directed Reading, pp. 21, 22 Lab Worksheet, pp. 7–8 **Home and Community Involvement,** p. 44 **Earth Science Critical Thinking/Problem Solving,** p. 18	**Portfolio** Differentiated Instruction, p. 234 **Performance** MiniLAB, p. 233 Applying Math, p. 239 **Content** Section Review, p. 239	🔊 Section Focus Transparency 🔊 Teaching Transparency 💿 Virtual Labs CD-ROM 🎧 Guided Reading Audio Program 💿 Interactive Chalkboard CD-ROM 📼 Video Lab

GLENCOE'S ASSESSMENT ADVANTAGE — End of Chapter Assessment

Blackline Masters	Technology	Professional Series
Chapter *FAST FILE* Resources Chapter Review, pp. 37–38 Chapter Tests, pp. 39–42 **Standardized Test Practice,** pp. 35–38	📼 MindJogger Videoquiz 💿 Virtual Labs CD-ROM 💿 ExamView® Pro Testmaker 💿 TeacherWorks CD-ROM 💿 Interactive Chalkboard CD-ROM	**Performance Assessment in the Science Classroom (PASC)**

Transparencies

Section Focus

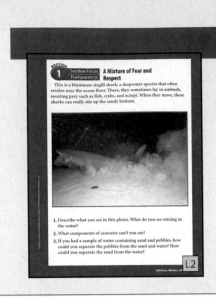

Section Focus Transparency 1 A Mixture of Fear and Respect

This is a bluntnose sixgill shark, a deepwater species that often resides near the ocean floor. There, they sometimes lay in ambush, awaiting prey such as fish, crabs, and octopi. When they move, these sharks can really stir up the sandy bottom.

1. Describe what you see in this photo. What do you see mixing in the water?
2. What components of seawater can't you see?
3. If you had a sample of water containing sand and pebbles, how could you separate the pebbles from the sand and water? How could you separate the sand from the water?

L2

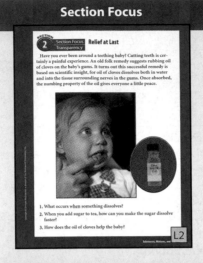

Section Focus Transparency 2 Relief at Last

Have you ever been around a teething baby? Cutting teeth is certainly a painful experience. An old folk remedy suggests rubbing oil of cloves on the baby's gums. It turns out this successful remedy is based on scientific insight, for oil of cloves dissolves both in water and into the tissue surrounding nerves in the gums. Once absorbed, the numbing property of the oil gives everyone a little peace.

1. What occurs when something dissolves?
2. When you add sugar to tea, how can you make the sugar dissolve faster?
3. How does the oil of cloves help the baby?

L2

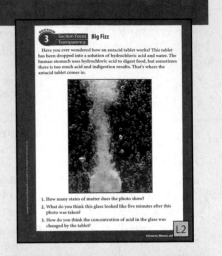

Section Focus Transparency 3 Big Fizz

Have you ever wondered how an antacid tablet works? This tablet has been dropped into a solution of hydrochloric acid and water. The human stomach uses hydrochloric acid to digest food, but sometimes there is too much acid and indigestion results. That's where the antacid tablet comes in.

1. How many states of matter does the photo show?
2. What do you think this glass looked like five minutes after this photo was taken?
3. How do you think the concentration of acid in the glass was changed by the tablet?

L2

This is a representation of key blackline masters available in the Teacher Classroom Resources. See Resource Manager boxes within the chapter for additional information.

Key to Teaching Strategies

The following designations will help you decide which activities are appropriate for your students.

L1 Level 1 activities should be appropriate for students with learning difficulties.

L2 Level 2 activities should be within the ability range of all students.

L3 Level 3 activities are designed for above-average students.

ELL ELL activities should be within the ability range of English-Language Learners.

COOP LEARN Cooperative Learning activities are designed for small group work.

LS Multiple Learning Styles logos, as described on page 12T, are used throughout to indicate strategies that address different learning styles.

P These strategies represent student products that can be placed into a best-work portfolio.

PBL Problem-Based Learning activities apply real-world situations to learning.

Assessment

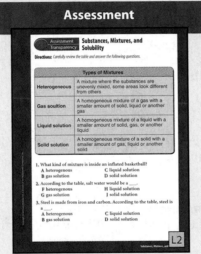

Assessment Transparency Substances, Mixtures, and Solubility

Directions: Carefully review the table and answer the following questions.

Types of Mixtures	
Heterogeneous	A mixture where the substances are unevenly mixed, some areas look different from others
Gas soultion	A homogeneous mixture of a gas with a smaller amount of solid, liquid or another gas
Liquid solution	A homogeneous mixture of a liquid with a smaller amount of solid, gas, or another liquid
Solid solution	A homogeneous mixture of a solid with a smaller amount of gas, liquid or another solid

1. What kind of mixture is inside an inflated basketball?
   A heterogenous   C liquid solution
   B gas solution   D solid solution
2. According to the table, salt water would be a ___.
   F heterogenous   H liquid solution
   G gas solution   J solid solution
3. Steel is made from iron and carbon. According to the table, steel is a ___.
   A heterogenous   C liquid solution
   B gas solution   D solid solution

L2

Teaching

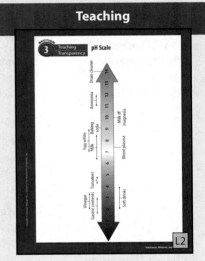

Teaching Transparency pH Scale

L2

Hands-on Activities

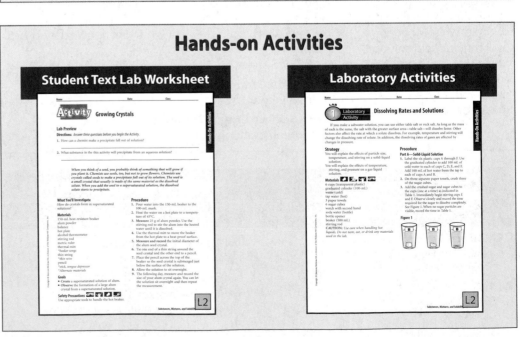

Student Text Lab Worksheet

Activity Growing Crystals

Lab Preview

Directions: Answer these questions before you begin the Activity.

1. How can a chemist make a precipitate fall out of solution?

2. What substance in the this activity will precipitate from an aqueous solution?

When you think of a seed, you probably think of something that will grow if you plant it. Chemists use seeds, too, but not to grow flowers. Chemists use crystals called seeds to make a precipitate fall out of its solution. The seed is a small crystal that usually is made of the same material as the dissolved solute. When you add the seed to a supersaturated solution, the dissolved solute starts to precipitate.

What You'll Investigate
How do crystals form in supersaturated solutions?

Materials
150-mL heat-resistant beaker
alum powder
balance
hot plate
alcohol thermometer
stirring rod
metric ruler
thermal mitt
*beaker tongs
thin string
*thin wire
pencil
*stick, tongue depressor
*Alternate materials

Goals
• Create a supersaturated solution of alum.
• Observe the formation of a large alum crystal from a supersaturated solution.

Safety Precautions
Use appropriate tools to handle the hot beaker.

Procedure
1. Pour water into the 150-mL beaker to the 100-mL mark.
2. Heat the water on a hot plate to a temperature of 65°C.
3. Measure 25 g of alum powder. Use the stirring rod to stir the alum into the heated water until it is dissolved.
4. Use the thermal mitt to move the beaker from the hot plate to a heat-proof surface.
5. Measure and record the initial diameter of the alum seed crystal.
6. Tie one end of a thin string around the seed crystal and the other end to a pencil.
7. Place the pencil across the top of the beaker so the seed crystal is submerged just below the surface of the solution.
8. Allow the solution to sit overnight.
9. The following day, measure and record the size of your alum crystal. You can let the solution sit overnight and then repeat the measurement.

L2

Laboratory Activities

Laboratory Activity 1 Dissolving Rates and Solutions

If you make a saltwater solution, you can use either table salt or rock salt. As long as the mass of each is the same, the salt with the greater surface area—table salt—will dissolve faster. Other factors also affect the rate at which a solute dissolves. For example, temperature and stirring will change the dissolving rate of solute. In addition, the dissolving rates of gases are affected by changes in pressure.

Strategy
You will explain the effects of particle size, temperature, and stirring on a solid-liquid solution.
You will explain the effects of temperature, stirring, and pressure on a gas-liquid solution.

Materials
6 cups (transparent plastic)
graduated cylinder (100-mL)
water (cold)
tap water (hot)
3 paper towels
6 sugar cubes
soda water (bottle)
bottle opener
beaker (500 mL)
stirring rod
CAUTION: Use care when handling hot liquids. Do not taste, eat, or drink any materials used in the lab.

Procedure

Part A—Solid-Liquid Solution
1. Label the six plastic cups A through F. Use the graduated cylinder to add 100 mL of cold water to each of cups C, D, E, and F. Add 100 mL of hot water from the tap to each of cups A and B.
2. On three separate paper towels, crush three of the sugar cubes.
3. Add the crushed sugar and sugar cubes to the cups (one at a time) as indicated in Table 1. Immediately begin stirring cups E and F. Observe closely and record the time required for the sugar to dissolve completely. See Figure 1. When no sugar particles are visible, record the time in Table 1.

Figure 1

L2

Meeting Different Ability Levels

Content Outline

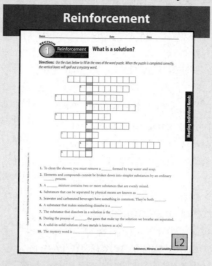

Note-taking Worksheet — Substances, Mixtures, and Solubility

L2

Reinforcement

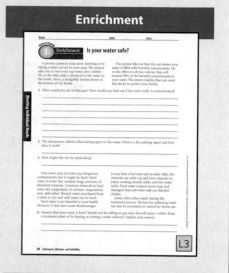

Reinforcement — What is a solution?

L2

Enrichment

Enrichment — Is your water safe?

L3

Directed Reading (English/Spanish)

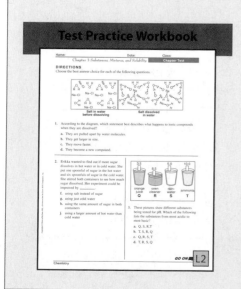

Directed Reading for Content Mastery — Overview — Substances, Mixtures, and Solubility

L1

Study Guide

Study Guide

Features
- Contains a study guide page for each section of the chapter
- Reviews key concepts
- Includes answer pages

L2

Reading Essentials

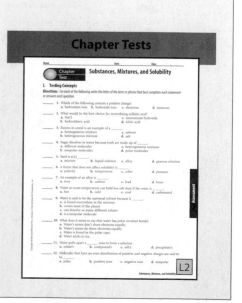

Reading Essentials for Glencoe Science — An Interactive Student Workbook

Features
- Condensed core content
- Actively involves students in reading
- Reinforces key vocabulary

L1

Assessment

Test Practice Workbook

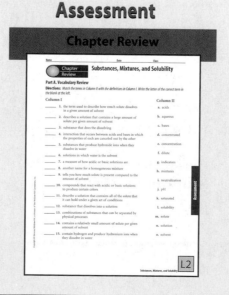

L2

Chapter Review

Chapter Review — Substances, Mixtures, and Solubility

L2

Chapter Tests

Chapter Test — Substances, Mixtures, and Solubility

L2

Science Content Background

section 1 What is a solution?
How Solutions Form

Attractive forces between the atoms, ions, or molecules of a substance hold liquid and solid substances together. When a substance is surrounded by a solvent, particles of the substance may be attracted to the solvent by various forces. If the attractive forces of the solvent are strong enough to overcome the internal attractive forces of the solute, the substance will be soluble to some extent. A substance with an extremely low solubility is usually said to be insoluble.

section 2 Solubility
Dissolution

The process of dissolving, called dissolution, involves energy. Energy is absorbed when the structure of the molecular solid is broken down or the ions of an ionic crystal are separated. Energy is released when the particles of solute form new bonds with the solvent. In the cold packs used by athletic trainers, more energy is absorbed in the first part of the dissolution process than released in the second. For that reason, the overall process is endothermic and the liquid becomes colder.

How much will dissolve?

A solution is saturated when solution equilibrium between the undissolved solute and dissolved solute in a solution is established at a particular temperature. In the state known as solution equilibrium, the solute is dissolving into the solution and forming from the solution at exactly equal rates. If a solution contains less dissolved solute than it can hold at a given temperature, the solution is unsaturated.

section 3 Acidic and Basic Solutions
Strengths of Acids and Bases

When a strong acid dissolves in water, the vast majority of acid molecules dissociate completely into ions. Strong bases react in the same way as strong acids. A weak acid only partially dissociates in water. Students might think this means that each acid molecule only separates partially. Students should understand that "partial dissociation" means that, in a solution of millions of weak acid molecules, only a few molecules completely dissociate, but the vast majority of molecules remain completely undissociated. Weak bases partially dissociate in the same manner as weak acids.

chapter content resources

Internet Resources
For additional content background, visit **ips.msscience.com** to:
- access your book online
- find references to related articles in popular science magazines
- access Web links with related content background
- access current events with science journal topics

Print Resources
Chemistry; The Molecular Nature of Matter and Change, by Martin S. Silberberg, McGraw-Hill, 2003
Crime Lab Chemistry: Grades 4–8, by Jacqueline Barber, University of California, Berkeley, Lawrence Hall of Science, 1999
Visualizing Chemistry: Investigations for Teachers, by Julie B. Ealy, James L. Ealy, and James L. Ealy Jr., American Chemical Society, 1995

IDENTIFYING Misconceptions

Find Out What Students Think

Students may think that . . .

When a material dissolves, it goes away.

An object that dissolves is melting.

A solid dissolves when it becomes part of a solution. For example, salt dissolves in water to produce a solution of salt water. After salt has dissolved in water students may think the salt is gone because it cannot be seen. Thus, they may equate dissolving with disappearing. Other students may think dissolving is the same as melting. Language may also play a role in these misconceptions. People say delicious foods "melt in their mouths" and speak of things that "dissolve into thin air."

Demonstration

As a class, find the mass of 100 mL of water, which should be about 100 g. Start adding and stirring in 5-g portions of table salt. Add a total of 20 g. Show that the salt can no longer be seen. Have students write down what they predict the new mass of the solution to be. Ask them to also write an explanation for what happened to the salt.

Promote Understanding

Activity L2 COOP LEARN

Have students work in groups to repeat the steps of the demonstration. Have each group find the mass of 100 mL of water and dissolve 20 g of table salt in it.

Ask each group to find the mass of its salt solution and compare this mass with the mass they predicted. They will find that the mass of the solution is equal to the mass of the water plus the mass of the salt.

Make sure students understand that even though we can't see the salt, it is still there.

Discuss with students ways you could show the salt is in the water. For example, if the water were boiled away, the salt would be left behind.

Now contrast melting with dissolving. Put an ice cube on your desk and allow students to watch as it melts. Light a candle, show students the liquid wax, and explain that some of the wax has melted.

Discuss the difference between dissolving and melting. Make sure students understand that

- dissolving involves at least two different materials (a solvent and a solute).

- melting happens because solids become warm enough to turn into liquids.

Explain that salt would have to be heated to a temperature of 800°C to melt.

Assess

After completing the chapter, see *Identifying Misconceptions* in the Study Guide at the end of the chapter.

Chapter Vocabulary

Science Journal Answers will vary. Look for depth and quality of information.

INTERACTIVE CHALKBOARD with Image Bank

PowerPoint® Presentations

This CD-ROM is an editable Microsoft® PowerPoint® presentation that includes:
- a pre-made presentation for every chapter
- interactive graphics
- animations
- audio clips
- image bank
- all new section and chapter questions
- Standardized Test Practice
- transparencies
- pre-lab questions for all labs
- Foldables directions
- links to ips.msscience.com

Substances, Mixtures, and Solubility

chapter preview

sections

1 **What is a solution?**

2 **Solubility**
   Lab Observing Gas Solubility

3 **Acidic and Basic Solutions**
   Lab Testing pH Using Natural Indicators

Virtual Lab What is the pH of common solutions?

Big-Band Mixtures

It's a parade and the band plays. Just as the mixing of notes produces music, the mixing of substances produces many of the things around you. From the brass in tubas to the lemonade you drink, you live in a world of mixtures. In this chapter, you'll learn why some substances form mixtures and others do not.

Science Journal Find and name four items around you that are mixtures.

216

Theme Connection

Systems and Interactions Solutions are systems in which ions, atoms, or molecules of solutes and solvents interact. Acid/base systems exist in solutions that produce hydronium ions or hydroxide ions. Acid/base systems have their own well-defined interactions.

About the Photo

Marching Bands While the tuba is the largest brass instrument in the marching band, a whole band of tubas would not be very exciting. Other instruments are needed to blend with the tubas to create the sounds you hear. The composer of the music took special care that the various instruments' sounds are interfused to produce the perfect mixture.

Start-Up Activities

Particle Size and Dissolving Rates

Why do drink mixes come in powder form? What would happen if you dropped a big chunk of drink mix into the water? Would it dissolve quickly? Powdered drink mix dissolves faster in water than chunks do because it is divided into smaller particles, exposing more of the mix to the water. See for yourself how particle size affects the rate at which a substance dissolves.

1. Pour 400 mL of water into each of two 600-mL beakers.
2. Carefully grind a bouillon cube into powder using a mortar and pestle.
3. Place the bouillon powder into one beaker and drop a whole bouillon cube into the second beaker.
4. Stir the water in each beaker for 10 s and observe.
5. **Think Critically** Write a paragraph in your Science Journal comparing the color of the two liquids and the amount of undissolved bouillon at the bottom of each beaker. How does the particle size affect the rate at which a substance dissolves?

 FOLDABLES Study Organizer

Solutions Make the following Foldable to help classify solutions based on their common features.

STEP 1 Fold a vertical sheet of paper from side to side. Make the front edge about 1.25 cm shorter than the back edge.

STEP 2 Turn lengthwise and **fold** into thirds.

STEP 3 Unfold and cut only the top layer along both folds to make three tabs.

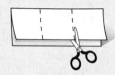

STEP 4 Label each tab as shown.

| Solid Solutions | Liquid Solutions | Gaseous Solutions |

Find Main Ideas As you read the chapter, classify solutions based on their states and list them under the appropriate tabs. On your Foldable, circle the solutions that are acids and underline the solutions that are bases.

Science Online
Preview this chapter's content and activities at
ips.msscience.com

217

 **Launch LAB**

Purpose Use the Launch Lab to introduce students to the effect of particle size on rate of dissolving. L1 ELL IS **Kinesthetic**

Preparation If you do not have enough mortars and pestles, grind a bouillon cube for each group before class.

Materials bouillon cubes, mortar and pestle, two large beakers, stirring rod, timer that can measure seconds

Alternate Materials Sugar cubes can be substituted for bouillon cubes.

Teaching Strategies
• Beef bouillon provides more observable results than does chicken bouillon.
• If timers are not available, instruct students to add the bouillon to both beakers simultaneously in order to compare the time it takes for the crushed bouillon and the cube of bouillon to dissolve.
• Using hot tap water will speed results.

Think Critically

The solution in the beaker containing the powdered bouillon is darker, and less bouillon remains undissolved in this beaker. The smaller the particle size, the faster the substance dissolves.

Assessment

Process Ask students to predict results if a bouillon cube cut in quarters were used. A quartered cube would dissolve faster than a whole cube, but slower than a crushed cube. Use **Performance Assessment in the Science Classroom,** p. 89.

 FOLDABLES Study Organizer **Dinah Zike Study Fold**

Student preparation materials for this Foldable are available in the **Chapter FAST FILE Resources.**

section 1

What is a solution?

as you read

What You'll Learn
- **Distinguish** between substances and mixtures.
- **Describe** two different types of mixtures.
- **Explain** how solutions form.
- **Describe** different types of solutions.

Why It's Important
The air you breathe, the water you drink, and even parts of your body are all solutions.

⚙ Review Vocabulary
proton: positively charged particle located in the nucleus of an atom

New Vocabulary
- ● substance
- ● heterogeneous mixture
- ● homogeneous mixture
- ● solution   ● solvent
- ● solute   ● precipitate

Table 1 Examples of Physical and Chemical Processes

Physical Processes	Chemical Processes
Boiling	Burning
Changing pressure	Reacting with other chemicals
Cooling	Reacting with light
Sorting	

Substances

Water, salt water, and pulpy orange juice have some obvious differences. These differences can be explained by chemistry. Think about pure water. No matter what you do to it physically—freeze it, boil it, stir it, or strain it—it still is water. On the other hand, if you boil salt water, the water turns to gas and leaves the salt behind. If you strain pulpy orange juice, it loses its pulp. How does chemistry explain these differences? The answer has to do with the chemical compositions of the materials.

Atoms and Elements Recall that atoms are the basic building blocks of matter. Each atom has unique chemical and physical properties which are determined by the number of protons it has. For example, all atoms that have eight protons are oxygen atoms. A **substance** is matter that has the same fixed composition and properties. It can't be broken down into simpler parts by ordinary physical processes, such as boiling, grinding, or filtering. Only a chemical process can change a substance into one or more new substances. **Table 1** lists some examples of physical and chemical processes. An element is an example of a pure substance; it cannot be broken down into simpler substances. The number of protons in an element, like oxygen, are fixed—it cannot change unless the element changes.

Compounds Water is another example of a substance. It is always water even when you boil it or freeze it. Water, however, is not an element. It is an example of a compound which is made of two or more elements that are chemically combined. Compounds also have fixed compositions. The ratio of the atoms in a compound is always the same. For example, when two hydrogen atoms combine with one oxygen atom, water is formed. All water—whether it's in the form of ice, liquid, or steam—has the same ratio of hydrogen atoms to oxygen atoms.

218   CHAPTER 8 Substances, Mixtures, and Solubility

Section 1 Resource Manager

Chapter *FAST FILE* Resources

Transparency Activity, p. 44

Directed Reading for Content Mastery, pp. 19, 20

Note-taking Worksheets, pp. 33–35

Lab Activity, pp. 9–12

Enrichment, p. 30

Reinforcement, p. 27

Separation by magnetism

Separation by straining

Figure 1 Mixtures can be separated by physical processes.
Explain why the iron-sand mixture and the pulpy lemonade are not pure substances.

Mixtures

Imagine drinking a glass of salt water. You would know right away that you weren't drinking pure water. Like salt water, many things are not pure substances. Salt water is a mixture of salt and water. Mixtures are combinations of substances that are not bonded together and can be separated by physical processes. For example, you can boil salt water to separate the salt from the water. If you had a mixture of iron filings and sand, you could separate the iron filings from the sand with a magnet. **Figure 1** shows some mixtures being separated.

Unlike compounds, mixtures do not always contain the same proportions of the substances that they are composed of. Lemonade is a mixture that can be strong tasting or weak tasting, depending on the amounts of water and lemon juice that are added. It also can be sweet or sour, depending on how much sugar is added. But whether it is strong, weak, sweet, or sour, it is still lemonade.

Heterogeneous Mixtures It is easy to tell that some things are mixtures just by looking at them. A watermelon is a mixture of fruit and seeds. The seeds are not evenly spaced through the whole melon—one bite you take might not have any seeds in it and another bite might have several seeds. A type of mixture where the substances are not mixed evenly is called a **heterogeneous** (he tuh ruh JEE nee us) **mixture.** The different areas of a heterogeneous mixture have different compositions. The substances in a heterogeneous mixture are usually easy to tell apart, like the seeds from the fruit of a watermelon. Other examples of heterogeneous mixtures include a bowl of cold cereal with milk and the mixture of pens, pencils, and books in your backpack.

Science Online

Topic: Desalination
Visit ips.msscience.com for Web links to information about how salt is removed from salt water to provide drinking water.

Activity Compare and contrast the two most common methods used for desalination.

SECTION 1 What is a solution? **219**

IDENTIFYING Misconceptions

Substances The word *substance* is often used to mean "any kind of matter." Make sure students know that in science, *substance* is used only to refer to an element or a compound. Provide students with several common items, such as wood, water, and an iron nail, and have them identify whether each is a substance.

Caption Answer

Figure 1 They can be separated by physical processes.

Make a Model

Marbles and Balls of Clay To emphasize the difference between compounds and mixtures, have students put marbles of different colors in one container and some soft balls of two different colors of modeling clay in another. Tell them to shake both containers. The clay balls will stick together, simulating the formation of compounds. The marbles will just mix. L2 ELL IS **Kinesthetic**

Visual Learning

Figure 1 Ask students whether straining the lemonade will completely separate it into its component parts. Ask them what might have to be done to further separate its parts. Straining lemonade does not separate the dissolved materials. Evaporating the water would separate the dissolved materials from the water. L2 IS **Logical-Mathematical**

Figure 2 Molecules of sugar and water are evenly mixed in frozen pops.

Figure 3 Minerals and soap react to form soap scum, which comes out of the water solution and coats the tiles of a shower.

220

Homogeneous Mixtures Your shampoo contains many ingredients, but you can't see them when you look at the shampoo. It is the same color and texture throughout. Shampoo is an example of a homogeneous (hoh muh JEE nee us) mixture. A **homogeneous mixture** contains two or more substances that are evenly mixed on a molecular level but still are not bonded together. Another name for a homogeneous mixture is a **solution**. The sugar and water in the frozen pops shown in **Figure 2,** are a solution—the sugar is evenly distributed in the water, and you can't see the sugar.

✔ Reading Check
What is another name for a homogeneous mixture?

How Solutions Form

How do you make sugar water for a hummingbird feeder? You might add sugar to water and heat the mixture until the sugar disappears. The sugar molecules would spread out until they were evenly spaced throughout the water, forming a solution. This is called dissolving. The substance that dissolves—or seems to disappear—is called the **solute.** The substance that dissolves the solute is called the **solvent.** In the hummingbird feeder solution, the solute is the sugar and the solvent is water. The substance that is present in the greatest quantity is the solvent.

Forming Solids from Solutions Under certain conditions, a solute can come back out of its solution and form a solid. This process is called crystallization. Sometimes this occurs when the solution is cooled or when some of the solvent evaporates. Crystallization is the result of a physical change. When some solutions are mixed, a chemical reaction occurs, forming a solid. This solid is called a **precipitate** (prih SIH puh tayt). A precipitate is the result of a chemical change. Precipitates probably have formed in your sink or shower because of chemical reactions. Minerals that are dissolved in tap water react chemically with soap. The product of this reaction leaves the water as a precipitate called soap scum, shown in **Figure 3.**

Curriculum Connection

Physical Education Have a physical education teacher bring to class hot and cold packs used for injuries and demonstrate their use. Explain that in a cold pack, a container of one chemical is broken, this chemical dissolves in another, and energy is absorbed. In a hot pack, a similar process occurs, but energy is released as the chemical dissolves. L2 LS **Visual-Spatial**

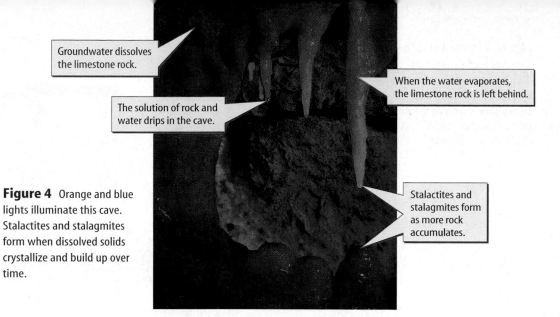

Groundwater dissolves the limestone rock.

The solution of rock and water drips in the cave.

When the water evaporates, the limestone rock is left behind.

Stalactites and stalagmites form as more rock accumulates.

Figure 4 Orange and blue lights illuminate this cave. Stalactites and stalagmites form when dissolved solids crystallize and build up over time.

INTEGRATE Environment

Stalactites and stalagmites in caves are formed from solutions, as shown in **Figure 4.** First, minerals dissolve in water as it flows through rocks at the top of the cave. This solution of water and dissolved minerals drips from the ceiling of the cave. When drops of the solution evaporate from the roof of the cave, the minerals are left behind. They create the hanging rock formations called stalactites. When drops of the solution fall onto the floor of the cave and evaporate, they form stalagmites. Very often, a stalactite develops downward while a stalagmite develops upward until the two meet. One continuous column of minerals is formed. This process will be discussed later.

Types of Solutions

So far, you've learned about types of solutions in which a solid solute dissolves in a liquid solvent. But solutions can be made up of different combinations of solids, liquids, and gases, as shown in **Table 2.**

Table 2 Examples of Common Solutions

	Solvent/ State	Solute/ State	State of Solution
Earth's atmosphere	nitrogen/gas	oxygen/gas carbon dioxide/gas argon/gas	gas
Ocean water	water/liquid	salt/solid oxygen/gas carbon dioxide/gas	liquid
Carbonated beverage	water/liquid	carbon dioxide/gas	liquid
Brass	copper/solid	zinc/solid	solid

Figure 5 Acetic acid (a liquid), carbon dioxide (a gas), and drink-mix crystals (a solid) can be dissolved in water (a liquid). **Determine** *whether one liquid solution could contain all three different kinds of solute.*

Liquid Solutions

You're probably most familiar with liquid solutions like the ones shown in **Figure 5,** in which the solvent is a liquid. The solute can be another liquid, a solid, or even a gas. You've already learned about liquid-solid solutions such as sugar water and salt water. When discussing solutions, the state of the solvent usually determines the state of the solution.

Liquid-Gas Solutions Carbonated beverages are liquid-gas solutions—carbon dioxide is the gaseous solute, and water is the liquid solvent. The carbon dioxide gas gives the beverage its fizz and some of its tartness. The beverage also might contain other solutes, such as the compounds that give it its flavor and color.

✔ Reading Check *What are the solutes in a carbonated beverage?*

Liquid-Liquid Solutions In a liquid-liquid solution, both the solvent and the solute are liquids. Vinegar, which you might use to make salad dressing, is a liquid-liquid solution made of 95 percent water (the solvent) and 5 percent acetic acid (the solute).

Gaseous Solutions

In gaseous solutions, a smaller amount of one gas is dissolved in a larger amount of another gas. This is called a gas-gas solution because both the solvent and solute are gases. The air you breathe is a gaseous solution. Nitrogen makes up about 78 percent of dry air and is the solvent. The other gases are the solutes.

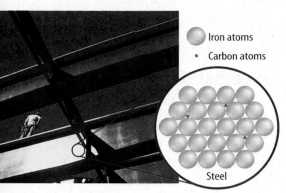

Figure 6 Metal alloys can contain either metal or nonmetal solutes dissolved in a metal solvent.

Iron atoms
· Carbon atoms

Steel

Copper atoms
Zinc atoms

Brass

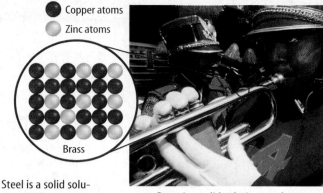

Steel is a solid solution of the metal iron and the nonmetal carbon.

Brass is a solid solution made of copper and zinc.

Solid Solutions In solid solutions, the solvent is a solid. The solute can be a solid, liquid, or gas. The most common solid solutions are solid-solid solutions—ones in which the solvent and the solute are solids. A solid-solid solution made from two or more metals is called an alloy. It's also possible to include elements that are not metals in alloys. For example, steel is an alloy that has carbon dissolved in iron. The carbon makes steel much stronger and yet more flexible than iron. Two alloys are shown in **Figure 6.**

section 1 review

Summary

Substances
- Elements are substances that cannot be broken down into simpler substances.
- A compound is made up of two or more elements bonded together.

Mixtures and Solutions
- Mixtures are either heterogeneous or homogeneous.
- Solutions have two parts—solute and solvent.
- Crystallization and precipitation are two ways that solids are formed from solutions.

Types of Solutions
- The solutes and solvents can be solids, liquids, or gases.

Self Check

1. **Compare and contrast** substances and mixtures. Give two examples of each.
2. **Describe** how heterogeneous and homogeneous mixtures differ.
3. **Explain** how a solution forms.
4. **Identify** the common name for a solid-solid solution of metals.
5. **Think Critically** The tops of carbonated-beverage cans usually are made with a different aluminum alloy than the pull tabs are made with. Explain.

Applying Skills

6. **Compare and contrast** the following solutions: a helium-neon laser, bronze (a copper-tin alloy), cloudy ice cubes, and ginger ale.

section 1 review

1. A substance is either an element or a compound. Examples may include water or elements, such as oxygen, carbon, or hydrogen. A mixture is two or more substances mixed together. Examples may include salt water, cold cereal and milk, or lemonade.
2. In a homogeneous mixture two or more substances are mixed evenly on a molecular level. In a heterogeneous mixture substances are not mixed evenly on a molecular level.
3. A solution is formed by a solute, a substance that dissolves, combining with a solvent, a substance that dissolves the solute. The substance in greater quantity is the solvent.
4. alloy
5. The alloy for the tab must be stronger so that it will open the can without breaking.
6. Helium-neon is a gas-gas solution; bronze is a solid-solid solution; cloudy ice cubes are a solid-gas solution; and ginger ale is a liquid solvent with gas and solid solutes.

section 2 Solubility

as you read

What You'll Learn

- **Explain** why water is a good general solvent.
- **Describe** how the structure of a compound affects which solvents it dissolves in.
- **Identify** factors that affect how much of a substance will dissolve in a solvent.
- **Describe** how temperature affects reaction rate.
- **Explain** how solute particles affect physical properties of water.

Why It's Important

How you wash your hands, clothes, and dishes depends on which substances can dissolve in other substances.

⦿ Review Vocabulary
polar bond: a bond resulting from the unequal sharing of electrons

New Vocabulary
- aqueous
- solubility
- saturated
- concentration

Figure 7 Some atoms share electrons to form covalent bonds.

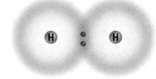

Two atoms of hydrogen share their electrons equally. Such a molecule is nonpolar.

Water—The Universal Solvent

In many solutions, including fruit juice and vinegar, water is the solvent. A solution in which water is the solvent is called an **aqueous** (A kwee us) solution. Because water can dissolve so many different solutes, chemists often call it the universal solvent. To understand why water is such a great solvent, you must first know a few things about atoms and bonding.

Molecular Compounds When certain atoms form compounds, they share electrons. Sharing electrons is called covalent bonding. Compounds that contain covalent bonds are called molecular compounds, or molecules.

If a molecule has an even distribution of electrons, like the one in **Figure 7,** it is called nonpolar. The atoms in some molecules do not have an even distribution of electrons. For example, in a water molecule, two hydrogen atoms share electrons with a single oxygen atom. However, as **Figure 7** shows, the electrons spend more time around the oxygen atom than they spend around the hydrogen atoms. As a result, the oxygen portion of the water molecule has a partial negative charge and the hydrogen portions have a partial positive charge. The overall charge of the water molecule is neutral. Such a molecule is said to be polar, and the bonds between its atoms are called polar covalent bonds.

(Partial negative charge)

The electrons spend more time around the oxygen atom than the hydrogen atoms. Such a molecule is polar.

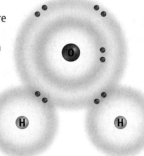

(Partial positive charge)

224 **CHAPTER 8** Substances, Mixtures, and Solubility

Section 2 Resource Manager

Chapter *FAST FILE* Resources

Transparency Activity, p. 45
Directed Reading for Content Mastery, p. 20
Enrichment, p. 31
Reinforcement, p. 28
MiniLAB, p. 3

Lab Activity, pp. 13–16
   Lab Worksheet, pp. 5–6
Lab Management and Safety, p. 65
Mathematical Skill Activities, p. 5
Cultural Diversity, p. 37
Science Inquiry Labs, pp. 43–44

Ionic Bonds Some atoms do not share electrons when they join with other atoms to form compounds. Instead, these atoms lose or gain electrons. When they do, the number of protons and electrons within an atom are no longer equal, and the atom becomes positively or negatively charged. Atoms with a charge are called ions. Bonds between ions that are formed by the transfer of electrons are called ionic bonds, and the compound that is formed is called an ionic compound. Table salt is an ionic compound that is made of sodium ions and chloride ions. Each sodium atom loses one electron to a chlorine atom and becomes a positively charged sodium ion. Each chlorine atom gains one electron from a sodium atom, becoming a negatively charged chloride ion.

 **Reading Check** *How does an ionic compound differ from a molecular compound?*

How Water Dissolves Ionic Compounds Now think about the properties of water and the properties of ionic compounds as you visualize how an ionic compound dissolves in water. Because water molecules are polar, they attract positive and negative ions. The more positive part of a water molecule—where the hydrogen atoms are—is attracted to negatively charged ions. The more negative part of a water molecule—where the oxygen atom is—attracts positive ions. When an ionic compound is mixed with water, the different ions of the compound are pulled apart by the water molecules. **Figure 8** shows how sodium chloride dissolves in water.

Solutions Seawater is a solution that contains nearly every element found on Earth. Most elements are present in tiny quantities. Sodium and chloride ions are the most common ions in seawater. Several gases, including oxygen, nitrogen, and carbon dioxide, also are dissolved in seawater.

Figure 8 Water dissolves table salt because its partial charges are attracted to the charged ions in the salt.

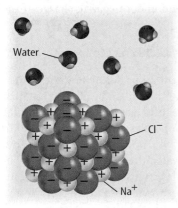

The partially negative oxygen in the water molecule is attracted to a positive sodium ion.

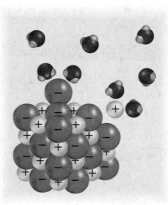

The partially positive hydrogen atoms in another water molecule are attracted to a negative chloride ion.

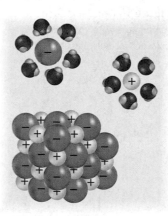

The sodium and chloride ions are pulled apart from each other, and more water molecules are attracted to them.

Quick Demo
Polar Molecules
Materials balloon, wool cloth or piece of fur, sink with running water
Estimated Time 15 minutes
Procedure To make the concept of polar molecules more accessible to students, blow up a balloon and rub it with a wool cloth or a piece of fur to give it a charge. Then hold the balloon next to a thin stream of water. Students will observe that the stream of water bends toward the balloon. The polar water molecules are attracted to the charge on the balloon.

 **Reading Check**

Answer Ionic compounds are made up of particles that have lost or gained electrons. Molecular compounds are made up of particles that share electrons to form molecules.

INTEGRATE Environment

Solutions Other elements found in some abundance in seawater include bromine and manganese. Earth's oceans also contain an estimated nine billion metric tons of gold, but obtaining gold from seawater is not cost effective.

Discussion
Water Conductivity Pure water is a poor conductor of electricity. Do you think water with ions dissolved in it conducts electricity? Explain. Water with ions dissolved in it conducts electricity easily because the ions are free to move in the water and can carry electric current. L3
LS **Logical-Mathematical**

Differentiated Instruction

Challenge Water alone can't dissolve everything needed to clean oil off your hands. You need to use soap as well. Have students find out how soap works. A soap molecule is hydrophilic (attracted to water) on one end, and hydrophobic (attracted to water-insoluble molecules) on the other end. Its hydrophilic end allows it to dissolve in water, and its hydrophobic end dissolves materials that are insoluble in water and washes them off. L3 **LS** **Logical-Mathematical**

Visual Learning

Figure 8 Review the three illustrations. Point out that an ion is not attracted to one certain water molecule but is attracted to the oppositely charged parts of many water molecules. Many water molecules are attracted to and surround each ion. L2 **LS** **Visual-Spatial**

Figure 9 Sugar molecules that are dissolved in water spread out until they are spaced evenly in the water.

Figure 10 Water and oil do not mix because water molecules are polar and oil molecules are nonpolar.

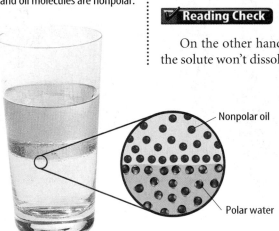

Nonpolar oil

Polar water

How Water Dissolves Molecular Compounds

Can water also dissolve molecular compounds that are not made of ions? Water does dissolve molecular compounds, such as sugar, although it doesn't break each sugar molecule apart. Water simply moves between different molecules of sugar, separating them. Like water, a sugar molecule is polar. Polar water molecules are attracted to the positive and negative portions of the polar sugar molecules. When the sugar molecules are separated by the water and spread throughout it, as **Figure 9** shows, they have dissolved.

What will dissolve?

When you stir a spoonful of sugar into iced tea, all of the sugar dissolves but none of the metal in the spoon does. Why does sugar dissolve in water, but metal does not? A substance that dissolves in another is said to be soluble in that substance. You would say that the sugar is soluble in water but the metal of the spoon is insoluble in water, because it does not dissolve readily.

Like Dissolves Like When trying to predict which solvents can dissolve which solutes, chemists use the rule of "like dissolves like." This means that polar solvents dissolve polar solutes and nonpolar solvents dissolve nonpolar solutes. In the case of sugar and water, both are made up of polar molecules, so sugar is soluble in water. In the case of salt and water, the sodium and chloride ion pair is like the water molecule because it has a positive charge at one end and a negative charge at the other end.

✔ Reading Check *What does "like dissolves like" mean?*

On the other hand, if a solvent and a solute are not similar, the solute won't dissolve. For example, oil and water do not mix. Oil molecules are nonpolar, so polar water molecules are not attracted to them. If you pour vegetable oil into a glass of water, the oil and the water separate into layers instead of forming a solution, as shown in **Figure 10.** You've probably noticed the same thing about the oil-and-water mixtures that make up some salad dressings. The oil stays on the top. Oils generally dissolve better in solvents that have nonpolar molecules.

226 CHAPTER 8 Substances, Mixtures, and Solubility

How much will dissolve?

Even though sugar is soluble in water, if you tried to dissolve 1 kg of sugar into one small glass of water, not all of the sugar would dissolve. **Solubility** (sahl yuh BIH luh tee) is a measurement that describes how much solute dissolves in a given amount of solvent. The solubility of a material has been described as the amount of the material that can dissolve in 100 g of solvent at a given temperature. Some solutes are highly soluble, meaning that a large amount of solute can be dissolved in 100 g of solvent. For example, 63 g of potassium chromate can be dissolved in 100 g of water at 25°C. On the other hand, some solutes are not very soluble. For example, only 0.00025 g of barium sulfate will dissolve in 100 g of water at 25°C. When a substance has an extremely low solubility, like barium sulfate does in water, it usually is considered insoluble.

Reading Check *What is an example of a substance that is considered to be insoluble in water?*

Solubility in Liquid-Solid Solutions Did you notice that the temperature was included in the explanation about the amount of solute that dissolves in a quantity of solvent? The solubility of many solutes changes if you change the temperature of the solvent. For example, if you heat water, not only does the sugar dissolve at a faster rate, but more sugar can dissolve in it. However, some solutes, like sodium chloride and calcium carbonate, do not become more soluble when the temperature of water increases. The graph in **Figure 11** shows how the temperature of the solvent affects the solubility of some solutes.

Solubility in Liquid-Gas Solutions Unlike liquid-solid solutions, an increase in temperature decreases the solubility of a gas in a liquid-gas solution. You might notice this if you have ever opened a warm carbonated beverage and it bubbled up out of control while a chilled one barely fizzed. Carbon dioxide is less soluble in a warm solution. What keeps the carbon dioxide from bubbling out when it is sitting at room temperature on a supermarket shelf? When a bottle is filled, extra carbon dioxide gas is squeezed into the space above the liquid, increasing the pressure in the bottle. This increased pressure increases the solubility of gas and forces most of it into the solution. When you open the cap, the pressure is released and the solubility of the carbon dioxide decreases.

Reading Check *Why does a bottle of carbonated beverage go "flat" after it has been opened for a few days?*

Figure 11 The solubility of some solutes changes as the temperature of the solvent increases.
Use a Graph *According to the graph, is it likely that warm ocean water contains any more sodium chloride than cold ocean water does?*

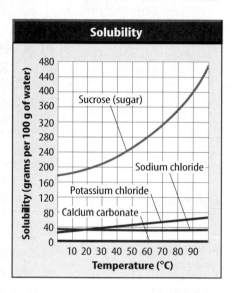

Solubility

SECTION 2 Solubility **227**

Fun Fact

Hot chocolate mix is a combination of sugars. The instructions say to combine the mix with hot water. More mix is dissolved in hot water since sugars are more soluble in hot water than cold water.

Mini LAB

Observing Chemical Processes

Procedure 🥽 ✋ 🧪

1. Pour **two small glasses of milk.**
2. Place one glass of milk in the **refrigerator.** Leave the second glass on the counter.
3. Allow the milk to sit overnight. **WARNING:** *Do not drink the milk that sat out overnight.*
4. On the following day, smell both glasses of milk. Record your observations.

Analysis

1. Compare and contrast the smell of the refrigerated milk to the non-refrigerated milk.
2. Explain why refrigeration is needed.

Try at Home

Figure 12 The Dead Sea has an extremely high concentration of dissolved minerals. When the water evaporates, the minerals are left behind and form pillars.

Saturated Solutions If you add calcium carbonate to 100 g of water at 25°C, only 0.0014 g of it will dissolve. Additional calcium carbonate will not dissolve. Such a solution—one that contains all of the solute that it can hold under the given conditions—is called a ~~saturated~~ solution. **Figure 12** shows a saturated solution. If a solution is a liquid-solid solution, the extra solute that is added will settle to the bottom of the container. It's possible to make solutions that have less solute than they would need to become saturated. Such solutions are unsaturated. An example of an unsaturated solution is one containing 50 g of sugar in 100 g of water at 25°C. That's much less than the 204 g of sugar the solution would need to be saturated.

A hot solvent usually can hold more solute than a cool solvent can. When a saturated solution cools, some of the solute usually falls out of the solution. But if a saturated solution is cooled slowly, sometimes the excess solute remains dissolved for a period of time. Such a solution is said to be supersaturated, because it contains more than the normal amount of solute.

Rate of Dissolving

Solubility does not tell you how fast a solute will dissolve—it tells you only how much of a solute will dissolve at a given temperature. Some solutes dissolve quickly, but others take a long time to dissolve. A solute dissolves faster when the solution is stirred or shaken or when the temperature of the solution is increased. These methods increase the rate at which the surfaces of the solute come into contact with the solvent. Increasing the area of contact between the solute and the solvent can also increase the rate of dissolving. This can be done by breaking up the solute into smaller pieces, which increases the surface area of the solute that is exposed to the solvent.

INTEGRATE Chemistry

Molecules are always moving and colliding. The collisions must take place for chemical processes to occur. The chemical processes take place at a given rate of reaction. Temperature has a large effect on that rate. The higher the temperature, the more collisions occur and the higher the rate of reaction. The opposite is also true. The lower the temperature, the less collisions occur and the lower the rate of reaction. Refrigerators are an example of slowing the reaction rate—and therefore the chemical process—down to prevent food spoilage.

Concentration

What makes strong lemonade strong and weak lemonade weak? The difference between the two drinks is the amount of water in each one compared to the amount of lemon. The lemon is present in different concentrations in the solution. The **concentration** of a solution tells you how much solute is present compared to the amount of solvent. You can give a simple description of a solution's concentration by calling it either concentrated or dilute. These terms are used when comparing the concentrations of two solutions with the same type of solute and solvent. A concentrated solution has more solute per given amount of solvent than a dilute solution.

Measuring Concentration Can you imagine a doctor ordering a dilute intravenous, or IV, solution for a patient? Because dilute is not an exact measurement, the IV could be made with a variety of amounts of medicine. The doctor would need to specify the exact concentration of the IV solution to make sure that the patient is treated correctly.

INTEGRATE Career

Pharmacist Doctors rely on pharmacists to formulate IV solutions. Pharmacists begin with a concentrated form of the drug, which is supplied by pharmaceutical companies. This is the solute of the IV solution. The pharmacist adds the correct amount of solvent to a small amount of the solute to achieve the concentration requested by the doctor. There may be more than one solute per IV solution in varying concentrations.

INTEGRATE Career

Pharmacist Besides making IV solutions, pharmacists are responsible for understanding the use, effects, and chemical composition of drugs including physical, chemical, and biological properties. Pharmacists also advise doctors on the selection, dosage, interactions, and side effects of the drugs.

Use an Analogy

Swimming Pools Suggest that students think of a public swimming pool as being like a solvent and individual swimmers as molecules of solute. A dozen swimmers in the pool would be like a dilute solution. A crowded pool would be like a concentrated solution. L1 ELL LS Visual-Spatial

---

Applying Science

How can you compare concentrations?

A solute is a substance that can be dissolved in another substance called a solvent. Solutions vary in concentration, or strength, depending on the amount of solute and solvent being used. Fruit drinks are examples of such a solution. Stronger fruit drinks appear darker in color and are the result of more drink mix being dissolved in a given amount of water. What would happen if more water were added to the solution?

Glucose Solutions (g/100 mL)		
Solute Glucose (g)	Solvent Water (mL)	Solution Concentration of Glucose (%)
2	100	2
4	100	4
10	100	10
20	100	20

Identifying the Problem

The table on the right lists different concentration levels of glucose solutions, a type of carbohydrate your body uses as a source of energy. The glucose is measured in grams, and the water is measured in milliliters.

Solving the Problem

A physician writes a prescription for a patient to receive 1,000 mL of a 20 percent solution of glucose. How many grams of glucose must the pharmacist add to 1,000 mL of water to prepare this 20 percent concentration level?

Applying Science

Answer

$$1000 \text{ mL} \times \frac{20 \text{ g}}{100 \text{ mL}} = 200 \text{ g}$$

Science Journal

Home Concentrates Most households contain a variety of solutions, such as frozen juice, or laundry detergent, that are concentrated. Have students list in their Science Journals the concentrated solutions in their homes, and describe why they think these products come in concentrated form. It makes them smaller so they can be shipped easily and cheaply. L2 LS
Logical-Mathematical

Differentiated Instruction

Learning Disabled Give the students a small box. Have them add five marbles to the box to mimic a dilute solution. Have them add 15 more marbles to exhibit a concentrated solution. L1 ELL
LS **Visual-Spatial**

Figure 13 Concentrations can be stated in percentages.
Identify *the percentage of this fruit drink that is water, assuming there are no other dissolved substances.*

One way of giving the exact concentration is to state the percentage of the volume of the solution that is made up of solute. Labels on fruit drinks show their concentration like the one in **Figure 13.** When a fruit drink contains 15 percent fruit juice, the remaining 85 percent of the drink is water and other substances such as sweeteners and flavorings. This drink is more concentrated than another brand that contains 10 percent fruit juice, but it's more dilute than pure juice, which is 100 percent juice. Another way to describe the concentration of a solution is to give the percentage of the total mass that is made up of solute.

Effects of Solute Particles All solute particles affect the physical properties of the solvent, such as its boiling point and freezing point. The effect that a solute has on the freezing or boiling point of a solvent depends on the number of solute particles.

When a solvent such as water begins to freeze, its molecules arrange themselves in a particular pattern. Adding a solute such as sodium chloride to this solvent changes the way the molecules arrange themselves. To overcome this interference of the solute, a lower temperature is needed to freeze the solvent.

When a solvent such as water begins to boil, the solvent molecules are gaining enough energy to move from the liquid state to the gaseous state. When a solute such as sodium chloride is added to the solvent, the solute particles interfere with the evaporation of the solvent particles. More energy is needed for the solvent particles to escape from the liquid, and the boiling point of the solution will be higher.

section 2 review

Summary

The Universal Solvent

- Water is known as the universal solvent.
- A molecule that has an even distribution of electrons is a nonpolar molecule.
- A molecule that has an uneven distribution of electrons is a polar molecule.
- A compound that loses or gains electrons is an ionic compound.

Dissolving a Substance

- Chemists use the rule "like dissolves like."

Concentration

- Concentration is the quantity of solute present compared to the amount of solvent.

Self Check

1. **Identify** the property of water that makes it the universal solvent.
2. **Describe** the two methods to increase the rate at which a substance dissolves.
3. **Infer** why it is important to add sodium chloride to water when making homemade ice cream.
4. **Think Critically** Why can the fluids used to dry-clean clothing remove grease even when water cannot?

Applying Skills

5. **Recognize Cause and Effect** Why is it more important in terms of reaction rate to take groceries straight home from the store when it is 25°C than when it is 2°C?

Science Online ips.msscience.com/self_check_quiz

section 2 review

1. Water is a polar molecule with a partial negative charge near the oxygen atom and a partial positive charge near the hydrogen atoms. The opposite charges allow water to attract both positive and negative charges on ions or molecules.

2. Possible answers: Change the temperature, increase surface area of solute, stir or shake, increase the pressure if the solute is a gas.

3. It is important to add sodium chloride to water when making homemade ice cream in order to lower the freezing point of the water.

4. The fluids are nonpolar, as are molecules that make up grease.

5. At 25°C the rate at which food spoils is much higher than the rate at 2°C.

Observing Gas Solubility

BENCH TESTED

On a hot day, a carbonated beverage will cool you off. If you leave the beverage uncovered at room temperature, it quickly loses its fizz. However, if you cap the beverage and place it in the refrigerator, it will still have its fizz hours later. In this lab you will explore why this happens.

● Real-World Question

What effect does temperature have on the fizz, or carbon dioxide, in your carbonated beverage?

Goals
■ **Observe** the effect that temperature has on solubility.
■ **Compare** the amount of carbon dioxide released at room temperature and in hot tap water.

Materials
carbonated beverages in plastic bottles,
　thoroughly chilled (2)
balloons (2)　　　　　　*ruler
tape　　　　　　　　　container
fabric tape measure　　hot tap water
*string　　　　　　　　*Alternative materials

Safety Precautions

WARNING: *DO NOT point the bottles at anyone at any time during the lab.*

● Procedure

1. Carefully remove the caps from the thoroughly chilled plastic bottles one at a time. Create as little agitation as possible.
2. Quickly cover the opening of each bottle with an uninflated balloon.

3. Use tape to secure and tightly seal the balloons to the top of the bottles.
4. Gently agitate one bottle from side to side for two minutes. Measure the circumference of the balloon.

WARNING: *Contents under pressure can cause serious accidents. Be sure to wear safety goggles, and DO NOT point the bottles at anyone.*

5. Gently agitate the second bottle in the same manner as in step 4. Then, place the bottle in a container of hot tap water for ten minutes. Measure the circumference of the balloon.

● Conclude and Apply

1. **Compare and contrast** the relative amounts of carbon dioxide gas released from the cold and the warm carbonated beverages.
2. **Infer** Why does the warmed carbonated beverage release a different amount of carbon dioxide than the chilled one?

𝒞ommunicating Your Data

Compare the circumferences of your balloons with those of members of your class. **For more help, refer to the Science Skill Handbook.**

☑ Assessment

Process Have students design an experiment that would produce a more qualitative way to measure the amount of carbon dioxide in a carbonated beverage. Use **Performance Assessment in the Science Classroom,** p. 95. P

𝒞ommunicating Your Data

Have students make line graphs. Plot the student's name (or team) versus the circumference of the balloons. Make two separate lines. Use blue pen to plot the cold carbonated beverage data. Use red pen to plot the warm carbonated beverage data. Be sure the students plot the cold and warm data on the same *x*-axis point for each team. A computer graphing program may be used.

● Real-World Question

Purpose Students observe how temperature effects solubility.
L2 ELL COOP LEARN

Process Skills observe, measure, record data

Time Required 30 minutes

● Procedure

Alternate Materials A string of known length can be substituted for a fabric tape measure. Have the students use a ruler to measure the amount of string that wraps around the balloon circumference.

Safety Precautions Be sure that all students are wearing safety goggles.

Teaching Strategy Consider having students work in pairs. One student can remove the cap from the plastic bottle while the other student covers the opening with a balloon.

Troubleshooting The connection between the bottle and the balloon must be secure.

● Conclude and Apply

1. The relative amount of carbon dioxide released from the cold carbonated beverage was less than the relative amount of carbon dioxide in the warm carbonated beverage.
2. The warm carbonated beverage releases more carbon dioxide because an increase of temperature decreases the solubility of a gas in a liquid-gas solution.

section 3

Acidic and Basic Solutions

as you read

What You'll Learn

- **Compare** acids and bases and their properties.
- **Describe** practical uses of acids and bases.
- **Explain** how pH is used to describe the strength of an acid or base.
- **Describe** how acids and bases react when they are brought together.

Why It's Important

Many common products, such as batteries and bleach, work because of acids or bases.

Review Vocabulary

physical property: any characteristic of a material that can be seen or measured without changing the material

New Vocabulary

- acid
- hydronium ion
- base
- pH
- indicator
- neutralization

Acids

What makes orange juice, vinegar, dill pickles, and grapefruit tangy? Acids cause the sour taste of these and other foods. **Acids** are substances that release positively charged hydrogen ions, H^+, in water. When an acid mixes with water, the acid dissolves, releasing a hydrogen ion. The hydrogen ion then combines with a water molecule to form a hydronium ion, as shown in **Figure 14. Hydronium ions** are positively charged and have the formula H_3O^+.

Properties of Acidic Solutions Sour taste is one of the properties of acidic solutions. The taste allows you to detect the presence of acids in your food. However, even though you can identify acidic solutions by their sour taste, you should never taste anything in the laboratory, and you should never use taste to test for the presence of acids in an unknown substance. Many acids can cause serious burns to body tissues.

Another property of acidic solutions is that they can conduct electricity. The hydronium ions in an acidic solution can carry the electric charges in a current. This is why some batteries contain an acid. Acidic solutions also are corrosive, which means they can break down certain substances. Many acids can corrode fabric, skin, and paper. The solutions of some acids also react strongly with certain metals. The acid-metal reaction forms metallic compounds and hydrogen gas, leaving holes in the metal in the process.

Figure 14 One hydrogen ion can combine with one water molecule to form one positively charged hydronium ion.
Identify *what kinds of substances are sources of hydrogen ions.*

$$H^+ \quad + \quad H_2O \quad \longrightarrow \quad H_3O^+$$

Hydrogen ion

Water molecule

Hydronium ion

232 CHAPTER 8 Substances, Mixtures, and Solubility

Section 3 Resource Manager

Chapter FAST FILE Resources

Directed Reading for Content Mastery, pp. 21, 22

Transparency Activity, pp. 46, 47–48

MiniLAB, p. 4

Enrichment, p. 32

Reinforcement, p. 29

Lab Worksheet, pp. 7–8

Figure 15 Each of these products contains an acid or is made with the help of an acid.
Describe *how your life would be different if acids were not available to make these products.*

The Better Battery

6 Volt
Lantern
Battery
Super
Heavy Duty – Long Life

Uses of Acids You're probably familiar with many acids. Vinegar, which is used in salad dressing, contains acetic acid. Lemons, limes, and oranges have a sour taste because they contain citric acid. Your body needs ascorbic acid, which is vitamin C. Ants that sting inject formic acid into their victims.

Figure 15 shows other products that are made with acids. Sulfuric acid is used in the production of fertilizers, steel, paints, and plastics. Acids often are used in batteries because their solutions conduct electricity. For this reason, it sometimes is referred to as battery acid. Hydrochloric acid, which is known commercially as muriatic acid, is used in a process called pickling. Pickling is a process that removes impurities from the surfaces of metals. Hydrochloric acid also can be used to clean mortar from brick walls. Nitric acid is used in the production of fertilizers, dyes, and plastics.

Acid in the Environment Carbonic acid plays a key role in the formation of caves and of stalactites and stalagmites. Carbonic acid is formed when carbon dioxide in soil is dissolved in water. When this acidic solution comes in contact with calcium carbonate—or limestone rock—it can dissolve it, eventually carving out a cave in the rock. A similar process occurs when acid rain falls on statues and eats away at the stone, as shown in **Figure 16.** When this acidic solution drips from the ceiling of the cave, water evaporates and carbon dioxide becomes less soluble, forcing it out of solution. The solution becomes less acidic and the limestone becomes less soluble, causing it to come out of solution. These solids form stalactites and stalagmites.

Mini LAB

Observing a Nail in a Carbonated Drink

Procedure

1. Observe the initial appearance of an **iron nail.**
2. Pour enough **carbonated soft drink** into a **cup or beaker** to cover the nail.
3. Drop the nail into the soft drink and observe what happens.
4. Leave the nail in the soft drink overnight and observe it again the next day.

Analysis

1. Describe what happened when you first dropped the nail into the soft drink and the appearance of the nail the following day.
2. Based upon the fact that the soft drink was carbonated, explain why you think the drink reacted with the nail as you observed.

Visualizing Acid Precipitation

Have students examine the pictures and read the captions. Then ask the following questions.

What are some ways to cut down on the emissions from power plants and cars? Possible answers: Improve catalytic converters that are currently on cars or have periodic inspections of cars to ensure that the catalytic converters are working properly. Power plants can continue to improve the scrubbers on their emission towers and to periodically inspect scrubbers to ensure that they are working properly.

What are some ways to repair the damage that has already occurred on statues and forests? Possible answers: Professionals can repair the damage that has already occurred to statues. Studies can be conducted to see if coatings or coverings can protect them. Soil can be treated and forests can be replanted.

Activity

Reducing Emissions Have students find out if cars and power plants in their area are significantly contributing to the acid rain problem. If so, ask them to determine what measures are being taken to reduce the emissions.
L2 **Linguistic**

NATIONAL
GEOGRAPHIC VISUALIZING
ACID PRECIPITATION

Figure 16

When fossil fuels such as coal and oil are burned, a variety of chemical compounds are produced and released into the air. In the atmosphere, some of these compounds form acids that mix with water vapor and fall back to Earth as acid precipitation—rain, sleet, snow, or fog. The effects of acid precipitation on the environment can be devastating. Winds carry these acids hundreds of miles from their source, damaging forests, corroding statues, and endangering human health.

B Sulfur dioxide and nitrogen oxides react with water vapor in the air to form highly acidic solutions of nitric acid (HNO_3) and sulfuric acid (H_2SO_4). These solutions eventually return to Earth as acid precipitation.

C Some acid rain in the United States has a pH as low as 2.3— close to the acidity of stomach acid.

A Power plants and cars burn fossil fuels to generate energy for human use. In the process, sulfur dioxide (SO_2) and nitrogen oxides are released into the atmosphere.

234

Differentiated Instruction

Challenge Challenge students to find out how scrubbers and catalytic converters work. Ask students to make diagrams illustrating their findings. L3 **LS** **Visual-Spatial** P

Teacher FYI

Binary Acids Acids that contain only two elements, one of which is hydrogen, are binary acids. An example is HCl. These acids are named by using the prefix *hydro*, the root of the nonhydrogen element, the suffix *-ic*, and the word *acid*. HCl is hydrochloric acid; HI is hydroiodic acid.

Bases

People often use ammonia solutions to clean windows and floors. These solutions have different properties from those of acidic solutions. Ammonia is called a base. **Bases** are substances that can accept hydrogen ions. When bases dissolve in water, some hydrogen atoms from the water molecules are attracted to the base. A hydrogen atom in the water molecule leaves behind the other hydrogen atom and oxygen atom. This pair of atoms is a negatively charged ion called a hydroxide ion. A hydroxide ion has the formula OH^-. Most bases contain a hydroxide ion, which is released when the base dissolves in water. For example, sodium hydroxide is a base with the formula NaOH. When NaOH dissolves in water, a sodium ion and the hydroxide ion separate.

Properties of Basic Solutions Most soaps are bases, so if you think about how soap feels, you can figure out some of the properties of basic solutions. Basic solutions feel slippery. Acids in water solution taste sour, but bases taste bitter—as you know if you have ever accidentally gotten soap in your mouth.

Like acids, bases are corrosive. Bases can cause burns and damage tissue. You should never touch or taste a substance to find out whether it is a base. Basic solutions contain ions and can conduct electricity. Basic solutions are not as reactive with metals as acidic solutions are.

Uses of Bases Many uses for bases are shown in **Figure 17.** Bases give soaps, ammonia, and many other cleaning products some of their useful properties. The hydroxide ions produced by bases can interact strongly with certain substances, such as dirt and grease.

Chalk and oven cleaner are examples of familiar products that contain bases. Your blood is a basic solution. Calcium hydroxide, often called lime, is used to mark the lines on athletic fields. It also can be used to treat lawns and gardens that have acidic soil. Sodium hydroxide, known as lye, is a strong base that can cause burns and other health problems. Lye is used to make soap, clean ovens, and unclog drains.

Science Online

Topic: Calcium Hydroxide
Visit ips.msscience.com for Web links to information about the uses for calcium hydroxide.

Activity Describe the chemical reaction that converts limestone (calcium carbonate) to calcium hydroxide.

Figure 17 Many products, including soaps, cleaners, and plaster contain bases or are made with the help of bases.

Discussion

Household Bases Household cleaners such as ammonia and oven cleaner have health warning labels on their containers. Explain what characteristics of these products make them dangerous. Possible answer: They are corrosive and can cause burns and irritation to the skin, eyes, and lungs. L2 **IS** **Logical-Mathematical**

IDENTIFYING
Misconceptions

Alcohol's Formula The formulas for alcohols might lead students to think that alcohols are bases because they contain an $-OH$ group. This group is nonionic and is known as a hydroxyl group. It is quite different from the hydroxide ion, OH^-.

Activity

Testing Soap Have students confirm that soap contains a base by testing a wet bar of soap with red litmus paper. Then have them wash their hands with the soap, observing the slippery feel. L2 **ELL** **IS** **Kinesthetic**

Fun Fact

Although they are named as acids, amino acids have properties of both acids and bases. In the glycine molecule, NH_2CH_2COOH, for example, the NH_2- group acts as a base, and the $-COOH$ group acts as an acid.

Curriculum Connection

Literature Preserving the best of writing from the past is a problem that has occupied archivists since people recognized that the life of paper is limited. In the nineteenth century, in an effort to preserve the quality of the printing, potassium aluminum sulfate, or alum, was used to absorb moisture and prevent ink from spreading. Have students find out the effect this had on paper and report their findings to the class. Unfortunately, the reaction of alum with water produces the $Al(H_2O)_6^{3+}$ ion, which is acidic. Over time, the acid reacted with the fibers of the paper, causing the paper to disintegrate. Thus, some books from earlier centuries are in better condition than those of the nineteenth century. L2 **IS** **Linguistic**

pH Levels Life-forms that normally exist in bodies of water are good examples of organisms that do not survive noticeable changes in pH. When lakes and streams become lower in pH because of acid precipitation, many organisms die. Adding lime to the water neutralizes the acid, making the water again safe for life.

Career Stream biologists test the pH of rivers and streams for neutral pH values. They also test for the amount of nitrogen, phosphorous, and dissolved oxygen. All of these factors tell if the stream is balanced for living organisms. Contact your local wildlife agency to have a biologist speak to the class. L2 LS **Interpersonal**

Reading Check

Answer They are equal.

Use Science Words

Word Origin Have students look up the origin of the symbol *pH*. The *p* stands for the German word *potenz*, which means "power." The *H* is the chemical symbol for hydrogen. Thus, pH means "the power of hydrogen." L2 LS **Linguistic**

Virtual Labs

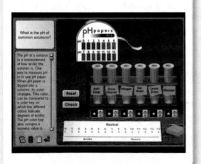

pH *What is the pH of common solutions?*

pH Levels Most life-forms can't exist at extremely low pH levels. However, some bacteria thrive in acidic environments. Acidophils are bacteria that exist at low pH levels. These bacteria have been found in the Hot Springs of Yellowstone National Park in areas with pH levels ranging from 1 to 3.

What is pH?

You've probably heard of pH-balanced shampoo or deodorant, and you might have seen someone test the pH of the water in a swimming pool. **pH** is a measure of how acidic or basic a solution is. The pH scale ranges from 0 to 14. Acidic solutions have pH values below 7. A solution with a pH of 0 is very acidic. Hydrochloric acid can have a pH of 0. A solution with a pH of 7 is neutral, meaning it is neither acidic nor basic. Pure water is neutral. Basic solutions have pH values above 7. A solution with a pH of 14 is very basic. Sodium hydroxide can have a pH of 14. **Figure 18** shows where various common substances fall on the pH scale.

The pH of a solution is related directly to its concentrations of hydronium ions (H_3O^+) and hydroxide ions (OH^-). Acidic solutions have more hydronium ions than hydroxide ions. Neutral solutions have equal numbers of the two ions. Basic solutions have more hydroxide ions than hydronium ions.

Reading Check

In a neutral solution, how do the numbers of hydronium ions and hydroxide ions compare?

pH Scale The pH scale is not a simple linear scale like mass or volume. For example, if one book has a mass of 2 kg and a second book has a mass of 1 kg, the mass of the first book is twice that of the second. However, a change of 1 pH unit represents a tenfold change in the acidity of the solution. For example, if one solution has a pH of 1 and a second solution has a pH of 2, the first solution is not twice as acidic as the second—it is ten times more acidic. To determine the difference in pH strength, use the following calculation: 10^n, where $n =$ the difference between pHs. For example: pH3 − pH1 = 2, $10^2 = 100$ times more acidic.

Figure 18 The pH scale classifies a solution as acidic, basic, or neutral.

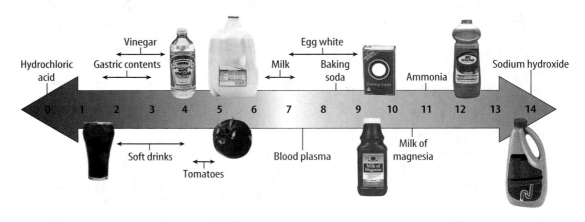

Cultural Diversity

Sandbox Trees Tall sandbox trees are found in the jungles of South and Central America. The sap from these trees is acidic. People throw the sap into lakes and streams that have been dammed. The sap solution stuns the fish, and the people gather the fish for food. Then they remove the dams, and water dilutes the sap so that the remaining fish recover completely.

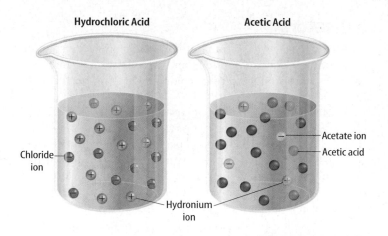

Hydrochloric Acid   Acetic Acid

Chloride ion

Acetate ion
Acetic acid

Hydronium ion

Figure 19 Hydrochloric acid separates into ions more readily than acetic acid does when it dissolves in water. Therefore, hydrochloric acid exists in water as separated ions. Acetic acid exists in water almost entirely as molecules.

Strengths of Acids and Bases You've learned that acids give foods a sour taste but also can cause burns and damage tissue. The difference between food acids and the acids that can burn you is that they have different strengths. The acids in food are fairly weak acids, while the dangerous acids are strong acids. The strength of an acid is related to how easily the acid separates into ions, or how easily a hydrogen ion is released, when the acid dissolves in water. Look at **Figure 19.** In the same concentration, a strong acid—like hydrochloric acid—forms more hydronium ions in solution than a weak acid does—like acetic acid. More hydronium ions means the strong-acid solution has a lower pH than the weak-acid solution. Similarly, the strength of a base is related to how easily the base separates into ions, or how easily a hydroxide ion is released, when the base dissolves in water. The relative strengths of some common acids and bases are shown in **Table 3.**

☑ Reading Check *What determines the strength of an acid or a base?*

An acid containing more hydrogen atoms, such as carbonic acid, H_2CO_3, is not necessarily stronger than an acid containing fewer hydrogen atoms, such as nitric acid, HNO_3. An acid's strength is related to how easily a hydrogen ion separates—not to how many hydrogen atoms it has. For this reason, nitric acid is stronger than carbonic acid.

Table 3 Strengths of Some Acids and Bases

	Acid	Base
Strong	hydrochloric (HCl) sulfuric (H_2SO_4) nitric (HNO_3)	sodium hydroxide (NaOH) potassium hydroxide (KOH)
Weak	acetic (CH_3COOH) carbonic (H_2CO_3) ascorbic ($H_2C_6H_6O_6$)	ammonia (NH_3) aluminum hydroxide (Al(OH)$_3$) iron (III) hydroxide (Fe(OH)$_3$)

SECTION 3 Acidic and Basic Solutions **237**

Quick Demo

Multi-use Indicator

Materials 0.1M potassium fluoride, 0.1M sodium nitrate, 0.1M ammonium chloride, 150-mL beakers (3), bromthymol blue indicator solution, dropper, marking pencil

Estimated Time 20 minutes

Procedure Label a beaker for each solution. Place 100 mL of each of the solutions in the corresponding beaker. Add several drops of bromthymol blue indicator solution to each. The potassium fluoride will be yellow, the sodium nitrate will be green and the ammonium chloride will be blue. This indicates basic, neutral, and acidic solutions respectively.

☑ Reading Check

Answer a salt and water

Caption Answer

Figure 20 The numbers of hydronium and hydroxide ions are equal.

Differentiated Instruction

Challenge Chemists use a wide array of acid-base indicator solutions. Have students find the names of several and the pH ranges over which they work. Possible answers: methyl violet: 0.0–1.6; methyl orange: 3.1–4.4; bromocresol green: 3.8–5.4; methyl red: 4.2–6.2; bromothymol blue: 6.0–7.6; phenolphthalein: 8.0–9.8; alizarin yellow R: 10.1–12.0 L3 [IS] **Linguistic**

Science Online

Topic: Indicators

Visit ips.msscience.com for Web links to information about the types of pH indicators.

Activity Describe how plants can act as indicators in acidic and basic solutions.

Figure 20 The pH of a solution is more acidic when greater amounts of hydronium ions are present.

Define what makes a pH 7 solution neutral.

Indicators

What is a safe way to find out how acidic or basic a solution is? **Indicators** are compounds that react with acidic and basic solutions and produce certain colors, depending on the solution's pH.

Because they are different colors at different pHs, indicators can help you determine the pH of a solution. Some indicators, such as litmus, are soaked into paper strips. When litmus paper is placed in an acidic solution, it turns red. When placed in a basic solution, litmus paper turns blue. Some indicators can change through a wide range of colors, with each different color appearing at a different pH value.

Neutralization

Perhaps you've heard someone complain about heartburn or an upset stomach after eating spicy food. To feel better, the person might have taken an antacid. Think about the word *antacid* for a minute. How do antacids work?

Heartburn or stomach discomfort is caused by excess hydrochloric acid in the stomach. Hydrochloric acid helps break down the food you eat, but too much of it can irritate your stomach or digestive tract. An antacid product, often made from the base magnesium hydroxide, $Mg(OH)_2$, neutralizes the excess acid. **Neutralization** (new truh luh ZAY shun) is the reaction of an acid with a base. It is called this because the properties of both the acid and base are diminished, or neutralized. In most cases, the reaction produces a water and a salt. **Figure 20** illustrates the relative amounts of hydronium and hydroxide ions between pH 0 and pH 14.

☑ Reading Check   *What are the products of neutralization?*

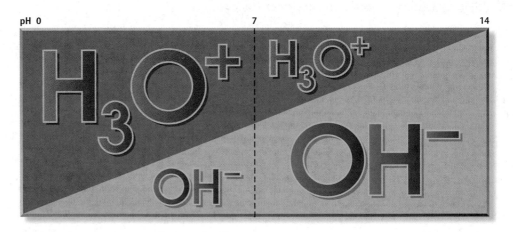

pH 0   7   14

238   CHAPTER 8 Substances, Mixtures, and Solubility

LAB DEMONSTRATION

Purpose to show neutralization and the use of an indicator

Materials 0.1M HCl, 0.1M NaOH, 10-mL graduated cylinder, 250-mL beaker, phenolphthalein solution, stirring rod, overhead projector, dropper, universal indicator paper

Procedure Test the pH of both solutions. Pour 10 mL of the acid into a beaker placed on the overhead projector. Add two drops of phenolphthalein. Gradually add the base while stirring until a slight pink color appears and stays. Test the pH of the final solution.

Expected Outcome The final solution is slightly basic.

Assessment

Why might the final solution be slightly basic? The pink color of the indicator occurs after neutralization (about pH=8).

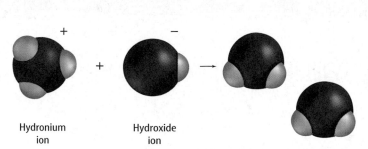

$$H_3O^+ \quad + \quad OH^- \quad \longrightarrow \quad 2H_2O$$

Hydronium ion

Hydroxide ion

Water molecules

Figure 21 When acidic and basic solutions react, hydronium and hydroxide ions react to form water.
Determine *why the pH of the solution changes.*

How does neutralization occur?

Recall that every water molecule contains two hydrogen atoms and one oxygen atom. As **Figure 21** shows, when one hydronium ion reacts with one hydroxide ion, the product is two water molecules. This reaction occurs during acid-base neutralization. Equal numbers of hydronium ions from the acidic solution and hydroxide ions from the basic solution react to produce water. Pure water has a pH of 7, which means that it's neutral.

✓ **Reading Check** *What happens to acids and bases during neutralization?*

section 3 review

Summary

Acids and Bases

- Acids are substances that release positively charged hydrogen ions in water.
- Substances that accept hydrogen ions in water are bases.
- Acidic and basic solutions can conduct electricity.

pH

- pH measures how acidic or basic a solution is.
- The scale ranges from 0 to 14.

Neutralization

- Neutralization is the interaction between an acid and a base to form water and a salt.

Self Check

1. **Identify** what ions are produced by acids in water and bases in water. Give two properties each of acids and bases.
2. **Name** three acids and three bases and list an industrial or household use of each.
3. **Explain** how the concentration of hydronium ions and hydroxide ions are related to pH.
4. **Think Critically** In what ways might a company that uses a strong acid handle an acid spill on the factory floor?

Applying Math

5. **Solve One-Step Equations** How much more acidic is a solution with a pH of 2 than one with a pH of 6? How much more basic is a solution with a pH of 13 than one with a pH of 10?

 **Science Online** ips.msscience.com/self_check_quiz

SECTION 3 Acidic and Basic Solutions **239**

section 3 review

1. Hydronium ions are produced by acids and hydroxide ions are produced by bases. Properties of acids include sour taste, corrosive, and conduct electricity. Properties of bases include bitter taste, slippery, corrosive, and conduct electricity.
2. Acids: acetic acid, vinegar; ascorbic acid, vitamin C; hydrochloric acid, pickling; sulfuric acid, fertilizer production; nitric acid, plastics and dyes production. Bases: calcium hydroxide, lawn treatments or lining athletic fields; sodium hydroxide, soap or oven cleaners; ammonia, cleaning products.
3. Solutions with more hydronium ions than hydroxide ions are acidic, pH below 7. Solutions with equal amounts are neutral, pH equal to 7. Solutions with more hydroxide ions than hydronium ions are basic, pH above 7.
4. Answers might include that a base could be used to neutralize it.
5. 10,000 times more acidic; 1,000 times more basic

Real-World Question

Purpose Students will measure pH using a red-cabbage-juice indicator. L2 ELL LS **Kinesthetic**

Process Skills observe, make and use tables, compare, classify, predict

Time Required 45 minutes

Procedure

Materials Prepare indicator solution by tearing three red cabbage leaves into small pieces and layering them in a 600-mL beaker. Add distilled water until the leaves are just covered. Boil the mixture for 5 minutes. Pour the cooled indicator into dropper bottles and refrigerate until needed.

Prepare 100 mL of 0.1M HCl solution by adding 10 mL 1M HCl to 90 mL distilled water.

Alternate Materials Other solutions that could be tested are lemon juice, sodium chloride solution, eyewash, and orange juice.

Safety Precautions Caution students not to inhale ammonia fumes, to avoid skin contact with the solutions, and to report any spillage.

Goals
■ **Determine** the relative acidity or basicity of several common solutions.
■ **Compare** the strengths of several common acids and bases.

Materials
small test tubes (9)
test-tube rack
concentrated red cabbage juice in a dropper bottle
labeled bottles containing:
household ammonia, baking soda solution, soap solution, 0.1M hydrochloric acid solution, white vinegar, colorless carbonated soft drink, borax soap solution, distilled water
grease pencil
droppers (9)

Safety Precautions

WARNING: *Many acids and bases are poisonous, can damage your eyes, and can burn your skin. Wear goggles and gloves AT ALL TIMES. Tell your teacher immediately if a substance spills. Wash your hands after you finish but before removing your goggles.*

Testing pH Using Natural Indicators

Real-World Question

You have learned that certain substances, called indicators, change color when the pH of a solution changes. The juice from red cabbage is a natural indicator. How do the pH values of various solutions compare to each other? How can you use red cabbage juice to determine the relative pH of several solutions?

Procedure

1. **Design** a data table to record the names of the solutions to be tested, the colors caused by the added cabbage juice indicator, and the relative strengths of the solutions.

2. Mark each test tube with the identity of the acid or base solution it will contain.

3. Half-fill each test tube with the solution to be tested.
   WARNING: *If you spill any liquids on your skin, rinse the area immediately with water. Alert your teacher if any liquid spills in the work area or on your skin.*

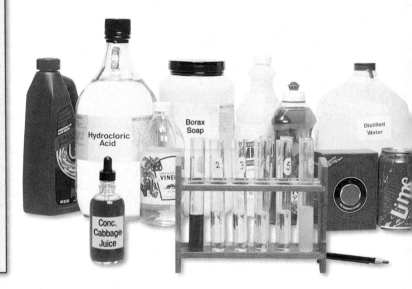

Solutions, Indicators, and Approximate pH Values

Solution	Indicator Color	pH	Solution	Indicator Color	pH
Ammonia solution	blue-green	11–12	White vinegar	red-purple	3–4
Baking soda solution	green	10–11	Soft drink	red-purple	3–4
Soap solution	green	10–11	Borax soap	purple	7–8
HCl	red	0–1	Distilled water	purple	6–8

4. Add ten drops of the cabbage juice indicator to each of the solutions to be tested. Gently agitate or wiggle each test tube to mix the cabbage juice with the solution.

5. **Observe** and record the color of each solution in your data table.

Analyze Your Data

1. **Compare** your observations with the table above. Record in your data table the relative acid or base strength of each solution you tested.

2. **List** the solutions by pH value starting with the most acidic and finishing with the most basic.

Conclude and Apply

1. **Classify** which solutions were acidic and which were basic.

2. **Identify** which solution was the weakest acid. The strongest base? The closest to neutral?

3. **Predict** what ion might be involved in the cleaning process based upon your data for the ammonia, soap, and borax soap solutions.

Form a Hypothesis

Form a hypothesis that explains why the borax soap solution was less basic than an ammonia solution of approximately the same concentration.

Determining pH Values	
Cabbage Juice Color	Relative Strength of Acid or Base
	strong acid
	medium acid
	weak acid
	neutral
	weak base
	medium base
	strong base

Communicating Your Data

Use your data to create labels for the solutions you tested. Include the relative strength of each solution and any other safety information you think is important on each label. **For more help, refer to the Science Skill Handbook.**

Conc. Cabbage Juice

LAB 241

Alternative Inquiry Lab

Indicator Inquiry Have students research other natural indicators, such as flowers, that change color due to soil acidity. Consult a garden center for specific pH-reliant flowers. Have students try to grow them with soils of different acidities. What methods do gardeners use to alter soil pH? NOTE: leaves changing color in the fall is NOT an acid/base effect.

Communicating Your Data

Student labels should show which solutions are dangerous to skin and eyes and which solutions might be harmful to metals or other materials they contact.

Teaching Strategies Advise students to compare the color of one solution with another and with the color chart. Students should observe the colors by setting the beakers on white paper. This will help them develop sensitivity to small differences in tint.

Analyze Your Data

Expected Outcome See table. Students should be able to classify each solution according to relative strength of acid or base.

Conclude and Apply

1. See data table.
2. acidic solutions: HCl, vinegar, soft drink; basic solutions: ammonia, baking soda, soap, borax soap solution
3. weakest acid: vinegar or soft drink; strongest base: ammonia solution; closest to neutral: distilled water
4. the hydroxide ion
5. HCl, soft drink, white vinegar, distilled water, borax soap, soap solution, baking soda solution, ammonia solution

Form a Hypothesis

The ammonia solution produces more hydroxide ions in solution than the borax.

Error Analysis Have groups compare results to determine whether they distinguished color in the same way. If data disagree, have students repeat the tests.

✔ Assessment

Content Ask students to use colored markers or colored pencils to draw and label each solution containing indicator.

Content Background

While salt is necessary for life, too much or too little salt is harmful. If too little salt is present in blood, blood cells swell and become ineffective. If too much salt is present in blood, the cells shrivel up and die.

Discussion

How much salt? Why should your diet limit, but not eliminate, salt? Too much salt can cause health problems, but salt is a part of many body fluids, such as saliva, tears, perspiration, and blood plasma. Correct concentrations of salt are also needed for proper transmission of nerve impulses. L2 LS
Logical-Mathematical

Activity

Create a Saline Lake Have students show how the Great Salt Lake formed. Set up a stream table containing a mixture of soil or sand containing a small amount of salt. Have students pour small streams of water over the soil, simulating rain. Have them collect the runoff in a bowl or beaker. Then, have them set the solution in a warm place so that the water can evaporate. Discuss how the salt concentration of the water changes over time. L2 ELL LS **Kinesthetic**

Applying Math

Answer 4,000 km²/32,000 km² × 100% = 12.5%

SCIENCE Stats

Salty Solutions

Did you know...

...Seawater is certainly a salty solution. Ninety-nine percent of all salt ions in the sea are sodium, chlorine, sulfate, magnesium, calcium, and potassium. The major gases in the sea are nitrogen, oxygen, carbon dioxide, argon, neon, and helium.

...Tears and saliva have a lot in common. Both are salty solutions that protect you from harmful bacteria, keep tissues moist, and help spread nutrients. Bland-tasting saliva, however, is 99 percent water. The remaining one percent is a combination of many ions, including sodium and several proteins.

...The largest salt lake in the United States is the Great Salt Lake. It covers more than 4,000 km² in Utah and is up to 13.4 m deep. The Great Salt Lake and the Salt Lake Desert were once part of the enormous, prehistoric Lake Bonneville, which was 305 m deep at some points.

WYOMING

Lake Bonneville — Great Salt Lake

UTAH

Applying Math At its largest, Lake Bonneville covered about 32,000 km². What percentage of that area does the Great Salt Lake now cover?

...Salt can reduce pain. Gargled salt water is a disinfectant; it fights the bacteria that cause some sore throats.

Graph It

Visit ips.msscience.com/science_stats to research and learn about other elements in seawater. Create a graph that shows the amounts of the ten most common elements in 1 L of seawater.

242   CHAPTER 8   Substances, Mixtures, and Solubility

Differentiated Instruction

English-Language Learners Each continent has saline lakes. Have students research a saline lake from their native continent. Instruct them to write a summary of their research including the location, the depth, and the area the lake covers. Ask them to present their summaries orally to a classmate. L2 ELL LS **Auditory-Musical**

Graph It

Seawater Elements Be sure student graphs reflect elements, not compounds. Students can use bar or circle graphs to present results. If they use circle graphs, review how to calculate the percentage of each element and how to multiply it by 360° to determine the number of degrees in the circle represented by the element.

Reviewing Main Ideas

Section 1 What is a solution?

1. Elements and compounds are pure substances, because their compositions are fixed. Mixtures are not pure substances.

2. Heterogeneous mixtures are not mixed evenly. Homogeneous mixtures, also called solutions, are mixed evenly on a molecular level.

3. Solutes and solvents can be gases, liquids, or solids, combined in many different ways.

Section 2 Solubility

1. Because water molecules are polar, they can dissolve many different solutes. Like dissolves like.

2. Temperature and pressure can affect solubility.

3. Solutions can be unsaturated, saturated, or supersaturated, depending on how much solute is dissolved compared to the solubility of the solute in the solvent.

4. The concentration of a solution is the amount of solute in a particular volume of solvent.

Section 3 Acidic and Basic Solutions

1. Acids release H+ ions and produce hydronium ions when they are dissolved in water. Bases accept H+ ions and produce hydroxide ions when dissolved in water.

2. pH expresses the concentrations of hydronium ions and hydroxide ions in aqueous solutions.

3. In a neutralization reaction, an acid reacts with a base to form water and a salt.

Visualizing Main Ideas

Copy and complete the concept map on the classification of matter.

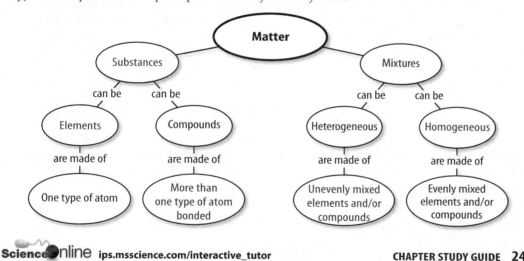

CHAPTER STUDY GUIDE 243

Reviewing Main Ideas

Summary statements can be used by students to review the major concepts of the chapter.

Visualizing Main Ideas

See student page.

Science⬤nline

Visit ips.msscience.com
 /self_check_quiz
 /interactive_tutor
 /vocabulary_puzzlemaker
 /chapter_review
 /standardized_test

Assessment Transparency

For additional assessment questions, use the *Assessment Transparency* located in the transparency book.

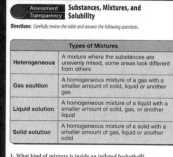

◆ Identifying Misconceptions   Assess

After students have done the activity on page F at the beginning of this chapter, have them perform this activity.

Materials beaker of water, salt

Procedure Give each group a set of materials. Ask them to write observations about the water and salt. Then have them drop the salt into the water and record what they observe. Have them allow the water to evaporate and observe the remaining salt. L2 COOP LEARN

Expected Outcome When the salt is dropped into the water, it seems to disappear. When the water is evaporated, the salt will remain, proving that it was there all the time.

Using Vocabulary

1. pH
2. concentration
3. solubility
4. solute
5. neutralization
6. substance

Checking Concepts

7. D	12. A
8. C	13. B
9. A	14. C
10. B	15. C
11. C	16. D

Using Vocabulary

acid p.232	neutralization p.238
aqueous p.224	pH p.236
base p.235	precipitate p.220
concentration p.229	saturated p.228
heterogeneous	solubility p.227
mixture p.219	solute p.220
homogeneous	solution p.220
mixture p.220	solvent p.220
hydronium ion p.232	substance p.218
indicator p.238	

Fill in the blanks with the correct vocabulary word.

1. A base has a(n) _____ value above 7.

2. A measure of how much solute is in a solution is its _____.

3. The amount of a solute that can dissolve in 100 g of solvent is its _____.

4. The _____ is the substance that is dissolved to form a solution.

5. The reaction between an acidic and basic solution is called _____.

6. A(n) _____ has a fixed composition.

Checking Concepts

Choose the word or phrase that best answers the question.

7. Which of the following is a solution?
   A) pure water
   B) an oatmeal-raisin cookie
   C) copper
   D) vinegar

8. What type of compounds will not dissolve in water?
   A) polar   C) nonpolar
   B) ionic   D) charged

9. What type of molecule is water?
   A) polar   C) nonpolar
   B) ionic   D) precipitate

10. When chlorine compounds are dissolved in pool water, what is the water?
    A) the alloy
    B) the solvent
    C) the solution
    D) the solute

11. A solid might become less soluble in a liquid when you decrease what?
    A) particle size   C) temperature
    B) pressure   D) container size

12. Which acid is used in the industrial process known as pickling?
    A) hydrochloric   C) sulfuric
    B) carbonic   D) nitric

13. A solution is prepared by adding 100 g of solid sodium hydroxide, NaOH, to 1,000 mL of water. What is the solid NaOH called?
    A) solution   C) solvent
    B) solute   D) mixture

14. Given equal concentrations, which of the following will produce the most hydronium ions in an aqueous solution?
    A) a strong base   C) a strong acid
    B) a weak base   D) a weak acid

15. Bile, an acidic body fluid used in digestion, has a high concentration of hydronium ions. Predict its pH.
    A) 11   C) less than 7
    B) 7   D) greater than 7

16. When you swallow an antacid, what happens to your stomach acid?
    A) It is more acidic.
    B) It is concentrated.
    C) It is diluted.
    D) It is neutralized.

Science Online ips.msscience.com/vocabulary_puzzlemaker

Use the ExamView® Pro Testmaker CD-ROM to:
- create multiple versions of tests
- create modified tests with one mouse click for inclusion students
- edit existing questions and add your own questions
- build tests aligned with state standards using built-in State Curriculum Tags
- change English tests to Spanish with one mouse click and vice versa

Thinking Critically

17. Infer why deposits form in the steam vents of irons in some parts of the country.

18. Explain if it is possible to have a dilute solution of a strong acid.

19. Draw Conclusions Antifreeze is added to water in a car's radiator to prevent freezing in cold months. It also prevents overheating or boiling. Explain how antifreeze does both.

Use the illustration below to answer question 20.

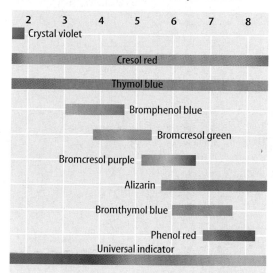

20. Interpret Chemists use a variety of indicators. Using the correct indicator is important. The color change must occur at the proper pH or the results could be misleading. Looking at the indicator chart, what indicators could be used to produce a color change at both pH 2 and pH 8?

21. Explain Water molecules can break apart to form H^+ ions and OH^- ions. Water is known as an amphoteric substance, which is something that can act as an acid or a base. Explain how this can be so.

 ips.msscience.com/chapter_review

22. Describe how a liquid-solid solution forms. How is this different from a liquid-gas solution? How are these two types of solutions different from a liquid-liquid solution? Give an example of each with your description.

23. Compare and contrast examples of heterogeneous and homogeneous mixtures from your daily life.

24. Form a Hypotheses A warm carbonated beverage seems to fizz more than a cold one when it is opened. Explain this based on the solubility of carbon dioxide in water.

Performance Activities

25. Poem Write a poem that explains the difference between a substance and a mixture.

Applying Math

Use the graph below to answer question 26.

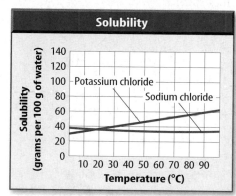

26. Solubility Using the solubility graph above, estimate the solubilities of potassium chloride and sodium chloride in grams per 100 g of water at 80°C.

27. Juice Concentration You made a one-liter (1,000 mL) container of juice. How much concentrate, in mL, did you add to make a concentration of 18 percent?

Thinking Critically

17. Minerals are dissolved in the water. When the water evaporates, the minerals are left behind.

18. Yes; if a small amount of a strong acid is dissolved in a large amount of water, the solution will be dilute.

19. Antifreeze lowers the freezing point of the water in cold months and raises the boiling point in hot months. This happens because antifreeze acts as a solute particle and changes the physical properties of the solvent, water.

20. cresol red, thymol blue, universal indicator

21. It meets the definition of a base because it produces hydroxide ions and that of an acid because it produces hydrogen (hydronium) ions.

22. A liquid-solid solution forms when the solvent, the liquid, dissolves the solute, the solid. In a liquid-gas solution the solvent is the liquid and the solute is the gas. In a liquid-liquid solution the liquid in the greater amount is the solvent and the other liquid is the solute. Examples may include: liquid-solid — salt water; liquid-gas — carbonated beverages; liquid-liquid — vinegar.

23. Accept all reasonable answers.

24. The higher the temperature, the less carbon dioxide can be dissolved in water. Therefore, more carbon dioxide gas escapes from the warm beverage than from the cold one.

Performance Activities

25. Check student poems for accuracy. Use **Performance Assessment in the Science Classroom**, p. 151.

Applying Math

National Math Standards

1, 4, 5, 9

26. potassium chloride: 60 g/100 g of water; sodium chloride: 35 g/100 g of water

27. x mL/1,000 mL = .18; x = 180 mL

✓ Assessment   Resources

📁 Reproducible Masters

Chapter *Fast File* Resources
Chapter Review, pp. 37–38
Chapter Tests, pp. 39–42
Assessment Transparency Activity, p. 49

Glencoe Science Web site
Chapter Review Test
Standardized Test Practice

Glencoe Technology
🔦 Assessment Transparency
ⓥ Exam*View*® Pro Testmaker
▣ MindJogger Videoquiz
🌐 Interactive Chalkboard

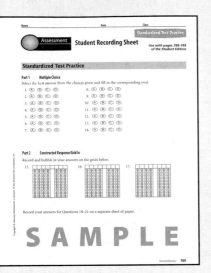

FAST FILE

Answer Sheet A practice answer sheet can be found at ips.msscience.com/answer_sheet.

Part 1 | Multiple Choice

1. B
2. A
3. D
4. A
5. C
6. A

Part 2 | Short Response

7. Steel is an alloy containing carbon dissolved in iron. The addition of carbon makes steel more flexible and stronger than iron.

8. The matter can be separated by a physical process. One of the mixture components has the physical property of magnetism.

9. The matter is a heterogeneous mixture, in which the components are not mixed evenly and have different compositions which can be distinguished. Additional examples include cereal with milk, a chocolate chip cookie, and vinegar and oil salad dressing.

Part 1 | Multiple Choice

Record your answers on the answer sheet provided by your teacher or on a sheet of paper.

Use the illustration below to answer questions 1 and 2.

Composition of Earth's Atmosphere

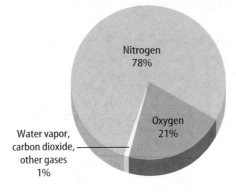

Nitrogen 78%

Oxygen 21%

Water vapor, carbon dioxide, other gases 1%

1. Which term best describes Earth's atmosphere?
  A. saturated   **C.** precipitate
  B. solution   **D.** indicator

2. Which of these is the solvent in Earth's atmosphere?
  A. nitrogen   **C.** water vapor
  B. oxygen   **D.** carbon dioxide

3. What characteristic do aqueous solutions share?
  A. They contain more than three solutes.
  B. No solids or gases are present as solutes in them.
  C. All are extremely concentrated.
  D. Water is the solvent in them.

Test-Taking Tip

Start the Day Right The morning of the test, eat a healthy breakfast with a balanced amount of protein and carbohydrates.

Use the illustration below to answer questions 4 and 5.

Solubility

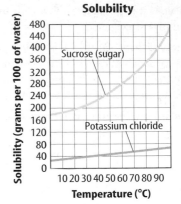

Sucrose (sugar)

Potassium chloride

Solubility (grams per 100 g of water): 0 40 80 120 160 200 240 280 320 360 400 440 480

Temperature (°C): 10 20 30 40 50 60 70 80 90

4. How does the solubility of sucrose change as the temperature increases?
  A. It increases.
  B. It does not change.
  C. It decreases.
  D. It fluctuates randomly.

5. Which statement is TRUE?
  A. Potassium chloride is more soluble in water than sucrose.
  B. As water temperature increases, the solubility of potassium chloride decreases.
  C. Sucrose is more soluble in water than potassium chloride.
  D. Water temperature has no effect on the solubility of these two chemicals.

6. Which of these is a property of acidic solutions?
  A. They taste sour.
  B. They feel slippery.
  C. They are in many cleaning products.
  D. They taste bitter.

---

10. Breaking the solute into smaller pieces increases the area of contact between the solute and the solvent, increasing the dissolving rate.

11. Solution B is more concentrated than Solution A. Solution A is dilute, while Solution B is concentrated. Neither is saturated.

12. The pH of vinegar ranges from 2 to 3. The pH of blood plasma is about 7.4, while the pH of ammonia is 11. Soft drinks are anywhere from 10 to 100 times more acidic than tomatoes, and tomatoes are about 100 times more acidic than milk.

13. Litmus is an indicator which is soaked into strips of paper. Litmus paper placed in an acidic solution turns red. Litmus paper placed in a basic solution turns blue.

Part 2 | Short Response/Grid In

Record your answers on the answer sheet provided by your teacher or on a sheet of paper.

7. Identify elements present in the alloy steel. Compare the flexibility and strength of steel and iron.

Use the illustration below to answer questions 8 and 9.

8. How can you tell that the matter in this bowl is a mixture?

9. What kind of mixture is this? Define this type of mixture, and give three additional examples.

10. Explain why a solute broken into small pieces will dissolve more quickly than the same type and amount of solute in large chunks.

11. Compare the concentration of two solutions: Solution A is composed of 5 grams of sodium chloride dissolved in 100 grams of water. Solution B is composed of 27 grams of sodium chloride dissolved in 100 grams of water.

12. Give the pH of the solutions vinegar, blood plasma, and ammonia. Compare the acidities of soft drinks, tomatoes, and milk.

13. Describe how litmus paper is used to determine the pH of a solution.

Part 3 | Open Ended

Record your answers on a sheet of paper.

14. Compare and contrast crystallization and a precipitation reaction.

15. Why is a carbonated beverage defined as a liquid-gas solution? In an open container, the ratio of liquid solvent to gas solute changes over time. Explain.

Use the illustration below to answer questions 16 and 17.

(Partial negative charge)

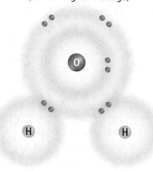

(Partial positive charge)

16. The diagram shows a water molecule. Use the distribution of electrons to describe this molecule's polarity.

17. Explain how the polarity of water molecules makes water effective in dissolving ionic compounds.

18. Marble statues and building facades in many of the world's cities weather more quickly today than when first constructed. Explain how the pH of water plays a role in this process.

19. Acetic acid, CH_3COOH, has more hydrogen atoms than the same concentration of hydrochloric acid, HCl. Hydrogen ions separate more easily from hydrochloric than acetic acid. Which acid is strongest? Why?

17. Water molecules are polar. The positive parts of water molecules attract the negative ions in an ionic compound, while the negative parts of water molecules attract the positive ions in an ionic compound. The ions are pulled away from each other and surrounded by additional polar water molecules, causing them to dissolve.

18. Precipitation in some cities is acidic, with a low pH. The acidity is caused by chemicals like nitric acid and sulfuric acid which are incorporated into snow and rainfall. The acidic liquid reacts chemically with some types of stone, dissolving the solid and washing it away. Acidic precipitation wears away the surface of landmarks more quickly than pure water.

19. Hydrochloric acid is stronger than acetic acid. The strength of an acid is not related to how many hydrogen atoms it has, but to how easily the acid separates into ions when the acid dissolves in water. The more hydronium ions in solution, the stronger the acid.

Rubrics

For more help evaluating open-ended assessment questions, see the rubric on p. 10T.

Part 3 | Open Ended

14. Both processes produce a solid from solution. Crystallization is caused by a physical change, such as the cooling of a solution or the evaporation of some or all of the solvent in a solution. A precipitation reaction is a chemical reaction in which a solid product, called a precipitate, is formed.

15. Water is the liquid solvent in a carbonated drink. Carbon dioxide gas is present in addition to other solutes. Over time, CO_2 gas escapes into the air, decreasing the amount of solute in the solvent.

16. Each hydrogen atom shares one electron with the oxygen atom. The electrons spend more time around the oxygen atom than the hydrogen atoms. The oxygen end of the water molecule has a partial negative charge, and the hydrogen end has a partial positive charge, resulting in a polar molecule.

Section/Objectives	Standards		Labs/Features
	National	**State/Local**	
Chapter Opener	See pp. 16T–17T for a Key to Standards.		**Launch Lab:** Model Carbon's Bonding, p. 249 **Foldables,** p. 249
Section 1 Simple Organic Compounds ● 2 sessions ▣ 1 block 1. **Explain** why carbon is able to form many compounds. 2. **Describe** how saturated and unsaturated hydrocarbons differ. 3. **Identify** isomers of organic compounds.	National Content Standards: UCP.1–UCP.3, UCP.5, A.1, A.2, B.1, C.1		**Integrate Earth Science,** p. 252 **MiniLAB:** Modeling Isomers, p. 254 **Visualizing Organic Chemistry Nomenclature,** p. 255 **Science Online,** p. 256
Section 2 Other Organic Compounds ● 2 sessions ▣ 1 block 4. **Describe** how new compounds are formed by substituting hydrogens in hydrocarbons. 5. **Identify** the classes of compounds that result from substitution.	National Content Standards: UCP.1–UCP.3, UCP.5, A.1, A.2, B.1, C.1		**Lab:** Conversion of Alcohols, p. 261
Section 3 Biological Compounds ● 4 sessions ▣ 2 blocks 6. **Describe** how large organic molecules are made. 7. **Explain** the roles of organic molecules in the body. 8. **Explain** why eating a balanced diet is important for good health.	National Content Standards: UCP.1–UCP.3, UCP.5, A.1, A.2, B.1, C.1, F.1, G.1, G.3		**MiniLAB:** Summing Up Protein, p. 263 **Integrate Career,** p. 264 **Applying Science:** Which foods are best for quick energy?, p. 266 **Science Online,** p. 267 **Lab:** Looking for Vitamin C, pp. 270–271 **Science and Society:** From Plants to Medicine, p. 272

Glencoe Exclusive!
TeacherWorks™
All-In-One Planner and Resource Center

Lab Materials	Reproducible Resources	Section Assessment	Technology
Launch Lab: clay or foam ball, toothpicks (4), raisins, grapes, gumdrops	**Chapter *FAST FILE* Resources** Foldables Worksheet, p. 19 Directed Reading Overview, p. 21 Note-taking Worksheets, pp. 35–37	**GLENCOE'S ASSESSMENT ADVANTAGE**	**TeacherWorks** includes: • Interactive Teacher Edition • Lesson Planner with calendar • Access to all program blacklines • Correlations to standards • Web links
MiniLAB: toothpicks, balls of colored clay or gumdrops *Need materials?* Contact Science Kit at 1-800-828-7777 or www.sciencekit.com on the Internet.	**Chapter *FAST FILE* Resources** Transparency Activity, p. 46 MiniLAB, p. 3 Enrichment, p. 32 Reinforcement, p. 29 Directed Reading, p. 22 Transparency Activity, pp. 49–50 **Cultural Diversity,** p. 45	**Portfolio** Make a Model, p. 253 **Performance** MiniLAB, p. 254 Applying Math, p. 256 **Content** Section Review, p. 256	Section Focus Transparency Teaching Transparency Virtual Labs CD-ROM Guided Reading Audio Program Interactive Chalkboard CD-ROM
Lab: test tube and stopper, test-tube rack, potassium permanganate solution, sodium hydroxide solution, ethanol, pH test paper, 10-mL graduated cylinders, dropper	**Chapter *FAST FILE* Resources** Transparency Activity, p. 47 Enrichment, p. 33 Reinforcement, p. 30 Directed Reading, p. 23 Lab Worksheet, pp. 5–6 **Lab Management and Safety,** p. 50	**Portfolio** Assessment, p. 260 **Performance** Applying Skills, p. 260 **Content** Section Review, p. 260	Section Focus Transparency Guided Reading Audio Program Interactive Chalkboard CD-ROM
MiniLAB: paper and pencil, calculator **Lab:** starch solution, iodine solution, vitamin–C solution, water, droppers (10), 15-mL test tubes (10), test-tube rack, 250-mL beaker, stirrer, 10-mL graduated cylinder, mortar and pestle, liquid foods (milk, orange juice, vinegar, cola), solid foods (tomatoes, onions, citrus fruits, potatoes, bread, salt, sugar)	**Chapter *FAST FILE* Resources** Transparency Activity, p. 48 MiniLAB, p. 4 Lab Activity, pp. 9–14, 15–18 Enrichment, p. 34 Reinforcement, p. 31 Directed Reading, pp. 23, 24 Lab Worksheet, pp. 7–8 **Mathematics Skill Activities,** p. 49	**Portfolio** Cultural Diversity, p. 264 **Performance** MiniLAB, p. 263 Applying Science, p. 266 Applying Skills, p. 269 **Content** Section Review, p. 269	Section Focus Transparency Guided Reading Audio Program Interactive Chalkboard CD-ROM Video Lab

GLENCOE'S ASSESSMENT ADVANTAGE — End of Chapter Assessment

Blackline Masters	Technology	Professional Series
Chapter *FAST FILE* Resources Chapter Review, pp. 39–40 Chapter Tests, pp. 41–44 **Standardized Test Practice,** pp. 39–42	MindJogger Videoquiz Virtual Labs CD-ROM ExamView® Pro Testmaker TeacherWorks CD-ROM Interactive Chalkboard CD-ROM	**Performance Assessment in the Science Classroom (PASC)**

Transparencies

Section Focus

SECTION 1 Section Focus Transparency **Something in Common**

In nature, fish eat insects and smaller fish, and bears eat the larger fish, as well as certain plants. Because living things eat other living things (or foods that were once living), they all have certain elements in common.

1. Categorize the things in the picture into living and nonliving things.
2. What does a bear need to stay alive? Are these living or nonliving things?
3. What do most plants need to live?

L2

SECTION 2 Section Focus Transparency **Ptoooey!**

Cobras are venomous snakes that live in parts of Africa, Asia, and the East Indies. Cobra venom is a complex mixture of compounds that includes proteins. These compounds are extremely toxic whether delivered internally through a bite or externally as demonstrated by the spitting cobra, below.

1. Venom is a hydrocarbon compound. Does that make it organic or inorganic?
2. Why might a spitting cobra pose a greater danger than a standard cobra?

L2

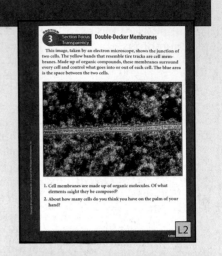

SECTION 3 Section Focus Transparency **Double-Decker Membranes**

This image, taken by an electron microscope, shows the junction of two cells. The yellow bands that resemble tire tracks are cell membranes. Made up of organic compounds, these membranes surround every cell and control what goes into or out of each cell. The blue area is the space between the two cells.

1. Cell membranes are made up of organic molecules. Of what elements might they be composed?
2. About how many cells do you think you have on the palm of your hand?

L2

This is a representation of key blackline masters available in the Teacher Classroom Resources. See Resource Manager boxes within the chapter for additional information.

Key to Teaching Strategies

The following designations will help you decide which activities are appropriate for your students.

L1 Level 1 activities should be appropriate for students with learning difficulties.

L2 Level 2 activities should be within the ability range of all students.

L3 Level 3 activities are designed for above-average students.

ELL ELL activities should be within the ability range of English Language Learners.

COOP LEARN Cooperative Learning activities are designed for small group work.

LS Multiple Learning Styles logos, as described on page 12T, are used throughout to indicate strategies that address different learning styles.

P These strategies represent student products that can be placed into a best-work portfolio.

PBL Problem-Based Learning activities apply real-world situations to learning.

Assessment

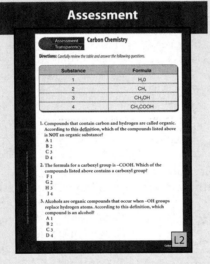

Assessment Transparency **Carbon Chemistry**

Directions: *Carefully review the table and answer the following questions.*

Substance	Formula
1	H_2O
2	CH_4
3	CH_3OH
4	CH_3COOH

1. Compounds that contain carbon and hydrogen are called organic. According to this definition, which of the compounds listed above is **NOT** an organic substance?
   A 1
   B 2
   C 3
   D 4
2. The formula for a carboxyl group is –COOH. Which of the compounds listed above contains a carboxyl group?
   F 1
   G 2
   H 3
   J 4
3. Alcohols are organic compounds that occur when –OH groups replace hydrogen atoms. According to this definition, which compound is an alcohol?
   A 1
   B 2
   C 3
   D 4

L2

Teaching

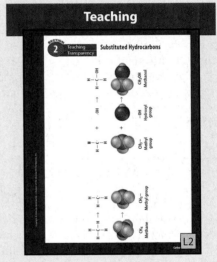

SECTION 2 Teaching Transparency **Substituted Hydrocarbons**

L2

Hands-on Activities

Student Text Lab Worksheet

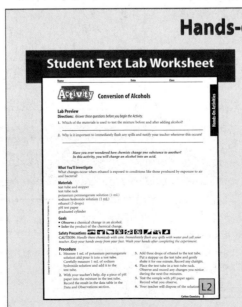

Activity Conversion of Alcohols

Lab Preview
Directions: *Answer these questions before you begin the Activity.*
1. Which of the materials is used to test the mixture before and after adding alcohol?

2. Why is it important to immediately flush any spills and notify your teacher whenever this occurs?

Have you ever wondered how chemists change one substance to another? In this activity, you will change an alcohol into an acid.

What You'll Investigate
What changes occur when ethanol is exposed to conditions like those produced by exposure to air and bacteria?

Materials
test tube and stopper
test tube rack
potassium permanganate solution (1 mL)
sodium hydroxide solution (1 mL)
ethanol (3 drops)
pH test paper
graduated cylinder

Goals
• Observe a chemical change in an alcohol.
• Infer the product of the chemical change.

Safety Precautions
CAUTION: *Handle these chemicals with care. Immediately flush any spills with water and call your teacher. Keep your hands away from your face. Wash your hands after completing the experiment.*

Procedure
1. Measure 1 mL of potassium permanganate solution and pour it into a test tube. Carefully measure 1 mL of sodium hydroxide solution and add it to the test tube.
2. With your teacher's help, dip a piece of pH paper into the mixture in the test tube. Record the result in the data table in the Data and Observations section.
3. Add three drops of ethanol to the test tube. Put a stopper on the test tube and gently shake it for one minute. Record any changes.
4. Place the test tube in a test-tube rack. Observe and record any changes you notice during the next five minutes.
5. Test the sample with pH paper again. Record what you observe.
6. Your teacher will dispose of the solution.

L2

Carbon Chemistry 5

Laboratory Activities

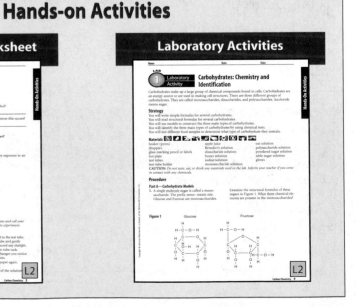

LAB 1 Laboratory Activity **Carbohydrates: Chemistry and Identification**

Carbohydrates make up a large group of chemical compounds found in cells. Carbohydrates are an energy source or are used in making cell structures. There are three different groups of carbohydrates. They are called monosaccharides, disaccharides, and polysaccharides. *Saccharide* means sugar.

Strategy
You will write simple formulas for several carbohydrates.
You will read structural formulas for several carbohydrates.
You will use models to construct the three main types of carbohydrates.
You will identify the three main types of carbohydrates by using chemical tests.
You will test different food samples to determine what type of carbohydrate they contain.

Materials
beaker (pyrex)   apple juice   oat solution
droppers   Benedict's solution   polysaccharide solution
glass marking pencil or labels   disaccharide solution   powdered sugar solution
hot plate   honey solution   table sugar solution
test tubes   iodine solution   gloves
test-tube holder   monosaccharide solution

CAUTION: *Do not taste, eat, or drink any materials used in the lab. Inform your teacher if you come in contact with any chemicals.*

Procedure
Part A—Carbohydrate Models
1. A single molecule sugar is called a monosaccharide. The prefix *mono-* means one. Glucose and fructose are monosaccharides.

Examine the structural formulas of these sugars in Figure 1. What three chemical elements are present in the monosaccharides?

Figure 1   Glucose   Fructose

L2

Carbon Chemistry 9

Meeting Different Ability Levels

Content Outline

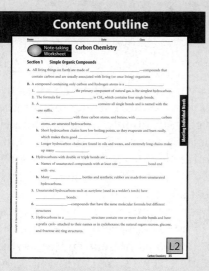

L2

Reinforcement

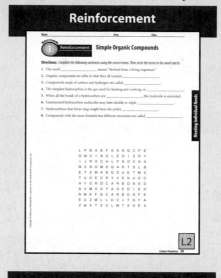

L2

Enrichment

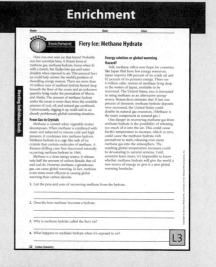

L3

Directed Reading (English/Spanish)

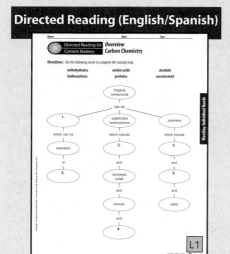

L1

Study Guide

L2

Reading Essentials

L1

Assessment

Test Practice Workbook

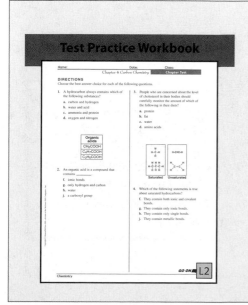

L2

Chapter Review

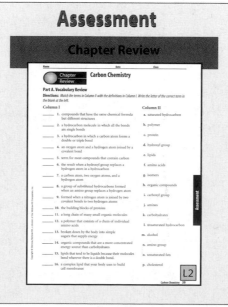

L2

Chapter Tests

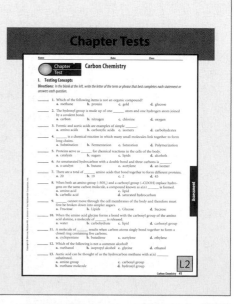

L2

Simple Organic Compounds

Organic Compounds

Organic molecules include a wide variety of substances, such as medicines, vitamins, plastics, and natural and synthetic fibers, as well as carbohydrates, proteins, and fats. In the 20th century, organic chemistry had a significant effect on people's lives. Natural materials have been improved and new materials developed that add convenience to nearly every product manufactured today. The beginning of organic chemistry is often associated with Friedrich Woehler's 1828 discovery of a method of converting ammonium cyanate, an inorganic compound, into the organic compound urea. Prior to this, it was thought that organic compounds could only be formed by life processes.

Hydrocarbons

The terms saturated and unsaturated, as applied to hydrocarbons, came into use by chemists before they knew how the bonding in the two types of hydrocarbons differed. They found from experience that some hydrocarbons took up hydrogen in the presence of a catalyst. When the substance stopped taking up hydrogen, it was said to be saturated. Hydrocarbons that would take up hydrogen were said to be unsaturated. Now chemists know that the unsaturated hydrocarbons contain double or triple bonds. For an unsaturated hydrocarbon to be converted to a saturated hydrocarbon, each double bond must add two atoms of hydrogen and each triple bond must add four atoms of hydrogen.

Saturated hydrocarbons are known as alkanes. They are named by using a prefix to indicate the number of carbon atoms present and the suffix –ane. For example C_5H_{12} is pentane. The general formula for a straight-chain alkane is C_nH_{2n+2}.

Unsaturated hydrocarbons with one or more double bonds are known as alkenes. They are named by using a prefix to indicate the number of carbon atoms present and the suffix –ene. For example C_5H_{10} is pentene. The general formula for a straight-chain alkene with one double bond is C_nH_{2n}. Unsaturated hydrocarbons with one or more triple bonds are known as alkynes.

Any of these types of hydrocarbons can have branches. Branched alkanes are named according to the longest carbon chain. Alkenes and alkynes are named according to the longest carbon chain that contains the double bond.

chapter content resources

Internet Resources
For additional content background, visit
ips.msscience.com to:
- access your book online
- find references to related articles in popular science magazines
- access Web links with related content background
- access current events with science journal topics

Print Resources
Chemistry; The Molecular Nature of Matter and Change, by Martin S. Silberberg, McGraw-Hill, 2003
Kids' Crafts: Polymer Clay: 30 Terrific Projects to Roll, Mold & Squish, by Irene Semanchuk Dean, Sterling Publishing Company, Incorporated, 2003
A Life in Magical Chemistry: Autobiographical Reflections, by George A. Olah, John Wiley & Sons, Incorporated, 2000

section 2 Other Organic Compounds
Substituted Hydrocarbons

Other substituted hydrocarbons exist in addition to those described in the section. Examples are esters, which are found in many natural and artificial flavorings and fragrances; aldehydes such as vanillin, which provides the flavor and fragrance of vanilla; and ketones, such as acetone, which is used in nail polish remover.

section 3 Biological Compounds
What's a Polymer?

Polymers can be biologically or artificially produced. Sometimes, the terms plastic and polymer are used synonymously, but not all polymers are plastics. Plastics are polymers that can be molded into different shapes. Although all polymers are large molecules formed by combining small molecules, or monomers, they are formed in two different ways. In one polymerization process, one bond of a double bond is broken in two monomers, and the monomers bond together at this location. This is called *addition polymerization*. The other type of polymerization process, called *condensation polymerization*, occurs when two or more different monomers form a polymer and eliminate a small compound, such as water.

Carbohydrates

In addition to uses in foods and biological processes, carbohydrates are used in the manufacture of fabrics, photographic film, plastics, and other products.

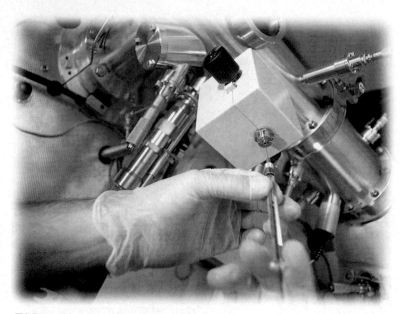

Tek Image/Photo Researchers, Inc.

Cholesterol

Medical experts disagree about the health effects of cholesterol. The ideal blood cholesterol level differs, depending on the source of the information. A desirable cholesterol level often given is less than 200 mg/dL. However, total cholesterol count is not as important as the ratio of the two different types of cholesterol present. LDL stands for low-density lipid. This is the type of cholesterol that clogs arteries. HDL stands for high-density lipid. HDL does not cause the vascular problems that LDL does. HDL actually helps prevent the damage that LDL can do. The most important information about cholesterol is the ratio of HDL to LDL.

In addition to building cell membranes, cholesterol and its derivatives are secreted through the oil glands of the skin to act as a lubricant and protective covering for the hair and skin.

Chapter Vocabulary

Science Journal Answers will vary. Look for depth and quality of information.

INTERACTIVE CHALKBOARD
with Image Bank

PowerPoint® Presentations

This CD-ROM is an editable Microsoft® PowerPoint® presentation that includes:

- a pre-made presentation for every chapter
- interactive graphics
- animations
- audio clips
- image bank
- all new section and chapter questions
- Standardized Test Practice
- transparencies
- pre-lab questions for all labs
- Foldables directions
- links to ips.msscience.com

Carbon Chemistry

chapter preview

sections

1 **Simple Organic Compounds**

2 **Other Organic Compounds**
   Lab **Conversion of Alcohols**

3 **Biological Compounds**
   Lab **Looking for Vitamin C**
   Virtual Lab *How can models of carbon compounds be built?*

Better Camping Through Carbon Chemistry

When you are camping, you spend your nights sleeping under the stars. But one thing remains the same—carbon. Your food, clothing, body, and living things around you contain carbon compounds.

Science Journal Find and name four items around your classroom that are made from carbon compounds.

Theme Connection

Scale and Structure The size and configuration of an organic molecule on the microscopic level determines many of its properties on the macroscopic level.

About the Photo

Carbon Chemistry Compounds made from carbon are all around us. Carbon is a very versatile atom that can combine with many other atoms. Hydrogen and other carbon atoms are the two elements that combine readily with carbon to form hydrocarbons. Hydrocarbons are a specific type of organic compound.

Start-Up Activities

Model Carbon's Bonding

Many of the compounds that compose your body and other living things are carbon compounds. This lab demonstrates some of the atomic combinations possible with one carbon and four other atoms. The ball represents a carbon atom. The toothpicks represent chemical bonds.

WARNING: *Do not eat any foods from this lab. Wash your hands before and after this lab.*

1. Insert four toothpicks into a small clay or plastic foam ball so they are evenly spaced around the sphere.
2. Make models of as many molecules as possible by adding raisins, grapes, and gumdrops to the ends of the toothpicks. Use raisins to represent hydrogen atoms, grapes to represent chlorine atoms, and gumdrops to represent fluorine atoms.
3. **Think Critically** Draw each model and write the formula for it in your Science Journal. What can you infer about the number of compounds a carbon atom can form?

Science Online Preview this chapter's content and activities at ips.msscience.com

---

FOLDABLES
Study Organizer

Hydrocarbons Make the following Foldable to help you learn the definitions of vocabulary words. This will help you understand the chapter content.

STEP 1 **Fold** a sheet of paper in half lengthwise. Make the back edge about 1.25 cm longer than the front edge.

STEP 2 **Fold** in half, then fold in half again to make three folds.

STEP 3 **Unfold and cut** only the top layer along the three folds to make four tabs.

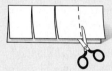

STEP 4 **Label** the tabs as shown.

Hydrocarbon | Saturated Hydrocarbon | Unsaturated Hydrocarbon | Substituted Hydrocarbon

Find Main Ideas As you read the chapter, find the definitions for each vocabulary word and write them under the appropriate tabs. Add additional words and definitions to help you understand your reading. List examples of each type of hydrocarbon under the appropriate tab.

Purpose Students model some carbon compounds. **L2** **ELL** **LS**
Kinesthetic

Preparation If using clay, make the balls of clay ahead of time.

Materials toothpicks (wood or plastic), clay or plastic foam ball, raisins, grapes, gumdrops

Alternate Materials Small balls of clay of three different colors could be used in place of the raisins, grapes, and gumdrops. The clay ball used to represent carbon should be of a fourth color.

Teaching Strategies
• Supply students with small cups in which to organize their materials.
• Have students cover work areas with newspaper for easier cleanup.

Safety Precautions Students should use caution when handling toothpicks and should not eat foods from the lab.

Think Critically

Fifteen different compounds can be constructed: CH_4, CH_3Cl, CH_2Cl_2, $CHCl_3$, CCl_4, CCl_3F, CCl_2F_2, $CClF_3$, CF_4, CHF_3, CH_2F_2, CH_3F, CH_2ClF, $CHCl_2F$, and $CHClF_2$. Students should infer that a single carbon atom could form hundreds of compounds with other elements.

Assessment

Portfolio Have students make posters showing additional models they could make if they used mini-marshmallows to represent bromine atoms. Use **Performance Assessment in the Science Classroom**, p. 145.

FOLDABLES **Dinah Zike**
Study Organizer **Study Fold**

Student preparation materials for this Foldable are available in the Chapter **FAST FILE** Resources.

section 1

Simple Organic Compounds

as you read

What You'll Learn

- **Explain** why carbon is able to form many compounds.
- **Describe** how saturated and unsaturated hydrocarbons differ.
- **Identify** isomers of organic compounds.

Why It's Important

Plants, animals, and many of the things that are part of your life are made of organic compounds.

⊘ Review Vocabulary

chemical bond: force that holds two atoms together

New Vocabulary
- organic compound
- hydrocarbon
- saturated hydrocarbon
- unsaturated hydrocarbon
- isomer

Organic Compounds

Earth's crust contains less than one percent carbon, yet all living things on Earth are made of carbon-containing compounds. Carbon's ability to bond easily and form compounds is the basis of life on Earth. A carbon atom has four electrons in its outer energy level, so it can form four covalent bonds with as many as four other atoms. When carbon atoms form four covalent bonds, they obtain the stability of a noble gas with eight electrons in their outer energy level. One of carbon's most frequent partners in forming covalent bonds is hydrogen.

Substances can be classified into two groups—those derived from living things and those derived from nonliving things, as shown in **Figure 1.** Most of the substances associated with living things contain carbon and hydrogen. These substances were called organic compounds, which means "derived from a living organism." However, in 1828, scientists discovered that living organisms are not necessary to form organic compounds. Despite this, scientists still use the term **organic compound** for most compounds that contain carbon.

✔ Reading Check
What is the origin of the term organic compound?

Figure 1 Most substances can be classified as living or nonliving things.

Living things and products made from living things such as this wicker chair contain carbon.

Most of the things in this photo are nonliving and are composed of elements other than carbon.

250 CHAPTER 9 Carbon Chemistry

Hydrocarbons

Many compounds are made of only carbon and hydrogen. A compound that contains only carbon and hydrogen atoms is called a **hydrocarbon**. The simplest hydrocarbon is methane, the primary component of natural gas. If you have a gas stove or gas furnace in your home, methane usually is the fuel that is burned in these appliances. Methane consists of a single carbon atom covalently bonded to four hydrogen atoms. The formula for methane is CH_4. **Figure 2** shows a model of the methane molecule and its structural formula. In a structural formula, the line between one atom and another atom represents a pair of electrons shared between the two atoms. This pair forms a single bond. Methane contains four single bonds.

Now, visualize the removal of one of the hydrogen atoms from a methane molecule, as in **Figure 3A.** A fragment of the molecule called a methyl group, $-CH_3$, would remain. The methyl group then can form a single bond with another methyl group. If two methyl groups bond with each other, the result is the two-carbon hydrocarbon ethane, C_2H_6, which is shown with its structural formula in **Figure 3B.**

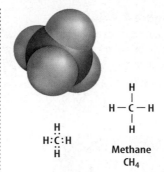

Figure 2 Methane is the simplest hydrocarbon molecule. **Explain** *why this is true.*

Figure 3 Here's a way to visualize how larger hydrocarbons are built up.

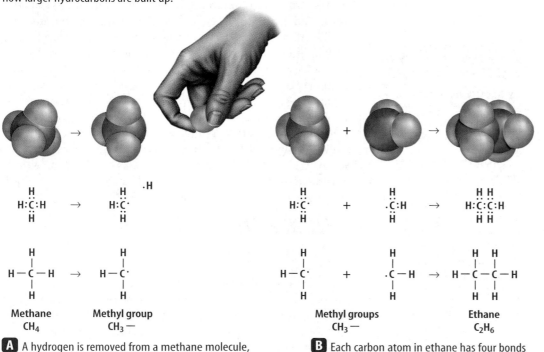

A A hydrogen is removed from a methane molecule, forming a methyl group.

B Each carbon atom in ethane has four bonds after the two methyl groups join.

SECTION 1 Simple Organic Compounds **251**

INTEGRATE Earth Science

Hydrocarbons Petroleum is a nonrenewable resource because it is being used faster than it is being produced. Petroleum is separated into its components by a process called fractional distillation. In fractional distillation, separation is possible because the components have different boiling points.

Research Have students research the process of fractional distillation. Students can make a diagram of this process. Also, have students research which hydrocarbons are found in gasoline. hydrocarbons with chains containing from five carbons to twelve carbons L3 **LS** Visual-Spatial

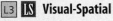
Reading Check

Answer a hydrocarbon in which all the bonds are single bonds; no additional hydrogen atoms can be added to the molecule

Quick Demo

Hydrocarbon Properties

Materials chalk, chalkboard

Estimated Time ten minutes

Procedure Make a table on the chalkboard. Column one is hydrocarbons. Column two is their respective boiling points. methane, −161.5°C; ethane, −88.7°C; propane, ?; butane, −0.6°C; pentane, 36.0°C. Have students predict the boiling point of propane. Students should guess around −44°C. The actual boiling point is −42.2°C. Ask students to draw a correlation between the number of carbon and hydrogen atoms in a compound with its boiling point. The larger the hydrocarbon chain, the higher the boiling point.

Figure 4 Propane and butane are two useful fuels. **Explain** why they are called "saturated."

$$H-\overset{\displaystyle H}{\underset{\displaystyle H}{C}}-\overset{\displaystyle H}{\underset{\displaystyle H}{C}}-\overset{\displaystyle H}{\underset{\displaystyle H}{C}}-H$$

Propane
C_3H_8

When propane burns, it releases energy as the chemical bonds are broken. Propane often is used to fuel camp stoves and outdoor grills.

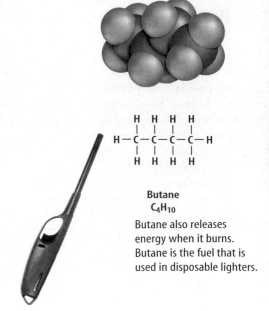

$$H-\overset{\displaystyle H}{\underset{\displaystyle H}{C}}-\overset{\displaystyle H}{\underset{\displaystyle H}{C}}-\overset{\displaystyle H}{\underset{\displaystyle H}{C}}-\overset{\displaystyle H}{\underset{\displaystyle H}{C}}-H$$

Butane
C_4H_{10}

Butane also releases energy when it burns. Butane is the fuel that is used in disposable lighters.

INTEGRATE Earth Science

Hydrocarbons Petroleum is a mixture of hydrocarbons that formed from plants and animals that lived in seas and lakes hundreds of millions of years ago. With the right temperature and pressure, this plant and animal matter, buried deep under Earth's surface, decomposed to form petroleum. Why is petroleum a nonrenewable resource?

Saturated Hydrocarbons Methane and ethane are members of a series of molecules in which carbon and hydrogen atoms are joined by single covalent bonds. When all the bonds in a hydrocarbon are single bonds, the molecule is called a **saturated hydrocarbon.** It is called *saturated* because no additional hydrogen atoms can be added to the molecule. The carbon atoms are saturated with hydrogen atoms. The formation of larger hydrocarbons occurs in a way similar to the formation of ethane. A hydrogen atom is removed from ethane and replaced by a $-CH_3$ group. Propane, with three carbon atoms, is the third member of the series of saturated hydrocarbons. Butane has four carbon atoms. Both of these hydrocarbons are shown in **Figure 4.** The names and the chemical formulas of a few of the smaller saturated hydrocarbons are listed in **Table 1.** Saturated hydrocarbons are named with an *-ane* ending. Another name for these hydrocarbons is alkanes.

Reading Check *What is a saturated hydrocarbon?*

These short hydrocarbon chains have low boiling points, so they evaporate and burn easily. That makes methane a good fuel for your stove or furnace. Propane is used in gas grills, lanterns, and to heat air in hot-air balloons. Butane often is used as a fuel for camp stoves and lighters. Longer hydrocarbons are found in oils and waxes. Carbon can form long chains that contain hundreds or even thousands of carbon atoms. These extremely long chains make up many of the plastics that you use.

Science Journal

Knock, Knock Gasoline is rated on the octane scale by its ability to burn smoothly, or not knock, in an engine. Pure isooctane, which knocks little, is rated 100, and heptane, which has a strong tendency to knock, is rated 0. Have students find out the octane ratings of the different types of gasoline sold at a local gasoline station and record their results in their Science Journals. L2 **LS**
Logical-Mathematical

Unsaturated Hydrocarbons Carbon also forms hydrocarbons with double and triple bonds. In a double bond, two pairs of electrons are shared between two atoms, and in a triple bond, three pairs of electrons are shared. Hydrocarbons with double or triple bonds are called **unsaturated hydrocarbons.** This is because the carbon atoms are not saturated with hydrogen atoms.

Ethene, the simplest unsaturated hydrocarbon, has two carbon atoms joined by a double bond. Propene is an unsaturated hydrocarbon with three carbons. Some unsaturated hydrocarbons have more than one double bond. Butadiene (byew tuh DI een) has four carbon atoms and two double bonds. The structures of ethene, propene, and butadiene are shown in **Figure 5.**

Unsaturated compounds with at least one double bond are named with an -*ene* ending. Notice that the names of the compounds below have an -*ene* ending. These compounds are called alkenes.

✔ Reading Check *What type of bonds are found in unsaturated hydrocarbons?*

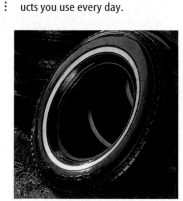

Table 1 The Structures of Hydrocarbons

Name	Structural Formula	Chemical Formula
Methane	H–C–H (with H above and below)	CH_4
Ethane	H–C–C–H (with H's above and below)	C_2H_6
Propane	H–C–C–C–H (with H's above and below)	C_3H_8
Butane	H–C–C–C–C–H (with H's above and below)	C_4H_{10}

Figure 5 You'll find unsaturated hydrocarbons in many of the products you use every day.

Ethene

Ethene helps ripen fruits and vegetables. It's also used to make milk and soft-drink bottles.

Propene

This detergent bottle contains the tough plastic polypropylene, which is made from propene.

Butadiene

Butadiene made it possible to replace natural rubber with synthetic rubber.

SECTION 1 Simple Organic Compounds **253**

Curriculum Connection

Social Studies Brazil was one of the world's leading producers of natural rubber. Natural rubber was harvested from rubber trees in the Amazon Basin. Have students write reports on the role of rubber in the economy of Brazil. In the late 19th century the need for electrical insulation and the invention of pneumatic tires dramatically increased the world's demand for rubber. Brazil went through a rubber boom between about 1880 and 1910. After 1910, competition from Asian rubber decreased the dominance of Brazil's rubber, and the development of relatively cheap synthetic rubber during World War II decreased the market for natural rubber. L3 LS **Linguistic**

Figure 6 In the welder's torch, ethyne, also called acetylene, is combined with oxygen to form a mixture that burns, releasing intense light and heat. The two carbon atoms in ethyne are joined by a triple bond.

$$H-C\equiv C-H$$

Ethyne or Acetylene
C_2H_2

Use Science Words

Word Origins Have students look up the origin of the word *isomer.* The word *isomer* can be broken into *isos,* meaning "same," and *meros,* meaning "parts." Isomers are substances made up of the same parts. L2 **LS** Linguistic

Mini LAB

Purpose Students model isomers of hydrocarbons. L2 **ELL** **LS** **Kinesthetic**

Materials 16 toothpicks, enough modeling clay to make 17 small balls or gumdrops

Teaching Strategies Have students sketch each isomer as they model it so that they don't model the same isomer more than once. Tell students that the chains of carbon atoms can bend, molecules can be flipped, and that the longest chain is the parent chain.

Analysis

1. There are three isomers of pentane and five of hexane.
2. Yes; as the number of carbon atoms increases, the number of isomers also increases.

Assessment

Process Have students compare isomers and make a display showing all of the structures. Use **Performance Assessment in the Science Classroom,** p. 135.

Mini LAB

Modeling Isomers

Procedure 🔲 🥽 🔬

WARNING: *Do not eat any foods in this lab.*

1. Construct a model of pentane, C_5H_{12}. Use **tooth-picks** for covalent bonds and small balls of different **colored clay or gumdrops** for carbon and hydrogen atoms.
2. Using the same materials, build a molecule with a different arrangement of the atoms. Are there any other possibilities?
3. Make a model of hexane, C_6H_{14}.
4. Arrange the atoms of hexane in different ways.

Analysis

1. How many isomers of pentane did you build? How many isomers of hexane?
2. Do you think there are more isomers of heptane, C_7H_{16}, than hexane? Explain.

Try at Home

Figure 7 Butane and isobutane both have four carbons and ten hydrogens but their structures and properties are different.

Triple Bonds Unsaturated hydrocarbons also can have triple bonds, as in the structure of ethyne (EH thine) shown in **Figure 6.** Ethyne, commonly called acetylene (uh SE tuh leen), is a gas used for welding because it produces high heat as it burns. Welding torches mix acetylene and oxygen before burning. These unsaturated compounds are called alkynes.

Hydrocarbon Isomers Suppose you had ten blocks that could be snapped together in different arrangements. Each arrangement of the same ten blocks is different. The atoms in an organic molecule also can have different arrangements but still have the same molecular formula. Compounds that have the same molecular formula but different arrangements, or structures, are called **isomers** (I suh murz). Two isomers, butane and isobutane, are shown in **Figure 7.** They have different chemical and physical properties because of their different structures. As the size of a hydrocarbon molecule increases, the number of possible isomers also increases.

By now, you might be confused about how organic compounds are named. **Figure 8** explains the system that is used to name simple organic compounds.

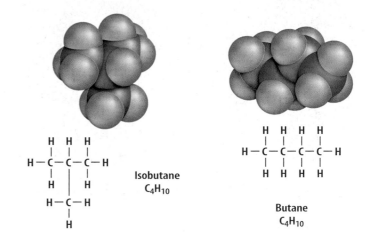

Isobutane
C_4H_{10}

Butane
C_4H_{10}

Differentiated Instruction

Learning Disabled Often, a structure can be drawn in different ways in two dimensions but the drawings represent the same structure. This is because of how the atoms bond in three dimensions. Use models to show students that **(A)** is the same isomer as **(B)** or that **(C)** is the same isomer as **(D)**. L1 **LS** **Visual-Spatial**

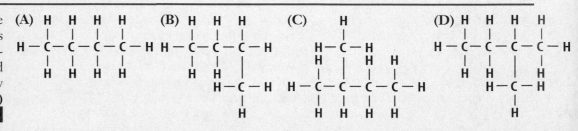

NATIONAL GEOGRAPHIC

Figure 8

More than one million organic compounds have been discovered and created, and thousands of new ones are synthesized in laboratories every year. To keep track of all these carbon-containing molecules, the International Union of Pure and Applied Chemistry, or IUPAC, devised a special naming system (a nomenclature) for organic compounds. As shown here, different parts of an organic compound's name—its root, suffix, or prefix—give information about its size and structure.

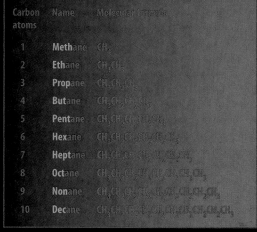

Carbon atoms	Name	Molecular formula
1	Methane	CH_4
2	Ethane	CH_3CH_3
3	Propane	$CH_3CH_2CH_3$
4	Butane	$CH_3CH_2CH_2CH_3$
5	Pentane	$CH_3CH_2CH_2CH_2CH_3$
6	Hexane	$CH_3CH_2CH_2CH_2CH_2CH_3$
7	Heptane	$CH_3CH_2CH_2CH_2CH_2CH_2CH_3$
8	Octane	$CH_3CH_2CH_2CH_2CH_2CH_2CH_2CH_3$
9	Nonane	$CH_3CH_2CH_2CH_2CH_2CH_2CH_2CH_2CH_3$
10	Decane	$CH_3CH_2CH_2CH_2CH_2CH_2CH_2CH_2CH_2CH_3$

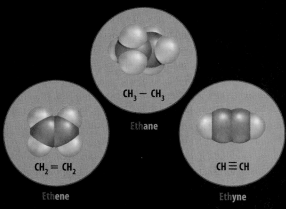

$CH_3 - CH_3$
Ethane

$CH_2 = CH_2$
Ethene

$CH \equiv CH$
Ethyne

ROOT WORDS The key to every name given to a compound in organic chemistry is its root word. This word tells how many carbon atoms are found in the longest continuous carbon chain in the compound. Except for compounds with one to four carbon atoms, the root word is based on Greek numbers.

SUFFIXES The suffix of the name for an organic compound indicates the kind of covalent bonds joining the compound's carbon atoms. If the atoms are joined by single covalent bonds, the compound's name will end in *-ane*. If there is a double covalent bond in the carbon chain, the compound's name ends in *-ene*. Similarly, if there is a triple bond in the chain, the compound's name will end in *-yne*.

PREFIXES The prefix of the name for an organic compound describes how the carbon atoms in the compound are arranged. Organic molecules that have names with the prefix *cyclo-* contain a ring of carbon atoms. For example, cyclopentane contains five carbon atoms all joined by single bonds in a ring.

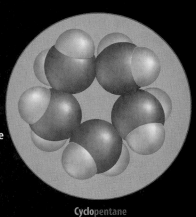

Cyclopentane

SECTION 1 Simple Organic Compounds **255**

Visualizing Organic Chemistry Nomenclature

Have students examine the illustrations and read the captions. Then ask the following questions.

Who devised this system of nomenclature? the International Union of Pure and Applied Chemistry (IUPAC)

Why is it important to have a system for naming organic compounds? Possible answers include: so that scientists all over the world can communicate effectively about new and old compounds; this particular system gives scientists information about the composition of compounds.

When you see the chemical name cyclopentane, what do you know about the molecular structure? The molecule has a ring structure with five carbon atoms and only single bonds within its structure.

Activity

Drawing Structure Have students draw and name four structural diagrams of straight-chain hydrocarbons that contain one to ten carbon atoms bonded with single bonds. Have students draw and name structural diagrams of hydrocarbons with three carbons and one double or triple bond. Propene, Propyne Have students draw and name a structural diagram of a seven-carbon hydrocarbon with a ring structure. Cycloheptane L2 LS **Visual-Spatial**

Caption Answer

Figure 9 The chemical formula for cyclohexane has 2 fewer hydrogen atoms than hexane.

✔ **Reading Check**

Answer that the molecule is ring shaped

3 Assess

✔ **Assessment**

Process Have students predict the formulas for the saturated hydrocarbons that contain five and seven carbon atoms. C_5H_{12} and C_7H_{16} Use **Performance Assessment in the Science Classroom,** p. 89.

Figure 9 Visualize a hydrogen atom removed from a carbon atom on both ends of a hexane chain. The two end carbons form a bond with each other. **Describe** *how the chemical formula changes.*

Hexane
C_6H_{14}

Cyclohexane
C_6H_{12}

Hydrocarbons in Rings You might be thinking that all hydrocarbons are chains of carbon atoms with two ends. Some molecules contain rings. You can see the structures of two different molecules in **Figure 9.** The carbon atoms of hexane bond together to form a closed ring containing six carbons. Each carbon atom still has four bonds. The prefix *cyclo-* in their names tells you that the molecules are cyclic, or ring shaped.

Ring structures are not uncommon in chemical compounds. Many natural substances such as sucrose, glucose, and fructose are ring structures. Ring structures can contain one or more double bonds.

✔ **Reading Check** *What does the prefix* cyclo- *tell you about a molecule?*

section 1 review

Summary

Organic Compounds
- All living things contain carbon.
- Carbon atoms form covalent bonds.

Hydrocarbons
- Hydrocarbons are compounds that contain only hydrogen and carbon.
- The simplest hydrocarbon is methane.
- Saturated hydrocarbons are compounds that contain only single covalent bonds.
- Unsaturated hydrocarbons are compounds that form double and triple bonds.

Isomers
- Isomers are compounds that have the same molecular formula but different structures.
- Isomers also have different chemical and physical properties.

Self Check

1. **Describe** a carbon atom.
2. **Identify** Give one example of each of the following: a compound with a single bond, a compound with a double bond, and a compound with a triple bond. Write the chemical formula and draw the structure for each.
3. **Draw** all the possible isomers for heptane, C_7H_{16}.
4. **Think Critically** Are propane and cylcopropane isomers? Draw their structures. Use the structures and formulas to explain your answer.

Applying Math

5. **Make and Use Graphs** From **Table 1,** plot the number of carbon atoms on the *x*-axis and the number of hydrogen atoms on the *y*-axis. Predict the formula for the saturated hydrocarbon that has 11 carbon atoms.

256 CHAPTER 9 Carbon Chemistry

 Science Online ips.msscience.com/self_check_quiz

section 1 review

1. A carbon atom has four electrons in its outer energy level making it able to form four covalent bonds.
2. Answers will vary. Check students' work.
3. Check students' drawings for the nine isomers of heptane.
4. No, propane is a straight chain hydrocarbon and cyclopropane is ring shaped. Also, their formulas are different—C_3H_8 and C_3H_6.
5. Students' graphs will result in a straight line. $C_{11}H_{24}$

2 Other Organic Compounds

Substituted Hydrocarbons

Suppose you pack an apple in your lunch every day. One day, you have no apples, so you substitute a pear. When you eat your lunch, you'll notice a difference in the taste and texture of your fruit. Chemists make substitutions, too. They change hydrocarbons to make compounds called substituted hydrocarbons. To make a substituted hydrocarbon, one or more hydrogen atoms are replaced by atoms such as halogens or by groups of atoms. Such changes result in compounds with chemical properties different from the original hydrocarbon. When one or more chlorine atoms are added to methane in place of hydrogens, new compounds are formed. **Figure 10** shows the four possible compounds formed by substituting chlorine atoms for hydrogen atoms in methane.

Chloromethane contains a single chlorine atom.

$$H - C - Cl$$

CH_3Cl

Dichloromethane contains two chlorine atoms. This is used in some paint and varnish removers.

$$H - C - Cl$$

CH_2Cl_2

Trichloromethane, or chloroform, has three chlorine atoms. It is used in the production of fluoropolymers—one of the raw materials used to make nonstick coating.

$$H - C - Cl$$

$CHCl_3$

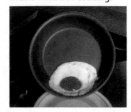

Carbon tetrachloride is a fully substituted methane molecule with four chlorines.

$$Cl - C - Cl$$

CCl_4

Figure 10 Chlorine can replace hydrogen atoms in methane.

What You'll Learn
- **Describe** how new compounds are formed by substituting hydrogens in hydrocarbons.
- **Identify** the classes of compounds that result from substitution.

Why It's Important

Many natural and manufactured organic compounds are formed by replacing hydrogen with other atoms.

Review Vocabulary
chemical formula: chemical shorthand that uses symbols to tell what elements are in a compound and their ratios

New Vocabulary
- hydroxyl group
- amino group
- carboxyl group
- amino acid

Section 2 Resource Manager

Chapter FAST FILE Resources
Transparency Activity, p. 47
Directed Reading for Content Mastery, p. 23
Enrichment, p. 33
Lab Worksheet, pp. 5–6

Reinforcement, p. 30
Earth Science Critical Thinking/Problem Solving, p. 17

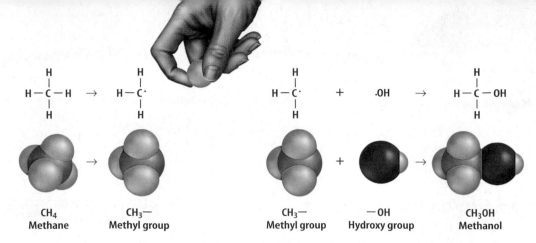

Visual Learning

Figure 10 Point out the different uses for dichloromethane and trichloromethane. Have students find out how the physical properties of chlorinated methane change as each successive hydrogen atom is replaced with a chlorine atom. As each chlorine atom is added, the boiling point and the density of the compounds increase. L3 **LS** Linguistic

Caption Answer

Figure 11 covalent

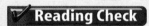

Answer a hydroxyl group

Misconceptions

Various Alcohols Students may think that alcohol refers only to the liquid in alcoholic beverages, or that all alcohols can be ingested. Remind students that an alcohol is any hydrocarbon in which an −OH group replaces a hydrogen atom. There are many alcohols, but the only one in alcoholic beverages is ethanol.

Figure 11 After the methane molecule loses one of its hydrogen atoms, it has an extra electron to share, as does the hydroxyl group. **Identify** the type of bond formed.

Alcohols Groups of atoms also can be added to hydrocarbons to make different compounds. The **hydroxyl (hi DROK sul) group** is made up of an oxygen atom and a hydrogen atom joined by a covalent bond. A hydroxyl group is represented by the formula −OH. An alcohol is formed when a hydroxyl group replaces a hydrogen atom in a hydrocarbon. **Figure 11** shows the formation of the alcohol methanol. A hydrogen atom in the methane molecule is replaced by a hydroxyl group.

✓ Reading Check *What does the formula* −OH *represent?*

Larger alcohol molecules are formed by adding more carbon atoms to the chain. Ethanol is an alcohol produced naturally when sugar in corn, grains, and fruit ferments. It is a combination of ethane, which contains two carbon atoms, and an −OH group. Its formula is C_2H_5OH. Isopropyl alcohol forms when the hydroxyl group is substituted for a hydrogen atom on the middle carbon of propane rather than one of the end carbons. **Table 2** lists three alcohols with their structures and uses. You've probably used isopropyl alcohol to disinfect injuries. Did you know that ethanol can be added to gasoline and used as a fuel for your car?

Table 2 Common Alcohols			
	H H−C−OH H	H H H−C−C−OH H H	H H H H−C−C−C−H H OH H
Uses	**Methanol**	**Ethanol**	**Isopropyl Alcohol**
Fuel	yes	yes	no
Cleaner	yes	yes	yes
Disinfectant	no	yes	yes
Manufacturing chemicals	yes	yes	yes

258 CHAPTER 9 Carbon Chemistry

 LAB DEMONSTRATION

Purpose to show how alcohol and water differ as solvents

Materials 2 small jars with lids, 40 whole cloves, water, rubbing alcohol, 2 droppers

Procedure Place 20 cloves in a half-filled jar of water. Place remaining cloves in a half-filled jar of alcohol. Label the jars and let sit undisturbed for one week. Have students put a few drops of the alcohol solution on one wrist and a few drops of the water solution on the other wrist. After the solutions evaporate, have them smell each wrist.

Expected Outcome The smell from the alcohol solution will be stronger.

Assessment

Which solution produced the stronger scent? the alcohol solution In which liquid did more of the cloves dissolve, alcohol or water? Why? Alcohol; cloves contain oils that are nonpolar, so they dissolve better in less polar alcohol than they do in highly polar water.

Carboxylic Acids Have you ever tasted vinegar? Vinegar is a solution of acetic acid and water. You can think of acetic acid as the hydrocarbon methane with a carboxyl (car BOK sul) group substituted for a hydrogen. A carboxyl group consists of a carbon atom that has a double bond with one oxygen atom and a single bond with a hydroxyl group. Its formula is −COOH. When a carboxyl group is substituted in a hydrocarbon, the substance formed is called a carboxylic acid. The simplest carboxylic acid is formic acid. Formic acid consists of a single hydrogen atom and a carboxyl group. You can see the structures of formic acid and acetic acid in **Figure 12.**

You probably can guess that many other carboxylic acids are formed from longer hydrocarbons. Many carboxylic acids occur in foods. Citric acid is found in citrus fruits such as oranges and grapefruit. Lactic acid is present in sour milk. Acetic acid dissolved in water—vinegar—often is used in salad dressings.

Amines Substituted hydrocarbons, called amines, formed when an amino (uh ME noh) group replaces a hydrogen atom. An amino group is a nitrogen atom joined by covalent bonds to two hydrogen atoms. It has the formula −NH₂. Methylamine, shown in **Figure 13,** is formed when one of the hydrogens in methane is replaced with an amino group. A more complex amine is the novocaine dentists once used to numb your mouth during dental work. Amino groups are important because they are a part of many biological compounds that are essential for life. When an amino group bonds with one additional hydrogen atom, the result is ammonia, NH_3.

Amino Acids You have seen that a carbon group can be substituted onto one end of a chain to make a new molecule. It's also possible to substitute groups on both ends of a chain and even to replace hydrogen atoms bonded to carbon atoms in the middle of a chain. When both an amino group (−NH₂) and a carboxyl acid group (−COOH) replace hydrogens on the same carbon atom in a molecule, a type of compound known as an amino acid is formed. Amino acids are essential for human life.

Methanoic, or formic, acid
HCOOH

Ethanoic, or acetic, acid
CH₃COOH

Figure 12 *Crematogaster* ants make the simplest carboxylic acid, formic acid. Notice the structure of the −COOH group.
Describe *how the structures of formic acid and acetic acid differ.*

Figure 13 Complex amines account for the strong smells of cheeses such as these.

Methylamine
CH₃NH₂

259

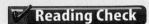
3 Assess

DAILY INTERVENTION

Check for Understanding

Kinesthetic Have the students use toothpicks and colored gum drops to make models of substituted hydrocarbons. Have students assign different colors to different elements. Make sure that they use the colors consistently. Begin with a methane molecule and substitute −OH groups, −COOH groups, and −NH₂ groups. L2 **LS**

Reteach

Memory Game Organize the class into groups and have each group prepare one set of index cards with names of types of substituted hydrocarbons and another set of cards with examples of formulas from the different groups. Have them play a game by laying all the cards face down. Each player turns over two cards and tries to match the name and formula for each group. If the two cards don't match, the cards get turned back over, and it's the next person's turn. If the cards do match, the person who turned them over keeps the cards. When all the cards are gone, the player with the most cards wins. L1 **COOP LEARN** **LS**
Interpersonal

Assessment

Content Ask students to draw diagrams illustrating the substitutions that make a hydrocarbon an amino acid. One hydrogen is replaced with a −COOH group and another hydrogen on the same carbon is replaced by an −NH₂ group. Use **Performance Assessment in the Science Classroom**, p. 127.
P

Key
Amine group
Carboxyl group

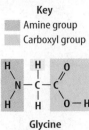

Glycine

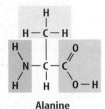

Alanine

Figure 14 The 20 amino acids needed for protein synthesis each contain a central carbon atom bonded to an amine group, a hydrogen atom, and a carboxyl group. The fourth bond, shown in yellow, is different for each amino acid.

The Building Blocks of Protein

Amino acids are the building blocks of proteins, which are an important class of biological molecules needed by living cells. Twenty different amino acids bond in different combinations to form the variety of proteins that are needed in the human body. Glycine and alanine are shown in **Figure 14.**

Glycine is the simplest amino acid. It is a methane molecule in which one hydrogen atom has been replaced by an amine group and another has been replaced by a carboxyl group. The other 19 amino acids are formed by replacing the yellow highlighted hydrogen atom with different groups. For example, in alanine, one hydrogen atom is replaced by a methyl (−CH₃) group.

Reading Check *What are the building blocks of protein?*

Some amino acids, such as glycine and alanine, are manufactured within the human body. They are called nonessential amino acids. This means that it is not essential to consume these types of amino acids. More than half of the twenty amino acids are considered nonessential. The essential amino acids, those that must be consumed, are obtained by eating protein-rich foods. These foods include meat, eggs, and milk.

---

section 2 review

Summary

Substituted Hydrocarbons

- A substituted hydrocarbon has one or more hydrogen atoms replaced.
- The chemical properties of the substituted hydrocarbon are different from the original hydrocarbon.

Types of Substitutions

- Alcohols are made when a hydroxyl group is substituted for a hydrogen atom.
- Carboxylic acids are formed when the carboxyl group is substituted for a hydrogen atom.
- When an amino group is substituted for hydrogen, an amine is formed.
- Amino acids have both an amino group and a carboxyl group.
- Twenty amino acids are building blocks of proteins needed in the human body.

Self Check

1. **Draw** Tetrafluoroethylene is a substituted hydrocarbon in which all four of the hydrogen atoms are replaced by fluorine. Draw the structural formula for this molecule.
2. **Describe** how the 20 amino acids differ from each other.
3. **Identify** Starting with a hexane molecule, C_6H_{14}, draw and label each new molecule when adding an alcohol group, a carboxylic group, and an amino group.
4. **Think Critically** The formula for one compound that produces the odor in skunk spray is $CH_3CH_2CH_2CH_2SH$. Draw and examine the structural formula. Does it fit the definition of a substituted hydrocarbon? Explain.

Applying Skills

5. **Define** Compounds in which hydrogen atoms have been replaced by chlorine and fluorine atoms are known as chlorofluorocarbons (CFCs). Draw the structures of the four CFCs using CH_4 as the starting point.

Science online ips.msscience.com/self_check_quiz

---

section 2 review

1. $F_2 - C = C - F_2$
2. They have different groups attached to the carbon atom that has the acid and amino groups bonded to it.
3. Check students' drawings for appropriate number of atoms. $C_6H_{13}OH$ for alcohol group; $C_5H_{11}COOH$ for carboxylic group; $C_6H_{13}NH_2$ for amino group.
4. Yes; one of the hydrogens in butane has been replaced with an −SH group.
5. CH_2ClF, $CHClF_2$, $CHCl_2F$, CCl_2F_2

Conversion of Alcohols

Have you ever wondered how chemists change one substance into another? In this lab, you will change an alcohol into an acid.

Real-World Question

What changes occur when ethanol is exposed to conditions like those produced by exposure to air and bacteria?

Goals

■ **Observe** a chemical change in an alcohol.
■ **Infer** the product of the chemical change.

Materials

test tube and stopper
test-tube rack
pH test paper
10-mL graduated cylinders (2)
dropper
0.01M potassium permanganate solution (1 mL)
6.0M sodium hydroxide solution (1 mL)
ethanol (3 drops)

Safety Precautions

WARNING: *Handle these chemicals with care. Immediately flush any spills with water and call your teacher. Keep your hands away from your face.*

Procedure

1. Measure 1 mL of potassium permanganate solution and pour it into a test tube. Carefully measure 1 mL of sodium hydroxide solution and add it to the test tube.

2. With your teacher's help, dip a piece of pH paper into the mixture in the test tube. Record the result in your Science Journal.

Alcohol Conversion

Procedure Step	Observations
Step 2	The solution is purple and basic.
Step 3	The color changes from purple to green.
Step 4	The color changes from green to brown.
Step 5	The solution is acidic.

3. Add three drops of ethanol to the test tube. Put a stopper on the test tube and gently shake it for one minute. Record any changes.

4. Place the test tube in a test-tube rack. Observe and record any changes you notice during the next five minutes.

5. Test the sample with pH paper again. Record what you observe.

6. Your teacher will dispose of the solutions.

Conclude and Apply

1. **Analyze Results** Did a chemical reaction take place? What leads you to infer this?

2. **Predict** Alcohols can undergo a chemical reaction to form carboxylic acids in the presence of potassium permanganate. If the alcohol used is ethanol, what would you predict to be the chemical formula of the acid produced?

*C*ommunicating
Your Data

Compare your conclusions with other students in your class. **For more help, refer to the Science Skill Handbook.**

☑ Assessment

Oral If the formulas of both an acid and an alcohol are written as C_3H_8O and $C_3H_6O_2$, which formula is for the organic acid and which is for the alcohol? $C_3H_6O_2$ is the organic acid and C_3H_8O is the alcohol. Organic acids must have at least two oxygen atoms.

*C*ommunicating
Your Data

Students should discuss why their conclusions did or did not agree and determine the causes of any differences.

Real-World Question

Purpose Students observe a chemical change in an alcohol.
L2 **ELL** **IS** Visual-Spatial

Process Skills observe, infer, measure, recognize cause and effect, classify

Time Required 30 minutes

Procedure

Safety Precautions Dilute $KMnO_4$ and NaOH solutions with water before pouring them down the drain.

Teaching Strategies

• Prepare 0.01M $KMnO_4$ solution by dissolving 0.16 g $KMnO_4$ in 100 mL of distilled water.

• Prepare 6.0M NaOH solution by dissolving 24 g of solid NaOH in 100 mL of distilled water. Prepare it in a heat-resistant glass container well ahead of use so that it has time to cool.

• Dispense NaOH in dropper bottles. Tell students that 20 drops equals 1 mL.

• Use at least 90% ethanol, which can be purchased in most pharmacies. If 70% ethanol is used, increase the amount.

Conclude and Apply

1. Yes; the color changed from purple to green to brown, indicating a chemical reaction; pH also changed.

2. CH_3COOH

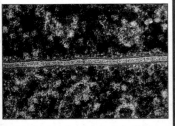
section 3
Biological Compounds

What's a polymer?

Now that you know about some simple organic molecules, you can begin to learn about more complex molecules. One type of complex molecule is called a polymer (PAH luh mur). A **polymer** is a molecule made up of many small organic molecules linked together with covalent bonds to form a long chain. The small, organic molecules that link together to form polymers are called **monomers.** Polymers can be produced by living organisms or can be made in a laboratory. Polymers produced by living organisms are called natural polymers. Polymers made in a laboratory are called synthetic polymers.

✔ **Reading Check** *What is a polymer, and how does it resemble a chain?*

To picture what polymers are, it is helpful to start with small synthetic polymers. You use such polymers every day. Plastics, synthetic fabrics, and nonstick surfaces on cookware are polymers. The unsaturated hydrocarbon ethylene, C_2H_4, is the monomer of a common polymer used often in plastic bags. The monomers are bonded together in a chemical reaction called **polymerization** (puh lih muh ruh ZAY shun). As you can see in **Figure 15,** the double bond breaks in each ethylene molecule. The two carbon atoms then form new bonds with carbon atoms in other ethylene molecules. This process is repeated many times and results in a much larger molecule called polyethylene. A polyethylene molecule can contain 10,000 ethylene units.

Figure 15 Small molecules called monomers link into long chains to form polymers.

The carbon atoms that were joined by the double bond each have an electron to share with another carbon in another molecule of ethylene. The process goes on until a long molecule is formed.

Section 3 Resource Manager

Chapter *FAST FILE* Resources

Transparency Activity, p. 48

Directed Reading for Content Mastery, pp. 23, 24

MiniLAB, p. 4

Enrichment, p. 34

Lab Activity, pp. 9–14, 15–18

Reinforcement, p. 31

Lab Worksheet, pp. 7–8

Life Science Critical Thinking/Problem Solving, p. 15

Physical Science Critical Thinking/Problem Solving, p. 15

Glycine + **Alanine** → + H_2O

Proteins are Polymers

You've probably heard about proteins when you've been urged to eat healthful foods. A **protein** is a polymer that consists of a chain of individual amino acids linked together. Your body cannot function properly without them. Proteins in the form of enzymes serve as catalysts and speed up chemical reactions in cells. Some proteins make up the structural materials in ligaments, tendons, muscles, cartilage, hair, and fingernails. Hemoglobin, which carries oxygen through the blood, is a protein polymer, and all body cells contain proteins.

The various functions in your body are performed by different proteins. Your body makes many of these proteins by assembling 20 amino acids in different ways. Nine of the amino acids that are needed to make proteins cannot be produced by your body. These amino acids, which are called essential amino acids, must come from the food you eat. That's why you need to eat a diet containing protein-rich foods, like those in **Table 3.**

The process by which your body converts amino acids to proteins is shown in **Figure 16.** In this reaction, the amino group of the amino acid alanine forms a bond with the carboxyl group of the amino acid glycine, and a molecule of water is released. Each end of this new molecule can form similar bonds with another amino acid. The process continues in this way until the amino acid chain, or protein, is complete.

✓ Reading Check *How is an amino acid converted to protein?*

Table 3 Protein Content (Approximate)	
Foods	**Protein Content (g)**
Chicken breast (113 g)	28
Eggs (2)	12
Whole milk (240 mL)	8
Peanut butter (30 g)	8
Kidney beans (127 g)	8

Figure 16 Both ends of an amino acid can link with other amino acids.
Identify *the molecule that is released in the process.*

Mini LAB

Summing Up Protein

Procedure
1. Make a list of the foods you ate during the last 24 h.
2. Use the data your teacher gives you to find the total number of grams of protein in your diet for the day. Multiply the grams of protein in one serving of food by the number of units of food you ate. The recommended daily allowance (RDA) of protein for girls 11 to 14 years old is 46 g per day. For boys 11 to 14 years old, the RDA is 45 g per day.

Analysis
1. Was your total greater or less than the RDA?
2. Which of the foods you ate supplied the largest amount of protein? What percent of the total grams of protein did that food supply?

SECTION 3 Biological Compounds **263**

Differentiated Instruction

Learning Disabled To help students see the difference between a polymer and a monomer, have students clip one spring-type clothespin onto the leg of another one. Continue this process to form a polymer chain. If clothespins are not available, paper clips can be used. L1 IS **Kinesthetic**

2 Teach

Caption Answer
Figure 16 water

✓ Reading Check

Answer The amino group of one amino acid forms a bond with the carboxyl group of another amino acid. Each end of this new molecule forms similar bonds with another amino acid until the amino acid chain, or protein, is complete.

Mini LAB

Purpose Students determine whether their diets for one day provided them with the RDA of protein. L3 ELL IS Logical-Mathematical

Teaching Strategy Provide students with this data:

Food	Protein
1 oz. meat, poultry, fish, or cheese	7 g
1 egg	6 g
1 c. milk or yogurt	8 g
2/3 c. peas or beans	6 g
2 T. peanut butter	9 g
1 c. rice or pasta	6 g
1 potato, baked with skin	5 g
1 c. cooked vegetables	4 g
1 slice bread	3 g

Analysis
1. Answers will vary with foods eaten.
2. Answers will vary.

Assessment

Content Have groups of students make up poems or songs about the power of protein to keep them healthy. Use **Performance Assessment in the Science Classroom,** p. 151.

Quick Demo

Carbohydrates

Materials 250-mL beaker, fume hood, 50 mL sugar, 25 mL concentrated sulfuric acid

Estimated Time 20 minutes

Procedure Show that carbohydrates are basically atoms of carbon and the atoms that make up water molecules bonded together. Place a 250-mL beaker in an operating fume hood. Add approximately 50 mL of sucrose (table sugar) to the beaker. Slowly add about 25 mL of concentrated sulfuric acid. Sulfuric acid is a dehydrating agent, a material that will remove water from another substance. The acid removes the water from the sugar, and carbon remains. Students will observe clouds of steam escaping and a column of black carbon forming in the beaker. After the reaction allow students to have a close look at the carbon but not to touch it. **WARNING:** *Demonstrate this reaction in a fume hood. Wear goggles, apron, and protective gloves. Be sure students are at least 3 m from the demonstration.*

Nutrition Science If your school or school district has a dietician, have that person visit the classroom. Ask the dietician to explain how their job impacts school lunches.

Figure 17 These foods contain a high concentration of carbohydrates.

Nutrition Science A dietician studies the science of nutrition. Their main focus is to help people maintain good health and prevent and control disease through the foods they eat. Dieticians assess the individual's nutritional needs and build a dietary program specifically to meet these needs. Dieticians work in a variety of fields from schools and company cafeterias to hospitals and nursing homes.

Carbohydrates

The day before a race, athletes often eat large amounts of foods containing carbohydrates like the ones in **Figure 17.** What's in pasta and other foods like bread and fruit that gives the body a lot of energy? These foods contain sugars and starches, which are members of the family of organic compounds called carbohydrates. A **carbohydrate** is an organic compound that contains only carbon, hydrogen, and oxygen, usually in a ratio of two hydrogen atoms to one oxygen atom. In the body, carbohydrates are broken down into simple sugars that the body can use for energy. The different types of carbohydrates are divided into groups—sugars, starches, and cellulose.

Table 4 below gives some approximate carbohydrate content for some of the common foods.

Table 4 Carbohydrates in Foods (Approximate)	
Foods	Carbohydrate Content (g)
Apple (1)	21
White rice ($\frac{1}{2}$ cup)	17
Baked potato ($\frac{1}{2}$ cup)	15
Wheat bread (1 slice)	13
Milk (240 mL)	12

Cultural Diversity

Bread Bread in some form is a major source of carbohydrates in the diets of most people in the world. Have students find out about different types of bread made by people of different cultures, and make drawings illustrating their findings. Suggest students identify the grains from which the bread is made and include illustations of the bread and a description of how it is made.

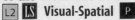 **Visual-Spatial**

Figure 18 Glucose and fructose are simple six-carbon carbohydrates found in many fresh and packaged foods. Glucose and fructose are isomers.
Explain why they are isomers.

Glucose

Fructose

Caption Answer
Figure 18 They both have the formula $C_6H_{12}O_6$.

Visual Learning

Figure 18 Point out the structural formulas of fructose and glucose. Ask a volunteer to describe the difference between the two compounds. Glucose forms a 6-membered ring and fructose forms a 5-membered ring. L2 [IS] **Visual-Spatial**

Fun Fact

The chief form in which carbohydrates are stored in plants is starch. In animals, it is glycogen.

Use Science Words

Word Origin Point out to students that the chemical formula for many carbohydrates is a multiple of the formula CH_2O, or carbon plus water. This formula is the basis of the word *carbohydrate*. L2 [IS] **Linguistic**

Sugars If you like chocolate-chip cookies or ice cream, then you're familiar with sugars. They are the substances that make fresh fruits and candy sweet. Simple **sugars** are carbohydrates containing five, six, or seven carbon atoms arranged in a ring. The structures of glucose and fructose, two common simple sugars, are shown in **Figure 18.** Glucose forms a six-carbon ring. It is found in many naturally sweet foods, such as grapes and bananas. Fructose is the sweet substance found in ripe fruit and honey. It often is found in corn syrup and added to many foods as a sweetener. The sugar you probably have in your sugar bowl or use in baking a cake is sucrose. Sucrose, shown in **Figure 19,** is a combination of the two simple sugars glucose and fructose. In the body, sucrose cannot move through cell membranes. It must be broken down into glucose and fructose to enter cells. Inside the cells, these simple sugars are broken down further, releasing energy for cell functions.

Starches Starches are large carbohydrates that exist naturally in grains such as rice, wheat, corn, potatoes, lima beans, and peas. **Starches** are polymers of glucose monomers in which hundreds or even thousands of glucose molecules are joined together. Because each sugar molecule releases energy when it is broken down, starches are sources of large amounts of energy.

Sucrose

Figure 19 Sucrose is a molecule of glucose combined with a molecule of fructose.
Identify What small molecule must be added to sucrose when it separates to form the two six-carbon sugars?

Caption Answer
Figure 19 water

Differentiated Instruction

Challenge Have students examine food labels and compile a list of the sugars they find. Sugars can be recognized by the *-ose* suffix. Did any labels state "no added sugar," yet contain sugars? How could such labeling be dangerous for someone with a sugar control problem, such as diabetes? Yes; many foods naturally contain sugars. People with diabetes should take these sugars into consideration. L3 [IS] **Linguistic**

Teacher FYI

Natural Polymers Chitin is an abundant natural polymer due to the large number of insects that produce it. Chitin is a structural carbohydrate that makes up the tough outer skeletons of arthropods such as lobsters, beetles, and other insects. The basic unit of chitin is similar to glucose but has a side chain containing an amide group.

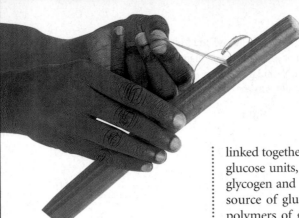

Figure 20 Your body cannot chemically break down the long cellulose fibers in celery, but it needs fiber to function properly.

Other Glucose Polymers Two other important polymers that are made up of glucose molecules are cellulose and glycogen. Cellulose makes up the long, stiff fibers found in the walls of plant cells, like the strands that pull off the celery stalk in **Figure 20.** It is a polymer that consists of long chains of glucose units linked together. Glycogen is a polymer that also contains chains of glucose units, but the chains are highly branched. Animals make glycogen and store it mainly in their muscles and liver as a ready source of glucose. Although starch, cellulose, and glycogen are polymers of glucose, humans can't use cellulose as a source of energy. The human digestive system can't convert cellulose into sugars. Grazing animals, such as cows, have special digestive systems that allow them to break down cellulose into sugars.

Reading Check
How do the location and structure of glycogen and cellulose differ?

Applying Science

Which foods are best for quick energy?

Foods high in carbohydrates are sources of energy.

Identifying the Problem

The chart shows some foods and their carbohydrate count. Look at the differences in how much energy they might provide, given their carbohydrate count.

Solving the Problem

1. Create a high-energy meal with the most carbohydrates. Include one choice from each category. Create another meal that contains a maximum of 60 g of carbohydrates.

2. Meat and many vegetables have only trace amounts of carbohydrates. How many grams of carbohydrates would a meal of turkey, stuffing, lettuce salad, and lemonade contain?

Carbohydrate Counts for Common Foods

Main Dish		Side Dish		Drink	
two slices wheat bread	26 g	fudge brownie	25 g	orange juice	27 g
macaroni and cheese	29 g	apple	21 g	cola	38 g
two pancakes	28 g	baked beans	27 g	sweetened iced tea	22 g
chicken and noodles	39 g	blueberry muffin	27 g	lemon-lime soda	38 g
hamburger with bun	34 g	cooked carrots	8 g	hot cocoa	25 g
hot oatmeal	25 g	banana	28 g	apple juice	29 g
plain bagel	38 g	baked potato	34 g	lemonade	28 g
bran flakes with raisins	47 g	stuffing	22 g	whole milk	12 g
lasagna	50 g	brown rice	22 g	chocolate milk	26 g
spaghetti with marinara	50 g	corn on the cob	14 g	sports drink	24 g

266 CHAPTER 9 Carbon Chemistry

Lipids

A **lipid** is an organic compound that contains the same elements as carbohydrates—carbon, hydrogen, and oxygen—but in different proportions. They are the reaction products of glycerol, which has three –OH groups and three long-chain carboxylic acids, as pictured in **Figure 21.** Lipids are in many of the foods you eat such as the ones shown in **Figure 22.** Lipids are commonly called fats and oils, but they also are found in greases and waxes such as beeswax. Wax is a lipid, but it is harder than fat because of its chemical composition. Bees secrete wax from a gland in the abdomen to form beeswax, which is part of the honeycomb.

Lipids Store Energy
Lipids store energy in their bonds, just as carbohydrates do, but they are a more concentrated source of energy than carbohydrates. If you eat more food than your body needs to supply you with the energy for usual activities, the excess energy from the food is stored by producing lipids.

How can energy be stored in a molecule? The chemical reaction that produces lipids is endothermic. An endothermic reaction is one in which energy is absorbed. This means that energy is stored in the chemical bonds of lipids. When your body needs energy, the bonds are broken and energy is released. This process protects your body when you need extra energy or when you might not be able to eat. If you regularly eat more food than you need, large amounts of lipids will be produced and stored as fat on your body.

Reading Check *What is a lipid and how does your body use lipids to store energy?*

Figure 21 Lipids consist of two parts—glycerol and three molecules of carboxylic acid.
Identify *which portion is from glycerol and which portion is from carboxylic acid.*

Science Online
Topic: Lipids
Visit ips.msscience.com for Web links to Information about your body's requirement for lipids.

Activity Lipids (fats) are important to your body's dietary needs. Make a table of saturated and unsaturated lipids that you consume. Try to list a total of ten.

Figure 22 Many of the foods that you eat contain fats and oils, which are lipids.

SECTION 3 Biological Compounds **267**

Caption Answer

Figure 21 The portion on the right is from glycerol. The three molecules of carboxylic acid are on the left. To produce this lipid glycerol loses three hydrogen atoms. Each carboxylic acid molecule loses a hydroxyl group. A total of three water molecules are produced in this reaction.

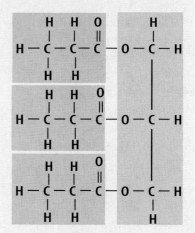

Activity

Calories of Energy Write the following problem on the board. Allow each student to calculate the answer, and then solve the problem together as a class.

One gram of carbohydrates releases 4 Calories of energy and 1 g of lipids releases 9 Calories. If your daily diet provides 400 g of carbohydrates and 100 g of lipids, how many Calories of energy will be available to you? $(400\,g \times 4\,Cal/g) + (100\,g \times 9\,Cal/g) = 1{,}600\,Cal + 900\,Cal = 2{,}500\,Cal$ Explain to students that the unit Calories, with a capital C, is used when dealing with food. It is actually a kilocalorie and is equal to 1,000 calories. L3 **LS Logical-Mathematical**

Reading Check

Answer A lipid is an organic compound similar to a carbohydrate in that it contains carbon, hydrogen, and oxygen, but it contains these elements in different proportions. The chemical reaction that produces lipids is endothermic. This means that energy is stored in the bonds in lipids. When the body needs energy, the bonds are broken and energy is released.

Oil v. Margarine

Purpose To identify the properties of saturated and unsaturated fats using models. L2 ELL LS
Kinesthetic

Possible Materials gum drop candies, mini marshmallows, toothpicks cut in half

Estimated Time one class session

Teaching Strategies

• Use toothpicks as bonds, gum drops for carbon, and marshmallows for hydrogen, or other elements.

• Construct saturated and unsaturated hydrocarbon chains.

• Ask students to experiment with the chains' ability to rotate, vibrate, and twist and coil up on itself. Saturated molecules have greater rotation and twisting ability and can pack closer to each other.

• Ask students to try to demonstrate why oils are liquid while saturated fats like margarine are solid. The double-bonded chains don't allow the molecules to pack close together.

• Show how the hydrogenation process would change the form of the chain.

For additional inquiry activities, see Science Inquiry Labs.

Discussion

Caribou Legs Explain to students that the bodies of caribou, which are arctic animals, contain fats that are saturated. However, the lower parts of their legs contain many unsaturated fats. Why is it beneficial for the caribou's lower legs to contain unsaturated, rather than saturated, fat? Unsaturated fats remain liquid at low temperatures. They allow the caribou's feet and legs to function properly in cold weather. L3 LS
Logical-Mathematical

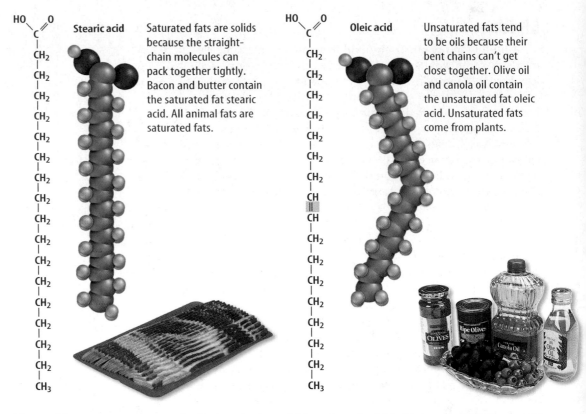

Stearic acid Saturated fats are solids because the straight-chain molecules can pack together tightly. Bacon and butter contain the saturated fat stearic acid. All animal fats are saturated fats.

Oleic acid Unsaturated fats tend to be oils because their bent chains can't get close together. Olive oil and canola oil contain the unsaturated fat oleic acid. Unsaturated fats come from plants.

Figure 23 Whether a lipid is a liquid or a solid depends on the type of bonds it has.

Saturated and Unsaturated Lipids Not all lipids are the same. Recall the difference between saturated and unsaturated hydrocarbons. Unsaturated molecules have one or more double or triple bonds between carbon atoms. Lipid molecules also can be saturated or unsaturated. As you can see in **Figure 23,** when a lipid is saturated, the acid chains are straight because all the bonds are single bonds. They are able to pack together closely. A compact arrangement of the molecules is typical of a solid such as margarine or shortening. These solid lipids consist mainly of saturated fats.

When a lipid is unsaturated, as in **Figure 23,** the molecule bends wherever there is a double bond. This prevents the chains from packing close together, so these lipids tend to be liquid oils such as olive or corn oil.

Doctors have observed that people who eat a diet high in saturated fats have an increased risk of developing cardiovascular problems such as heart disease. The effect of saturated fat seems to be increased blood cholesterol, which may be involved in the formation of deposits on artery walls. Fortunately, many foods containing unsaturated fats are available. Making wise choices in the foods that you eat can help keep your body healthy.

268 CHAPTER 9 Carbon Chemistry

Active Reading

Write-Draw-Discuss This strategy encourages students to actively participate in reading and lectures, assimilating content creatively. Have students write about an idea, clarify it, and make an illustration or drawing. Ask students to share responses and examples with the class about types of biological compounds. L2

Fun Fact

Unsaturated fats can be turned into saturated fats by a process known as hydrogenation. Nickel is often the catalyst used for this reaction.

Cholesterol

Cholesterol is a complex lipid that is present in foods that come from animals, such as meat, butter, eggs, and cheese. However, cholesterol is not a fat. Even if you don't eat foods containing cholesterol, your body makes its own supply. Your body needs cholesterol for building cell membranes. Cholesterol is not found in plants, so oils derived from plants are free of cholesterol. However, the body can convert fats in these oils to cholesterol.

Deposits of cholesterol, called plaque, can build up on the inside walls of arteries. This condition, known as atherosclerosis, is shown in **Figure 24.** When arteries become clogged, the flow of blood is restricted, which results in high blood pressure. This, in turn, can lead to heart disease. Although the cause of plaque build up on the inside walls of arteries is unknown, limiting the amount of saturated fat and cholesterol might help to lower cholesterol levels in the blood and might help reduce the risk of heart problems.

Heart disease is a major health concern in the United States. As a result, many people are on low-cholesterol diets. What types of foods should people choose to lower their cholesterol level?

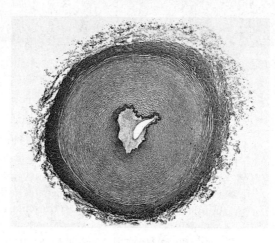

Figure 24 This view of an artery shows atherosclerosis, a dangerous condition in which arteries in the body become clogged. Deposits build up on the inside walls of the artery, leaving less room for blood to flow.

Reading Check *What is atherosclerosis and why is this condition dangerous?*

section 3 review

Summary

Polymers and Proteins
- A polymer is a molecule made up of small, repeating units.
- The small molecules that link together to form a polymer are called monomers.
- A protein is a polymer that consists of individual amino acids linked together.

Carbohydrates, Lipids, and Cholesterol
- Carbohydrates and lipids are organic compounds that contain carbon, hydrogen, and oxygen.
- Lipids store energy in their bonds.
- Unsaturated lipids have one or more double or triple bonds between carbon atoms.
- Cholesterol is a complex lipid.

Self Check

1. **Define** the process by which proteins are made. What other product is formed along with a protein molecule?
2. **Explain** how carbohydrates, proteins, and lipids are important to body functions.
3. **Analyze** how cellulose, starch, and glycogen are different.
4. **Describe** how your body obtains and uses cholesterol.
5. **Think Critically** Explain why even people who eat a healthful diet might gain weight if they don't get enough exercise.

Applying Skills

6. **Draw a Conclusion** Polyunsaturated fats are recommended for a healthful diet. Using what you know about lipids, what might *polyunsaturated* mean?

 **Science Online** ips.msscience.com/self_check_quiz

SECTION 3 Biological Compounds **269**

Text Question Answer

fruits, vegetables, and nonfatty foods

Reading Check

Answer It is a build up of cholesterol deposits on the inside of artery walls. The deposits restrict the flow of blood, leading to high blood pressure.

3 Assess

DAILY INTERVENTION

Check for Understanding

Linguistic Have students write a news report describing proteins, carbohydrates, and lipids and their roles in the body. Have students read their papers in front of the class as a news broadcast. `L2` `LS`

Reteach

Food Guide Pyramid Show students a copy of a Food Guide Pyramid. Discuss with them why the different types of foods are present in the quantities and locations found in the pyramid. `L2` `LS` **Visual-Spatial**

Assessment

Content Ask students to make Venn diagrams showing the similarities and differences between saturated and unsaturated fats. Both are fats. Saturated fats contain only single bonds in the carbon chain. They are usually solids at room temperature. Unsaturated fats contain double bonds. They are often liquids at room temperature. Use **PASC**, p. 167.

section 3 review

1. The amino group from one amino acid combines with the carboxyl group from another amino acid to form a protein. Water also is formed.
2. Carbohydrates are broken down into simple sugars that the body can use for energy. Proteins serve as catalysts in chemical reactions in cells; make up structure in ligaments, tendons, muscles, cartilage, hair, and fingernails; and form hemoglobin. Lipids store energy until it is needed.
3. Cellulose and glycogen are more complex and more difficult to break down and use than starch is.
4. You obtain cholesterol by eating foods that come from animals or by converting fats from other foods. Your body uses cholesterol for building cell membranes.
5. If a person takes in more food energy than he or she uses, he or she will gain weight.
6. Polyunsaturated means having two or more double or triple bonds.

● Real-World Question

Purpose Students will test foods for the presence of vitamin C.
L2 ELL LS **Kinesthetic**

Process Skills observe, collect data, measure, make and use tables, interpret data, infer

Time Required one class period

● Procedure

Materials Prepare the vitamin C solution by using a mortar and pestle to crush a 250-mg vitamin C tablet. Add the crushed tablet to 200 mL of distilled water and stir until it dissolves.

Prepare a starch solution by mixing 5 g of cornstarch with 15 mL of distilled water to form a paste. Add another 235 mL of distilled water and heat on a hot plate until the cornstarch is dissolved. Allow the mixture to cool before pouring it into a jar and securing the lid.

Tincture of iodine is available at drug stores and grocery stores.

Alternate Materials You might want to also test drinks or cereals to which vitamin C has been added.

Safety Precautions Remind students not to taste any materials used in the lab.

LAB

Goals
- **Prepare** an indicator solution.
- **Verify** a positive test by using a known material.
- **Apply** the test to various foods.
- **Infer** some foods your diet should contain.

Possible Materials
starch solution
iodine solution
vitamin-C solution
water
droppers (10)
15-mL test tubes (10)
test-tube rack
250-mL beaker
stirrer
10-mL graduated cylinder
mortar and pestle
liquid foods such as milk, orange juice, vinegar, and cola
solid foods such as tomatoes, onions, citrus fruits, potatoes, bread, salt, and sugar

Safety Precautions

WARNING: *Do not taste any materials used in the lab. Use care when mashing food samples.*

Looking for Vitamin C

● Real-World Question

Vitamin C is essential to humans for good health and the prevention of disease. Your body cannot produce this necessary organic molecule, so you must consume it in your food. How do you know which foods are good sources of vitamin C? Reactions that cause color changes are useful as chemical tests. This activity uses the disappearance of the dark-blue color of a solution of starch and iodine to show the presence of vitamin C. Can you test foods for vitamin C? Could the starch-iodine solution be used to show the presence of vitamin C in food?

● Procedure

1. Collect all the materials and equipment you will need.
2. Obtain 10 mL of the starch solution from your teacher.
3. Add the starch solution to 200 mL of water in a 250-mL beaker. Stir.
4. Add four drops of iodine solution to the beaker to make a dark-blue indicator solution. Stir in the drops.

Data Table

Food tested	Number of Drops	Results
Orange juice	*The number of drops*	Positive
Milk	*added to cause*	Negative
Tomatoes	*a color change will*	Positive
Potatoes	*depend on the*	Negative
Sugar	*amount of vitamin C*	Negative
Vinegar	*in each sample.*	Negative
Lemon		Positive

Alternative Inquiry Lab

Extend the Lab Have students research the purposes of vitamin C in the body and the symptoms of vitamin C deficiency (scurvy). Allow students to explore related questions. More advanced students might titrate orange juice to find the percentage of vitamin C.

5. Obtain your teacher's approval of your indicator solution before proceeding.

6. **Measure** and place 5 mL of the indicator solution in a clean test tube.

7. Obtain 5 mL of vitamin-C solution from your teacher.

8. Using a clean dropper, add one drop of the vitamin-C solution to the test tube. Stir. Continue adding drops and stirring until you notice a color change. Place a piece of white paper behind the test tube to show the color clearly. Record the number of drops added and any observations.

9. Using a clean test tube and dropper for each test, repeat steps 6 through 8, replacing the vitamin-C solution with other liquids and solids. Add drops of liquid foods or juices until a color change is noted or until you have added about 40 drops of the liquid. Mash solid foods such as onion and potato. Add about 1 g of the food directly to the test tube and stir. Test at least four liquids and four solids.

10. Record the amount of each food added and observations in a table.

⬤ Analyze Your Data

1. **Infer** What indicates a positive test for vitamin C? How do you know?

2. **Describe** a negative test for vitamin C.

3. **Observe** Which foods tested positive for vitamin C? Which foods, if any, tested negative for vitamin C?

⬤ Conclude and Apply

1. **Explain** which foods you might include in your diet to make sure you get vitamin C every day.

2. **Determine** if a vitamin-C tablet could take the place of these foods. Explain.

Communicating
Your Data

Compare your results with other class members. Were your results consistent? Make a record of the foods you eat for two days. Does your diet contain the minimum RDA of vitamin C?

LAB 271

☑ Assessment

Process Have students rank the vitamin-C content of the foods that tested positive according to the number of drops they added to cause the color change. Foods with the highest vitamin C content required fewer drops to cause a color change. Use **Performance Assessment in the Science Classroom,** p. 99.

Communicating
Your Data

Suggest students use an electronic spreadsheet for recording the foods they eat for two days.

Teaching Strategies

- The test solution will fade with time. It should be prepared fresh for every lab session. Students should look for a fairly quick color change. A slow fading of color is not a positive test.

- Remind students that the iodine solution will stain skin and clothing.

⬤ Analyze Your Data

Expected Outcomes Results should indicate positive tests for citrus fruits and juices, tomatoes, and any processed foods to which vitamin C has been added.

Answers to Questions

1. When vitamin C is added to the indicator solution, the dark-blue color disappears quickly. This is what happened with the vitamin-C solution.

2. When 40 drops of the food or juice have been added and no color change has been observed, the test is negative.

3. Foods that tested positive include orange juice, citrus fruits, and tomatoes. Foods that tested negative included milk, vinegar, cola, bread, salt, and sugar.

Error Analysis Have each group compare its results with those of another group. If the test results disagree, have students list possible reasons for the discrepancy.

⬤ Conclude and Apply

1. Include foods that tested positive for vitamin C such as orange juice, citrus fruits, and tomatoes.

2. Citrus fruits and juices and tomatoes provide vitamin C. A vitamin-C tablet would not provide the other nutrients found in those foods.

TIME

SCIENCE AND Society

SCIENCE ISSUES THAT AFFECT YOU!

Content Background

Ethnobotany is the study of how different cultures make use of their native plants. One area of particular interest is how native peoples use local plants for medicinal purposes. These plants are then collected and taken to a lab to be chemically analyzed. The goal is to identify the chemical component of the plant that is responsible for its medicinal value. Once the active ingredient is identified and isolated, pharmacologists attempt to manufacture the substance.

Herbal medicines associated with health food stores use the whole plant while ethnobotanists deal with individual chemical substances derived from the plants.

The growing awareness of the medicinal potential of plants in areas such as the rain forest has renewed interest in the field of ethnobotany. This, in turn, has raised public interest in conservation and in unconventional sources for medicines.

Discussion

Compensation Should the local healer be compensated for his or her knowledge of a native plant provided to a pharmaceutical company? Accept all well-supported answers. [L1]

Activity

Home Remedies Have students survey family members and friends for home remedies they have used. Have students write their responses in a class remedy book. Responses may include: slippery elm for digestive troubles, aloe vera for burns, comfrey to promote healing, and peppermint for indigestion. [L1] [ELL]
[LS] **Interpersonal**

From Plants to Medicine

Wild plants help save lives

Look carefully at those plants growing in your backyard or neighborhood. With help from scientists, they could save a life. Many of the medicines that doctors prescribe were first developed from plants. For example, aspirin was extracted from the bark of a willow tree. A cancer medication was extracted from the bark of the Pacific yew tree. Aspirin and the cancer medication are now made synthetically—their carbon structures are duplicated in the lab and factory.

Throughout history, and in all parts of the world, traditonal healers have used different parts of plants and flowers to help treat people. Certain kinds of plants have been mashed up and applied to the body to heal burns and sores, or have been swallowed or chewed to help people with illnesses.

Modern researchers are studying the medicinal value of plants and then figuring out the plants' properties and makeup. This is giving scientists important information as they turn to more and more plants to help make medicine in the lab. Studying these plants—and how people in different cultures use them— is the work of scientists called ethnobotanists (eth noh BAH tuhn ihsts). Ethnobotanist Memory Elvin-Lewis notes that plants help treat illnesses.

Promising cancer medications are made from the bark of the Pacific yew tree.

She visits healers who show her the plants that they find most useful. "Plants are superior chemists producing substances with sophisticated molecular structures that protect the plant from injury and disease," writes Professor Michele L. Trankina. It's these substances in plants that are used as sources of medicines. And it's these substances that are giving researchers and chemists leads to making similar substances in the lab. That can only mean good news—and better health—for people!

Memory Elvin-Lewis has spent part of her career studying herbal medicines.

Investigate Research the work of people like Carole L. Cramer. She's modifying common farm plants so that they produce human antibodies used to treat human illnesses. Use the link on the right or your school's media center to get started in your search.

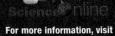
Science Online

For more information, visit ips.msscience.com/time

Investigate Carole L. Cramer is a professor of plant pathology and physiology at Virginia Polytechnical Institute. She is also one of the founders of CropTech Corporation. CropTech is using tobacco plants to produce the human enzyme glucocerebrosidase. People who can't manufacture this necessary enzyme currently pay about $160,000 per year for treatment.

Resources for Teachers and Students

The National Health Museum 1155 15th Street, NW, Suite 810, Washington, DC 20005

Herbal Medicine in Primary Care. Sue Eldin and Andrew Dunford, Butterworth-Heinemann, 1999

Earthly Goods: Medicine Hunting in the Rainforest. Christopher Joyce, Little, Brown and Company, 1994

Reviewing Main Ideas

Section 1 Simple Organic Compounds

1. Hydrocarbons are compounds containing only carbon and hydrogen.

2. If a hydrocarbon has only single bonds, it is called a saturated hydrocarbon.

3. Unsaturated hydrocarbons have one or more double or triple bonds in their structure.

Section 2 Other Organic Compounds

1. Hydrogens can be substituted with other atoms or with groups of atoms.

2. An amino acid contains an amino group and a carboxyl group substituted on the same carbon atom.

3. An alcohol is formed when a hydroxyl group is substituted for a hydrogen atom in a hydrocarbon.

4. A carboxylic acid is made when a carboxyl group is substituted and an amine is formed when an amino group ($-NH_2$) is substituted.

Section 3 Biological Compounds

1. Many biological compounds are large molecules called polymers.

2. Proteins serve a variety of functions, including catalyzing many cell reactions.

3. Carbohydrates and lipids are energy sources and the means of storing energy.

Visualizing Main Ideas

Copy and complete the following concept map on simple organic compounds.

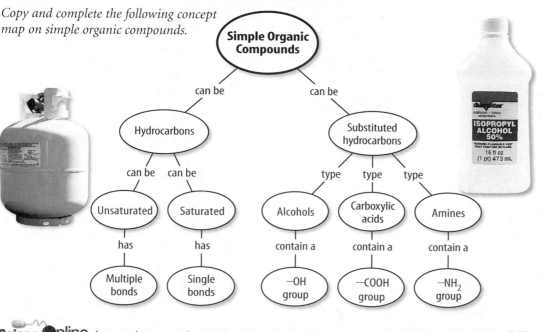

Reviewing Main Ideas

Summary statements can be used by students to review the major concepts of the chapter.

Visualizing Main Ideas

See student page.

Science Online

Visit ips.msscience.com

/self_check_quiz

/interactive_tutor

/vocabulary_puzzlemaker

/chapter_review

/standardized_test

Assessment Transparency

For additional assessment questions, use the *Assessment Transparency* located in the transparency book.

Assessment

Assessment Transparency **Carbon Chemistry**

Directions: *Carefully review the table and answer the following questions.*

Substance	Formula
1	H_2O
2	CH_4
3	CH_3OH
4	CH_3COOH

1. Compounds that contain carbon and hydrogen are called organic. According to this definition, which of the compounds listed above is NOT an organic substance?
   A 1
   B 2
   C 3
   D 4

2. The formula for a carboxyl group is –COOH. Which of the compounds listed above contains a carboxyl group?
   F 1
   G 2
   H 3
   J 4

3. Alcohols are organic compounds that occur when –OH groups replace hydrogen atoms. According to this definition, which compound is an alcohol?
   A 1
   B 2
   C 3
   D 4

Carbon Chemistry

Using Vocabulary

1. An amino group is —NH2. An amino acid is a substituted hydrocarbon that contains both an amino group and a carboxyl group, —COOH.
2. A hydroxyl group is —OH, and a carboxyl group is —COOH.
3. Carbohydrates can be easily converted into energy by the body.
4. A protein is a type of polymer.
5. Both are made from carbon, hydrogen, and oxygen. Both store energy.
6. A saturated hydrocarbon has only single bonds. An unsaturated hydrocarbon has at least one double or triple bond.

Checking Concepts

7. B
8. D
9. C
10. A
11. D
12. C
13. C
14. B
15. C
16. C

Using Vocabulary

amino acid p. 259	organic compound p. 250
amino group p. 259	polymer p. 262
carbohydrate p. 264	polymerization p. 262
carboxyl group p. 259	protein p. 263
cholesterol p. 269	saturated hydrocarbon
hydrocarbon p. 251	p. 252
hydroxyl group p. 258	starches p. 265
isomer p. 254	sugars p. 265
lipid p. 267	unsaturated hydrocarbon
monomer p. 262	p. 253

Answer the following questions using complete sentences.

1. Explain the difference between an amino group and an amino acid.
2. How does a hydroxyl group differ from a carboxyl group?
3. Explain why eating carbohydrates would be beneficial to an athlete before a race.
4. What is the connection between a polymer and a protein?
5. What do carbohydrates and lipids have in common?
6. Explain the difference between a saturated and an unsaturated compound.

Checking Concepts

Choose the word or phrase that best answers the question.

7. A certain carbohydrate molecule has ten oxygen atoms. How many hydrogen atoms does it contain?
   A) five   C) ten
   B) 20   D) 16
8. Which is NOT a group that can be substituted in a hydrocarbon?
   A) amino   C) hydroxyl
   B) carboxyl D) lipid

9. Which chemical formula represents an alcohol?
   A) CH_3COOH C) CH_3OH
   B) CH_3NH_2 D) CH_4
10. Which substance can build up in arteries and lead to heart disease?
    A) cholesterol   C) glucose
    B) fructose   D) starch
11. What is an organic molecule that contains a triple bond called?
    A) polymer
    B) saturated hydrocarbon
    C) isomer
    D) unsaturated hydrocarbon
12. What is the name of the substituted hydrocarbon with the chemical formula CH_2F_2?
    A) methane
    B) fluoromethane
    C) difluoromethane
    D) trifluoromethane

$$\begin{array}{c} H \\ | \\ F - C - F \\ | \\ H \end{array}$$

13. Which chemical formula below represents an amino acid?
    A) CH_3COOH C) NH_2CH_2COOH
    B) CH_3NH_2 D) CH_4
14. Proteins are biological polymers made up of what type of monomers?
    A) alcohols   C) ethene molecules
    B) amino acids   D) propene molecules
15. Excess energy is stored in your body as which of the following?
    A) proteins
    B) isomers
    C) lipids
    D) saturated hydrocarbons
16. Which is a ring-shaped molecule?
    A) acetone   C) cyclopentane
    B) ethylene   D) dichloroethane

Science Online ips.msscience.com/vocabulary_puzzlemaker

Use the Exam*View*® Pro Testmaker CD-ROM to:
- create multiple versions of tests
- create modified tests with one mouse click for inclusion students
- edit existing questions and add your own questions
- build tests aligned with state standards using built-in State Curriculum Tags
- change English tests to Spanish with one mouse click and vice versa

Thinking Critically

Use the figures below to answer question 17.

17. Compare and Contrast Benzene and cyclohexane are both ring molecules. Discuss the similarities and differences of the two molecules.

18. Explain Ethanol is used as a fuel for cars. Explain how energy is obtained from ethanol to fuel a car.

19. Analyze Candle wax is one of the longer hydrocarbons. Explain why heat and light are produced in a burning candle.

20. Infer In the polymerization of amino acids to make proteins, water molecules are produced as part of the reaction. However, in the polymerization of ethylene, no water is produced. Explain.

21. Recognize Cause and Effect Marathon runners go through a process known as hitting the wall. They have used up all their readily available glucose and start using stored lipids as fuel. What is the advantage of eating lots of carbohydrates the day before a race?

22. Hypothesize PKU is a genetic disorder that can lead to brain damage. People with this disorder cannot process one of the amino acids. Luckily, damage can be prevented by a proper diet. How is this possible?

23. Explain Medicines previously obtained from plants are now manufactured. Can these two medicines be the same?

Science⊚nline ips.msscience.com/chapter_review

Performance Activities

24. Scientific Drawing Research an amino acid that was not mentioned in the chapter. Draw its structural formula and highlight the portion that substitutes for a hydrogen atom.

Applying Math

Use the graph below to answer question 25.

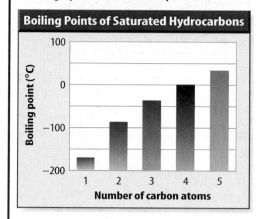

25. Hydrocarbons Using the graph above, explain how the boiling point varies with the number of carbon atoms. What do you predict would be the approximate boiling point of hexane?

Use the figure below to answer question 26.

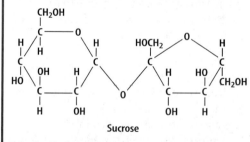

Sucrose

26. Simple Sugar What are the percentages of carbon, oxygen, and hydrogen in a sucrose molecule?

27. Polyethylene If one polyethylene molecule contains 10,000 ethylene units, how many can be made from 3 million ethylene units?

CHAPTER REVIEW 275

Thinking Critically

17. Both molecules are rings with six carbon atoms. Cyclohexane's chemical formula is C_6H_{12} and benzene's chemical formula is C_6H_6. Cyclohexane has only single bonds between carbon atoms (saturated) and benzene has single and double bonds between carbon atoms (unsaturated).

18. Energy is stored in the bonds of ethanol. When these bonds are broken the energy is released.

19. Energy is stored in the bonds of the candle wax. When the bonds are broken, energy is released in the form of heat and light.

20. No oxygen is present in ethylene.

21. Excess sugars have not had time to be stored as lipids. They are still in the blood and are available for energy, so the runner will go longer before hitting the wall.

22. People can eat only foods that do not contain this amino acid.

23. Yes. They are the same so long as the same atoms are arranged in the same way in the molecules.

Performance Activities

24. Check students' drawings. Use **Performance Assessment in the Science Classroom,** p. 127.

Applying Math

National Math Standards
1, 2, 5, 9

25. The boiling point increases as the number of carbon atoms increases. Students may estimate hexane's boiling point to be between 50°C and 100°C. Hexane's actual boiling point is 69°C.

26. 27% carbon, 49% hydrogen, 24% oxygen

27. 300 polyethylene molecules

✓ Assessment · Resources

📁 Reproducible Masters

Chapter *Fast File* Resources
Chapter Review, pp. 39–40
Chapter Tests, pp. 41–44
Assessment Transparency Activity, p. 51

Glencoe Science Web site
Chapter Review Test
Standardized Test Practice

Glencoe Technology

🔦 Assessment Transparency
⊛ Exam*View*® Pro Testmaker
📺 MindJogger Videoquiz
💿 Interactive Chalkboard

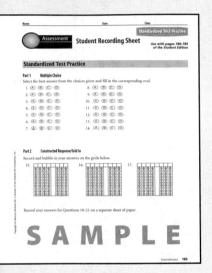

Answer Sheet A practice answer sheet can be found at ips.msscience.com/answer_sheet.

S A M P L E

Part 1 | Multiple Choice

1. C	6. D
2. B	7. B
3. A	8. D
4. C	9. A
5. D	

Part 2 | Short Response

10. $x = 12$, $y = 22$, $z = 11$; that is $C_{12}H_{22}O_{11}$

11. The ratio of two hydrogen atoms to one oxygen atom denotes a carbohydrate.

12. $CH_3CH_2CH_2$ is an propyl group

13. $C_3H_7NH_2$

14. 30 units; $(12 \times 2) + (1 \times 6) = 30$

15. 75% for methane; $(12/16) \times 100 = 75\%$
80% for ethane; $(24/30) \times 100 = 80\%$

Part 1 | Multiple Choice

Record your answers on the answer sheet provided by your teacher or on a sheet of paper.

Use the table below to answer questions 1 and 2.

Double Bonded Hydrocarbons			
Name	**Formula**	**Name**	**Formula**
Ethene	C_2H_4	Pentene	C_5H_{10}
Propene	C_3H_6	Octene	?
Butene	C_4H_8	Decene	$C_{10}H_{20}$

1. What is the general formula for this family?
A. $C_{2n}H_n$ C. C_nH_{2n}
B. C_nH_{2n+2} D. C_nH_{2n-2}

2. What is the formula of octene?
A. C_6H_{12} C. C_6H_{10}
B. C_8H_{16} D. C_8H_{18}

3. Based on its root name and suffix, what is the structural formula of propyne?
A. $H-C\equiv C-CH_3$
B. $CH_3-CH_2-CH_3$
C. $H_2C=CHCH_3$
D. $HC\equiv CH$

4. As five amino acids polymerize to form a protein, how many water molecules split off?
A. 6   C. 4
B. 5   D. none

5. As a NH_2 group replaces a hydrogen in a hydrocarbon, which type of compound is formed?
A. carboxylic acid   C. alcohol
B. amino acid   D. amine

6. One of the freons used in refrigerators is dichloro-difluoromethane. How many H atoms are in this molecule ?
A. 4   C. 1
B. 2   D. none

Use the structures below to answer questions 7–9.

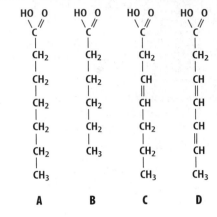

A   B   C   D

7. Which is saturated and has the fewest number of carbon atoms?
A. A   C. C
B. B   D. D

8. Which is a polyunsaturated acid?
A. A   C. C
B. B   D. D

9. These are all considered to be carboxylic acids because they contain which of the following?
A. a $-COOH$ group
B. a $-CH_3$ group
C. a double bond
D. C, H, and O atoms

Test-Taking Tip

Figures and Illustrations Be sure you understand all symbols in a figure or illustration before attempting to answer any questions about them.

Question 7 Even though the hydrogen molecules are shown on the same side of the carboxylic acid molecules, the structural formula places one hydrogen on either side of the carbon.

Part 3 | Open Ended

16. "eth" indicates two carbon atoms

17. "ane" indicates a single bond between carbon atoms

18. "ol" indicates —OH group attached to a carbon atom

19. No. The graph is exponential, not linear.

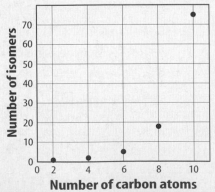

20. Predict either three or four isomers based on the trend. There are three isomers.

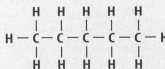

Part 2 | Short Response/Grid In

Record answers on the answer sheet provided by your teacher or on a sheet of paper.

Use the illustration below to answer questions 10 and 11.

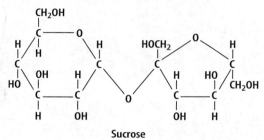

Sucrose

10. If its formula is given as $C_xH_yO_z$ what are the values of x, y, and z?

11. Sucrose is a carbohydrate. What ratio between atoms denotes a carbohydrate?

12. What is the structural formula of the propyl group?

13. What is the molecular formula of propylamine?

Use the following explanation to answer questions 14 and 15.

A carbon atom has a mass of 12 units and hydrogen 1. A molecule of methane has a molecular mass of $(12 \times 1) + (1 \times 4) = 16$ units, and is $\frac{4}{16} = 25\%$ hydrogen by mass.

Methane   **Ethane**

14. What is molecular mass of C_2H_6?

15. What is the percent carbon by mass for methane and ethane?

Part 3 | Open Ended

Record your answers on a sheet of paper.

Use the following explanation to answer questions 16–18.

Glycol is a chief component of antifreeze. It IUPAC name is 1, 2-ethanediol.

16. The root "eth" indicates how many carbon atoms?

17. The "ane" suffix indicates which bond between carbons: single, double, or triple?

18. What functional group does "ol" indicate?

Use the table below to answer questions 19 and 20.

Hydrocarbon Isomers	
Formula	**Number of Isomers**
C_2H_6	1
C_4H_{10}	2
C_6H_{14}	5
C_8H_{18}	18
$C_{10}H_{22}$	75

19. Sketch a graph of this data. Is it linear?

20. Predict how many isomers of C_5H_{12} might exist. Draw them.

21. Draw a reasonable structural formula for carbon dioxide. Recall how many bonds each carbon atom can form.

Rubrics

The following rubrics are sample scoring devices for short response and open-ended questions.

Short Response

Points	Description
2	The student demonstrates a thorough understanding of the science of the task. The response may contain minor flaws that do not detract from the demonstration of a thorough understanding.
1	The student has provided a response that is only partially correct.
0	The student has provided a completely incorrect solution or no response at all.

Open Ended

Points	Description
4	The student demonstrates a thorough understanding of the science of the task. The response may contain minor flaws that do not detract from the demonstration of a thorough understanding.
3	The student demonstrates an understanding of the science of the task. The response is essentially correct and demonstrates an essential but less than thorough understanding of the science.
2	The student demonstrates only a partial understanding of the science of the task. Although the student may have used the correct approach to a solution or may have provided a correct solution, the work lacks an essential understanding of the underlying science concepts.
1	The student demonstrates a very limited understanding of the science of the task. The response is incomplete and exhibits many flaws.
0	The student provides a completely incorrect solution or no response at all.

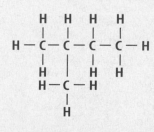

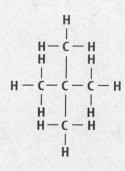

21. $O = C = O$

Carbon forms a double bond with one oxygen atom and then forms another double bond with a second oxygen atom for a total of four bonds.

Unit Contents

WebQuest **Roller Coaster Physics** is an investigation of coaster design, laws of motion, gravity, velocity, and acceleration. Students will use virtual programming to engineer, test, and evaluate roller coaster simulations. As a culminating activity, students will create their own roller coaster model and report on their results.

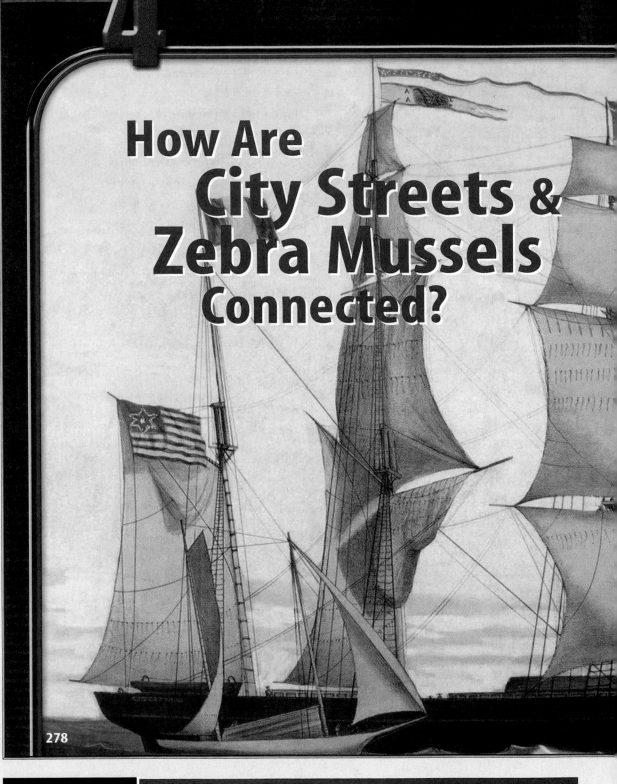

How Are City Streets & Zebra Mussels Connected?

278

PROJECT

CRISS℠

Study Skills

Expand Vocabulary Capsule vocabulary strategies help students with the way words are used. To begin, write several vocabulary words related to a single topic on the board. Select terms related to concepts that have been introduced in this unit such as *energy* and *force*. Use the terms as part of a class discussion, then group the students into pairs. Each pair decides on the best definition for each term and uses the terms correctly and meaningfully in a sentence or two.

NATIONAL GEOGRAPHIC

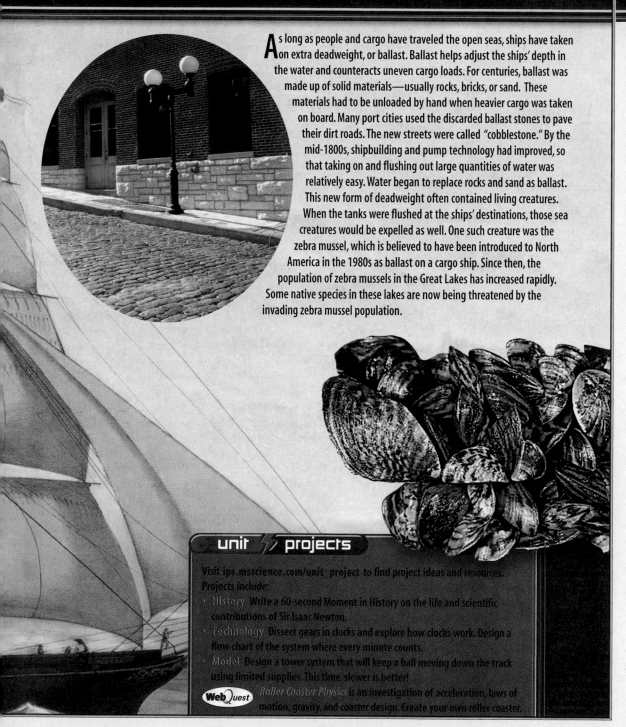

As long as people and cargo have traveled the open seas, ships have taken on extra deadweight, or ballast. Ballast helps adjust the ships' depth in the water and counteracts uneven cargo loads. For centuries, ballast was made up of solid materials—usually rocks, bricks, or sand. These materials had to be unloaded by hand when heavier cargo was taken on board. Many port cities used the discarded ballast stones to pave their dirt roads. The new streets were called "cobblestone." By the mid-1800s, shipbuilding and pump technology had improved, so that taking on and flushing out large quantities of water was relatively easy. Water began to replace rocks and sand as ballast. This new form of deadweight often contained living creatures. When the tanks were flushed at the ships' destinations, those sea creatures would be expelled as well. One such creature was the zebra mussel, which is believed to have been introduced to North America in the 1980s as ballast on a cargo ship. Since then, the population of zebra mussels in the Great Lakes has increased rapidly. Some native species in these lakes are now being threatened by the invading zebra mussel population.

unit ⚡ projects

Visit ips.msscience.com/unit_project to find project ideas and resources. Projects include:

- **History** Write a 60-second Moment in History on the life and scientific contributions of Sir Isaac Newton.
- **Technology** Dissect gears in clocks and explore how clocks work. Design a flow chart of the system where every minute counts.
- **Model** Design a tower system that will keep a ball moving down the track using limited supplies. This time, slower is better!
- **WebQuest** *Roller Coaster Physics* is an investigation of acceleration, laws of motion, gravity, and coaster design. Create your own roller coaster.

unit ⚡ projects

History Have students research Sir Issac Newton—his life and contributions to science. Using their new information, have students write a 60-second Moment in History to share 15 interesting "Newton facts."

Technology Have students bring in broken or donated cuckoo, pendulum, or wind-up clocks to dissect. Have students explore how stuff works—in this case, their clock. Ask students to design a flow chart that represents the process that takes place inside the clock each minute and hour as the gears turn and the minute and hour hands move.

Model Using only 25 sheets of copy paper, a stopwatch, a table-tennis ball, 5-meters of tape, and a sheet of poster board for a base, have pairs of students design and construct a system of tubes, troughs, turns, ramps, and funnels to see how long they can keep the ball moving while remaining inside the boundaries of the poster board. The longer and slower the system, the better.

Additional Resources For more information, resources, and assessment rubrics, visit ips.msscience.com/unit_project

NATIONAL GEOGRAPHIC   How Are City Streets & Zebra Mussels Connected?

Ballast can be defined as "any heavy material carried in a ship to help it achieve a desired draft and degree of stability." The design and operation of a ship is a balancing act between forces, structural materials, and the ultimate utility of the vessel.

All ships are designed to optimize speed and stability with a certain percentage of the hull in the water. If there is too much mass above the waterline, the ship will tend to roll over. Too much mass below the waterline will cause it to wallow and swamp. Ballast is used to adjust the load and bring the ship within its design specifications. Adjusting the amount of ballast also can enable a ship to navigate shallow waters.

Section/Objectives	Standards		Labs/Features
Chapter Opener	**National**	**State/Local**	**Launch Lab:** Motion After a Collision, p. 281 **Foldables,** p. 281
	See pp. 16T–17T for a Key to Standards.		
Section 1 What is motion? ● 2 sessions 🖭 1 block 1. **Define** distance, speed, and velocity. 2. **Graph** motion.	National Content Standards: UCP.2, UCP.3, UCP.5, A.1, A.2, B.1, B.2		**Integrate Life Science,** p. 284 **Applying Math:** Speed of a Swimmer, p. 284 **MiniLAB:** Measuring Average Speed, p. 285 **Science Online,** p. 286
Section 2 Acceleration ● 3 sessions 🖭 1.5 blocks 3. **Define** acceleration. 4. **Predict** what effect acceleration will have on motion.	National Content Standards: UCP.2, UCP.3, UCP.5, A.1, A.2, B.1, B.2		**Applying Math:** Acceleration of a Bus, p. 290 **MiniLAB:** Modeling Acceleration, p. 291
Section 3 Momentum ● 4 sessions 🖭 2 blocks 5. **Explain** the relationship between mass and inertia. 6. **Define** momentum. 7. **Predict** motion using the law of conservation of momentum.	National Content Standards: UCP.2, UCP.3, UCP.5, A.1, A.2, B.1, B.2		**Integrate Social Studies,** p. 294 **Applying Math:** Momentum of a Bicycle, p. 294 **Science Online,** p. 296 **Visualizing Conservation of Momentum,** p. 297 **Lab:** Collisions, p. 299 **Lab:** Care Safety Testing, pp. 300–301 **Oops! Accidents in Science:** What Goes Around Comes Around, p. 302

Lab Materials	Reproducible Resources	Section Assessment	Technology
Launch Lab: 2 baseballs, 2 tennis balls	**Chapter FAST FILE Resources** Foldables Worksheet, p. 17 Directed Reading Overview, p. 19 Note-taking Worksheets, pp. 33–34	**GLENCOE'S ASSESSMENT ADVANTAGE**	**TeacherWorks** includes: • Interactive Teacher Edition • Lesson Planner with calendar • Access to all program blacklines • Correlations to standards • Web links
MiniLAB: masking tape, meterstick, stopwatch *Need materials?* Contact Science Kit at 1-800-828-7777 or www.sciencekit.com on the Internet.	**Chapter FAST FILE Resources** Transparency Activity, p. 44 MiniLAB, p. 3 Enrichment, p. 30 Reinforcement, p. 27 Directed Reading, p. 20 Lab Activity, pp. 9–11 Transparency Activity, pp. 47–48 **Physical Science Critical Thinking/Problem Solving,** pp. 2, 21	**Portfolio** Active Reading, p. 283 **Performance** Applying Math, p. 284 MiniLAB, p. 285 Applying Math, p. 287 **Content** Section Review, p. 287	Section Focus Transparency Teaching Transparency Virtual Labs CD-ROM Guided Reading Audio Program Interactive Chalkboard CD-ROM
MiniLAB: masking tape, meterstick	**Chapter FAST FILE Resources** Transparency Activity, p. 45 MiniLAB, p. 4 Enrichment, p. 31 Reinforcement, p. 28 Directed Reading, p. 20 Transparency Activity, pp. 47–48 Lab Activity, pp. 13–15	**Portfolio** Assessment, p. 292 **Performance** Applying Math, p. 290 MiniLAB, p. 291 Applying Math, p. 292 **Content** Section Review, p. 292	Section Focus Transparency Guided Reading Audio Program Interactive Chalkboard CD-ROM
Lab: 5 small marbles, 2 large marbles, 2 metersticks, tape **Lab:** insulated foam meat trays or fast-food trays, insulated foam cups, straws, straight pins, tape, plastic eggs	**Chapter FAST FILE Resources** Transparency Activity, p. 46 Enrichment, p. 32 Reinforcement, p. 29 Directed Reading, pp. 21, 22 Lab Worksheets, pp. 5–6, 7–8 **Home and Community Involvement,** p. 48	**Portfolio** Currculum Connection, p. 294 **Performance** Applying Math, p. 294 Applying Math, p. 298 **Content** Section Review, p. 298	Section Focus Transparency Guided Reading Audio Program Interactive Chalkboard CD-ROM Video Lab

End of Chapter Assessment

GLENCOE'S ASSESSMENT ADVANTAGE

Blackline Masters	Technology	Professional Series
Chapter Fast File Resources Chapter Review, pp. 37–38 Chapter Tests, pp. 39–42 **Standardized Test Practice,** pp. 43–46	MindJogger Videoquiz Virtual Labs CD-ROM ExamView® Pro Testmaker TeacherWorks CD-ROM Interactive Chalkboard CD-ROM	**Performance Assessment in the Science Classroom (PASC)**

Transparencies

Section Focus

Section Focus Transparency 1 — Air Canvas

This is a photo of the artist Pablo Picasso. While he often worked with paints, here he is creating an image with a flashlight. The photograph recorded the path of the flashlight as he moved it through the air.

1. What creature did Picasso draw with his flashlight?
2. Can you see where the light started? Estimate the distance between the starting point and the end point.
3. Is the distance between the starting point and the end point greater than, equal to, or less than the overall distance traveled by the light?

L2

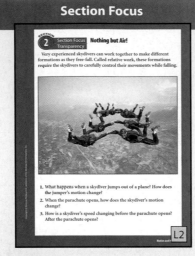

Section Focus Transparency 2 — Nothing but Air!

Very experienced skydivers can work together to make different formations as they free-fall. Called relative work, these formations require the skydivers to carefully control their movements while falling.

1. What happens when a skydiver jumps out of a plane? How does the jumper's motion change?
2. When the parachute opens, how does the skydiver's motion change?
3. How is a skydiver's speed changing before the parachute opens? After the parachute opens?

L2

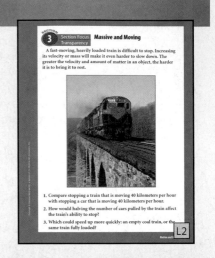

Section Focus Transparency 3 — Massive and Moving

A fast-moving, heavily loaded train is difficult to stop. Increasing its velocity or mass will make it even harder to slow down. The greater the velocity and amount of matter in an object, the harder it is to bring it to rest.

1. Compare stopping a train that is moving 40 kilometers per hour with stopping a car that is moving 40 kilometers per hour.
2. How would halving the number of cars pulled by the train affect the train's ability to stop?
3. Which could speed up more quickly: an empty coal train, or the same train fully loaded?

L2

This is a representation of key blackline masters available in the Teacher Classroom Resources. See Resource Manager boxes within the chapter for additional information.

Key to Teaching Strategies

The following designations will help you decide which activities are appropriate for your students.

L1 Level 1 activities should be appropriate for students with learning difficulties.

L2 Level 2 activities should be within the ability range of all students.

L3 Level 3 activities are designed for above-average students.

ELL ELL activities should be within the ability range of English Language Learners.

COOP LEARN Cooperative Learning activities are designed for small group work.

LS Multiple Learning Styles logos, as described on page 12T, are used throughout to indicate strategies that address different learning styles.

P These strategies represent student products that can be placed into a best-work portfolio.

PBL Problem-Based Learning activities apply real-world situations to learning.

Assessment

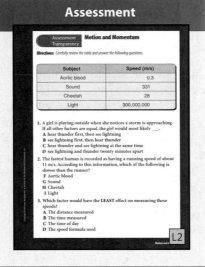

Assessment Transparency — Motion and Momentum

Directions: Carefully review the table and answer the following questions.

Subject	Speed (m/s)
Aortic blood	0.3
Sound	331
Cheetah	28
Light	300,000,000

1. A girl is playing outside when she notices a storm is approaching. If all other factors are equal, the girl would most likely ___.
   A hear thunder first, then see lightning
   B see lightning first, then hear thunder
   C hear thunder and see lightning at the same time
   D see lightning and thunder twenty minutes apart
2. The fastest human is recorded as having a running speed of about 11 m/s. According to this information, which of the following is slower than the runner?
   F Aortic blood
   G Sound
   H Cheetah
   J Light
3. Which factor would have the LEAST effect on measuring these speeds?
   A The distance measured
   B The time measured
   C The time of day
   D The speed formula used

L2

Teaching

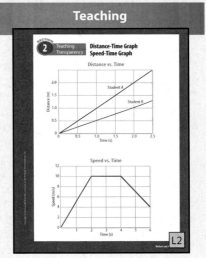

Teaching Transparency 2 — Distance-Time Graph / Speed-Time Graph

L2

Hands-on Activities

Student Text Lab Worksheet

Laboratory Activities

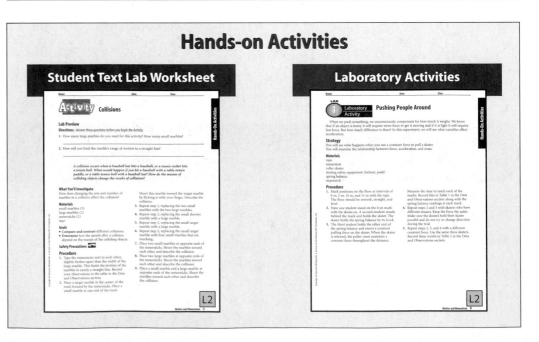

Activity — Collisions

Lab Preview
Directions: Answer these questions before you begin the Activity.
1. How many large marbles do you need for this activity? How many small marbles?
2. How will you limit the marble's range of motion to a straight line?

A collision occurs when a baseball bat hits a baseball, or a tennis racket hits a tennis ball. What would happen if you hit a baseball with a table-tennis paddle, or a table-tennis ball with a baseball bat? How do the masses of colliding objects change the results of collisions?

What You'll Investigate
How does changing the size and number of marbles in a collision affect the collision?

Materials
small marbles (3)
large marbles (2)
metersticks (2)
tape

Goals
• Compare and contrast different collisions.
• Determine how the speeds after a collision depend on the masses of the colliding objects.

Safety Precautions

Procedure
1. Tape the metersticks next to each other, slightly farther apart than the width of the large marble. This limits the motion of the marble to nearly a straight line. Record your observations in the table in the Data and Observations section.
2. Place a target marble in the center of the track formed by the metersticks. Place a small marble at one end of the track.

Shoot this marble toward the target marble by flicking it with your finger. Describe the collision.
3. Repeat step 2, replacing the two small marbles with the two large marbles.
4. Repeat step 2, replacing the small shooter marble with a large marble.
5. Repeat step 2, replacing the small target marble with a large marble.
6. Repeat step 2, placing the small target marble with four small marbles that are touching.
7. Place two small marbles at opposite ends of the metersticks. Shoot the marbles toward each other and describe the collision.
8. Place two large marbles at opposite ends of the metersticks. Shoot the marbles toward each other and describe the collision.
9. Place a small marble and a large marble at opposite ends of the metersticks. Shoot the marbles toward each other and describe the collisions.

L2

Laboratory Activity 1 — Pushing People Around

When we push something, we unconsciously compensate for how much it weighs. We know that if an object is heavy it will require more force to get it moving and if it is light it will require less force. But how much difference is there? In this experiment, we will see what variables affect acceleration.

Strategy
You will see what happens when you use a constant force to pull a skater.
You will examine the relationship between force, acceleration, and mass.

Materials
tape
meterstick
roller skates
skating safety equipment (helmet, pads)
spring balance
stopwatch

Procedure
1. Mark positions on the floor at intervals of 0 m, 5 m, 10 m, and 15 m with the tape. The floor should be smooth, straight, and level.
2. Have one student stand on the 0-m mark with the skates on. A second student stands behind the mark and holds the skater. The skater holds the spring balance by its hook.
3. The third student holds the other end of the spring balance and exerts a constant pulling force on the skater. When the skater is released, the puller must maintain a constant force throughout the distance.

Measure the time to reach each of the marks. Record this in Table 1 in the Data and Observations section along with the spring balance readings at each mark.
4. Repeat steps 2 and 3 with skaters who have different masses. Keep the force the same. Make sure the skaters hold their skates parallel and do not try to change direction during the trial.
5. Repeat steps 2, 3, and 4 with a different constant force. Use the same three skaters. Record these results in Table 2 in the Data and Observations section.

L2

Meeting Different Ability Levels

Content Outline

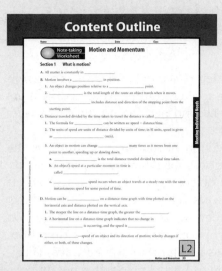

L2

Reinforcement

L2

Enrichment

L3

Directed Reading (English/Spanish)

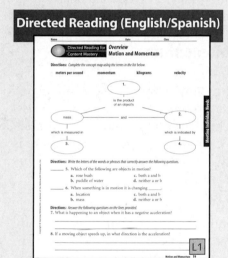

L1

Study Guide

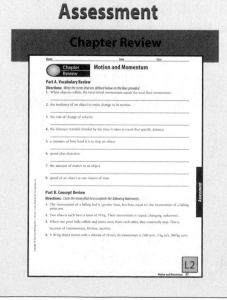

L2

Reading Essentials

L1

Assessment

Test Practice Workbook

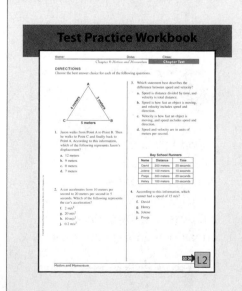

L2

Chapter Review

L2

Chapter Tests

L2

Science Content Background

section 1 What is motion?

Changing Position

Distance is a scalar quantity. This means that it has only a magnitude, such as 6 km. Displacement is a vector quantity; it has both magnitude and direction, such as 8 km south. A car or bike odometer displays distance, not displacement.

Speed

Speed, unlike displacement and velocity, is a scalar quantity. Speedometers display speed, not velocity, because they do not indicate direction. Speedometers indicate instantaneous speed, which is the speed at a given instant of time. In planning a trip, however, average speed is more useful for determining the time required to travel.

Graphing Motion

Because distance is how far an object has traveled, a distance-time graph can never have a line that slopes downward in the positive-time direction (has a negative slope). This is because it is impossible to travel a negative distance. However, a displacement-time graph can have a negative slope, which means the object is moving closer to its point of reference.

section 2 Acceleration

Acceleration and Motion

Acceleration is the rate of change of an object's velocity. If velocity is expressed as meters/second and time is given in seconds, then acceleration is expressed in units of meters per second per second, m/s/s or (m/s × 1/s) or m/s².

If the direction of motion is defined as the positive direction, then when an object's velocity increases, the object experiences positive acceleration. When its velocity decreases, the object experiences negative acceleration. Acceleration also occurs when an object changes direction. For example, as Earth orbits the Sun, it is accelerating. Although Earth travels at a nearly constant speed, its direction is constantly changing.

section 3 Momentum

Mass and Inertia

Students may attribute inertia to an object's weight instead of mass, so that a weightless object would have no inertia. However, even in deep space where there is almost no gravitational force on an object, its inertia is unchanged.

Momentum

Momentum and force are related. The time rate of change of an object's momentum is equal to the force exerted on the object or exerted by the object. In collisions, momentum is conserved only if there are no external forces, such as friction, acting on the colliding objects.

chapter content resources

Internet Resources
For additional content background, visit **ips.msscience.com** to:
- access your book online
- find references to related articles in popular science magazines
- access Web links with related content background
- access current events with science journal topics

Print Resources
Eyewitness: Force & Motion, by Peter Lafferty, Dorling Kindersley Publishing, 2000
Hands-On Physics Activities with Real-Life Applications : Easy-to-Use Labs and Demonstrations for Grades 8–12, by James Cunningham & Norman Herr, Jossey-Bass, 1994

IDENTIFYING Misconceptions

Find Out What Students Think

Students may think that . . .

distance and displacement are the same, and speed and velocity are the same.

One difficulty with the terms velocity and displacement is that they are both vector quantities, and students are much more familiar with scalar quantities. To confuse matters more, the term velocity is sometimes used in everyday language in a non-scientific way. Finally, the terms displacement and distance sound similar, and this may make it easier to confuse them.

Demonstration

After initially teaching the difference between distance and displacement, ask students whether the phrase "as the crow flies," when estimating how far something is, is more like distance or more like displacement.

Promote Understanding

Activity

- Draw Figures 1 and 2 on the board. Explain that the distance-time graph and the displacement-time graph both show Samantha's walking motion after she left her house.

- Ask students to supply a possible story to describe her motion. Ask them what she might be doing when the lines of the two graphs are horizontal.

- Students should see that the distance-time graph and displacement-time graph for the same motion look very different. In this case, the distance traveled is how far Samantha actually walked. Her displacement shows how far she is from her house.

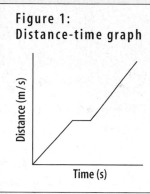

Figure 1: Distance-time graph

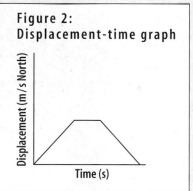

Figure 2: Displacement-time graph

- A plausible story for both graphs has Samantha walking at constant speed directly away from her house, then resting a bit, and then walking at constant speed directly back to her house.

Assess

After completing the chapter, see *Identifying Misconceptions* in the Study Guide at the end of a chapter.

Chapter Vocabulary

speed, p. 284
average speed, p. 285
instantaneous speed, p. 285
velocity, p. 287
acceleration, p. 288
mass, p. 293
inertia, p. 293
momentum, p. 294
law of conservation of
  momentum, p. 295

 **Science Journal** Student
responses will vary.

INTERACTIVE CHALKBOARD
with Image Bank

PowerPoint® Presentations

This CD-ROM is an editable
Microsoft® PowerPoint®
presentation that includes:

• a pre-made presentation for
  every chapter
• interactive graphics
• animations
• audio clips
• image bank
• all new section and chapter
  questions
• Standardized Test Practice
• transparencies
• pre-lab questions for all labs
• Foldables directions
• links to ips.msscience.com

Motion and Momentum

chapter preview

sections

1 What is motion?

2 Acceleration

3 Momentum
  Lab Collisions
  Lab Car Safety Testing
  *Virtual Lab How does
  horizontal motion affect
  vertical motion?*

A Vanishing Act

You hear the crack of the bat and an instant
later the ball disappears into a diving infielder's glove. Think of how the motion of the
ball changed—it moved toward the batter,
changed direction when it collided with the
bat, and then stopped when it collided with
the infielder's glove.

Science Journal Describe how your motion changed
as you moved from your school's entrance to your classroom.

280

Theme Connection

Stability and Change An object can be in motion
or at rest. If in motion, the motion can be constant or accelerated. If accelerated, the acceleration can be constant or changing.

About the Photo

Home-Run Hitting Many baseball fans love the
excitement of seeing long balls hit far into the
outfield. The distance the ball travels depends, in
part, on the momentum of the bat and ball when
they collide. Every year, it seems like hitters send
the ball flying further, so some people think the
ball must be being changed somehow. However,
the mass and size of the baseball has remained the
same since 1872.

Start-Up Activities

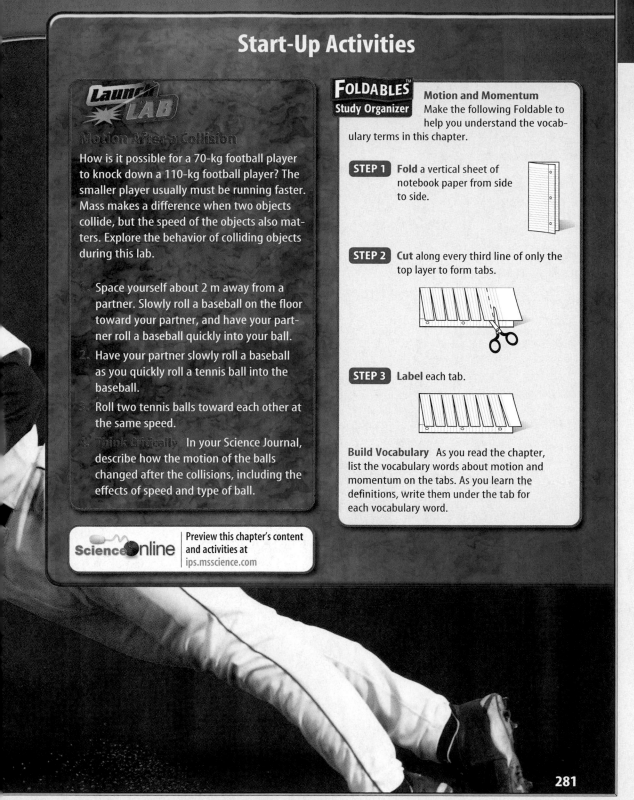

Motion After a Collision

How is it possible for a 70-kg football player to knock down a 110-kg football player? The smaller player usually must be running faster. Mass makes a difference when two objects collide, but the speed of the objects also matters. Explore the behavior of colliding objects during this lab.

1. Space yourself about 2 m away from a partner. Slowly roll a baseball on the floor toward your partner, and have your partner roll a baseball quickly into your ball.

2. Have your partner slowly roll a baseball as you quickly roll a tennis ball into the baseball.

3. Roll two tennis balls toward each other at the same speed.

4. **Think Critically** In your Science Journal, describe how the motion of the balls changed after the collisions, including the effects of speed and type of ball.

Science Online | Preview this chapter's content and activities at ips.msscience.com

---

FOLDABLES™ Study Organizer

Motion and Momentum Make the following Foldable to help you understand the vocabulary terms in this chapter.

STEP 1 **Fold** a vertical sheet of notebook paper from side to side.

STEP 2 **Cut** along every third line of only the top layer to form tabs.

STEP 3 **Label** each tab.

Build Vocabulary As you read the chapter, list the vocabulary words about motion and momentum on the tabs. As you learn the definitions, write them under the tab for each vocabulary word.

Launch LAB

Purpose Use the Launch Lab to introduce students to the way the speeds and masses of the objects in a collision affect the collision. L2 **LS** **Kinesthetic**

Preparation Ask students to bring in balls, or arrange to borrow them at your school.

Materials two baseballs, two tennis balls

Alternate Materials Different types of balls can be used as long as the balls in each pair have identical masses.

Teaching Strategy Remind students of what they have observed in other collisions. For example, which ball is harder to catch?

Think Critically

In the first case, the slower ball reversed direction and increased speed after the collision. The faster ball reversed direction, and its speed decreased. In the second case, both balls reversed direction. The baseball slightly increased in speed, and the tennis ball decreased in speed. In the third case, the balls reversed direction when they collided, but moved off at about the same speed as before.

Assessment

Process Ask students to predict what would happen if a small child, running fast, ran into an adult who wasn't moving. In the collision, the child would slow down, and the adult would move. Both would stumble in the direction the child was first moving, but at a slower speed. Use **Performance Assessment in the Science Classroom,** p. 89.

FOLDABLES™ Study Organizer **Dinah Zike Study Fold**

Student preparation materials for this Foldable are available in the Chapter *FAST FILE* Resources.

Bellringer

INTERACTIVE CHALKBOARD
PowerPoint® Presentations

Section Focus Transparencies also are available on the Interactive Chalkboard CD-ROM.

L2 ELL

Section Focus Transparency   **Air Canvas**

This is a photo of the artist Pablo Picasso. While he often worked with paints, here he is creating an image with a flashlight. The photograph recorded the path of the flashlight as he moved it through the air.

1. What creature did Picasso draw with his flashlight?
2. Can you see where the light started? Estimate the distance between the starting point and the end point.
3. Is the distance between the starting point and the end point greater than, equal to, or less than the overall distance traveled by the light?

L2

Tie to Prior Knowledge

Races Ask students to describe races they have watched or in which they have participated. Possibilities include running, swimming, bicycling, car racing, and horse racing, among others. Discuss what is being measured in each type of race.

---

section 1 What is motion?

Matter and Motion

All matter in the universe is constantly in motion, from the revolution of Earth around the Sun to electrons moving around the nucleus of an atom. Leaves rustle in the wind. Lava flows from a volcano. Bees move from flower to flower as they gather pollen. Blood circulates through your body. These are all examples of matter in motion. How can the motion of these different objects be described?

Changing Position

To describe an object in motion, you must first recognize that the object is in motion. Something is in motion if it is changing position. It could be a fast-moving airplane, a leaf swirling in the wind, or water trickling from a hose. Even your school, attached to Earth, is moving through space. When an object moves from one location to another, it is changing position. The runners shown in **Figure 1** sprint from the start line to the finish line. Their positions change, so they are in motion.

as you read

What You'll Learn
- **Define** distance, speed, and velocity.
- **Graph** motion.

Why It's Important
The different motions of objects you see every day can be described in the same way.

⊙ Review Vocabulary
meter: SI unit of distance, abbreviated m; equal to approximately 39.37 in

New Vocabulary
- speed
- average speed
- instantaneous speed
- velocity

Figure 1 When running a race, you are in motion because your position changes.

Section 1 Resource Manager

Chapter FAST FILE Resources

Transparency Activity, pp. 44, 47–48

Directed Reading for Content Mastery, pp. 19, 20

Note-taking Worksheets, pp. 33–34

MiniLAB, p. 3

Enrichment, p. 30

Reinforcement, p. 27

Lab Activity, pp. 9–11

Relative Motion Determining whether something changes position requires a point of reference. An object changes position if it moves relative to a reference point. To visualize this, picture yourself competing in a 100-m dash. You begin just behind the start line. When you pass the finish line, you are 100 m from the start line. If the start line is your reference point, then your position has changed by 100 m relative to the start line, and motion has occurred. Look at **Figure 2.** How can you determine that the dog has been in motion?

 *How do you know if an object has changed position?*

Distance and Displacement Suppose you are to meet your friends at the park in five minutes. Can you get there on time by walking, or should you ride your bike? To help you decide, you need to know the distance you will travel to get to the park. This distance is the length of the route you will travel from your house to the park.

Suppose the distance you traveled from your house to the park was 200 m. When you get to the park, how would you describe your location? You could say that your location was 200 m from your house. However, your final position depends on both the distance you travel and the direction. Did you go 200 m east or west? To describe your final position exactly, you also would have to tell the direction from your starting point. To do this, you would specify your displacement. Displacement includes the distance between the starting and ending points and the direction in which you travel. **Figure 3** shows the difference between distance and displacement.

Figure 2 Motion occurs when something changes position relative to a reference point. **Explain** *whether the dog's position would depend on the reference point chosen.*

Figure 3 Distance is how far you have walked. Displacement is the direction and difference in position between your starting and ending points.

Distance: 40 m
Displacement: 40 m east

Distance: 70 m
Displacement: 50 m northeast

Distance: 140 m
Displacement: 0 m

SECTION 1 What is motion? **283**

Reading Check

Answer It has moved relative to a reference point.

Caption Answer
Figure 2 Yes, the description of the dog's position depends on the reference point.

Activity
Walking Motion Have students work in pairs. Ask one student to walk forward while the other stands still. Then have the first student stand still while the other walks forward. Have students describe their motion relative to each other. L2 LS **Kinesthetic**

Quick Demo
Distance v. Displacement
Material ball
Estimated Time 15 minutes
Procedure Toss a ball to a student. Maintaining the same distance from the student, vary the toss. Throw the ball quickly and along a fairly flat path, bounce it, and toss it high in the air. Point out that the ball's displacement remains the same, but its total path (distance) varies. L2 LS **Visual-Spatial**

Differentiated Instruction

English-Language Learners Help these students by assigning each one a partner to provide support in understanding new concepts. Encourage partners to demonstrate or illustrate ideas to add meaning to verbal explanations.

Cultural Diversity

Chinese Mapmaking By the second century A.D., Chang Heng, inventor of the seismometer, was applying uniform grids to maps to make it easier to calculate distances. This was eventually developed to the point where, by the 1300s, some maps eliminated the physical features and simply showed place names and grid lines, as a modern computer might model a map.

Active Reading

Concept Maps Have students create concept maps using the vocabulary words introduced throughout the chapter. Have students pair up and take turns explaining their concept maps to each other. P

Speed

To describe motion, you usually want to describe how fast something is moving. The faster something is moving, the less time it takes to travel a certain distance. **Speed** is the distance traveled divided by the time taken to travel the distance. Speed can be calculated from this equation:

> **Speed Equation**
>
> $$\text{speed (in meters/second)} = \frac{\text{distance (in meters)}}{\text{time (in seconds)}}$$
>
> $$s = \frac{d}{t}$$

Because speed equals distance divided by time, the unit of speed is the unit of distance divided by the unit of time. In SI units, distance is measured in m and time is measured in s. As a result, the SI unit of speed is the m/s—the SI distance unit divided by the SI time unit.

Applying Math — Solve a Simple Equation

SPEED OF A SWIMMER Calculate the speed of a swimmer who swims 100 m in 56 s.

Solution

1 *This is what you know:*
- distance: $d = 100$ m
- time: $t = 56$ s

2 *This is what you need to know:*
speed: $s = ?$ m/s

3 *This is the procedure you need to use:*
Substitute the known values for distance and time into the speed equation and calculate the speed:
$$s = \frac{d}{t} = \frac{100 \text{ m}}{56 \text{ s}} = \frac{100}{56} \frac{\text{m}}{\text{s}} = 1.8 \text{ m/s}$$

4 *Check your answer:*
Multiply your answer by the time. You should get the distance that was given.

Practice Problems

1. A runner completes a 400-m race in 43.9 s. In a 100-m race, he finishes in 10.4 s. In which race was his speed faster?

2. A passenger train travels from Boston to New York, a distance of 350 km, in 3.5 h. What is the train's speed?

Science Online For more practice, visit ips.msscience.com/math_practice

Curriculum Connection

Music Ask students to identify the units used to measure speed in music and to demonstrate how speed is used in music. Beats per minute are the units used. A rapid beat or slow beat affects the mood of a piece. **L3** **ELL** **LS** **Auditory-Musical**

Average Speed If a sprinter ran the 100-m dash in 10 s, she probably couldn't have run the entire race with a speed of 10 m/s. Consider that when the race started, the sprinter wasn't moving. Then, as she started running, she moved faster and faster, which increased her speed. During the entire race, the sprinter's speed could have been different from instant to instant. However, the sprinter's motion for the entire race can be described by her average speed, which is 10 m/s. **Average speed** is found by dividing the total distance traveled by the time taken.

Reading Check *How is average speed calculated?*

An object in motion can change speeds many times as it speeds up or slows down. The speed of an object at one instant of time is the object's **instantaneous speed.** To understand the difference between average and instantaneous speeds, think about walking to the library. If it takes you 0.5 h to walk 2 km to the library, your average speed would be as follows:

$$s = \frac{d}{t}$$
$$= \frac{2\ km}{0.5\ h} = 4\ km/h$$

However, you might not have been moving at the same speed throughout the trip. At a crosswalk, your instantaneous speed might have been 0 km/h. If you raced across the street, your speed might have been 7 km/h. If you were able to walk at a steady rate of 4 km/h during the entire trip, you would have moved at a constant speed. Average speed, instantaneous speed, and constant speed are illustrated in **Figure 4.**

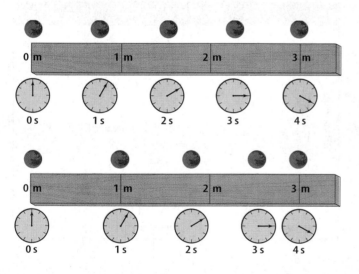

Figure 4 The average speed of each ball is the same from 0 s to 4 s.

The top ball is moving at a constant speed. In each second, the ball moves the same distance.

The bottom ball has a varying speed. Its instantaneous speed is fast between 0 s and 1 s, slower between 2 s and 3 s, and even slower between 3 s and 4 s.

Fun Fact

People climbing Mt. Everest by the North Ridge Ascent start at a base camp with an elevation of 5,170 m. Because the summit of Mt. Everest has an elevation of 8,850 m, the ascent has a vertical displacement of only 3,680 m. However, the distance along the ridge from the base camp to the summit is 20 km (20,000 m)!

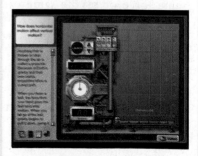

Slope Tell students that to calculate speed from a distance-time graph, they must find the slope of the line. The slope is a measure of the steepness of the graph and is found by dividing the rise, or vertical change, by the run, or horizontal change. In **Figure 5**, the slope of line A between 1 and 2 seconds is (2 m − 1 m) ÷ (2 s − 1 s) = 1 m/s. Have students find the slope of line B for that period of time. (1 m − 0.5 m) ÷ (2 s − 1 s) = 0.5 m/s L3 **LS Logical-Mathematical**

Caption Answer

Figure 5 student A

Inquiry Lab

Mass, Acceleration, and Inertia

Purpose Students will explore the role of mass in inertia and in acceleration.

Possible Materials several toy cars of varying masses, toy car track, rubber bands, stopwatch

Safety Precaution Caution students never to direct rubber bands at one another.

Estimated Time one class session

Teaching Strategies

• Students can use the rubber bands as slingshots to propel the cars and the tracks to keep the cars moving in a straight line.

• Students can predict and then observe how the mass of a car affects how quickly it's accelerated by the rubber bands. They can compare the distances traveled by different cars for the same force or by the same car for different forces.

• Students can also explore how the relative masses of cars (one moving, one initially at rest) affect their velocities after a collision.

For additional inquiry activities, see *Science Inquiry Labs.*

Topic: Land Speed Record
Visit ips.msscience.com for Web links to information about how the land speed record has changed over the past century.

Activity Make a graph showing the increase in the land speed over time.

Figure 5 The motion of two students walking across a classroom is plotted on this distance-time graph.
Use the graph *to determine which student had the faster average speed.*

Graphing Motion

You can represent the motion of an object with a distance-time graph. For this type of graph, time is plotted on the horizontal axis and distance is plotted on the vertical axis. **Figure 5** shows the motion of two students who walked across a classroom plotted on a distance-time graph.

Distance-Time Graphs and Speed A distance-time graph can be used to compare the speeds of objects. Look at the graph shown in **Figure 5.** According to the graph, after 1 s student A traveled 1 m. Her average speed during the first second is as follows:

$$\text{speed} = \frac{\text{distance}}{\text{time}} = \frac{1 \text{ m}}{1 \text{ s}} = 1 \text{ m/s}$$

Student B, however, traveled only 0.5 m in the first second. His average speed is

$$\text{speed} = \frac{\text{distance}}{\text{time}} = \frac{0.5 \text{ m}}{1 \text{ s}} = 0.5 \text{ m/s}$$

So student A traveled faster than student B. Now compare the steepness of the lines on the graph in **Figure 5.** The line representing the motion of student A is steeper than the line for student B. A steeper line on the distance-time graph represents a greater speed. A horizontal line on the distance-time graph means that no change in position occurs. In that case, the speed, represented by the line on the graph, is zero.

286   CHAPTER 10 Motion and Momentum

Curriculum Connection

Math The horizontal axis of a graph represents the independent variable; that is, the variable in which a change causes a change in the other variable. In distance-time graphs the independent variable is time. The vertical axis shows the dependent variable, in this case distance.

Differentiated Instruction

Challenge The motion of groups of objects can be modeled using graph paper. Have students divide a sheet of graph paper into six regions to represent one-second intervals from 0 to 5 s. Have students use the graph paper to illustrate what happens to four objects moving at different speeds and directions at t = 0, 1, 2, 3, 4, and 5 s. Then ask them to predict when and if various pairs of objects meet. L3 **LS Visual-Spatial**

Velocity

If you are hiking in the woods, it is important to know in which direction you should walk in order to get back to camp. You want to know not only your speed, but also the direction in which you are moving. The **velocity** of an object is the speed of the object and the direction of its motion. This is why a compass and a map, like the one shown in **Figure 6,** are useful to hikers. The map and the compass help the hikers to determine what their velocity must be. Velocity has the same units as speed, but it includes the direction of motion.

The velocity of an object can change if the object's speed changes, its direction of motion changes, or they both change. For example, suppose a car is traveling at a speed of 40 km/h north and then turns left at an intersection and continues on with a speed of 40 km/h. The speed of the car is constant at 40 km/h, but the velocity changes from 40 km/h north to 40 km/h west. Why can you say the velocity of a car changes as it comes to a stop at an intersection?

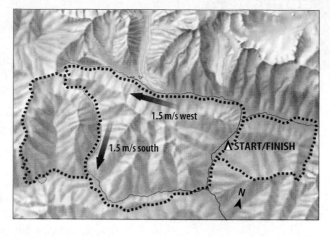

Figure 6 A map helps determine the direction in which you need to travel. Together with your speed, this gives your velocity.

---

section 1 review

Summary

Changing Position

- An object is in motion if it changes position relative to a reference point.
- Motion can be described by distance, speed, displacement, and velocity, where displacement and velocity also include direction.

Speed and Velocity

- The speed of an object can be calculated by dividing the distance traveled by the time needed to travel the distance.
- For an object traveling at constant speed, its average speed is the same as its instantaneous speed.
- The velocity of an object is the speed of the object and its direction of motion.

Graphing Motion

- A line on a distance-time graph becomes steeper as an object's speed increases.

Self Check

1. **Identify** the two pieces of information you need to know the velocity of an object.

2. **Make and Use Graphs** You walk forward at 1.5 m/s for 8 s. Your friend decides to walk faster and starts out at 2.0 m/s for the first 4 s. Then she slows down and walks forward at 1.0 m/s for the next 4 s. Make a distance-time graph of your motion and your friend's motion. Who walked farther?

3. **Think Critically** A bee flies 25 m north of the hive, then 10 m east, 5 m west, and 10 m south. How far north and east of the hive is it now? Explain how you calculated your answer.

Applying Math

4. **Calculate** the average velocity of a dancer who moves 5 m toward the left of the stage over the course of 15 s.

5. **Calculate Travel Time** An airplane flew a distance of 650 km at an average speed of 300 km/h. How much time did the flight take?

---

section 1 review

1. speed and direction
2. The horizontal axis should be marked from 0 s to 8 s, and the vertical axis should be marked from 0 m to 12 m. The graph of your motion is a diagonal line from (0,0)

to (8,12). The graph of your friend's motion is a 2-part line extending from (0,0) to (4,8) and from (4,8) to (8,12). You and your friend walked the same distance, 12 m.

3. 15 m north (25 − 10) and 5 m east (10 − 5)
4. 5 m left ÷ 15 s = 0.33 m/s left
5. 650 km ÷ 300 km/h = 2.17 h

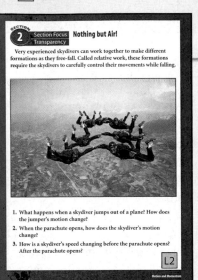
Acceleration

as you read

What You'll Learn
- **Define** acceleration.
- **Predict** what effect acceleration will have on motion.

Why It's Important
Whenever the motion of an object changes, it is accelerating.

⟳ Review Vocabulary
kilogram: SI unit of mass, abbreviated kg; equal to approximately 2.2 lbs

New Vocabulary
● acceleration

Acceleration and Motion

When you watch the first few seconds of a liftoff, a rocket barely seems to move. With each passing second, however, you can see it move faster until it reaches an enormous speed. How could you describe the change in the rocket's motion? When an object changes its motion, it is accelerating. **Acceleration** is the change in velocity divided by the time it takes for the change to occur.

Like velocity, acceleration has a direction. If an object speeds up, the acceleration is in the direction that the object is moving. If an object slows down, the acceleration is opposite to the direction that the object is moving. What if the direction of the acceleration is at an angle to the direction of motion? Then the direction of motion will turn toward the direction of the acceleration.

Speeding Up You get on a bicycle and begin to pedal. The bike moves slowly at first, and then accelerates because its speed increases. When an object that is already in motion speeds up, it also is accelerating. Imagine that you are biking along a level path and you start pedaling harder. Your speed increases. When the speed of an object increases, it is accelerating.

Suppose a toy car is speeding up, as shown in **Figure 7.** Each second, the car moves at a greater speed and travels a greater distance than it did in the previous second. When the car stops accelerating, it will move in a straight line at the speed it had when the acceleration stopped.

Figure 7 The toy car is accelerating to the right. Its speed is increasing.

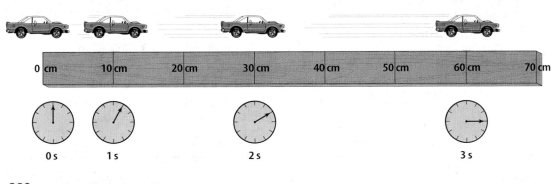

Section 2 Resource Manager

Chapter *FAST FILE* Resources
Transparency Activity, p. 45
Directed Reading for Content Mastery, p. 20
MiniLAB, p.4

Enrichment, p. 31
Reinforcement, p. 28
Lab Activity, pp. 13–15

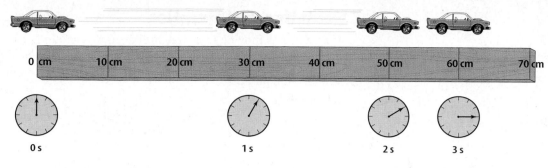

0 cm 10 cm 20 cm 30 cm 40 cm 50 cm 60 cm 70 cm

0 s   1 s   2 s   3 s

Slowing Down Now suppose you are biking at a speed of 4 m/s and you apply the brakes. This causes you to slow down. It might sound odd, but because your speed is changing, you are accelerating. Acceleration occurs when an object slows down, as well as when it speeds up. The car in **Figure 8** is slowing down. During each time interval, the car travels a smaller distance, so its speed is decreasing.

In both of these examples, speed is changing, so acceleration is occurring. Because speed is decreasing in the second example, the direction of the acceleration is opposite to the direction of motion. Any time an object slows down, its acceleration is in the direction opposite to the direction of its motion.

Changing Direction Motion is not always along a straight line. If the acceleration is at an angle to the direction of motion, the object will turn. At the same time, it might speed up, slow down, or not change speed at all.

Again imagine yourself riding a bicycle. When you lean to one side and turn the handlebars, the bike turns. Because the direction of the bike's motion has changed, the bike has accelerated. The acceleration is in the direction that the bicycle turned.

Figure 9 shows another example of an object that is accelerating. The ball starts moving upward, but its direction of motion changes as its path turns downward. Here the acceleration is downward. The longer the ball accelerates, the more its path turns toward the direction of acceleration.

✓ Reading Check *What are three ways to accelerate?*

Figure 8 The car is moving to the right but accelerating to the left. In each time interval, it covers less distance and moves more slowly.
Determine *how the car's velocity is changing.*

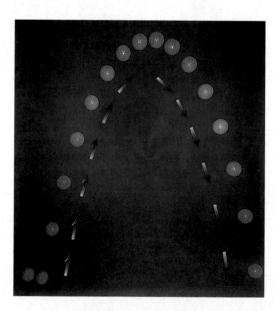

Figure 9 The ball starts out by moving forward and upward, but the acceleration is downward, so the ball's path turns in that direction.

2 Teach

Caption Answer

Figure 8 The car's speed is decreasing but its direction of motion is unchanged.

Use Science Words

Word Origins Ask students to look up the origin of the word *accelerate* and explain how it relates to the scientific use of the word. Accelerate comes from the Latin prefix *ac-*, meaning "toward," the Latin root word *celer*, meaning "swift," and the Latin suffix *-ate*, meaning "cause to become." These together mean "cause to become swift toward." This covers one meaning, to move faster, of the scientific use of the word accelerate. It does not cover slowing down or turning. L3 LS **Linguistic**

Quick Demo

Circular Motion

Materials spool, length of string (about 1 m)

Estimated Time 15 minutes

Procedure Tie a small spool to the end of a piece of string and whirl it around your head. **WARNING:** *Make sure that the spool is fastened tightly to the string and that you have enough space so the spool won't hit anyone.* Discuss with students the motion of the spool and the fact that the string pulls on the spool, accelerating it, to keep it moving in a circle. L2 ELL LS **Visual-Spatial**

✓ Reading Check

Answer speeding up, slowing down, and changing direction

Science Journal

Accelerating to School Have students note each time they accelerate on their way to school and write their observations in their Science Journals. Make sure they include each time they stop, start, and turn on their journeys. L2 ELL LS **Linguistic**

Fun Fact

The velocity any object needs to reach to escape Earth's gravity and get into space is about 11 km/s. That's equivalent to almost 40,000 km/h (about 25,000 miles per hour)!

290 CHAPTER 10 Motion and Momentum

Discussion

Squared Seconds Have students look at the equations on this page. Why is acceleration measured in meters divided by seconds *squared*? Velocity is measured in meters per second. To find acceleration, you divide velocity by time, which has units of seconds. Therefore, the final answer has units of distance divided by time (velocity) divided by time = m/s^2.

L2 LS **Logical-Mathematical**

Applying Math

National Math Standards

Correlation to Mathematics Objectives

1, 2, 9

Answers to Practice Problems

1. $a = (17 \text{ m/s} - 7 \text{ m/s}) \div 120 \text{ s} = 0.083 \text{ m/s}^2$

2. $a = (6 \text{ m/s} - 0 \text{ m/s}) \div 2 \text{ s} = 3 \text{ m/s}^2$

Differentiated Instruction

Learning Disabled Provide extra practice problems for students who have difficulty understanding the mathematics discussed on these pages. Make sure students understand the basic principles used both to set up and solve the problems.

Calculating Acceleration

If an object is moving in a straight line, its acceleration can be calculated using this equation.

Acceleration Equation

acceleration (in m/s^2) =

$$\frac{(\textbf{final speed (in m/s)} - \textbf{initial speed (in m/s)})}{\textbf{time (in s)}}$$

$$a = \frac{(s_f - s_i)}{t}$$

In this equation, time is the length of time over which the motion changes. In SI units, acceleration has units of meters per second squared (m/s^2).

Applying Math   Solve a Simple Equation

ACCELERATION OF A BUS Calculate the acceleration of a bus whose speed changes from 6 m/s to 12 m/s over a period of 3 s.

Solution

1 *This is what you know:*
- initial speed: $s_i = 6$ m/s
- final speed: $s_f = 12$ m/s
- time: $t = 3$ s

2 *This is what you need to know:*

acceleration: $a = ?$ m/s^2

3 *This is the procedure you need to use:*

Substitute the known values of initial speed, final speed and time in the acceleration equation and calculate the acceleration:

$$a = \frac{(s_f - s_i)}{t} = \frac{(12 \text{ m/s} - 6 \text{ m/s})}{3 \text{ s}} = 6\frac{\text{m}}{\text{s}} \times \frac{1}{3 \text{ s}} = 2 \text{ m/s}^2$$

4 *Check your answer:*

Multiply the calculated acceleration by the known time. Then add the known initial speed. You should get the final speed that was given.

Practice Problems

1. Find the acceleration of a train whose speed increases from 7 m/s to 17 m/s in 120 s.

2. A bicycle accelerates from rest to 6 m/s in 2 s. What is the bicycle's acceleration?

Science Online   **For more practice, visit ips.msscience.com/ math_practice**

Differentiated Instruction

Challenge When doing calculations, students may be helped by doing unit analysis. In doing unit analysis, you write the initial problem with units included and cancel appropriately to see what units the answer will have. If the answer does not have the right units, the problem is set up incorrectly. Have students do a unit analysis of the problem of finding the time needed to accel- erate from 3 m/s to 8 m/s at 2 m/s^2. The units should cancel leaving the unit of time, seconds. The change in velocity is 5 m/s. Rearrange the equation for acceleration to: time = change in velocity ÷ acceleration. Substituting units in this equation gives

time = (m/s − m/s) ÷ m/s^2 = m/s × s^2/m = s

$t = (5 \text{ m/s}) \div (2 \text{ m/s}^2) = 2.5$ s   L3 LS

Logical-Mathematical

Figure 10 When skidding to a stop, you are slowing down. This means you have a negative acceleration.

Positive and Negative Acceleration An object is accelerating when it speeds up, and the acceleration is in the same direction as the motion. An object also is accelerating when it slows down, but the acceleration is in the direction opposite to the motion, such as the bicycle in **Figure 10.** How else is acceleration different when an object is speeding up and slowing down?

Suppose you were riding your bicycle in a straight line and increased your speed from 4 m/s to 6 m/s in 5 s. You could calculate your acceleration from the equation on the previous page.

$$a = \frac{(s_f - s_i)}{t}$$
$$= \frac{(6 \text{ m/s} - 4 \text{ m/s})}{5 \text{ s}} = \frac{+2 \text{ m/s}}{5 \text{ s}}$$
$$= +0.4 \text{ m/s}^2$$

When you speed up, your final speed always will be greater than your initial speed. So subtracting your initial speed from your final speed gives a positive number. As a result, your acceleration is positive when you are speeding up.

Suppose you slow down from a speed of 4 m/s to 2 m/s in 5 s. Now the final speed is less than the initial speed. You could calculate your acceleration as follows:

$$a = \frac{(s_f - s_i)}{t}$$
$$= \frac{(2 \text{ m/s} - 4 \text{ m/s})}{5 \text{ s}} = \frac{-2 \text{ m/s}}{5 \text{ s}}$$
$$= -0.4 \text{ m/s}^2$$

Because your final speed is less than your initial speed, your acceleration is negative when you slow down.

Modeling Acceleration

Procedure
1. Use **masking tape** to lay a course on the floor. Mark a starting point and place marks along a straight path at 10 cm, 40 cm, 90 cm, 160 cm, and 250 cm from the start.
2. Clap a steady beat. On the first beat, the person walking the course should be at the starting point. On the second beat, the walker should be on the first mark, and so on.

Analysis
1. Describe what happens to your speed as you move along the course. Infer what would happen if the course were extended farther.
2. Repeat step 2, starting at the other end. Are you still accelerating? Explain.

Mini LAB

Purpose Students observe constant acceleration. L2 LS
Kinesthetic

Materials meterstick or other measuring device, masking tape

Teaching Strategy Explain to students that the actual time interval used doesn't matter, as long as it is constant—it could be 1 s–1 s–1 s, or 3 s–3 s–3 s, or any other regular time interval. Clapping steadily is easier than trying to watch the clock and the course at the same time.

Safety Precaution Suggest that students leave space at the fast end of the course to come to a stop.

Analysis
1. I speed up. I would go faster and faster with each clap, because I would be covering a greater distance in the same amount of time.
2. Yes, because my speed is changing. In this case, I am slowing down.

Assessment

Process Ask students to repeat the experiment using different steady beats—very slow or very fast. How does this affect the acceleration they experience? The faster the beat, the greater the acceleration, because the time between beats decreases. Use **Performance Assessment in the Science Classroom,** p. 97.

Activity

Final Speed Have students calculate the final speed of a bicyclist who accelerates at 0.3 m/s² for 10 s from an initial speed of 4 m/s.

Curriculum Connection

History An early problem in the study of motion was to measure the acceleration of an object due to gravity. Does the acceleration of an object depend on its mass? Have students do research to find Galileo's contributions to understanding the answers to these problems. He showed that gravity causes all falling objects to have the same constant acceleration. L3 LS **Linguistic**

Teacher FYI

Negative Velocity A negative number multiplied by a positive number results in a negative number. Because time is always positive, a negative acceleration multiplied by a positive time will always give a negative change in velocity.

3 Assess

Check for Understanding

Logical-Mathematical Ask students to draw a speed-time graph showing the speed of an object with a constant acceleration of 8 m/s² after starting from rest for 10 s. Have them use points on this graph to calculate the average speed after 8 seconds and the distance traveled in 8 seconds. The average speed is (speed after 8 s − initial speed) ÷ 2 = (64 m/s − 0 m/s) ÷ 2 = 32 m/s. The distance traveled in 8 s is 32 m/s × 8 s = 256 m. [L2]

Reteach

Graphing Acceleration Draw the following speed-time graph on the board: straight line sloping up, flat line, straight line sloping partway down, another flat line, then a line curving down. Where does the graph show positive acceleration? sloping up Negative acceleration? sloping down No acceleration? flat Constant acceleration? any straight line [L2] [LS]
Visual-Spatial

Assessment

Portfolio Ask students to make speed-time graphs for a possible trip from their homes to school. The graphs should indicate where students speed up, slow down, or move at constant speed and give an idea of the comparative speeds and accelerations. Use **Performance Assessment in the Science Classroom**, p. 111. [P]

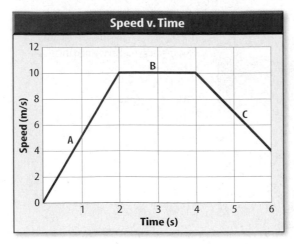

Figure 11 A speed-time graph can be used to find acceleration. When the line rises, the object is speeding up. When the line falls, the object is slowing down.
Infer *what acceleration a horizontal line represents.*

Graphing Accelerated Motion The motion of an object that is accelerating can be shown with a graph. For this type of graph, speed is plotted on the vertical axis and time on the horizontal axis. Take a look at **Figure 11.** On section A of the graph, the speed increases from 0 m/s to 10 m/s during the first 2 s, so the acceleration is +5 m/s². The line in section A slopes upward to the right. An object that is speeding up will have a line on a speed-time graph that slopes upward.

Now look at section C. Between 4 s and 6 s, the object slows down from 10 m/s to 4 m/s. The acceleration is −3 m/s². On the speed-time graph, the line in section C is sloping downward to the right. An object that is slowing down will have a line on a speed-time graph that slopes downward.

On section B, where the line is horizontal, the change in speed is zero. So a horizontal line on the speed-time graph represents an acceleration of zero or constant speed.

section 2 review

Summary

Acceleration and Motion

- Acceleration is the change in velocity divided by the time it takes to make the change. Acceleration has direction.

- Acceleration occurs whenever an object speeds up, slows down, or changes direction.

Calculating Acceleration

- For motion in a straight line, acceleration can be calculated from this equation:

$$a = \frac{s_f - s_i}{t}$$

- If an object is speeding up, its acceleration is positive; if an object is slowing down, its acceleration is negative.

- On a speed-time graph, a line sloping up represents positive acceleration, a line sloping down represents negative acceleration, and a horizontal line represents zero acceleration or constant speed.

Self Check

1. **Compare and contrast** speed, velocity, and acceleration.

2. **Infer** the motion of a car whose speed-time graph shows a horizontal line, followed by a straight line that slopes downward to the bottom of the graph.

3. **Think Critically** You start to roll backward down a hill on your bike, so you use the brakes to stop your motion. In what direction did you accelerate?

Applying Math

4. **Calculate** the acceleration of a runner who accelerates from 0 m/s to 3 m/s in 12 s.

5. **Calculate Speed** An object falls with an acceleration of 9.8 m/s². What is its speed after 2 s?

6. **Make and Use a Graph** A sprinter had the following speeds at different times during a race: 0 m/s at 0 s, 4 m/s at 2 s, 7 m/s at 4 s, 10 m/s at 6 s, 12 m/s at 8 s, and 10 m/s at 10 s. Plot these data on a speed-time graph. During what time intervals is the acceleration positive? Negative? Is the acceleration ever zero?

Science Online ips.msscience.com/self_check_quiz

section 2 review

1. Speed and velocity both include rate of change in position. Acceleration measures rate of change in velocity. Both velocity and acceleration include direction; speed does not.

2. The car first travels at constant speed (horizontal line) and then slows down (sloping line) and comes to a stop (bottom of the graph).

3. Against the motion; I accelerated uphill.

4. $a = (3\ \text{m/s} - 0\ \text{m/s}) \div 12\ \text{s} = 0.25\ \text{m/s}^2$

5. $s_f = 0\ \text{m/s} + 9.8\ \text{m/s}^2 \times 2\ \text{s} = 19.6\ \text{m/s}$

6. Check students' graphs; positive from 0 s to 8 s; negative from 8 s to 10 s. The acceleration must become zero for some short time as it changes from positive to negative between 8 and 10 s.

Momentum

Mass and Inertia

The world you live in is filled with objects in motion. How can you describe these objects? Objects have many properties such as color, size, and composition. One important property of an object is its mass. The **mass** of an object is the amount of matter in the object. In SI units, the unit for mass is the kilogram.

The weight of an object is related to the object's mass. Objects with more mass weigh more than objects with less mass. A bowling ball has more mass than a pillow, so it weighs more than a pillow. However, the size of an object is not the same as the mass of the object. For example, a pillow is larger than a bowling ball, but the bowling ball has more mass.

Objects with different masses are different in an important way. Think about what happens when you try to stop someone who is rushing toward you. A small child is easy to stop. A large adult is hard to stop. The more mass an object has, the harder it is to start it moving, slow it down, speed it up, or turn it. This tendency of an object to resist a change in its motion is called **inertia**. Objects with more mass have more inertia, as shown in **Figure 12.** The more mass an object has, the harder it is to change its motion.

> **Reading Check** *What is inertia?*

as you read

What You'll Learn

- **Explain** the relationship between mass and inertia.
- **Define** momentum.
- **Predict** motion using the law of conservation of momentum.

Why It's Important

Objects in motion have momentum. The motion of objects after they collide depends on their momentum.

⊚ Review Vocabulary
triple-beam balance: scientific instrument used to measure mass precisely by comparing the mass of a sample to known masses

New Vocabulary
- mass
- inertia
- momentum
- law of conservation of momentum

Figure 12 The more mass an object has, the greater its inertia is. A table-tennis ball responds to a gentle hit that would move a tennis ball only slightly.

SECTION 3 Momentum **293**

Section 3 Resource Manager

Chapter *FAST FILE* Resources
Transparency Activity, p. 46
Directed Reading for Content Mastery, pp. 21, 22
Enrichment, p. 32

Lab Worksheets, pp. 5–6, 7–8
Reinforcement, p. 29
Cultural Diversity, p. 63

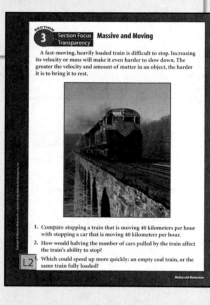

INTEGRATE
Social Studies

Forensics and Momentum
Forensic investigations of accidents and crimes often involve determining the momentum of an object. For example, the law of conservation of momentum sometimes is used to reconstruct the motion of vehicles involved in a collision. Research other ways momentum is used in forensic investigations.

Momentum

You know that the faster a bicycle moves, the harder it is to stop. Just as increasing the mass of an object makes it harder to stop, so does increasing the speed or velocity of the object. The **momentum** of an object is a measure of how hard it is to stop the object, and it depends on the object's mass and velocity. Momentum is usually symbolized by p.

> **Momentum Equation**
> **momentum** (in kg · m/s) = **mass** (in kg) × **velocity** (in m/s)
> $$p = mv$$

Mass is measured in kilograms and velocity has units of meters per second, so momentum has units of kilograms multiplied by meters per second (kg · m/s). Also, because velocity includes a direction, momentum has a direction that is the same as the direction of the velocity.

Reading Check *Explain how an object's momentum changes as its velocity changes.*

Applying Math   Solve a Simple Equation

MOMENTUM OF A BICYCLE Calculate the momentum of a 14-kg bicycle traveling north at 2 m/s.

Solution

1 *This is what you know:*
- mass: $m = 14$ kg
- velocity: $v = 2$ m/s north

2 *This is what you need to find:*
momentum: $p = ?$ kg · m/s

3 *This is the procedure you need to use:*
Substitute the known values of mass and velocity into the momentum equation and calculate the momentum:
$p = mv = (14$ kg$)$ $(2$ m/s north$) = 28$ kg · m/s north

4 *Check your answer:*
Divide the calculated momentum by the mass of the bicycle. You should get the velocity that was given.

Practice Problems

1. A 10,000-kg train is traveling east at 15 m/s. Calculate the momentum of the train.
2. What is the momentum of a car with a mass of 900 kg traveling north at 27 m/s?

Science Online   For more practice, visit ips.msscience.com/ math_practice

Curriculum Connection

Physical Education Momentum and inertia are part of all sports. Ask each student to choose a sport and prepare a poster illustrating how momentum and inertia are important in that sport. Possibilities include the inertia of a runner racing around an oval track, the momentum of a soccer ball going past a goalie, and the inertia of a wrestler. L2 LS Visual-Spatial P

Fun Fact

When an object falls toward Earth, its momentum downward is balanced by Earth's momentum upward — but Earth is so massive that its velocity is too tiny to be felt!

Conservation of Momentum

If you've ever played billiards, you know that when the cue ball hits another ball, the motions of both balls change. The cue ball slows down and may change direction, so its momentum decreases. Meanwhile, the other ball starts moving, so its momentum increases. It seems as if momentum is transferred from the cue ball to the other ball.

In fact, during the collision, the momentum lost by the cue ball was gained by the other ball. This means that the total momentum of the two balls was the same just before and just after the collision. This is true for any collision, as long as no outside forces such as friction act on the objects and change their speeds after the collision. According to the **law of conservation of momentum,** the total momentum of objects that collide is the same before and after the collision. This is true for the collisions of the billiard balls shown in **Figure 13,** as well as for collisions of atoms, cars, football players, or any other matter.

Using Momentum Conservation

Outside forces, such as gravity and friction, are almost always acting on objects that are colliding. However, sometimes, the effects of these forces are small enough that they can be ignored. Then the law of conservation of momentum enables you to predict how the motions of objects will change after a collision.

There are many ways that collisions can occur. Two examples are shown in **Figure 14.** Sometimes, the objects that collide will bounce off of each other, like the bowling ball and bowling pins. In other collisions, objects will stick to each other after the collision, like the two football players. In both of these types of collisions, the law of conservation of momentum enables the speeds of the objects after the collision to be calculated.

Figure 13 When the cue ball hits the other billiard balls, it slows down because it transfers some of its momentum to the other billiard balls.
Predict *what would happen to the speed of the cue ball if all of its momentum were transferred to the other billiard balls.*

Figure 14 In these collisions, the total momentum before the collision equals the total momentum after the collision.

When the bowling ball hits the pins, some of its momentum is transferred to the pins. The ball slows down, and the pins speed up.

When one player tackles the other, they both change speeds, but momentum is conserved.

Discussion

Ball Motion Suppose two balls approach each other at 1 m/s from opposite directions. Their total momentum is zero. After the collision, they both zoom off at 1 m/s in opposite directions. What is their momentum? It is still zero. What do you know about the masses of the two balls? If the total momentum is zero and the two balls have the same speed in opposite directions, the balls must have the same mass. L2 **LS** **Logical-Mathematical**

Quick Demo

Momentum Conservation

Materials ball, rolling cart or roller skates

Estimated Time 15 minutes

Procedure While sitting on a rolling cart or standing on roller skates, use both hands to throw a ball forcefully forward. Explain that, because you and the ball were initially at rest, the total initial momentum was zero. When you threw the ball, you gave it positive momentum in the forward direction. As a result, you started to roll backward (negative momentum) so that the total momentum would still be zero.

Before the student on skates and the backpack collide, she is not moving.

After the collision, the student and the backpack move together at a slower speed than the backpack had before the collision.

Figure 15 Momentum is conserved in the collision of the backpack and the student.

Science **Online**

Topic: Collisions

Visit ips.msscience.com for Web links to information about collisions between objects with different masses.

Activity Draw diagrams showing the results of collisions between a bowling ball and a tennis ball if they are moving in the same direction and if they are in opposite directions.

Sticking Together Imagine being on skates when someone throws a backpack to you, as in **Figure 15**. When you catch the backpack, you and the backpack continue to move in the same direction as the backpack was moving before the collision.

The law of conservation of momentum can be used to find your velocity after you catch the backpack. Suppose a 2-kg backpack is tossed at a speed of 5 m/s. Your mass is 48 kg, and initially you are at rest. Then the total initial momentum is

$$\text{total momentum} = \text{momentum of backpack} + \text{your momentum}$$
$$= 2 \text{ kg} \times 5 \text{ m/s} + 48 \text{ kg} \times 0 \text{ m/s}$$
$$= 10 \text{ kg} \cdot \text{m/s}$$

After the collision, the total momentum remains the same, and only one object is moving. Its mass is the sum of your mass and the mass of the backpack. You can use the equation for momentum to find the final velocity.

$$\text{total momentum} = (\text{mass of backpack} + \text{your mass}) \times \text{velocity}$$
$$10 \text{ kg} \cdot \text{m/s} = (2 \text{ kg} + 48 \text{ kg}) \times \text{velocity}$$
$$10 \text{ kg} \cdot \text{m/s} = (50 \text{ kg}) \times \text{velocity}$$
$$0.2 \text{ m/s} = \text{velocity}$$

This is your velocity right after you catch the backpack. As you continue to move on your skates, the force of friction between the ground and the skates slows you down. Because of friction, the momentum of you and the backpack together continually decreases until you come to a stop. **Figure 16** shows the results of some collisions between two objects with various masses and velocities.

LAB DEMONSTRATION

Purpose to observe and measure momentum during an inelastic collision

Materials 2 toy cars, 2 metersticks, balance, timer

Preparation Set up a straight course bounded by two metersticks set end to end.

Procedure Measure and record the mass of each toy car. Place one car at the zero mark of the second meterstick. Push the other car so that it starts rolling at the zero mark of the first meterstick and hits the first car. Measure the time it takes the rolling car to reach the standing car, and measure the time and distance the two cars roll after the collision. Calculate the momentum before and after the collision.

Assessment

Was momentum conserved in this collision? Answers will depend on experimental results. If not, why not? Friction caused the toy cars to slow down, so their total momentum decreased.

Figure 16

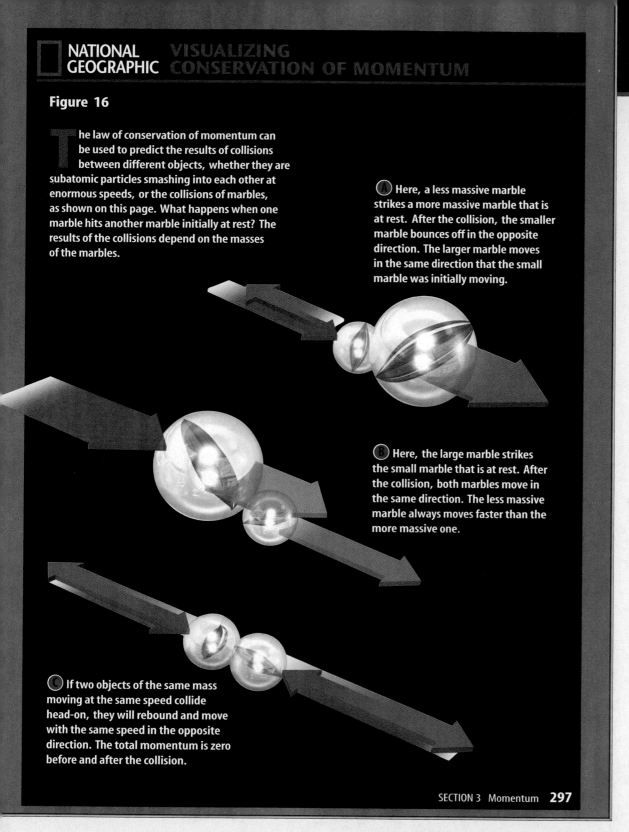

The law of conservation of momentum can be used to predict the results of collisions between different objects, whether they are subatomic particles smashing into each other at enormous speeds, or the collisions of marbles, as shown on this page. What happens when one marble hits another marble initially at rest? The results of the collisions depend on the masses of the marbles.

Ⓐ Here, a less massive marble strikes a more massive marble that is at rest. After the collision, the smaller marble bounces off in the opposite direction. The larger marble moves in the same direction that the small marble was initially moving.

Ⓑ Here, the large marble strikes the small marble that is at rest. After the collision, both marbles move in the same direction. The less massive marble always moves faster than the more massive one.

Ⓒ If two objects of the same mass moving at the same speed collide head-on, they will rebound and move with the same speed in the opposite direction. The total momentum is zero before and after the collision.

SECTION 3 Momentum **297**

Visualizing Conservation of Momentum

Have students examine the pictures and read the captions. Then ask the following questions.

If a small car is stopped at a traffic light and is hit from behind by a truck, what will happen? Both vehicles will move forward, with the car moving faster than the truck.

What will happen if two marbles of the same mass, traveling toward each other, collide? The marbles will collide and reverse directions, moving away from each other at the same speed as before the collision.

Activity

Marble Tracks Have small groups of students tape two metersticks to a flat surface. The space between them should be wide enough to allow marbles to travel in the space. Have students form a ramp by placing one end of a grooved ruler on two or three books and the other end at one end of the track. They should place three marbles in the track and roll one marble down the ruler into the track and observe what happens. Ask students to repeat the procedure rolling two and three marbles down the ramp together. Ask them to explain their observations in terms of conservation of momentum. L2 LS **Kinesthetic**

Differentiated Instruction

Challenge Have students research collision tests that are used to rate cars. Ask them to present oral reports on the tests and how the conservation of momentum applies. L3 LS **Linguistic**

Check for Understanding

Logical-Mathematical Ask students to calculate the final velocity of the baseball in the following problem: A tennis ball (57 g) is rolling at a velocity of 5 m/s north. It collides with a baseball (142 g) that is initially at rest. The tennis ball bounces off at a speed of 2 m/s in the opposite direction. (Assume the collision is perfectly elastic.) 2.8 m/s north

Reteach

Inertia Toss a table-tennis ball, tennis ball, and basketball to students. Have the students compare the amounts of force they had to use to stop the three balls and the inertias of the three balls. It took the most force to stop the basketball, which had the most inertia. It took less force to stop the tennis ball, which had less inertia than the basketball. It took very little force to stop the table-tennis ball, which had the least inertia. **L2** **ELL** **LS** **Kinesthetic**

Assessment

Process Ask students to design an experiment to demonstrate qualitatively what happens to velocity in different collisions. Use **Performance Assessment in the Science Classroom,** p. 95.

Figure 17 When bumper cars collide, they bounce off each other, and momentum is transferred.

Colliding and Bouncing Off In some collisions, the objects involved, like the bumper cars in **Figure 17,** bounce off each other. The law of conservation of momentum can be used to determine how these objects move after they collide.

For example, suppose two identical objects moving with the same speed collide head on and bounce off. Before the collision, the momentum of each object is the same, but in opposite directions. So the total momentum before the collision is zero. If momentum is conserved, the total momentum after the collision must be zero also. This means that the two objects must move in opposite directions with the same speed after the collision. Then the total momentum once again is zero.

section 3 review

Summary

Mass, Inertia, and Momentum

- Mass is the amount of matter in an object.
- Inertia is the tendency of an object to resist a change in motion. Inertia increases as the mass of an object increases.
- The momentum of an object in motion is related to how hard it is to stop the object, and can be calculated from the following equation:
  $$p = mv$$
- Because velocity has a direction, momentum also has a direction.

The Law of Conservation of Momentum

- The law of conservation of momentum states that in a collision, the total momentum of the objects that collide is the same before and after the collision.

Self Check

1. **Explain** how momentum is transferred when a golfer hits a ball with a golf club.
2. **Determine** if the momentum of an object moving in a circular path at constant speed is constant.
3. **Explain** why the momentum of a billiard ball rolling on a billiard table changes.
4. **Think Critically** Two identical balls move directly toward each other with equal speeds. How will the balls move if they collide and stick together?

Applying Math

5. **Calculate Momentum** What is the momentum of a 0.1-kg mass moving with a speed of 5 m/s?
6. **Calculate Speed** A 1-kg ball moving at 3 m/s strikes a 2-kg ball and stops. If the 2-kg ball was initially at rest, find its speed after the collision.

298 CHAPTER 10 Motion and Momentum

Science Online ips.msscience.com/self_check_quiz

section 3 review

1. Some of the momentum of the moving club is transferred to the ball when the club collides with the ball.
2. No, because momentum depends on velocity and velocity includes direction, which is constantly changing.

3. The momentum of a rolling billiard ball decreases because its velocity decreases as a result of friction with the table.
4. Momentum must be conserved. Before the collision, the momentum is zero because $m_1v_1 = -m_2v_2$, so

$m_1v_1 + m_2v_2 = 0$. After the collision, the momentum must also be zero. If the balls stick together, the only way for momentum to be zero is if the balls are at rest ($v = 0$).
5. $p = 0.1$ kg $\times$ 5 m/s $= 0.5$ kg·m/s

6. Before the collision, the momentum is 1 kg $\times$ 3 m/s left + 2 kg $\times$ 0 m/s = 3 kg·ms/s left. After the collision, the momentum must also be 3 kg·m/s left, so 1 kg $\times$ v = 3 kg·m/s. v = 3 kg·m/s left $\div$ 2 kg = 1.5 m/s left.

Collisions

A collision occurs when a baseball bat hits a baseball or a tennis racket hits a tennis ball. What would happen if you hit a baseball with a table-tennis paddle or a table-tennis ball with a baseball bat? How do the masses of colliding objects change the results of collisions?

● Real-World Question

How does changing the size and number of objects in a collision affect the collision?

Goals
- **Compare and contrast** different collisions.
- **Determine** how the speeds after a collision depend on the masses of the colliding objects.

Materials
small marbles (5)   metersticks (2)
large marbles (2)   tape

Safety Precautions 🥽 🧪

● Procedure

1. Tape the metersticks next to each other, slightly farther apart than the width of the large marbles. This limits the motion of the marbles to nearly a straight line.

2. Place a small target marble in the center of the track formed by the metersticks. Place another small marble at one end of the track. Flick the small marble toward the target marble. Describe the collision.

3. Repeat step 2, replacing the two small marbles with the two large marbles.

4. Repeat step 2, replacing the small shooter marble with a large marble.

5. Repeat step 2, replacing the small target marble with a large marble.

6. Repeat step 2, replacing the small target marble with four small marbles that are touching.

7. Place two small marbles at opposite ends of the metersticks. Shoot the marbles toward each other and describe the collision.

8. Place two large marbles at opposite ends of the metersticks. Shoot the marbles toward each other and describe the collision.

9. Place a small marble and a large marble at opposite ends of the metersticks. Shoot the marbles toward each other and describe the collision.

● Conclude and Apply

1. **Describe** In which collisions did the shooter marble change direction? How did the mass of the target marble compare with the mass of the shooter marble in these collisions?

2. **Explain** how momentum was conserved in these collisions.

Communicating Your Data

Make a chart showing your results. You might want to make before-and-after sketches, with short arrows to show slow movement and long arrows to show fast movement.

LAB 299

● *Real-World Question*

Purpose Students will construct a car that will protect an egg from a rapid deceleration.

Time Required approximately 70 minutes

Alternate Materials The list for materials that can be used to create the car is nearly endless. Don't use items that are sharp or breakable.

Safety Precautions Because the cars are intended to crash, students should wear safety goggles.

● *Form a Hypothesis*

Possible Hypothesis The egg will be most likely to survive in a car that gradually brings the egg to a stop, thus cushioning it.

● *Test Your Hypothesis*

Possible Procedures The car must roll freely to be fast. The egg must be protected or slowed gradually to a stop by some sort of layers or barriers or restraints.

Teaching Strategy Students will often have elaborate and complex ideas that may be too difficult to be practical. Try to steer them clear of such ideas without stifling their creativity

---

LAB Design Your Own

C🚗r Safety Testing

Goals
- **Construct** a fast car.
- **Design** a safe car that will protect a plastic egg from the effects of inertia when the car crashes.

Possible Materials
insulated foam meat trays or fast food trays
insulated foam cups
straws, narrow and wide
straight pins
tape
plastic eggs

Safety Precautions
🥽 👟 🧤

WARNING: *Protect your eyes from possible flying objects.*

● *Real-World Question*

Imagine that you are a car designer. How can you create an attractive, fast car that is safe? When a car crashes, the passengers have inertia that can keep them moving. How can you protect the passengers from stops caused by sudden, head-on impacts?

● *Form a Hypothesis*

Develop a hypothesis about how to design a car to deliver a plastic egg quickly and safely through a race course and a crash at the end.

● *Test Your Hypothesis*

Make a Plan

1. Be sure your group has agreed on the hypothesis statement.
2. **Sketch** the design for your car. List the materials you will need. Remember that to make the car move smoothly, narrow straws will have to fit into the wider straws.

Differentiated Instruction

Learning Disabled Students who have learning challenges are sometimes good at manipulating or building things. Perhaps one student in a group could design an idea and another could physically create it.

Alternative Inquiry Lab

Real World Connection Partner with an elementary classroom and ask your students to develop a demonstration for the younger students of the value of seat belts and air bags in automobiles, using their eggs and the provided materials.

3. As a group, make a detailed list of the steps you will take to test your hypothesis.

4. Gather the materials you will need to carry out your experiment.

Follow Your Plan

1. Make sure your teacher approves your plan before you start. Include any changes suggested by your teacher in your plans.

2. Carry out the experiment as planned.

3. **Record** any observations that you made while doing your experiment. Include suggestions for improving your design.

Analyze Your Data

1. **Compare** your car design to the designs of the other groups. What made the fastest car fast? What slowed the slowest car?

2. **Compare** your car's safety features to those of the other cars. What protected the eggs the best? How could you improve the unsuccessful designs?

3. **Predict** What effect would decreasing the speed of your car have on the safety of the egg?

Conclude and Apply

1. **Summarize** How did the best designs protect the egg?

2. **Apply** If you were designing cars, what could you do to better protect passengers from sudden stops?

Communicating Your Data

Write a descriptive paragraph about ways a car could be designed to protect its passengers effectively. Include a sketch of your ideas.

Expected Outcome Cars that cushioned their eggs will be most successful. Students should try to discover why some were successful and others weren't.

Analyze Your Data

Answers to Questions

1. Reducing friction and air resistance makes the cars go faster.

2. Eggs with layers of protection to gradually slow them to a stop work best. Such protections have the same effects as car seat belts and air bags.

3. Decreasing the speed would give the egg a better chance for survival because the egg would experience a smaller deceleration during a crash.

Error Analysis Ask students to name features that allowed eggs to survive.

Conclude and Apply

1. The best designs protected the egg in the same way seat belts and airbags protect people.

2. Provide devices to restrain people from being thrown as the car stops.

Assessment

Content Divide the class into groups and ask each group to develop and perform a short skit comparing the cart with the egg to a real car carrying people. Use **Performance Assessment in the Science Classroom**, p. 147.

Active Reading

Synthesis Journal In this strategy, students reflect on a project, paper, or performance in light of their own experiences and plan to apply it personally. Ask students to write a Synthesis Journal entry for this activity. Have each student divide a sheet of paper into three sections. For this activity, have them record *What I did, What I learned,* and *How I can use it.*

Communicating Your Data

To complete their writing, students could also briefly research how the automobile industry tests vehicle safety. Students may also find photos or videos of industry tests to incorporate into their writing.

Content Background

Not all boomerangs return to their throwers. A true boomerang is nothing more than a curved stick that is thrown. The early boomerangs used for hunting by peoples of many ancient cultures (including many tribes in the western United States) were much longer, straighter, and heavier than the more familiar returning types. Returning boomerangs are too light and thin to do much damage to any living thing. Returning boomerangs became popular primarily as playthings for Aborigines in Australia. Some hunters there used them to imitate hawks in flight and so to serve as a decoy to drive other game birds into nets strung from trees. Otherwise, they don't have any real practical uses because they are difficult to throw very accurately. They also probably wouldn't have enough momentum to return to the thrower after hitting something.

Activity

Varying Throw Angle Take students outside and have volunteers throw boomerangs first from a horizontal starting position and then from varying angles. Ask students what is different about the paths of the boomerangs. A boomerang thrown from a horizontal position flies off until it stops spinning and then falls. Boomerangs thrown at different angles curve. Explain to students that when a boomerang is thrown from an angle slightly different from the horizontal, the motions of its wings and its speed through the air cause it to experience a force that makes it circle back to the thrower. L2 LS
Kinesthetic

What Goes Around Comes Around

The Story of Boomerangs

Imagine a group gathered on a flat, yellow plain on the Australian Outback. One youth steps forward and, with the flick of an arm, sends a long, flat, angled stick soaring and spinning into the sky. The stick's path curves until it returns right back into the thrower's hand. Thrower after thrower steps forward, and the contest goes on all afternoon.

This contest involved throwing boomerangs—elegantly curved sticks. Because of how boomerangs are shaped, they always return to the thrower's hand

This amazing design is over 15,000 years old. Scientists believe that boomerangs developed from simple clubs thrown to stun and kill animals for food. Differently shaped clubs flew in different ways. As the shape of the club was refined, people probably started throwing them for fun too. In fact, today, using boomerangs for fun is still a popular sport, as world-class throwers compete in contests of strength and skill.

Boomerangs come in several forms, but all of them have several things in common. First a boomerang is shaped like an airplane's wing: flat on one side and curved on the other. Second, boomerangs are angled, which makes them spin as they fly. These two features determine the aerodynamics that give the boomerang its unique flight path.

From its beginning as a hunting tool to its use in today's World Boomerang Championships, the boomerang has remained a source of fascination for thousands of years.

Design Boomerangs are made from various materials. Research to find instructions for making boomerangs. After you and your friends build some boomerangs, have a competition of your own.

Science Online
For more information, visit
ips.msscience.com/oops

Design Possible competitions might include the best catch, longest flight time, and greatest curvature in flight. Students might also construct targets to hit or paper barriers to curve through. Caution students that, although boomerangs are very light, they can hit hard when moving fast, so students should be careful when throwing them and wear protective goggles and gloves.

Resources for Teachers and Students

Boomerang: Behind an Australian Icon, by Philip Jones, Ten Speed Press, 1997

Many Happy Returns, Quarterly Newsletter of the United States Boomerang Association

Reviewing Main Ideas

Section 1 What is motion?

1. The position of an object depends on the reference point that is chosen.

2. An object is in motion if the position of the object is changing.

3. The speed of an object equals the distance traveled divided by the time:

$$s = \frac{d}{t}$$

4. The velocity of an object includes the speed and the direction of motion.

5. The motion of an object can be represented on a speed-time graph.

Section 2 Acceleration

1. Acceleration is a measure of how quickly velocity changes. It includes a direction.

2. An object is accelerating when it speeds up, slows down, or turns.

3. When an object moves in a straight line, its acceleration can be calculated by

$$a = \frac{(s_f - s_i)}{t}$$

Section 3 Momentum

1. Momentum equals the mass of an object times its velocity:

$$p = mv$$

2. Momentum is transferred from one object to another in a collision.

3. According to the law of conservation of momentum, the total amount of momentum of a group of objects doesn't change unless outside forces act on the objects.

Reviewing Main Ideas

Summary statements can be used by students to review the major concepts of the chapter.

Visualizing Main Ideas

See student page.

Science Online

Visit ips.msscience.com
/self_check_quiz
/interactive_tutor
/vocabulary_puzzlemaker
/chapter_review
/standardized_test

Visualizing Main Ideas

Copy and complete the following table on motion.

Describing Motion

Quantity	Definition	Direction
Distance	length of path traveled	no
Displacement	direction and change in position	yes
Speed	rate of change in position	no
Velocity	rate of change in position and direction	yes
Acceleration	rate of change in velocity	yes
Momentum	mass times velocity	yes

Science Online ips.msscience.com/interactive_tutor

CHAPTER STUDY GUIDE 303

Identifying Misconceptions

Assess

Use the assessment as follow-up to page 280F after students have completed the chapter.
Materials protractor, paper, ruler, string
Procedure Have each student use the protractor to draw a large circle and label four 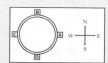 points 90 degrees apart A, B, C and D. Have them place an object at point A, and tell them the object will travel around the circle. Their mission is to find the object's distance trav- eled and displacement at points B, C, and D. Tell them the top of the paper is north.
Expected Outcome Ways to find the distance traveled include using the string to measure the circle or using the formula for a perimeter of a circle.

Using Vocabulary

1. Both measure rate of change in position, but velocity includes a direction.

2. Both are rates of change in motion. Velocity is the rate of change in position, and acceleration is the rate of change in velocity.

3. Momentum is mass multiplied by velocity. The higher the velocity, the higher the momentum.

4. The law of conservation of momentum states that the total momentum of a group of objects is the same before and after they collide unless some outside force acts on the objects.

5. Momentum is mass multiplied by velocity. The higher the mass, the higher the momentum.

6. Mass is a measure of inertia.

7. An object always has inertia. It only has momentum when it is in motion. Both indicate how hard it is to change the object's motion.

8. Both measure rate of change in position. Instantaneous speed gives the speed at a moment in time; average speed gives the average of instantaneous speeds over a given time or distance interval.

Checking Concepts

9. D
10. A
11. C
12. C
13. D
14. B
15. C
16. D
17. C
18. C

Using Vocabulary

acceleration p. 288	mass p. 293
average speed p. 285	momentum p. 294
inertia p. 293	speed p. 284
instantaneous speed p. 285	velocity p. 287
law of conservation	
of momentum p. 295	

Explain the relationship between each pair of words.

1. speed—velocity

2. velocity—acceleration

3. velocity—momentum

4. momentum—law of conservation of momentum

5. mass—momentum

6. mass—inertia

7. momentum—inertia

8. average speed—instantaneous speed

Checking Concepts

Choose the word or phrase that best answers the question.

9. What measures the quantity of matter?
   A) speed   C) acceleration
   B) weight   D) mass

10. Which of the following objects is NOT accelerating?
   A) a jogger moving at a constant speed
   B) a car that is slowing down
   C) Earth orbiting the Sun
   D) a car that is speeding up

11. Which of the following equals speed?
   A) acceleration/time
   B) (change in velocity)/time
   C) distance/time
   D) displacement/time

---

12. A parked car is hit by a moving car, and the two cars stick together. How does the speed of the combined cars compare to the speed of the car before the collision?
   A) Combined speed is the same.
   B) Combined speed is greater.
   C) Combined speed is smaller.
   D) Any of these could be true.

13. What is a measure of inertia?
   A) weight   C) momentum
   B) gravity   D) mass

14. What is 18 cm/h north an example of?
   A) speed
   B) velocity
   C) acceleration
   D) momentum

15. Ball A bumps into ball B. Which is the same before and after the collision?
   A) the momentum of ball A
   B) the momentum of ball B
   C) the sum of the momentums
   D) the difference in the momentums

16. Which of the following equals the change in velocity divided by the time?
   A) speed
   B) displacement
   C) momentum
   D) acceleration

17. You travel to a city 200 km away in 2.5 hours. What is your average speed in km/h?
   A) 180 km/h   C) 80 km/h
   B) 12.5 km/h   D) 500 km/h

18. Two objects collide and stick together. How does the total momentum change?
   A) Total momentum increases.
   B) Total momentum decreases.
   C) The total momentum doesn't change.
   D) The total momentum is zero.

Science Online ips.msscience.com/vocabulary_puzzlemaker

Use the Exam*View*® Pro Testmaker CD-ROM to:

- create multiple versions of tests
- create modified tests with one mouse click for inclusion students
- edit existing questions and add your own questions
- build tests aligned with state standards using built-in State Curriculum Tags
- change English tests to Spanish with one mouse click and vice versa

Thinking Critically

19. Explain You run 100 m in 25 s. If you later run the same distance in less time, explain if your average speed increase or decrease.

Use the graph below to answer questions 20 and 21.

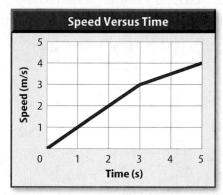

Speed Versus Time

20. Compare For the motion of the object plotted on the speed-time graph above, how does the acceleration between 0 s and 3 s compare to the acceleration between 3 s and 5 s?

21. Calculate the acceleration of the object over the time interval from 0 s to 3 s.

22. Infer The molecules in a gas are often modeled as small balls. If the molecules all have the same mass, infer what happens if two molecules traveling at the same speed collide head on.

23. Calculate What is your displacement if you walk 100 m north, 20 m east, 30 m south, 50 m west, and then 70 m south?

24. Infer You are standing on ice skates and throw a basketball forward. Infer how your motion after you throw the basketball compares with the motion of the basketball.

25. Determine You throw a ball upward and then it falls back down. How does the velocity of the ball change as it rises and falls?

Scienceonline ips.msscience.com/chapter_review

Use the graph below to answer question 26.

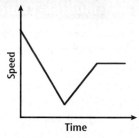

26. Make and Use Graphs The motion of a car is plotted on the speed-time graph above. Over which section of the graph is the acceleration of the car zero?

Performance Activities

27. Demonstrate Design a racetrack and make rules that specify the types of motion allowed. Demonstrate how to measure distance, measure time, and calculate speed accurately.

Applying Math

28. Speed of a Ball Calculate the speed of a 2-kg ball that has a momentum of 10 kg · m/s.

29. Distance Traveled A car travels for a half hour at a speed of 40 km/h. How far does the car travel?

Use the graph below to answer question 30.

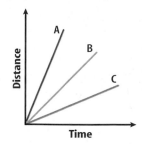

30. Speed From the graph determine which object is moving the fastest and which is moving the slowest.

Thinking Critically

19. It increases; when you divide the same distance by a smaller time, the speed increases.

20. The acceleration between 0 s and 3 s is greater because the slope of this part of the line is steeper.

21. 1 m/s^2

22. The molecules reverse direction and travel at the same speed away from each other.

23. 30 m west

24. The basketball and I experience the same force in opposite directions, so we are accelerated in opposite directions. The basketball's acceleration is greater than my acceleration because its mass is lower.

25. The ball slows down as it moves upward, comes to a stop at the top of the throw, and speeds up as it falls back down

26. the horizontal section

Performance Activities

27. Check students' work. Use **Performance Assessment in the Science Classroom,** p. 145.

Applying Math

National Math Standards
1, 2, 5, 9
28. 10 kg·m/s ÷ 2 kg = 5 m/s
29. 40 km/h × 0.5 h = 20 km
30. Object A is moving fastest; object C is moving slowest.

Part 1 | Multiple Choice

1. C	**7.** B
2. B	**8.** B
3. A	**9.** B
4. A	**10.** D
5. D	**11.** C
6. D	

Part 2 | Short Response

12. No; because inertia depends on mass and two objects of the same size can have different masses. An object with more mass will have greater inertia

13. 1,500 kg·m/s north

14. The sports car will be easier to stop. It has a lower mass and less inertia, so it is easier to change its motion.

15. The ball's momentum decreases because some of it is transferred to the bowling pins.

16. The ball slows down, and the pins speed up.

17. 12 m/s

18. 410 km

Part 1 | Multiple Choice

Record your answers on the answer sheet provided by your teacher or on a sheet of paper.

1. What is the distance traveled divided by the time taken to travel that distance?
  A. acceleration   **C.** speed
  B. velocity   **D.** inertia

2. Sound travels at a speed of 330 m/s. How long does it take for the sound of thunder to travel 1,485 m?
  A. 45 s   **C.** 4,900 s
  B. 4.5 s   **D.** 0.22 s

Use the figure below to answer questions 3 and 4.

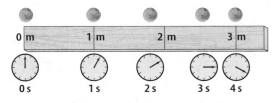

3. During which time period is the ball's average speed the fastest?
  A. between 0 and 1 s
  B. between 1 and 2 s
  C. between 2 and 3 s
  D. between 3 and 4 s

4. What is the average speed of the ball?
  A. 0.8 m/s   **C.** 10 m/s
  B. 1 m/s   **D.** 0.7 m/s

5. A car accelerates from 15 m/s to 30 m/s in 3.0 s. What is the car's acceleration?
  A. 10 m/s^2 **C.** 15 m/s^2
  B. 25 m/s^2 **D.** 5.0 m/s^2

6. Which of the following can occur when an object is accelerating?
  A. It speeds up.   **C.** It changes direction.
  B. It slows down.   **D.** all of the above

---

7. What is the momentum of a 21-kg bicycle traveling west at 3.0 m/s?
  A. 7 kg · m/s west   **C.** 18 kg · m/s west
  B. 63 kg · m/s west   **D.** 24 kg · m/s west

Use the figure below to answer questions 8–10.

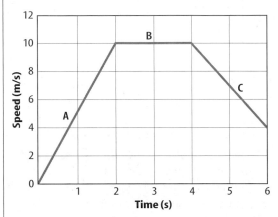

Speed v. Time

8. What is the acceleration between 0 and 2 s?
  A. 10 m/s^2 **C.** 0 m/s^2
  B. 5 m/s^2 **D.** −5 m/s^2

9. During what time period does the object have a constant speed?
  A. between 1 and 2 s
  B. between 2 and 3 s
  C. between 4 and 5 s
  D. between 5 and 6 s

10. What is the acceleration between 4 and 6 s?
  A. 10 m/s^2 **C.** 6 m/s^2
  B. 4 m/s^2 **D.** −3 m/s^2

11. An acorn falls from the top of an oak and accelerates at 9.8 m/s^2. It hits the ground in 1.5 s. What is the speed of the acorn when it hits the ground?
  A. 9.8 m/s   **C.** 15 m/s
  B. 20 m/s   **D.** 30 m/s

---

19. No; because even if the speed is constant, the car could be changing direction, which is also a form of acceleration.

20. The distance she traveled is 8 km. Her displacement is zero because she ends up back at her starting point.

21. Its speed is decreasing as it rises and increasing as it falls. Its velocity is changing the whole time because its speed and direction are changing. The acceleration of the ball is downward, so the ball's path turns in that direction.

22. The ball has positive acceleration when it is falling because it is speeding up. It has negative acceleration when it is rising because it is slowing down.

Part 2 | Short Response/Grid In

Record your answers on the answer sheet provided by your teacher or on a sheet of paper.

12. Do two objects that are the same size always have the same inertia? Why or why not?

13. What is the momentum of a 57 kg cheetah running north at 27 m/s?

14. A sports car and a moving van are traveling at a speed of 30 km/h. Which vehicle will be easier to stop? Why?

Use the figure below to answer questions 15 and 16.

15. What happens to the momentum of the bowling ball when it hits the pins?

16. What happens to the speed of the ball and the speed of the pins?

17. What is the speed of a race horse that runs 1500 m in 125 s?

18. A car travels for 5.5 h at an average speed of 75 km/h. How far did it travel?

19. If the speedometer on a car indicates a constant speed, can you be certain the car is not accelerating? Explain.

20. A girl walks 2 km north, then 2 km east, then 2 km south, then 2 km west. What distance does she travel? What is her displacement?

Part 3 | Open Ended

Record your answers on a sheet of paper.

Use the figure below to answer questions 21 and 22.

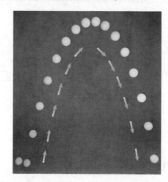

21. Describe the motion of the ball in terms of its speed, velocity, and acceleration.

22. During which part of its path does the ball have positive acceleration? During which part of its path does it have negative acceleration? Explain.

23. Describe what will happen when a baseball moving to the left strikes a bowling ball that is at rest.

24. A girl leaves school at 3:00 and starts walking home. Her house is 2 km from school. She gets home at 3:30. What was her average speed? Do you know her instantaneous speed at 3:15? Why or why not?

25. Why is it dangerous to try to cross a railroad track when a very slow-moving train is approaching?

Test-Taking Tip

Look for Missing Information Questions sometimes will ask about missing information. Notice what is missing as well as what is given.

Rubrics

The following rubrics are sample scoring devices for short response and open-ended questions.

Short Response

Points	Description
2	The student demonstrates a thorough understanding of the science of the task. The response may contain minor flaws that do not detract from the demonstration of a thorough understanding.
1	The student has provided a response that is only partially correct.
0	The student has provided a completely incorrect solution or no response at all.

Open Ended

Points	Description
4	The student demonstrates a thorough understanding of the science of the task. The response may contain minor flaws that do not detract from the demonstration of a thorough understanding.
3	The student demonstrates an understanding of the science of the task. The response is essentially correct and demonstrates an essential but less than thorough understanding of the science.
2	The student demonstrates only a partial understanding of the science of the task. Although the student may have used the correct approach to a solution or may have provided a correct solution, the work lacks an essential understanding of the underlying science concepts.
1	The student demonstrates a very limited understanding of the science of the task. The response is incomplete and exhibits many flaws.
0	The student provides a completely incorrect solution or no response at all.

Part 3 | Open Ended

23. After the collision, the baseball will bounce off the bowling ball and move in the opposite direction, or to the right, at a lower speed. The bowling ball will move slowly in the direction in which the baseball was originally moving, or to the left.

24. Her average speed was 2 km/0.5 h = 4 km/h. It is impossible to know her instantaneous speed at 3:15 because she may not have been walking at a constant speed. Only her average speed can be found.

25. A train has a huge mass, so its momentum is huge even when it is moving very slowly. The train's large mass makes slowing it down difficult. Even if the engineer sees a vehicle on a track, the train might not be able to stop in time.

Section/Objectives	Standards		Labs/Features
Chapter Opener	**National**	**State/Local**	**Launch Lab:** How do forces affect a ball? p. 309
	See pp. 16T–17T for a Key to Standards.		**Foldables,** p. 309
Section 1 Newton's First Law 2 sessions 1 block 1. **Distinguish** between balanced and net forces. 2. **Describe** Newton's first law of motion. 3. **Explain** how friction affects motion.	National Content Standards: UCP.1–UCP.3, UCP.5, A.1, A.2, B.1, G.2, G.3		**Integrate Life Science,** p. 311 **Science Online,** p. 313 **MiniLAB:** Observing Friction, p. 314
Section 2 Newton's Second Law 3 sessions 1.5 blocks 4. **Explain** Newton's second law of motion. 5. **Explain** why the direction of force is important.	National Content Standards: UCP.1–UCP.3, UCP.5, A.1, A.2, B.1–B.3		**Integrate History,** p. 317 **Applying Math:** Acceleration of a Car, p. 319
Section 3 Newton's Third Law 4 sessions 2 blocks 6. **Identify** the relationship between the forces that objects exert on each other.	National Content Standards: UCP.1–UCP.3, UCP.5, A.1, B.1–B.3, F.5		**Science Online,** p. 324 **Visualizing Newton's Laws in Sports,** p. 325 **MiniLAB:** Measuring Force Pairs, p. 327 **Lab:** Balloon Races, p. 329 **Lab:** Modeling Motion in Two Directions, pp. 330–331 **Science and Society:** Air Bag Safety, p. 332

Lab Materials	Reproducible Resources	Section Assessment	Technology
Launch Lab: metersticks (2), books (3), marble	**Chapter** *FAST FILE* **Resources** Foldables Worksheet, p. 17 Directed Reading Overview, p. 19 Note-taking Worksheets, pp. 33–35	GLENCOE'S **ASSESSMENT** ADVANTAGE	**TeacherWorks** includes: • Interactive Teacher Edition • Lesson Planner with calendar • Access to all program blacklines • Correlations to standards • Web links
MiniLAB: flat bar of soap, flat eraser, key, hard-sided notebook	**Chapter** *FAST FILE* **Resources** Transparency Activity, p. 44 MiniLAB, p. 3 Lab Activity, pp. 9–12 Enrichment, p. 30 Reinforcement, p. 27 Directed Reading, p. 20 Transparency Activity, pp. 47–48 **Home and Community Involvement,** p. 23	**Portfolio** Assessment, p. 315 **Performance** MiniLAB, p. 314 Applying Skills, p. 315 **Content** Section Review, p. 315	▪ Section Focus Transparency ▪ Teaching Transparency ∩ Guided Reading Audio Program ◉ Interactive Chalkboard CD-ROM
Need materials? Contact Science Kit at 1-800-828-7777 or www.sciencekit.com on the Internet.	**Chapter** *FAST FILE* **Resources** Transparency Activity, p. 45 Lab Activity, pp. 13–16 Enrichment, p. 31 Reinforcement, p. 28 Directed Reading, p. 21 Transparency Activity, pp. 47–48 **Mathematics Skill Activities,** p. 9	**Performance** Applying Math, p. 319 Applying Math, p. 322 **Content** Section Review, p. 322	▪ Section Focus Transparency ◉ Virtual Labs CD-ROM ∩ Guided Reading Audio Program ◉ Interactive Chalkboard CD-ROM
MiniLAB: spring scales (2), **Lab:** balloons of different sizes and shapes, drinking straws, string, tape, meterstick, stopwatch **Lab:** masking tape, stop-watch, meterstick, spring scales (2), plastic lid, golf ball	**Chapter** *FAST FILE* **Resources** Transparency Activity, p. 46 MiniLAB, p. 4 Enrichment, p. 32 Reinforcement, p. 29 Directed Reading, pp. 20, 22 Lab Worksheets, pp. 5–6, 7–8 Transparency Activity, pp. 47–48 **Lab Management and Safety,** p. 65	**Portfolio** MiniLAB Assessment, p. 327 **Performance** MiniLAB, p. 327 Applying Math, p. 328 **Content** Section Review, p. 328	▪ Section Focus Transparency ∩ Guided Reading Audio Program ◉ Interactive Chalkboard CD-ROM ▭ Video Lab

End of Chapter Assessment

GLENCOE'S **ASSESSMENT** ADVANTAGE

Blackline Masters	Technology	Professional Series
Chapter *FAST FILE* **Resources** Chapter Review, pp. 37–38 Chapter Tests, pp. 39–42 **Standardized Test Practice,** pp. 47–50	▭ MindJogger Videoquiz ◉ Virtual Labs CD-ROM ◉ Exam*View*® Pro Testmaker ◉ TeacherWorks CD-ROM ◉ Interactive Chalkboard CD-ROM	**Performance Assessment in the Science Classroom (PASC)**

Transparencies

Section Focus

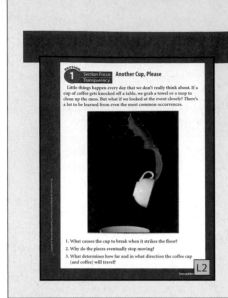

Section Focus Transparency 1 — Another Cup, Please

Little things happen every day that we don't really think about. If a cup of coffee gets knocked off a table, we grab a towel or a mop to clean up the mess. But what if we looked at the event closely? There's a lot to be learned from even the most common occurrences.

1. What causes the cup to break when it strikes the floor?
2. Why do the pieces eventually stop moving?
3. What determines how far and in what direction the coffee cup (and coffee) will travel?

L2

Section Focus Transparency 2 — Loop D'loop

Have you ever gone upside down on a roller coaster? What kept the car on the track? In the cartoon, Calvin is pulling the sled far up the hill so he can get a good start.

1. Does it make a difference where Calvin begins his descent? Explain.
2. How does friction figure into Calvin's scheme?
3. How will gravity affect Calvin if he makes it into the loop?

L2

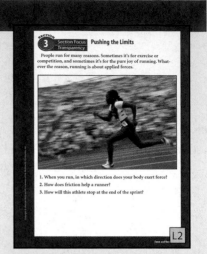

Section Focus Transparency 3 — Pushing the Limits

People run for many reasons. Sometimes it's for exercise or competition, and sometimes it's for the pure joy of running. Whatever the reason, running is about applied forces.

1. When you run, in which direction does your body exert force?
2. How does friction help a runner?
3. How will this athlete stop at the end of the sprint?

L2

Assessment

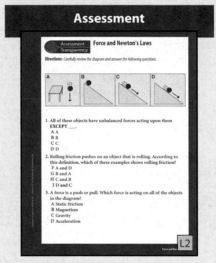

Assessment Transparency — Force and Newton's Laws

Directions: Carefully review the diagram and answer the following questions.

1. All of these objects have unbalanced forces acting upon them EXCEPT ___.
   A A
   B B
   C C
   D D
2. Rolling friction pushes on an object that is rolling. According to this definition, which of these examples shows rolling friction?
   F A and D
   G B and A
   H C and B
   J D and C
3. A force is a push or pull. Which force is acting on all of the objects in the diagram?
   A Static friction
   B Magnetism
   C Gravity
   D Acceleration

L2

Teaching

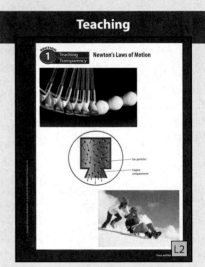

Teaching Transparency 1 — Newton's Laws of Motion

L2

This is a representation of key blackline masters available in the Teacher Classroom Resources. See Resource Manager boxes within the chapter for additional information.

Key to Teaching Strategies

The following designations will help you decide which activities are appropriate for your students.

L1 Level 1 activities should be appropriate for students with learning difficulties.

L2 Level 2 activities should be within the ability range of all students.

L3 Level 3 activities are designed for above-average students.

ELL ELL activities should be within the ability range of English Language Learners.

COOP LEARN Cooperative Learning activities are designed for small group work.

LS Multiple Learning Styles logos, as described on page 12T, are used throughout to indicate strategies that address different learning styles.

P These strategies represent student products that can be placed into a best-work portfolio.

PBL Problem-Based Learning activities apply real-world situations to learning.

Hands-on Activities

Student Text Lab Worksheet

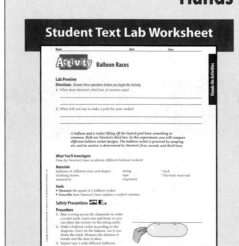

Activity — Balloon Races

Lab Preview
Directions: Answer these questions before you begin the Activity.
1. What does Newton's third law of motion state?

2. What will you use to make a path for your rocket?

A balloon and a rocket lifting off the launch pad have something in common. Both use Newton's third law. In this experiment, you will compare different balloon rocket designs. The balloon rocket is powered by escaping air, and its motion is determined by Newton's first, second, and third laws.

What You'll Investigate
How do Newton's laws accelerate different balloon rockets?

Materials
balloons of different sizes and shapes
drinking straws
meterstick
string
tape
stopwatch
*clock
*Alternate materials

Goals
• **Measure** the speed of a balloon rocket.
• **Describe** how Newton's laws explain a rocket's motion.

Safety Precautions

Procedure
1. Run a string across the classroom to make a rocket path. Leave one end loose so you can place the rockets on the string easily.
2. Make a balloon rocket according to the diagram. Don't tie the balloon. Let it run down the track. Measure the distance it travels and the time it takes.
3. Repeat step 2 with different balloons.

L2

Laboratory Activities

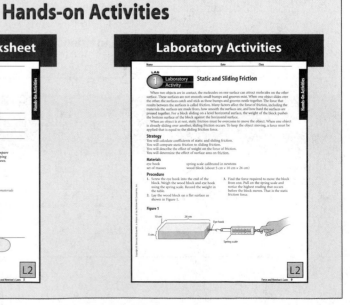

Laboratory Activity 1 — Static and Sliding Friction

When two objects are in contact, the molecules on one surface can attract molecules on the other surface. These surfaces are not smooth; small bumps and grooves exist. When one object slides over the other, the surfaces catch and stick as these bumps and grooves nestle together. The force that results between the surfaces is called friction. Many factors affect the force of friction, including the materials the surfaces are made from, how smooth the surfaces are, and how hard the surfaces are pressed together. For a block sliding on a level horizontal surface, the weight of the block pushes the bottom surface of the block against the horizontal surface.

When an object is at rest, static friction must be overcome to move the object. When one object is already sliding over another, sliding friction occurs. To keep the object moving, a force must be applied that is equal to the sliding friction force.

Strategy
You will calculate coefficients of static and sliding friction.
You will compare static friction to sliding friction.
You will describe the effect of weight on the force of friction.
You will determine the effect of surface area on friction.

Materials
eye hook
set of masses
spring scale calibrated in newtons
wood block (about 5 cm × 10 cm × 26 cm)

Procedure
1. Screw the eye hook into the end of the block. Weigh the wood block and eye hook using the spring scale. Record the weight in the table.
2. Lay the wood block on a flat surface as shown in Figure 1.
3. Find the force required to move the block from rest. Pull on the spring scale and notice the highest reading that occurs before the block moves. That is the static friction force.

Figure 1

L2

Meeting Different Ability Levels

Content Outline
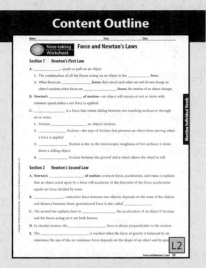

Reinforcement
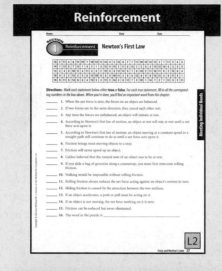

Enrichment
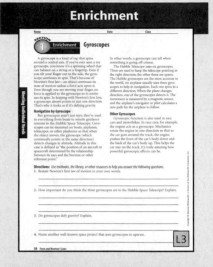

Directed Reading (English/Spanish)
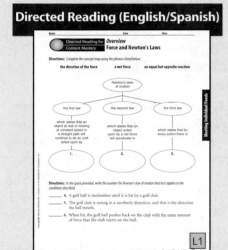

Study Guide

Reading Essentials

Assessment

Test Practice Workbook
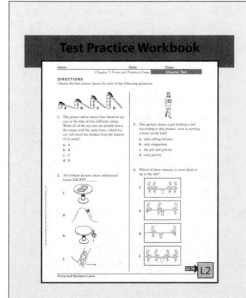

Chapter Review
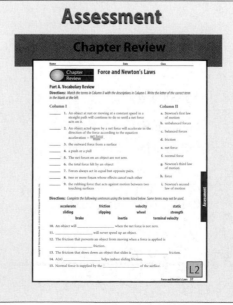

Chapter Tests
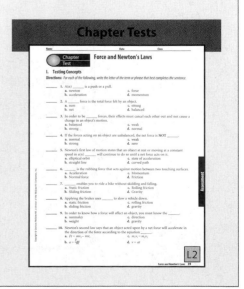

Science Content Background

section 1 Newton's First Law

Force

A force is a push or a pull. If two objects must be in contact to exert forces on each other, it is a contact force, like friction between two surfaces. Other forces, such as the gravitational force, are long-ranged forces.

Newton's First Law of Motion

According to Newton's first law of motion, a change in motion, or acceleration, is caused by a force. Because forces cause a change in motion, an object can be moving even if there are no forces acting on it. Then the object's velocity will be constant, and the object will move in a straight line with constant speed. When more than one force is acting on an object, the combination of the forces, is called the net force.

Friction

Friction is a force that acts between any two surfaces in contact. Electromagnetic forces act between the atoms and molecules on the two surfaces. These electromagnetic forces cause bonds to be formed that weld the surfaces together in some places. These welds must be broken before the surfaces can slide past each other. This is the source of static friction.

section 2 Newton's Second Law

Gravity

Gravity acts between all objects and causes them to be attracted to each other. According to Newton's law of universal gravitation, the gravitational force between two objects is $F = G\,m_1 m_2/d_2$, where G is the universal gravitational constant, m_1 and m_2 are the masses of the objects, and d is the distance between them. Near Earth's surface, this equation gives the force between Earth and any other object as $F = m(9.8\ \text{m/s}^2)$.

section 3 Newton's Third Law

Action and Reaction

According to Newton's third law, forces always act in action-reaction pairs. When one object exerts a force on another, the second object always exerts a force of the same size, but in the opposite direction, on the first object. For example, the force of gravity between two objects is exerted on both objects. The size of the force is the same on both objects, and the direction of the force on one object is opposite to the direction of the force on the other.

chapter content resources

Internet Resources

For additional content background, visit **ips.msscience.com** to:

- access your book onlineonline
- find references to related articles in popular science magazines
- access Web links with related content background
- access current events with science journal topics

Print Resources

The Spinning Blackboard, by Paul Doherty, Don Rothjen, The Exploratorium Teacher Institute, John Wiley and Sons, 1996

Hands-on Physics Activities with Real-Life Applications, by James Cunningham, Norman Herr, Jossey-Bass, 2002

Turning the World Inside Out and 174 Other Simple Physics Demonstrations, by Robert Ehrlich, Jearl Walker, Princeton University Press, 1990

 **IDENTIFYING** ▷ # Misconceptions

Find Out What Students Think

Students may think that . . .

An object at rest resists acceleration only because of friction.
Students have probably learned about friction in the past and view it as the thing that works against motion.

Demonstration

Place a small cart or car on your desk. Give it a push and give a humorous grunt to show that it is hard work to get it going. Once it is moving make the pushing seem effortless. Ask students whether they have ever had to help push a stalled car. Did they notice that it takes a lot of effort to get the car going and less effort to keep it going?

Ask students why it takes a larger force to move a stopped car than it does to push a moving car. Give students a few minutes to think about the question. Then have them share their thoughts with a partner. Ask some of the pairs to share their answers with the whole class. Finally, see if the class can come to consensus about the correct answer to this question.

Promote Understanding

Activity

Give each group a cart, a hanging spring scale that reads force in Newtons, five objects with different masses, and string. Show them how to find the amount of force needed to pull the cart as shown in the diagram below.

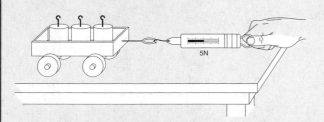

5N

- Have students practice slowly pulling the cart and measuring the maximum force needed to get the cart moving. Then have them practice measuring the force needed to move the cart with constant velocity.

Once students are proficient in these techniques, ask them to investigate how increasing the cart's mass affects these two forces.

- They will need to know or measure the mass of the cart and the masses of each of the added objects.

- Suggest students graph their data with mass on the *x*-axis and force on the *y*-axis.

After students complete the activity, discuss with them the following questions:

- What is the relationship between the mass of the cart and the maximum force needed to get the cart moving? The greater the mass, the greater the force needed.

- Why is a force needed to have the cart move with constant velocity? to overcome friction

- Why is the force needed to start the cart moving always greater than the force to keep it moving? The friction between the cart and the table is greater when the cart is at rest.

Assess

After completing the chapter, see *Identifying Misconceptions* in the Study Guide at the end of the chapter.

Force and Newton's Laws

Chapter Vocabulary

force, p. 310
net force, p. 311
balanced forces, p. 311
unbalanced forces, p. 311
Newton's first law of motion, p. 312
friction, p. 312
Newton's second law of motion, p. 316
weight, p. 317
center of mass, p. 322
Newton's third law of motion, p. 323

Science Journal Possible answers: pulling a sled—a person supplied the force to overcome the sled's inertia; pulling an anchored boat closer to the dock—a person supplied the force to overcome the boat's inertia

PowerPoint® Presentations

This CD-ROM is an editable Microsoft® PowerPoint® presentation that includes:
• a pre-made presentation for every chapter
• interactive graphics
• animations
• audio clips
• image bank
• all new section and chapter questions
• Standardized Test Practice
• transparencies
• pre-lab questions for all labs
• Foldables directions
• links to ips.msscience.com

chapter preview

sections

1   Newton's First Law
2   Newton's Second Law
3   Newton's Third Law
    Lab Balloon Races
    Lab Modeling Motion in Two Directions
    Virtual Labs What is Newton's second law of motion?

Moving at a Crawl

This enormous vehicle is a crawler that moves a space shuttle to the launch pad. The crawler and space shuttle together have a mass of about 7,700,000 kg. To move the crawler at a speed of about 1.5 km/h requires a force of about 10,000,000 N. This force is exerted by 16 electric motors in the crawler.

Science Journal Describe three examples of pushing or pulling an object. How did the object move?

Theme Connection

Systems and Interactions Newton's laws of motion form a system that can be used to determine an object's future motions. Objects interacting with each other also follow these laws. If you know the forces acting between objects, you can determine the changes in the objects' future motion.

About the Photo

Crawlers When these crawlers were built, they were the largest tracked vehicles ever made. One crawler requires eleven drivers. The electric motors are powered by huge diesel engines that use 350 liters of diesel per kilometer.

Start-Up Activities

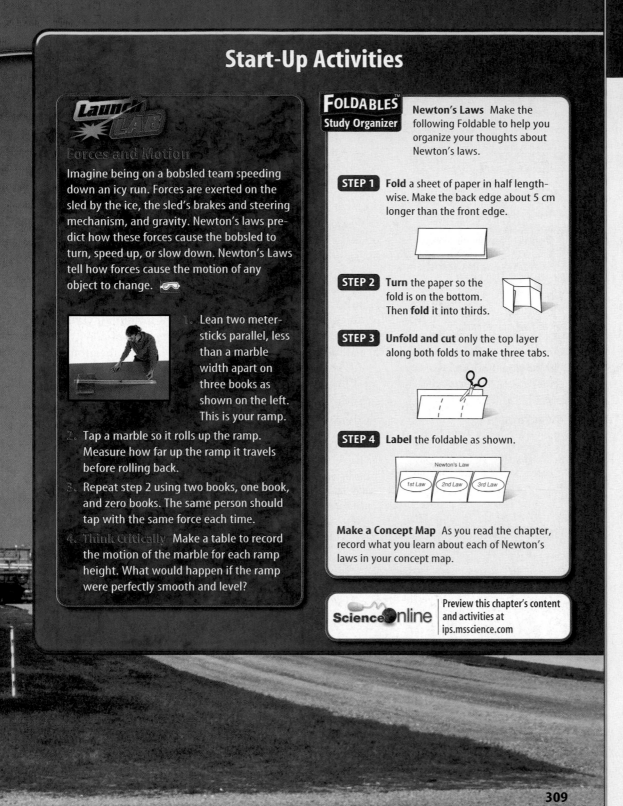

Forces and Motion

Imagine being on a bobsled team speeding down an icy run. Forces are exerted on the sled by the ice, the sled's brakes and steering mechanism, and gravity. Newton's laws predict how these forces cause the bobsled to turn, speed up, or slow down. Newton's Laws tell how forces cause the motion of any object to change.

1. Lean two meter-sticks parallel, less than a marble width apart on three books as shown on the left. This is your ramp.

2. Tap a marble so it rolls up the ramp. Measure how far up the ramp it travels before rolling back.

3. Repeat step 2 using two books, one book, and zero books. The same person should tap with the same force each time.

4. **Think Critically** Make a table to record the motion of the marble for each ramp height. What would happen if the ramp were perfectly smooth and level?

FOLDABLES
Study Organizer

Newton's Laws Make the following Foldable to help you organize your thoughts about Newton's laws.

STEP 1 **Fold** a sheet of paper in half lengthwise. Make the back edge about 5 cm longer than the front edge.

STEP 2 **Turn** the paper so the fold is on the bottom. Then **fold** it into thirds.

STEP 3 **Unfold and cut** only the top layer along both folds to make three tabs.

STEP 4 **Label** the foldable as shown.

> Newton's Law
> 1st Law   2nd Law   3rd Law

Make a Concept Map As you read the chapter, record what you learn about each of Newton's laws in your concept map.

Science Online
Preview this chapter's content and activities at
ips.msscience.com

Launch LAB

Purpose Use the Launch Lab to help students see the effect the steepness of a ramp has on the motion of a marble. L2 ELL LS **Kinesthetic**

Preparation Make sure that the books used are of similar thickness.

Materials 3 books, 2 metersticks, 1 marble

Teaching Strategies To make sure the initial speed of the marble is constant, use a flexible strip to make a launch ramp. Always release the marble from the same point on the ramp, and be sure there isn't a significant bump where the ramps join.

Thinking Critically

Students' data should show that the flatter the incline, the longer the distance traveled by the marble. If the ramp were perfectly smooth and flat, the marble would roll forever.

Assessment

Oral Show students a picture of a bobsled track, ski run, or slide. Ask them to identify the points at which a rider would have maximum speed. Ask students to write a sentence or two defending their choices. Use **Performance Assessment in the Science Classroom**, p. 159.

FOLDABLES
Study Organizer

Dinah Zike Study Fold

Student preparation materials for this Foldable are available in the Chapter *FAST FILE* Resources.

309

Newton's First Law

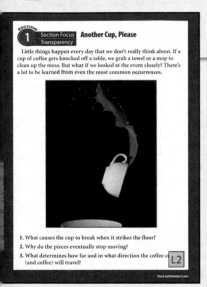
as you read

What You'll Learn

- **Distinguish** between balanced and net forces.
- **Describe** Newton's first law of motion.
- **Explain** how friction affects motion.

Why It's Important

Newton's first law explains why objects change direction.

Review Vocabulary

velocity: the speed and direction of a moving object

New Vocabulary

- force
- net force
- balanced forces
- unbalanced forces
- Newton's first law of motion
- friction

Force

A soccer ball sits on the ground, motionless, until you kick it. Your science book sits on the table until you pick it up. If you hold your book above the ground, then let it go, gravity pulls it to the floor. In every one of these cases, the motion of the ball or book was changed by something pushing or pulling on it. An object will speed up, slow down, or turn only if something is pushing or pulling on it.

A **force** is a push or a pull. Examples of forces are shown in **Figure 1.** Think about throwing a ball. Your hand exerts a force on the ball, and the ball accelerates forward until it leaves your hand. After the ball leaves your hand, the force of gravity causes its path to curve downward. When the ball hits the ground, the ground exerts a force, stopping the ball.

A force can be exerted in different ways. For instance, a paper clip can be moved by the force a magnet exerts, the pull of Earth's gravity, or the force you exert when you pick it up. These are all examples of forces acting on the paper clip.

The magnet on the crane pulls the pieces of scrap metal upward.

Figure 1 A force is a push or a pull.

This golf club exerts a force by pushing on the golf ball.

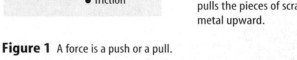

Section 1 Resource Manager

Chapter *FAST FILE* Resources

Transparency Activity, pp. 44, 47–48

Directed Reading for Content Mastery, pp. 19, 20

Note-taking Worksheets, pp. 33–35

Enrichment, p. 30

Lab Activity, pp. 9–12

MiniLAB, p. 3

Reinforcement, p. 27

Home and Community Involvement, p. 23

This door is not moving because the forces exerted on it are equal and in opposite directions.

The door is closing because the force pushing the door closed is greater than the force pushing it open.

Combining Forces More than one force can act on an object at the same time. If you hold a paper clip near a magnet, you, the magnet, and gravity all exert forces on the paper clip. The combination of all the forces acting on an object is the **net force**. When more than one force is acting on an object, the net force determines the motion of the object. In this example, the paper clip is not moving, so the net force is zero.

How do forces combine to form the net force? If the forces are in the same direction, they add together to form the net force. If two forces are in opposite directions, then the net force is the difference between the two forces, and it is in the direction of the larger force.

Balanced and Unbalanced Forces A force can act on an object without causing it to accelerate if other forces cancel the push or pull of the force. Look at **Figure 2.** If you and your friend push on a door with the same force in opposite directions, the door does not move. Because you both exert forces of the same size in opposite directions on the door, the two forces cancel each other. Two or more forces exerted on an object are **balanced forces** if their effects cancel each other and they do not cause a change in the object's motion. If the forces on an object are balanced, the net force is zero. If the forces are **unbalanced forces,** their effects don't cancel each other. Any time the forces acting on an object are unbalanced, the net force is not zero and the motion of the object changes.

Figure 2 When the forces on an object are balanced, no change in motion occurs. A change in motion occurs only when the forces acting on an object are unbalanced.

Biomechanics Whether you run, jump, or sit, forces are being exerted on different parts of your body. Biomechanics is the study of how the body exerts forces and how it is affected by forces acting on it. Research how biomechanics has been used to reduce job-related injuries. Write a paragraph on what you've learned in your Science Journal.

SECTION 1 Newton's First Law **311**

Curriculum Connection

Art Mobiles are based on the principle of balanced forces. Have each student make a mobile with at least three arms. The only criterion students must follow is that each arm must be balanced. Hang students' mobiles in the classroom. L2 **LS Kinesthetic**

Newton's First Law of Motion

If you stand on a skateboard and someone gives you a push, then you and your skateboard will start moving. You will begin to move when the force was applied. An object at rest—like you on your skateboard—remains at rest unless an unbalanced force acts on it and causes it to move.

Because a force had to be applied to make you move when you and your skateboard were at rest, you might think that a force has to be applied continually to keep an object moving. Surprisingly, this is not the case. An object can be moving even if the net force acting on it is zero.

The Italian scientist Galileo Galilei, who lived from 1564 to 1642, was one of the first to understand that a force doesn't need to be constantly applied to an object to keep it moving. Galileo's ideas helped Isaac Newton to better understand the nature of motion. Newton, who lived from 1642 to 1727, explained the motion of objects in three rules called Newton's laws of motion.

Newton's first law of motion describes how an object moves when the net force acting on it is zero. According to **Newton's first law of motion,** if the net force acting on an object is zero, the object remains at rest, or if the object is already moving, continues to move in a straight line with constant speed.

Friction

Galileo realized the motion of an object doesn't change until an unbalanced force acts on it. Every day you see moving objects come to a stop. The force that brings nearly everything to a stop is **friction,** which is the force that acts to resist sliding between two touching surfaces, as shown in **Figure 3.** Friction is why you never see objects moving with constant velocity unless a net force is applied. Friction is the force that eventually brings your skateboard to a stop unless you keep pushing on it. Friction also acts on objects that are sliding or moving through substances such as air or water.

Figure 3 When two objects in contact try to slide past each other, friction keeps them from moving or slows them down.

Without friction, the rock climber would slide down the rock.

Force due to friction

Force due to friction

Force due to friction

Force due to gravity

Friction slows down this sliding baseball player.

Force due to friction

Friction Opposes Sliding Although several different forms of friction exist, they all have one thing in common. If two objects are in contact, frictional forces always try to prevent one object from sliding on the other object. If you rub your hand against a tabletop, you can feel the friction push against the motion of your hand. If you rub the other way, you can feel the direction of friction change so it is again acting against your hand's motion. Friction always will slow a moving object.

 **Reading Check** *What do the different forms of friction have in common?*

Older Ideas About Motion It took a long time to understand motion. One reason was that people did not understand the behavior of friction and that friction was a force. Because moving objects eventually come to a stop, people thought the natural state of an object was to be at rest. For an object to be in motion, something always had to be pushing or pulling it to keep the object moving. As soon as the force stopped, the object would stop moving.

Galileo understood that an object in constant motion is as natural as an object at rest. It was usually friction that made moving objects slow down and eventually come to a stop. To keep an object moving, a force had to be applied to overcome the effects of friction. If friction could be removed, an object in motion would continue to move in a straight line with constant speed. **Figure 4** shows motion where there is almost no friction.

Science Online

Topic: Galileo and Newton
Visit ips.msscience.com for Web links to information about the lives of Galileo and Newton.

Activity Make a time line showing important events in the lives of either Galileo or Newton.

Figure 4 In an air hockey game, the puck floats on a layer of air, so that friction is almost eliminated. As a result, the puck moves in a straight line with nearly constant speed after it's been hit.
Infer *how the puck would move if there was no layer of air.*

SECTION 1   Newton's First Law   **313**

Differentiated Instruction

Purpose Students observe the static and sliding friction between various objects. L2 **ELL**

LS Kinesthetic

Materials flat bar of soap, flat eraser, key, notebook

Teaching Strategies Students should conduct the experiment several times. On occasion, one of the objects may abnormally stick, which could give misleading results if not rechecked.

Analysis

1. The eraser had the greatest static friction since it was the last to slide. The soap had the least since it was the first to slide.
2. The key slid the fastest, it had the least sliding friction. The eraser slid the slowest, it had the most sliding friction.
3. Increase the friction by pushing the surfaces together. Decrease the friction by placing a lubricant between the surfaces.

Assessment

Process Ask students to explain why keeping a bicycle chain properly lubricated helps make the bicycle easier to ride. The lubricant decreases the friction between the links of the chain. Use **Performance Assessment in the Science Classroom,** p. 89.

Reading Check

Answer Static friction prevents two objects at rest from moving past one another; sliding friction slows down two objects moving against each other.

Mini LAB

Observing Friction

Procedure

1. Lay a **bar of soap,** a **flat eraser,** and a **key** side by side on one end of a **hard-sided notebook.**
2. At a constant rate, slowly lift the end of notebook with objects on it. Note the order in which the objects start sliding.

Analysis

1. For which object was static friction the greatest? For which object was it the smallest? Explain, based on your observations.
2. Which object slid the fastest? Which slid the slowest? Explain why there is a difference in speed.
3. How could you increase and decrease the amount of friction between two materials?

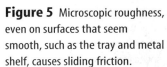

Static Friction If you've ever tried pushing something heavy, like a refrigerator, you might have discovered that nothing happened at first. Then as you push harder and harder, the object suddenly will start to move. When you first start to push, friction between the heavy refrigerator and the floor opposes the force you are exerting and the net force is zero. The type of friction that prevents an object from moving when a force is applied is called static friction.

Static friction is caused by the attraction between the atoms on the two surfaces that are in contact. This causes the surfaces to stick or weld together where they are in contact. Usually, as the surface gets rougher and the object gets heavier, the force of static friction will be larger. To move the object, you have to exert a force large enough to break the bonds holding two surfaces together.

Sliding Friction While static friction keeps an object at rest, sliding friction slows down an object that slides. If you push an object across a room, you notice the sliding friction between the bottom of the object and the floor. You have to keep pushing to overcome the force of sliding friction. Sliding friction is due to the microscopic roughness of two surfaces, as shown in **Figure 5.** A force must be applied to move the rough areas of one surface past the rough areas of the other. A sliding friction force is produced when the brake pads in a car's brakes rub against the wheels. This force slows the car. Bicycle brakes, shown in **Figure 6,** work the same way.

Reading Check
What is the difference between static friction and sliding friction?

Figure 5 Microscopic roughness, even on surfaces that seem smooth, such as the tray and metal shelf, causes sliding friction.

Differentiated Instruction

Challenge Have each student choose a part of an automobile that is affected by some form of friction. Have students state the type of friction, whether the friction decreases or increases the efficiency of the car, and how the friction can be increased or decreased to improve the performance of the car. L3 **LS Logical-Mathematical**

Visually Impaired When these students do the MiniLAB, have them place the objects at the edge of the notebook by feel. Have a sighted student lift the end of the notebook while the first student puts his or her hand at the bottom of the notebook to catch the objects as they slide. Have students repeat the process several times, until they have had a chance to discover by feel the order in which the objects slide.

Figure 6 A bicycle uses sliding friction and rolling friction.

Sliding friction is used to stop this bicycle tire. Friction between the brake pads and the wheel brings the wheel to a stop.

Rolling friction with the ground pushes the bottom of the bicycle tire, so it rolls forward.

Rolling Friction Another type of friction, rolling friction, is needed to make a wheel or tire turn. Rolling friction occurs between the ground and the part of the tire touching the ground, as shown in **Figure 6.** Rolling friction keeps the tire from slipping on the ground. If the bicycle tires are rolling forward, rolling friction exerts the force on the tires that pushes the bicycle forward.

It's usually easier to pull a load on a wagon or cart that has wheels rather than to drag the load along the ground. This is because rolling friction between the wheels and the ground is less than the sliding friction between the load and the ground.

section 1 review

Summary

Force

- A force is a push or a pull.
- The net force on an object is the combination of all the forces acting on the object.
- The forces acting on an object can be balanced or unbalanced. If the forces are balanced, the net force is zero.

Newton's First Law of Motion

- If the net force on an object at rest is zero, the object remains at rest, or if the object is moving, it continues moving in a straight line with constant speed.

Friction

- Friction is the force that acts to resist sliding between two surfaces that are touching.
- Three types of friction are static friction, sliding friction, and rolling friction.

Self Check

1. **Explain** whether a force is acting on a car that is moving at 20 km/h and turns to the left.
2. **Describe** the factors that cause static friction between two surfaces to increase.
3. **Discuss** why friction made it difficult to discover Newton's first law of motion.
4. **Discuss** whether an object can be moving if the net force acting on the object is zero.
5. **Think Critically** For the following actions, explain whether the forces involved are balanced or unbalanced.
   a. You push a box until it moves.
   b. You push a box but it doesn't move.
   c. You stop pushing a box and it slows down.

Applying Skills

6. **Compare and contrast** static, sliding, and rolling friction.

3 Assess

DAILY INTERVENTION

Check for Understanding

Kinesthetic Give each student a paper clip and a magnet. Have students move their paperclip with different types of forces and try to create situations of balanced and unbalanced forces. Have them list the different forces present as they moved their paperclip. magnetic, applied, gravity, and friction

Reteach

Types of Friction Ask students to identify the type of friction in each of the following situations: a bicycle tire rolling along a road; rolling friction a basketball player slipping on a wet spot on the floor; sliding friction a box resting on a ramp. static friction L2 LS
Logical-Mathematical

✔ Assessment

Process Ask each student to draw an events chain concept map illustrating why the space shuttle heats up to about 3,000°C when it re-enters the atmosphere. The friction of the atmosphere against the shuttle fuselage moving at 28,000 km/h heats it up to that temperature. Use **Performance Assessment in the Science Classroom,** p. 163. P

section 1 review

1. Yes; a force is needed to keep the car moving and to change direction.
2. Static friction increases if the surface is rougher or the object is heavier.
3. Because friction usually causes objects in motion to eventually stop, it seemed that rest was the natural state of matter.
4. Yes; if an object is already in motion, it will continue at a constant velocity until acted upon by an outside force.
5. a. unbalanced, box starts moving;
   b. balanced, box doesn't move;
   c. unbalanced, box slows down
6. All three types of friction act against

the direction an object moves. Static friction keeps an object from moving; sliding friction is the friction between two objects moving against each other; rolling friction is the static friction between the rolling object and the surface on which it is rolling.

Newton's Second Law

Bellringer

Section Focus Transparencies also are available on the Interactive Chalkboard CD-ROM.

L2 **ELL**

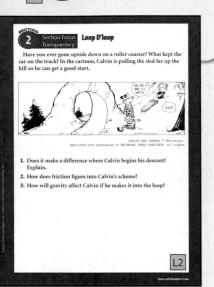

Tie to Prior Knowledge

Mass and Acceleration Have students recall the definitions of mass and acceleration. In this section they will learn how the mass, acceleration and net force acting on an object are related.

☑ Reading Check

Answer An object acted upon by an unbalanced force will accelerate in the direction of the force according to $a = F_{net}/m$.

Caption Answer

Figure 7 The cart with less food; it has less mass.

---

as you read

What **You'll Learn**

■ **Explain** Newton's second law of motion.
■ **Explain** why the direction of force is important.

Why **It's Important**

Newton's second law of motion explains how any object, from a swimmer to a satellite, moves when acted on by forces.

② Review Vocabulary

acceleration: the change in velocity divided by the time over which the change occurred

New Vocabulary

● Newton's second law of motion
● weight
● center of mass

Figure 7 The force needed to change the motion of an object depends on its mass.
Predict *which grocery cart would be easier to stop.*

Force and Acceleration

When you go shopping in a grocery store and push a cart, you exert a force to make the cart move. If you want to slow down or change the direction of the cart, a force is required to do this, as well. Would it be easier for you to stop a full or empty grocery cart suddenly, as in **Figure 7?** When the motion of an object changes, the object is accelerating. Acceleration occurs any time an object speeds up, slows down, or changes its direction of motion. Newton's second law describes how forces cause an object's motion to change.

Newton's second law of motion connects force, acceleration, and mass. According to the second law of motion, an object acted upon by a force will accelerate in the direction of the force. The acceleration is given by the following equation

Acceleration Equation

$$\text{acceleration (in meters/second}^2) = \frac{\text{net force (in newtons)}}{\text{mass (in kilograms)}}$$

$$a = \frac{F_{net}}{m}$$

In this equation, a is the acceleration, m is the mass, and F_{net} is the net force. If both sides of the above equation are multiplied by the mass, the equation can be written this way:

$$F_{net} = ma$$

☑ Reading Check *What is Newton's second law?*

Section 2 Resource Manager

Chapter *FAST FILE* Resources
Transparency Activity, pp. 45, 47–48
Directed Reading for Content Mastery, p. 21
Lab Activity, pp. 13–16
Enrichment, p. 31

Reinforcement, p. 28
Mathematics Skill Activities, p. 9
Physical Science Critical Thinking/ Problem Solving, p. 4

Units of Force

Force is measured in newtons, abbreviated N. Because the SI unit for mass is the kilogram (kg) and acceleration has units of meters per second squared (m/s^2), 1 N also is equal to $1 \text{ kg} \cdot m/s^2$. In other words, to calculate a force in newtons from the equation shown on the prior page, the mass must be given in kg and the acceleration in m/s^2.

Gravity

One force that you are familiar with is gravity. Whether you're coasting down a hill on a bike or a skateboard or jumping into a pool, gravity is at work pulling you downward. Gravity also is the force that causes Earth to orbit the Sun and the Moon to orbit Earth.

What is gravity? The force of gravity exists between any two objects that have mass. Gravity always is attractive and pulls objects toward each other. A gravitational attraction exists between you and every object in the universe that has mass. However, the force of gravity depends on the mass of the objects and the distance between them. The gravitational force becomes weaker the farther apart the objects are and also decreases as the masses of the objects involved decrease.

For example, there is a gravitational force between you and the Sun and between you and Earth. The Sun is much more massive than Earth, but is so far away that the gravitational force between you and the Sun is too weak to notice. Only Earth is close enough and massive enough to exert a noticeable gravitational force on you. The force of gravity between you and Earth is about 1,650 times greater than between you and the Sun.

Weight The force of gravity causes all objects near Earth's surface to fall with an acceleration of 9.8 m/s^2. By Newton's second law, the gravitational force on any object near Earth's surface is:

$$F = ma = m \times (9.8 \text{ m/s}^2)$$

This gravitational force also is called the weight of the object. Your **weight** on Earth is the gravitational force between you and Earth. Your weight would change if you were standing on a planet other than Earth, as shown in **Table 1.** Your weight on a different planet would be the gravitational force between you and the planet.

INTEGRATE History

Newton and Gravity
Isaac Newton was the first to realize that gravity—the force that made objects fall to Earth—was also the force that caused the Moon to orbit Earth and the planets to orbit the Sun. In 1687, Newton published a book that included the law of universal gravitation. This law showed how to calculate the gravitational force between any two objects. Using the law of universal gravitation, astronomers were able to explain the motions of the planets in the solar system, as well as the motions of distant stars and galaxies.

Table 1 Weight of 60-kg Person on Different Planets

Place	Weight in Newtons If Your Mass Were 60 kg	Percent of Your Weight on Earth
Mars	221	37.6
Earth	588	100.0
Jupiter	1,387	235.9
Pluto	39	6.6

2 Teach

Discussion

Weight In the United States, people usually measure their weight in pounds. In European countries, people speak of their weight in kilograms. When converting your weight to the metric system, should you convert it to kilograms or newtons? Why? Convert it to newtons. Weight is a measure of the force of gravity, and newtons is the unit of force. L2 LS **Logical-Mathematical**

INTEGRATE History

Newton and Gravity Isaac Newton made many contributions to science during his lifetime.

Research Have students research to find out about the works of Newton. Have students prepare oral reports to share their information with the class.

Virtual Labs

Second Law *What is Newton's second law of motion?*

Curriculum Connection

History Galileo was the first person to understand gravity's effect on objects. Have students learn more about Galileo and his understanding of gravity. Galileo discovered that the rate at which a body falls is independent of its weight or density, as long as air resistance can be neglected. He was also the first person to use mathematics to analyze his results. L2 LS **Linguistic**

Differentiated Instruction

English-Language Learners Explain to students, especially those who are more familiar with seeing their "weight" in kilograms, that weight is a force, not a mass. A pound and a Newton are both forces—these are measurements of weight. A kilogram is a measure of mass. When you step on a scale, it assumes that the acceleration is always 9.8 m/s^2, but it varies with altitude.

Figure 8 The girl on the sled is speeding up because she is being pushed in the same direction that she is moving.

Figure 9 The boy is slowing down because the force exerted by his feet is in the opposite direction of his motion.

Weight and Mass Weight and mass are different. Weight is a force, just like the push of your hand is a force, and is measured in newtons. When you stand on a bathroom scale, you are measuring the pull of Earth's gravity—a force. However, mass is the amount of matter in an object, and doesn't depend on location. Weight will vary with location, but mass will remain constant. A book with a mass of 1 kg has a mass of 1 kg on Earth or on Mars. However, the weight of the book would be different on Earth and Mars. The two planets would exert a different gravitational force on the book.

Using Newton's Second Law

How does Newton's second law determine how an object moves when acted upon by forces? The second law tells how to calculate the acceleration of an object if its mass and the forces acting on it are known. You may remember that the motion of an object can be described by its velocity. The velocity tells how fast an object is moving and in what direction. Acceleration tells how velocity changes. If the acceleration of an object is known, then the change in velocity can be determined.

Speeding Up Think about a soccer ball sitting on the ground. If you kick the ball, it starts moving. You exert a force on the ball, and the ball accelerates only while your foot is in contact with the ball. If you look back at all of the examples of objects speeding up, you'll notice that something is pushing or pulling the object in the direction it is moving, as in **Figure 8.** The direction of the push or pull is the direction of the force. It also is the direction of the acceleration.

318 CHAPTER 11 Force and Newton's Laws

Slowing Down If you wanted to slow down an object, you would have to push or pull it against the direction it is moving. An example is given in **Figure 9.**

Suppose you push a book across a tabletop. When you start pushing, the book speeds up. Sliding friction also acts on the book. After you stop pushing, sliding friction causes the book to slow down and stop.

Calculating Acceleration Newton's second law of motion can be used to calculate acceleration. For example, suppose you pull a 10-kg sled so that the net force on the sled is 5 N. The acceleration can be found as follows:

$$a = \frac{F_{net}}{m} = \frac{5\ N}{10\ kg} = 0.5\ m/s^2$$

The sled keeps accelerating as long as you keep pulling on it. The acceleration does not depend on how fast the sled is moving. It depends only on the net force and the mass of the sled.

Applying Math | Solving a Simple Equation

ACCELERATION OF A CAR A net force of 4,500 N acts on a car with a mass of 1,500 kg. What is the acceleration of the car?

Solution

1 *This is what you know:*
- net force: $F_{net} = 4,500\ N^2$
- mass: $m = 1,500\ kg$

2 *This is what you need to find:* acceleration: $a = ?\ m/s^2$

3 *This is the procedure you need to use:*

Substitute the known values for net force and mass into the equation for Newton's second law of motion to calculate the acceleration:

$$a = \frac{F_{net}}{m} = \frac{4,500\ N}{1,500\ kg} = 3.0\ \frac{N}{kg} = 3.0\ m/s^2$$

4 *Check your answer:* Multiply your answer by the mass, 1,500 kg. The result should be the given net force, 4,500 N.

Practice Problems

1. A book with a mass of 2.0 kg is pushed along a table. If the net force on the book is 1.0 N, what is the book's acceleration?

2. A baseball has a mass of 0.15 kg. What is the net force on the ball if its acceleration is 40 m/s²?

 Science Online | For more practice visit **ips.msscience.com/math_practice**

Science Journal

Forces on You Ask students to calculate their mass in kilograms and write the results in their Science Journals. Then, ask them to calculate the amount of force it would take to accelerate them from standing still to a velocity of 10 km/h in 10 seconds. $a = (v_2 - v_1)/t; v_2 = 10\ km/h = 10,000\ m/3,600\ s = 2.8\ m/s; v_1 = 0$; therefore, $a = 2.8\ m/s \div 10\ s = 0.28\ m/s^2; F = ma$, so the force needed will be the student's mass in kilograms times 0.28 m/s². **L2** **LS** **Logical-Mathematical**

Activity

Toy Car Have students measure the mass of a toy car, then roll it down a ramp. Have one student measure the distance the car rolled down the ramp, and have another student time how long it takes the car to get to the bottom of the ramp. Add some mass to the car and repeat. Change the mass 5 times. Have students calculate the average speed for each trial by dividing the distance traveled down the ramp by the time. Ask students whether the acceleration depended on the mass of the car. No, because the average speed was the same. Ask students whether the force on each car was different. Yes, because according to $F = ma$ the force will depend on the mass if a is constant. **L2** **COOP LEARN**
LS **Kinesthetic**

Teacher FYI

Translational and Angular Acceleration This section explains how to calculate the acceleration of an object moving in a straight line. This is called the object's translational acceleration. Acceleration that causes an object to change direction is called angular acceleration. If the object is changing both speed and direction, its total acceleration is the sum of both its translational acceleration and its angular acceleration.

Applying Math

National Math Standards
Correlation to Mathematics Objectives
1, 2, 9

Answers to Practice Problems
1. $a = \frac{F}{m} = \frac{1.0\ N}{2.0\ kg} = .5 m/s^2$
2. $F = ma = 0.15\ kg \times 40\ m/s^2 = 6\ N$

Caption Answer

Figure 10 The ball would fall towards Earth in a curved path.

Visual Learning

Figure 10 Ask students to identify the forces acting on the ball as it is being thrown and while it is in the air. Ask them to describe the motion of the ball in both of these situations. The force of the hand accelerates the ball forward and up until it loses contact with the hand. Ignoring air resistance, then only gravity acts on the ball, accelerating it downward. L2 LS **Visual-Spatial**

Discussion

Ball on the Moon Tell students to imagine throwing a baseball on Earth, and then throwing the ball with the same force on the Moon. How would the paths of the ball differ? Why? The ball would travel farther in the horizontal direction before falling to the ground on the Moon. The ball would have the same horizontal force acting on it, but the force pulling it down would be less on the Moon because of the Moon's lower gravity. L2 LS **Logical-Mathematical**

Discussion

Gravity What is the centripetal force that keeps the Moon in orbit around Earth? gravity L2 LS **Logical-Mathematical**

Figure 10 When the ball is thrown, it doesn't keep moving in a straight line. Gravity exerts a force downward that makes it move in a curved path. **Infer** *how the ball would move if it were thrown horizontally.*

Direction of motion

Force due to gravity

Turning Sometimes forces and motion are not in a straight line. If a net force acts at an angle to the direction an object is moving, the object will follow a curved path. The object might be going slower, faster, or at the same speed after it turns.

For example, when you shoot a basketball, the ball doesn't continue to move in a straight line after it leaves your hand. Instead it starts to curve downward, as shown in **Figure 10.** The force of gravity pulls the ball downward. The ball's motion is a combination of its original motion and the downward motion due to gravity. This causes the ball to move in a curved path.

Circular Motion

A rider on a merry-go-round ride moves in a circle. This type of motion is called circular motion. If you are in circular motion, your direction of motion is constantly changing. This means you are constantly accelerating. According to Newton's second law of motion, if you are constantly accelerating, there must be a force acting on you the entire time.

Think about an object on the end of a string whirling in a circle. The force that keeps the object moving in a circle is exerted by the string. The string pulls on the object to keep it moving in a circle. The force exerted by the string is the centripetal force and always points toward the center of the circle. In circular motion the centripetal force is always perpendicular to the motion.

Active Reading

Jigsaw In this collaborative learning technique, individuals become experts on a portion of a text and share their expertise with a small group, called their home group. Everyone shares responsibility for learning the assigned reading. Assign each person in each home group an expert number (1 through 5, for example). Have students gather into the expert groups that correspond to the number they were assigned. Have them read, discuss, and master chapter concepts and determine how best to teach them to their home groups. Have students return to their home groups and share the content they learned in their expert groups. Have students use the Jigsaw strategy with the material on Newton's laws of motion covered in this chapter.

Satellite Motion Objects that orbit Earth are satellites of Earth. Satellites go around Earth in nearly circular orbits, with the centripetal force being gravity. Why doesn't a satellite fall to Earth like a baseball does? Actually, a satellite is falling to Earth just like a baseball.

Suppose Earth were perfectly smooth and you throw a baseball horizontally. Gravity pulls the baseball downward so it travels in a curved path. If the baseball is thrown faster, its path is less curved, and it travels farther before it hits the ground. If the baseball were traveling fast enough, as it fell, its curved path would follow the curve of Earth's surface as shown in **Figure 11.** Then the baseball would never hit the ground. Instead, it would continue to fall around Earth.

Satellites in orbit are being pulled toward Earth just as baseballs are. The difference is that satellites are moving so fast horizontally that Earth's surface curves downward at the same rate that the satellites are falling downward. The speed at which a object must move to go into orbit near Earth's surface is about 8 km/s, or about 29,000 km/h.

To place a satellite into orbit, a rocket carries the satellite to the desired height. Then the rocket fires again to give the satellite the horizontal speed it needs to stay in orbit.

Air Resistance

Whether you are walking, running, or biking, air is pushing against you. This push is air resistance. Air resistance is a form of friction that acts to slow down any object moving in the air. Air resistance is a force that gets larger as an object moves faster. Air resistance also depends on the shape of an object. A piece of paper crumpled into a ball falls faster than a flat piece of paper falls.

When an object falls it speeds up as gravity pulls it downward. At the same time, the force of air resistance pushing up on the object is increasing as the object moves faster. Finally, the upward air resistance force becomes large enough to equal the downward force of gravity.

When the air resistance force equals the weight, the net force on the object is zero. By Newton's second law, the object's acceleration then is zero, and its speed no longer increases. When air resistance balances the force of gravity, the object falls at a constant speed called the terminal velocity.

Figure 11 The faster a ball is thrown, the farther it travels before gravity pulls it to Earth. If the ball is traveling fast enough, Earth's surface curves away from it as fast as it falls downward. Then the ball never hits the ground.

SECTION 2 Newton's Second Law **321**

Use Science Words

Word Meaning Ask students to look up the meaning of the adjective *terminal* and use the definition they find to explain the meaning of the term *terminal velocity.* *Terminal* means "of or relating to an end, extremity, boundary, or terminus." Terminal velocity is the end velocity, or the final velocity with which a particular object falls. It is also the extreme velocity, i.e., the fastest velocity with which the object falls. L2 LS **Linguistic**

Make a Model

Parachutes Have each student use coffee filters to make three different models of parachutes. Ask them to make the first parachute using a single coffee filter. Then, have them add coffee filters to make larger parachutes. Have them attach small objects to the parachutes, drop them, and measure the duration of their fall. L2 LS **Kinesthetic**

Use an Analogy

Sails Increasing the area of an object to increase air resistance in free fall is analogous to spreading a larger sail on a sailboat to increase the force of the wind against the sail.

Fun Fact

The maximum speed (or terminal velocity) of a sky diver is about 320 km/h.

Science Journal

Skydiving Ask students to draw pictures and write descriptions of what happens from the time a skydiver jumps out of a plane until he or she lands on the ground. Ask students to use the following terms: free fall, terminal velocity, air resistance, gravity, and acceleration due to gravity. Make sure they indicate when the forces on the skydiver are balanced and when they are unbalanced.

Differentiated Instruction

Challenge A 0.15-kg baseball is pitched at 45 m/s and is struck by the bat and sent back toward the pitcher at −45 m/s. If the ball is in contact with the bat for 0.0025 s, how hard does the bat hit the ball? What forces act on the ball after the bat hits it? $F = (0.15 \text{ kg})[(45 \text{ m/s}) - (-45 \text{ m/s})] \div 0.0025 \text{ s} = 5,400 \text{ N}$. After the bat hits the ball, the only forces acting on the ball are gravity and air resistance. L3 **Logical-Mathematical**

Figure 12 The wrench is spinning as it slides across the table. The center of mass of the wrench, shown by the dots, moves as if the force of friction is acting at that point.

Center of Mass

When you throw a stick, the motion of the stick might seem to be complicated. However, there is one point on the stick, called the center of mass, that moves in a smooth path. The **center of mass** is the point in an object that moves as if all the object's mass were concentrated at that point. For a symmetrical object, such as a ball, the center of mass is at the object's center. However, for any object the center of mass moves as if the net force is being applied there.

Figure 12 shows how the center of mass of a wrench moves as it slides across a table. The net force on the wrench is the force of friction between on the wrench and the table. This causes the center of mass to move in a straight line with decreasing speed.

---

section 2 review

Summary

Force and Acceleration

- According to Newton's second law, the net force on an object, its mass, and its acceleration are related by

$$F_{net} = ma$$

Gravity

- The force of gravity between any two objects is always attractive and depends on the masses of the objects and the distance between them.

Using Newton's Second Law

- A moving object speeds up if the net force is in the direction of the motion.
- A moving object slows down if the net force is in the direction opposite to the motion.
- A moving object turns if the net force is at an angle to the direction of motion.

Circular Motion

- A centripetal force exerted toward the center of the circle keeps an object moving in circular motion.

Self Check

1. **Make a diagram** showing the forces acting on a coasting bike rider traveling at 25 km/h on a flat roadway.

2. **Analyze** how your weight would change with time if you were on a space ship traveling away from Earth toward the Moon.

3. **Explain** how the force of air resistance depends on an object's speed.

4. **Infer** the direction of the net force acting on a car as it slows down and turns right.

5. **Think Critically** Three students are pushing on a box. Under what conditions will the motion of the box change?

Applying Math

6. **Calculate Net Force** A car has a mass of 1,500 kg. If the car has an acceleration of 2.0 m/s^2, what is the net force acting on the car?

7. **Calculate Mass** During a softball game, a softball is struck by a bat and has an acceleration of 1,500 m/s^2. If the net force exerted on the softball by the bat is 300 N, what is the softball's mass?

---

section 2 review

1. Check students' diagrams. The downward force of gravity is balanced by the upward force exerted by the ground. Rolling friction will cause the bike to slow down and stop.

2. The force of Earth's gravity will decrease so your weight will decrease.

3. The greater the speed, the greater the air resistance, but air resistance remains constant at terminal velocity.

4. The net force is pushing diagonally (at some angle) on the car and to the right.

5. When their forces are unbalanced.

6. $F = ma; F = 1,500\ kg \times 2.0\ m/s^2 = 3,000\ N$

7. $F = ma; m = F/a = 300\ N / 1,500\ m/s^2 = 0.2\ kg$

Newton's Third Law

Action and Reaction

Newton's first two laws of motion explain how the motion of a single object changes. If the forces acting on the object are balanced, the object will remain at rest or stay in motion with constant velocity. If the forces are unbalanced, the object will accelerate in the direction of the net force. Newton's second law tells how to calculate the acceleration, or change in motion, of an object if the net force acting on it is known.

Newton's third law describes something else that happens when one object exerts a force on another object. Suppose you push on a wall. It may surprise you to learn that if you push on a wall, the wall also pushes on you. According to **Newton's third law of motion**, forces always act in equal but opposite pairs. Another way of saying this is for every action, there is an equal but opposite reaction. This means that when you push on a wall, the wall pushes back on you with a force equal in strength to the force you exerted. When one object exerts a force on another object, the second object exerts the same size force on the first object, as shown in **Figure 13.**

as you read

What You'll Learn

■ **Identify** the relationship between the forces that objects exert on each other.

Why It's Important

Newton's third law can explain how birds fly and rockets move.

Review Vocabulary

force: a push or a pull

New Vocabulary

● Newton's third law of motion

Figure 13 The car jack is pushing up on the car with the same amount of force with which the car is pushing down on the jack. **Identify** *the other force acting on the car.*

Section 3 Resource Manager

Chapter FAST FILE Resources
Transparency Activity, pp. 46, 47–48
Directed Reading for Content Mastery, pp. 20, 22
MiniLAB, p. 4
Enrichment, p. 32
Reinforcement, p. 29

Lab Worksheets, pp. 5–6, 7–8
Cultural Diversity, p. 63
Performance Assessment in the Science Classroom, p. 36
Lab Management and Safety, p. 65

---

1 Motivate

Bellringer

Section Focus Transparencies also are available on the Interactive Chalkboard CD-ROM.
L2 ELL

Tie to Prior Knowledge

Force Pairs Ask students to describe the force exerted on them by their chairs. The force of the chairs pushes up on them, countering the force of gravity pulling them down. Ask students if they exert a force on their chairs. Explain that according to Newton's third law of motion, all forces act in pairs. They will learn more about these pairs of forces in this section.

Caption Answer
Figure 13 gravity

Caption Answer

Figure 14 The car with the smaller mass accelerates more.

Inquiry Lab

Describing the Motion of Balls

Purpose to explore how mass, velocity, and size affect balls' interactions

Possible Materials at least ten balls having different mass and size; such as marbles, bowling, table-tennis, golf, tennis, and wiffle balls, volleyballs, raquet-balls, softballs, and basketballs

Estimated Time 20 minutes

Teaching Strategies

• Students can experiment with the ways different balls interact.

• Students can plan how they want the balls to collide (one at rest, both in motion, three at a time, etc.), and then draw a diagram of the planned motion (have students indicate with arrow thickness or length the velocity of the balls).

• Student can test their plans and draw a diagram of how their balls interacted.

• Students can compare and contrast their plans with their tests.

For additional inquiry activities, see *Science Inquiry Labs.*

Science Online

Topic: How Birds Fly
Visit ips.msscience.com for Web links to information about how birds and other animals fly.

Activity Make a diagram showing the forces acting on a bird as it flies.

Figure 14 In this collision, the first car exerts a force on the second. The second exerts the same force in the opposite direction on the first car.
Explain *whether both cars will have the same acceleration.*

Figure 15 When the child pushes against the wall, the wall pushes against the child.

Reaction force

Action force

Action and Reaction Forces Don't Cancel The forces exerted by two objects on each other are often called an action-reaction force pair. Either force can be considered the action force or the reaction force. You might think that because action-reaction forces are equal and opposite that they cancel. However, action and reaction force pairs don't cancel because they act on different objects. Forces can cancel only if they act on the same object.

For example, imagine you're driving a bumper car and are about to bump a friend in another car, as shown in **Figure 14.** When the two cars collide, your car pushes on the other car. By Newton's third law, that car pushes on your car with the same force, but in the opposite direction. This force causes you to slow down. One force of the action-reaction force pair is exerted on your friend's car, and the other force of the force pair is exerted on your car. Another example of an action-reaction pair is shown in **Figure 15.**

You constantly use action-reaction force pairs as you move about. When you jump, you push down on the ground. The ground then pushes up on you. It is this upward force that pushes you into the air. **Figure 16** shows some examples of how Newton's laws of motion are demonstrated in sporting events.

INTEGRATE Life Science Birds and other flying creatures also use Newton's third law. When a bird flies, its wings push in a downward and a backward direction. This pushes air downward and backward. By Newton's third law, the air pushes back on the bird in the opposite directions—upward and forward. This force keeps a bird in the air and propels it forward.

Teacher FYI

How Birds Fly Newton's third law helps birds to fly, but most birds would not fly very well with Newton's third law alone. Other factors such as lift (due to Bernoulli's Principle), air currents, and air resistance help birds to fly as well.

Differentiated Instruction

Physically Challenged Have a student in a wheelchair with the brakes off push against a student in rollerskates (or in another wheelchair or on a skate board) to demonstrate Newton's third law. Have them repeat with one student in motion, if desired.

NATIONAL GEOGRAPHIC

Figure 16

Although it is not obvious, Newton's laws of motion are demonstrated in sports activities all the time. According to the first law, if an object is in motion, it moves in a straight line with constant speed unless a net force acts on it. If an object is at rest, it stays at rest unless a net force acts on it. The second law states that a net force acting on an object causes the object to accelerate in the direction of the force. The third law can be understood this way—for every action force, there is an equal and opposite reaction force.

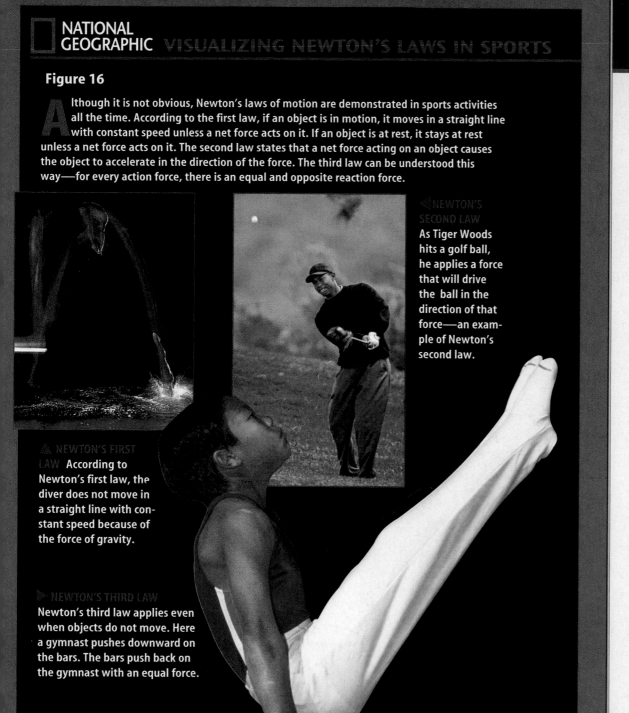

◁ NEWTON'S SECOND LAW As Tiger Woods hits a golf ball, he applies a force that will drive the ball in the direction of that force—an example of Newton's second law.

△ NEWTON'S FIRST LAW According to Newton's first law, the diver does not move in a straight line with constant speed because of the force of gravity.

▷ NEWTON'S THIRD LAW Newton's third law applies even when objects do not move. Here a gymnast pushes downward on the bars. The bars push back on the gymnast with an equal force.

SECTION 3 Newton's Third Law **325**

Visualizing Newton's Laws in Sports

Have students examine the pictures and read the captions. Then ask the following questions.

A shot put has a much greater mass than a discus. How does Newton's second law explain why a discus can be thrown about twice as far as a shot put? Because of its greater mass, the shot put must be thrown with much more force than the discus to reach the same acceleration.

How does Newton's third law explain the direction a boat crew must move the oars in order to move the boat forward? The crew applies a backward force to the water through the oars. The water applies an equal and opposite force on the oars. This force propels the oars and thus the boat through the water.

Activity

Motion in Sports Have groups of students cut out magazine pictures showing examples of Newton's laws of motion in sports. Have them mount each picture on poster board. Ask each group to present their pictures to the class, explaining the forces at work in each example.
LS **Visual-Spatial**

Cultural Diversity

Lacrosse The game of lacrosse is derived from an Iroquois game known as Galahs. This game involves catching and tossing a ball using a thin basket on a stick. Have students learn more about this game and describe it in relation to Newton's laws.

Discussion

Space Shuttle Two minutes after the space shuttle's launch, all fuel in the solid rocket boosters is used up, and these boosters drop off and fall back to Earth. This makes the shuttle lighter and easier to accelerate. Predict what happens to keep the shuttle accelerating smoothly. The rate of combustion in the engine is decreased.

L3 LS **Logical-Mathematical**

Visual Learning

Figure 18 Review with students the action-reaction force pairs between the gas molecules and the rocket. Tell students that the force on the rocket, called the thrust, is equal to the mass ejected per second times the velocity of the expelled gases. How is this equivalent to $F = ma$? Thrust = $(m/t)v = m(v/t) = ma = f$

L2 LS **Logical-Mathematical**

Quick Demo

Thrust in Action-Reaction

Materials CO_2 cartridge, nail to puncture cartridge, apparatus that rotates like a helicopter wing

Estimated Time five minutes

Procedure Attach the CO_2 cartridge to the end of the 'wing'. Puncture the CO_2 cartridge and release it to allow the apparatus to spin. Have the students explain what caused the spinning. Action-reaction similar to a rocket caused the motion.

Figure 17 The force of the ground on your foot is equal and opposite to the force of your foot on the ground. If you push back harder, the ground pushes forward harder.
Determine *In what direction does the ground push on you if you are standing still?*

Large and Small Objects Sometimes it's easy not to notice an action-reaction pair is because one of the objects is often much more massive and appears to remain motionless when a force acts on it. It has so much inertia, or tendency to remain at rest, that it hardly accelerates. Walking is a good example. When you walk forward, you push backward on the ground. Your shoe pushes Earth backward, and Earth pushes your shoe forward, as shown in **Figure 16.** Earth has so much mass compared to you that it does not move noticeably when you push it. If you step on something that has less mass than you do, like a skateboard, you can see it being pushed back.

A Rocket Launch The launching of a space shuttle is a spectacular example of Newton's third law. Three rocket engines supply the force, called thrust, that lifts the rocket. When the rocket fuel is ignited, a hot gas is produced. As the gas molecules collide with the inside engine walls, the walls exert a force that pushes them out of the bottom of the engine, as shown in **Figure 18.** This downward push is the action force. The reaction force is the upward push on the rocket engine by the gas molecules. This is the thrust that propels the rocket upward.

Figure 18 Newton's third law enables a rocket to fly. The rocket pushes the gas molecules downward, and the gas molecules push the rocket upward.

Gas particles

Engine compartment

Cultural Diversity

Chinese Rockets The Chinese were the first to fire rockets. Have students find out more about Chinese rockets. By the 1200s, the Chinese were filling sections of bamboo tubing with gunpowder and shooting them off as fireworks and as weapons. They knew how to weight the rockets to make them fly farther. With time, they learned to make multistage rockets, in which one set of rockets lit the next set. L3 LS **Linguistic**

Differentiated Instruction

Challenge Two ice-skaters push off each other. The first skater has a mass of 50 kg and is accelerated 10 m/s² by the push. The second is accelerated 15 m/s² by the push. What is the mass of the second skater? $F_1 = F_2$, so $m_1a_1 = m_2a_2$, and $m_2 = m_1a_1/a_2 = (50 \text{ kg} \times 10 \text{ m/s}^2) \div 15 \text{ m/s}^2 = 33.3 \text{ kg}$ L3 LS
Logical-Mathematical

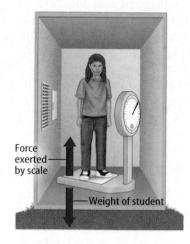

Force exerted by scale

Weight of student — Weight of student

Figure 19 Whether you are standing on Earth or falling, the force of Earth's gravity on you doesn't change. However, your weight measured by a scale would change.

Weightlessness

You might have seen pictures of astronauts floating inside a space shuttle as it orbits Earth. The astronauts are said to be weightless, as if Earth's gravity were no longer pulling on them. Yet the force of gravity on the shuttle is almost 90 percent as large as at Earth's surface. Newton's laws of motion can explain why the astronauts float as if there were no forces acting on them.

Measuring Weight Think about how you measure your weight. When you stand on a scale, your weight pushes down on the scale. This causes the scale pointer to point to your weight. At the same time, by Newton's third law the scale pushes up on you with a force equal to your weight, as shown in **Figure 19.** This force balances the downward pull of gravity on you.

Free Fall and Weightlessness Now suppose you were standing on a scale in an elevator that is falling, as shown in **Figure 19.** A falling object is in free fall when the only force acting on the object is gravity. Inside the free-falling elevator, you and the scale are both in free fall. Because the only force acting on you is gravity, the scale no longer is pushing up on you. According to Newton's third law, you no longer push down on the scale. So the scale pointer stays at zero and you seem to be weightless. Weightlessness is the condition that occurs in free fall when the weight of an object seems to be zero.

However, you are not really weightless in free fall because Earth is still pulling down on you. With nothing to push up on you, such as your chair, you would have no sensation of weight.

Figure 20 These oranges seem to be floating because they are falling around Earth at the same speed as the space shuttle and the astronauts. As a result, they aren't moving relative to the astronauts in the cabin.

Weightlessness in Orbit To understand how objects move in the orbiting space shuttle, imagine you were holding a ball in the free-falling elevator. If you let the ball go, the position of the ball relative to you and the elevator wouldn't change, because you, the ball, and the elevator are moving at the same speed.

However, suppose you give the ball a gentle push downward. While you are pushing the ball, this downward force adds to the downward force of gravity. According to Newton's second law, the acceleration of the ball increases. So while you are pushing, the acceleration of the ball is greater than the acceleration of both you and the elevator. This causes the ball to speed up relative to you and the elevator. After it speeds up, it continues moving faster than you and the elevator, and it drifts downward until it hits the elevator floor.

When the space shuttle orbits Earth, the shuttle and all the objects in it are in free fall. They are falling in a curved path around Earth, instead of falling straight downward. As a result, objects in the shuttle appear to be weightless, as shown in **Figure 20.** A small push causes an object to drift away, just as a small downward push on the ball in the free-falling elevator caused it to drift to the floor.

section 3 review

Summary

Action and Reaction

- According to Newton's third law, when one object exerts a force on another object, the second object exerts the same size force on the first object.
- Either force in an action-reaction force pair can be the action force or the reaction force.
- Action and reaction force pairs don't cancel because they are exerted on different objects.
- When action and reaction forces are exerted by two objects, the accelerations of the objects depend on the masses of the objects.

Weightlessness

- A falling object is in free fall if the only force acting on it is gravity.
- Weightlessness occurs in free fall when the weight of an object seems to be zero.
- Objects orbiting Earth appear to be weightless because they are in free fall in a curved path around Earth.

Self Check

1. **Evaluate** the force a skateboard exerts on you if your mass is 60 kg and you push on the skateboard with a force of 60 N.
2. **Explain** why you move forward and a boat moves backward when you jump from a boat to a pier.
3. **Describe** the action and reaction forces when a hammer hits a nail.
4. **Infer** You and a child are on skates and you give each other a push. If the mass of the child is half your mass, who has the greater acceleration? By what factor?
5. **Think Critically** Suppose you are walking in an airliner in flight. Use Newton's third law to describe the effect of your walk on the motion on the airliner.

Applying Math

6. **Calculate Acceleration** A person standing in a canoe exerts a force of 700 N to throw an anchor over the side. Find the acceleration of the canoe if the total mass of the canoe and the person is 100 kg.

Science Online ips.msscience.com/self_check_quiz

section 3 review

BALLOON *RACES*

● *Real-World Question*

The motion of a rocket lifting off a launch pad is determined by Newton's laws of motion. Here you will make a balloon rocket that is powered by escaping air. How do Newton's laws of motion explain the motion of balloon rockets?

Goals

■ **Measure** the speed of a balloon rocket.
■ **Describe** how Newton's laws explain a rocket's motion.

Materials

balloons   meterstick
drinking straws   stopwatch
string   *clock
tape   *Alternate materials

Safety Precautions

● *Procedure*

1. Make a rocket path by threading a string through a drinking straw. Run the string across the classroom and fasten at both ends.

2. Blow up a balloon and hold it tightly at the end to prevent air from escaping. Tape the balloon to the straw on the string.

3. Release the balloon so it moves along the string. Measure the distance the balloon travels and the time it takes.

4. Repeat steps 2 and 3 with different balloons.

● *Conclude and Apply*

1. **Compare and contrast** the distances traveled. Which rocket went the greatest distance?

2. **Calculate** the average speed for each rocket. Compare and contrast them. Which rocket has the greatest average speed?

3. **Infer** which aspects of these rockets made them travel far or fast.

4. **Draw** a diagram showing all the forces acting on a balloon rocket.

5. Use Newton's laws of motion to explain the motion of a balloon rocket from launch until it comes to a stop.

*C*ommunicating
Your Data

Discuss with classmates which balloon rocket traveled the farthest. Why? **For more help, refer to the Science Skill Handbook.**

● *Real-World Question*

Purpose Students observe Newton's third law of motion acting on rocket balloons. L2

ELL **COOP LEARN** **LS** **Kinesthetic**

Process Skills observe, infer, compare and contrast, recognize cause and effect, control variables, measure, interpret data

Time Required 45 minutes

● *Procedure*

Teaching Strategies Suggest that one student handle the balloon while another measures time.

● *Analyze Your Data*

Answers to Questions

1. Answers will vary.
2. To calculate a balloon's average speed, students will need to note the time and the distance the balloon travels.

● *Conclude and Apply*

1. Answers might include the balloon's size, shape, and air capacity; the thickness of the rubber from which the balloon is made; and the size of the opening.
2. Drawings should include gravity, upward force of the straw, force of the escaping air, and friction.
3. Escaping air pushes the balloon forward (third law). When it runs out of air, it continues a short way (first law) as friction slows it to a stop (second law).

● **Assessment**

Performance Ask students to design nozzles that control the flow of air out the back of the balloon. Test the designs, and award a prize for the best one. Use **Performance Assessment in the Science Classroom,** p. 117.

*C*ommunicating
Your Data

Students should discuss the process of troubleshooting their designs to get them to fly smoothly. The more successful techniques should be highlighted.

● Real-World Question

Purpose Students observe how to move an object from any point to another point using only two forces at right angles to each other. **L2** **LS** **Kinesthetic**

Process Skills observe and infer, communicate, interpret data, diagram, hypothesize, compare and contrast, form a hypothesis, design an experiment, predict, separate and control variables, recognize cause and effect

Time Required 45 minutes

Possible Materials Any small ball can be used for the activity, but heavier balls, such as a golf ball, work best.

● Form a Hypothesis

Possible Hypothesis Students might hypothesize that one person can move the skid in one direction and two people can move the sled diagonally by pulling at right angles to each other.

Design Your Own

Goals
■ **Move** the skid across the ground using two forces.
■ **Measure** how fast the skid can be moved.
■ **Determine** how smoothly the direction can be changed.

Possible Materials
masking tape
stopwatch
* *watch or clock with a*
  second hand
meterstick
metric tape measure
spring scales marked in
  newtons (2)
plastic lid
golf ball
tennis ball
Alternate materials

Safety Precautions
🥽 📖

MODELING M⊙TION IN TWO DIRECTI⊙NS

● Real-World Question

When you move a computer mouse across a mouse pad, how does the rolling ball tell the computer cursor to move in the direction that you push the mouse? Inside the housing for the mouse's ball are two or more rollers that the ball rubs against as you move the mouse. They measure up-and-down and back-and-forth motions. The motion of the cursor on the screen is based on the movement of the up-and-down rollers and the back-and-forth rollers. Can any object be moved along a path by a series of motions in only two directions?

● Form a Hypothesis

How can you combine forces to move in a straight line, along a diagonal, or around corners? Place a golf ball on something that will slide, such as a plastic lid. The plastic lid is called a skid. Lay out a course to follow on the floor. Write a plan for moving your golf ball along the path without having the golf ball roll away.

● Test Your Hypothesis

Make a Plan

1. Lay out a course that involves two directions, such as always moving forward or left.

2. Attach two spring scales to the skid. One always will pull straight forward. One always will pull to one side. You cannot turn the skid. If one scale is pulling toward the door of your classroom, it always must pull in that direction. (It can pull with zero force if needed, but it can't push.)

3. How will you handle movements along diagonals and turns?

4. How will you measure speed?

Alternative Inquiry Lab

Motion in All Directions Make this Lab an Inquiry Lab by building on their experience. Have students make groups of four. Give each group masking tape to make their own course that moves through all four directions. Connect the courses and time each group in an "obstacle course" race. Make sure each group stays within the taped off area, has all four members of the group at right angles, and that the students stay in the same direction.

5. Experiment with your skid. How hard do you have to pull to counteract sliding friction at a given speed? How fast can you accelerate? Can you stop suddenly without spilling the golf ball, or do you need to slow down?

6. Write a plan for moving your golf ball along the course by pulling only forward or to one side. Be sure you understand your plan and have considered all the details.

Follow Your Plan

1. Make sure your teacher approves your plan before you start.

2. Move your golf ball along the path.

3. Modify your plan, if needed.

4. Organize your data so they can be used to run your course and write them in your Science Journal.

5. Test your results with a new route.

● Analyze Your Data

1. What was the difference between the two routes? How did this affect the forces you needed to use on the golf ball?

2. How did you separate and control variables in this experiment?

3. Was your hypothesis supported? Explain.

● Conclude and Apply

1. What happens when you combine two forces at right angles?

2. If you could pull on all four sides (front, back, left, right) of your skid, could you move anywhere along the floor? Make a hypothesis to explain your answer.

Communicating
Your Data

Compare your conclusions with those of other students in your class. **For more help, refer to the Science Skill Handbook.**

LAB 331

● Test Your Hypothesis

Teaching Strategies Suggest that students try moving the skid by applying forces in one direction followed by the other, and then by applying forces in the two directions at the same time.

Expected Outcome Students will find it much easier to move the skid by moving one direction at a time. Moving the skid in both directions simultaneously requires them to be more responsive to what they see happening as they pull.

● Analyze Your Data

Answers to Questions

1. Students should find the new route easier than the first if they have learned from their experience.

2. The variables were the forces in each direction. The two spring scales enabled each force to be measured separately.

3. Check students' explanations.

Error Analysis Have students discuss problems they may have had moving the skid through their courses.

● Conclude and Apply

1. The object moves on a diagonal between the two forces.

2. Yes; forces in these four directions can be combined to move an object along any line.

☑ Assessment

Performance Ask students to examine a computer mouse and determine how it tells the screen how to move the cursor. Most have one roller for horizontal motion, one for vertical motion, and a third roller for stability. The information from the rollers is combined to move the cursor on the screen in any direction. Use **Performance Assessment in the Science Classroom,** p. 89.

Communicating
Your Data

Encourage students to discuss how Newton's three laws affected the results of the activity. Ask them to describe how the activity would have differed if it had been done on an almost frictionless surface such as ice.

Content Background

Air bags were originally designed as an inflatable device for use in crash landings of airplanes in World War II. Air bags inflate after a chemical reaction, triggered by an impact, releases hot nitrogen gas that expands into the bag. The inflation lasts only a fraction of a second. Between 1986 and 2000, the National Highway Traffic Safety Association estimated that air bags prevented over 5,300 fatalities. Air bags are designed to supplement, not replace, the use of seat belts. Improper use can result in injuries caused by the safety devices themselves. The NHTSA recorded 195 confirmed fatalities caused by air bags between 1990 and 2000.

Discussion

Collision Injuries In addition to air bags and seat restraints, how else can injuries be avoided in collisions? Students may suggest improvements in designs of car frames such as crumpling structural frames. Also, proper use of children's seats and appropriate placement of children in the passenger compartments.

Activity

Egg Drop Have students drop eggs one inch above a hard floor. Have them increase the height of the drop by half-inch increments until the eggshells break. Then have them repeat the activity several times with increasingly thick layers of fabric placed on the floor. Direct students to graph their data. Students should see that a yielding material that absorbs energy allows the eggs to withstand falls from greater heights. For further experimentation, allow the class to try different materials like balloons and pillows on the floor. L2 LS **Kinesthetic**

TIME **SCIENCE** AND **Society**

SCIENCE ISSUES THAT AFFECT YOU!

Air Bag Safety

After complaints and injuries, air bags in cars are helping all passengers

The car in front of yours stops suddenly. You hear the crunch of car against car and feel your seat belt grab you. Your mom is covered with, not blood, thank goodness, but with a big white cloth. Your seat belts and air bags worked perfectly.

Popcorn in the Dash

Air bags have saved more than a thousand lives since 1992. They are like having a giant popcorn kernel in the dashboard that pops and becomes many times its original size. But unlike popcorn, an air bag is triggered by impact, not heat. In a crash, a chemical reaction produces a gas that expands in a split second, inflating a balloonlike bag to cushion the driver and possibly the front-seat passenger. The bag deflates quickly so it doesn't trap people in the car.

Newton and the Air Bag

When you're traveling in a car, you move with it at whatever speed it is going. According to Newton's first law, you are the object in motion, and you will continue in motion unless acted upon by a force, such as a car crash.

Unfortunately, a crash stops the car, but it doesn't stop you, at least, not right away. You continue moving forward if your car doesn't have air bags or if you haven't buckled your seat belt. You stop when you strike the inside of the car. You hit the dashboard or steering wheel while traveling at the speed of the car. When an air bag inflates, you come to a stop move slowly, which reduces the force that is exerted on you.

A test measures the speed at which an air bag deploys.

Measure Hold a paper plate 26 cm in front of you. Use a ruler to measure the distance. That's the distance drivers should have between the chest and the steering wheel to make air bags safe. Inform adult drivers in your family about this safety distance.

For more information, visit
ips.msscience.com/time

Measure Ask students to investigate the proper use of seat belts and shoulder restraints. Improper placement of seat belts can result in neck injuries caused as a passenger's momentum carries them forward and under a belt. Improper positioning of shoulder restraints can result in chest and upper limb injuries.

Resources for Teachers and Students

Air Bag and Seat Belt Safety Campaign National Safety Council
1025 Connecticut Ave., NW, Suite 1200 Washington, DC 20036

National Highway Traffic Safety Administration Auto Safety Hotline 1-800-424-9393

Reviewing Main Ideas

Section 1 Newton's First Law

1. A force is a push or a pull.

2. Newton's first law states that objects in motion tend to stay in motion and objects at rest tend to stay at rest unless acted upon by a nonzero net force.

3. Friction is a force that resists motion between surfaces that are touching each other.

Section 2 Newton's Second Law

1. Newton's second law states that an object acted upon by a net force will accelerate in the direction of this force.

2. The acceleration due to a net force is given by the equation $a = F_{net}/m$.

3. The force of gravity between two objects depends on their masses and the distance between them.

4. In circular motion, a force pointing toward the center of the circle acts on an object.

Section 3 Newton's Third Law

1. According to Newton's third law, the forces two objects exert on each other are always equal but in opposite directions.

2. Action and reaction forces don't cancel because they act on different objects.

3. Objects in orbit appear to be weightless because they are in free fall around Earth.

Visualizing Main Ideas

Copy and complete the following concept map on Newton's laws of motion.

Newton's Laws of Motion

- First — An object at rest will remain at rest until a force is applied
- Third — Forces act in equal, but opposite pairs
- Second — Force = (mass) × (acceleration)

Science Online ips.msscience.com/interactive_tutor

CHAPTER STUDY GUIDE 333

Reviewing Main Ideas

Summary statements can be used by students to review the major concepts of the chapter.

Visualizing Main Ideas

See student page.

Science Online

Visit ips.msscience.com
/self_check_quiz
/interactive_tutor
/vocabulary_puzzlemaker
/chapter_review
/standardized_test

Assessment Transparency

For additional assessment questions, use the *Assessment Transparency* located in the transparency book.

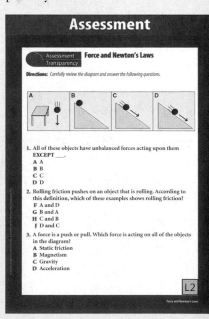

Assessment

Assessment Transparency — **Force and Newton's Laws**

Directions: *Carefully review the diagram and answer the following questions.*

1. All of these objects have unbalanced forces acting upon them EXCEPT ___.
   A A
   B B
   C C
   D D

2. Rolling friction pushes on an object that is rolling. According to this definition, which of these examples shows rolling friction?
   F A and D
   G B and A
   H C and B
   J D and C

3. A force is a push or pull. Which force is acting on all of the objects in the diagram?
   A Static friction
   B Magnetism
   C Gravity
   D Acceleration

L2

Force and Newton's Laws

◆ **Identifying Misconceptions**   **Assess**

Use the assessment as a follow up to page F at the beginning of the chapter.

Procedure Ask students to imagine a bowling ball and a table-tennis ball in outer space so far from other objects that they experience almost no gravity. Will the force required to move the bowling ball be greater than the force required to move the ping pong ball? Why? yes, because it has more mass How do we know friction does not play a part? In outer space there is no air and thus no friction.

Expected Outcome Students should begin to realize that a larger mass has more inertia, and thus a greater tendency to remain at rest.

Using Vocabulary

1. force—a push or pull; inertia—resistance to change in motion; weight—a force due to gravity
2. Newton's first law—a body has inertia; Newton's third law—for every force there is an equal and opposite force
3. Friction is a type of force.
4. net force—total of all forces on an object; balanced forces—net force equals zero
5. weight
6. balanced forces—object does not accelerate; unbalanced forces—object accelerates
7. friction—opposing force; weight—force due to gravity
8. Newton's first law of motion—a body has inertia; Newton's second law—$a = F/m$
9. friction—opposing force; unbalanced force—accelerates an object
10. net force—sum of forces; Newton's third law—for every force there is an equal and opposite force

Checking Concepts

11. B	14. C	17. D
12. C	15. A	18. D
13. B	16. B	

Thinking Critically

19. acceleration due to gravity increases the speed
20. Yes; the ball changed direction
21. Because Earth is so massive, the forces people exert on it cause very little acceleration.
22. The car is held on the hill by static friction. When the car moves at a constant speed, rolling friction and air resistance balance the force exerted on the wheels by the motor. When the brakes are applied, sliding friction between the brake pads and the wheels slows down the car.

Using Vocabulary

balanced forces p. 311	Newton's second law of motion p. 316
center of mass p. 322	
force p. 310	Newton's third law of motion p. 323
friction p. 312	
net force p. 311	unbalanced forces p. 311
Newton's first law of motion p. 312	weight p. 317

Explain the differences between the terms in the following sets.

1. force—inertia—weight
2. Newton's first law of motion—Newton's third law of motion
3. friction—force
4. net force—balanced forces
5. weight—weightlessness
6. balanced forces—unbalanced forces
7. friction—weight
8. Newton's first law of motion—Newton's second law of motion
9. friction—unbalanced force
10. net force—Newton's third law of motion

Checking Concepts

Choose the word or phrase that best answers the question.

11. Which of the following changes when an unbalanced force acts on an object?
    A) mass   **C)** inertia
    B) motion   **D)** weight

12. Which of the following is the force that slows a book sliding on a table?
    A) gravity
    B) static friction
    C) sliding friction
    D) inertia

Use the illustration below to answer question 13.

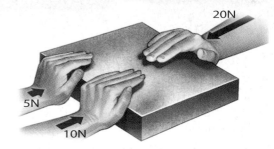

13. Two students are pushing on the left side of a box and one student is pushing on the right. The diagram above shows the forces they exert. Which way will the box move?
    A) up   **C)** down
    B) left   **D)** right

14. What combination of units is equivalent to the newton?
    A) m/s^2 **C)** $kg \cdot m/s^2$
    B) $kg \cdot m/s$ **D)** kg/m

15. Which of the following is a push or a pull?
    A) force   **C)** acceleration
    B) momentum   **D)** inertia

16. An object is accelerated by a net force in which direction?
    A) at an angle to the force
    B) in the direction of the force
    C) in the direction opposite to the force
    D) Any of these is possible.

17. You are riding on a bike. In which of the following situations are the forces acting on the bike balanced?
    A) You pedal to speed up.
    B) You turn at constant speed.
    C) You coast to slow down.
    D) You pedal at constant speed.

18. Which of the following has no direction?
    A) force   **C)** weight
    B) acceleration   **D)** mass

Science Online ips.msscience.com/vocabulary_puzzlemaker

Use the ExamView® Pro Testmaker CD-ROM to:
- create multiple versions of tests
- create modified tests with one mouse click for inclusion students
- edit existing questions and add your own questions
- build tests aligned with state standards using built-in State Curriculum Tags
- change English tests to Spanish with one mouse click and vice versa

Thinking Critically

19. Explain why the speed of a sled increases as it moves down a snow-covered hill, even though no one is pushing on the sled.

20. Explain A baseball is pitched east at a speed of 40 km/h. The batter hits it west at a speed of 40 km/h. Did the ball accelerate?

21. Form a Hypothesis Frequently, the pair of forces acting between two objects are not noticed because one of the objects is Earth. Explain why the force acting on Earth isn't noticed.

22. Identify A car is parked on a hill. The driver starts the car, accelerates until the car is driving at constant speed, drives at constant speed, and then brakes to put the brake pads in contact with the spinning wheels. Explain how static friction, sliding friction, rolling friction, and air resistance are acting on the car.

23. Draw Conclusions You hit a hockey puck and it slides across the ice at nearly a constant speed. Is a force keeping it in motion? Explain.

24. Infer Newton's third law describes the forces between two colliding objects. Use this connection to explain the forces acting when you kick a soccer ball.

25. Recognize Cause and Effect Use Newton's third law to explain how a rocket accelerates upon takeoff.

26. Predict Two balls of the same size and shape are dropped from a helicopter. One ball has twice the mass of the other ball. On which ball will the force of air resistance be greater when terminal velocity is reached?

Use the figure below to answer question 27.

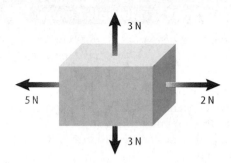

27. Interpreting Scientific Illustrations Is the force on the box balanced? Explain.

Performance Activities

28. Oral Presentation Research one of Newton's laws of motion and compose an oral presentation. Provide examples of the law. You might want to use a visual aid.

29. Writing in Science Create an experiment that deals with Newton's laws of motion. Document it using the following subject heads: *Title of Experiment, Partners' Names, Hypothesis, Materials, Procedures, Data, Results,* and *Conclusion.*

Applying Math

30. Acceleration If you exert a net force of 8 N on a 2-kg object, what will its acceleration be?

31. Force You push against a wall with a force of 5 N. What is the force the wall exerts on your hands?

32. Net Force A 0.4-kg object accelerates at 2 m/s². Find the net force.

33. Friction A 2-kg book is pushed along a table with a force of 4 N. Find the frictional force on the book if the book's acceleration is 1.5 m/s².

23. When the puck is sliding on the ice, there is no force being exerted on the puck to keep it moving forward. Instead, inertia keeps the puck moving forward. Friction between the puck and the ice gradually slows the puck down.

24. When the foot connects with the ball, the foot accelerates the ball forward (ball has low mass) and the ball accelerates the foot backward, slowing its forward motion somewhat (foot attached to body has high mass).

25. The fuel inside the rocket explodes. The gas particles that are formed push against the rocket, and the rocket pushes against them. This pushes the rocket up and the gases out the bottom.

26. the ball with the greater mass

27. No; the net force is pushing to the left with a strength of 3 N

Performance Activities

28. Check students' work. Use **PASC,** p. 143.

29. Check students' work. Use **PASC,** p. 159.

Applying Math

National Math Standards
1, 2, 9

30. $a = F/m = 8\,N/2\,kg = 4\,m/s^2$

31. 5 N

32. $F = ma = 0.4\,kg \times 2\,m/s^2 = 0.8\,N$

33. $F = ma = (2\,kg)(1.5\,m/s^2) = 3\,N$; $4\,N - 3\,N = 1\,N$

✓ **Assessment** **Resources**

📁 **Reproducible Masters**
Chapter *Fast File* Resources
  Chapter Review, pp. 39–40
  Chapter Tests, pp. 41–44
  Assessment Transparency Activity, p. 51
Glencoe Science Web site
  Chapter Review Test
  Standardized Test Practice

Glencoe Technology
  🔦 Assessment Transparency
  🌐 Exam*View*® Pro Testmaker
  📺 MindJogger Videoquiz
  💿 Interactive Chalkboard

chapter 11 Standardized Test Practice

Answer Sheet A practice answer sheet can be found at **ips.msscience.com/answer_sheet**.

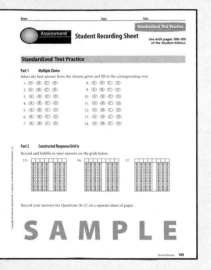

SAMPLE

Part 1 | Multiple Choice

1. B **4.** B **7.** C
2. D **5.** B **8.** C
3. C **6.** A

Part 2 | Short Response

9. Newton's first law of motion
10. gravity and air resistance
11. 45.7 N
12. The forces are equal and opposite.
13. The accelerations will vary due to the masses of the vehicles.
14. No, acceleration does not depend on the speed of an object. It depends only on the net force and the mass of the object.
15. 0.78 kg
16. $[(9.8 \text{ m/s}^2) \times (1.4 \text{ kg})] - 2.5 \text{ N}$
$= 11.2 \text{ N}$
17. speed up, slow down, or change direction

Part 1 | Multiple Choice

Record your answers on the answer sheet provided by your teacher or on a sheet of paper.

1. Which of the following descriptions of gravitational force is *not* true?
   A. It depends on the mass of objects.
   B. It is a repulsive force.
   C. It depends on the distance between objects.
   D. It exists between all objects.

Use the table below to answer questions 2 and 3.

Mass of Common Objects	
Object	**Mass (g)**
Cup	380
Book	1,100
Can	240
Ruler	25
Stapler	620

2. Which object would have an acceleration of 0.89 m/s^2 if you pushed on it with a force of 0.55 N?
   A. book   **C.** ruler
   B. can   **D.** stapler

3. Which object would have the greatest acceleration if you pushed on it with a force of 8.2 N?
   A. can   **C.** ruler
   B. stapler   **D.** book

Test-Taking Tip

Check Symbols Be sure you understand all symbols on a table or graph before answering any questions about the table or graph.

Question 3 The mass of the objects are given in grams, but the force is given in newtons which is a kg·m/s². The mass must be converted from grams to kilograms.

336 STANDARDIZED TEST PRACTICE

---

4. What is the weight of a book that has a mass of 0.35 kg?
   A. 0.036 N   **C.** 28 N
   B. 3.4 N   **D.** 34 N

5. If you swing an object on the end of a string around in a circle, the string pulls on the object to keep it moving in a circle. What is the name of this force?
   A. inertial   **C.** resistance
   B. centripetal **D.** gravitational

6. What is the acceleration of a 1.4-kg object if the gravitational force pulls downward on it, but air resistance pushes upward on it with a force of 2.5 N?
   A. 11.6 m/s^2, downward
   B. 11.6 m/s^2, upward
   C. 8.0 m/s^2, downward
   D. 8.0 m/s^2, upward

Use the figure below to answer questions 7 and 8.

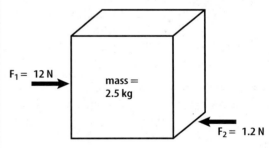

7. The figure above shows the horizontal forces that act on a box that is pushed from the left with a force of 12 N. What force is resisting the horizontal motion in this illustration?
   A. friction   **C.** inertia
   B. gravity   **D.** momentum

8. What is the acceleration of the box?
   A. 27 m/s^2 **C.** 4.3 m/s^2
   B. 4.8 m/s^2 **D.** 0.48 m/s^2

Part 3 | Open Ended

18. The force of gravity causes the astronauts and the spaceship to fall toward Earth with the same acceleration. Because the spaceship doesn't exert a force on the astronauts, their weight relative to the spaceship is zero and they are able to float. However, the weight of the astronauts relative to Earth is their mass multiplied by the gravitational pull they experience from Earth.

19. A satellite's forward motion tends to keep it traveling in a straight line, but gravity continually pulls it in toward Earth. Satellites move so fast horizontally that Earth's surface curves downward at the same rate that the satellites fall downward.

20. The initial force on the ball causes it to move outward and upward. The force of gravity on the ball pulls it downward. These forces combined cause the ball to travel along a curved path.

21. If the ball were thrown harder, the initial direction of the ball would be the same, but it would travel

Part 2 | Short Response/Grid In

*Record your answers on the answer sheet
provided by your teacher or on a sheet of paper.*

9. A skater is coasting along the ice without
exerting any apparent force. Which law of
motion explains the skater's ability to continue moving?

10. After a soccer ball is kicked into the air,
what force or forces are acting on it?

11. What is the force on an 8.55-kg object that
accelerates at 5.34 m/s².

Use the figure below to answer questions 12 and 13.

12. Two bumper cars collide and then move
away from each other. How do the forces the
bumper cars exert on each other compare?

13. After the collision, determine whether both
bumper cars will have the same acceleration.

14. Does acceleration depend on the speed of
an object? Explain.

15. An object acted on by a force of 2.8 N has
an acceleration of 3.6 m/s². What is the
mass of the object?

16. What is the acceleration a 1.4-kg object
falling through the air if the force of air
resistance on the object is 2.5 N?

17. Name three ways you could accelerate if
you were riding a bicycle.

Part 3 | Open Ended

Record your answers on a sheet of paper.

18. When astronauts orbit Earth, they float
inside the spaceship because of weightlessness. Explain this effect.

19. Describe how satellites are able to remain
in orbit around Earth.

Use the figure below to answer questions 20 and 21.

20. The figure above shows the path a ball
thrown into the air follows. What causes
the ball to move along a curved path?

21. What effect would throwing the ball
harder have on the ball's path? Explain.

22. How does Newton's second law determine
the motion of a book as you push it across
a desktop?

23. A heavy box sits on a sidewalk. If you push
against the box, the box moves in the direction of the force. If the box is replaced with
a ball of the same mass, and you push with
the same force against the ball, will it have
the same acceleration as the box? Explain.

24. According to Newton's third law of motion,
a rock sitting on the ground pushes against
the ground, and the ground pushes back
against the rock with an equal force. Explain
why this force doesn't cause the rock to
accelerate upward from the ground according to Newton's second law.

24. Newton's second law states that an
object's acceleration equals the force
on the object divided by the object's
mass. However, this refers to the *net*
force on the object. The rock experiences an upward force from the
ground and an equal downward
force due to gravity. The net force on
the rock is zero. According to
Newton's second law, the acceleration of the rock is therefore zero.

Rubrics

For more help evaluating open-
ended assessment questions, see
the rubric on p. 4T.

faster. Gravity would still pull the
ball downward with the same
force. However, the ball would
travel a greater horizontal distance
in the time required for the ball to
fall down. The ball's path would be
a wider arc.

22. Newton's second law describes
how to calculate the acceleration
of an object if you know the
object's mass and the force acting
on the object. The book has no vertical motion because the gravitational force acting down on it
equals the upward force on the
book by the desktop. The horizontal acceleration of the book equals
the mass of the book divided by

the force you exert upon the book.

23. No, the ball will have a greater acceleration. The sliding friction resisting
the motion of the box is greater than
the rolling friction resisting the
motion of the ball. The box therefore
has a smaller net force, resulting in a
smaller acceleration.

Section/Objectives	Standards		Labs/Features
Chapter Opener	**National**	**State/Local**	**Launch Lab:** Forces and Air Pressure, p. 339 **Foldables,** p. 339
	See pp. 16T–17T for a Key to Standards.		
Section 1 Pressure ⏱ 2 sessions 💾 1 block 1. **Define and calculate** pressure. 2. **Model** how pressure varies in a fluid.	National Content Standards: UCP.1–UCP.3, UCP.5, A.1, A.2, B.1, B.2, D.1		**Science Online,** p. 341 **Applying Math:** Calculating Pressure, p. 341 **MiniLAB:** Interpreting Footprints, p. 342 **Integrate Astronomy,** p. 343 **Visualizing Pressure at Varying Elevations,** p. 346
Section 2 Why do objects float? ⏱ 2 sessions 💾 1 block 3. **Explain** how the pressure in a fluid produces a buoyant force. 4. **Define** density. 5. **Explain** floating and sinking using Archimedes' principle.	National Content Standards: UCP.1–UCP.3, UCP.5, A.1, A.2, B.1, B.2, G.3		**Integrate Career,** p. 352 **Applying Science:** Layering Liquids, p. 352 **Lab:** Measuring Buoyant Force, p. 355
Section 3 Doing Work with Fluids ⏱ 4 sessions 💾 2 blocks 6. **Explain** how forces are transmitted through fluids. 7. **Describe** how a hydraulic system increases force. 8. **Describe** Bernoulli's principle.	National Content Standards: UCP.1–UCP.3, UCP.5, A.1, A.2, B.1, B.2, F.3		**Science Online,** p. 358 **MiniLAB:** Observing Bernoulli's Principle, p. 359 **Lab:** Barometric Pressure and Weather, pp. 362–363 **Science and Language Arts:** Hurricane, p. 364

Lab Materials	Reproducible Resources	Section Assessment	Technology
Launch Lab: water, drinking straw, cup or glass for water	**Chapter FAST FILE Resources** Foldables Worksheet, p. 17 Directed Reading Overview, p. 19 Note-taking Worksheets, pp. 33–35	**GLENCOE'S ASSESSMENT ADVANTAGE**	**TeacherWorks** includes: • Interactive Teacher Edition • Lesson Planner with calendar • Access to all program blacklines • Correlations to standards • Web links
MiniLAB: an area of dirt, sand or snow; metric ruler *Need materials?* Contact Science Kit at 1-800-828-7777 or www.sciencekit.com on the Internet.	**Chapter FAST FILE Resources** Transparency Activity, p. 44 MiniLAB, p. 3 Lab Activity, pp. 9–12 Enrichment, p. 30 Reinforcement, p. 27 Directed Reading, p. 20 **Life Science Critical Thinking/ Problem Solving,** p. 14	**Portfolio** Active Reading, p. 343 **Performance** Applying Math, p. 341 MiniLAB, p. 342 Applying Math, p. 347 **Content** Section Review, p. 347	🔊 Section Focus Transparency 🎧 Guided Reading Audio Program 💿 Interactive Chalkboard CD-ROM
Lab: aluminum pan, spring scale, 500-mL beaker, graduated cylinder, funnel, metal object	**Chapter FAST FILE Resources** Transparency Activity, p. 45 Enrichment, p. 31 Reinforcement, p. 28 Directed Reading, p. 20 Lab Worksheet, pp. 5–6 **Reading and Writing Skill Activities,** p. 19	**Portfolio** Curriculum Connection, p. 353 **Performance** Applying Science, p. 352 Applying Math, p. 354 **Content** Section Review, p. 354	🔊 Section Focus Transparency 💿 Virtual Labs CD-ROM 🎧 Guided Reading Audio Program 💿 Interactive Chalkboard CD-ROM 📼 Video Lab
MiniLAB: string, plastic spoon, stream of water from a faucet **Lab:** no materials needed	**Chapter FAST FILE Resources** Transparency Activity, p. 46 MiniLAB, p. 4 Lab Activity, pp. 13–16 Enrichment, p. 32 Reinforcement, p. 29 Directed Reading, pp. 21, 22 Lab Worksheet, pp. 7–8 Transparency Activity, pp. 47–48 **Lab Management and Safety,** p. 38	**Portfolio** Assessment, p. 359 **Performance** MiniLAB, p. 359 Applying Math, p. 361 **Content** Section Review, p. 361	🔊 Section Focus Transparency 🔊 Teaching Transparency 🎧 Guided Reading Audio Program 💿 Interactive Chalkboard CD-ROM

End of Chapter Assessment

GLENCOE'S ASSESSMENT ADVANTAGE

Blackline Masters	Technology	Professional Series
Chapter FAST FILE Resources Chapter Review, pp. 37–38 Chapter Tests, pp. 39–42 **Standardized Test Practice,** pp. 51–54	📼 MindJogger Videoquiz 💿 Virtual Labs CD-ROM 💿 ExamView® Pro Testmaker 💿 TeacherWorks CD-ROM 💿 Interactive Chalkboard CD-ROM	**Performance Assessment in the Science Classroom (PASC)**

Transparencies

Section Focus

SECTION 1 Section Focus Transparency Well, This Is Deep

Have you ever felt your ears pop as you reached for the bottom at the deep end of a pool? This happens because factors affecting your body change as you go deeper. In the ocean, divers need to be aware of this, too. For the deepest dives, a hard suit, like the one being tested below, is necessary for protection.

1. When might people feel their ears pop?
2. Describe the two diving suits you see in the picture. What advantages are there to the hard suit? Disadvantages?
3. How might conditions change as you dive far beneath the surface of the sea? How might conditions change as you climb a mountain?

L2

SECTION 2 Section Focus Transparency Connecticut floats?

Icebergs can be pretty big, but even the largest icebergs float. The pieces shown below were once part of an iceberg roughly the size of Connecticut! This monster iceberg, known as B15, broke off the Ross Ice Shelf in Antarctica.

1. Does shape affect whether or not an object will float? Illustrate your answer with an example.
2. What happens to the water level when a person gets in a bath tub?
3. How is a blimp filled with helium gas similar to an iceberg floating in the ocean?

L2

SECTION 3 Section Focus Transparency Again with the Fluids

Hydraulic lifts can hoist some really heavy objects, like cars and houses. They do so by exploiting the properties of fluids.

1. What happens when you squeeze the bottom of a toothpaste tube?
2. What does a toothpaste tube have to do with a hydraulic lift?
3. How can a small force at one end of a hydraulic lift be translated to a big force at the other end? (Hint: remember the part in section one about force, pressure, and area?)

L2

This is a representation of key blackline masters available in the Teacher Classroom Resources. See Resource Manager boxes within the chapter for additional information.

Assessment

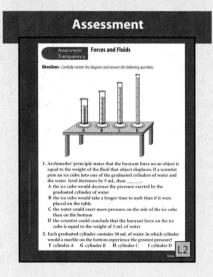

Assessment Transparency Forces and Fluids

Directions: Carefully review the diagram and answer the following questions.

1. Archimedes' principle states that the buoyant force on an object is equal to the weight of the fluid that object displaces. If a scientist puts an ice cube into one of the graduated cylinders of water and the water level increases by 5 mL, then ____.
   A the ice cube would decrease the pressure exerted by the graduated cylinder of water
   B the ice cube would take a longer time to melt than if it were placed on the table
   C the water could exert more pressure on the side of the ice cube than on the bottom
   D the scientist could conclude that the buoyant force on the ice cube is equal to the weight of 5 mL of water
2. Each graduated cylinder contains 50 mL of water. In which cylinder would a marble on the bottom experience the greatest pressure?
   F cylinder A   G cylinder B   H cylinder C   J cylinder D

L2

Teaching

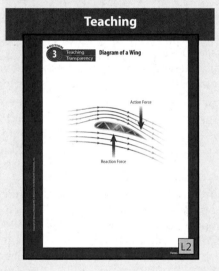

SECTION 3 Teaching Transparency Diagram of a Wing

Action Force

Reaction Force

L2

Key to Teaching Strategies

The following designations will help you decide which activities are appropriate for your students.

L1 Level 1 activities should be appropriate for students with learning difficulties.

L2 Level 2 activities should be within the ability range of all students.

L3 Level 3 activities are designed for above-average students.

ELL ELL activities should be within the ability range of English Language Learners.

COOP LEARN Cooperative Learning activities are designed for small group work.

LS Multiple Learning Styles logos, as described on page 12T, are used throughout to indicate strategies that address different learning styles.

P These strategies represent student products that can be placed into a best-work portfolio.

PBL Problem-Based Learning activities apply real-world situations to learning.

Hands-on Activities

Student Text Lab Worksheet

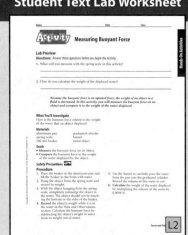

Activity Measuring Buoyant Force

Lab Preview
Directions: Answer these questions before you begin the Activity.
1. What will you measure with the spring scale in this activity?

2. How do you calculate the weight of the displaced water?

Because the buoyant force is an upward force, the weight of an object in a fluid is decreased. In this activity, you will measure the buoyant force on an object and compare it to the weight of the water displaced.

What You'll Investigate
How is the buoyant force related to the weight of the water that an object displaces?

Materials
aluminum pan
spring scale
500-mL beaker
graduated cylinder
funnel
metal object

Goals
• **Measure** the buoyant force on an object.
• **Compare** the buoyant force to the weight of the water displaced by the object.

Safety Precautions

Procedure
1. Place the beaker in the aluminum pan and fill beaker to the brim with water.
2. Hang the object from the spring scale and record its weight.
3. With the object hanging from the spring scale, completely submerge the object in the water. The object should not be touching the bottom or the sides of the beaker.
4. **Record** the object's weight while it is in the water in the Data and Observations section. Calculate the buoyant force by subtracting the object's weight in water from its weight out of water.
5. Use the funnel to carefully pour the water from the pan into the graduated cylinder. Record the volume of this water in cm³.
6. **Calculate** the weight of water displaced by multiplying the volume of the water by 0.0098 N.

L2

Laboratory Activities

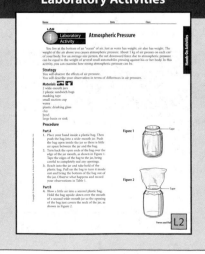

LAB 1 Laboratory Activity Atmospheric Pressure

You live at the bottom of an "ocean" of air. Just as water has weight, air also has weight. The weight of the air above you causes atmospheric pressure. About 1 kg of air presses on each cm² of your body. For an average-size person, the net downward force due to atmospheric pressure can be equal to the weight of several small automobiles pressing against his or her body. In this activity, you can examine how strong atmospheric pressure can be.

Strategy
You will observe the effects of air pressure.
You will describe your observation in terms of differences in air pressure.

Materials
2 wide-mouth jars
2 plastic sandwich bags
masking tape
small suction cup
water
plastic drinking glass
clay
bowl
large basin or sink

Procedure
Part A
1. Place your hand inside a plastic bag. Then push the bag into a wide-mouth jar. Push the bag open inside the jar so there is little air space between the jar and the bag.
2. Turn back the open ends of the bag over the edge of the jar mouth, as shown in Figure 1. Tape the edges of the bag to the jar, being careful to completely seal any openings.
3. Reach into the jar and take hold of the plastic bag. Pull on the bag to turn it inside out and bring the bottom of the bag out of the jar. Observe what happens and record your observations in Table 1.

Part B
4. Blow a little air into a second plastic bag. Hold the bag upside-down over the mouth of the bag just covers the neck of the jar, as shown in Figure 2.

Figure 1

Figure 2

L2

Meeting Different Ability Levels

Content Outline

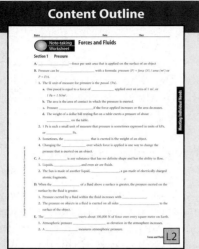

L2

Reinforcement

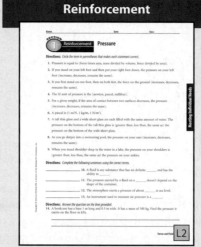

L2

Enrichment

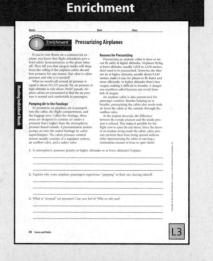

L3

Directed Reading (English/Spanish)

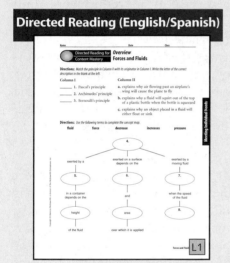

L1

Study Guide

L2

Reading Essentials

L1

Assessment

Test Practice Workbook

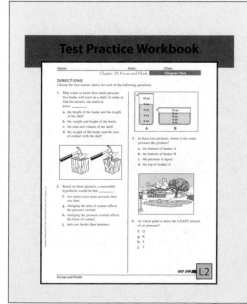

L2

Chapter Review

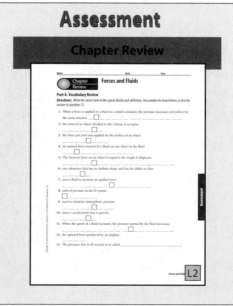

L2

Chapter Tests

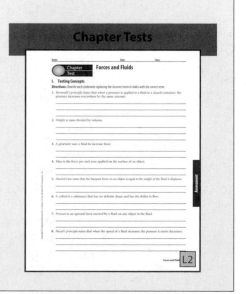

L2

Science Content Background

section 1 Pressure
What is pressure?

Forces exerted on an object sometimes can cause the object to deform. For example, the force exerted by your hand on a thin piece of metal can cause it to bend or deform. For most materials the deformation depends not on the force exerted, but on the pressure exerted. The pressure on an object is the force exerted on the object divided by the area over which the force is exerted, or $P = F/A$. By making the area over which the force is exerted very small, a large pressure can be exerted. For example, an ice pick has a narrow tip with a small area. This enables an ice pick to exert a large pressure on an ice surface that can cause the ice to crack.

Pressure in Fluid

In any material the atoms and molecules that make up the material are in constant motion. In a fluid, these particles can move from place to place. When a fluid is placed in a container, particles continually collide with the surfaces of the container. Each collision causes a force to be exerted on the container surface. The total force on a surface due to the collisions is the sum of forces exerted by all the collisions. Because the particles are moving randomly, the components of the forces in all directions—except those perpendicular to the surface—cancel out. As a result, the force and the pressure exerted by the fluid is always perpendicular to the surface, regardless of the orientation of the surface. This is true for any surface placed in the fluid.

Atmospheric Pressure

Atmospheric pressure on a surface is caused by the weight of the atmosphere above the surface. Just as for any other fluid, the atmospheric pressure on a surface is perpendicular to the surface. The atmosphere becomes more diffuse with altitude. At sea level, the weight of the atmosphere above a surface with an area of 1 m^2 is

about 100,000 N, corresponding to a pressure of about 100,000 Pa. The pressure exerted by water at a depth of only about 10 m is equal to atmospheric pressure at sea level.

section 2 Why do objects float?
The Buoyant Force

An upward force, called the buoyant force, acts on an object placed in a fluid. The buoyant force results from the increase in pressure with depth in the fluid. The pressure on a surface at any depth in a fluid equals the weight of the fluid above the surface divided by the surface area.

If the object is totally submerged, the pressure on the object's bottom surface is greater than the pressure on the top surface. Because the fluid forces exerted on the vertical sides cancel, the net force exerted by the fluid is upward.

Archimedes' Principle

An object floats if the buoyant force on the object equals the object's weight. When an object is placed in a fluid it begins to sink. As the object sinks and is not totally submerged, the buoyant force on the object increases. When the object's bottom surface is at a depth where the buoyant force equals the object's weight, the object stops moving downward and floats.

Bill Brooks/Masterfile

At a given depth, the force exerted by a fluid on a surface is the weight of the fluid above the force. If an object floats, the weight of the fluid above the bottom surface of the object is the same as the weight of the fluid the object displaced. This is Archimedes' principle—the buoyant force on an object in a fluid equals the weight of the fluid displaced by the object.

section 3 Doing Work with Fluids

Hydraulic systems use Pascal's principle to increase an applied force. A force applied to a small piston increases the pressure in a fluid. This pressure increase is transmitted through the fluid to the bottom of a larger piston, increasing the force applied on the piston. However, by the conservation of energy, the work done by the smaller piston is the same as the work done by the larger piston. As a result, the larger piston moves a shorter distance than the smaller piston.

Teacher to Teacher

Pam Griffiths
Havelock High School
Havelock, NC

"Ask the students to tape together two strips of paper that measure 5" × 1/2" to form a ring. Have students place the ring in front of them. With a straw, blow outside the ring about midway on the side. Practice different positions until the correct placement of air is achieved. The ring of paper will move toward the straw because of the decrease in pressure from the moving air."

Pam Griffiths

Wings and Flight

The lift on an airplane wing is often explained by Bernoulli's principle. According to this explanation, the curved shape of the upper surface of a wing makes air flow faster over the upper surface, reducing the pressure on the upper surface. However, planes can fly upside down and some wings have identical upper and lower surfaces. The shape of the wing surfaces has little to do with creating lift.

Instead, lift is produced primarily by the angle a wing makes with the airflow. When the wing is at an angle it deflects the air flow downward. Most of the deflection is caused by the upper surface. By Newton's third law, the downward force exerted on the air by the wing results in an upward force exerted by the air on the wing. This is the source of lift.

chapter content resources

Internet Resources

For additional content background, visit **ips.msscience.com** to:
- access your book online
- find references to related articles in popular science magazines
- access Web links with related content background
- access current events with science journal topics

Print Resources

An Introduction to Fluid Dynamics, by G.K. Batchelor, Cambridge University Press, 2000

Introduction to Fluid Mechanics, by Robert W. Fox, Alan T. McDonald, and Philip J. Prichard, John Wiley & Sons, 2003

The Works of Archimedes, by Thomas L. Heath (editor), Dover Publications, Inc., 2002

On Shoulders of Giants: Great Scientists and their Discoveries: From Archimedes to Watson and Crick, by Melvyn Bragg, John Wiley & Sons, 1999

Chapter Vocabulary

Science Journal Student responses will vary. Possible answer: objects that float—leaves, lily pads, corks, boats, and gliders; objects that sink—coins, rocks, ship anchors, lead weights, and concreate blocks

INTERACTIVE CHALKBOARD
with Image Bank

PowerPoint® Presentations

This CD-ROM is an editable Microsoft® PowerPoint® presentation that includes:
• a pre-made presentation for every chapter
• interactive graphics
• animations
• audio clips
• image bank
• all new section and chapter questions
• Standardized Test Practice
• transparencies
• pre-lab questions for all labs
• Foldables directions
• links to ips.msscience.com

Forces and Fluids

chapter preview

sections

1 **Pressure**

2 **Why do objects float?**
   Lab Measuring Buoyant Force

3 **Doing Work with Fluids**
   Lab Barometric Pressure and Weather

⊙ Virtual Lab Why do things float?

A Very Fluid Situation

This swimmer seems to be defying gravity as he skims over the water. Even though the swimmer floats, a rock with the same mass would sink to the bottom of the pool. What forces cause something to float? Why does a swimmer float, while a rock sinks?

Science Journal Compare and contrast five objects that float with five objects that sink.

338

Theme Connection

Fluids and Forces Fluids exert forces. These forces enable ships to float and aircraft to fly. Understanding the dynamics of fluids can lead to improvements in vessel design and to advances in aviation technology.

About the Photo

Human Floating On average the human body has a density very close to the density of water. As a result, most people will float only if they are submerged almost totally. Fat tissue has a density of about 0.8 g/cm³, so bodies with more fat tissue float more easily. Also, the density of the body is decreased by inhaling air.

Start-Up Activities

Forces Exerted by Air

When you are lying down, something is pushing down on you with a force equal to the weight of several small cars. What is the substance that is applying all this pressure on you? It's air, a fluid that exerts forces on everything it is in contact with.

1. Suck water into a straw. Try to keep the straw completely filled with water.

2. Quickly cap the top of the straw with your finger and observe what happens to the water.

3. Release your finger from the top of the straw for an instant and replace it as quickly as possible. Observe what happens to the water.

4. Release your finger from the top of the straw and observe.

5. **Think Critically** Write a paragraph describing your observations of the water in the straw. When were the forces acting on the water in the straw balanced and when were they unbalanced?

Fluids Make the following Foldable to compare and contrast the characteristics of two types of fluids—liquids and gases.

STEP 1 **Fold** one sheet of paper lengthwise.

STEP 2 **Fold** into thirds.

STEP 3 **Unfold and draw** overlapping ovals. **Cut** the top sheet along the folds.

STEP 4 **Label** the ovals as shown.

Construct a Venn Diagram As you read the chapter, list the characteristics of liquids under the left tab, those characteristics of gases under the right tab, and those characteristics common to both under the middle tab.

Preview this chapter's content and activities at
ips.msscience.com

Purpose Students explore the concept of air pressure. L2 LS Kinesthetic

Preparation Purchase straws.

Materials water, drinking straw, cup or glass for water

Teaching Strategies To avoid a mess, be certain students experiment with their straws while holding the bottom ends of the straws over the drinking glasses. Have paper towels available to clean up spills.

Think Critically

When the straw is capped, the downward force of gravity on the water is balanced by the upward force exerted by air pressure on the water surface at the bottom of the straw. When the straw is uncapped, the forces on the water are unbalanced. The force exerted by air pressure on the upper and lower water surfaces are balanced, and gravity pulls the water downward.

Assessment

Performance Tell students that the density of air is about 1.3 kg/m^3. Have them measure the dimensions of the classroom and calculate its volume, and then calculate the mass of the air in the room. Use **Performance Assessment in the Science Classroom,** p. 101.

FOLDABLES **Dinah Zike**
Study Organizer **Study Fold**

Student preparation materials for this Foldable are available in the Chapter *FAST FILE* Resources.

340 **CHAPTER 12** Forces and Fluids

Bellringer

Section Focus Transparencies also are available on the Interactive Chalkboard CD-ROM.

L2 **ELL**

Tie to Prior Knowledge

Force and Weight Review the concepts of force and weight, including the fact that a force has a direction. You may also want to review the states of matter (solid, liquid, gas, plasma) and calculating area.

---

section

1 Pressure

as you read

What You'll Learn
■ **Define and calculate** pressure.
■ **Model** how pressure varies in a fluid.

Why It's Important
Some of the processes that help keep you alive, such as inhaling and exhaling, depend on differences in pressure.

⟳ Review Vocabulary
weight: on Earth, the gravitational force between an object and Earth

New Vocabulary
● pressure
● fluid

What is pressure?

What happens when you walk in deep, soft snow or dry sand? Your feet sink into the snow or sand and walking can be difficult. If you rode a bicycle with narrow tires over these surfaces, the tires would sink even deeper than your feet.

How deep you sink depends on your weight as well as the area over which you make contact with the sand or snow. Like the person in **Figure 1,** when you stand on two feet, you make contact with the sand over the area covered by your feet. However, if you were to stand on a large piece of wood, your weight would be distributed over the area covered by the wood.

In both cases, your weight exerted a downward force on the sand. What changed was the area of contact between you and the sand. By changing the area of contact, you changed the pressure you exerted on the sand due to your weight. **Pressure** is the force per unit area that is applied on the surface of an object. When you stood on the board, the area of contact increased, so that the same force was applied over a larger area. As a result, the pressure that was exerted on the sand decreased and you didn't sink as deep.

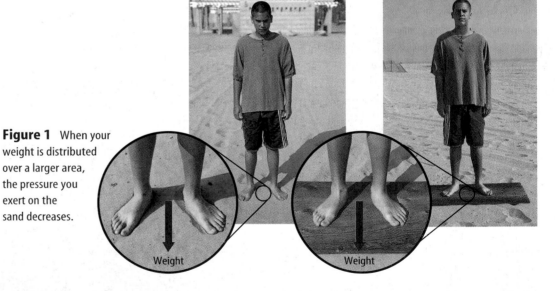

Figure 1 When your weight is distributed over a larger area, the pressure you exert on the sand decreases.

340 **CHAPTER 12** Forces and Fluids

Section 1 Resource Manager

Chapter *FAST FILE* Resources
Transparency Activity, p. 44
Directed Reading for Content Mastery, pp. 19, 20
Note-taking Worksheets, pp. 33–35

MiniLAB, p. 3
Lab Activity, pp. 9–12
Enrichment, p. 30
Reinforcement, p. 27

Calculating Pressure What would happen to the pressure exerted by your feet if your weight increased? You might expect that you would sink deeper in the sand, so the pressure also would increase. Pressure increases if the force applied increases, and decreases if the area of contact increases. Pressure can be calculated from this formula.

> **Pressure Equation**
>
> $$\text{Pressure (in pascals)} = \frac{\text{force (in newtons)}}{\text{area (in meters squared)}}$$
>
> $$P = \frac{F}{A}$$

The unit of pressure in the SI system is the pascal, abbreviated Pa. One pascal is equal to a force of 1 N applied over an area of 1 m², or 1 Pa = 1 N/m². The weight of a dollar bill resting completely flat on a table exerts a pressure of about 1 Pa on the table. Because 1 Pa is a small unit of pressure, pressure sometimes is expressed in units of kPa, which is 1,000 Pa.

Science Online

Topic: Snowshoes
Visit ips.msscience.com for Web links to information about the history and use of snowshoes. These devices have been used for centuries in cold, snowy climates.

Activity Use simple materials, such as pipe cleaners, string, or paper, to make a model of a snowshoe.

Applying Math — Solve One-Step Equations

CALCULATING PRESSURE A water glass sitting on a table weighs 4 N. The bottom of the water glass has a surface area of 0.003 m². Calculate the pressure the water glass exerts on the table.

Solution

1 *This is what you know:*
- force: $F = 4$ N
- area: $A = 0.003$ m²

2 *This is what you need to find out:*
- pressure: $P = ?$ Pa

3 *This is the procedure you need to use:*

Substitute the known values for force and area into the pressure equation and calculate the pressure:

$$P = \frac{F}{A} = \frac{(4\ \text{N})}{(0.003\ \text{m}^2)}$$

$$= 1{,}333\ \text{N/m}^2 = 1{,}333\ \text{Pa}$$

4 *Check your answer:*

Multiply pressure by the given area. You should get the force that was given.

Practice Problems

1. A student weighs 600 N. The student's shoes are in contact with the floor over a surface area of 0.012 m². Calculate the pressure exerted by the student on the floor.

2. A box that weighs 250 N is at rest on the floor. If the pressure exerted by the box on the floor is 25,000 Pa, over what area is the box in contact with the floor?

Science Online For more practice, visit ips.msscience.com/math_practice

Curriculum Connection

History The pascal is named for Blaise Pascal (1623–1662) a French scientist, philosopher and mathematician. Pascal carried out a number of experiments on the behavior of fluids, and also is credited with constructing the first digital calculator. Ask students to find out more about the life of Blaise Pascal.

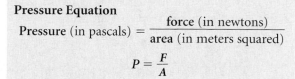

2 Teach

Discussion
Pressure Phrases What do people mean when they say they are under pressure? *that they are being pushed; or are being stressed* What do they mean when they say the pressure is letting up? *Pressure lets up when the stress is reduced.* [L2] [LS] **Linguistic**

Activity
Inverse Relationships Some students have trouble with inverse relationships such as $P = F/A$. Have each student make a pair of tables and graphs showing what happens to pressure when area is held constant and force varies, and what happens to pressure when force is held constant and area varies. [L2] [LS] **Visual-Spatial**

Discussion
Snow Walking Why is it easier to walk in snow when you are wearing skis or snowshoes than when you are wearing winter boots? *Skis and snowshoes increase the area in contact with the snow, reducing the pressure so you don't sink as far into the snow when you stand or walk.* [L2] [LS] **Logical-Mathematical**

Applying Math

National Math Standards
Correlation to Mathematics Objectives
1, 2, 9

Answers to Practice Problems
1. (600 N)/(0.012 m²) = 50,000 Pa
2. $A = \dfrac{F}{P} = \dfrac{250\ \text{N}}{25{,}000\ \text{N/m}^2} = 0.01$ m²

Purpose Students compare and contrast the pressures exerted by different types of movement. L2 LS **Kinesthetic**

Materials metric ruler, outside area that will take tracks

Teaching Strategy Try the ground before class to make sure it will take tracks, and observe how detailed the tracks are. A dusting of snow, for example, won't make tracks with varying depth. Slightly damp sand will hold clearer tracks than dry sand.

Analysis

1. Students should measure to the 0.10 cm.
2. Possible answers: A running person puts more pressure on the ball of the foot than the heel. A person carrying a load puts more pressure on the whole foot. A person walking backward puts more pressure on the heel than on the ball of the foot.
3. Answers should include some reasoning such as the tracks are deep at the ball of the foot and shallow at the heel, so the person was running.

Assessment

Process Ask students how a naturalist would use animal tracks to study animals. Possible answer: Look at the depths of different parts of the track and the distance between tracks to determine if the animal was walking or running. Use **Performance Assessment in the Science Classroom,** p. 89.

Interpreting Footprints

Procedure

1. Go outside to **an area of dirt, sand, or snow** where you can make footprints. Smooth the surface.
2. Make tracks in several different ways. Possible choices include walking forward, walking backward, running, jumping a short or long distance, walking carrying a load, and tiptoeing.

Analysis

1. Measure the depth of each type of track at two points: the ball of the foot and the heel. Compare the depths of the different tracks.
2. The depth of the track corresponds to the pressure on the ground. In your **Science Journal,** explain how different means of motion put pressure on different parts of the sole.
3. Have one person make a track while the other looks away. Then have the second person determine what the motion was.

Pressure and Weight To calculate the pressure that is exerted on a surface, you need to know the force and the area over which it is applied. Sometimes the force that is exerted is the weight of an object, such as when you are standing on sand, snow, or a floor. Suppose you are holding a 2-kg book in the palm of your hand. To find out how much pressure is being exerted on your hand, you first must know the force that the book is exerting on your hand—its weight.

$$\text{Weight} = \text{mass} \times \text{acceleration due to gravity}$$
$$W = (2 \text{ kg}) \times (9.8 \text{ m/s}^2)$$
$$W = 19.6 \text{ N}$$

If the area of contact between your hand and the book is 0.003 m², the pressure that is exerted on your hand by the book is:

$$P = \frac{F}{A}$$
$$P = \frac{(19.6 \text{ N})}{(0.003 \text{ m}^2)}$$
$$P = 6,533 \text{ Pa} = 6.53 \text{ kPa}$$

Pressure and Area One way to change the pressure that is exerted on an object is to change the area over which the force is applied. Imagine trying to drive a nail into a piece of wood, as shown in **Figure 2.** Why is the tip of a nail pointed instead of flat? When you hit the nail with a hammer, the force you apply is transmitted through the nail from the head to the tip. The tip of the nail comes to a point and is in contact with the wood over a small area. Because the contact area is so small, the pressure that is exerted by the nail on the wood is large—large enough to push the wood fibers apart. This allows the nail to move downward into the wood.

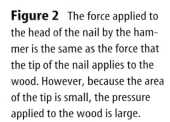
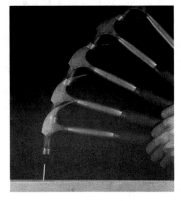

Figure 2 The force applied to the head of the nail by the hammer is the same as the force that the tip of the nail applies to the wood. However, because the area of the tip is small, the pressure applied to the wood is large.

Teacher FYI

Kinetic Theory of Matter According to the kinetic theory of matter, all matter is composed of small particles (atoms and molecules) in constant motion. The pressure of a fluid is due to the movement of the molecules in it. When the molecules of a fluid collide with the walls of a container or with objects submerged in the fluid, they exert pressure. Pressure depends on the mass of the molecules, their velocity, and how often collisions occur.

The water can be squeezed from its container into the pan.

Water flows from the jug to the canteen, taking the shape of the canteen.

The gas completely fills the propane tank. After it is attached to the stove, the gas can flow to be used as fuel.

Fluids

What do the substances in **Figure 3** have in common? Each takes the shape of its container and can flow from one place to another. A **fluid** is any substance that has no definite shape and has the ability to flow. You might think of a fluid as being a liquid, such as water or motor oil. But gases are also fluids. When you are outside on a windy day, you can feel the air flowing past you. Because air can flow and has no definite shape, air is a fluid. Gases, liquids, and the state of matter called plasma, which is found in the Sun and other stars, are fluids and can flow.

Pressure in a Fluid

Suppose you placed an empty glass on a table. The weight of the glass exerts pressure on the table. If you fill the glass with water, the weight of the water and glass together exert a force on the table. So the pressure exerted on the table increases.

Because the water has weight, the water itself also exerts pressure on the bottom of the glass. This pressure is the weight of the water divided by the area of the glass bottom. If you pour more water into the glass, the height of the water in the glass increases and the weight of the water increases. As a result, the pressure exerted by the water increases.

Figure 3 Fluids all have the ability to flow and take the shape of their containers.
Classify *What are some other examples of fluids?*

Plasma The Sun is a star with a core temperature of about 16 million°C. At this temperature, the particles in the Sun move at tremendous speeds, crashing into each other in violent collisions that tear atoms apart. As a result, the Sun is made of a type of fluid called a plasma. A plasma is a gas made of electrically charged particles.

SECTION 1 Pressure **343**

Discussion

Water Level Explain that air pressure is also important to water level in a system. What happens to the level of water if the air pressure over the top of one tube is lower than the air pressure over the top of a second tube connected to the first? The water will be pushed farther up the tube on which the pressure is lower. **L2** **LS**
Logical-Mathematical

Observing Pressure

Purpose To explore and observe pressure in fluids, have students design an experiment showing that, as the height of a fluid increases, the pressure at the bottom of the fluid increases.

Possible Materials water, recycled materials such as cans or plastic containers

Estimated Time one week outside class time

Teaching Strategies

• Students can make simple lab set-ups that show that the pressure increases at the bottom of a container as the height of the fluid increases.
• Encourage students to use inexpensive items such as recycled containers from home.
• Have students show their set-ups to the class.
• Allow students to explore other questions that arise.

For additional inquiry activities, see *Science Inquiry Labs.*

Caption Answer

Figure 4 The pressure becomes greater as the water column becomes narrower because the height of the column increases.

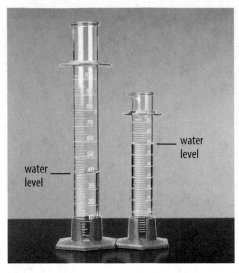

Figure 4 Even though each graduated cylinder contains the same volume of water, the pressure exerted by the higher column of water is greater.
Infer *how the pressure exerted by a water column would change as the column becomes narrower.*

Pressure and Fluid Height Suppose you poured the same amount of water into a small and a large graduated cylinder, as shown in **Figure 4.** Notice that the height of the water in the small cylinder is greater than in the large cylinder. Is the water pressure the same at the bottom of each cylinder? The weight of the water in each cylinder is the same, but the contact area at the bottom of the small cylinder is smaller. Therefore, the pressure is greater at the bottom of the small cylinder.

The height of the water can increase if more water is added to a container or if the same amount of water is added to a narrower container. In either case, when the height of the fluid is greater, the pressure at the bottom of the container is greater. This is always true for any fluid or any container. The greater the height of a fluid above a surface, the greater the pressure exerted by the fluid on that surface. The pressure exerted at the bottom of a container doesn't depend on the shape of the container, but only on the height of the fluid above the bottom, as **Figure 5** shows.

Pressure Increases with Depth If you swim underwater, you might notice that you can feel pressure in your ears. As you go deeper, you can feel this pressure increase. This pressure is exerted by the weight of the water above you. As you go deeper in a fluid, the height of the fluid above you increases. As the height of the fluid above you increases, the weight of the fluid above you also increases. As a result, the pressure exerted by the fluid increases with depth.

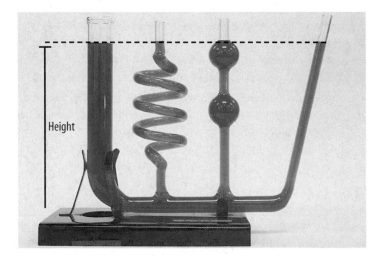

Figure 5 Pressure depends only on the height of the fluid above a surface, not on the shape of the container. The pressure at the bottom of each section of the tube is the same.

Differentiated Instruction

Challenge Deep-sea diving is challenging because of the high pressures that divers must contend with. Have students research what methods are used for deep-sea diving and what equipment is used. Have students present their reports to their class. **L3**

Visual Learning

Figure 5 The height of the water in the vertical tubes in this closed system is constant even though the shapes of the tubes are different. If the center section of the tube is sealed so that the two sides are independent, what will happen? The water in the left two vertical tubes would be isolated from the water in the right two tubes, so the water would behave independently on each side. **L3** **LS** **Visual-Spatial**

Pressure in All Directions

If the pressure that is exerted by a fluid is due to the weight of the fluid, is the pressure in a fluid exerted only downward? **Figure 6** shows a small, solid cube in a fluid. The fluid exerts a pressure on each side of this cube, not just on the top. The pressure on each side is perpendicular to the surface, and the amount of pressure depends only on the depth in the fluid. As shown in **Figure 6,** this is true for any object in a fluid, no matter how complicated the shape. The pressure at any point on the object is perpendicular to the surface of the object at that point.

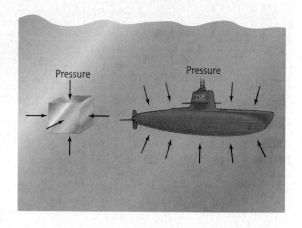

Reading Check *In what direction is pressure exerted by a fluid on a surface?*

Atmospheric Pressure

Even though you don't feel it, you are surrounded by a fluid that exerts pressure on you constantly. That fluid is the atmosphere. The atmosphere at Earth's surface is only about one-thousandth as dense as water. However, the thickness of the atmosphere is large enough to exert a large pressure on objects at Earth's surface. For example, look at **Figure 7.** When you are sitting down, the force pushing down on your body due to atmospheric pressure can be equal to the weight of several small cars. Atmospheric pressure is approximately 100,000 Pa at sea level. This means that the weight of Earth's atmosphere exerts about 100,000 N of force over every square meter on Earth.

Why doesn't this pressure cause you to be crushed? Your body is filled with fluids such as blood that also exert pressure. The pressure exerted outward by the fluids inside your body balances the pressure exerted by the atmosphere.

Going Higher As you go higher in the atmosphere, atmospheric pressure decreases as the amount of air above you decreases. The same is true in an ocean, lake, or pond. The water pressure is highest at the ocean floor and decreases as you go upward. The changes in pressure at varying heights in the atmosphere and depths in the ocean are illustrated in **Figure 8.**

Figure 6 The pressure on all objects in a fluid is exerted on all sides, perpendicular to the surface of the object, no matter what its shape.

Figure 7 Atmospheric pressure on your body is a result of the weight of the atmosphere exerting force on your body.
Infer *Why don't you feel the pressure exerted by the atmosphere?*

SECTION 1 Pressure **345**

LAB DEMONSTRATION

Purpose to observe that water and oil come to rest at different levels when balanced in a closed system

Materials clear plastic tube, water colored with food coloring, funnel, vegetable oil

Procedure Fill the tube partway with water and hang it in a U-shape. Mark the water level on each side. Pour some water out, and add oil to one side. Hang the tube in a U. Mark the level of the liquid on each side.

Expected Outcome When the tube contains only water, the liquid rises to the same level on each side. When the tube contains water and oil, the levels differ.

Assessment

Why are the levels different with oil on one side of the tube and water on the other? Oil is less dense than water, so oil at a depth of, for example, 10 cm exerts less pressure than water at a depth of 10 cm. The water pushes the oil up until equilibrium is reached.

Visualizing Pressure at Varying Elevations

Have students examine the pictures and read the captions. Then ask the following questions.

Commercial jets often fly 10 km above sea level. Why is air added to the passenger cabins of the planes to pressurize them? People would find it difficult or impossible to breathe the air at that altitude.

What could happen to a submarine if it went too deep in the ocean? It could be crushed by the water pressure.

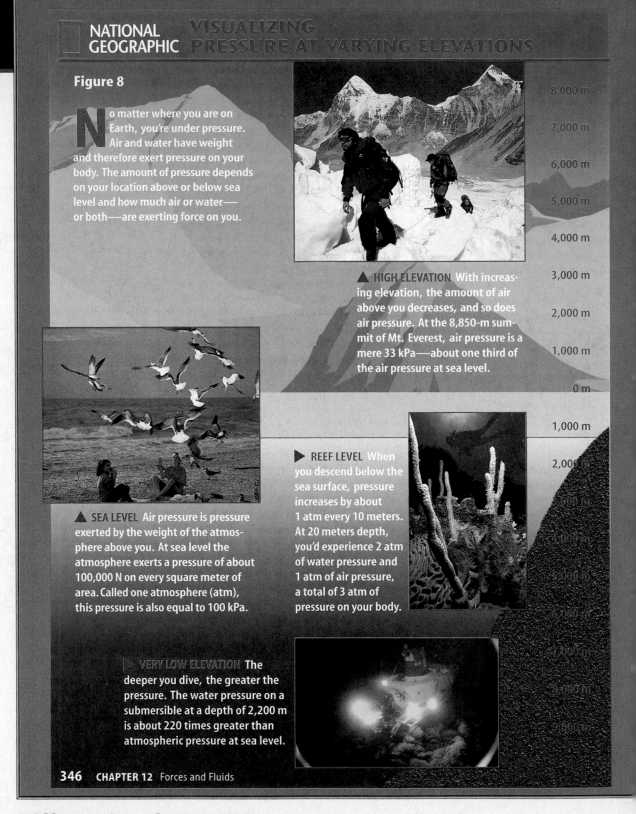

NATIONAL GEOGRAPHIC VISUALIZING PRESSURE AT VARYING ELEVATIONS

Figure 8

No matter where you are on Earth, you're under pressure. Air and water have weight and therefore exert pressure on your body. The amount of pressure depends on your location above or below sea level and how much air or water—or both—are exerting force on you.

▲ **HIGH ELEVATION** With increasing elevation, the amount of air above you decreases, and so does air pressure. At the 8,850-m summit of Mt. Everest, air pressure is a mere 33 kPa—about one third of the air pressure at sea level.

▲ **SEA LEVEL** Air pressure is pressure exerted by the weight of the atmosphere above you. At sea level the atmosphere exerts a pressure of about 100,000 N on every square meter of area. Called one atmosphere (atm), this pressure is also equal to 100 kPa.

▶ **REEF LEVEL** When you descend below the sea surface, pressure increases by about 1 atm every 10 meters. At 20 meters depth, you'd experience 2 atm of water pressure and 1 atm of air pressure, a total of 3 atm of pressure on your body.

▷ **VERY LOW ELEVATION** The deeper you dive, the greater the pressure. The water pressure on a submersible at a depth of 2,200 m is about 220 times greater than atmospheric pressure at sea level.

8,000 m
7,000 m
6,000 m
5,000 m
4,000 m
3,000 m
2,000 m
1,000 m
0 m
1,000 m
2,000 m

346 CHAPTER 12 Forces and Fluids

Differentiated Instruction

Learning Disabled Have students copy the meter measurements given in the above page on notebook paper using one line for each number. Have students label and draw brackets around the elevations above sea level, at sea level, and below sea level. Reread the captions and mark the atmospheric pressure given in the passage beside the correct elevation. Use the same units, such as atmospheres, for each entry. Students should see that atmospheric pressure increases as you go toward the center of the Earth.

Barometer An instrument called a barometer is used to measure atmospheric pressure. A barometer has something in common with a drinking straw. When you drink through a straw, it seems like you pull your drink up through the straw. But actually, atmospheric pressure pushes your drink up the straw. By removing air from the straw, you reduce the air pressure in the straw. Meanwhile, the atmosphere is pushing down on the surface of your drink. When you pull the air from the straw, the pressure in the straw is less than the pressure pushing down on the liquid, so atmospheric pressure pushes the drink up the straw.

One type of barometer works in a similar way, as shown in **Figure 9.** The space at the top of the tube is a vacuum. Atmospheric pressure pushes liquid up a tube. The liquid reaches a height where the pressure at the bottom of the column of liquid balances the pressure of the atmosphere. As the atmospheric pressure changes, the force pushing on the surface of the liquid changes. As a result, the height of the liquid in the tube increases as the atmospheric pressure increases.

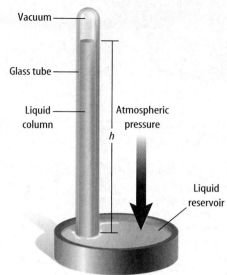

Vacuum

Glass tube

Liquid column

Atmospheric pressure

h

Liquid reservoir

Figure 9 In this type of barometer, the height of the liquid column increases as the atmospheric pressure increases.

DAILY INTERVENTION

Check for Understanding
Logical-Mathematical Suppose a gas is contained in a cylinder with a piston at one end. Ask students what happens to the pressure the gas exerts if you pull on the piston to increase the volume. Pressure decreases. What happens to the pressure if you push on the piston, making the volume smaller? Pressure increases. ☐L3

Reteach
Fluids Ask students to identify all the fluids in the classroom. Make sure they include such things as sealed containers that have air inside. ☐L1 ☐IS **Visual-Spatial**

---

section 1 review

Summary

Pressure
- Pressure is the force exerted on a unit area of a surface. Pressure can be calculated from this equation:

$$P = \frac{F}{A}$$

- The SI unit for pressure is the pascal, abbreviated Pa.

Pressure in a Fluid
- The pressure exerted by a fluid depends on the depth below the fluid surface.
- The pressure exerted by a fluid on a surface is always perpendicular to the surface.

Atmospheric Pressure
- Earth's atmosphere exerts a pressure of about 100,000 Pa at sea level.
- A barometer is an instrument used to measure atmospheric pressure.

Self Check

1. **Compare** One column of water has twice the diameter as another water column. If the pressure at the bottom of each column is the same, how do the heights of the two columns compare?

2. **Explain** why the height of the liquid column in a barometer changes as atmospheric pressure changes.

3. **Classify** the following as fluids or solids: warm butter, liquid nitrogen, paper, neon gas, ice.

4. **Explain** how the pressure at the bottom of a container depends on the container shape and the fluid height.

5. **Think Critically** Explain how the diameter of a balloon changes as it rises higher in the atmosphere.

Applying Math

6. **Calculate Force** The palm of a person's hand has an area of 0.0135 m². If atmospheric pressure is 100,000 N/m², find the force exerted by the atmosphere on the person's palm.

Assessment

Performance Have students place a small amount of hot water in a plastic soda bottle and screw on the cap. Have them describe the forces at work as they observe what happens when they submerge the bottle in ice water. As the gases inside the bottle cool, they exert less pressure on the container walls. When the outside pressure becomes so much larger than the inside pressure that the walls of the bottle are no longer strong enough to balance the force pushing inward, the bottle is crushed. Use **Performance Assessment in the Science Classroom,** p. 89.

---

section 1 review

1. The heights must be equal if the pressures are equal.

2. When atmospheric pressure changes, the force pushing on the open reservoir of liquid changes. This causes the pressure exerted by the fluid in the reservoir on the fluid in the tube to change. If atmospheric pressure increases, the upward force on the liquid in the tube increases and the liquid rises.

3. fluids—warm butter, liquid nitrogen, neon gas; solids—paper, ice

4. Pressure depends only on the height of the fluid above a surface, not on the shape of the container.

5. The balloon will expand and its diameter will increase. As the altitude of the balloon increases, the pressure exerted by the air surrounding the balloon decreases. Because the pressure inside the balloon is greater, the balloon expands. As the balloon expands, the surface area of the balloon increases. This causes the pressure exerted by the air inside the balloon to decrease. The balloon expands until the air pressure inside and outside the balloon are the same.

6. $F = PA = (100,000 \text{ N/m}^2) \times (0.0135 \text{ m}^2) = 1,350 \text{ m}^2$

Section Focus Transparencies also are available on the Interactive Chalkboard CD-ROM.

L2 ELL

Tie to Prior Knowledge

Balanced v. Unbalanced Review previous work on forces and ask students to give examples of balanced and unbalanced forces.

Caption Answer

Figure 10 zero

Why do objects float?

as you read

What You'll Learn
- **Explain** how the pressure in a fluid produces a buoyant force.
- **Define** density.
- **Explain** floating and sinking using Archimedes' principle.

Why It's Important
Knowing how fluids exert forces helps you understand how boats can float.

⊙ Review Vocabulary
Newton's second law of motion: the acceleration of an object is in the direction of the total force and equals the total force divided by the object's mass

New Vocabulary
- buoyant force
- Archimedes' principle
- density

The Buoyant Force

Can you float? Think about the forces that are acting on you as you float motionless on the surface of a pool or lake. You are not moving, so according to Newton's second law of motion, the forces on you must be balanced. Earth's gravity is pulling you downward, so an upward force must be balancing your weight, as shown in **Figure 10.** This force is called the buoyant force. The **buoyant force** is an upward force that is exerted by a fluid on any object in the fluid.

What causes the buoyant force?

The buoyant force is caused by the pressure that is exerted by a fluid on an object in the fluid. **Figure 11** shows a cube-shaped object submerged in a glass of water. The water exerts pressure everywhere over the surface of the object. Recall that the pressure exerted by a fluid has two properties. One is that the direction of the pressure on a surface is always perpendicular to the surface. The other is that the pressure exerted by a fluid increases as you go deeper into the fluid.

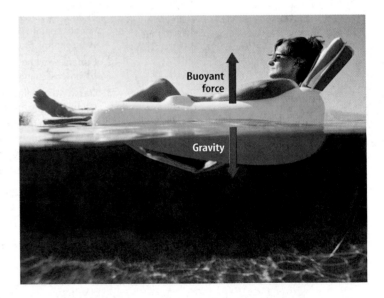

Figure 10 When you float, the forces on you are balanced. Gravity pulls you downward and is balanced by the buoyant force pushing you upward.

Infer *What is the acceleration of the person shown here?*

Section 2 Resource Manager	
Chapter *FAST FILE* Resources	**Reading and Writing Skill Activities,** p. 19
Transparency Activity, p. 12	**Mathematics Skill Activities,** p. 24
Directed Reading for Content Mastery, p. 20	**Performance Assessment in the Science Classroom,** p. 39
Enrichment, p. 31	
Reinforcement, p. 28	
Lab Worksheet, pp. 5–6	

Buoyant Force and Unbalanced Pressure The pressure that is exerted by the water on the cube is shown in **Figure 11.** The bottom of the cube is deeper in the water. Therefore, the pressure that is exerted by the water at the bottom of the cube is greater than it is at the top of the cube. The higher pressure near the bottom means that the water exerts an upward force on the bottom of the cube that is greater than the downward force that is exerted at the top of the cube. As a result, the force that is exerted on the cube due to water pressure is not balanced, and a net upward force is acting on the cube due to the pressure of the water. This upward force is the buoyant force. A buoyant force acts on all objects that are placed in a fluid, whether they are floating or sinking.

Reading Check *When does the buoyant force act on an object?*

Sinking and Floating

If you drop a stone into a pool of water, it sinks. But if you toss a twig on the water, it floats. An upward buoyant force acts on the twig and the stone, so why does one float and one sink?

The buoyant force pushes an object in a fluid upward, but gravity pulls the object downward. If the weight of the object is greater than the buoyant force, the net force on the object is downward and it sinks. If the buoyant force is equal to the object's weight, the forces are balanced and the object floats. As shown in **Figure 12,** the fish floats because the buoyant force on it balances its weight. The rocks sink because the buoyant force acting on them is not large enough to balance their weight.

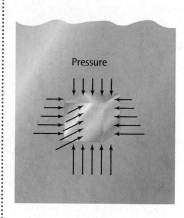

Pressure

Figure 11 The pressure exerted on the bottom of the cube is greater than the pressure on the top. The fluid exerts a net upward force on the cube.

Figure 12 The weight of a rock is more than the buoyant force exerted by the water, so it sinks to the bottom.
Infer *Why do the fish float?*

Use Science Words

Words Usage Have students use the word *buoyant* in a sentence indicating its meaning. Possible answer: The bottle was sufficiently buoyant to float. L2 ELL LS Linguistic

Reading Check

Answer when an object is placed in a fluid

Teacher FYI

Attractive Forces Surface tension is due to the attractive forces between molecules at the surface of a fluid. Within the fluid, a molecule is surrounded on all sides by other molecules, so that the attractive forces on a molecule nearly cancel. But the attractive forces on molecules at the surface do not cancel because there are no fluid molecules above them. As a result, molecules at the surface are more strongly attracted to each other and the surface behaves somewhat like a thin, elastic sheet. Surface tension causes a fluid to exert a small upward force on objects placed on the fluid's surface.

Activity

Surface Tension Drop a needle into a glass of water. It will sink, being denser than water. Now carefully place the needle on the water surface, using a fork to lower it in. Explain to students that surface tension keeps the needle from sinking, not the buoyant force. L2 LS Visual-Spatial

Caption Answer

Figure 12 The buoyant force on the fish is the same as the weight of the fish.

Diving Forces Ask students to compare the forces on a diver at a depth of 10 m and at a depth of 50 m. The downward force of gravity on the diver and the upward buoyant force don't change with depth. However, the pressure exerted on the diver does increase with depth. L3 [IS] **Logical-Mathematical**

Teacher FYI

Pressure Equation What is the pressure on an object at a depth h in a fluid? If a fluid has density d, the weight W of the fluid above a given area, A, is found as follows.

$W = mg$, where m is mass and g is the acceleration due to gravity, 9.8 m/s^2.

$W = mg$

$= d$ (volume of fluid)g

$= dAhg$

The pressure at depth h is then the weight of the fluid divided by the area, or $P = W/A = dAhg/A = dhg$.

Note that the pressure is independent of the area of the object.

Virtual Labs

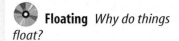

Floating *Why do things float?*

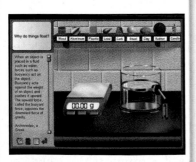

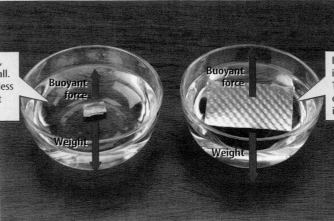

If the foil is folded up, its surface area is small. The buoyant force is less than the foil's weight and it sinks.

Buoyant force

Weight

Buoyant force

Weight

If the foil is unfolded, its surface area is larger. The buoyant force is equal to its weight and it floats.

Figure 13 The buoyant force on a piece of aluminum foil increases as the surface area of the foil increases.

Figure 14 The hull of this oil tanker has a large surface area in contact with the water. As a result, the buoyant force is so large that the ship floats.

Changing the Buoyant Force

Whether an object sinks or floats depends on whether the buoyant force is smaller than its weight. The weight of an object depends only on the object's mass, which is the amount of matter the object contains. The weight does not change if the shape of the object changes. A piece of modeling clay contains the same amount of matter whether it's squeezed into a ball or pressed flat.

Buoyant Force and Shape Buoyant force does depend on the shape of the object. The fluid exerts upward pressure on the entire lower surface of the object that is in contact with the fluid. If this surface is made larger, then more upward pressure is exerted on the object and the buoyant force is greater. **Figure 13** shows how a piece of aluminum can be made to float. If the aluminum is crumpled, the buoyant force is less than the weight, so the aluminum sinks. When the aluminum is flattened into a thin, curved sheet, the buoyant force is large enough that the sheet floats. This is how large, metal ships, like the one in **Figure 14,** are able to float. The metal is formed into a curved sheet that is the hull of the ship. The contact area of the hull with the water is much greater than if the metal were a solid block. As a result, the buoyant force on the hull is greater than it would be on a metal block.

Differentiated Instruction

Challenge There is a legend that Archimedes (287–212 B.C.) was asked by King Hiero II whether a crown was made of pure gold or also contained silver. Have students find out how Archimedes is supposed to have solved this problem. Archimedes realized that when submerged in water, equal weights of gold and silver displace different amounts of water because gold and silver have different densities. This allowed him to show that the crown was not pure gold. L3 [IS] **Linguistic**

The Buoyant Force Doesn't Change with Depth

Suppose you drop a steel cube into the ocean. You might think that the cube would sink only to a depth where the buoyant force on the cube balances its weight. However, the steel sinks to the bottom, no matter how deep the ocean is.

The buoyant force on the cube is the difference between the downward force due to the water pressure on the top of the cube and the upward force due to water pressure on the bottom of the cube. **Figure 15** shows that when the cube is deeper, the pressure on the top surface increases, but the pressure on the bottom surface also increases by the same amount. As a result, the difference between the forces on the top and bottom surfaces is the same, no matter how deep the cube is submerged. The buoyant force on the submerged cube is the same at any depth.

Archimedes' Principle

A way of determining the buoyant force was given by the ancient Greek mathematician Archimedes(ar kuh MEE deez) more than 2,200 years ago. According to **Archimedes' principle,** the buoyant force on an object is equal to the weight of the fluid it displaces.

To understand Archimedes' principle, think about what happens if you drop an ice cube in a glass of water that's filled to the top. The ice cube takes the place of some of the water and causes this water to overflow, as shown in **Figure 16.** Another way to say this is that the ice cube displaced water that was in the glass.

Suppose you caught all the overflow water and weighed it. According to Archimedes' principle, the weight of the overflow, or displaced water, would be equal to the buoyant force on the ice cube. Because the ice cube is floating, the buoyant force is balanced by the weight of the ice cube. So the weight of the water that is displaced, or the buoyant force, is equal to the weight of the ice cube.

 **A**

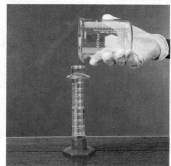 **B**

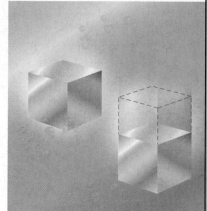

Figure 15 Because the cube on the right is deeper, the pressure on its upper surface is increased due to the weight of the water inside the dashed lines. The pressure on the bottom surface also increases by this amount.
Explain *how the buoyant force on the cube would change if it moved only to the left or right.*

Figure 16 The buoyant force exerted on this ice cube is equal to the weight of the water displaced by the ice cube.

SECTION 2 Why do objects float? **351**

Activity

Density Fill a clear glass with warm water and add a grape. The grape will sink to the bottom because it is denser than the water. Remove the grape and stir a tablespoon of salt into the water. Now replace the grape. This time it floats, because it is less dense then the salt water.

L2 ℕ **Visual-Spatial**

Naval Architect Many universities do not offer a degree in naval architecture. Have students find universities that offer this as a major.

Research Have students research the courses that are required to become an engineer or architect. Have them find the employment outlook for navel architects.

Applying Science

Answers

1. From bottom to top: blue, red, green, purple, yellow; the water layer (clear) would be between the purple and green layers, because the density of water, 1 g/cm^3, is between 0.78 and 1.2.
2. A) 76.8 g; B) 43.5 g; C) 24 g; D) 14.4 g; E) 14.8 g

Naval Architect Naval architects design the ships and submarines for the U.S. Naval Fleet, Coast Guard, and Military Sealift Command. Naval architects need math, science, and English skills for designing and communicating design ideas to others.

Density Archimedes' principle leads to a way of determining whether an object placed in a fluid will float or sink. The answer depends on comparing the density of the fluid and the density of the object. The **density** of a fluid or an object is the mass of the object divided by the volume it occupies. Density can be calculated by the following formula:

Density Equation

$$\text{density (in g/cm}^3) = \frac{\text{mass (in g)}}{\text{volume (in cm}^3)}$$

$$D = \frac{m}{V}$$

For example, water has a density of 1.0 g/cm^3. The mass of any volume of a substance can be calculated by multiplying both sides of the above equation by volume. This gives the equation

$$\text{mass} = \text{density} \times \text{volume}$$

Then if the density and volume are known, the mass of the material can be calculated.

Applying Science

Layering Liquids

The density of an object or substance determines whether it will sink or float in a fluid. Just like solid objects, liquids also have different densities. If you pour vegetable oil into water, the oil doesn't mix. Instead, because the density of oil is less than the density of water, the oil floats on top of the water.

Identifying the Problem

In science class, a student is presented with five unknown liquids and their densities. He measures the volume of each and organizes his data into the table at the right. He decides to experiment with these liquids by carefully pouring them, one at a time, into a graduated cylinder.

Liquid Density and Volume

Liquid	Color	Density (g/cm^3)	Volume (cm^3)
A	red	2.40	32.0
B	blue	2.90	15.0
C	green	1.20	20.0
D	yellow	0.36	40.0
E	purple	0.78	19.0

Solving the Problem

1. Assuming the liquids don't mix with each other, draw a diagram and label the colors, illustrating how these liquids would look when poured into a graduated cylinder. If 30 cm^3 of water were added to the graduated cylinder, explain how your diagram would change.
2. Use the formula for density to calculate the mass of each of the unknown liquids in the chart.

352 CHAPTER 12 Forces and Fluids

Differentiated Instruction

English-Language Learners Have students create an illustrated glossary of the science terms in this chapter. Students should write each new term on an index card. Divide the word into parts (prefix, root word, suffix) if needed. Have students write down the meaning of the word, its pronunciation, an illustration representing the word, and a sentence using the word correctly on the index card. For students with limited English proficiency, pair them with another student to assist in translations.

Sinking and Density Suppose you place a copper block with a volume of 1,000 cm³ into a container of water. This block weighs about 88 N. As the block sinks, it displaces water, and an upward buoyant force acts on it. If the block is completely submerged, the volume of water it has displaced is 1,000 cm³—the same as its own volume. This is the maximum amount of water the block can displace. The weight of 1,000 cm³ of water is about 10 N, and this is the maximum buoyant force that can act on the block. This buoyant force is less than the weight of the copper, so the copper block continues to sink.

The copper block and the displaced water had the same volume. Because the copper block had a greater density, the mass of the copper block was greater than the mass of the displaced water. As a result, the copper block weighed more than the displaced water because its density was greater. Any material with a density that is greater than the density of water will weigh more than the water that it displaces, and it will sink. This is true for any object and any fluid. Any object that has a density greater than the density of the fluid it is placed in will sink.

Floating and Density Suppose you place a block of wood with a volume of 1,000 cm³ into a container of water. This block weighs about 7 N. The block starts to sink and displaces water. However, it stops sinking and floats before it is completely submerged, as shown in **Figure 17.** The density of the wood was less than the density of the water. So the wood was able to displace an amount of water equal to its weight before it was completely submerged. It stopped sinking after it had displaced about 700 cm³ of water. That much water has a weight of about 7 N, which is equal to the weight of the block. Any object with a density less than the fluid it is placed in will float.

> **Reading Check** How can you determine whether an object will float or sink?

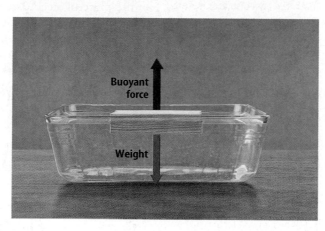

Figure 17 An object, such as this block of wood, will continue to sink in a fluid until it has displaced an amount of fluid that is equal to its mass. Then the buoyant force equals its weight.

Discussion

Floating on Water Is it easier to float in salt water or in fresh water? salt water Is salt water more dense or less dense than fresh water? more dense In salt water the buoyant force acting on a swimmer is greater than it is in fresh water—less of the swimmer is submerged in saltwater. A smaller volume of saltwater is displaced which has a weight equal to the swimmer's weight.
L2 LS **Logical-Mathematical**

Fun Fact

Archimedes' writings were concerned with calculating the areas and volumes of curved surfaces and solids. His work influenced the development of mathematics and quantitative science in the middle ages as people studied the rediscovered writings of ancient scientists.

Visual Learning

Figure 17 Point out that when the block starts to enter the water, only a small amount of water is displaced. The buoyant force is not large enough to balance the block's weight, so the block continues sinking. As the block displaces more and more water, the buoyant force becomes greater and greater, until it balances the block's weight. L2 LS **Visual-Spatial**

> **Reading Check**

Answer If its density is less than that of the fluid, it will float; if its density is greater than that of the fluid, it will sink.

Science Journal

Weather The density of air is affected by its temperature and by how much water vapor it contains. Have students write short paragraphs in their Science Journals about how this might affect weather cycles. Warm air can hold more water vapor than cool air. Clouds and rain form when warm, moist, less dense air is pushed up from the surface into the colder atmosphere above. L2 LS **Linguistic**

Curriculum Connection

History Have students find out more about the life of Archimedes and make pamphlets illustrating their findings. Archimedes lived from approximately 287–212 B.C. He was a mathematician, engineer, and scientist. He is said to have created several military devices to defend his city of Syracuse, in Greece. The city eventually fell to the Romans in 212 B.C., and Archimedes was killed in the siege. L2 LS **Visual-Spatial** P

Check for Understanding

Visual-Spatial Have students make illustrations showing buoyancy and density for a scenario of their choice. Students should include labels and explanations on their illustrations.

Reteach

Density Place an air-filled ball and a solid ball, such as a marble, into a glass of water. Ask students to explain why the air-filled ball floats and the solid ball sinks. The air-filled ball is less dense than water; the solid ball is more dense than water. L2 LS Visual-Spatial

Assessment

Performance Have students make miniposters illustrating why it is easier to float in salt water than in fresh water. Miniposters should indicate that the density of salt water is greater than the density of fresh water. Use **Performance Assessment in the Science Classroom,** p. 145.

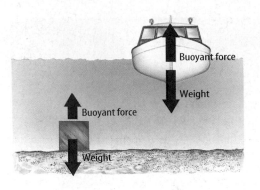

Figure 18 Even though the boat and the cube have the same mass, the boat displaces more water because of its shape. Therefore the boat floats, but the cube sinks.

Boats

Archimedes' principle provides an-other way to understand why boats that are made of metal can float. Look at **Figure 18.** By making a piece of steel into a boat that occupies a large volume, more water is displaced by the boat than by the piece of steel. According to Archimedes' principle, increasing the weight of the water that is displaced increases the buoyant force. By making the volume of the boat large enough, enough water can be displaced so that the buoyant force is greater than the weight of the steel.

How does the density of the boat compare to the density of the piece of steel? The steel now surrounds a volume that is filled with air that has little mass. The mass of the boat is nearly the same as the mass of the steel, but the volume of the boat is much larger. As a result, the density of the boat is much less than the density of the steel. The boat floats when its volume becomes large enough that its density is less than the density of water.

section 2 review

Summary

The Buoyant Force

- The buoyant force is an upward force that is exerted by a fluid on any object in the fluid.
- The buoyant force is caused by the increase in pressure with depth in a fluid.
- Increasing the surface area in contact with a fluid increases the buoyant force on an object.

Sinking and Floating

- An object sinks when the buoyant force on an object is less than the object's weight.
- An object floats when the buoyant force on an object equals the object's weight.

Archimedes' Principle

- Archimedes' principle states that the buoyant force on a object equals the weight of the fluid the object displaces.
- According to Archimedes' principle, an object will float in a fluid only if the density of the object is less than the density of the fluid.

Self Check

1. **Explain** whether the buoyant force on a submerged object depends on the weight of the object.
2. **Determine** whether an object will float or sink in water if it has a density of 1.5 g/cm^3. Explain.
3. **Compare** the buoyant force on an object when it is partially submerged and when it's completely submerged.
4. **Explain** how the buoyant force acting on an object placed in water can be measured.
5. **Think Critically** A submarine changes its mass by adding or removing seawater from tanks inside the sub. Explain how this can enable the sub to dive or rise to the surface.

Applying Math

6. **Buoyant Force** A ship displaces 80,000 L of water. One liter of water weighs 9.8 N. What is the buoyant force on the ship?
7. **Density** The density of 14k gold is 13.7 g/cm^3. A ring has a mass of 7.21 g and a volume of 0.65 cm^3. Find the density of the ring. Is it made from 14k gold?

Science online ips.msscience.com/self_check_quiz

section 2 review

1. No. The buoyant force on the submerged object depends on the object's volume.
2. It will sink because its density is greater than 1 g/cm^3, the density of water.
3. The buoyant force depends on the weight of fluid displaced. When the object is partially submerged it displaces less fluid than when it is fully submerged. So the buoyant force on the partially submerged object is less.
4. One way would be to weigh the object in air, and then weigh the object in the water. The difference between the two weights is the upward buoyant force on the object.
5. When the sub displaces air in its tanks with seawater, its density increases and becomes greater than the surrounding water. Then the sub dives. When the sub expels seawater from its tanks, its density decreases and the sub rises.
6. Water has a density of 1 kg/L, so that 1 L has a weight of 9.8 N. So the buoyant force is (80,000 L)(9.8 N/L) = 784,000 N.
7. The density of the ring is $D = m/V$ = (7.21 g)/(0.65 cm^3) = 11.1 g/cm^3. Because the density of the ring is not the same as the density of 14k gold, the ring cannot be made of pure 14k gold.

Measuring Buoyant Force

The total force on an object in a fluid is the difference between the object's weight and the buoyant force. In this lab, you will measure the buoyant force on an object and compare it to the weight of the water displaced.

Real-World Question

How is the buoyant force related to the weight of the water that an object displaces?

Goals

- **Measure** the buoyant force on an object.
- **Compare** the buoyant force to the weight of the water displaced by the object.

Materials

aluminum pan	graduated cylinder
spring scale	funnel
500-mL beaker	metal object

Safety Precautions

Procedure

1. Place the beaker in the aluminum pan and fill the beaker to the brim with water.
2. Hang the object from the spring scale and record its weight.
3. With the object hanging from the spring scale, completely submerge the object in the water. The object should not be touching the bottom or the sides of the beaker.
4. **Record** the reading on the spring scale while the object is in the water. Calculate the buoyant force by subtracting this reading from the object's weight.

5. Use the funnel to carefully pour the water from the pan into the graduated cylinder. Record the volume of this water in cm³.
6. **Calculate** the weight of the water displaced by multiplying the volume of water by 0.0098 N.

Conclude and Apply

1. **Explain** how the total force on the object changed when it was submerged in water.
2. **Compare** the weight of the water that is displaced with the buoyant force.
3. **Explain** how the buoyant force would change if the object were submersed halfway in water.

Communicating Your Data

Make a poster of an empty ship, a heavily loaded ship, and an overloaded, sinking ship. Explain how Archimedes' principle applies in each case. **For more help, refer to the Science Skill Handbook.**

Communicating Your Data

Posters should show that as more material is loaded onto the boat, it sinks lower into the water. The overloaded ship starts taking in water over the sides, causing it to become even heavier.

Real-World Question

Purpose to measure the buoyant force and compare it to the weight of water displaced by an object L2 IS **Kinesthetic**

Process Skills observe, infer, measure, test a hypothesis, collect data, compare and contrast, recognize cause and effect

Time Required 45 minutes

Procedure

Safety Precautions Caution students not to spill water on the floor.

Teaching Strategy Make sure the objects will sink in water, and are large enough to displace a noticeable amount of water. For example, a hollow metal bead won't sink, and a necklace chain will have too small a volume to displace much water.

Conclude and Apply

1. The total force decreased.
2. The two should be equal.
3. If only half of the object were submerged, only half the volume of water would be displaced, so the buoyant force would be half what it was on the completely submerged object.

Assessment

Oral Ask students to hypothesize why birds that dive and do not fly, such as penguins, tend to have heavier bones than birds that fly. The heavier bones make the birds denser than flying birds of similar shape. This makes it easier for the birds to dive. Use **Performance Assessment in the Science Classroom,** p. 93.

Doing Work with Fluids

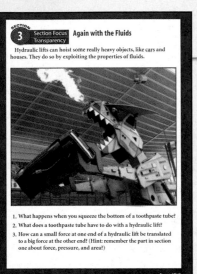
as you read

What You'll Learn

- **Explain** how forces are transmitted through fluids.
- **Describe** how a hydraulic system increases force.
- **Describe** Bernoulli's principle.

Why It's Important

Fluids can exert forces that lift heavy objects and enable aircraft to fly.

⟳ Review Vocabulary

work: the product of the force applied to an object and the distance the object moves in the direction of the force

New Vocabulary

- Pascal's principle
- hydraulic system
- Bernoulli's principle

Using Fluid Forces

You might have watched a hydraulic lift raise a car off the ground. It might surprise you to learn that the force pushing the car upward is being exerted by a fluid. When a huge jetliner soars through the air, a fluid exerts the force that holds it up. Fluids at rest and fluids in motion can be made to exert forces that do useful work, such as pumping water from a well, making cars stop, and carrying people long distances through the air. How are these forces produced by fluids?

Pushing on a Fluid The pressure in a fluid can be increased by pushing on the fluid. Suppose a watertight, movable cover, or piston, is sitting on top of a column of fluid in a container. If you push on the piston, the fluid can't escape past the piston, so the height of the fluid in the container doesn't change. As a result, the piston doesn't move. But now the force exerted on the bottom of the container is the weight of the fluid plus the force pushing the piston down. Because the force exerted by the fluid at the bottom of the container has increased, the pressure exerted by the fluid also has increased. **Figure 19** shows how the force exerted on a brake pedal is transmitted to a fluid.

Figure 19 Because the fluid in this piston can't escape, it transmits the force you apply throughout the fluid.

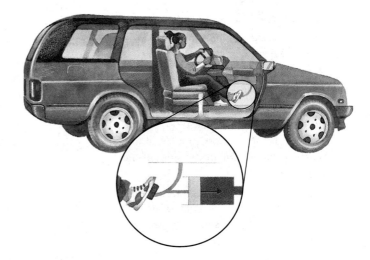

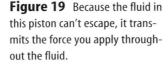

Pascal's Principle

Suppose you fill a plastic bottle with water and screw the cap back on. If you poke a hole in the bottle near the top, water will leak out of the hole. However, if you squeeze the bottle near the bottom, as shown in **Figure 20,** water will shoot out of the hole. When you squeezed the bottle, you applied a force on the fluid. This increased the pressure in the fluid and pushed the water out of the hole faster.

No matter where you poke the hole in the bottle, squeezing the bottle will cause the water to flow faster out of the hole. The force you exert on the fluid by squeezing has been transmitted to every part of the bottle. This is an example of Pascal's principle. According to **Pascal's principle,** when a force is applied to a fluid in a closed container, the pressure in the fluid increases everywhere by the same amount.

Hydraulic Systems

Pascal's principle is used in building hydraulic systems like the ones used by car lifts. A **hydraulic system** uses a fluid to increase an input force. The fluid enclosed in a hydraulic system transfers pressure from one piston to another. An example is shown in **Figure 21.** An input force that is applied to the small piston increases the pressure in the fluid. This pressure increase is transmitted throughout the fluid and acts on the large piston. The force the fluid exerts on the large piston is the pressure in the fluid times the area of the piston. Because the area of the large piston is greater than the area of the small piston, the output force exerted on the large piston is greater than the input force exerted on the small piston.

Figure 20 When you squeeze the bottle, the pressure you apply is distributed throughout the fluid, forcing the water out the hole.

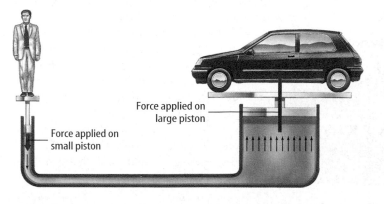

Force applied on large piston

Force applied on small piston

Figure 21 A hydraulic system uses Pascal's principle to make the output force applied on the large piston greater than the input force applied on the small piston. **Infer** *how the force on the large piston would change if its area increased.*

SECTION 3   Doing Work with Fluids   **357**

Fun Fact

Pascal's principle does not hold for solids. Because of their rigid structure, an increase in pressure at one point is not smoothly transferred throughout the material.

Differentiated Instruction

Physically Challenged Students with asthma and other breathing problems may not be able to do many of the experiments described in this section. Suggest these students use a hairdryer set to cool to produce a steady, high pressure stream of air.

SECTION 3   Doing Work with Fluids   **357**

Science Online

Topic: Hydraulic Systems
Visit ips.msscience.com for Web links to information about hydraulic systems.

Activity Draw a diagram showing how one of the hydraulic systems that you find works. Share your diagram with the class.

Figure 22 By blowing on one side of the can, you decrease the air pressure on that side. Because the pressure on the opposite side is now greater, the can moves toward the side you're blowing on.

Increasing Force What is the force pushing upward on the larger piston? For example, suppose that the area of the small piston is 1 m² and the area of the large piston is 2 m². If you push on the small piston with a force of 10 N, the increase in pressure at the bottom of the small piston is

$$P = F/A$$
$$= (10\ N)/(1\ m^2)$$
$$= 10\ Pa$$

According to Pascal's principle, this increase in pressure is transmitted throughout the fluid. This causes the force exerted by the fluid on the larger piston to increase. The increase in the force on the larger piston can be calculated by multiplying both sides of the above formula by A.

$$F = P \times A$$
$$= 10\ Pa \times 2\ m^2$$
$$= 20\ N$$

The force pushing upward on the larger piston is twice as large as the force pushing downward on the smaller piston. What happens if the larger piston increases in size? Look at the calculation above. If the area of the larger piston increases to 5 m², the force pushing up on this piston increases to 50 N. So a small force pushing down on the left piston as in **Figure 21** can be made much larger by increasing the size of the piston on the right.

Reading Check *How does a hydraulic system increase force?*

Pressure in a Moving Fluid

What happens to the pressure in a fluid if the fluid is moving? Try the following experiment. Place an empty soda can on the desktop and blow to the right of the can, as shown in **Figure 22.** In which direction will the can move?

When you blow to the right of the can, the can moves to the right, toward the moving air. The air pressure exerted on the right side of the can, where the air is moving, is less than the air pressure on the left side of the can, where the air is not moving. As a result, the force exerted by the air pressure on the left side is greater than the force exerted on the right side, and the can is pushed to the right. What would happen if you blew between two empty cans?

Bernoulli's Principle

The reason for the surprising behavior of the can in **Figure 22** was discovered by the Swiss scientist Daniel Bernoulli in the eighteenth century. It is an example of Bernoulli's principle. According to **Bernoulli's principle,** when the speed of a fluid increases, the pressure exerted by the fluid decreases. When you blew across the side of the can, the pressure exerted by the air on that side of the can decreased because the air was moving faster than it was on the other side. As a result, the can was pushed toward the side you blew across.

Chimneys and Bernoulli's Principle In a fireplace the hotter, less dense air above the fire is pushed upward by the cooler, denser air in the room. Wind outside of the house can increase the rate at which the smoke rises. Look at **Figure 23.** Air moving across the top of the chimney causes the air pressure above the chimney to decrease according to Bernoulli's principle. As a result, more smoke is pushed upward by the higher pressure of the air in the room.

Damage from High Winds You might have seen photographs of people preparing for a hurricane by closing shutters over windows or nailing boards across the outside of windows. In a hurricane, the high winds blowing outside the house cause the pressure outside the house to be less than the pressure inside. This difference in pressure can be large enough to cause windows to be pushed out and to shatter.

Hurricanes and other high winds sometimes can blow roofs from houses. When wind blows across the roof of a house, the pressure outside the roof decreases. If the wind outside is blowing fast enough, the outside pressure can become so low that the roof can be pushed off the house by the higher pressure of the still air inside.

Wings and Flight

You might have placed your hand outside the open window of a moving car and felt the push on it from the air streaming past. If you angled your hand so it tilted upward into the moving air, you would have felt your hand pushed upward. If you increased the tilt of your hand, you felt the upward push increase. You might not have realized it, but your hand was behaving like an airplane wing. The force that lifted your hand was provided by a fluid—the air.

Mini LAB

Observing Bernoulli's Principle

Procedure
1. Tie a piece of **string** to the handle of a **plastic spoon.**
2. Turn on a faucet to make a stream of water.
3. Holding the string, bring the spoon close to the stream of water.

Analysis
Use Bernoulli's principle to explain the motion of the spoon.

Try at Home

Figure 23 The air moving past the chimney lowers the air pressure above the chimney. As a result, smoke is forced up the chimney faster than when air above the chimney is still.

SECTION 3 Doing Work with Fluids **359**

Mini LAB

Purpose to observe Bernoulli's principle [L2] [LS] **Kinesthetic**

Materials plastic spoon, faucet with running water, string

Analysis
The pressure of the air close to the flowing water is lower than the pressure of the air farther away. This pulled the spoon toward the water.

Assessment

Content Ask students to draw diagrams with arrows illustrating the forces involved in this activity. Use **Performance Assessment in the Science Classroom,** p. 127. [P]

Try at Home

Quick Demo

Bending Flame

Materials candle and match

Estimated Time 10 minutes

Procedure Light a candle. Blow directly at the flame to show students that the flame bends away from you, as expected. The force of your breath pushes the flame. Blow to one side of the flame to show students that the flame is pushed towards the moving air. The pressure in the air moving past the flame is lower than the pressure of the still air on the other side of the flame.

Differentiated Instruction

Challenge Have students research how a perfume atomizer works. Have students make a poster detailing how it works to present to the class. When the bulb of an atomizer is squeezed, a puff of air is sent over the top of a narrow tube. This decreases the air pressure at the top, so that perfume is drawn up into the air flow and sprays out as a fine mist. [L3]

Science Journal

Flight How has learning to fly changed human history? Have students each write a paragraph in their Science Journals describing what the world would be like if people could not yet fly. [L2] [LS] **Linguistic**

Reading Check

Answer by increasing the surface area of the wing

Visual Learning

Figure 25 People have made many attempts to fly by building wings, attaching them to their arms, and flapping them. All attempts have been unsuccessful. Why can't humans fly by flapping artificial wings? Birds have a number of adaptations that enable them to fly, including hollow bones that reduce their body mass, and powerful chest muscles to flap their wings. Because of their relatively high body mass, humans would need artificial wings with a large surface area to provide enough lift. However, humans do not have the muscles that would be needed to flap these large wings. L2

LS **Logical-Mathematical**

Producing Lift How is the upward force, or lift, on an airplane wing produced? A jet engine pushes the plane forward, or a propeller pulls the plane forward. Air flows over the wings as the plane moves. The wings are tilted upward into the airflow, just like your hand was tilted outside the car window. **Figure 24** shows how the tilt of the wing causes air that has flowed over the wing's upper and lower surfaces to be directed downward.

Lift is created by making the air flow downward. To understand this, remember that air is made of different types of molecules. The motion of these molecules is changed only when a force acts on them. When the air is directed downward, a force is being exerted on the air molecules by the wing.

However, according to Newton's third law of motion, for every action force there is an equal but opposite reaction force. The wing exerts a downward action force on the air. So the air must exert an upward reaction force on the wing. This reaction force is the lift that enables paper airplanes and jet airliners to fly.

Airplane Wings Airplanes have different wing shapes, depending on how the airplane is used. The lift on a wing depends on the amount of air that the wing deflects downward and how fast that air is moving. Lift can be increased by increasing the size or surface area of the wing. A larger wing is able to deflect more air downward.

Look at the planes in **Figure 25.** A plane designed to fly at high speeds, such as a jet fighter, can have small wings. A large cargo plane that carries heavy loads needs large wings to provide a great deal of lift. A glider flies at low speeds and uses long wings that have a large surface area to provide the lift it needs.

Reading Check
How can a wing's lift be increased?

Figure 24 An airplane wing forces air to be directed downward. As a result, the air exerts an upward reaction force on the wing, producing lift.

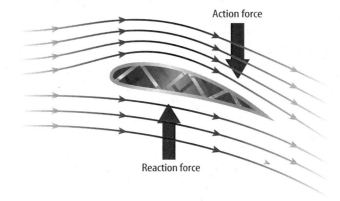

Action force

Reaction force

360 CHAPTER 12 Forces and Fluids

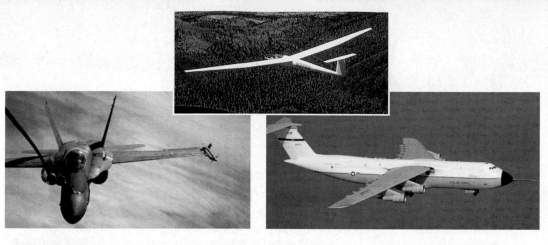

Birds' Wings A bird's wing provides lift in the same way that an airplane wing does. The wings also act as propellers that pull the bird forward when it flaps its wings up and down. Bird wings also have different shapes depending on the type of flight. Seabirds have long, narrow wings, like the wings of a glider, that help them glide long distances. Forest and field birds, such as pheasants, have short, rounded wings that enable them to take off quickly and make sharp turns. Swallows, swifts, and falcons, which fly at high speeds, have small, narrow, tapered wings like those on a jet fighter.

Figure 25 Different wing shapes are used for different types of planes. Larger wings provide more lift.

section 3 review

Summary

Pascal's Principle

- Pascal's principle states that when a force is applied to a fluid in a closed container, the pressure in the fluid increases by the same amount everywhere in the fluid.
- Hydraulic systems use Pascal's principle to produce an output force that is greater than an applied input force.
- Increasing the surface area in contact with a fluid increases the buoyant force on an object.

Bernoulli's Principle

- Bernoulli's principle states that when the speed of a fluid increases, the pressure exerted by the fluid decreases.

Wings and Flight

- An airplane wing exerts a force on air and deflects it downward. By Newton's third law, the air exerts an upward reaction force.

Self Check

1. **Explain** why making an airplane wing larger enables the wing to produce more lift.
2. **Infer** If you squeeze a plastic water-filled bottle, where is the pressure change in the water the greatest?
3. **Explain** Use Bernoulli's principle to explain why a car passing a truck tends to be pushed toward the truck.
4. **Infer** why a sheet of paper rises when you blow across the top of the paper.
5. **Think Critically** Explain why the following statement is false: In a hydraulic system, because the increase in the pressure on both pistons is the same, the increase in the force on both pistons is the same.

Applying Math

6. **Calculate Force** The small piston of a hydraulic lift, has an area of 0.01 m². If a force of 250 N is applied to the small piston, find the force on the large piston if it has an area of 0.05 m².

section 3 review

1. A larger wing is able to deflect more air downward which results in a greater reaction force pushing upward, resulting in greater lift.
2. The change in pressure is the same throughout the water.

3. The air flowing between the car and the truck is moving faster than the air on the other side of the car. So the pressure exerted by the air between the car and the truck is less than the pressure exerted on the other side of the car.

4. Blowing across the top of a sheet of paper creates a low pressure area above the paper. The higher pressure air below the paper pushes the paper up.
5. The pressure increase is the same on both pistons. The increase in force is

greater on the piston with the greater surface area.

6. The increase in pressure in the fluid is $P = F/A = (250 \text{ N})/(0.01 \text{ m}^2) = 25{,}000$ Pa. The increase in force on the larger piston is $F = PA = (25{,}000 \text{ Pa})(0.05 \text{ m}^2) = 1{,}250$ N.

BENCH TESTED

Real-World Question

Purpose

Internet Students use Internet sites that can be accessed through **ips.msscience.com/internet_lab**.

Non-Internet Sources Weather information from a newspaper or other sources.

Time Required

90 minutes spread over five days or more

Make a Plan

Preparation

Internet To run through the steps that the students will follow, visit **ips.msscience.com/internet_lab**.

Non-Internet Sources Bring weather information to class.

Follow Your Plan

Teaching Strategies

- **Troubleshooting** Data and observations may not exactly coincide. Students may have a difficult time understanding that meteorology is not an exact science. Depending on the area and season, wide variations may not even occur.

- Direct students to make sure they observe the weather for the prescribed number of days. Incomplete data will make it difficult to draw conclusions.

LAB — **Use the Internet**

Barometric Pressure and Weather

Goals

- **Collect** barometric pressure and other weather data.
- **Compare** barometric pressure to weather conditions.
- **Predict** weather patterns based on barometric pressure, wind speed and direction, and visual conditions.

Data Source

Science Online

Visit ips.msscience.com/internet_lab for more information about barometric pressure, weather information, and data collected by other students.

Real-World Question

What is the current barometric pressure where you are? How would you describe the weather today where you are? What is the weather like in the region to the west of you? To the east of you? What will your weather be like tomorrow? The atmosphere is a fluid and flows from one place to another as weather patterns change. Changing weather conditions also cause the atmospheric pressure to change. By collecting barometric pressure data and observing weather conditions, you will be able to make a prediction about the next day's weather.

Make a Plan

1. Visit the Web site on the left for links to information about weather in the region where you live.

2. Find and record the current barometric pressure and whether the pressure is rising, falling, or remaining steady. Also record the wind speed and direction.

3. **Observe and record** other weather conditions, such as whether rain is falling, the Sun is shining, or the sky is cloudy.

4. Based on the data you collect and your observations, predict what you think tomorrow's weather will be. Record your prediction.

5. Repeat the data collection and observation for a total of five days.

Alternative Inquiry Lab

Star Gazing To make this Lab an Inquiry Lab, give students a more personal investment in the problem by connecting it to the real world. Tell the students that they are in charge of planning a star-gazing party for their class. The class is going into the countryside with telescopes and observing the stars on two consecutive nights. Have students collect weather data and predict which two consecutive nights would be the best for this party. Remind the students that you cannot look at stars on cloudy nights.

Barometric Pressure Weather Data	
Location of weather station	Carlsbad, CA
Barometric pressure	99.7 kPa
Status of barometric pressure	Falling
Wind speed	2 m/s
Wind direction	Variable
Current weather conditions	Cloudy and cool
Predictions of tomorrow's weather conditions	Continue to be cloudy and cool

Follow Your Plan

1. Make sure your teacher approves your plan before you start.
2. Visit the link below to post your data.

Analyze Your Data

1. **Analyze** Look at your data. What was the weather the day after the barometric pressure increased? The day after the barometric pressure decreased? The day after the barometric pressure was steady?
2. **Draw Conclusions** How accurate were your weather predictions?

Conclude and Apply

1. **Infer** What is the weather to the west of you today? How will that affect the weather in your area tomorrow?
2. **Compare** What was the weather to the east of you today? How does that compare to the weather in your area yesterday?
3. **Evaluate** How does increasing, decreasing, or steady barometric pressure affect the weather?

Communicating Your Data

Find this lab using the link below. Use the data on the Web site to predict the weather where you are two days from now.

Science Online
ips.msscience.com/internet_lab

Expected Outcome If students look broadly at their data, they should notice that lower pressure often brings rain and higher pressure usually brings fairer skies.

Analyze Your Data

Answers to Questions

1. Increasing pressure brings clear skies, decreasing pressure brings rain or clouds, and steady pressure brings no changes.
2. A general trend should be seen, but precise, exact correlations may be difficult to find.

Error Analysis If the expected results are not seen, another series of observations may bring clearer results.

Conclude and Apply

1. Since weather patterns generally move west to east, the weather to the west is an indicator of your weather for tomorrow.
2. The weather to the east should be similar to the weather you experienced yesterday.
3. Increasing pressure brings clear skies, while decreasing pressure brings clouds or rain. Steady pressure means there will not be a change in weather.

Assessment

Performance Have students take additional data and predict the weather for the next day. Do several predictions, list the reasons for the predictions, and assess the accuracy. Use **Performance Assessment in the Science Classroom,** p. 89.

Communicating Your Data

To clearly communicate their recorded data, be sure that students have a large chart that has space for each item to be recorded on each day. If it is not clear what they are to record, students may not take all data needed.

Science and Language Arts

Understanding Literature

Sense Impressions Sample examples: smell: "ozoned light" sight: "day arrived in queer light" sound: "crashed" touch: "sickening August heat"

Respond to the Reading

1. The hurricane destroyed houses, caused trees to snap, and caused other living things such as snakes to die.
2. Elling brought much needed supplies.
3. **Linking Science and Writing** Lead students in a brainstorming activity to think of words that suggest sense impressions.

 **Bernoulli's Principle**

Daniel Bernoulli was the second son of Johann Bernoulli, who first taught him mathematics. In his important work entitled *Hydrodynamica*, he considered how pressure, density, and velocity of fluids affect fluid flow and established their basic relationship. He put forward what is called Bernoulli's principle, which states that the pressure in a fluid decreases as its velocity increases. He also established the basis for the kinetic theory of gases and heat by demonstrating that the impact of molecules on a surface could explain pressure and that, assuming the constant, random motion of molecules, pressure and motion would increase with temperature.

"Hurricane"
by John Balaban

Near dawn our old live oak sagged over
then crashed on the tool shed
rocketing off rakes paintcans flower pots.

All night, rain slashed the shutters until
it finally quit and day arrived in queer light,
silence, and ozoned air. Then voices calling

as neighbors crept out to see the snapped trees,
leaf mash and lawn chairs driven in heaps
with roof bits, siding, sodden birds, dead snakes.

For days, bulldozers clanked by our houses
in sickening August heat as heavy cranes
scraped the rotting tonnage from the streets.

Then our friend Elling drove in from Sarasota
in his old . . . van packed with candles, with
dog food, cat food, flashlights and batteries . . . .

Understanding Literature

Sense Impressions In this poem, John Balaban uses sense impressions to place the reader directly into the poem's environment. For example, the words *rotting tonnage* evoke the sense of smell. Give examples of other sense impressions mentioned.

Respond to the Reading

1. What kinds of damage did the hurricane cause?
2. Why do you think the poet felt relief when his friend, Elling, arrived?
3. **Linking Science and Writing** Write a poem describing a natural phenomenon involving forces and fluids. Use words that evoke at least one of the five sense impressions.

 In the poem, bits of roofs and siding from houses are part of the debris that is everywhere in heaps. According to Bernoulli's principle, the high winds in a hurricane blowing past a house causes the air pressure outside the house to be less than the air pressure inside. In some cases, the forces exerted by the air inside causes the roof to be pushed off the house, and the walls to be blown outward.

Resources for Teachers and Students

Locust at the Edge of Summer: New and Selected Poems, by John Balaban, Copper Canyon Press, 1997

Blue Mountain, by John Balaban, Unicorn Press, 1982

Reviewing Main Ideas

Section 1 Pressure

1. Pressure equals force divided by area.

2. Liquids and gases are fluids that flow.

3. Pressure increases with depth and decreases with elevation in a fluid.

4. The pressure exerted by a fluid on a surface is always perpendicular to the surface.

Section 2 Why do objects float?

1. A buoyant force is an upward force exerted on all objects placed in a fluid.

2. The buoyant force depends on the shape of the object.

3. According to Archimedes' principle, the buoyant force on the object is equal to the weight of the fluid displaced by the object.

4. An object floats when the buoyant force exerted by the fluid is equal to the object's weight.

5. An object will float if it is less dense than the fluid it is placed in.

Section 3 Doing Work with Fluids

1. Pascal's principle states that the pressure applied at any point to a confined fluid is transmitted unchanged throughout the fluid.

2. Bernoulli's principle states that when the velocity of a fluid increases, the pressure exerted by the fluid decreases.

3. A wing provides lift by forcing air downward.

Visualizing Main Ideas

Copy and complete the following table.

Relationships Among Forces and Fluids		
Idea	What does it relate?	How?
Density	mass and volume	
Pressure		force/area
Archimedes' principle	buoyant force and weight of fluid that is displaced	
Bernoulli's principle		velocity increases, pressure decreases
Pascal's principle	pressure applied to enclosed fluid at one point and pressure at other points in a fluid	

Science Online ips.msscience.com/interactive_tutor

CHAPTER STUDY GUIDE **365**

Reviewing Main Ideas

Summary statements can be used by students to review the major concepts of the chapter.

Visualizing Main Ideas

See student page.

Science Online

Visit ips.msscience.com
/self_check_quiz
/interactive_tutor
/vocabulary_puzzlemaker
/chapter_review
/standardized_test

Assessment Transparency

For additional assessment questions, use the *Assessment Transparency* located in the transparency book.

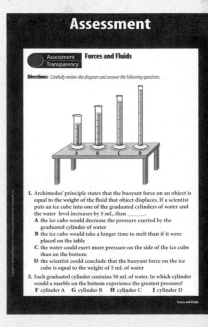

chapter 12 Review

Using Vocabulary

1. fluid
2. pressure
3. Archimedes' principle
4. hydraulic system
5. density
6. density
7. Bernoulli's principle

Checking Concepts

8. A
9. C
10. D
11. B
12. B
13. B

Thinking Critically

14. When the sandbag is dropped, the weight of the balloon decreases. The buoyant force of air on the balloon remains the same, so the balloon rises.

15. The statement is not correct because the density determines whether or not an object floats, not its weight. A heavy aircraft carrier is less dense than water so it will float, while a much lighter pebble will sink because it is denser than water.

16. The boat takes in water, increasing its mass and its density. Eventually the boat becomes more dense than water and sinks.

17. The forces due to water pressure on either side of the cube balance each other, because they are at the same depth. The top and bottom of the cube are at different depths, and the force at the greater depth, the bottom of the cube, is greater. So the net force is upward.

18. Steel is denser than the material making up the balloon, so the steel tank filled with helium is denser than air while the balloon filled with helium is less dense than air. The balloon rises and the steel tank stays on the ground.

Using Vocabulary

Archimedes' principle p. 351	fluid p. 343
Bernoulli's principle p. 359	hydraulic system p. 357
buoyant force p. 348	Pascal's principle p. 357
density p. 352	pressure p. 340

Answer each of the following questions using complete sentences that include vocabulary from the list above.

1. How would you describe a substance that can flow?

2. When the area over which a force is applied decreases, what increases?

3. What principle relates the weight of displaced fluid to the buoyant force?

4. How is a fluid used to lift heavy objects?

5. If you increase an object's mass but not its volume, what have you changed?

6. How is a log able to float in a river?

7. What principle explains why hurricanes can blow the roof off of a house?

Checking Concepts

Choose the word or phrase that best answers the question.

8. Which always equals the weight of the fluid displaced by an object?
   A) the weight of the object
   B) the force of gravity on the object
   C) the buoyant force on the object
   D) the net force on the object

9. What is the net force on a rock that weighs 500 N if the weight of the water it displaces is 300 N?
   A) 200 N   C) 500 N
   B) 300 N   D) 800 N

10. The pressure exerted by a fluid on a surface is always in which direction?
    A) upward
    B) downward
    C) parallel to the surface
    D) perpendicular to the surface

Use the photo below to answer question 11.

water level

water level

11. Each graduated cylinder contains the same amount of water. Which of the following statements is true?
    A) The pressure is greater at the bottom of the large cylinder.
    B) The pressure is greater at the bottom of the small cylinder.
    C) The pressure is equal at the bottom of both cylinders.
    D) There is zero pressure at the bottom of both cylinders.

12. Which would increase the lift provided by an airplane wing?
    A) decreasing the volume of the wing
    B) increasing the area of the wing
    C) decreasing the length of the wing
    D) increasing the mass of the wing

13. An airplane wing produces lift by forcing air in which direction?
    A) upward   C) under the wing
    B) downward   D) over the wing

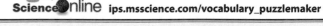

Science Online   ips.msscience.com/vocabulary_puzzlemaker

19. The graph should be a curved line from upper left to lower right, showing that pressure decreases as area increases.

20. An upward buoyant force acts on an object in water. As a result, the net downward force due to gravity is less. The upward force needed to lift the object is less when it is in water.

21. The object that sinks has a greater density than the object that floats. Because the objects have identical volumes, the object that sinks has a greater mass.

Use the Exam*View*® Pro Testmaker CD-ROM to:
• customize tests
• create multiple versions of tests
• generate tests in Spanish
• build tests aligned with state standards

Thinking Critically

14. Explain A sandbag is dropped from a hot-air balloon and the balloon rises. Explain why this happens.

15. Determine whether or not this statement is true: Heavy objects sink, and light objects float. Explain your answer.

16. Explain why a leaking boat sinks.

17. Explain why the direction of the buoyant force on a submerged cube is upward and not left or right.

18. Recognizing Cause and Effect A steel tank and a balloon are the same size and contain the same amount of helium. Explain why the balloon rises and the steel tank doesn't.

19. Make and Use Graphs Graph the pressure exerted by a 75-kg person wearing different shoes with areas of 0.01 m², 0.02 m², 0.03 m², 0.04 m², and 0.05 m². Plot pressure on the vertical axis and area on the horizontal axis.

20. Explain why it is easier to lift an object that is underwater, than it is to lift the object when it is out of the water.

21. Infer Two objects with identical shapes are placed in water. One object floats and the other object sinks. Infer the difference between the two objects that causes one to sink and the other to float.

22. Compare Two containers with different diameters are filled with water to the same height. Compare the force exerted by the fluid on the bottom of the two containers.

Performance Activities

23. Oral Presentation Research the different wing designs in birds or aircraft. Present your results to the class.

24. Experiment Partially fill a plastic dropper with water until it floats just below the surface of the water in a bowl or beaker. Place the dropper inside a plastic bottle, fill the bottle with water, and seal the top. Now squeeze the bottle. What happens to the water pressure in the bottle? How does the water level in the dropper change? How does the density of the dropper change? Use your answers to these questions to explain how the dropper moves when you squeeze the bottle.

Applying Math

25. Buoyant Force A rock is attached to a spring scale that reads 10 N. If the rock is submerged in water, the scale reads 6 N. What is the buoyant force on the submerged rock?

26. Hydraulic Force A hydraulic lift with a large piston area of 0.04 m² exerts a force of 5,000 N. If the smaller piston has an area of 0.01 m², what is the force on it?

Use the table below to answer questions 27 and 28.

Material Density	
Substance	**Density (g/cm³)**
Ice	0.92
Lead	11.34
Balsa wood	0.12
Sugar	1.59

27. Density Classify which of the above substances will and will not float in water.

28. Volume Find the volumes of each material, if each has a mass of 25 g.

29. Pressure What is the pressure due to a force of 100 N on an area 4 m²?

30. Pressure A bottle of lemonade sitting on a table weighs 6 N. The bottom of the bottle has a surface area of 0.025 m². Calculate the pressure the bottle of lemonade exerts on the table.

CHAPTER REVIEW 367

22. Because the water has the same height, the pressure exerted at the bottom of each container is the same. The container with the larger diameter has a greater surface area at the bottom, so the force exerted by the fluid is greater at the bottom of this container.

Performance Activities

23. Answers will vary. Students should contrast at least two wing designs, listing the benefits and limitations of each. Use **PASC,** p. 143.

24. The water pressure in the bottle increases as you squeeze it, as does the water pressure in the dropper. The air in the dropper is compressed by incoming water. This increased pressure is transferred, by Pascal's principle, to the water and air in the dropper. More water is pushed into the dropper, thus increasing the density of the dropper, so it sinks. Use **PASC,** p. 119.

Applying Math

National Math Standards
1, 2, 3, 5, 9

25. 4 N

26. The pressure equals $F/A = (5{,}000 \text{ N})/(0.04 \text{ m}^2) = 125{,}000$ Pa. The force on the smaller piston then is $F = PA = (125{,}000 \text{ Pa})(0.01 \text{ m}^2) = 1{,}250$ N.

27. Ice and balsa wood float; lead and sugar do not float.

28. $V = m/D$; ice, 27 cm³; lead, 2.2 cm³; balsa wood, 208 cm³; sugar, 16 cm³

29. $P = F/A = (100 \text{ N})/(4 \text{ m}^2) = 25$ Pa

30. $P = F/A = (6 \text{ N})/(0.025 \text{ m}^2) = 240$ Pa

☑ **Assessment** **Resources**

📁 Reproducible Masters

Chapter *Fast File* Resources
   Chapter Review, pp. 37–38
   Chapter Tests, pp. 39–42
   Assessment Transparency Activity, p. 49

Glencoe Science Web site
   Chapter Review Test
   Standardized Test Practice

Glencoe Technology
   🔊 Assessment Transparency
   ⊛ Exam*View*® Pro Testmaker
   📺 MindJogger Videoquiz
   ⊛ Interactive Chalkboard

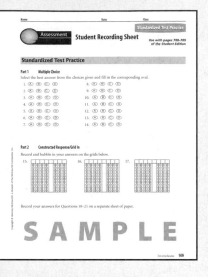

Answer Sheet A practice answer sheet can be found at ips.msscience.com/answer_sheet.

Part 1 Multiple Choice

1. B
2. D
3. B
4. A
5. C
6. A
7. C

Part 2 Short Response

8. Snowshoes turn the bottoms of feet into large, flat surfaces. This increases the area over which the force of body weight is exerted. The pressure is decreased, making it easier to walk without sinking.

9. A fluid is any substance that has no definite shape and has the ability to flow. Gases meet both of these criteria.

10. The fluids in your body exert an outward pressure which balances the inward pressure exerted by the atmosphere.

Part 1 Multiple Choice

Record your answers on the answer sheet provided by your teacher or on a sheet of paper.

1. A force of 15 N is exerted on an area of 0.1 m². What is the pressure?
   - **A.** 150 N
   - **B.** 150 Pa
   - **C.** 1.5 Pa
   - **D.** 0.007 Pa

Use the illustration below to answer questions 2 and 3.

2. Which statement is TRUE?
   - **A.** The contact area between the board and the nail tip is large.
   - **B.** The contact area between the nail tip and the board is greater than the contact area between the nail head and the hammer head.
   - **C.** The nail exerts no pressure on the board because its weight is so small.
   - **D.** The pressure exerted by the nail is large because the contact area between the nail tip and the board is small.

3. Which increases the pressure exerted by the nail tip on the board?
   - **A.** increasing the area of the nail tip
   - **B.** decreasing the area of the nail tip
   - **C.** increasing the length of the nail
   - **D.** decreasing the length of the nail

Test-Taking Tip

Check the Answer Number For each question, double check that you are filling in the correct answer bubble for the question number you are working on.

---

4. A 15-g block of aluminum has a volume of 5.5 cm³. What is the density?
   - **A.** 2.7 g/cm³
   - **B.** 82.5 g/cm³
   - **C.** 0.37 g/cm³
   - **D.** 2.7 cm³/g

Use the illustration below to answer questions 5 and 6.

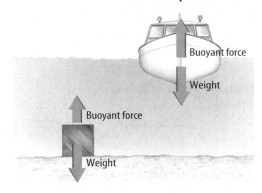

5. Assume the boat and cube have the same mass. Which of these is correct?
   - **A.** The boat displaces less water than the cube.
   - **B.** The densities of the boat and cube are equal.
   - **C.** The density of the boat is less than the density of the cube.
   - **D.** The density of the boat is greater than the density of the water.

6. Which of the following would make the cube more likely to float?
   - **A.** increasing its volume
   - **B.** increasing its density
   - **C.** increasing its weight
   - **D.** decreasing its volume

7. Which of the following instruments is used to measure atmospheric pressure?
   - **A.** altimeter
   - **B.** hygrometer
   - **C.** barometer
   - **D.** anemometer

---

11. The buoyant force increases because the boat displaces more water.

12. Any change in the boat's weight that made it greater than the buoyant force would result in the boat sinking. This could happen if large amounts of water entered the boat through holes in the hull or if the boat was overloaded.

13. High winds blowing across the outside of windows cause the pressure to be less outside of the house than inside. If the difference in pressure is large enough, the windows can be pushed out.

14. Lift is affected by the amount of air deflected downward by the wing and how fast the air is moving.

15. $F = (1,000 \text{ Pa}) \times (0.05 \text{ m}^2) = 50 \text{ N}$

Part 2 | Short Response/Grid In

Record your answers on the answer sheet provided by your teacher or on a sheet of paper.

8. Explain why wearing snowshoes makes it easier to walk over deep, soft snow.

9. Why is a gas, such as air considered to be a fluid?

10. Explain why the pressure exerted by the atmosphere does not crush your body.

Use the illustration below to answer questions 11 and 12.

11. How does the buoyant force on the boat change if the boat is loaded so that it floats lower in the water?

12. What changes in the properties of this boat could cause it to sink?

13. People sometimes prepare for a coming hurricane by nailing boards over the outside of windows. How can high winds damage windows?

14. What factors influence the amount of lift on an airplane wing?

15. The pressure inside the fluid of a hydraulic system is increased by 1,000 Pa. What is the increase in the force exerted on a piston that has an area of 0.05 m²?

Part 3 | Open Ended

Record your answers on a sheet of paper.

16. Explain why the interior of an airplane is pressurized when flying at high altitude. If a hole were punctured in an exterior wall, what would happen to the air pressure inside the plane?

17. In an experiment, you design small boats using aluminum foil. You add pennies to each boat until it sinks. Sketch several different shapes you might create. Which will likely hold the most pennies? Why?

18. You squeeze a round, air-filled balloon slightly, changing its shape. Describe how the pressure inside the balloon changes.

Use the illustration below to answer questions 19 and 20.

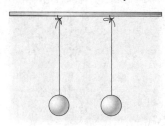

19. Describe the motion of the table tennis balls when air is blown between the two balls. Explain.

20. Describe the motion of the table tennis balls if air blown to the left of the ball on the left and to the right of the ball on the right at the same time. Explain.

21. Compare the pressure you exert on a floor when you are standing on the floor and when you are lying on the floor.

22. In order to drink a milk shake through a straw, how must the air pressure inside the straw change, compared with the air pressure outside the straw?

Part 3 | Open Ended

16. At a high altitude, atmospheric pressure decreases. In order to maintain comfortable air pressure and adequate oxygen supply, cabins are pressurized. Should a puncture occur, the air inside the plane will attempt to move to an area of lower pressure outside the plane. Eventually, the pressures inside and outside the plane would equalize.

17. Shapes might include flat-bottomed boats, hulls which are slightly rounded, and hulls which have steep sides. Boats that hold the most pennies will be those with the largest volume that displace the most water.

18. According to Pascal's principle, the pressure of the gas inside the balloon increases throughout the balloon by the same amount because the force is transmitted to all parts of the fluid.

19. According to Bernoulli's principle, the pressure exerted by the moving air is less than the pressure exerted by the still air. This will cause the balls to move toward each other.

20. The pressure exerted by the moving air is less than the pressure exerted by the still air between the balls. This will cause the balls to move away from each other.

21. The force you exert on the floor equals your weight and is the same in each case. When you are standing, the area in contact with the floor is less, so the pressure is greater.

22. The air pressure in the straw must decrease.

Rubrics

For more help evaluating open-ended assessment questions, see the rubric on p. 10T.

unit 5

Unit Contents

WebQuest *MagLev Trains: Floating Locomotives* is an investigation of magnets and how they work. Students will study different types of magnetic levitation, design and build a maglev train, then test and refine their models. Class presentations reflect student designs, procedures, refinements, and results.

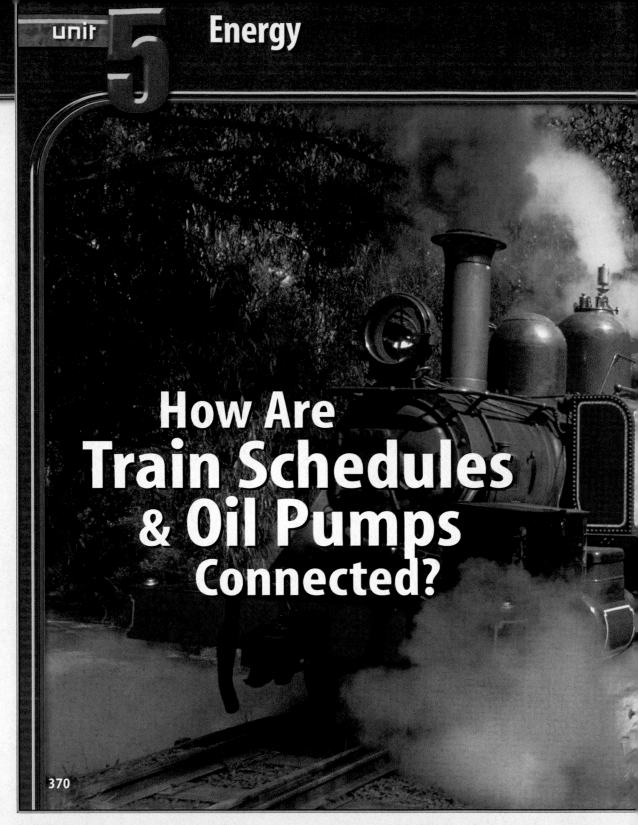

unit 5 Energy

How Are Train Schedules & Oil Pumps Connected?

370

PROJECT *Study Skills*

CRISS℠

Illustrate Key Concepts When students actively engage in meaningful conversation and activities, deeper understanding of topics takes place. As a post-reading exercise, divide the class into cooperative groups, and ask them to describe and draw pictures that illustrate the conversion of one kind of energy to another. Have them share these picture maps with the class followed by a whole-class discussion.

NATIONAL GEOGRAPHIC

In the 1800s, trains had to make frequent stops so that their moving parts could be lubricated. Without lubrication, the parts would have worn out due to friction. When the train stopped, a worker had to get out and oil the parts by hand. The process was very time-consuming and made it hard for trains to stay on schedule. Around 1870, an engineer named Elijah McCoy developed the first automatic lubricating device, which oiled the engine while the train was running. (A later version of his automatic lubricator is seen at lower right.) Since then, many kinds of automatic lubricating devices have been developed. Today, automobiles have oil pumps that automatically circulate oil to the moving parts of the engine. When you go for a ride in a car, you can thank Elijah McCoy that you don't have to stop every few miles to oil the engine by hand!

unit projects

Visit ips.msscience.com/unit_project to find project ideas and resources.
Projects include:
- **Career** As a class, design a chart of the many fields of engineering and how they relate to conserving and protecting the environment.
- **Technology** Design and construct miniature models of energy-producing devices. Explain how your model works.
- **Model** Analyze locations for a future city. Consider what characteristics will make the best location and make a model of a portion of your design.

WebQuest *Mag Lev Trains: Floating Locomotives* encourages understanding of magnets and their application in the transportation field. Design a mag lev train and present it to the class.

unit projects

Career Have students study aspects of the field of engineering and how this career option influences resources, energy, and development. Careers include environmental, mechanical, electrical, civil, and ceramic engineers, as well as hydrologists, geologists, and metallurgists. As a class, design a chart that lists the field of engineering and how it relates to conserving and protecting the environment.

Technology Have students research, design, and construct energy resource saving models of windmills, wave and water mills, solar panels, dams, geothermal stations, and composting gas for energy. Students should be able to explain how their model works, saves energy resources, money, and the environment.

Model Working in small groups, have students analyze different locations to build a city. Student decisions should take into account natural resources, climate, food and water sources, economic development, and environmental concerns and how energy can best be used to conserve those resources. Using recycled materials, have students build a portion of their city as a model. Students should consider size limits and scale, and how to best present their energy efficient community.

Additional Resources For more information, resources, and assessment rubrics, visit ips.msscience.com/unit_project

---

NATIONAL GEOGRAPHIC — How Are Train Schedules & Oil Pumps Connected?

A rough surface has high spots and low spots that are large enough that you can feel or sometimes see. If you try to slide these surfaces past each other, the high spots hit each other, and impede the motion of the surfaces.

However, friction also exists between smooth surfaces. On a microscopic scale, the surface is rough. Lubricants can reduce friction by forming a thin film between the surfaces. This film separates the surfaces so that the high spots no longer make contact with each other. The result is longer-lasting parts and a more efficient use of fuels to produce motion.

Section/Objectives	Standards		Labs/Features
	National	State/Local	
Chapter Opener	See pp. 16T–17T for a Key to Standards.		**Launch Lab:** Marbles and Energy, p. 373 **Foldables,** p. 373
Section 1 What is energy? ● 3 sessions ◫ 1.5 blocks 1. **Explain** what energy is. 2. **Distinguish** between kinetic energy and potential energy. 3. **Identify** the various forms of energy.	National Content Standards: UCP.1, UCP.2, UCP.3, UCP.5, A.1, A.2, B.1, B.2, B.3, G.2, G.3		
Section 2 Energy Transformations ● 3 sessions ◫ 1.5 blocks 4. **Apply** the law of conservation of energy to energy transformations. 5. **Identify** how energy changes form. 6. **Describe** how electric power plants produce energy.	National Content Standards: UCP.1, UCP.2, UCP.3, UCP.5, A.1, A.2, B.1, B.2, B.3		**Science Online,** p. 380 **MiniLAB:** Analyzing Energy Transformations, p. 381 **Visualizing Energy Transformations,** p. 382 **Integrate Life Science,** p. 383 **Lab:** Hearing with Your Jaw, p. 386
Section 3 Sources of Energy ● 4 sessions ◫ 2 blocks 7. **Explain** what renewable, nonrenewable, and alternative resources are. 8. **Describe** the advantages and disadvantages of using various energy sources.	National Content Standards: UCP.1, UCP.2, UCP.3, UCP.5, A.1, A.2, B.3, F.2, F.4		**Integrate Earth Science,** p. 388 **Science Online,** p. 390 **Applying Science:** Is energy consumption outpacing production?, p. 390 **MiniLAB:** Building a Solar Collector, p. 391 **Lab:** Energy to Power Your Life, p. 396 **Science Stats:** Energy to Burn, p. 398

Lab Materials	Reproducible Resources	Section Assessment	Technology
Launch Lab: book, glass marble, steel marbles, 3 metersticks	**Chapter FAST FILE Resources** Foldables Worksheet, p. 15 Directed Reading Overview, p. 17 Note-taking Worksheets, pp. 31–32	GLENCOE'S ASSESSMENT ADVANTAGE	**TeacherWorks** includes: • Interactive Teacher Edition • Lesson Planner with calendar • Access to all program blacklines • Correlations to standards • Web links ▭ Video Lab
Need materials? Contact Science Kit at 1-800-828-7777 or www.sciencekit.com on the Internet.	**Chapter FAST FILE Resources** Transparency Activity, p. 42 Enrichment, p. 28 Reinforcement, p. 25 Directed Reading, p. 18 **Reading and Writing Skill Activities,** p. 35	**Portfolio** Curriculum Connection, p. 375 **Performance** Applying Skills, p. 378 **Content** Section Review, p. 378	Section Focus Transparency Virtual Labs CD-ROM Guided Reading Audio Program Interactive Chalkboard CD-ROM
MiniLAB: soft clay, golf ball, steel ball, rubber ball, table-tennis ball, metric ruler **Lab:** radio or CD player, small electrical motor, headphone jack	**Chapter FAST FILE Resources** Transparency Activity, p. 43 MiniLAB, p. 3 Enrichment, p. 29 Reinforcement, p. 26 Directed Reading, p. 19 Lab Activity, pp. 9–10 Lab Worksheet, pp. 5–6	**Portfolio** Curriculum Connection, p. 384 **Performance** MiniLAB, p. 381 Applying Skills, p. 385 **Content** Section Review, p. 385	Section Focus Transparency Guided Reading Audio Program Interactive Chalkboard CD-ROM
MiniLAB: black plastic garbage bag, scissors, large pot, water, clear plastic wrap, tape, computer temperature probe or thermometer, watch **Lab:** Internet and other resources on energy	**Chapter FAST FILE Resources** Transparency Activity, p. 44 MiniLAB, p. 4 Enrichment, p. 30 Reinforcement, p. 27 Directed Reading, pp. 19, 20 Lab Activity, pp. 11–13 Lab Worksheet, pp. 7–8 Transparency Activity, pp. 45–46 **Lab Management and Safety,** p. 37	**Portfolio** Activity, p. 393 **Performance** Applying Science, p. 390 MiniLAB, p. 391 Applying Math, p. 395 **Content** Section Review, p. 395	Section Focus Transparency Teaching Transparency Guided Reading Audio Program Interactive Chalkboard CD-ROM

End of Chapter Assessment

GLENCOE'S ASSESSMENT ADVANTAGE

Blackline Masters	Technology	Professional Series
Chapter FAST FILE Resources Chapter Review, pp. 35–36 Chapter Tests, pp. 37–40 **Standardized Test Practice,** pp. 55–58	▭ MindJogger Videoquiz ◉ Virtual Labs CD-ROM ◉ ExamView® Pro Testmaker ◉ TeacherWorks CD-ROM ◉ Interactive Chalkboard CD-ROM	**Performance Assessment in the Science Classroom (PASC)**

Transparencies

Section Focus

Zot!

Lightning is a natural electrical spark. Sometimes the lightning we see goes from the clouds to the ground, but lightning also travels within a single cloud and between two clouds.

1. When do you most often see lightning?
2. Since lightning is a form of electricity, do you think it could be used by people to run appliances? Why or why not?

L2

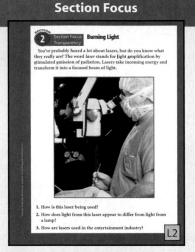

Burning Light

You've probably heard a lot about lasers, but do you know what they really are? The word *laser* stands for **l**ight **a**mplification by **s**timulated **e**mission of **r**adiation. Lasers take incoming energy and transform it into a focused beam of light.

1. How is this laser being used?
2. How does light from this laser appear to differ from light from a lamp?
3. How are lasers used in the entertainment industry?

L2

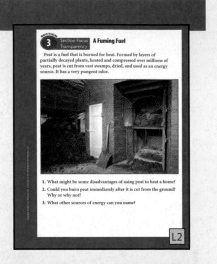

A Fuming Fuel

Peat is a fuel that is burned for heat. Formed by layers of partially decayed plants, heated and compressed over millions of years, peat is cut from vast swamps, dried, and used as an energy source. It has a very pungent odor.

1. What might be some disadvantages of using peat to heat a home?
2. Could you burn peat immediately after it is cut from the ground? Why or why not?
3. What other sources of energy can you name?

L2

This is a representation of key blackline masters available in the Teacher Classroom Resources. See Resource Manager boxes within the chapter for additional information.

Key to Teaching Strategies

The following designations will help you decide which activities are appropriate for your students.

L1 Level 1 activities should be appropriate for students with learning difficulties.

L2 Level 2 activities should be within the ability range of all students.

L3 Level 3 activities are designed for above-average students.

ELL ELL activities should be within the ability range of English-Language Learners.

COOP LEARN Cooperative Learning activities are designed for small group work.

LS Multiple Learning Styles logos, as described on page 12T, are used throughout to indicate strategies that address different learning styles.

P These strategies represent student products that can be placed into a best-work portfolio.

PBL Problem-Based Learning activities apply real-world situations to learning.

Assessment

Energy

Directions: Carefully review the diagrams and answer the following questions.

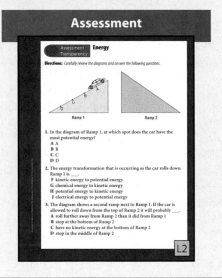

Ramp 1   Ramp 2

1. In the diagram of Ramp 1, at which spot does the car have the most potential energy?
   A A
   B B
   C C
   D D
2. The energy transformation that is occurring as the car rolls down Ramp 1 is ___.
   F kinetic energy to potential energy
   G chemical energy to kinetic energy
   H potential energy to kinetic energy
   J electrical energy to potential energy
3. The diagram shows a second ramp next to Ramp 1. If the car is allowed to roll down from the top of Ramp 2 it will probably ___.
   A roll further away from Ramp 2 than it did from Ramp 1
   B stop at the bottom of Ramp 2
   C have no kinetic energy at the bottom of Ramp 2
   D stop in the middle of Ramp 2

L2

Teaching

Energy Transformations

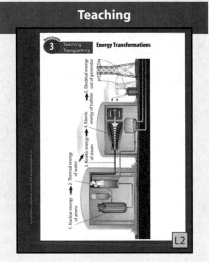

L2

Hands-on Activities

Student Text Lab Worksheet

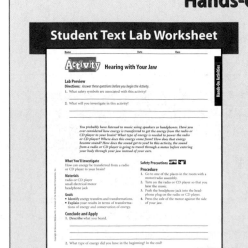

Activity — Hearing with Your Jaw

Lab Preview
Directions: Answer these questions before you begin the Activity.
1. What safety symbols are associated with this activity?

2. What will you investigate in this activity?

You probably have listened to music using speakers or headphones. Have you ever considered how energy is transferred to get the energy from the radio or CD player to your brain? What type of energy is needed to power the radio or CD player? Where does this energy come from? How does that energy become sound? How does the sound get to you? In this activity, the sound from a radio or CD player is going to travel through a motor before entering your body through your jaw instead of your ears.

What You'll Investigate
How can energy be transferred from a radio or CD player to your brain?

Materials
radio or CD player
small electrical motor
headphone jack

Goals
- **Identify** energy transfers and transformations.
- **Explain** your results in terms of transformations of energy and conservation of energy.

Conclude and Apply
1. Describe what you heard.

2. What type of energy did you have in the beginning? In the end?

Safety Precautions
Procedure
1. Go to one of the places in the room with a motor/radio assembly.
2. Turn on the radio or CD player so that you hear the music.
3. Push the headphone jack into the head-phone plug on the radio or CD player.
4. Press the axle of the motor against the side of your jaw.

L2

Laboratory Activities

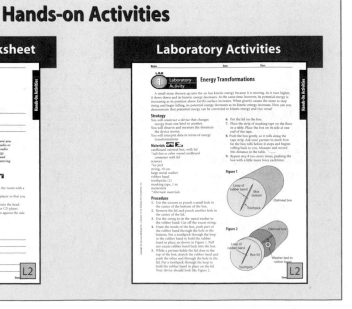

Laboratory Activity — Energy Transformations

A small stone thrown up into the air has kinetic energy because it is moving. As it rises higher, it slows down and its kinetic energy decreases. At the same time, however, its potential energy is increasing as its position above Earth's surface increases. When gravity causes the stone to stop rising and begin falling, its potential energy decreases as its kinetic energy increases. How can you demonstrate that potential energy can be converted to kinetic energy and vice versa?

Strategy
You will construct a device that changes energy from one kind to another.
You will observe and measure the distances the device moves.
You will interpret data in terms of energy transformations.

Materials
cardboard oatmeal box, with lid
*salt box or other round cardboard container with lid
scissors
*ice pick
string, 10 cm
large metal washer
rubber band
toothpicks (2)
masking tape, 1 m
meterstick
*Alternate materials

Procedure
1. Use the scissors to punch a small hole in the center of the bottom of the box.
2. Remove the lid and punch another hole in the center of the lid.
3. Use the string to tie the metal washer to the rubber band. Cut off the excess string.
4. From the inside of the box, push part of the rubber band through the hole in the bottom. Put a toothpick through the loop in the rubber band to hold the rubber band in place, as shown in Figure 1. Pull any excess rubber band back into the box.
5. While a partner holds the lid close to the top of the box, stretch the rubber band and push the other end through the hole in the lid. Put a toothpick through the loop to hold the rubber band in place on the lid. Your device should look like Figure 2.

6. Put the lid on the box.
7. Place the strip of masking tape on the floor or a table. Place the box on its side at one end of the tape.
8. Push the box gently, so it rolls along the tape strip. Ask your partner to mark how far the box rolls before it stops and begins rolling back to you. Measure and record this distance in the table.
9. Repeat step 8 two more times, pushing the box with a little more force each time.

Figure 1

Figure 2

L2

Meeting Different Ability Levels

Content Outline

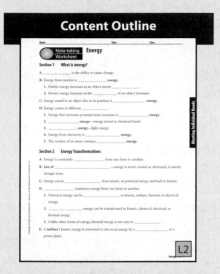

L2

Reinforcement

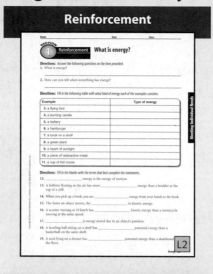

L2

Enrichment

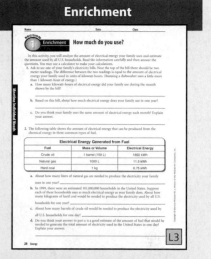

L3

Directed Reading (English/Spanish)

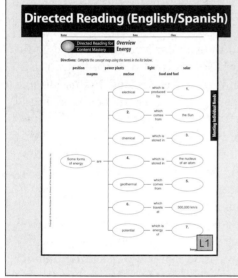

L1

Study Guide

L2

Reading Essentials

L1

Assessment

Test Practice Workbook

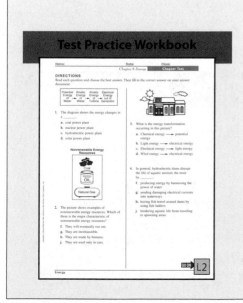

L2

Chapter Review

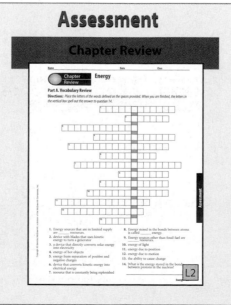

L2

Chapter Tests

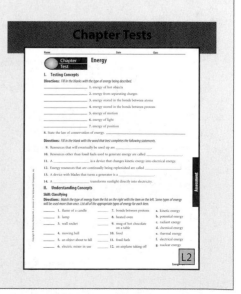

L2

Science Content Background

section 1

What is energy?
The Nature of Energy

Energy is not matter. Some forms of energy, such as light, can exist independent of matter. Other forms, such as chemical and kinetic energy, only can exist with matter.

section 2

Energy Transformations
Changing Forms of Energy

In our common experience on Earth, energy is neither created nor destroyed, just transformed from one form into another. Heat often is produced from energy transformations.

The Law of Conservation of Energy

The law of conservation of energy states that energy is neither created nor destroyed, only converted from one form into another. Sometimes energy may appear to be lost. For example, when a moving object slows down kinetic energy appears to be lost. However, friction converts kinetic energy into thermal energy so that the sum of the kinetic energy and thermal energy stays constant.

In processes involving nuclear fission or nuclear fusion matter can be changed to energy. Energy also can be changed to matter. According to Einstein's equation $E = mc^2$, a small amount of mass can be converted into an enormous amount of energy. However, even when nuclear reactions are involved the law of conservation of energy still is true.

section 3

Sources of Energy
Fossil Fuels

Fossil fuels were once living organisms that obtained energy from the Sun, and could thus be considered a type of solar energy. Unlike more direct forms of solar energy, burning fossil fuels produces carbon dioxide gas and other pollutants.

Geothermal Energy

You don't need to live near a volcano to use geothermal energy. Geothermal heat pumps, in use in 400,000 homes in the United States alone, take advantage of fairly constant below-ground temperatures. The temperature range in the first ten feet of soil is 10°C to 15.5°C (50°F to 60°F). This usually means the soil is warmer than the winter air and cooler than the summer air. In a heat pump, air gains or loses heat to the ground before entering a heating or cooling unit.

Iceland leads the world in its use of geothermal energy for heating. Almost 50% of its buildings are warmed using water heated by hot magma below Earth's surface. The Philippines is a leader in the use of geothermal energy to produce electricity. Approximately 22% of its electricity is produced with geothermal energy.

chapter content resources

Internet Resources

For additional content background, visit **ips.msscience.com** to:

- access your book online
- find references to related articles in popular science magazines
- access Web links with related content background
- access current events with science journal topics

Print Resources

Renewable Energy, Sorensen, Brent, Academic Press, 2000

The Feynman Lectures on Physics: Feynman on Fundamentals, Feynman, Richard P., Perseus Publishing, 1999

The Energy of Nature, Pielou, E.C., University of Chicago Press, 2001

IDENTIFYING ▸ Misconceptions

Find Out What Students Think

Students may think that . . .

Energy is something that is used and then disappears.

Students may have this misconception because people commonly talk about energy as though we use it and then it's gone. An athlete may say, "I ran out of energy." A parent may say, "Turn off the lights. You're wasting energy." An environmentalist may caution that the world is running out of energy. Another problem is that energy can seem abstract. Perhaps it is easy to understand that food contains energy. But energy contained by a book sitting on a desk is more difficult to comprehend.

Demonstration and Discussion

Hold up a windup toy. As you wind it, explain that your actions take energy. Release the toy and allow it to move until it winds down. Ask students to explain what has happened to the energy that you put into the toy. If students say that the toy used it up, ask them to explain what they mean. Did it disappear or become something else? Have students share their ideas.

Promote Understanding

Activity

Use books and tag board to make a U-shaped ramp. Students may have observed similar ramps used in skateboarding and bicycle stunt competitions.

- Hold a marble on top of one side of the ramp. Explain that the marble has potential energy due to its position. Gravity is pulling down on it.

- Release the marble. Explain that as the marble falls, its potential energy is converted to kinetic energy. Then, as the marble rises up the other side of the ramp, the kinetic energy is converted into potential energy.

- Now have students release the marble. Direct them to observe how high the marble rises up on each side of the ramp. Have them mark the heights achieved on each side of the ramp. Have students repeat this process at least five times.

- How does the maximum height reached by the marble change throughout each trial? Why does the marble go a little less high each time? How do we know the marble will eventually stop rolling? Help students realize that in this energy transformation between potential energy and kinetic energy, some energy is lost due to friction. This converts some kinetic energy of the marble into heat energy. Have the students rub their hands together to experience friction producing heat energy.

Assess

After completing the chapter, see *Identifying Misconceptions* in the Study Guide at the end of the chapter.

Chapter Vocabulary

Science Journal Possible answers: hair dryer produces heat and blows air, toaster produces heat, TV produces sound and images, CD player produces sound

INTERACTIVE CHALKBOARD with Image Bank

PowerPoint® Presentations

This CD-ROM is an editable Microsoft® PowerPoint® presentation that includes:
- a pre-made presentation for every chapter
- interactive graphics
- animations
- audio clips
- image bank
- all new section and chapter questions
- Standardized Test Practice
- transparencies
- pre-lab questions for all labs
- Foldables directions
- links to ips.msscience.com

Energy and Energy Resources

chapter preview

sections

1 What is energy?

2 Energy Transformations
Lab Hearing with Your Jaw

3 Sources of Energy
Lab Energy to Power Your Life

Virtual Lab What are the relationships between kinetic energy and potential energy?

Blowing Off Steam

The electrical energy you used today might have been produced by a coal-burning power plant like this one. Energy contained in coal is transformed into heat, and then into electrical energy. As boiling water heated by the burning coal is cooled, steam rises from these cone-shaped cooling towers.

Science Journal Choose three devices that use electricity, and identify the function of each device.

Theme Connection

Systems and Interactions This chapter explores the various forms of energy, the interactions among them, and how they are harnessed for use in various systems.

About the Photo

Running on Steam In fossil-fuel-burning power plants and nuclear power plants, water is heated to produce steam. The steam drives turbines that are connected to electric generators. After the steam passes through the turbine, it is condensed by passing the steam over pipes containing cold water. This water then is cooled in the cooling towers.

Start-Up Activities

Marbles and Energy

What's the difference between a moving marble and one at rest? A moving marble can hit something and cause a change to occur. How can a marble acquire energy—the ability to cause change?

1. Make a track on a table by slightly separating two metersticks placed side by side.

2. Using a book, raise one end of the track slightly and measure the height.

3. Roll a marble down the track. Measure the distance from its starting point to where it hits the floor. Repeat. Calculate the average of the two measurements.

4. Repeat steps 2 and 3 for three different heights. Predict what will happen if you use a heavier marble. Test your prediction and record your observations.

5. **Think Critically** In your Science Journal, describe how the distance traveled by the marble is related to the height of the ramp. How is the motion of the marble related to the ramp height?

FOLDABLES
Study Organizer

Energy Make the following Foldable to help identify what you already know, what you want to know, and what you learned about energy.

STEP 1 **Fold** a vertical sheet of paper from side to side. Make the front edge about 1 cm shorter than the back edge.

STEP 2 **Turn** lengthwise and **fold** into thirds

STEP 3 **Unfold, cut, and label** each tab for only the top layer along both folds to make three tabs.

| Know? | Like to know? | Learned? |

Identify Questions Before you read the chapter, write what you know and what you want to know about the types, sources, and transformation of energy under the appropriate tabs. As you read the chapter, correct what you have written and add more questions under the *Learned* tab.

 Preview this chapter's content and activities at ips.mscience.com

Launch LAB

Purpose Use the Launch Lab to help students see how the height from which an object is released on a ramp affects the distance it will roll. L2 ELL COOP LEARN
IS Kinesthetic

Materials book, glass marble, steel marble, 3 metersticks

Teaching Strategy Make sure students always release the marble at the same point on the ramp, and be sure there isn't a significant bump where the ramp contacts the table. An index card can be used to smooth out the bump.

Think Critically
The higher the ramp, the farther from the table the marble hits the floor. The more massive marble lands the same distance from the table because it has the same horizontal velocity when it leaves the table as the less massive marble has.

Assessment
Performance Have students redesign the experiment to explore how changes in the mass of the marble affect an object it strikes. Use **Performance Assessment in the Science Classroom,** p. 105.

FOLDABLES **Dinah Zike**
Study Organizer **Study Fold**

Student preparation materials for this Foldable are available in the Chapter *FAST FILE* Resources.

Section Focus Transparencies also are available on the Interactive Chalkboard CD-ROM.

L2 ELL

Tie to Prior Knowledge

Changes in Surroundings Ask students to name changes they have observed going on around them since they got up this morning. Possible answers include lights going on or off, changes in the positions of objects and of themselves, changes in temperature, and so on. Tell students that in this section they will learn about some of the causes of these changes.

Text Question Answer

They can cause change.

Text Question Answer

The person is changing position, the sun is warming up the desk, and the leaves are changing position.

---

section 1

What is energy?

as you read

What You'll Learn
- **Explain** what energy is.
- **Distinguish** between kinetic energy and potential energy.
- **Identify** the various forms of energy.

Why It's Important
Energy is involved whenever a change occurs.

Review Vocabulary
mass: a measure of the amount of matter in an object

New Vocabulary
- energy
- kinetic energy
- potential energy
- thermal energy
- chemical energy
- radiant energy
- electrical energy
- nuclear energy

The Nature of Energy

What comes to mind when you hear the word *energy*? Do you picture running, leaping, and spinning like a dancer or a gymnast? How would you define energy? When an object has energy, it can make things happen. In other words, energy is the ability to cause change. What do the items shown in **Figure 1** have in common?

Look around and notice the changes that are occurring—someone walking by or a ray of sunshine that is streaming through the window and warming your desk. Maybe you can see the wind moving the leaves on a tree. What changes are occurring?

Transferring Energy You might not realize it, but you have a large amount of energy. In fact, everything around you has energy, but you notice it only when a change takes place. Anytime a change occurs, energy is transferred from one object to another. You hear a footstep because energy is transferred from a foot hitting the ground to your ears. Leaves are put into motion when energy in the moving wind is transferred to them. The spot on the desktop becomes warmer when energy is transferred to it from the sunlight. In fact, all objects, including leaves and desktops, have energy.

Figure 1 Energy is the ability to cause change.
Explain *how these objects cause change.*

Section 1 Resource Manager

Chapter *FAST FILE* Resources
Transparency Activity, p. 42
Directed Reading for Content Mastery, pp. 17, 18
Note-taking Worksheets, pp. 31–32

Enrichment, p. 28
Reinforcement, p. 25
Reading and Writing Skill Activities, p. 35

Energy of Motion

Things that move can cause change. A bowling ball rolls down the alley and knocks down some pins, as in **Figure 2A.** Is energy involved? A change occurs when the pins fall over. The bowling ball causes this change, so the bowling ball has energy. The energy in the motion of the bowling ball causes the pins to fall. As the ball moves, it has a form of energy called kinetic energy. **Kinetic energy** is the energy an object has due to its motion. If an object isn't moving, it doesn't have kinetic energy.

Kinetic Energy and Speed If you roll the bowling ball so it moves faster, what happens when it hits the pins? It might knock down more pins, or it might cause the pins to go flying farther. A faster ball causes more change to occur than a ball that is moving slowly. Look at **Figure 2B.** The professional bowler rolls a fast-moving bowling ball. When her ball hits the pins, pins go flying faster and farther than for a slower-moving ball. All that action signals that her ball has more energy. The faster the ball goes, the more kinetic energy it has. This is true for all moving objects. Kinetic energy increases as an object moves faster.

✓ Reading Check *How does kinetic energy depend on speed?*

Kinetic Energy and Mass Suppose, as shown in **Figure 2C,** you roll a volleyball down the alley instead of a bowling ball. If the volleyball travels at the same speed as a bowling ball, do you think it will send pins flying as far? The answer is no. The volleyball might not knock down any pins. Does the volleyball have less energy than the bowling ball even though they are traveling at the same speed?

An important difference between the volleyball and the bowling ball is that the volleyball has less mass. Even though the volleyball is moving at the same speed as the bowling ball, the volleyball has less kinetic energy because it has less mass. Kinetic energy also depends on the mass of a moving object. Kinetic energy increases as the mass of the object increases.

Figure 2 The kinetic energy of an object depends on the mass and speed of the object.

A This ball has kinetic energy because it is rolling down the alley.

B This ball has more kinetic energy because it has more speed.

C This ball has less kinetic energy because it has less mass.

Curriculum Connection

Art Kinetic sculptures move using motors, pendulum action, or slight breezes that act upon sails. Among the most famous are the mobiles of artist Alexander Calder, who invented the art form in the 1920s. Have students research kinetic sculpture and build a sculpture of their own that models this art form. L2 **LS Kinesthetic**

Figure 3 The potential energy of an object depends on its mass and height above the ground.
Determine *which vase has more potential energy, the red one or the blue one.*

Figure 4 The hotter an object is, the more thermal energy it has. A cup of hot chocolate has more thermal energy than a cup of cold water, which has more thermal energy than a block of ice with the same mass.

Energy of Position

An object can have energy even though it is not moving. For example, a glass of water sitting on the kitchen table doesn't have any kinetic energy because it isn't moving. If you accidentally nudge the glass and it falls on the floor, changes occur. Gravity pulls the glass downward, and the glass has energy of motion as it falls. Where did this energy come from?

When the glass was sitting on the table, it had potential (puh TEN chul) energy. **Potential energy** is the energy stored in an object because of its position. In this case, the position is the height of the glass above the floor. The potential energy of the glass changes to kinetic energy as the glass falls. The potential energy of the glass is greater if it is higher above the floor. Potential energy also depends on mass. The more mass an object has, the more potential energy it has. Which object in **Figure 3** has the most potential energy?

Forms of Energy

Food, sunlight, and wind have energy, yet they seem different because they contain different forms of energy. Food and sunlight contain forms of energy different from the kinetic energy in the motion of the wind. The warmth you feel from sunlight is another type of energy that is different from the energy of motion or position.

Thermal Energy The feeling of warmth from sunlight signals that your body is acquiring more thermal energy. All objects have **thermal energy** that increases as its temperature increases. A cup of hot chocolate has more thermal energy than a cup of cold water, as shown in **Figure 4.** Similarly, the cup of water has more thermal energy than a block of ice of the same mass. Your body continually produces thermal energy. Many chemical reactions that take place inside your cells produce thermal energy. Where does this energy come from? Thermal energy released by chemical reactions comes from another form of energy called chemical energy.

376 CHAPTER 13 Energy and Energy Resources

Figure 5 Complex chemicals in food store chemical energy. During activity, the chemical energy transforms into kinetic energy.

Sugar

Reading Check

Answer when chemicals are broken apart and new chemicals are formed

Discussion

Chemical Energy Tell your class that chemical energy is a very important form of energy. It includes burning gasoline in cars among other things. Ask your students what some other examples of chemical engery might be. Answers could include burning natural gas or oil for heat, burning logs, body metabolism, burning natural gas in electricity generators, natural gas stoves, natural gas clothes dryers, and battery-operated things.

Chemical Energy When you eat a meal, you are putting a source of energy inside your body. Food contains chemical energy that your body uses to provide energy for your brain, to power your movements, and to fuel your growth. As in **Figure 5,** food contains chemicals, such as sugar, which can be broken down in your body. These chemicals are made of atoms that are bonded together, and energy is stored in the bonds between atoms. **Chemical energy** is the energy stored in chemical bonds. When chemicals are broken apart and new chemicals are formed, some of this energy is released. The flame of a candle is the result of chemical energy stored in the wax. When the wax burns, chemical energy is transformed into thermal energy and light energy.

Reading Check *When is chemical energy released?*

Light Energy Light from the candle flame travels through the air at an incredibly fast speed of 300,000 km/s. This is fast enough to circle Earth almost eight times in 1 s. When light strikes something, it can be absorbed, transmitted, or reflected. When the light is absorbed by an object, the object can become warmer. The object absorbs energy from the light and this energy is transformed into thermal energy. Then energy carried by light is called **radiant energy. Figure 6** shows a coil of wire that produces radiant energy when it is heated. To heat the metal, another type of energy can be used—electrical energy.

Differentiated Instruction

Learning Disabled Light a candle and explain that the flame is a chemical reaction between the carbon compounds in the candle and the oxygen in the air. The flame gives off heat and light.

Figure 6 Electrical energy is transformed into thermal energy in the metal heating coil. As the metal becomes hotter, it emits more radiant energy.

Science Journal

Chemical Energy Have students list all the chemical energy transformations they encounter in a day. For each item have them list how the chemical energy was transformed or from what it was obtained. Possible answers include combustion of fuel in a car, digestion of food, use of oxygen by the body, photosynthesis in plants, use of battery-powered toys or appliances. L2 **LS** **Visual-Spatial**

Differentiated Instruction

Challenge In living things, the chemical energy in food is released through the process of respiration. Have students research and report on the chemical changes that occur in this process. During respiration, oxygen joins with glucose to release energy that is then used by the cells. Carbon dioxide and water are released as waste products. L3 **LS** **Linguistic**

Check For Understanding

Interpersonal Have students discuss why bat speed is the key factor in hitting homeruns in baseball. When a bat hits a ball, some of the kinetic energy of the bat is transferred to the ball. The more kinetic energy that is transferred to the ball, the farther it will travel. More kinetic energy can be transferred to the ball by increasing the bat's kinetic energy. The kinetic energy of an object is given by the equation $KE = \frac{1}{2}mv^2$. Because the velocity is squared in this equation, a fractional increase in the speed of the bat will have a greater effect on the bat's kinetic energy than the same fractional increase in the mass of the bat.

Reteach

Energy Types Have students identify the different types of energy that they rely upon. Discuss the specific tasks each type of energy is used to perform. L1 LS

Logical-Mathematical

☑ Assessment

Oral During the Explore Activity, the more massive marble had the same speed as the less massive marble. What conclusion can you draw about the energy of the two marbles? Explain. The more massive marble had more kinetic energy than the less massive marble. Use **Performance Assessment in the Science Classroom,** p. 89.

Figure 7 Complex power plants are required to obtain useful energy from the nucleus of an atom.

Electrical Energy Electrical lighting is one of the many ways electrical energy is used. Look around at all the devices that use electricity. Electric current flows in these devices when they are connected to batteries or plugged into an electric outlet. **Electrical energy** is the energy that is carried by an electric current. An electric device uses the electrical energy provided by the current flowing in the device. Large electric power plants generate the enormous amounts of electrical energy used each day. About 20 percent of the electrical energy used in the United States is generated by nuclear power plants.

Nuclear Energy Nuclear power plants use the energy stored in the nucleus of an atom to generate electricity. Every atomic nucleus contains energy—**nuclear energy**—that can be transformed into other forms of energy. However, releasing the nuclear energy is a difficult process. It involves the construction of complex power plants, shown in **Figure 7.** In contrast, all that is needed to release chemical energy from wood is a lighted match.

section 1 review

Summary

The Nature of Energy
- Energy is the ability to cause change.
- Kinetic energy is the energy an object has due to its motion. Kinetic energy depends on an object's speed and mass.
- Potential energy is the energy an object has due to its position. Potential energy depends on an object's height and mass.

Forces of Energy
- Thermal energy increases as temperature increases.
- Chemical energy is the energy stored in chemical bonds in molecules.
- Light energy, also called radiant energy, is the energy contained in light.
- Electrical energy is the energy carried by electric current.
- Nuclear energy is the energy contained in the nucleus of an atom.

Self Check

1. **Explain** why a high-speed collision between two cars would cause more damage than a low-speed collision between the same two cars.
2. **Describe** the energy transformations that occur when a piece of wood is burned.
3. **Identify** the form of energy that is converted into thermal energy by your body.
4. **Explain** how, if two vases are side by side on a shelf, one could have more potential energy.
5. **Think Critically** A golf ball and a bowling ball are moving and both have the same kinetic energy. Which one is moving faster? If they move at the same speed, which one has more kinetic energy?

Applying Skills

6. **Communicate** In your Science Journal, record different ways the word *energy* is used. Which ways of using the word *energy* are closest to the definition of energy given in this section?

378 CHAPTER 13 Energy and Energy Resources

Science Online ips.msscience.com/self_check_quiz

section 1 review

1. At high speed, both cars have more kinetic energy. This greater kinetic energy will result in more damage occurring when the cars collide.
2. Chemical energy in the wood is transformed into thermal energy and radiant energy.
3. chemical energy
4. The vase with the larger mass would have more potential energy.
5. The golf ball has less mass so it must be moving faster. If they move at the same speed, the bowling ball has more kinetic energy.
6. Answers will vary.

Energy Transformations

1 **Motivate**

Changing Forms of Energy

Chemical, thermal, radiant, and electrical are some of the forms that energy can have. In the world around you, energy is transforming continually between one form and another. You observe some of these transformations by noticing a change in your environment. Forest fires are a dramatic example of an environmental change that can occur naturally as a result of lightning strikes. A number of changes occur that involve energy as the mountain biker in **Figure 8** pedals up a hill. What energy transformations cause these changes to occur?

Tracking Energy Transformations As the mountain biker pedals, his leg muscles transform chemical energy into kinetic energy. The kinetic energy of his leg muscles transforms into kinetic energy of the bicycle as he pedals. Some of this energy transforms into potential energy as he moves up the hill. Also, some energy is transformed into thermal energy. His body is warmer because chemical energy is being released. Because of friction, the mechanical parts of the bicycle are warmer, too. Energy in the form of heat is almost always one of the products of an energy transformation. The energy transformations that occur when people exercise, when cars run, when living things grow and even when stars explode, all produce heat.

as you read

What **You'll Learn**
- **Apply** the law of conservation of energy to energy transformations.
- **Identify** how energy changes form.
- **Describe** how electric power plants produce energy.

Why **It's Important**
Changing energy from one form to another is what makes cars run, furnaces heat, telephones work, and plants grow.

🔁 **Review Vocabulary**
transformation: a change in composition or structure

New Vocabulary
- law of conservation of energy
- generator
- turbine

Figure 8 The ability to transform energy allows the biker to climb the hill.
Identify *all the forms of energy that are represented in the photograph.*

379

Bellringer

Section Focus Transparencies also are available on the Interactive Chalkboard CD-ROM.
L2 **ELL**

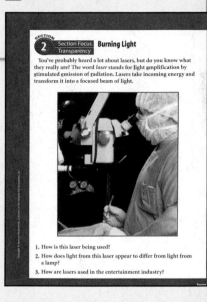

SECTION 2
Section Focus Transparency **Burning Light**

You've probably heard a lot about lasers, but do you know what they really are? The word *laser* stands for light amplification by stimulated emission of radiation. Lasers take incoming energy and transform it into a focused beam of light.

1. How is this laser being used?
2. How does light from this laser appear to differ from light from a lamp?
3. How are lasers used in the entertainment industry?

Tie to Prior Knowledge
Changing Energy Ask students to give examples of energy they used to get ready for school. Possible answers: thermal energy to dry hair, electricity to run appliances. Point out that energy changes from one form to another. For example, electrical energy was transformed to thermal energy by a hairdryer.

Caption Answer
Figure 8 kinetic energy of the bike and rider, potential energy of the bike and rider due to the height of the hill, and chemical energy in the rider's muscles

Section 2 Resource Manager

Chapter *FAST FILE* Resources
Transparency Activity, p. 43
Directed Reading for Content Mastery, p. 19
MiniLAB, p. 3
Lab Activity, pp. 9–10
Enrichment, p. 29

Reinforcement, p. 26
Lab Worksheet, pp. 5–6
Physical Science Critical Thinking/Problem Solving, p. 17

Answer Energy is never lost. It may be changed into a different form of energy.

Caption Answer

Figure 9 The ball has the most kinetic energy as it leaves and returns to the hand. The ball's total energy is constant.

IDENTIFYING Misconceptions

Where Energy Goes Students may think that energy is something that is used and then disappears. See page F at the beginning of this chapter for teacher strategies that address this misconception.

Science Online

Topic: Energy Transformations
Visit ips.msscience.com for Web links to information about energy transformations that occur during different activities and processes.

Activity Choose an activity or process and make a graph showing how the kinetic and potential energy change during it.

The Law of Conservation of Energy

It can be a challenge to track energy as it moves from object to object. However, one extremely important principle can serve as a guide as you trace the flow of energy. According to the **law of conservation of energy,** energy is never created or destroyed. The only thing that changes is the form in which energy appears. When the biker is resting at the summit, all his original energy is still around. Some of the energy is in the form of potential energy, which he will use as he coasts down the hill. Some of this energy was changed to thermal energy by friction in the bike. Chemical energy was also changed to thermal energy in the biker's muscles, making him feel hot. As he rests, this thermal energy moves from his body to the air around him. No energy is missing—it can all be accounted for.

✓ **Reading Check** *Can energy ever be lost? Why or why not?*

Changing Kinetic and Potential Energy

The law of conservation of energy can be used to identify the energy changes in a system. For example, tossing a ball into the air and catching it is a simple system. As shown in **Figure 9,** as the ball leaves your hand, most of its energy is kinetic. As the ball rises, it slows and its kinetic energy decreases. But, the total energy of the ball hasn't changed. The decrease in kinetic energy equals the increase in potential energy as the ball flies higher in the air. The total amount of energy remains constant. Energy moves from place to place and changes form, but it never is created or destroyed.

Figure 9 During the flight of the baseball, energy is transforming between kinetic and potential energy.
Determine *where the ball has the most kinetic energy. Where does the ball have the most total energy?*

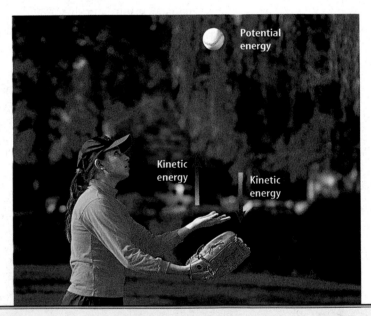

Potential energy

Kinetic energy

Kinetic energy

LAB DEMONSTRATION

Purpose to observe the exchange of potential and kinetic energy
Materials 1.0-kg mass attached to a 2-m string
Procedure Hang the pendulum so the bob just misses the floor at its lowest point. Release the bob at different heights, and measure the height to which it rises at the other end of its swing.
Expected Outcome The pendulum will swing up to nearly the original height from which it was released. The final height will be slightly lower due to the effects of air resistance and friction.

Assessment

Where does the bob have the greatest potential energy? just before it is released The greatest kinetic energy? at the bottom of its swing How does the height at which the bob is released affect the energy? Greater height means more total energy.

Figure 10 Hybrid cars that use an electric motor and a gasoline engine for power are now available. Hybrid cars make energy transformations more efficient.

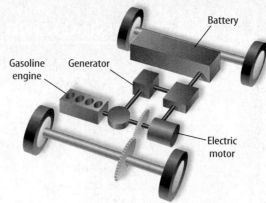

Battery

Generator

Gasoline engine

Electric motor

Quick Demo
Radiant Energy

Materials bright light source (such as a flashlight), radiometer

Estimated Time 1–3 minutes

Procedure Shine a bright light on a radiometer so that the vanes rotate. Show how the radiometer vanes stop rotating when the light is turned off. Explain that the radiant energy carried by the light is transferred to the radiometer and converted into the kinetic energy of the moving radiometer vanes.

Energy Changes Form

Energy transformations occur constantly all around you. Many machines are devices that transform energy from one form to another. For example, an automobile engine transforms the chemical energy in gasoline into energy of motion. However, not all of the chemical energy is converted into kinetic energy. Instead, some of the chemical energy is converted into thermal energy, and the engine becomes hot. An engine that converts chemical energy into more kinetic energy is a more efficient engine. New types of cars, like the one shown in **Figure 10,** use an electric motor along with a gasoline engine. These engines are more efficient so the car can travel farther on a gallon of gas.

Transforming Chemical Energy Inside your body, chemical energy also is transformed into kinetic energy. Look at **Figure 11.** The transformation of chemical to kinetic energy occurs in muscle cells. There, chemical reactions take place that cause certain molecules to change shape. Your muscle contracts when many of these changes occur, and a part of your body moves.

The matter contained in living organisms, also called biomass, contains chemical energy. When organisms die, chemical compounds in their biomass break down. Bacteria, fungi, and other organisms help convert these chemical compounds to simpler chemicals that can be used by other living things.

Thermal energy also is released as these changes occur. For example, a compost pile can contain plant matter, such as grass clippings and leaves. As the compost pile decomposes, chemical energy is converted into thermal energy. This can cause the temperature of a compost pile to reach 60°C.

Mini LAB

Analyzing Energy Transformations

Procedure 🌐 🤚

1. Place soft **clay** on the floor and smooth out its surface.
2. Hold a **marble** 1.5 m above the clay and drop it. Measure the depth of the crater made by the marble.
3. Repeat this procedure using a **golf ball** and a **plastic golf ball.**

Analysis

1. Compare the depths of the craters to determine which ball had the most kinetic energy as it hit the clay.
2. Explain how potential energy was transformed into kinetic energy during your activity.

Try at Home

Mini LAB

Purpose Students observe the difference in kinetic energy of balls of different masses. L2

ELL **LS** **Kinesthetic**

Materials soft clay, marble, steel ball, rubber ball, table-tennis ball, metric ruler

Teaching Strategies Suggest that students hold a pencil in the crater and mark the depth of the crater on the pencil. Then they can measure the distance marked on the pencil with the metric ruler.

Analysis

1. The ball with the most mass had the greatest kinetic energy. This was probably the steel ball.
2. The balls had potential energy because of the height to which they were raised above the clay. This energy was transformed into kinetic energy as they fell.

Assessment

Oral Ask students to explain what happened to the kinetic energy of the balls as they landed in the clay. It changed to kinetic energy in the clay and then to thermal energy. Use **Performance Assessment in the Science Classroom,** p. 89.

Try at Home

Visual Learning

Figure 10 Hybrid cars use an internal combustion engine as the primary power source of the car, but use a battery-powered electrical motor to assist with acceleration. The electric motor can be used alone for low speed driving. A generator converts some of the car's kinetic energy into electrical energy that keeps the batteries charged. The batteries convert chemical energy to electrical energy, which runs the electric motor.

Fun Fact

Chemical energy is used to put on fireworks shows. Potassium nitrate, ammonium nitrate, saltpeter, sulfur, silicon, aluminum powder, and other materials give off different colors and luminescence when they burn to give off the colorful fireworks shows seen at festive times of the year.

Visualizing Energy Transformations

Have students examine the pictures and read the captions. Then ask the following questions.

Why is it necessary for skeletal muscles in the arm to be arranged in pairs? This is necessary so that the arm can move in more than one direction. For instance, when the arm is raised by the biceps, as shown in the art drawing, the triceps are needed to lower it.

What is the source of chemical energy for the muscles? Chemical energy is provided by breaking the chemical bonds in the foods we eat.

Activity

Leg Muscles Have your students research the major muscles in the human leg. Have students make drawings in their Science Journals of their leg muscles. Encourage them to make their drawings similar to those shown for the arm in **Figure 11.** L2

LS Visual-Spatial

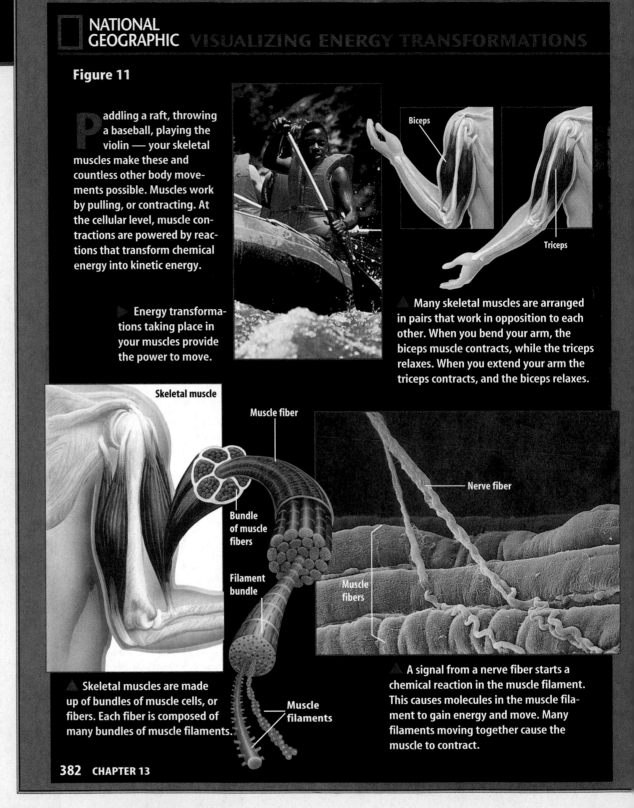

NATIONAL GEOGRAPHIC VISUALIZING ENERGY TRANSFORMATIONS

Figure 11

Paddling a raft, throwing a baseball, playing the violin — your skeletal muscles make these and countless other body movements possible. Muscles work by pulling, or contracting. At the cellular level, muscle contractions are powered by reactions that transform chemical energy into kinetic energy.

► Energy transformations taking place in your muscles provide the power to move.

▲ Many skeletal muscles are arranged in pairs that work in opposition to each other. When you bend your arm, the biceps muscle contracts, while the triceps relaxes. When you extend your arm the triceps contracts, and the biceps relaxes.

Biceps

Triceps

Skeletal muscle

Muscle fiber

Bundle of muscle fibers

Filament bundle

Nerve fiber

Muscle fibers

Muscle filaments

▲ Skeletal muscles are made up of bundles of muscle cells, or fibers. Each fiber is composed of many bundles of muscle filaments.

▲ A signal from a nerve fiber starts a chemical reaction in the muscle filament. This causes molecules in the muscle filament to gain energy and move. Many filaments moving together cause the muscle to contract.

382 CHAPTER 13

Differentiated Instruction

Challenge Have students research how electrical stimulation is being used to help paraplegics walk again. Encourage students to report their findings to the class. L2

Figure 12 The simple act of listening to a radio involves many energy transformations. A few are diagrammed here.

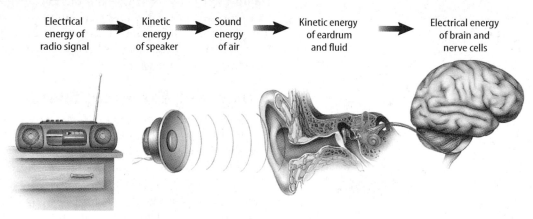

Electrical energy of radio signal → Kinetic energy of speaker → Sound energy of air → Kinetic energy of eardrum and fluid → Electrical energy of brain and nerve cells

Transforming Electrical Energy

Every day you use electrical energy. When you flip a light switch, or turn on a radio or television, or use a hair drier, you are transforming electrical energy to other forms of energy. Every time you plug something into a wall outlet, or use a battery, you are using electrical energy. **Figure 12** shows how electrical energy is transformed into other forms of energy when you listen to a radio. A loudspeaker in the radio converts electrical energy into sound waves that travel to your ear—energy in motion. The energy that is carried by the sound waves causes parts of the ear to move also. This energy of motion is transformed again into chemical and electrical energy in nerve cells, which send the energy to your brain. After your brain interprets this energy as a voice or music, where does the energy go? The energy finally is transformed into thermal energy.

Transforming Thermal Energy

Different forms of energy can be transformed into thermal energy. For example, chemical energy changes into thermal energy when something burns. Electrical energy changes into thermal energy when a wire that is carrying an electric current gets hot. Thermal energy can be used to heat buildings and keep you warm. Thermal energy also can be used to heat water. If water is heated to its boiling point, it changes to steam. This steam can be used to produce kinetic energy by steam engines, like the steam locomotives that used to pull trains. Thermal energy also can be transformed into radiant energy. For example, when a bar of metal is heated to a high temperature, it glows and gives off light.

Controlling Body Temperature Most organisms have some adaptation for controlling the amount of thermal energy in their bodies. Some living in cooler climates have thick fur coats that help prevent thermal energy from escaping, and some living in desert regions have skin that helps keep thermal energy out. Research some of the adaptations different organisms have for controlling the thermal energy in their bodies.

SECTION 2 Energy Transformations **383**

Figure 13 Thermal energy moves from the hot chocolate to the cooler surroundings. **Explain** what happens to the hot chocolate as it loses thermal energy.

Figure 14 A coal-burning power plant transforms the chemical energy in coal into electrical energy. **List** some of the other energy sources that power plants use.

How Thermal Energy Moves Thermal energy can move from one place to another. Look at **Figure 13.** The hot chocolate has thermal energy that moves from the cup to the cooler air around it, and to the cooler spoon. Thermal energy only moves from something at a higher temperature to something at a lower temperature.

Generating Electrical Energy

The enormous amount of electrical energy that is used every day is too large to be stored in batteries. The electrical energy that is available for use at any wall socket must be generated continually by power plants. Every power plant works on the same principle—energy is used to turn a large generator. A **generator** is a device that transforms kinetic energy into electrical energy. In fossil fuel power plants, coal, oil, or natural gas is burned to boil water. As the hot water boils, the steam rushes through a **turbine,** which contains a set of narrowly spaced fan blades. The steam pushes on the blades and turns the turbine, which in turn rotates a shaft in the generator to produce the electrical energy, as shown in **Figure 14.**

Reading Check *What does a generator do?*

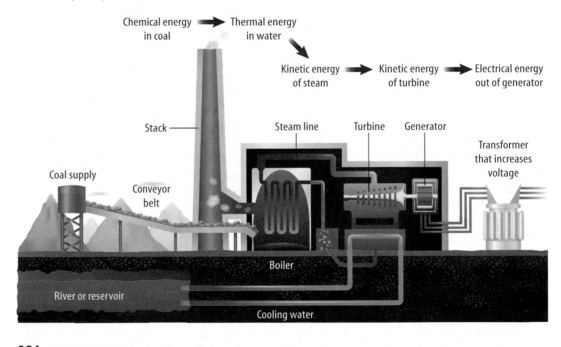

Power Plants Almost 90 percent of the electrical energy generated in the United States is produced by nuclear and fossil fuel power plants, as shown in **Figure 15.** Other types of power plants include hydroelectric (hi droh ih LEK trihk) and wind. Hydroelectric power plants transform the kinetic energy of moving water into electrical energy. Wind power plants transform the kinetic energy of moving air into electrical energy. In these power plants, a generator converts the kinetic energy of moving water or wind to electrical energy.

To analyze the energy transformations in a power plant, you can diagram the energy changes using arrows. A coal-burning power plant generates electrical energy through the following series of energy transformations.

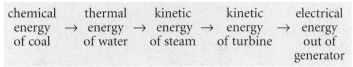

chemical energy of coal	→	thermal energy of water	→	kinetic energy of steam	→	kinetic energy of turbine	→	electrical energy out of generator

Nuclear power plants use a similar series of transformations. Hydroelectric plants, however, skip the steps that change water into steam because the water strikes the turbine directly.

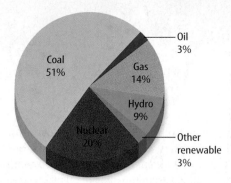

Figure 15 The graph shows sources of electrical energy in the United States.
Name *the energy source that you think is being used to provide the electricity for the lights overhead.*

Caption Answer
Figure 15 Possible answers: fossil fuels, uranium, falling water.

3 Assess

DAILY INTERVENTION

Check For Understanding
Linguistic Have students write in their Science Journals, using **Figure 12,** how the electrical energy of a radio signal is transformed into electrical energy in the brain and nerve cells. The energy in radio waves is transformed by the radio into kinetic energy in the form of sound waves. The sound waves strike the eardrum and are transformed from kinetic energy to electrical energy in the cochlea, which is then transmitted through nerve tissue to the brain.

Reteach
Energy Type Have volunteers explain each type of energy discussed in this section. As each energy type is discussed, challenge students to explain how this form of energy is used in their daily lives. L2 LS **Linguistic**

section 2 review

Summary

Changing Forms of Energy
- Heat usually is one of the forms of energy produced in energy transformations.
- The law of conservation of energy states that energy cannot be created or destroyed; it can only change form.
- The total energy doesn't change when an energy transformation occurs.
- As an object rises and falls, kinetic and potential energy are transformed into each other, but the total energy doesn't change.

Generating Electrical Energy
- A generator converts kinetic energy into electrical energy.
- Burning fossil fuels produces thermal energy that is used to boil water and produce steam.
- In a power plant, steam is used to spin a turbine which then spins an electric generator.

Self Check

1. **Describe** the conversions between potential and kinetic energy that occur when you shoot a basketball at a basket.
2. **Explain** whether your body gains or loses thermal energy if your body temperature is 37°C and the temperature around you is 25°C.
3. **Describe** a process that converts chemical energy to thermal energy.
4. **Think Critically** A lightbulb converts 10 percent of the electrical energy it uses into radiant energy. Make a hypothesis about the other form of energy produced.

Applying Math

5. **Use a Ratio** How many times greater is the amount of electrical energy produced in the United States by coal-burning power plants than the amount produced by nuclear power plants?

section 2 review

1. Ball has kinetic energy when it leaves your hand; kinetic energy is converted to potential energy as ball rises; potential energy is converted to kinetic energy as ball falls

2. Your temperature is higher than your surroundings, so thermal energy is transferred from you to your surroundings.

3. Possible answer: burning of wood
4. The other 90 percent is converted into thermal energy.
5. (51%)/(20%) = 2.5 times greater

Assessment

Performance Have students make posters illustrating the energy transformations that occur when oil is used to generate electricity. Chemical energy of oil → thermal energy of water → kinetic energy of steam → kinetic energy of turbine → electrical energy out of generator Use **Performance Assessment in the Science Classroom,** p. 145.

● Real-World Question

Purpose Students track energy conversions from electrical energy to vibrations to sound.
L2 | LS | **Auditory-Musical**

Process Skills observing, inferring, predicting

Time Required 20 minutes

● Procedure

Teaching Strategy Have reference books about sound and electricity available.

Troubleshooting Make sure the wiring is securely connected. The motor will not turn even though students will be able to "hear" the music when they press the axle against their jaws.

● Conclude and Apply

1. Students should hear the sound of the radio or disc.
2. sound energy
3. Transformation should start with electrical energy (from a wall outlet or from a battery), change to mechanical energy, and end with sound energy. If a CD player is used, students also might include light energy.
4. The motor will probably get warmer as it runs. Some of the energy changes to heat because of friction.
5. All of the energy put into the system can be accounted for as motion, heat, light, or sound.

☑ Assessment

Content Have students work in groups to write a song or poem or make a picture about transfers of energy. Use **Performance Assessment in the Science Classroom**, p. 151.

Hearing with Your Jaw

You probably have listened to music using speakers or headphones. Have you ever considered how energy is transferred to get the energy from the radio or CD player to your brain? What type of energy is needed to power the radio or CD player? Where does this energy come from? How does that energy become sound? How does the sound get to you? In this activity, the sound from a radio or CD player is going to travel through a motor before entering your body through your jaw instead of your ears.

● Real-World Question

How can energy be transferred from a radio or CD player to your brain?

Goals
■ **Identify** energy transfers and transformations.
■ **Explain** your observations using the law of conservation of energy.

Materials
radio or CD player
small electrical motor
headphone jack

● Procedure

1. Go to one of the places in the room with a motor/radio assembly.
2. Turn on the radio or CD player so that you hear the music.
3. Push the headphone jack into the headphone plug on the radio or CD player.
4. Press the axle of the motor against the side of your jaw.

● Conclude and Apply

1. **Describe** what you heard in your Science Journal.
2. **Identify** the form of energy produced by the radio or CD player.
3. **Draw** a diagram to show all of the energy transformations taking place.
4. **Evaluate** Did anything get hotter as a result of this activity? Explain.
5. **Explain** your observations using the law of conservation of energy.

𝒞ommunicating Your Data

Compare your conclusions with those of other students in your class. **For more help, refer to the Science Skill Handbook.**

𝒞ommunicating Your Data

Students could use an electronic presentation program to present their picture and/or events chain to the rest of the class.

Sources of Energy

Using Energy

Every day, energy is used to provide light and to heat and cool homes, schools, and workplaces. According to the law of conservation of energy, energy can't be created or destroyed. Energy only can change form. If a car or refrigerator can't create the energy they use, then where does this energy come from?

Energy Resources

Energy cannot be made, but must come from the natural world. As you can see in **Figure 16,** the surface of Earth receives energy from two sources—the Sun and radioactive atoms in Earth's interior. The amount of energy Earth receives from the Sun is far greater than the amount generated in Earth's interior. Nearly all the energy you used today can be traced to the Sun, even the gasoline used to power the car or school bus you came to school in.

as you read

What You'll Learn

- **Explain** what renewable, non-renewable, and alternative resources are.
- **Describe** the advantages and disadvantages of using various energy sources.

Why It's Important

Energy is vital for survival and making life comfortable. Developing new energy sources will improve modern standards of living.

Review Vocabulary

resource: a natural feature or phenomenon that enhances the quality of life

New Vocabulary

- nonrenewable resource
- renewable resource
- alternative resource
- inexhaustible resource
- photovoltaic

Bellringer

Section Focus Transparencies also are available on the Interactive Chalkboard CD-ROM.

L2 ELL

A Fuming Fuel

Peat is a fuel that is burned for heat. Formed by layers of partially decayed plants, heated and compressed over millions of years, peat is cut from vast swamps, dried, and used as an energy source. It has a very pungent odor.

1. What might be some disadvantages of using peat to heat a home?
2. Could you burn peat immediately after it is cut from the ground? Why or why not?
3. What other sources of energy can you name?

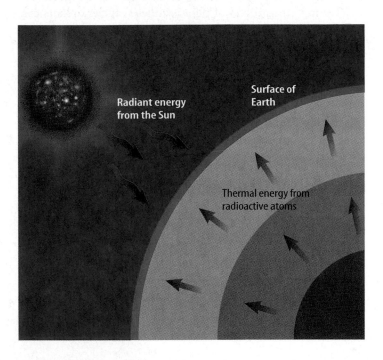

Radiant energy from the Sun

Surface of Earth

Thermal energy from radioactive atoms

Figure 16 All the energy you use can be traced to one of two sources—the Sun or radioactive atoms in Earth's interior.

Tie to Prior Knowledge

Energy Sources Ask students how their homes are heated. Possible answers: by burning oil or natural gas, or using electricity. Have them recall the sources of energy, such as fossil fuels, used to produce electricity in some power plants, and the energy transformations involved. Explain that they learn about other energy sources in this section.

SECTION 3 Sources of Energy **387**

Section 3 Resource Manager

Chapter FAST FILE Resources

Transparency Activity, pp. 44, 45–46

Directed Reading for Content Mastery, pp. 19, 20

MiniLAB, p. 4

Lab Activity, pp. 11–13

Enrichment, p. 30

Reinforcement, p. 27

Lab Worksheet, pp. 7–8

Cultural Diversity, p. 45

Home and Community Involvement, p. 26

Lab Management and Safety, p. 73

Use an Analogy

Building Energy In fossil fuels, the chemical energy between the carbon atoms and the other atoms of the original organic matter has been concentrated. Burning fossil fuel yields a high amount of energy for a period of time that is fleeting compared with the time it took to transform the organic material into fossil fuel. In the same way, professional musicians and players of professional sports spend years learning to concentrate their energy and perfecting techniques that may take mere seconds to perform.

INTEGRATE Earth Science

Energy Source Origins Coal was formed from the remains of partially decomposed plants that had accumulated hundreds of millions of years ago. Coal formation gradually occurred after the plant debris had been covered and compressed by rocks, soil, and water and then subjected to great pressure and heat over long periods of time. Oil and natural gas formed from the remains of marine life and plants that had been rapidly buried in fine-grained sediment. This rapid burial prevented these organic debris from completely decomposing; and, along with increases in temperature and pressure, oil and natural gas deposits gradually formed.

Radiant energy

Radiant energy from the Sun is stored as chemical energy in molecules.

Time Heat Pressure

Coal mine

Figure 17 Coal is formed after the molecules in ancient plants are heated under pressure for millions of years. The energy stored by the molecules in coal originally came from the Sun.

INTEGRATE Earth Science

Energy Source Origins
The kinds of fossil fuels found in the ground depend on the kinds of organisms (animal or plant) that died and were buried in that spot. Research coal, oil, and natural gas to find out what types of organisms were primarily responsible for producing each.

Fossil Fuels

Fossil fuels are coal, oil, and natural gas. Oil and natural gas were made from the remains of microscopic organisms that lived in Earth's oceans millions of years ago. Heat and pressure gradually turned these ancient organisms into oil and natural gas. Coal was formed by a similar process from the remains of ancient plants that once lived on land, as shown in **Figure 17.**

Through the process of photosynthesis, ancient plants converted the radiant energy in sunlight to chemical energy stored in various types of molecules. Heat and pressure changed these molecules into other types of molecules as fossil fuels formed. Chemical energy stored in these molecules is released when fossil fuels are burned.

Using Fossil Fuels The energy used when you ride in a car, turn on a light, or use an electric appliance usually comes from burning fossil fuels. However, it takes millions of years to replace each drop of gasoline and each lump of coal that is burned. This means that the supply of oil on Earth will continue to decrease as oil is used. An energy source that is used up much faster than it can be replaced is a **nonrenewable resource.** Fossil fuels are nonrenewable resources.

Burning fossil fuels to produce energy also generates chemical compounds that cause pollution. Each year billions of kilograms of air pollutants are produced by burning fossil fuels. These pollutants can cause respiratory illnesses and acid rain. Also, the carbon dioxide gas formed when fossil fuels are burned might cause Earth's climate to warm.

388   CHAPTER 13 Energy and Energy Resources

Science Journal

Energy Matters Some people believe the demand for energy in the world will quadruple in the next fifty years. Have students write paragraphs in their Science Journals speculating how people will meet the demands for more energy. L2 LS
Intrapersonal P

Nuclear Energy

Can you imagine running an automobile on 1 kg of fuel that releases almost 3 million times more energy than 1 L of gas? What could supply so much energy from so little mass? The answer is the nuclei of uranium atoms. Some of these nuclei are unstable and break apart, releasing enormous amounts of energy in the process. This energy can be used to generate electricity by heating water to produce steam that spins an electric generator, as shown in **Figure 18.** Because no fossil fuels are burned, generating electricity using nuclear energy helps make the supply of fossil fuels last longer. Also, unlike fossil fuel power plants, nuclear power plants produce almost no air pollution. In one year, a typical nuclear power plant generates enough energy to supply 600,000 homes with power and produces only 1 m³ of waste.

Nuclear Wastes Like all energy sources, nuclear energy has its advantages and disadvantages. One disadvantage is the amount of uranium in Earth's crust is nonrenewable. Another is that the waste produced by nuclear power plants is radioactive and can be dangerous to living things. Some of the materials in the nuclear waste will remain radioactive for many thousands of years. As a result the waste must be stored so no radioactivity is released into the environment for a long time. One method is to seal the waste in a ceramic material, place the ceramic in protective containers, and then bury the containers far underground. However, the burial site would have to be chosen carefully so underground water supplies aren't contaminated. Also, the site would have to be safe from earthquakes and other natural disasters that might cause radioactive material to be released.

Figure 18 To obtain electrical energy from nuclear energy, a series of energy transformations must occur.

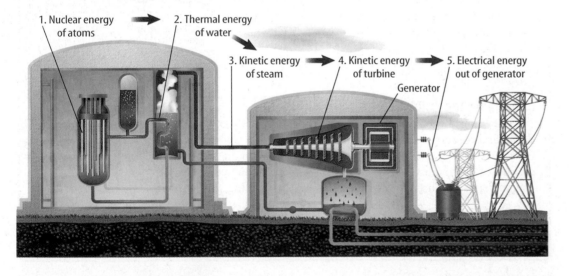

1. Nuclear energy of atoms
2. Thermal energy of water
3. Kinetic energy of steam
4. Kinetic energy of turbine
Generator
5. Electrical energy out of generator

Quick Demo

Chain Reaction

Materials many mousetraps, large box with short walls

Estimated Time 2–5 minutes

Procedure To model the chain reaction that can occur in nuclear fission, place many set mousetraps into a large box with fairly short walls. **Warning:** *Keep fingers clear of trap area.* The traps should be fairly close together for a good response. Drop a table-tennis ball into the box and have students observe what happens. Explain that the ball represents a loose neutron that initiates the fission process while the mousetraps model uranium-235 nuclei.

Differentiated Instruction

Challenge The first human use of nuclear fission was in atomic weapons. Have students research the development of these weapons and give speeches describing their findings. During World War II, Albert Einstein twice wrote to President Franklin Delano Roosevelt to warn him that the technology needed to build nuclear weapons existed and that such weapons might be developed by Germany, which could lead to a global disaster. Einstein's warnings led to the formation of the Manhattan Project, which led to development of the world's first atomic weapons. L2 LS **Linguistic**

Active Reading

Four-Corner Discussion This strategy encourages the class to debate a complex issue. Make four signs: Strongly Agree, Agree, Disagree, and Strongly Disagree. Place one sign in each corner of the room. Write on the chalkboard a statement that will elicit reactions from students. Have the students respond on paper to the statement. After several minutes, direct them to move to the corner with the sign that most closely reflects their opinions. In the corners, students share responses. Each group then selects a spokesperson to report the opinions of the group. After all groups have reported, open the floor for debate. Allow students who have changed their opinions to change corners. Have students conduct a Four-Corner Discussion about the use of nuclear energy.

Make a Model

Pinwheel Have students make a pinwheel by folding each corner of a large index card into the center and attaching it to a pencil eraser with a pin. Have students place their pinwheels under a stream of water running from a faucet to observe that the kinetic energy of moving water can be transferred to the blades of a turbine. L1 [LS] **Kinesthetic**

Science Online

Topic: Hydroelectricity

Visit ips.msscience.com for Web links to information about the use of hydroelectricity in various parts of the world.

Activity On a map of the world, show where the use of hydroelectricity is the greatest.

Hydroelectricity

Currently, transforming the potential energy of water that is trapped behind dams supplies the world with almost 20 percent of its electrical energy. Hydroelectricity is the largest renewable source of energy. A **renewable resource** is an energy source that is replenished continually. As long as enough rain and snow fall to keep rivers flowing, hydroelectric power plants can generate electrical energy, as shown in **Figure 19.**

Although production of hydroelectricity is largely pollution free, it has one major problem. It disrupts the life cycle of aquatic animals, especially fish. This is particularly true in the Northwest where salmon spawn and run. Because salmon return to the spot where they were hatched to lay their eggs, the development of dams has hindered a large fraction of salmon from reproducing. This has greatly reduced the salmon population. Efforts to correct the problem have resulted in plans to remove a number of dams. In an attempt to help fish bypass some dams, fish ladders are being installed. Like most energy sources, hydroelectricity has advantages and disadvantages.

Applying Science

Is energy consumption outpacing production?

You use energy every day—to get to school, to watch TV, and to heat or cool your home. The amount of energy consumed by an average person has increased over time. Consequently, more energy must be produced.

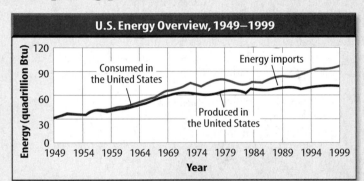

U.S. Energy Overview, 1949–1999

Identifying the Problem

The graph above shows the energy produced and consumed in the United States from 1949 to 1999. How does energy that is consumed by Americans compare with energy that is produced in the United States?

Solving the Problem

1. Determine the approximate amount of energy produced in 1949 and in 1999 and how much it has increased in 50 years. Has it doubled or tripled?

2. Do the same for consumption. Has it doubled or tripled?

3. Using your answers for steps 1 and 2 and the graph, where does the additional energy that is needed come from? Give some examples.

390   CHAPTER 13 Energy and Energy Resources

Differentiated Instruction

Challenge Have groups of students build solar-powered toy cars. The cars should be built from scratch with parts from other toys. Upon completion, students should make diagrams describing how the cars work. L3 **ELL** **COOP LEARN** [LS] **Kinesthetic**

Cultural Diversity

Three Gorges Dam The largest hydroelectric dam in the world, Three Gorges Dam, is under construction in China. Have students find out more about this dam and present their findings to the class. The dam will produce 18,200 megawatts of electricity and is to be completed in 2009. It will submerge 13 cities, 140 towns, and 1,352 villages. L2 [LS] **Linguistic**

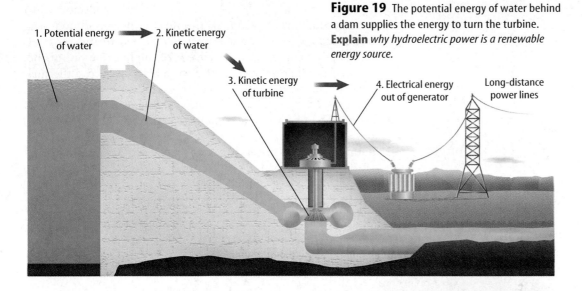

1. Potential energy of water → 2. Kinetic energy of water

3. Kinetic energy of turbine → 4. Electrical energy out of generator

Long-distance power lines

Figure 19 The potential energy of water behind a dam supplies the energy to turn the turbine. **Explain** why hydroelectric power is a renewable energy source.

Alternative Sources of Energy

Electrical energy can be generated in several ways. However, each has disadvantages that can affect the environment and the quality of life for humans. Research is being done to develop new sources of energy that are safer and cause less harm to the environment. These sources often are called **alternative resources**. These alternative resources include solar energy, wind, and geothermal energy.

Solar Energy

The Sun is the origin of almost all the energy that is used on Earth. Because the Sun will go on producing an enormous amount of energy for billions of years, the Sun is an inexhaustible source of energy. An **inexhaustible resource** is an energy source that can't be used up by humans.

Each day, on average, the amount of solar energy that strikes the United States is more than the total amount of energy used by the entire country in a year. However, less than 0.1 percent of the energy used in the United States comes directly from the Sun. One reason is that solar energy is more expensive to use than fossil fuels. However, as the supply of fossil fuels decreases, the cost of finding and mining these fuels might increase. Then, it may be cheaper to use solar energy or other energy sources to generate electricity and heat buildings than to use fossil fuels.

Reading Check *What is an inexhaustible energy source?*

Mini LAB

Building a Solar Collector

Procedure
1. Line a **large pot** with **black plastic** and fill with **water.**
2. Stretch **clear-plastic wrap** over the pot and tape it taut.
3. Make a slit in the top and slide a **thermometer** or a **computer probe** into the water.
4. Place your solar collector in direct sunlight and monitor the temperature change every 3 min for 15 min.
5. Repeat your experiment without using any black plastic.

Analysis
1. Graph the temperature changes in both setups.
2. Explain how your solar collector works.

Teacher FYI

Geothermal Energy Geothermal energy can be used for heating in the winter and cooling in the summer. A loop of pipe with water running through it is inserted below the frost line where the ground stays at a constant temperature of about 10°C to 20°C, as in a cave. In summer, when the house air is warmer than this underground temperature, water in the pipe carries underground heat out of the house and underground, where the water is cooled. The water then returns above ground to collect more heat. In the winter, the reverse takes place. This method of heating and cooling is more efficient than many other methods and has recently become cost effective. Also, this method does not depend on thermal vents, which occur in only a few isolated regions of the world, and it can be used nearly everywhere.

Discussion

Advantages of Geothermal Energy
What advantages does geothermal energy have over burning fossil fuels or using nuclear energy? Possible answers: Geothermal energy is a renewable resource. Using it instead of a nonrenewable resource such as coal or petroleum reserves fossil fuels for other uses, produces less air pollution, and eliminates waste disposal problems associated with nuclear power.

Figure 20 Solar energy can be collected and utilized by individuals using thermal collectors or photovoltaic collectors.

Collecting the Sun's Energy Two types of collectors capture the Sun's rays. If you look around your neighborhood, you might see large, rectangular panels attached to the roofs of buildings or houses. If, as in **Figure 20,** pipes come out of the panel, it is a thermal collector. Using a black surface, a thermal collector heats water by directly absorbing the Sun's radiant energy. Water circulating in this system can be heated to about 70°C. The hot water can be pumped through the house to provide heat. Also, the hot water can be used for washing and bathing. If the panel has no pipes, it is a photovoltaic (foh toh vol TAY ihk) collector, like the one pictured in **Figure 20.** A **photovoltaic** is a device that transforms radiant energy directly into electrical energy. Photovoltaics are used to power calculators and satellites, including the *International Space Station.*

✔ **Reading Check** *What does a photovoltaic do?*

Geothermal Energy

Imagine you could take a journey to the center of Earth—down to about 6,400 km below the surface. As you went deeper and deeper, you would find the temperature increasing. In fact, after going only about 3 km, the temperature could have increased enough to boil water. At a depth of 100 km, the temperature could be over 900°C. The heat generated inside Earth is called geothermal energy. Some of this heat is produced when unstable radioactive atoms inside Earth decay, converting nuclear energy to thermal energy.

At some places deep within Earth the temperature is hot enough to melt rock. This molten rock, or magma, can rise up close to the surface through cracks in the crust. During a volcanic eruption, magma reaches the surface. In other places, magma gets close to the surface and heats the rock around it.

Geothermal Reservoirs In some regions where magma is close to the surface, rainwater and water from melted snow can seep down to the hot rock through cracks and other openings in Earth's surface. The water then becomes hot and sometimes can form steam. The hot water and steam can be trapped under high pressure in cracks and pockets called geothermal reservoirs. In some places, the hot water and steam are close enough to the surface to form hot springs and geysers.

392 CHAPTER 13 Energy and Energy Resources

Differentiated Instruction

Learning Disabled Light from different sources, most notably the sun, can be transformed directly into electricity. Have a light-powered calculator available to demonstrate this. When the photovoltaic cell is in the light the light energy turns into electricity which runs the calculator. Cover the cell and the source of electricity is gone. The calculator runs out of energy and goes off.

Cultural Diversity

Geothermal Iceland Iceland gets 50% of its energy from geothermal sources. Fossil fuels are only used to power automobiles, ships, and airplanes. About 86% of all space heating in Iceland is provided by geothermal energy and about 16% of Iceland's electricity is generated using geothermal energy. Geothermal energy is also used to heat outdoor pools, where people swim year round.

Geothermal Power Plants In places where the geothermal reservoirs are less than several kilometers deep, wells can be drilled to reach them. The hot water and steam produced by geothermal energy then can be used by geothermal power plants, like the one in **Figure 21,** to generate electricity.

Most geothermal reservoirs contain hot water under high pressure. **Figure 22** shows how these reservoirs can be used to generate electricity. While geothermal power is an inexhaustible source of energy, geothermal power plants can be built only in regions where geothermal reservoirs are close to the surface, such as in the western United States.

Heat Pumps Geothermal heat helps keep the temperature of the ground at a depth of several meters at a nearly constant temperature of about 10° to 20°C. This constant temperature can be used to cool and heat buildings by using a heat pump.

A heat pump contains a water-filled loop of pipe that is buried to a depth where the temperature is nearly constant. In summer the air is warmer than this underground temperature. Warm water from the building is pumped through the pipe down into the ground. The water cools and then is pumped back to the house where it absorbs more heat, and the cycle is repeated. During the winter, the air is cooler than the ground below. Then, cool water absorbs heat from the ground and releases it into the house.

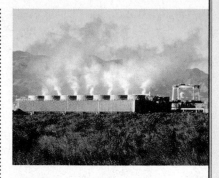

Figure 21 This geothermal power plant in Nevada produces enough electricity to power about 50,000 homes.

Figure 22 The hot water in a geothermal reservoir is used to generate electricity in a geothermal power plant.

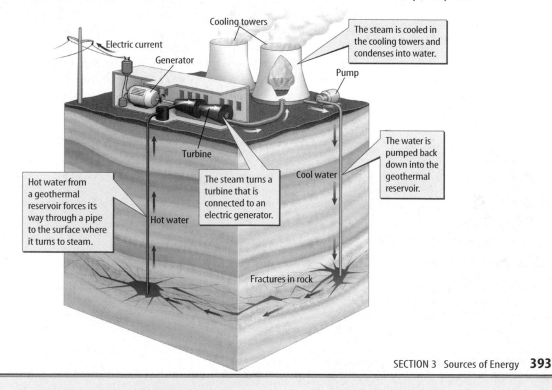

Cooling towers

Electric current

Generator

The steam is cooled in the cooling towers and condenses into water.

Pump

Turbine

The water is pumped back down into the geothermal reservoir.

Hot water from a geothermal reservoir forces its way through a pipe to the surface where it turns to steam.

The steam turns a turbine that is connected to an electric generator.

Cool water

Hot water

Fractures in rock

Water Energy What produces the mechanical energy used in a tidal power plant? The flow of water through a turbine, which causes the turbine to spin; in this way mechanical energy can be changed to electrical energy. Why is this system available in only a few locations around the world? There are only a few locations that have a large enough difference between the height of high and low tides.

Make a Model

Tidal Energy Have groups of students make simple models demonstrating how tidal energy can be used to generate electricity. Instruct students to use their models to explain this process to a group of younger students or another class. [LS] **Interpersonal**

Activity

Venn Diagram Have students make a Venn diagram to compare and contrast hydroelectric and tidal power. [LS] **Visual-Spatial**

Figure 23 This tidal power plant in Annapolis Royal, Nova Scotia, is the only operating tidal power plant in North America.

Figure 24 A tidal power plant can generate electricity when the tide is coming in and going out.

Energy from the Oceans

The ocean is in constant motion. If you've been to the seashore you've seen waves roll in. You may have seen the level of the ocean rise and fall over a period of about a half day. This rise and fall in the ocean level is called a tide. The constant movement of the ocean is an inexhaustible source of mechanical energy that can be converted into electric energy. While methods are still being developed to convert the motion in ocean waves to electric energy, several electric power plants using tidal motion have been built.

Using Tidal Energy A high tide and a low tide each occur about twice a day. In most places the level of the ocean changes by less than a few meters. However, in some places the change is much greater. In the Bay of Fundy in Eastern Canada, the ocean level changes by 16 m between high tide and low tide. Almost 14 trillion kg of water move into or out of the bay between high and low tide.

Figure 23 shows an electric power plant that has been built along the Bay of Fundy. This power plant generates enough electric energy to power about 12,000 homes. The power plant is constructed so that as the tide rises, water flows through a turbine that causes an electric generator to spin, as shown in **Figure 24A.** The water is then trapped behind a dam. When the tide goes out, the trapped water behind the dam is released through the turbine to generate more electricity, as shown in **Figure 24B.** Each day electric power is generated for about ten hours when the tide is rising and falling.

While tidal energy is a nonpolluting, inexhaustible energy source, its use is limited. Only in a few places is the difference between high and low tide large enough to enable a large electric power plant to be built.

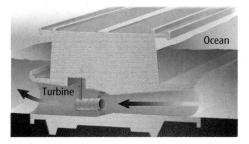

Ocean

Turbine

A As the tide comes in, it turns a turbine connected to a generator. When high tide occurs, gates are closed that trap water behind a dam.

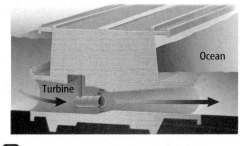

Ocean

Turbine

B As the tide goes out and the ocean level drops, the gates are opened and water from behind the dam flows through the turbine, causing it to spin and turn a generator.

736 **CHAPTER 24** Energy and Energy Resources

Curriculum Connection

Geography The first large-scale tidal plant was constructed on the Rance River in Saint-Malo, France. Have students locate this area on a map. [LS] **Visual-Spatial**

Wind

Wind is another inexhaustible supply of energy. Modern windmills, like the ones in **Figure 25,** convert the kinetic energy of the wind to electrical energy. The propeller is connected to a generator so that electrical energy is generated when wind spins the propeller. These windmills produce almost no pollution. Some disadvantages are that windmills produce noise and that large areas of land are needed. Also, studies have shown that birds sometimes are killed by windmills.

Conserving Energy

Fossil fuels are a valuable resource. Not only are they burned to provide energy, but oil and coal also are used to make plastics and other materials. One way to make the supply of fossil fuels last longer is to use less energy. Reducing the use of energy is called conserving energy.

You can conserve energy and also save money by turning off lights and appliances such as televisions when you are not using them. Also keep doors and windows closed tightly when it's cold or hot to keep heat from leaking out of or into your house. Energy could also be conserved if buildings are properly insulated, especially around windows. The use of oil could be reduced if cars were used less and made more efficient, so they went farther on a liter of gas. Recycling materials such as aluminum cans and glass also helps conserve energy.

Figure 25 Windmills work on the same basic principles as a power plant. Instead of steam turning a turbine, wind turns the rotors. **Describe** *some of the advantages and disadvantages of using windmills.*

---

section 3 review

Summary

Nonrenewable Resources

- All energy resources have advantages and disadvantages.
- Nonrenewable energy resources are used faster than they are replaced.
- Fossil fuels include oil, coal, and natural gas and are nonrenewable resources. Nuclear energy is a nonrenewable resource.

Renewable and Alternative Resources

- Renewable energy resources, such as hydroelectricity, are resources that are replenished continually.
- Alternative energy sources include solar energy, wind energy, and geothermal energy.

Self Check

1. **Diagram** the energy conversions that occur when coal is formed, and then burned to produce thermal energy.
2. **Explain** why solar energy is considered an inexhaustible source of energy.
3. **Explain** how a heat pump is used to both heat and cool a building.
4. **Think Critically** Identify advantages and disadvantages of using fossil fuels, hydroelectricity, and solar energy as energy sources.

Applying Math

5. **Use a Ratio** Earth's temperature increases with depth. Suppose the temperature increase inside Earth is 500°C at a depth of 50 km. What is the temperature increase at a depth of 10 km?

Figure 25 Advantages include lack of pollution and the availability of wind. Disadvantages are the potential for killing birds, variability of the wind, towers are unsightly, and a large amount of land is required.

3 Assess

DAILY INTERVENTION

Check for Understanding

Linguistic Have students answer the following questions in their Science Journals: "What kind of energy source is ethanol derived from corn, and why does adding it to gasoline prolong the supply of oil?" Ethanol derived from corn is a renewable source of energy. As long as corn keeps being planted and grown, there will be a source for ethanol to burn in cars. Adding ethanol to gasoline allows us to reduce our usage of gasoline, slowing down the rate at which we are using that non-renewable source of energy.

Reteach

Sources of Energy Have each student make a list of all of the sources of energy discussed in this section. Ask students to explain how each energy source releases its energy and classify each source as renewable or nonrenewable. L2 IS **Linguistic**

Assessment

Oral Where does all the electrical energy produced in power plants end up? It is converted into energy forms such as thermal, radiant, or sound energy.

---

section 3 review

1. Radiant energy from the Sun is converted into chemical energy when coal is formed; chemical energy in coal is converted into thermal energy and radiant energy when coal is burned.
2. The Sun's energy cannot be used up by humans because the Sun will produce an enormous amount of energy for billions of years and humans can use only a small amount of the energy the Sun produces.
3. The ground at several meters' depth is cooler than the outside air in summer and warmer than the outside air in winter. Heat can be transferred from the building to the ground in summer, and from the ground to the building in winter.
4. fossil fuels: cheap, plentiful, but nonrenewable and produces pollution; hydroelectricity: nonpolluting, renewable, but can alter local ecosystems and available only in certain areas; solar energy: inexhaustible, but expensive
5. 100°C

Real-World Question

Purpose Students will investigate the types of energy they use in everyday activities.

Process Skills Locate and evaluate sources of information on the Internet, in books, and in periodicals.

Time Required about two days

Internet Students use Internet sites that can be accessed through **ips.msscience.com/internet_lab**.

They will investigate the types of energy they use in everyday activities. L2

LS Logical-Mathematical

Non-Internet Sources Identify different science books to research energy sources.

Make a Plan

Preparation

Internet To run through the steps that the students will follow, visit **ips.msscience.com/internet_lab**.

Non-Internet Sources Collect books and materials that contain information about energy sources such as gasoline, coal, and solar energy.

Follow Your Plan

Teaching Strategy Ahead of time, do some Internet searches to locate and evaluate several Web sites noting their strengths and weaknesses. This will help you guide your students as they research Internet sites. Also, ask your librarian to give a short presentation on using library materials as part of their research.

Use the Internet

Energy to Power Your Life

Goals

- **Identify** how energy you use is produced and delivered.
- **Investigate** alternative sources for the energy you use.
- **Outline** a plan for how these alternative sources of energy could be used.

Data Source

Science Online

Visit **ips.msscience.com/internet_lab** for more information about sources of energy and for data collected by other students.

Real-World Question

Over the past 100 years, the amount of energy used in the United States and elsewhere has greatly increased. Today, a number of energy sources are available, such as coal, oil, natural gas, nuclear energy, hydroelectric power, wind, and solar energy. Some of these energy sources are being used up and are nonrenewable, but others are replaced as fast as they are used and, therefore, are renewable. Some energy sources are so vast that human usage has almost no effect on the amount available. These energy sources are inexhaustible.

Think about the types of energy you use at home and school every day. In this lab, you will investigate how and where energy is produced, and how it gets to you. You will also investigate alternative ways energy can be produced, and whether these sources are renewable, nonrenewable, or inexhaustible. What are the sources of the energy you use every day?

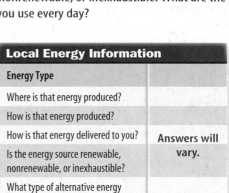

Local Energy Information	
Energy Type	
Where is that energy produced?	
How is that energy produced?	
How is that energy delivered to you?	**Answers will vary.**
Is the energy source renewable, nonrenewable, or inexhaustible?	
What type of alternative energy source could you use instead?	

396 CHAPTER 13 Energy and Energy Resources

Alternative Inquiry Lab

Energy Types and Sources When students feel as though their research could have an impact, they learn more. Every energy resource has its pros and cons. Have students research the energy resources utilized in your community and the issues surrounding them. They should summarize the pros and cons of these resources and take a position on the advisability of staying with or changing to that source of energy for your local community. Students should prepare their findings in a report to be presented to your city council or other governing body.

Make a Plan

1. Think about the activities you do every day and the things you use. When you watch television, listen to the radio, ride in a car, use a hair drier, or turn on the air conditioning, you use energy. Select one activity or appliance that uses energy.
2. **Identify** the type of energy that is used.
3. **Investigate** how that energy is produced and delivered to you.
4. **Determine** if the energy source is renewable, nonrenewable, or inexhaustible.
5. If your energy source is nonrenewable, describe how the energy you use could be produced by renewable sources.

Follow Your Plan

1. Make sure your teacher approves your plan before you start.
2. Organize your findings in a data table, similar to the one that is shown.

Analyze Your Data

1. **Describe** the process for producing and delivering the energy source you researched. How is it created, and how does it get to you?
2. How much energy is produced by the energy source you investigated?
3. Is the energy source you researched renewable, nonrenewable, or inexhaustible? Why?

Conclude and Apply

1. **Describe** If the energy source you investigated is nonrenewable, how can the use of this energy source be reduced?
2. **Organize** What alternative sources of energy could you use for everyday energy needs? On the computer, create a plan for using renewable or inexhaustible sources.

Communicating
Your Data

Find this lab using the link below. Post your data in the table that is provided. **Compare** your data to those of other students. **Combine** your data with those of other students and make inferences using the combined data.

Science Online
ips.msscience.com/internet_lab

Analyze Your Data

1. Answers may vary. One example would be the process for producing gasoline, which involves drilling crude oil from wells, and the process involved in refining the crude oil into the product that we pump at the gas station.
2. If students investigated gasoline, they may discover that it is a small part of their daily energy use.
3. Gasoline is an example of a non-renewable energy source, because it is a fossil fuel.

Conclude and Apply

1. Answers will vary.
2. One strategy may be to replace a calculator that runs on nonrechargeable batteries with one that is powered by solar cells.

✔ Assessment

Process Have students make displays that show their research about an activity or appliance and its energy source. They should include pictures and descriptions of how the energy source used is produced and delivered so it can be used. Use **Performance Assessment in the Science Classroom**, p.135.

Communicating
Your Data

Have students make a chart that compares the energy source they investigated with other energy sources that could be used, including alternative or renewable energy sources. Students should also compare costs and environmental impacts.

SCIENCE Stats

Content Background

Solar, wind, and geothermal are inexhaustible energy sources, and biomass and hydroelectric powered systems are considered renewable energy sources. Not all sources can be used to produce a continuous supply of energy in all areas. Also, the technology needed to store and supply this energy on demand is insufficient and often far too costly to use. As technology improves, these alternative sources will supplement and possibly even replace fossil fuels.

Discussion

Energy Sources What are some possible explanations for why only 18 percent of the energy used worldwide is from renewable and inexhaustible resources? Answers will vary. Currently the technology does not exist to supply energy from these sources on demand and at an affordable price.

Activity

Alternatives Have students research alternative energy sources available in their area. Students should make posters showing how energy is obtained from these sources. [L2] [LS] **Visual-Spatial**

Applying Math

Answer 320 calories

Find Out About It

Solar collectors would do well in the southwestern United States because it is sunny there for most of the year.

SCIENCE Stats

Energy to Burn

Did you know...

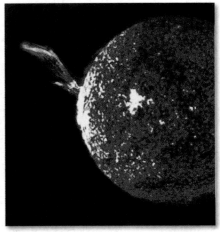

... The energy released by the average hurricane is equal to about 200 times the total energy produced by all of the world's power plants. Almost all of this energy is released as heat when raindrops form.

... The energy Earth gets each half hour from the Sun is enough to meet the world's demands for a year. Renewable and inexhaustible resources, including the Sun, account for only 18 percent of the energy that is used worldwide.

... The Calories in one medium apple will give you enough energy to walk for about 15 min, swim for about 10 min, or jog for about 9 min.

> **Applying Math** If walking for 15 min requires 80 Calories of fuel (from food), how many Calories would someone need to consume to walk for 1 h?

Write About It

Where would you place solar collectors in the United States? Why? For more information on solar energy, go to ips.msscience.com/science_stats.

Reviewing Main Ideas

Section 1 What is energy?

1. Energy is the ability to cause change.

2. A moving object has kinetic energy that depends on the object's mass and speed.

3. Potential energy is energy due to position and depends on an object's mass and height.

4. Light carries radiant energy, electric current carries electrical energy, and atomic nuclei contain nuclear energy.

Section 2 Energy Transformations

1. Energy can be transformed from one form to another. Thermal energy is usually produced when energy transformations occur.

2. The law of conservation of energy states that energy cannot be created or destroyed.

3. Electric power plants convert a source of energy into electrical energy. Steam spins a turbine which spins an electric generator.

Section 3 Sources of Energy

1. The use of an energy source has advantages and disadvantages.

2. Fossil fuels and nuclear energy are nonrenewable energy sources that are consumed faster than they can be replaced.

3. Hydroelectricity is a renewable energy source that is continually being replaced.

4. Alternative energy sources include solar, wind, and geothermal energy. Solar energy is an inexhaustible energy source.

Visualizing Main Ideas

Copy and complete the concept map using the following terms: fossil fuels, hydroelectric, solar, wind, oil, coal, photovoltaic, *and* nonrenewable resources.

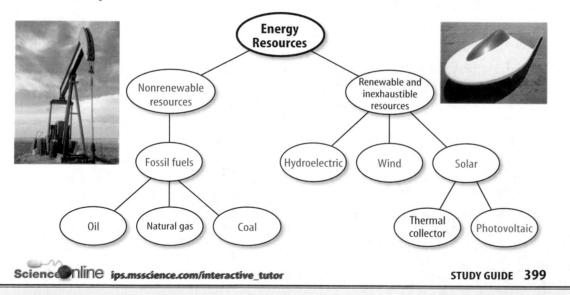

Identifying Misconceptions

Assess

Use the assessment as follow-up to page F at the beginning of the chapter.

Activity Display examples of the work of the famous cartoonist Rube Goldberg. Have students draw their own Rube Goldberg style invention that includes four energy transformations. Direct students to draw red arrows to indicate areas where heat loss would occur.

Expected Outcome Students recognize that energy is transferred from one form into another.

Reinforcement Have students exchange drawings and describe the energy transformations depicted.

Reviewing Main Ideas

Summary statements can be used by students to review the major concepts of the chapter.

Visualizing Main Ideas

See student page.

Science Online

Visit **ips.msscience.com**

/self_check_quiz

/interactive_tutor

/vocabulary_puzzlemaker

/chapter_review

/standardized_test

/field_guide

Assessment Transparency

For additional assessment questions, use the *Assessment Transparency* located in the transparency book.

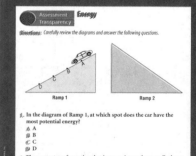

chapter 13 Review

Using Vocabulary

1. Nuclear energy is sometimes used to generate electrical energy.
2. A rotating turbine helps produce electrical energy by causing a generator to spin.
3. A photovoltaic collector changes radiant energy from the Sun directly into electrical energy.
4. Inexhaustible resources are resources that can't be used up by humans. Renewable resources are replenished by nature. Neither source gets used up.
5. Potential energy due to gravity changes to kinetic energy as an object falls.
6. In an electrical generator, kinetic energy is changed into electrical energy.
7. Thermal energy and radiant energy are two forms of energy that can be converted into each other or other forms of energy.
8. The law of conservation of energy states that in energy transformations, energy can be neither created nor destroyed. It only can change from one form to another.
9. Some sources of chemical energy, such as fossil fuels, are nonrenewable. Some, such as biomass, are renewable.

Checking Concepts

10. C	14. A	18. D
11. D	15. A	19. B
12. D	16. B	
13. C	17. A	

Thinking Critically

20. When the swing is pulled back, its potential energy increases. When the swing is released, potential energy is converted into kinetic energy as it moves downward. As it moves upward, kinetic energy is converted into potential energy.

Using Vocabulary

alternative resource p. 391	nonrenewable
chemical energy p. 377	resource p. 388
electrical energy p. 378	nuclear energy p. 378
energy p. 374	photovoltaic p. 392
generator p. 384	potential energy p. 376
inexhaustible	radiant energy p. 377
resource p. 391	renewable resource p. 390
kinetic energy p. 375	thermal energy p. 376
law of conservation	turbine p. 384
of energy p. 380	

For each of the terms below, explain the relationship that exists.

1. electrical energy—nuclear energy
2. turbine—generator
3. photovoltaic—radiant energy—electrical energy
4. renewable resource—inexhaustible resource
5. potential energy—kinetic energy
6. kinetic energy—electrical energy—generator
7. thermal energy—radiant energy
8. law of conservation of energy—energy transformations
9. nonrenewable resource—chemical energy

Checking Concepts

Choose the word or phrase that best answers the question.

10. Objects that are able to fall have what type of energy?
    A) kinetic
    B) radiant
    C) potential
    D) electrical

11. Which form of energy does light have?
    A) electrical
    B) nuclear
    C) kinetic
    D) radiant

12. Muscles perform what type of energy transformation?
    A) kinetic to potential
    B) kinetic to electrical
    C) thermal to radiant
    D) chemical to kinetic

13. Photovoltaics perform what type of energy transformation?
    A) thermal to radiant
    B) kinetic to electrical
    C) radiant to electrical
    D) electrical to thermal

14. The form of energy that food contains is which of the following?
    A) chemical
    B) potential
    C) radiant
    D) electrical

15. Solar energy, wind, and geothermal are what type of energy resource?
    A) inexhaustible
    B) inexpensive
    C) nonrenewable
    D) chemical

16. Which of the following is a nonrenewable source of energy?
    A) hydroelectricity
    B) nuclear
    C) wind
    D) solar

17. A generator is NOT required to generate electrical energy when which of the following energy sources is used?
    A) solar
    B) wind
    C) hydroelectric
    D) nuclear

18. Which of the following are fossil fuels?
    A) gas
    B) coal
    C) oil
    D) all of these

19. Almost all of the energy that is used on Earth's surface comes from which of the following energy sources?
    A) radioactivity
    B) the Sun
    C) chemicals
    D) wind

 Science Online ips.msscience.com/vocabulary_puzzlemaker

Use the Exam*View*® Pro Testmaker CD-ROM to:
- create multiple versions of tests
- create modified tests with one mouse click for inclusion students
- edit existing questions and add your own questions
- build tests aligned with state standards using built-in State Curriculum Tags
- change English tests to Spanish with one mouse click and vice versa

Thinking Critically

20. Explain how the motion of a swing illustrates the transformation between potential and kinetic energy.

21. Explain what happens to the kinetic energy of a skateboard that is coasting along a flat surface, slows down, and comes to a stop.

22. Describe the energy transformations that occur in the process of toasting a bagel in an electric toaster.

23. Compare and contrast the formation of coal and the formation of oil and natural gas.

24. Explain the difference between the law of conservation of energy and conserving energy. How can conserving energy help prevent energy shortages?

25. Make a Hypothesis about how spacecraft that travel through the solar system obtain the energy they need to operate. Do research to verify your hypothesis.

26. Concept Map Copy and complete this concept map about energy.

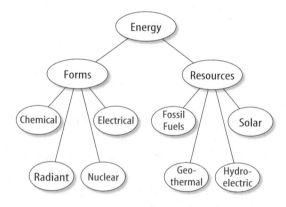

27. Diagram the energy transformations that occur when you rub sandpaper on a piece of wood and the wood becomes warm.

Science⌇nline ips.msscience.com/chapter_review

Performance Activities

28. Multimedia Presentation Alternative sources of energy that weren't discussed include biomass energy, wave energy, and hydrogen fuel cells. Research an alternative energy source and then prepare a digital slide show about the information you found. Use the concepts you learned from this chapter to inform your classmates about the future prospects of using such an energy source on a large scale.

Applying Math

29. Calculate Number of Power Plants A certain type of power plant is designed to provide energy for 10,000 homes. How many of these power plants would be needed to provide energy for 300,000 homes?

Use the table below to answer questions 30 and 31.

Energy Sources Used in the United States	
Energy Source	**Percent of Energy Used**
Coal	23%
Oil	39%
Natural gas	23%
Nuclear	8%
Hydroelectric	4%
Other	3%

30. Use Percentages According to the data in the table above, what percentage of the energy used in the United States comes from fossil fuels?

31. Calculate a Ratio How many times greater is the amount of energy that comes from fossil fuels than the amount of energy from all other energy sources?

Thinking Critically

21. The kinetic energy of the skate is converted into thermal energy by friction.

22. In the toaster, electrical energy is converted into thermal energy. Thermal energy is converted into chemical energy in the bagel, causing it to become toasted.

23. Both formed over millions of years. Coal formed from the effects of heat and pressure on buried vegetation. Oil and natural gas formed from the effects of heat and pressure on the buried remains of microscopic organisms on the ocean floor.

24. Law of conservation of energy states that energy cannot be created or destroyed. Conserving energy means reducing energy usage, which can prevent energy shortages by reducing the consumption of nonrenewable energy sources.

25. Possible answers: spacecrafts use solar cells, spacecrafts use batteries

26. See student page.

27. chemical energy in muscles → kinetic energy of sandpaper → thermal energy of wood

Performance Activities

28. Check students' work. Use **Performance Assessment in the Science Classroom,** p. 149.

Applying Math

National Math Standards

1, 2, 9
29. 30
30. 85%
31. 5.7 times greater

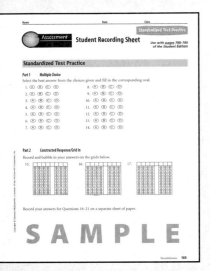

Answer Sheet A practice answer sheet can be found at ips.msscience.com/answer_sheet.

SAMPLE

Part 1 | Multiple Choice

1. B
2. B
3. D
4. D
5. C
6. C
7. A
8. B

Part 1 | Multiple Choice

Record your answers on the answer sheet provided by your teacher or on a sheet of paper.

1. The kinetic energy of a moving object increases if which of the following occurs?
  A. Its mass decreases.
  B. Its speed increases.
  C. Its height above the ground increases.
  D. Its temperature increases.

Use the graph below to answer questions 2–4.

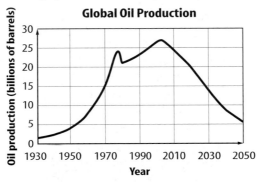

Global Oil Production

2. According to the graph above, in which year will global oil production be at a maximum?
  A. 1974   **C.** 2010
  B. 2002   **D.** 2050

3. Approximately how many times greater was oil production in 1970 than oil production in 1950?
  A. 2 times   **C.** 6 times
  B. 10 times   **D.** 3 times

4. In which year will the production of oil be equal to the oil production in 1970?
  A. 2010   **C.** 2022
  B. 2015   **D.** 2028

5. Which of the following energy sources is being used faster than it can be replaced?
  A. tidal   **C.** fossil fuels
  B. wind   **D.** hydroelectric

402 STANDARDIZED TEST PRACTICE

Use the circle graph below to answer question 6.

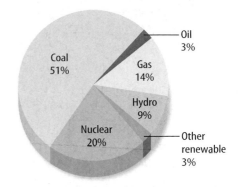

6. The circle graph shows the sources of electrical energy in the United States. In 2002, the total amount of electrical energy produced in the United States was 38.2 quads. How much electrical energy was produced by nuclear power plants?
  A. 3.0 quads   **C.** 7.6 quads
  B. 3.8 quads   **D.** 35.1 quads

7. When chemical energy is converted into thermal energy, which of the following must be true?
  A. The total amount of thermal energy plus chemical energy changes.
  B. Only the amount of chemical energy changes.
  C. Only the amount of thermal energy changes.
  D. The total amount of thermal energy plus chemical energy doesn't change.

8. A softball player hits a fly ball. Which of the following describes the energy conversion that occurs as it falls from its highest point?
  A. kinetic to potential
  B. potential to kinetic
  C. thermal to potential
  D. thermal to kinetic

Part 2 | Short Response/Grid In

9. The law of conservation of energy would prevent such a machine from being built.

10. The kinetic energy is the same.

11. The basketball dropped from a height of 4 m.

12. about two times

13. 1970–1975

Part 2 | Short Response/Grid In

Record your answers on the answer sheet provided by your teacher or on a sheet of paper.

9. Why is it impossible to build a machine that produces more energy than it uses?

10. You toss a ball upward and then catch it on the way down. The height of the ball above the ground when it leaves your hand on the way up and when you catch it is the same. Compare the ball's kinetic energy when it leaves your hand and just before you catch it.

11. A basket ball is dropped from a height of 2 m and another identical basketball is dropped from a height of 4 m. Which ball has more kinetic energy just before it hits the ground?

Use the graph below to answer questions 12 and 13.

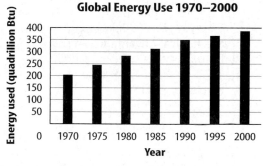

Global Energy Use 1970–2000

12. According to the graph above, by about how many times did the global use of energy increase from 1970 to 2000?

13. Over which five-year time period was the increase in global energy use the largest?

Test-Taking Tip

Do Your Studying Regularly Do not "cram" the night before the test. It can hamper your memory and make you tired.

Part 3 | Open Ended

Record your answers on a sheet of paper.

14. When you drop a tennis ball, it hits the floor and bounces back up. But it does not reach the same height as released, and each successive upward bounce is smaller than the one previous. However, you notice the tennis ball is slightly warmer after it finishes bouncing. Explain how the law of conservation of energy is obeyed.

Use the graph below to answer questions 15–17.

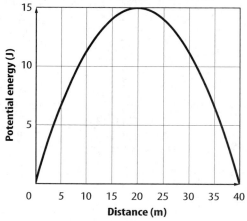

Potential Energy of Batted Ball

15. The graph shows how the potential energy of a batted ball depends on distance from the batter. At what distances is the kinetic energy of the ball the greatest?

16. At what distance from the batter is the height of the ball the greatest?

17. How much less is the kinetic energy of the ball at a distance of 20 m from the batter than at a distance of 0 m?

18. List advantages and disadvantages of the following energy sources: fossil fuels, nuclear energy, and geothermal energy.

Rubrics

The following rubrics are sample scoring devices for short response and open-ended questions.

Short Response

Points	Description
2	The student demonstrates a thorough understanding of the science of the task. The response may contain minor flaws that do not detract from the demonstration of a thorough understanding.
1	The student has provided a response that is only partially correct.
0	The student has provided a completely incorrect solution or no response at all.

Open Ended

Points	Description
4	The student demonstrates a thorough understanding of the science of the task. The response may contain minor flaws that do not detract from the demonstration of a thorough understanding.
3	The student demonstrates an understanding of the science of the task. The response is essentially correct and demonstrates an essential but less than thorough understanding of the science.
2	The student demonstrates only a partial understanding of the science of the task. Although the student may have used the correct approach to a solution or may have provided a correct solution, the work lacks an essential understanding of the underlying science concepts.
1	The student demonstrates a very limited understanding of the science of the task. The response is incomplete and exhibits many flaws.
0	The student provides a completely incorrect solution or no response at all.

Part 3 | Open Ended

14. During each bounce, some of the kinetic energy of the ball is converted into thermal energy. As a result, energy is not created or destroyed, but only changes form, so that the law of conservation of energy is obeyed.

15. The kinetic energy of the ball is greatest at the distances where the potential energy is smallest. This is at distances of 0 m and 40 m.

16. The height of the ball is greatest where the ball's potential energy is greatest. This is at a distance of 20 m.

17. In moving from 0 m to 20 m, the increase in potential energy of the ball equals the decrease in the ball's kinetic energy. The ball's potential energy increases by 15 J, so its kinetic energy decreases by 15 J.

18. fossil fuels: currently cheap and plentiful, but nonrenewable and produces pollution; nuclear energy: does not produce pollution, cheap, but produces nuclear waste and is nonrenewable; geothermal energy: inexhaustible, but only available in a few places

Section/Objectives	Standards		Labs/Features
Chapter Opener	National	State/Local	**Launch Lab:** Compare forces, p. 405 **Foldables,** p. 405
	See pp. 16T–17T for a Key to Standards.		
Section 1 Work and Power ⏱ 3 sessions ▨ 1.5 blocks 1. **Recognize** when work is done. 2. **Calculate** how much work is done. 3. **Explain** the relationship between work and power.	National Content Standards: UCP.2, UCP.3, A.1, A.2, B.2, B.3		**Integrate History,** p. 408 **Applying Math:** Calculating Work, p. 408 **MiniLAB:** Work and Power, p. 409 **Applying Math:** Calculating Power, p. 409 **Science Online,** p. 410 **Lab:** Building the Pyramids, p. 411
Section 2 Using Machines ⏱ 3 sessions ▨ 1.5 blocks 4. **Explain** how a machine makes work easier. 5. **Calculate** the mechanical advantages and efficiency of a machine. 6. **Explain** how friction reduces efficiency.	National Content Standards: UCP.2, UCP.3, A.1, A.2, B.2, B.3		**Science Online,** p. 413 **Applying Math:** Calculating Mechanical Advantage, p. 413 **Integrate Life Science,** p. 415 **Applying Math:** Calculating Efficiency, p. 415
Section 3 Simple Machines ⏱ 4 sessions ▨ 2 blocks 7. **Distinguish** among the different simple machines. 8. **Describe** how to find the mechanical advantage of each simple machine.	National Content Standards: UCP.2, UCP.3, A.1, A.2, B.2, B.3		**Visualizing Levers,** p. 421 **MiniLAB:** Observing Pulleys, p. 422 **Lab:** Pulley Power, pp. 424–425 **Science and Society:** Bionic People, p. 426

Lab Materials	Reproducible Resources	Section Assessment	Technology
Launch Lab: ruler, flat eraser, book	**Chapter _FAST FILE_ Resources** Foldables Worksheet, p. 17 Directed Reading Overview, p. 19 Note-taking Worksheets, pp. 33–35	GLENCOE'S **ASSESSMENT** ADVANTAGE	**TeacherWorks** includes: • Interactive Teacher Edition • Lesson Planner with calendar • Access to all program blacklines • Correlations to standards • Web links
MiniLAB: bathroom scale, meterstick, stopwatch, calculator **Lab:** wood block, tape, spring scale, ruler, thin notebooks, meterstick, several books	**Chapter _FAST FILE_ Resources** Transparency Activity, p. 44 MiniLAB, p. 3 Lab Activity, pp. 9–12 Enrichment, p. 30 Reinforcement, p. 27 Directed Reading, pp. 19, 20 Lab Worksheets, pp. 5–6 **Cultural Diversity,** p. 63 **Mathematics Skill Activities,** p. 11	**Portfolio** Integrate History, p. 408 **Performance** Applying Math, pp. 408, 409 MiniLAB, p. 409 Applying Math, p. 410 **Content** Section Review, p. 410	Section Focus Transparency Virtual Labs CD-ROM Guided Reading Audio Program Interactive Chalkboard CD-ROM Video Lab
Need materials? Contact Science Kit at 1-800-828-7777 or www.sciencekit.com on the Internet.	**Chapter _FAST FILE_ Resources** Transparency Activity, p. 45 Enrichment, p. 31 Reinforcement, p. 28 Directed Reading, p. 21 Transparency Activity, pp. 47–48 **Reading and Writing Skill Activities,** p. 35	**Portfolio** Active Reading, p. 415 **Performance** Applying Math, pp. 413, 415 Applying Math, p. 416 **Content** Section Review, p. 416	Section Focus Transparency Teaching Transparency Guided Reading Audio Program Interactive Chalkboard CD-ROM
MiniLAB: 2 broomsticks, rope **Lab:** single- and multiple-pulley systems, nylon rope, steel bar to support the pulley system, meterstick, variety of weights, force spring scale, brick, balance	**Chapter _FAST FILE_ Resources** Transparency Activity, p. 46 MiniLAB, p. 4 Lab Activity, pp. 13–16 Enrichment, p. 32 Reinforcement, p. 29 Directed Reading, pp. 21, 22 Lab Worksheets, pp. 7–8 **Lab Management and Safety,** p. 39	**Portfolio** Differentiated Instruction, p. 418 **Performance** MiniLAB, p. 422 Applying Math, p. 423 **Content** Section Review, p. 423	Section Focus Transparency Guided Reading Audio Program Interactive Chalkboard CD-ROM

GLENCOE'S **ASSESSMENT** ADVANTAGE

End of Chapter Assessment

Blackline Masters	Technology	Professional Series
Chapter _FAST FILE_ Resources Chapter Review, pp. 37–38 Chapter Tests, pp. 39–42 **Standardized Test Practice,** pp. 59–62	MindJogger Videoquiz Virtual Labs CD-ROM _ExamView_® Pro Testmaker TeacherWorks CD-ROM Interactive Chalkboard CD-ROM	**Performance Assessment in the Science Classroom (PASC)**

Transparencies

Section Focus

SECTION 1 — Section Focus Transparency — **Weighted Down** — Chapter 4

A heavy backpack can be a load to carry. Just lifting it can take a lot of effort, but it's easier to take it off your back.

1. What forces are acting on the backpack?
2. Compare the direction the backpack moves when it is lifted by the girl with the direction it moves when the girl is walking.
3. Why is it easier to lower something down than it is to lift it up?

L2

SECTION 2 — Section Focus Transparency — **The Puck Stops Here**

If you've ever tried to walk or run on ice, you know how difficult it can be. Because ice can be so slippery, hockey players on skates can move quickly, making hockey a fast and exciting sport.

1. Why do you sometimes slip when you step onto a patch of ice on the sidewalk?
2. Why can a hockey player move faster than a runner?
3. When a player takes a shot, is work being done on the puck? Explain.

L2

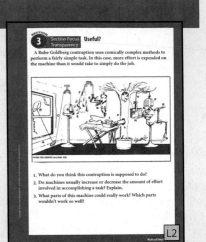

SECTION 3 — Section Focus Transparency — **Useful?**

A Rube Goldberg contraption uses comically complex methods to perform a fairly simple task. In this case, more effort is expended on the machine than it would take to simply do the job.

RUBE GOLDBERG (tm) POST 338

1. What do you think this contraption is supposed to do?
2. Do machines usually increase or decrease the amount of effort involved in accomplishing a task? Explain.
3. What parts of this machine could really work? Which parts wouldn't work so well?

L2

This is a representation of key blackline masters available in the Teacher Classroom Resources. See Resource Manager boxes within the chapter for additional information.

Key to Teaching Strategies

The following designations will help you decide which activities are appropriate for your students.

L1 Level 1 activities should be appropriate for students with learning difficulties.

L2 Level 2 activities should be within the ability range of all students.

L3 Level 3 activities are designed for above-average students.

ELL ELL activities should be within the ability range of English Language Learners.

COOP LEARN Cooperative Learning activities are designed for small group work.

LS Multiple Learning Styles logos, as described on page 12T, are used throughout to indicate strategies that address different learning styles.

P These strategies represent student products that can be placed into a best-work portfolio.

PBL Problem-Based Learning activities apply real-world situations to learning.

Assessment

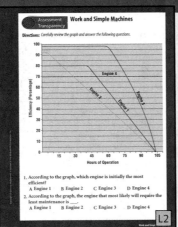

Assessment Transparency — **Work and Simple Machines**

Directions: *Carefully review the graph and answer the following questions.*

Engine 4
Engine 2
Engine 1
Engine 3

Efficiency (Percentage) vs. Hours of Operation

1. According to the graph, which engine is initially the most efficient?
   A Engine 1   B Engine 2   C Engine 3   D Engine 4
2. According to the graph, the engine that most likely will require the least maintenance is ___.
   A Engine 1   B Engine 2   C Engine 3   D Engine 4

L2

Teaching

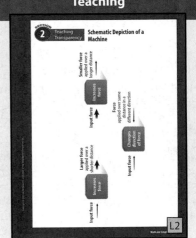

SECTION 2 — Teaching Transparency — **Schematic Depiction of a Machine**

Smaller force applied over a longer distance — Increases force

Force applied over same distance in a different direction — Changes direction of force

Larger force applied over a shorter distance — Increases force

Input force

L2

Hands-on Activities

Student Text Lab Worksheet

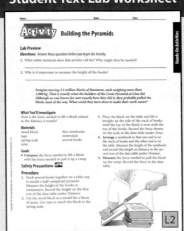

Activity — Building the Pyramids

Lab Preview

Directions: *Answer these questions before you begin the Activity.*

1. What safety materials does this activity call for? Why might they be needed?

2. Why is it important to measure the height of the books?

Imagine moving 2.3 million blocks of limestone, each weighing more than 1,000 kg. That is exactly what the builders of the Great Pyramid at Giza did. Although no one knows for sure exactly how they did it, they probably pulled the blocks most of the way. What could they have done to make their work easier?

What You'll Investigate
How is the force needed to lift a block related to the distance it travels?

Materials
wood block   thin notebooks
tape   meterstick
spring scale   several books
ruler

Goals
• **Compare** the force needed to lift a block with the force needed to pull it up a ramp.

Safety Precautions

Procedure
1. Stack several books together on a table-top to model a half-completed pyramid. Measure the height of the books in centimeters. Record the height on the first row of the data table under *Distance*.
2. Use the wood block as a model for a block of stone. Use tape to attach the block to the spring scale.
3. Place the block on the table and lift it straight up the side of the stack of books until the top of the block is even with the top of the books. Record the force shown on the scale in the data table under *Force*.
4. **Arrange** a notebook so that one end is on the stack of books and the other end is on the table. Measure the length of the notebook and record this length as distance in the second row of the data table under *Distance*.
5. **Measure** the force needed to pull the block up the ramp. Record the force in the data table.

L2

Laboratory Activities

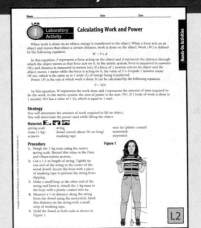

LAB 1 — Laboratory Activity — **Calculating Work and Power**

When work is done on an object, energy is transferred to the object. When a force acts on an object and moves that object a certain distance, work is done on the object. Work (*W*) is defined by the following equation.

$$W = F \times d$$

In this equation, *F* represents a force acting on the object and *d* represents the distance through which the object moves as that force acts on it. In the metric system, force is measured in newtons (N), and distance is measured in meters (m). If a force of 1 newton acts on an object and the object moves 1 meter while the force is acting on it, the value of *F* × *d* equals 1 newton-meter (N-m), which is the same as to 1 joule (J) of energy being transferred.

Power (*P*) is the rate at which work is done. It can be calculated by the following equation.

$$P = W/t$$

In this equation, *W* represents the work done and *t* represents the amount of time required to do the work. In the metric system, the unit of power is the watt (W). If 1 joule of work is done in 1 second, *W/t* has a value of 1 J/s, which is equal to 1 watt.

Strategy
You will determine the amount of work required to lift an object.
You will determine the power used while lifting the object.

Materials
spring scale   string   wire tie (plastic-coated)
mass (1-kg)   dowel (wood, about 30 cm long)
scissors   masking tape   meterstick
                                        stopwatch

Procedure   Figure 1
1. Weigh the 1-kg mass using the metric spring scale. Record this value in the Data and Observations section.
2. Cut a 1.3-m length of string. Tightly tie one end of the string to the center of the wood dowel. Secure the knot with a piece of masking tape to prevent the string from slipping.
3. Make a small loop at the other end of the string and knot it. Attach the 1-kg mass to the loop with a plastic-coated wire tie.
4. Measure a 1-m distance along the string from the dowel using the meterstick. Mark this distance on the string with a small strip of masking tape.
5. Hold the dowel at both ends as shown in Figure 1.

L2

Meeting Different Ability Levels

Content Outline

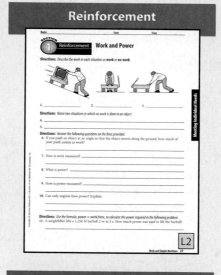

Reinforcement

Enrichment

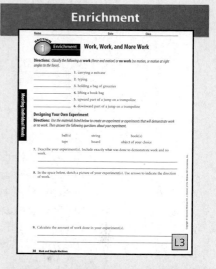

Directed Reading (English/Spanish)

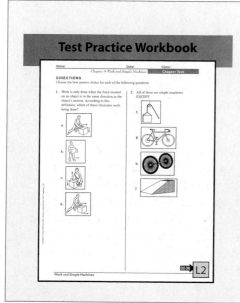

Study Guide

Reading Essentials

Assessment

Test Practice Workbook

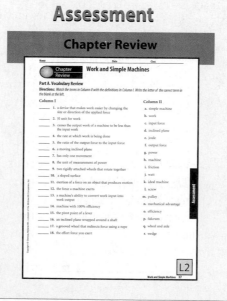

Chapter Review

Chapter Tests

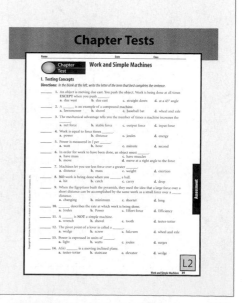

Science Content Background

section 1 Work and Power
What is work?

Energy is the ability to produce change. One way to produce change is to do work. Energy is the ability to perform work. When work is done on an object, energy is transferred to the object. The work-energy theorem states that when work is done on an object, the object's kinetic energy changes. The work done is equal to the change in kinetic energy.

Calculating Work

Both energy and work are measured in joules, kg (m^2/s^2). When an object falls, gravity does work equal to (force)(distance) = (mass)(g)(distance) where g is the acceleration due to gravity, 9.8 m/s^2. The kinetic energy changes from 0 to $\frac{1}{2}mv^2$ at the end of the fall. By letting $mgd = \frac{1}{2}mv^2$, you can find the velocity of an object when it hits the ground.

The concept of negative work is somewhat abstract. It is most easily grasped in situations where objects slow down. Here, an object is subjected to a force, usually friction, that reduces the object's kinetic energy. When an object is lifted, Earth's gravitational force does negative work. The lifter does positive work, which is stored as potential energy. When the object is held up, the lifter's muscles move microscopically. The object, however, does not move, so no work is done on it.

Michael Lichter/International Stock

Teacher to Teacher

Kevin Finnegan
McCord Middle School
Worthington, OH

"When examining compound machines, have students search the classroom, the school, or magazines to identify the compound machine that includes the greatest number of simple machines. Have them identify each simple machine they find and share their information with the class."

Kevin Finnegan

section 2 Using Machines
Mechanical Advantage

Mechanical advantage is a measure of a machine's leverage. It relates either the resistance force overcome by the machine to the load force, or the distance through which the effort force acts to the distance the resistance is moved. Together these quantities form the equality: $F_e d_e = F_r d_r$. This is the equation of balance for a lever and other simple machines.

Efficiency

When a machine leverages a force, the law of conservation of energy states that the smaller force must act through a greater distance. The work to perform a task is the same no matter how it is done. In reality, with a machine, you must do some extra work because some of the work supplied is lost as heat. The lower the loss, the more efficient the machine.

A perpetual-motion machine is a fictitious device that is said to convert all of the input work into an equal or greater amount of output work. An inventor always aspires to make a machine that is 100 percent efficient, but there is always some energy lost to friction. A carefully designed machine can get close. Getting more out of the machine than is put into it would be a clear violation of the law of energy conservation.

The source of energy that allows a machine to work is called the prime mover. Although machines make a job easier, the job may still require a backbreaking effort if you have to supply the energy. The steam engine and the electric motor were invented to ease this burden. They get their energy from coal, oil, electricity, and other sources. An automobile engine has the ability to supply the power of 200 horses, hence the term horsepower for engine capacity.

section 3 Simple Machines
Inclined Plane

Archaeologists believe the ancient Egyptians constructed enormous ramps to move the pyramids' limestone blocks into place. Without the use of wheels or other means of facilitating the move, the ramp needed to drag one of these blocks would require more material than the pyramid itself. Archaeologists discovered the Egyptians used a type of clay called tafla which becomes slippery when wet. Tests indicate that by using tafla as a lubricant, the Egyptians could have made steeper ramps, requiring much less fill.

Wheel and Axle

The wheel and axle discussed in this chapter is a simple machine. Some wheels and axles, such as those in a car, are more complicated.

You may want to point out to students the two uses of wheels. The wheels on a car or wagon are designed to avoid sliding friction: it's easier to push a grocery cart with wheels than without. Wheels that appear as handles, such as faucets and doorknobs, are designed to take advantage of the mechanical advantage of a wheel and axle.

chapter content resources

Internet Resources
For additional content background, visit
ips.msscience.com to:
- access your book onlineonline
- find references to related articles in popular science magazines
- access Web links with related content background
- access current events with science journal topics

Print Resources
On the Shoulders of Giants: The Great Works of Physics and Astronomy, by Stephen Hawking (Commentary), Running Press Book Publishers, 2003

Work (Early Bird Physics Series), by Sally M. Walker and Roseann Feldmann, Lerner Publications Company, 2001

Physics, by David Halliday, Kenneth S. Krane, and Robert Resnick, John Wiley & Sons, 2001

Physics, by James S. Walker, Prentice Hall, 2003

Chapter Vocabulary

Science Journal Student answers will vary. Accept all reasonable responses.

INTERACTIVE CHALKBOARD with Image Bank

PowerPoint® Presentations

This CD-ROM is an editable Microsoft® PowerPoint® presentation that includes:
- a pre-made presentation for every chapter
- interactive graphics
- animations
- audio clips
- image bank
- all new section and chapter questions
- Standardized Test Practice
- transparencies
- pre-lab questions for all labs
- Foldables directions
- links to ips.msscience.com

Work and Simple Machines

chapter preview

sections

1 **Work and Power**
   Lab **Building the Pyramids**
2 **Using Machines**
3 **Simple Machines**
   Lab **Pulley Power**
   Virtual Lab What is the relationship between work, force, and distance?

Heavy Lifting

It took the ancient Egyptians more than 100 years to build the pyramids without machines like these. But now, even tall skyscrapers can be built in a few years. Complex or simple, machines have the same purpose. They make doing work easier.

Science Journal Describe three machines you used today, and how they made doing a task easier.

Theme Connection

Systems and Interactions A simple machine interacts with an input force and converts it to an output force. Compound machines are systems of interacting simple machines.

About the Photo

Cranes Pieces of heavy equipment are common on modern construction sites. Cranes often are used to lift support beams and other heavy objects. Cranes were introduced in the nineteenth century when steam engines, internal-combustion engines, and electric motors were developed.

Start-Up Activities

Compare Forces

Two of the world's greatest structures were built using different tools. The Great Pyramid at Giza in Egypt was built nearly 5,000 years ago using blocks of limestone moved into place by hand with ramps and levers. In comparison, the Sears Tower in Chicago was built in 1973 using tons of steel that were hoisted into place by gasoline-powered cranes. How do machines such as ramps, levers, and cranes change the forces needed to do a job?

1. Place a ruler on an eraser. Place a book on one end of the ruler.

2. Using one finger, push down on the free end of the ruler to lift the book.

3. Repeat the experiment, placing the eraser in various positions beneath the ruler. Observe how much force is needed in each instance to lift the book.

4. **Think Critically** In your Science Journal, describe your observations. How did changing the distance between the book and the eraser affect the force needed to lift the book?

Simple Machines Many of the devices that you use every day are simple machines. Make the following Foldable to help you understand the characteristics of simple machines.

STEP 1 Draw a mark at the midpoint of a sheet of paper along the side edge. Then **fold** the top and bottom edges in to touch the midpoint.

STEP 2 **Fold** in half from side to side.

STEP 3 **Turn** the paper vertically. **Open and cut** along the inside fold lines to form four tabs.

STEP 4 Label the tabs *Inclined Plane, Lever, Wheel and Axle,* and *Pulley.*

Read for Main Ideas As you read the chapter, list the characteristics of inclined planes, levers, wheels and axles, and pulleys under the appropriate tab.

Preview this chapter's content and activities at
ips.msscience.com

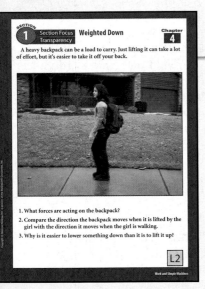

Tie to Prior Knowledge

Force and Motion Have students recall what they know about force and motion. Ask students to recall situations where they apply a force to an object and it doesn't move; and situations where they apply a force and an object moves. Ask students how the energy of the object changes in these situations. When the object moves its energy increases. Tell students they will study how work and energy are related in this section.

---

section 1
Work and Power

as you read

What You'll Learn
- **Recognize** when work is done.
- **Calculate** how much work is done.
- **Explain** the relation between work and power.

Why It's Important
If you understand work, you can make your work easier.

Review Vocabulary
force: a push or a pull

New Vocabulary
- work
- power

What is work?

What does the term *work* mean to you? You might think of household chores; a job at an office, a factory, a farm; or the homework you do after school. In science, the definition of work is more specific. **Work** is done when a force causes an object to move in the same direction that the force is applied.

Can you think of a way in which you did work today? Maybe it would help to know that you do work when you lift your books, turn a doorknob, raise window blinds, or write with a pen or pencil. You also do work when you walk up a flight of stairs or open and close your school locker. In what other ways do you do work every day?

Work and Motion Your teacher has asked you to move a box of books to the back of the classroom. Try as you might, though, you just can't budge the box because it is too heavy. Although you exerted a force on the box and you feel tired from it, you have not done any work. In order for you to do work, two things must occur. First, you must apply a force to an object. Second, the object must move in the same direction as your applied force. You do work on an object only when the object moves as a result of the force you exert. The girl in **Figure 1** might think she is working by holding the bags of groceries. However, if she is not moving, she is not doing any work because she is not causing something to move.

 Reading Check *To do work, how must a force make an object move?*

Figure 1 This girl is holding bags of groceries, yet she isn't doing any work.
Explain *what must happen for work to be done.*

406 CHAPTER 14 Work and Simple Machines

Force

Motion

The boy's arms do work when they exert an upward force on the basket and the basket moves upward.

Force

Motion

The boy's arms still exert an upward force on the basket. But when the boy walks forward, no work is done by his arms.

Figure 2 To do work, an object must move in the direction a force is applied.

Applying Force and Doing Work Picture yourself lifting the basket of clothes in **Figure 2.** You can feel your arms exerting a force upward as you lift the basket, and the basket moves upward in the direction of the force your arms applied. Therefore, your arms have done work. Now, suppose you carry the basket forward. You can still feel your arms applying an upward force on the basket to keep it from falling, but now the basket is moving forward instead of upward. Because the direction of motion is not in the same direction of the force applied by your arms, no work is done by your arms.

Force in Two Directions Sometimes only part of the force you exert moves an object. Think about what happens when you push a lawn mower. You push at an angle to the ground as shown in **Figure 3.** Part of the force is to the right and part of the force is downward. Only the part of the force that is in the same direction as the motion of the mower—to the right—does work.

Forward force

Total force

Downward force

Motion

Figure 3 When you exert a force at an angle, only part of your force does work—the part that is in the same direction as the motion of the object.

SECTION 1 Work and Power **407**

Caption Answer

Figure 1 A force must move an object in the same direction that the force is applied.

Reading Check

Answer in the direction of the force

Activity

Pushing on a Book To help students understand how one force can be divided into components in two directions, have them push on two sides of a book—for example, left and bottom—using different amounts of force. They will observe how the two forces acting in different directions are added. L2 **ELL** **LS** **Kinesthetic**

Quick Demo

Work and a Toy Car

Materials table or another flat space, tape, spring scale, toy car

Estimated Time 15 minutes

Procedure Mark a distance of one or two meters on a tabletop with a tape. Fasten a spring scale to a toy car and pull the car from one tape mark to the other. Read the force on the spring scale as you pull, and calculate the amount of work done on the car. Repeat the demonstration, but increase the force exerted on the car. Calculate the work done on the car. Point out to students that the car was moving faster and had greater kinetic energy when more work was done on the car.

Visual Learning

Figure 3 Point out to students the angle between the handle of the lawn mower and the ground. Ask students whether more of the force applied by the boy would be down or forward if the angle between the handle and the ground were smaller. More of the force would be forward. L2 **LS** **Visual-Spatial**

James Prescott Joule This British physicist lived from 1818 to 1889. Joule is best known for his research in electricity and thermodynamics. He discovered that heat produced in a wire by an electric current is proportional to the product of the resistance of the wire and the square of the current. This is known as Joule's law. Joule and Lord Kelvin discovered that the temperature of a gas falls without doing work when the gas is allowed to expand. This is known as the Joule-Thomson effect and is the underlying principle of refrigeration.

Research William Thomson, who later became Lord Kelvin, made many contributions to science. Have students prepare a short biography of Lord Kelvin. Have selected students make a short presentation to the class about his life. P

James Prescott Joule This English physicist experimentally verified the law of conservation of energy. He showed that various forms of energy—mechanical, electrical, and thermal—are essentially the same and can be converted one into another. The SI unit of energy and work, the joule, is named after him. Research the work of Joule and write what you learn in your Science Journal.

Applying Math

National Math Standards
Correlation to Mathematics Objectives
1, 2, 9

Answers to Practice Problems

1. work = force × distance =
300 N × 500 m = 150,000 J

2. work = force × distance =
93 N × 1.5 m = 140 J

Teacher FYI

Power There are two units used to express power—watt and horsepower. One horsepower is equal to the amount of power required to lift 33,000 pounds a distance of 1 foot in 1 minute. There are 746 watts in 1 horsepower.

Calculating Work

Work is done when a force makes an object move. More work is done when the force is increased or the object is moved a greater distance. Work can be calculated using the work equation below. In SI units, the unit for work is the joule, named for the nineteenth-century scientist James Prescott Joule.

> **Work Equation**
> **work** (in joules) = **force** (in newtons) × **distance** (in meters)
> $$W = Fd$$

Work and Distance Suppose you give a book a push and it slides across a table. To calculate the work you did, the distance in the above equation is not the distance the book moved. The distance in the work equation is the distance an object moves while the force is being applied. So the distance in the work equation is the distance the book moved while you were pushing.

Applying Math — Solve a One-Step Equation

CALCULATING WORK A painter lifts a can of paint that weighs 40 N a distance of 2 m. How much work does she do? *Hint: to lift a can weighing 40 N, the painter must exert a force of 40 N.*

Solution

1 *This is what you know:*
- force: F = 40 N
- distance: d = 2 m

2 *This is what you need to find out:*
work: W = ? J

3 *This is the procedure you need to use:*
Substitute the known values F = 40 N and d = 2 m into the work equation:

$$W = Fd = (40\ N)(2\ m) = 80\ N\cdot m = 80\ J$$

4 *Check your answer:*
Check your answer by dividing the work you calculated by the distance given in the problem. The result should be the force given in the problem.

Practice Problems

1. As you push a lawn mower, the horizontal force is 300 N. If you push the mower a distance of 500 m, how much work do you do?

2. A librarian lifts a box of books that weighs 93 N a distance of 1.5 m. How much work does he do?

Science Online — For more practice, visit **ips.msscience.com/math_practice**

Differentiated Instruction

Challenge A 7,500-W engine is used to lift an I beam with a mass of 1,000 kg to a height of 150 m. How much work must be done to lift this mass at constant speed? How long will it take? Have students write down a detailed solution to the problems. $W = F \times d = m \times g \times d = (1,000\ kg)\ (9.8\ m/s^2)\ (150\ m) = 1,470,000\ J$; $t = W/P = 1,470,000\ J/7,500\ W = 196\ s$ L3

Physically Challenged Help students who use hand-powered wheelchairs understand how force and distance affect work by having them think about how much effort they must use to move their wheelchairs in various situations, such as starting, moving up a ramp, or moving at a constant rate along a flat surface. L1 **I.S. Intrapersonal**

What is power?

What does it mean to be powerful? Imagine two weightlifters lifting the same amount of weight the same vertical distance. They both do the same amount of work. However, the amount of power they use depends on how long it took to do the work. **Power** is how quickly work is done. The weightlifter who lifted the weight in less time is more powerful.

Calculating Power Power can be calculated by dividing the amount of work done by the time needed to do the work.

Power Equation

$$\text{power (in watts)} = \frac{\text{work (in joules)}}{\text{time (in seconds)}}$$

$$P = \frac{W}{t}$$

In SI units, the unit of power is the watt, in honor of James Watt, a nineteenth-century British scientist who invented a practical version of the steam engine.

Applying Math   Solve a One-Step Equation

CALCULATING POWER You do 200 J of work in 12 s. How much power did you use?

Solution

1 *This is what you know:*
- work: $W = 200$ J
- time: $t = 12$ s

2 *This is what you need to find out:*
- power: $P = ?$ watts

3 *This is the procedure you need to use:*

Substitute the known values $W = 200$ J and $t = 12$ s into the power equation:

$$P = \frac{W}{t} = \frac{200 \text{ J}}{12 \text{ s}} = 17 \text{ watts}$$

4 *Check your answer:*

Check your answer by multiplying the power you calculated by the time given in the problem. The result should be the work given in the problem.

Practice Problems

1. In the course of a short race, a car does 50,000 J of work in 7 s. What is the power of the car during the race?

2. A teacher does 140 J of work in 20 s. How much power did he use?

Science Online For more practice, visit ips.msscience.com/math_practice

Work and Power

Procedure

1. Weigh yourself on a **scale**.
2. Multiply your weight in pounds by 4.45 to convert your weight to newtons.
3. Measure the vertical height of a **stairway**. **WARNING:** *Make sure the stairway is clear of all objects.*
4. Time yourself walking slowly and quickly up the stairway.

Analysis

Calculate and compare the work and power in each case.

 Try at Home

Purpose Students measure and compare work and power. L2
ELL **IS** **Kinesthetic**
Materials scale, meterstick, stairway, stopwatch

Analysis

Work will be the same in both cases, but power will be greater when a student runs.

Assessment

Process One dietary Calorie is 4,184 J. Have students calculate the number of Calories used to climb the stairs. Use **Performance Assessment in the Science Classroom**, p. 101.

Try at Home

Discussion

SI Units To help students understand the relationship between force, work, and power, have them express each in terms of their basic SI units. $F = ma = $ kg m/s^2 = N; $W = F \times d = mad = $ kg m/s^2 m = J; $P = W/t = (F \times d)/t = mad/t = $ (kg m/s^2)m/s = watt L2
IS **Logical-Mathematical**

Applying Math

National Math Standards
Correlation to Mathematics Objectives
1, 2, 9

Answers to Practice Problems

1. Power = work done/time needed
   50,000 J/7 s = 7,143 watts
2. $P = W/t = $ 140 J/20 s = 7 watts

Curriculum Connection

History Explain to students that another unit for measuring work is the calorie. One calorie is equal to 4.184 joules. The kilocalorie, written with a capital C as Calorie, is often used when discussing the energy available from food. One Calorie = 4,184 joules. Tell students that walking and running a given distance burn about the same number of Calories. Under what conditions does running result in a greater number of Calories being burned than walking does? A greater number of Calories are burned when running for a given period of time rather than walking for the same time period, because a greater distance is covered and therefore more work is done. Which requires more power, running or walking? Why? running, because it covers the distance in less time. L2 **IS** **Logical-Mathematical**

Work, Force, Distance
What is the relationship between work, force, and distance?

DAILY INTERVENTION

Check for Understanding

Logical-Mathematical Have students use a science textbook and a stop watch to determine the amount of power and work done to carry the textbook a predetermined distance in the classroom. L2

Reteach

Power Ask students to explain how the time it takes to lift a mass is related to the height it is raised, if the same power is used. The higher the mass is lifted, the more time it will take. L2

☑ Assessment

Content How much power is used when 600 joules of work are done in 1 min? 10 W L2

Science Online

Topic: James Watt
Visit ips.msscience.com for Web links to information about James Watt and his steam engine.

Activity Draw a diagram showing how his steam engine worked.

Work and Energy If you push a chair and make it move, you do work on the chair and change its energy. Recall that when something is moving it has energy of motion, or kinetic energy. By making the chair move, you increase its kinetic energy.

You also change the energy of an object when you do work and lift it higher. An object has potential energy that increases when it is higher above Earth's surface. By lifting an object, you do work and increase its potential energy.

Power and Energy When you do work on an object you increase the energy of the object. Because energy can never be created or destroyed, if the object gains energy then you must lose energy. When you do work on an object you transfer energy to the object, and your energy decreases. The amount of work done is the amount of energy transferred. So power is also equal to the amount of energy transferred in a certain amount of time.

Sometimes energy can be transferred even when no work is done, such as when heat flows from a warm to a cold object. In fact, there are many ways energy can be transferred even if no work is done. Power is always the rate at which energy is transferred, or the amount of energy transferred divided by the time needed.

---

section 1 review

Summary

What is work?

- Work is done when a force causes an object to move in the same direction that the force is applied.

- If the movement caused by a force is at an angle to the direction the force is applied, only the part of the force in the direction of motion does work.

- Work can be calculated by multiplying the force applied by the distance:

$$W = Fd$$

- The distance in the work equation is the distance an object moves while the force is being applied.

What is power?

- Power is how quickly work is done. Something is more powerful if it can do a given amount of work in less time.

- Power can be calculated by dividing the work done by the time needed to do the work:

$$P = \frac{W}{t}$$

Self Check

1. **Describe** a situation in which work is done on an object.

2. **Evaluate** which of the following situations involves more power: 200 J of work done in 20 s or 50 J of work done in 4 s? Explain your answer.

3. **Determine** two ways power can be increased.

4. **Calculate** how much power, in watts, is needed to cut a lawn in 50 min if the work involved is 100,000 J.

5. **Think Critically** Suppose you are pulling a wagon with the handle at an angle. How can you make your task easier?

Applying Math

6. **Calculate Work** How much work was done to lift a 1,000-kg block to the top of the Great Pyramid, 146 m above ground?

7. **Calculate Work Done by an Engine** An engine is used to lift a beam weighing 9,800 N up to 145 m. How much work must the engine do to lift this beam? How much work must be done to lift it 290 m?

Science Online ips.msscience.com/self_check_quiz

---

section 1 review

1. Answers will vary. The students may describe any situation where a force moves an object in the direction of the force.

2. In the first case, 10 W are used; in the second case, 12.5 W are used. Even though less work is done in the second case, it uses more power because the work is done at a faster rate.

3. increasing the amount of work or decreasing the time

4. $P = 100,000$ J/[(50 min) $\times$ (60 s/min)] $= 100,000$ J/3,000 s $= 33$ W

5. Pull the wagon by the handle, making as small an angle with the ground as possible.

6. $W = mgh = (1,000$ kg$) \times (9.8$ m/s$^2) \times (146$ m$) = 1,430,800$ J

7. $W = mgh = (9,800$ N$)(145$ m$) = 1,420,000$ J. To lift the beam 290 m, twice as much work, 2,840,000 J, must be done, because it is lifted twice as high.

Building the Pyramids

Imagine moving 2.3 million blocks of limestone, each weighing more than 1,000 kg. That is exactly what the builders of the Great Pyramid at Giza did. Although no one knows for sure exactly how they did it, they probably pulled the blocks most of the way.

● *Real-World Question*

How is the force needed to lift a block related to the distance it travels?

Goals
■ **Compare** the force needed to lift a block with the force needed to pull it up a ramp.

Materials
wood block	thin notebooks
tape	meterstick
spring scale	several books
ruler	

Safety Precautions

● *Procedure*

1. Stack several books together on a tabletop to model a half-completed pyramid. Measure the height of the books in centimeters. Record the height on the first row of the data table under *Distance*.

2. Use the wood block as a model for a block of stone. Use tape to attach the block to the spring scale.

3. Place the block on the table and lift it straight up the side of the stack of books until the top of the block is even with the top of the books. Record the force shown on the scale in the data table under *Force*.

Work Done Using Different Ramps		
Distance (cm)	Force (N)	Work (J)
Answers will vary.		

4. **Arrange** a notebook so that one end is on the stack of books and the other end is on the table. Measure the length of the notebook and record this length as distance in the second row of the data table under *Distance*.

5. **Measure** the force needed to pull the block up the ramp. Record the force in the data table.

6. Repeat steps 4 and 5 using a longer notebook to make the ramp longer.

7. **Calculate** the work done in each row of the data table.

● *Conclude and Apply*

1. **Evaluate** how much work you did in each instance.

2. **Determine** what happened to the force needed as the length of the ramp increased.

3. **Infer** How could the builders of the pyramids have designed their task to use less force than they would lifting the blocks straight up? Draw a diagram to support your answer.

*C*ommunicating
Your Data

Add your data to that found by other groups. **For more help, refer to the Science Skill Handbook.**

*C*ommunicating
Your Data

Encourage students to use a spreadsheet to display their data. If the groups use different ramp lengths, have students plot the results using the graphing feature of the spreadsheet program.

● *Real-World Question*

Purpose Students investigate the mechanical advantage of a ramp. L2 ELL COOP LEARN LS **Kinesthetic**

Process Skills observe, infer, compare and contrast, make and use tables, interpret data, make models, separate and control variables, work with numbers

Time Required 45 minutes

● *Procedure*

Teaching Strategy Have students determine the force used to pull the block while the block is moving at a constant speed.

Troubleshooting Zero the spring scales before use and secure the ramps so they do not move when a block is pulled along them.

● *Conclude and Apply*

1. Work should be similar in each instance.
2. It decreased.
3. They could have built ramps along the sides of the pyramids.

☑ Assessment

Content Have each student write a short essay explaining whether he or she thinks the hypothesis that the Egyptians used ramps to build the pyramids is feasible. Use **Performance Assessment in the Science Classroom,** p. 157.

as you read

What You'll Learn
- **Explain** how a machine makes work easier.
- **Calculate** the mechanical advantages and efficiency of a machine.
- **Explain** how friction reduces efficiency.

Why It's Important

Machines can't change the amount of work you need to do, but they can make doing work easier.

⊙ **Review Vocabulary**
friction: force that opposes motion between two touching surfaces

New Vocabulary
- input force
- output force
- mechanical advantage
- efficiency

What is a machine?

Did you use a machine today? When you think of a machine you might think of a device, such as a car, with many moving parts powered by an engine or an electric motor. But if you used a pair of scissors or a broom, or cut your food with a knife, you used a machine. A machine is simply a device that makes doing work easier. Even a sloping surface can be a machine.

Mechanical Advantage

Even though machines make work easier, they don't decrease the amount of work you need to do. Instead, a machine changes the way in which you do work. When you use a machine, you exert a force over some distance. For example, you exert a force to move a rake or lift the handles of a wheelbarrow. The force that you apply on a machine is the **input force.** The work you do on the machine is equal to the input force times the distance over which your force moves the machine. The work that you do on the machine is the input work.

The machine also does work by exerting a force to move an object over some distance. A rake, for example, exerts a force to move leaves. Sometimes this force is called the resistance force because the machine is trying to overcome some resistance. The force that the machine applies is the **output force.** The work that the machine does is the output work. **Figure 4** shows how a machine transforms input work to output work.

When you use a machine, the output work can never be greater than the input work. So what is the advantage of using a machine? A machine makes work easier by changing the amount of force you need to exert, the distance over which the force is exerted, or the direction in which you exert your force.

Figure 4 No matter what type of machine is used, the output work is never greater than the input work.

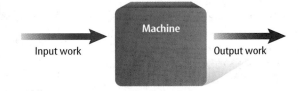

Section 2 Resource Manager

Chapter *FAST FILE* Resources
Transparency Activity, pp. 45, 47–48
Directed Reading for Content Mastery, p. 21
Enrichment, p. 31
Reinforcement, p. 28
Reading and Writing Skill Activities, p. 35

Changing Force Some machines make doing work easier by reducing the force you have to apply to do work. This type of machine increases the input force, so that the output force is greater than the input force. The number of times a machine increases the input force is the **mechanical advantage** of the machine. The mechanical advantage of a machine is the ratio of the output force to the input force and can be calculated from this equation:

Mechanical Advantage Equation

$$\text{mechanical advantage} = \frac{\text{output force (in newtons)}}{\text{input force (in newtons)}}$$

$$MA = \frac{F_{\text{out}}}{F_{\text{in}}}$$

Mechanical advantage does not have any units, because it is the ratio of two numbers with the same units.

Science Online

Topic: Historical Tools
Visit ips.msscience.com for Web links to information about early types of tools and how they took advantage of simple machines.

Activity Write a paragraph describing how simple machines were used to design early tools.

Applying Math   Solve a One-Step Equation

CALCULATING MECHANICAL ADVANTAGE To pry the lid off a paint can, you apply a force of 50 N to the handle of the screwdriver. What is the mechanical advantage of the screwdriver if it applies a force of 500 N to the lid?

Solution

1 *This is what you know:*

- input force: $F_{\text{in}} = 50$ N
- output force: $F_{\text{out}} = 500$ N

2 *This is what you need to find out:*

mechanical advantage: $MA = ?$

3 *This is the procedure you need to use:*

Substitute the known values $F_{\text{in}} = 50$ N and $F_{\text{out}} = 500$ N into the mechanical advantage equation:

$$MA = \frac{F_{\text{out}}}{F_{\text{in}}} = \frac{500 \text{ N}}{50 \text{ N}} = 10$$

4 *Check your answer:*

Check your answer by multiplying the mechanical advantage you calculated by the input force given in the problem. The result should be the output force given in the problem.

Practice Problems

1. To open a bottle, you apply a force of 50 N to the bottle opener. The bottle opener applies a force of 775 N to the bottle cap. What is the mechanical advantage of the bottle opener?

2. To crack a pecan, you apply a force of 50 N to the nutcracker. The nutcracker applies a force of 750 N to the pecan. What is the mechanical advantage of the nutcracker?

For more practice, visit ips.msscience.com/math_practice

2 Teach

Discussion

Building Variations How is building skyscrapers today similar to and different from the building of the pyramids? Both are large construction projects in which tools are used. Pyramid construction relied largely on people power, but skyscrapers are built using machines with engines powered by fossil fuels.

Applying Math

National Math Standards
Correlation to Mathematics Objectives
1, 2, 9

Answers to Practice Problems

1. $MA = F_{out}/F_{in}$
   $= 775 \text{ N}/50 \text{ N} = 15.5$
2. $MA = F_{out}/F_{in}$
   $= 750 \text{ N}/50 \text{ N} = 15$

Activity

Problem-Solving Contest Give students practice solving problems from this section by having a contest. Divide the students into two groups. Have a member from each group go to the board and give them a problem to solve. The first one to solve the problem wins and the team gets one point. Allow each student on the team to have a turn. If the student at the board cannot solve the problem, let the team help them. The team with the most points wins.

Differentiated Instruction

Challenge In the late 1800s and early 1900s, many people tried to develop perpetual motion machines. Have interested students research perpetual motion machines and attempts to develop them. Ask students to prepare written reports explaining why these machines are impossible to develop. A perpetual motion machine is a device that can either deliver more work than is put into it or can continue to work with no energy input other than that which was used to start it. L3 **LS Linguistic**

Figure 6 Spend a few moments reviewing with students how machines make work easier. Once students understand the benefits of machines, have them identify which machines in **Figure 5** work in the same way as those in **Figure 6.** The rake works like the machine at the top on the right by multiplying the distance over which the force is applied. The pulley on the flagpole works like the machine at the bottom by changing the direction of the force. L1 **LS Visual-Spatial**

Use an Analogy

Prying Open a Lid Ask students whether they have ever used a screwdriver to pry open the lid of a can, such as that on a can of paint. Explain that the movement involved in this process (which actually involves a lever) is the same as that illustrated by the pulley on the flagpole in **Figure 5.** In each case, an input force applied in a downward direction causes the output force to move upward.

Teacher FYI

Pulleys According to legend, Archimedes (287–212 B.C.), used a system of pulleys to pull a ship onto dry land.

Figure 5 Changing the direction or the distance that a force is applied can make a task easier.

Sometimes it is easier to exert your force in a certain direction. This boy would rather pull down on the rope to lift the flag than to climb to the top of the pole and pull up.

When you rake leaves, you move your hands a short distance, but the end of the rake moves over a longer distance.

Changing Distance Some machines allow you to exert your force over a shorter distance. In these machines, the output force is less than the input force. The rake in **Figure 5** is this type of machine. You move your hands a small distance at the top of the handle, but the bottom of the rake moves a greater distance as it moves the leaves. The mechanical advantage of this type of machine is less than one because the output force is less than the input force.

Changing Direction Sometimes it is easier to apply a force in a certain direction. For example, it is easier to pull down on the rope in **Figure 5** than to pull up on it. Some machines enable you to change the direction of the input force. In these machines neither the force nor the distance is changed. The mechanical advantage of this type of machine is equal to one because the output force is equal to the input force. The three ways machines make doing work easier are summarized in **Figure 6.**

Figure 6 Machines are useful because they can increase force, increase distance, or change the direction in which a force is applied.

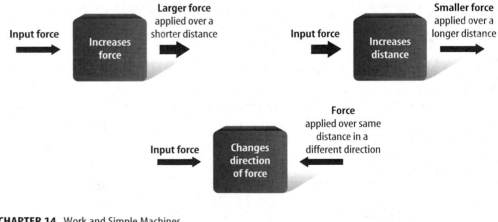

Curriculum Connection

History One type of wheelbarrow was used in Europe during the construction of the cathedrals. It was derived from the barrow, or handbarrow, a stretcherlike device carried by two people. Have interested students research to find out what tools were available for the building of the cathe-drals or other historic structures. Ask them to find out how existing tools were improved during the projects they research, and have them report their findings to the class in oral presentations. L2 **LS Linguistic**

Efficiency

A machine doesn't increase the input work. For a real machine, the output work done by the machine is always less than the input work that is done on the machine. In a real machine, there is friction as parts of the machine move. Friction converts some of the input work into heat, so that the output work is reduced. The **efficiency** of a machine is the ratio of the output work to the input work, and can be calculated from this equation:

Efficiency Equation

$$\text{efficiency (in percent)} = \frac{\textbf{output work (in joules)}}{\textbf{input work (in joules)}} \times 100\%$$

$$eff = \frac{W_{out}}{W_{in}} \times 100\%$$

If the amount of friction in the machine is reduced, the efficiency of the machine increases.

INTEGRATE Life Science

Body Temperature
Chemical reactions that enable your muscles to move also produce heat that helps maintain your body temperature. When you shiver, rapid contraction and relaxation of muscle fibers produces a large amount of heat that helps raise your body temperature. This causes the efficiency of your muscles to decrease as more energy is converted into heat.

INTEGRATE Life Science

Body Temperature Each time a muscle contracts, molecules of adenosine triphosphate (ATP) react with water to form adenosine diphosphate (ADP) and release energy. Some of this energy is used by other chemical reactions and some is lost as heat.

Applying Math

National Math Standards
Correlation to Mathematics Objectives
1, 2, 9

Answers to Practice Problems
1. $Eff = (W_{out}/W_{in}) \times 100\% = (70 \text{ J}/100 \text{ J}) \times 100\% = 70\%$
2. $Eff = (W_{out}/W_{in}) \times 100\% = (105 \text{ J}/150 \text{ J}) \times 100\% = 70\%$

Applying Math   Solve a One-Step Equation

CALCULATING EFFICIENCY Using a pulley system, a crew does 7,500 J of work to load a box that requires 4,500 J of work. What is the efficiency of the pulley system?

Solution

1 *This is what you know:*
- input work: $W_{in} = 7{,}500$ J
- output work: $W_{out} = 4{,}500$ J

2 *This is what you need to find out:*
efficiency: $eff = ?$ %

3 *This is the procedure you need to use:*
Substitute the known values $W_{in} = 7{,}500$ J and $W_{out} = 4{,}500$ J into the efficiency equation:

$$eff = \frac{W_{out}}{W_{in}} = \frac{4{,}500 \text{ J}}{7{,}500 \text{ J}} \times 100\% = 60\%$$

4 *Check your answer:*
Check your answer by dividing the efficiency by 100% and then multiplying your answer times the work input. The product should be the work output given in the problem.

Practice Problems

1. You do 100 J of work in pulling out a nail with a claw hammer. If the hammer does 70 J of work, what is the hammer's efficiency?

2. You do 150 J of work pushing a box up a ramp. If the ramp does 105 J of work, what is the efficiency of the ramp?

 Science Online
For more practice, visit ips.msscience.com/ math_practice

Differentiated Instruction

Learning Disabled Have students show you how they would do the Applying Math example step-by-step. Answer any questions and correct any misconceptions they may have. Make sure they show all of their work. Check their practice problems to make sure they understand how to do the problems.

Active Reading

Bubble Map In a bubble map, words are clustered to describe a topic or idea. A bubble map can be used for prewriting, to generate ideas before writing, or to review for a test. Have students design a bubble map to help them find the relationship between mechanical advantage and efficiency. L2 **LS** **Logical-Mathematical** P

Misconceptions

Frictional Force The frictional force depends on the force pushing two surfaces together and not on the area of contact. This is because friction depends on the total contact area between microscopic bumps on the two surfaces. Making the surface area larger increases the number of microscopic bumps in contact. However, this also decreases the pressure pushing the bumps together, so the contact area between individual bumps decreases. As a result, the total microscopic contact area stays the same, and the frictional force is unchanged.

3 Assess

DAILY INTERVENTION

Check for Understanding

Visual-Spatial Have students investigate how a car jack works and explain the process in an illustrated drawing. L3 **LS**

Reteach

Efficiency Why is it impossible to have a machine that is perfectly efficient? There is always some amount of friction changing some of the work done by the machine into heat. L2
LS Logical-Mathematical

☑ Assessment

Performance Have students suggest methods other than using oil for reducing friction in machines. Possible answers: Use another lubricant such as graphite; sand surfaces to make them as smooth as possible; use wheels or similar devices to slide one surface over another Use **PASC**, p. 93. L2

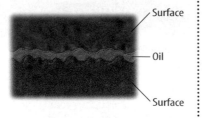

Figure 7 Lubrication can reduce the friction between two surfaces. Two surfaces in contact can stick together where the high spots on each surface come in contact. Adding oil or another lubricant separates the surface so that fewer high spots make contact.

Friction To help understand friction, imagine pushing a heavy box up a ramp. As the box begins to move, the bottom surface of the box slides across the top surface of the ramp. Neither surface is perfectly smooth—each has high spots and low spots, as shown in **Figure 7**.

As the two surfaces slide past each other, high spots on the two surfaces come in contact. At these contact points, shown in **Figure 7,** atoms and molecules can bond together. This makes the contact points stick together. The attractive forces between all the bonds in the contact points added together is the frictional force that tries to keep the two surfaces from sliding past each other.

To keep the box moving, a force must be applied to break the bonds between the contact points. Even after these bonds are broken and the box moves, new bonds form as different parts of the two surfaces come into contact.

Friction and Efficiency One way to reduce friction between two surfaces is to add oil. **Figure 7** shows how oil fills the gaps between the surfaces, and keeps many of the high spots from making contact. Because there are fewer contact points between the surfaces, the force of friction is reduced. More of the input work then is converted to output work by the machine.

section 2 review

Summary

What is a machine?
- A machine is a device that makes doing work easier.
- A machine can make doing work easier by reducing the force exerted, changing the distance over which the force is exerted, or changing the direction of the force.
- The output work done by a machine can never be greater than the input work done on the machine.

Mechanical Advantage and Efficiency
- The mechanical advantage of a machine is the number of times the machine increases the input force:
$$MA = \frac{F_{out}}{F_{in}}$$
- The efficiency of a machine is the ratio of the output work to the input work:
$$eff = \frac{W_{out}}{W_{in}} \times 100\%$$

Self Check

1. **Identify** three specific situations in which machines make work easier.
2. **Infer** why the output force exerted by a rake must be less than the input force.
3. **Explain** how the efficiency of an ideal machine compares with the efficiency of a real machine.
4. **Explain** how friction reduces the efficiency of machines.
5. **Think Critically** Can a machine be useful even if its mechanical advantage is less than one? Explain and give an example.

Applying Math

6. **Calculate Efficiency** Find the efficiency of a machine if the input work is 150 J and the output work is 90 J.
7. **Calculate Mechanical Advantage** To lift a crate, a pulley system exerts a force of 2,750 N. Find the mechanical advantage of the pulley system if the input force is 250 N.

Science Online ips.msscience.com/self_check_quiz

section 2 review

1. Possible answers: using ramps to move heavy furniture, using a screwdriver to turn a screw, using a wheelbarrow to move heavy loads
2. The output arm of the rake moves a greater distance than the input arm moves. Because the output work cannot be greater than the input work, the output force must be less than the input force.
3. The efficiency of an ideal machine is 100%, but real machines always have an efficiency less than 100%.
4. Friction converts some of the input work into heat, so that the output work is always less than the input work.
5. Yes. This type of machine increases the distance over which the output force is applied. An example is a rake or a baseball bat.
6. 60%
7. 11

Simple Machines

What is a simple machine?

What do you think of when you hear the word *machine*? Many people think of machines as complicated devices such as cars, elevators, or computers. However, some machines are as simple as a hammer, shovel, or ramp. A **simple machine** is a machine that does work with only one movement. The six simple machines are the inclined plane, lever, wheel and axle, screw, wedge, and pulley. A machine made up of a combination of simple machines is called a **compound machine**. A can opener is a compound machine. The bicycle in **Figure 8** is a familiar example of another compound machine.

Inclined Plane

Ramps might have enabled the ancient Egyptians to build their pyramids. To move limestone blocks weighing more than 1,000 kg each, archaeologists hypothesize that the Egyptians built enormous ramps. A ramp is a simple machine known as an inclined plane. An **inclined plane** is a flat, sloped surface. Less force is needed to move an object from one height to another using an inclined plane than is needed to lift the object. As the inclined plane becomes longer, the force needed to move the object becomes smaller.

What You'll Learn

- **Distinguish** among the different simple machines.
- **Describe** how to find the mechanical advantage of each simple machine.

Why It's Important

All machines, no matter how complicated, are made of simple machines.

⟳ Review Vocabulary

compound: made of separate pieces or parts

New Vocabulary

- simple machine
- compound machine
- inclined plane
- wedge
- screw
- lever
- wheel and axle
- pulley

Figure 8 Devices that use combinations of simple machines, such as this bicycle, are called compound machines.

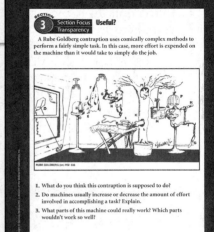

Bellringer

Section Focus Transparencies also are available on the Interactive Chalkboard CD-ROM.
L2 ELL

Tie to Prior Knowledge

Mechanical Advantage and Efficiency Remind students of the definition of mechanical advantage and the concept of efficiency as you prepare them to explore the different types of simple machines.

Section 3 Resource Manager

Chapter *FAST FILE* Resources
  Transparency Activity, p. 46
  Directed Reading for Content Mastery, pp. 21–22
  Enrichment, p. 32
  Reinforcement, p. 29
  MiniLAB, p. 4

  Lab Activity, pp. 13–16
  Lab Worksheets, pp. 7–8
Lab Management and Safety, p. 39
Physical Science Critical Thinking/Problem Solving, p. 7
Performance Assessment in the Science Classroom, p. 37

Machines v. Tools Many people refer to simple devices such as knives or screwdrivers as tools. Students may think that a machine must be a more complicated device, such as an electric drill. In science, however, there is no distinction between machines and tools. A machine is any device that is used to multiply or change the direction of a force. Thus, a hammer or a knife is as much a machine as is a lathe or an electric drill.

Inquiry Lab

Tools and Gadgets

Purpose To invent a new gadget using simple machines

Possible Materials wood, plastic, cardboard, rubber hose, recycled materials, rope

Estimated Time one week outside class time

Teaching Strategies

• Challenge students to invent a new gadget using simple machines.

• Have students construct their gadget from inexpensive materials.

• Students should present their new gadget to the class. Students should identify the simple machines they used to construct the gadget.

For additional inquiry activities, see *Science Inquiry Labs.*

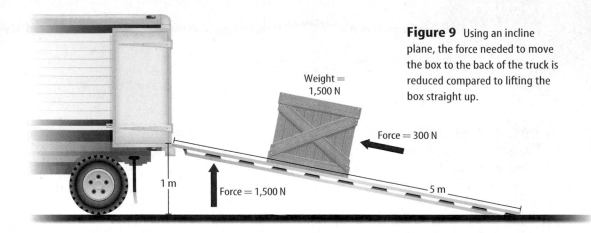

Figure 9 Using an incline plane, the force needed to move the box to the back of the truck is reduced compared to lifting the box straight up.

Weight = 1,500 N

Force = 300 N

1 m

Force = 1,500 N

5 m

Using Inclined Planes Imagine having to lift a box weighing 1,500 N to the back of a truck that is 1 m off the ground. You would have to exert a force of 1,500 N, the weight of the box, over a distance of 1 m, which equals 1,500 J of work. Now suppose that instead you use a 5-m-long ramp, as shown in **Figure 9.** The amount of work you need to do does not change. You still need to do 1,500 J of work. However, the distance over which you exert your force becomes 5 m. You can calculate the force you need to exert by dividing both sides of the equation for work by distance.

$$\text{Force} = \frac{\text{work}}{\text{distance}}$$

If you do 1,500 J of work by exerting a force over 5 m, the force is only 300 N. Because you exert the input force over a distance that is five times as long, you can exert a force that is five times less.

The mechanical advantage of an inclined plane is the length of the inclined plane divided by its height. In this example, the ramp has a mechanical advantage of 5.

Wedge An inclined plane that moves is called a **wedge.** A wedge can have one or two sloping sides. The knife shown in **Figure 10** is an example of a wedge. An axe and certain types of doorstops are also wedges. Just as for an inclined plane, the mechanical advantage of a wedge increases as it becomes longer and thinner.

Figure 10 This chef's knife is a wedge that slices through food.

418 **CHAPTER 14** Work and Simple Machines

Science Journal

Inclined Planes Ask students to note all the inclined planes they see in a two-day period. Have them list each one in their Science Journals and describe how it is used. [L2] **IS** **Visual-Spatial**

Differentiated Instruction

Challenge Encourage students with a strong interest in nature to look for examples of the use of simple machines by animals. Examples include the way a parrot uses its powerful bill to crack nuts and the use of sticks by chimpanzees to obtain food that is hard to reach. Ask students to prepare a poster with examples to share with the class. [L3] **IS** **Naturalist** [P]

Figure 11 Wedge-shaped teeth help tear food.

Your front teeth help tear an apple apart.

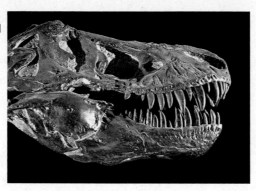

The wedge-shaped teeth of this *Tyrannosaurus rex* show that it was a carnivore.

INTEGRATE Life Science

Wedges in Your Body You have wedges in your body. The bite marks on the apple in **Figure 11** show how your front teeth are wedge shaped. A wedge changes the direction of the applied effort force. As you push your front teeth into the apple, the downward effort force is changed by your teeth into a sideways force that pushes the skin of the apple apart.

The teeth of meat eaters, or carnivores, are more wedge shaped than the teeth of plant eaters, or herbivores. The teeth of carnivores are used to cut and rip meat, while herbivores' teeth are used for grinding plant material. By examining the teeth of ancient animals, such as the dinosaur in **Figure 11,** scientists can determine what the animal ate when it was living.

The Screw Another form of the inclined plane is a screw. A **screw** is an inclined plane wrapped around a cylinder or post. The inclined plane on a screw forms the screw threads. Just like a wedge changes the direction of the effort force applied to it, a screw also changes the direction of the applied force. When you turn a screw, the force applied is changed by the threads to a force that pulls the screw into the material. Friction between the threads and the material holds the screw tightly in place. The mechanical advantage of the screw is the length of the inclined plane wrapped around the screw divided by the length of the screw. The more tightly wrapped the threads are, the easier it is to turn the screw. Examples of screws are shown in **Figure 12.**

Reading Check How are screws related to the inclined plane?

Figure 12 The thread around a screw is an inclined plane. Many familiar devices use screws to make work easier.

Cultural Diversity

Pyramid Construction Until the early part of the twentieth century, the Great Pyramid of Khufu in Egypt was the world's largest building, standing more than 145 m tall, covering an area of seven city blocks and weighing 6.5 million tons. Archaeologists believe the ancient Egyptians constructed enormous ramps to move more than 2 million 1,000-kg limestone blocks into place. A ramp with a length that would enable about ten people to drag one of these blocks would require more material than the pyramid itself! Archaeologists discovered that the Egyptians used a type of clay called tafla that is strong and becomes slippery when wet. Tests indicate that if the Egyptians used tafla as a lubricant on the ramps, they could have made steeper ramps, which would have required much less material.

Use Science Words

Word Origin Have students use a dictionary to find the source of the word *fulcrum* and relate their findings to what a fulcrum does. *Fulcrum* is derived from the Latin *fulcire,* which means "to support." A fulcrum provides the support around which a lever turns. L2 **LS** Linguistic

Make a Model

First-Class Levers Have students use a pencil, a ruler, and books to model a first-class lever. Have students experiment to find out how changing the distance between the fulcrum (pencil) and the resistance (books) changes the amount of force that must be exerted to lift the books. L2

Caption Answer

Figure 14 by making the radius of the wheel larger or the radius of the axle smaller

Teacher FYI

Inventing the Wheel The wheel was invented about the time of the building of the pyramids (3600 B.C.). It was used initially not for transporting heavy loads but to turn a potter's table. A heavy, round stone was attached to a shaft under the potter's table. With a small kick of the foot, the potter could keep the table turning while shaping the clay.

Figure 13 The mechanical advantage of a lever changes as the position of the fulcrum changes. The mechanical advantage increases as the fulcrum is moved closer to the output force.

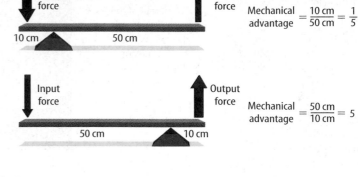

$$\text{Mechanical advantage} = \frac{10\ cm}{50\ cm} = \frac{1}{5}$$

$$\text{Mechanical advantage} = \frac{50\ cm}{10\ cm} = 5$$

Figure 14 A faucet handle is a wheel and axle. A wheel and axle is similar to a circular lever. The center is the fulcrum, and the wheel and axle turn around it. **Explain** *how you can increase the mechanical advantage of a wheel and axle.*

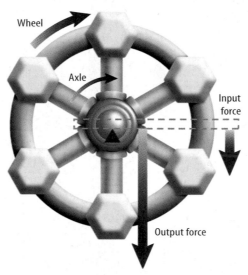

Wheel

Axle

Input force

Output force

Lever

You step up to the plate. The pitcher throws the ball and you swing your lever to hit the ball? That's right! A baseball bat is a type of simple machine called a lever. A **lever** is any rigid rod or plank that pivots, or rotates, about a point. The point about which the lever pivots is called a fulcrum.

The mechanical advantage of a lever is found by dividing the distance from the fulcrum to the input force by the distance from the fulcrum to the output force, as shown in **Figure 13.** When the fulcrum is closer to the output force than the input force, the mechanical advantage is greater than one.

Levers are divided into three classes according to the position of the fulcrum with respect to the input force and output force. **Figure 15** shows examples of three classes of levers.

Wheel and Axle

Do you think you could turn a doorknob easily if it were a narrow rod the size of a pencil? It might be possible, but it would be difficult. A doorknob makes it easier for you to open a door because it is a simple machine called a wheel and axle. A **wheel and axle** consists of two circular objects of different sizes that are attached in such a way that they rotate together. As you can see in **Figure 14,** the larger object is the wheel and the smaller object is the axle.

The mechanical advantage of a wheel and axle is usually greater than one. It is found by dividing the radius of the wheel by the radius of the axle. For example, if the radius of the wheel is 12 cm and the radius of the axle is 4 cm, the mechanical advantage is 3.

420 CHAPTER 14 Work and Simple Machines

LAB DEMONSTRATION

Purpose to demonstrate the mechanical advantage of a wheel and axle

Materials wheel and axle, rod, 2 strings, 500-g mass

Preparation Mount the wheel and axle on the support rod.

Procedure Wrap one string clockwise around the axle and the other counterclockwise around the wheel. Hang the 500-g mass from the end of the wheel string. Have student volunteers pull down on the axle string until the mass is lifted about 10 cm.

Expected Outcome The force used is large, and the distance moved is small.

Assessment

Ask students to explain the results, using the concept of mechanical advantage. The mechanical advantage is less than one, because a large input force over a small distance produced a smaller output force over a larger distance. L2

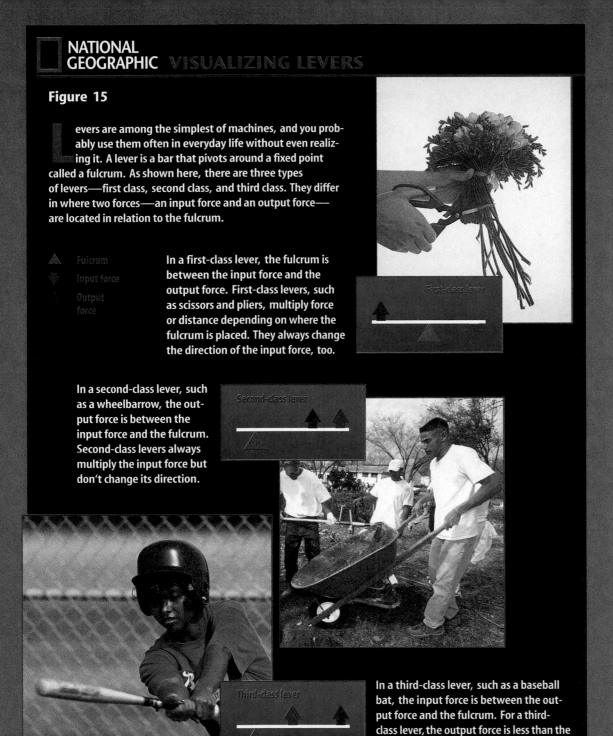

NATIONAL GEOGRAPHIC VISUALIZING LEVERS

Figure 15

Levers are among the simplest of machines, and you probably use them often in everyday life without even realizing it. A lever is a bar that pivots around a fixed point called a fulcrum. As shown here, there are three types of levers—first class, second class, and third class. They differ in where two forces—an input force and an output force—are located in relation to the fulcrum.

- ▲ Fulcrum
- ↓ Input force
- ↑ Output force

In a first-class lever, the fulcrum is between the input force and the output force. First-class levers, such as scissors and pliers, multiply force or distance depending on where the fulcrum is placed. They always change the direction of the input force, too.

First-class lever

In a second-class lever, such as a wheelbarrow, the output force is between the input force and the fulcrum. Second-class levers always multiply the input force but don't change its direction.

Second-class lever

In a third-class lever, such as a baseball bat, the input force is between the output force and the fulcrum. For a third-class lever, the output force is less than the input force, but is in the same direction.

Third-class lever

SECTION 3   Simple Machines   **421**

Visualizing Levers

Have students examine the pictures and read the captions. Then ask the following questions.

What are the fundamental differences between 1st-, 2nd-, and 3rd-class levers? They differ in the locations of the input force, output force, and fulcrum.

What are other examples of 1st-class levers? Answers will vary. Possible answers include crowbar, teeter totter or see-saw, and laboratory balances.

What are other examples of 2nd-class levers? Answers will vary. Possible answers include nutcrackers, bottle openers, and doors.

What are other examples of 3rd-class levers? Answers will vary. Possible answers include hammers, tweezers, shovels, rakes, and fishing poles.

Activity

Collecting Levers Have students assemble collections of the three types of levers. Encourage students to find examples that are not listed in this text. L2 LS **Kinesthetic**

Fun Fact

The ancient Greek mathematician Archimedes was the first to understand the full potential of the lever. According to legend, when he announced his discovery to the king, he said, "Give me a place to stand, and I will move the Earth!" He then proceeded to move a grounded ship with an enormous lever.

Differentiated Instruction

English-Language Learners Have students find photos of levers in magazines, catalogues, or other sources. Have students make a poster using their examples. Students should identify which class of lever each example represents. L2

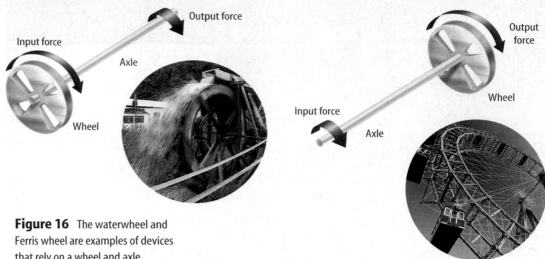

Figure 16 The waterwheel and Ferris wheel are examples of devices that rely on a wheel and axle. **Compare and contrast** *waterwheels and Ferris wheels in terms of wheels and axles.*

Using Wheels and Axles In some devices, the input force is used to turn the wheel and the output force is exerted by the axle. Because the wheel is larger than the axle, the mechanical advantage is greater than one. So the output force is greater than the input force. A doorknob, a steering wheel, and a screwdriver are examples of this type of wheel and axle.

In other devices, the input force is applied to turn the axle and the output force is exerted by the wheel. Then the mechanical advantage is less than one and the output force is less than the input force. A fan and a ferris wheel are examples of this type of wheel and axle. **Figure 16** shows an example of each type of wheel and axle.

Pulley

To raise a sail, a sailor pulls down on a rope. The rope uses a simple machine called a pulley to change the direction of the force needed. A **pulley** consists of a grooved wheel with a rope or cable wrapped over it.

Fixed Pulleys Some pulleys, such as the one on a sail, a window blind, or a flagpole, are attached to a structure above your head. When you pull down on the rope, you pull something up. This type of pulley, called a fixed pulley, does not change the force you exert or the distance over which you exert it. Instead, it changes the direction in which you exert your force, as shown in **Figure 17.** The mechanical advantage of a fixed pulley is 1.

☑ **Reading Check** *How does a fixed pulley affect the input force?*

Visual Learning

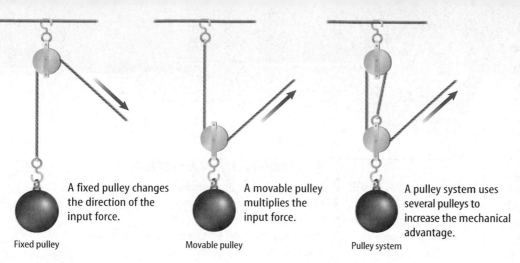

A fixed pulley changes the direction of the input force.

Fixed pulley

A movable pulley multiplies the input force.

Movable pulley

A pulley system uses several pulleys to increase the mechanical advantage.

Pulley system

Movable Pulleys Another way to use a pulley is to attach it to the object you are lifting, as shown in **Figure 17.** This type of pulley, called a movable pulley, allows you to exert a smaller force to lift the object. The mechanical advantage of a movable pulley is always 2.

More often you will see combinations of fixed and movable pulleys. Such a combination is called a pulley system. The mechanical advantage of a pulley system is equal to the number of sections of rope pulling up on the object. For the pulley system shown in **Figure 17** the mechanical advantage is 3.

Figure 17 Pulleys can change force and direction.

3 Assess

DAILY INTERVENTION

Check for Understanding
Linguistic Organize the class into groups, and give each group a machine to present to the class. Group members should describe the features, mechanical advantage, and efficiency of the group's machine and give an example of how it is used. L2

Reteach
Compound Machines Ask each student to bring in a compound machine or a picture of a compound machine. Have them identify the simple machines that make up the machine they selected and explain how they work together to perform the machine's intended function. L2
ELL **IS** **Visual-Spatial**

---

section 3 review

Summary

Simple and Compound Machines
- A simple machine is a machine that does work with only one movement.
- A compound machine is made from a combination of simple machines.

Types of Simple Machines
- An inclined plane is a flat, sloped surface.
- A wedge is an inclined plane that moves.
- A screw is an inclined plane that is wrapped around a cylinder or post.
- A lever is a rigid rod that pivots around a fixed point called the fulcrum.
- A wheel and axle consists of two circular objects of different sizes that rotate together.
- A pulley is a grooved wheel with a rope or cable wrapped over it.

Self Check

1. **Determine** how the mechanical advantage of a ramp changes as the ramp becomes longer.
2. **Explain** how a wedge changes an input force.
3. **Identify** the class of lever for which the fulcrum is between the input force and the output force.
4. **Explain** how the mechanical advantage of a wheel and axle change as the size of the wheel increases.
5. **Think Critically** How are a lever and a wheel and axle similar?

Applying Math

6. **Calculate Length** The Great Pyramid is 146 m high. How long is a ramp from the top of the pyramid to the ground that has a mechanical advantage of 4?
7. **Calculate Force** Find the output force exerted by a moveable pulley if the input force is 50 N.

---

section 3 review

1. The mechanical advantage of a ramp increases as the ramp becomes longer if the height remains the same.
2. A wedge changes the direction of the input force.
3. first class lever
4. As the size of the wheel increases, so does the mechanical advantage.
5. The point that the wheel and axle rotate around would be the fulcrum. The radius of the axle would be the output arm, and the radius of the wheel would be the input arm. The wheel and axle would make a second-class lever.
6. 4×146 m $= 584$ m
7. 2×50 N $= 100$ N

Design Your Own

Pulley Power

Goals
■ **Design** a pulley system.
■ **Measure** the mechanical advantage and efficiency of the pulley system.

Possible Materials
single- and multiple-
    pulley systems
nylon rope
steel bar to support the
    pulley system
meterstick
*metric tape measure
variety of weights to test
    pulleys
force spring scale
brick
*heavy book
balance
*scale
*Alternate materials

Safety Precautions

WARNING: *The brick could be dangerous if it falls. Keep your hands and feet clear of it.*

● **Real-World Question**

Imagine how long it might have taken to build the Sears Tower in Chicago without the aid of a pulley system attached to a crane. Hoisting the 1-ton I beams to a maximum height of 110 stories required large lifting forces and precise control of the beam's movement.

Construction workers also use smaller pulleys that are not attached to cranes to lift supplies to where they are needed. Pulleys are not limited to construction sites. They also are used to lift automobile engines out of cars, to help load and unload heavy objects on ships, and to lift heavy appliances and furniture. How can you use a pulley system to reduce the force needed to lift a load?

● **Form a Hypothesis**

Write a hypothesis about how pulleys can be combined to make a system of pulleys to lift a heavy load, such as a brick. Consider the efficiency of your system.

● **Test Your Hypothesis**

Make a Plan

1. Decide how you are going to support your pulley system. What materials will you use?

2. How will you measure the effort force and the resistance force? How will you determine the mechanical advantage? How will you measure efficiency?

3. **Experiment** by lifting small weights with a single pulley, double pulley, and so on. How efficient are the pulleys? In what ways can you increase the efficiency of your setup?

424   CHAPTER 14 Work and Simple Machines

Alternative Inquiry Lab

Real-World Connection To make this Lab an Inquiry Lab, give the students more personal investment into the problem by connecting it to the real world. Tell the students that they are construction engineers. They must design a pulley system that will lift the construction materials for their construction project. Have students brainstorm how they can design their system so that it can be used on a multiple-story building. The same pulley system should be used throughout the construction project with slight modifications to allow for the increased height of the building. L2

4. Use the results of step 3 to design a pulley system to lift the brick. Draw a diagram of your design. Label the different parts of the pulley system and use arrows to indicate the direction of movement for each section of rope.

Follow Your Plan

1. Make sure your teacher approves your plan before you start.

2. **Assemble** the pulley system you designed. You might want to test it with a smaller weight before attaching the brick.

3. **Measure** the force needed to lift the brick. How much rope must you pull to raise the brick 10 cm?

● Analyze Your Data

1. **Calculate** the ideal mechanical advantage of your design.

2. **Calculate** the actual mechanical advantage of the pulley system you built.

3. **Calculate** the efficiency of your pulley system.

4. How did the mechanical advantage of your pulley system compare with those of your classmates?

● Conclude and Apply

1. **Explain** how increasing the number of pulleys increases the mechanical advantage.

2. **Infer** How could you modify the pulley system to lift a weight twice as heavy with the same effort force used here?

3. **Compare** this real machine with an ideal machine.

Communicating
Your Data

Show your design diagram to the class. Review the design and point out good and bad characteristics of your pulley system. **For more help, refer to the Science Skill Handbook.**

LAB 425

Teaching Strategy
Point out that every time a pulley is added to the system, it introduces more weight and friction. This lowers the efficiency of the pulley system.

Troubleshooting
You may want to divide the class into groups to tackle different parts of the problem during the design phase.

Expected Outcome
A multiple-pulley system can use a small force to raise a heavy load.

● Analyze Your Data

Answers to Questions

1. (length of rope pulled)/(distance load is raised) = MA

2. (weight of load)/(input force) = MA

3. $(W_{out}/W_{in})(100\%) = E$, where $W_{out} = $ (weight)(distance raised) and $W_{in} = $ (input force)(length of rope pulled)

4. Answers will depend on the number of pulleys used and the efficiencies of the pulley systems.

Error Analysis
Have students compare their results and their hypotheses and explain any differences in their results.

● Conclude and Apply

1. Each pulley added increases the mechanical advantage by one.

2. Double the number of pulleys in the system.

3. An ideal pulley system would have an efficiency of 100%. The real system has noticeable loss of efficiency because of friction.

☑ Assessment

Oral How much work would it take for a simple pulley to lift a 910-kg I-beam 460 m? Does the weight of the cable affect the efficiency of the crane as it lifts an I-beam? 4,100,000 J; Yes; the cable is heavy and the crane must lift the cable as well as the I-beam. Use **Performance Assessment in the Science Classroom**, p. 101. L2

Communicating
Your Data

Have each student write a paragraph using information learned in the lab to explain how to design a pulley system with which one person could lift a building stone into position on a wall. L2

Content Background

By using sensors that stimulate nerve cells to send signals to the brain, it is possible to restore some function in senses damaged by injury or disease. For example, researchers are currently developing a retinal implant that will help transmit light messages from the eye to the brain. It is called an Artificial Retina Component Chip. Designed to be implanted near the vision center of the retina, the device transmits messages to the brain via a silicon microchip that is embedded with photosensor cells and electrodes. The photosensor converts patterns of light and dark into electric impulses, stimulating nerves behind the retina that send the information to the brain.

A device called a cochlear implant has enabled many deaf and hearing-impaired individuals to significantly increase their hearing. A cochlear implant is a device implanted in the ear that replaces the function of the cochlea, the organ that translates sound energy into nerve impulses and then sends the impulses to the brain. The device includes a transmitter implanted in the temporal bone and electrodes threaded through the cochlea that help stimulate the nerve fibers. Cochlear implants are no longer considered experimental and are used by thousands worldwide.

Discussion

Reasons What are some reasons people need the prosthetic devices discussed in the article? Possible answers include because of loss of the use of limbs due to accidents, birth defects, or disease. L1 [LS] **Logical-Mathematical**

TIME

SCIENCE AND Society

SCIENCE ISSUES THAT AFFECT YOU!

Bionic People

Artificial limbs can help people lead normal lives

People in need of transplants usually receive human organs. But many people's medical problems can only be solved by receiving artificial body parts. These synthetic devices, called prostheses, are used to replace anything from a heart valve to a knee joint. Bionics is the science of creating artificial body parts. A major focus of bionics is the replacement of lost limbs. Through accident, birth defect, or disease, people sometimes lack hands or feet, or even whole arms or legs.

For centuries, people have used prostheses to replace limbs. In the past, physically challenged people used devices like peg legs or artificial arms that ended in a pair of hooks. These prostheses didn't do much to replace lost functions of arms and legs.

The knowledge that muscles respond to electricity has helped create more effective prostheses. One such prostheses is the myoelectric arm. This battery-powered device connects muscle nerves in an amputated arm to a sensor.

The sensor detects when the arm tenses, then transmits the signal to an artificial hand, which opens or closes. New prosthetic hands even give a sense of touch, as well as cold and heat.

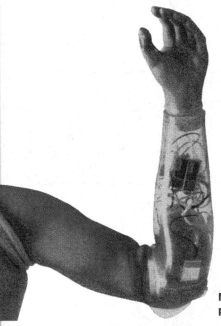

Myoelectric arms make life easier for people who have them.

Research Use your school's media center to find other aspects of robotics such as walking machines or robots that perform planetary exploration. What are they used for? How do they work? You could take it one step further and learn about cyborgs. Report to the class.

Science Online

For more information, visit ips.msscience.com/time

Research Visit ips.msscience.com for information and illustrations on the use of robots for space exploration. Ask students to include information on the success and failure rates of robotics in space. Encourage them to find out why some designs were used more than once and why some were discarded after one excursion.

Resources for Teachers and Students

Spare Parts, by Wendy Murphy. 21st Century Books, 2001

Orthotics and Prosthetics in Rehabilitation, by editors Michelle M. Lusardi and Caroline Nielsen, Butterworth and Heinemann Medical, 2000

Reviewing Main Ideas

Section 1 Work and Power

1. Work is done when a force exerted on an object causes the object to move.

2. A force can do work only when it is exerted in the same direction as the object moves.

3. Work is equal to force times distance, and the unit of work is the joule.

4. Power is the rate at which work is done, and the unit of power is the watt.

Section 2 Using Machines

1. A machine can change the size or direction of an input force or the distance over which it is exerted.

2. The mechanical advantage of a machine is its output force divided by its input force.

Section 3 Simple Machines

1. A machine that does work with only one movement is a simple machine. A compound machine is a combination of simple machines.

2. Simple machines include the inclined plane, lever, wheel and axle, screw, wedge, and pulley.

3. Wedges and screws are inclined planes.

4. Pulleys can be used to multiply force and change direction.

Visualizing Main Ideas

Copy and complete the following concept map on simple machines.

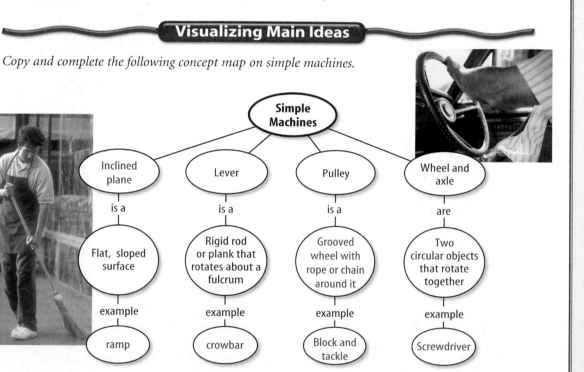

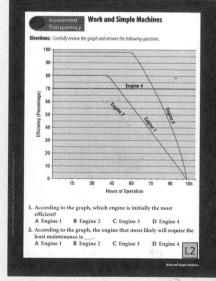

---

chapter
Study Guide **14**

Reviewing Main Ideas

Summary statements can be used by students to review the major concepts of the chapter.

Visualizing Main Ideas

See student page.

Science Online

Visit ips.msscience.com
  /self_check_quiz
  /interactive_tutor
  /vocabulary_puzzlemaker
  /chapter_review
  /standardized_test

Assessment Transparency

For additional assessment questions, use the *Assessment Transparency* located in the transparency book.

Assessment

Assessment Transparency — **Work and Simple Machines**

Directions: *Carefully review the graph and answer the following questions.*

1. According to the graph, which engine is initially the most efficient?
   A Engine 1   B Engine 2   C Engine 3   D Engine 4

2. According to the graph, the engine that most likely will require the least maintenance is ___.
   A Engine 1   B Engine 2   C Engine 3   D Engine 4

L2

Work and Simple Machines

Using Vocabulary

1. efficiency
2. input force
3. output force
4. wheel and axle
5. mechanical advantage
6. simple machine
7. wedge
8. lever
9. inclined plane
10. power

Checking Concepts

11. C   16. C
12. D   17. B
13. B   18. B
14. A   19. B
15. B

Thinking Critically

20. No; it would need to be at least 3 m from the fulcrum.

21. When work is done on the machine, energy is transferred to the machine. When work is done by the machine, the machine transfers energy to another object. According to the law of conservation of energy, energy cannot be created or destroyed. Therefore, the machine cannot create energy, so the energy transferred from the machine cannot be greater than the energy transferred to the machine.

22. The radius of the knob is greater than the radius of the axle. This means that when a force is applied to the knob, the knob moves a greater distance than the axle. The knob and the axle do the same amount of work. Therefore, the axle must multiply the force.

Using Vocabulary

compound machine p. 417	output force p. 412
efficiency p. 415	power p. 409
inclined plane p. 417	pulley p. 422
input force p. 412	screw p. 419
lever p. 420	simple machine p. 417
mechanical advantage p. 413	wedge p. 418
	wheel and axle p. 420
	work p. 406

Each phrase below describes a vocabulary word. Write the vocabulary word that matches the phrase describing it.

1. percentage of work in to work out
2. force put into a machine
3. force exerted by a machine
4. two rigidly attached wheels
5. input force divided by output force
6. a machine with only one movement
7. an inclined plane that moves
8. a rigid rod that rotates about a fulcrum
9. a flat, sloped surface
10. amount of work divided by time

Checking Concepts

Choose the word or phrase that best answers the question.

11. Which of the following is a requirement for work to be done?
    A) Force is exerted.
    B) Object is carried.
    C) Force moves an object.
    D) Machine is used.

12. How much work is done when a force of 30 N moves an object a distance of 3 m?
    A) 3 J   C) 30 J
    B) 10 J   D) 90 J

Science Online ips.msscience.com/vocabulary_puzzlemaker

13. How much power is used when 600 J of work are done in 10 s?
    A) 6 W   C) 600 W
    B) 60 W   D) 610 W

14. Which is a simple machine?
    A) baseball bat   C) can opener
    B) bicycle   D) car

15. Mechanical advantage can be calculated by which of the following expressions?
    A) input force/output force
    B) output force/input force
    C) input work/output work
    D) output work/input work

16. What is the ideal mechanical advantage of a machine that changes only the direction of the input force?
    A) less than 1   C) 1
    B) zero   D) greater than 1

Use the illustration below to answer question 17.

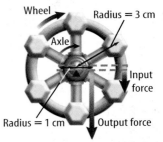

17. What is the output force if the input force on the wheel is 100 N?
    A) 5 N   C) 500 N
    B) 200 N   D) 2,000 N

18. Which of the following is a form of the inclined plane?
    A) pulley   C) wheel and axle
    B) screw   D) lever

19. For a given input force, a ramp increases which of the following?
    A) height   C) output work
    B) output force   D) efficiency

Use the ExamView® Pro Testmaker CD-ROM to:
- create multiple versions of tests
- create modified tests with one mouse click for inclusion students
- edit existing questions and add your own questions
- build tests aligned with state standards using built-in State Curriculum Tags
- change English tests to Spanish with one mouse click and vice versa

Thinking Critically

Use the illustration below to answer question 20.

9 N

3 m

20. **Evaluate** Would a 9-N force applied 2 m from the fulcrum lift the weight? Explain.

21. **Explain** why the output work for any machine can't be greater than the input work.

22. **Explain** A doorknob is an example of a wheel and axle. Explain why turning the knob is easier than turning the axle.

23. **Infer** On the Moon, the force of gravity is less than on Earth. Infer how the mechanical advantage of an inclined plane would change if it were on the Moon, instead of on Earth.

24. **Make and Use Graphs** A pulley system has a mechanical advantage of 5. Make a graph with the input force on the *x*-axis and the output force on the *y*-axis. Choose five different values of the input force, and plot the resulting output force on your graph.

Use the diagram below to answer question 25.

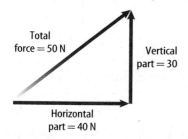

Total force = 50 N

Vertical part = 30

Horizontal part = 40 N

25. **Work** The diagram above shows a force exerted at an angle to pull a sled. How much work is done if the sled moves 10 m horizontally?

Science**Online** ips.msscience.com/chapter_review

Performance Activities

26. **Identify** You have levers in your body. Your muscles and tendons provide the input force. Your joints act as fulcrums. The output force is used to move everything from your head to your hands. Describe and draw any human levers you can identify.

27. **Display** Make a display of everyday devices that are simple and compound machines. For devices that are simple machines, identify which simple machine it is. For compound machines, identify the simple machines that compose it.

Applying Math

28. **Mechanical Advantage** What is the mechanical advantage of a 6-m long ramp that extends from a ground-level sidewalk to a 2-m high porch?

29. **Input Force** How much input force is required to lift an 11,000-N beam using a pulley system with a mechanical advantage of 20?

30. **Efficiency** The input work done on a pulley system is 450 J. What is the efficiency of the pulley system if the output work is 375 J?

Use the table below to answer question 31.

Output Force Exerted by Machines

Machine	Input Force (N)	Output Force (N)
A	500	750
B	300	200
C	225	225
D	800	1,100
E	75	110

31. **Mechanical Advantage** According to the table above, which of the machines listed has the largest mechanical advantage?

23. The mechanical advantage of an inclined plane would be the same on Earth as on the Moon. The mechanical advantage of an inclined plane depends only on its length and height.

24. Check students' graphs.

25. work = force in direction of motion × distance moved by this force = 40 N × 10 m = 400 J

Performance Activities

26. Arms and legs are examples of levers. The elbows and knees are the fulcrums. Forces are exerted by muscles.

27. Check students' displays.

Applying Math

National Math Standards

1, 2, 5, 9

28. $MA = 6/2 = 3$

29. $MA = F_{out}/F_{in}; F_{in} = F_{out}/MA = 11,000 \text{ N}/20 = 550 \text{ N}$

30. $eff = \dfrac{W_{out}}{W_{in}} \times 100\% = \dfrac{375 \text{ J}}{450 \text{ J}} \times 100\% = 83\%$

31. Using the equation $MA = F_{out}/F_{in}$ shows that machine *A* has the largest mechanical advantage.

☑ Assessment Resources

📁 Reproducible Masters

Chapter *Fast File* Resources
Chapter Review, pp. 37–38
Chapter Tests, pp. 39–42
Assessment Transparency Activity, p. 49

Glencoe Science Web site
Chapter Review Test
Standardized Test Practice

Glencoe Technology

- Assessment Transparency
- Exam*View*® Pro Testmaker
- MindJogger Videoquiz
- Interactive Chalkboard

FAST FILE

Answer Sheet A practice answer sheet can be found at ips.msscience.com/answer_sheet.

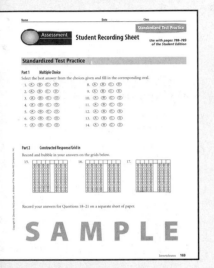

S A M P L E

Part 1 | Multiple Choice

1. B	5. C	9. C
2. A	6. B	
3. C	7. C	
4. D	8. C	

Part 2 | Short Response

10. fulcrum

11. The mechanical advantage of a pulley or pulley system is the number of sections of rope pulling up on the object supported by the pulleys.

12. The tip of the dart is a wedge. The feathers function as wedges as they push the air aside while the dart flies toward its target.

13. Yes, the mechanical advantage of the tip would increase.

14. $W = P \times t = 75 \text{ W} \times 15 \text{ s} = 1{,}125 \text{ J}$

15. $MA = 2 \text{ m}/1 \text{ m} = 2$

16. Possible answers: wedge—teeth; forearm—lever

17. The efficiency of the machine increases because the lubricant decreases friction and less work is converted to thermal energy.

Part 1 | Multiple Choice

Record your answers on the answer sheet provided by your teacher or on a sheet of paper.

1. The work done by a boy pulling a snow sled up a hill is 425 J. What is the power expended by the boy if he pulls on the sled for 10.5 s?
- **A.** 24.7 W
- **B.** 40.5 W
- **C.** 247 W
- **D.** 4460 W

Use the illustration below to answer questions 2 and 3.

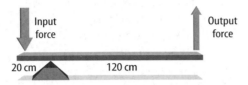

Input force   Output force

20 cm   120 cm

2. What is the mechanical advantage of the lever shown above?
- **A.** $\frac{1}{6}$
- **B.** $\frac{1}{2}$
- **C.** 2
- **D.** 6

3. What would the mechanical advantage of the lever be if the triangular block were moved to a position 40 cm from the edge of the output force side of the plank?
- **A.** $\frac{1}{4}$
- **B.** $\frac{1}{2}$
- **C.** 2
- **D.** 4

4. Which of the following causes the efficiency of a machine to be less than 100%?
- **A.** work
- **B.** power
- **C.** mechanical advantage
- **D.** friction

Test-Taking Tip

Simplify Diagrams Write directly on complex charts, such as a Punnett square.

Use the illustration below to answer questions 5 and 6.

5. The pulley system in the illustration above uses several pulleys to increase the mechanical advantage. What is the mechanical advantage of this system?
- **A.** 1
- **B.** 2
- **C.** 3
- **D.** 4

6. Suppose the lower pulley was removed so that the object was supported only by the upper pulley. What would the mechanical advantage be?
- **A.** 0
- **B.** 1
- **C.** 2
- **D.** 3

7. You push a shopping cart with a force of 12 N for a distance of 1.5 m. You stop pushing the cart, but it continues to roll for 1.1 m. How much work did you do?
- **A.** 8.0 J
- **B.** 13 J
- **C.** 18 J
- **D.** 31 J

8. What is the mechanical advantage of a wheel with a radius of 8.0 cm connected to an axle with a radius of 2.5 cm?
- **A.** 0.31
- **B.** 2.5
- **C.** 3.2
- **D.** 20

9. You push a 5-kg box across the floor with a force of 25 N. How far do you have to push the box to do 63 J of work?
- **A.** 0.40 m
- **B.** 1.6 m
- **C.** 2.5 m
- **D.** 13 m

Part 3 | Open Ended

18. In a real machine, the output work is always less than the input work because some of the work is converted into heat by friction. Energy is conserved in the machine because input work = output work + thermal energy.

19. changing the amount of force exerted; examples: scissors or pliers; changing the distance over which the force is exerted; examples: inclined plane or ramp; changing the direction in which the force is exerted; example: a fixed pulley

20. For some systems, the F_{in} is used to turn the wheel, and the F_{out} is exerted by the axle. The *MA* is greater than one. Examples: doorknob, a steering wheel, and a screwdriver. In other systems, the F_{in} is applied to turn the axle, and

Part 2 | Short Response/Grid In

Record your answers on the answer sheet provided by your teacher or on a sheet of paper.

10. What is the name of the point about which a lever rotates?

11. Describe how you can determine the mechanical advantage of a pulley or a pulley system.

Use the figure below to answer questions 12 and 13.

12. What type of simple machine is the tip of the dart in the photo above?

13. Would the mechanical advantage of the dart tip change if the tip were longer and thinner? Explain.

14. How much energy is used by a 75-W lightbulb in 15 s?

15. The input and output forces are applied at the ends of the lever. If the lever is 3 m long and the output force is applied 1 m from the fulcrum, what is the mechanical advantage?

16. Your body contains simple machines. Name one part that is a wedge and one part that is a lever.

17. Explain why applying a lubricant, such as oil, to the surfaces of a machine causes the efficiency of the machine to increase.

18. Apply the law of conservation of energy to explain why the output work done by a real machine is always less than the input work done on the machine.

Part 3 | Open Ended

Record your answers on a sheet of paper.

19. The output work of a machine can never be greater than the input work. However, the advantage of using a machine is that it makes work easier. Describe and give an example of the three ways a machine can make work easier.

20. A wheel and axle may have a mechanical advantage that is either greater than 1 or less than 1. Describe both types and give some examples of each.

21. Draw a sketch showing the cause of friction as two surfaces slide past each other. Explain your sketch, and describe how lubrication can reduce the friction between the two surfaces.

22. Draw the two types of simple pulleys and an example of a combination pulley. Draw arrows to show the direction of force on your sketches.

Use the figure below to answer question 23.

23. Identify two simple machines in the photo above and describe how they make riding a bicycle easier.

24. Explain why the mechanical advantage of an inclined plane can never be less than 1.

lever, and the pedal crank is a wheel and axle.

24. For the mechanical advantage of an inclined plane to be less than one, the height must be greater than the length of the plane. This is impossible.

Rubrics

For more help evaluating open-ended assessment questions, see the rubric on p. 10T.

the F_{out} is exerted by the wheel. The *MA* is less than one. Examples: fan and Ferris wheel

21. Sketches should show contact points between two irregular surfaces. Applying a lubricant such as oil to the surfaces fills in the gaps between the surfaces, reducing the friction between the surfaces.

22. (1) a fixed pulley supporting an object; (2) rope tied to an upper support and a movable pulley on the rope supporting an object; (3) a pulley system consisting of a fixed pulley and one or more movable pulleys. In each sketch, the F_{in} should be along the rope away from the last pulley in the system.

23. Possible answers: the brakes on the handlebars are levers, the gearshift on the handlebar is a

Section/Objectives	Standards		Labs/Features
Chapter Opener	**National**	**State/Local**	**Launch Lab:** Measuring Temperature, p. 433 **Foldables,** p. 433
	See pp. 16T–17T for a Key to Standards.		A data-collection lab using Probeware technology can be found in the **Probeware Lab Manual,** pp. 49–52
Section 1 Temperature and Thermal Energy ● 3 sessions 📷 1.5 blocks 1. **Explain** how temperature is related to kinetic energy. 2. **Describe** three scales used for measuring temperature. 3. **Define** thermal energy.	National Content Standards: UCP.1, UCP.2, UCP.3, UCP.5, A.1, A.2, B.1, B.3		**Applying Math:** Converting to Celsius, p. 436
Section 2 Heat ● 3 sessions 📷 1.5 blocks 4. **Explain** the difference between thermal energy and heat. 5. **Describe** three ways heat is transferred. 6. **Identify** materials that are insulators or conductors.	National Content Standards: UCP.1, UCP.2, UCP.3, UCP.5, A.1, A.2, B.1, B.2, B.3		**MiniLAB:** Comparing Rates of Melting, p. 440 **MiniLAB:** Observing Convection, p. 441 **Integrate Life Science,** p. 442 **Lab:** Heating Up and Cooling Down, p. 444
Section 3 Engines and Refrigerators ● 4 sessions 📷 2 blocks 7. **Identify** what a heat engine does. 8. **Explain** that energy can exist in different forms, but is never created or destroyed. 9. **Describe** how an internal combustion engine works. 10. **Explain** how refrigerators move heat.	National Content Standards: UCP.1, UCP.2, UCP.3, UCP.5, A.1, A.2, B.2, B.3		**Science Online,** p. 446 **Visualizing the Four-Stroke Cycle,** p. 447 **Integrate Career,** p. 448 **Lab:** Comparing Thermal Insulators, p. 450 **Science and Society:** The Heat is On, p. 452

Lab Materials	Reproducible Resources	Section Assessment	Technology
Launch Lab: water, ice, three pans, refrigerator	**Chapter FAST FILE Resources** Foldables Worksheet, p. 17 Directed Reading Overview, p. 19 Note-taking Worksheets, pp. 33–35	GLENCOE'S **ASSESSMENT** ADVANTAGE	**TeacherWorks** includes: • Interactive Teacher Edition • Lesson Planner with calendar • Access to all program blacklines • Correlations to standards • Web links
Need materials? Contact Science Kit at 1-800-828-7777 or www.sciencekit.com on the Internet.	**Chapter FAST FILE Resources** Transparency Activity, p. 44 Lab Activity, pp. 9–12 Enrichment, p. 30 Reinforcement, p. 27 Directed Reading, p. 20 **Earth Science Critical Thinking/Problem Solving,** p. 10	**Portfolio** Use Science Words, p. 436 **Performance** Applying Math, p. 436 Applying Math, p. 437 **Content** Section Review, p. 437	Section Focus Transparency Guided Reading Audio Program Interactive Chalkboard CD-ROM
MiniLAB: glass, ice, water, 2 coffee cups, clock or watch **MiniLAB:** 250-mL beaker, water, hot plate, 50-mL beaker, penny, metal tongs, dropper, food coloring **Lab:** 5 thermometers, 400-mL beakers (5), stopwatch, refrigerator, stirring rod, hot plate, water, ice	**Chapter FAST FILE Resources** Transparency Activity, p. 45 MiniLABS, pp. 3, 4 Lab Activity, pp. 13–16 Enrichment, p. 31 Reinforcement, p. 28 Directed Reading, p. 20 Lab Worksheets, pp. 5–6 **Physical Science Critical Thinking/Problem Solving,** p. 5 **Cultural Diversity,** p. 41	**Portfolio** Active Reading, p. 440 **Performance** MiniLAB, p. 440 MiniLAB, p. 441 Applying Skills, p. 443 **Content** Section Review, p. 443	Section Focus Transparency Virtual Labs CD-ROM Guided Reading Audio Program Interactive Chalkboard CD-ROM Video Lab
Lab: hot plate, large beaker, water, graduated cylinder, thermometers, various beverage containers (each about the same size and shape), covers for the containers, tongs, stopwatch, thermal gloves or mitts	**Chapter FAST FILE Resources** Transparency Activity, p. 46 Enrichment, p. 32 Reinforcement, p. 29 Directed Reading, pp. 21, 22 Transparency Activity, pp. 47–48 Lab Worksheets, pp. 7–8 **Home and Community Involvement,** p. 49	**Portfolio** Differentiated Instruction, p. 446 **Performance** Applying Skills, p. 449 **Content** Section Review, p. 449	Section Focus Transparency Teaching Transparency Guided Reading Audio Program Interactive Chalkboard CD-ROM

End of Chapter Assessment

GLENCOE'S **ASSESSMENT** ADVANTAGE

Blackline Masters	Technology	Professional Series
Chapter FAST FILE Resources Chapter Review, pp. 37–38 Chapter Tests, pp. 39–42 **Standardized Test Practice,** pp. 63–66	MindJogger Videoquiz Virtual Labs CD-ROM ExamView® Pro Testmaker TeacherWorks CD-ROM Interactive Chalkboard CD-ROM	**Performance Assessment in the Science Classroom (PASC)**

Transparencies

Section Focus

1 Section Focus Transparency — **Coping with Winter**

Japanese macaques are one of the few species of primates that can live outside of the tropics. These macaques live on Honshu Island in Japan.

1. What do you think the air temperature is like in this photo? What is the water temperature like?
2. What do you think might explain the water's temperature?
3. If you were told that the temperature of the water was 40 degrees, would that be meaningful? Why or why not?

L2

2 Section Focus Transparency — **Hot Times**

The image below was made with heat sensitive camera on a cool day. The colors show thermal energy escaping from this building. The color green indicates the coolest areas of the building while the color white shows the warmest. Purple, red, and yellow respresent the stages from green to white.

1. From which parts of the house is the most thermal energy escaping?
2. In what ways might the information from the photo be useful?
3. How do you feel if you sit in the shade on a sunny day? How do you feel in the sun?

L2

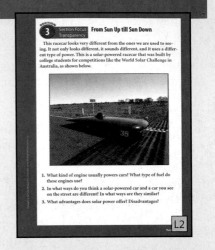

3 Section Focus Transparency — **From Sun Up till Sun Down**

This racecar looks very different from the ones we are used to seeing. It not only looks different, it sounds different, and it uses a different type of power. This is a solar-powered racecar that was built by college students for competitions like the World Solar Challenge in Australia, as shown below.

1. What kind of engine usually powers cars? What type of fuel do these engines use?
2. In what ways do you think a solar-powered car and a car you see on the street are different? In what ways are they similar?
3. What advantages does solar power offer? Disadvantages?

L2

This is a representation of key blackline masters available in the Teacher Classroom Resources. See Resource Manager boxes within the chapter for additional information.

Key to Teaching Strategies

The following designations will help you decide which activities are appropriate for your students.

[L1] Level 1 activities should be appropriate for students with learning difficulties.

[L2] Level 2 activities should be within the ability range of all students.

[L3] Level 3 activities are designed for above-average students.

[ELL] ELL activities should be within the ability range of English Language Learners.

[COOP LEARN] Cooperative Learning activities are designed for small group work.

[LS] Multiple Learning Styles logos, as described on page 12T, are used throughout to indicate strategies that address different learning styles.

[P] These strategies represent student products that can be placed into a best-work portfolio.

[PBL] Problem-Based Learning activities apply real-world situations to learning.

Assessment

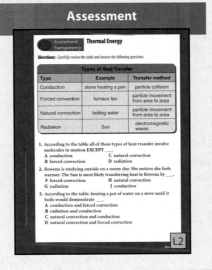

Assessment Transparency — **Thermal Energy**

Directions: Carefully review the table and answer the following questions.

Types of Heat Transfer		
Type	**Example**	**Transfer method**
Conduction	stove heating a pan	particle collision
Forced convection	furnace fan	particle movement from area to area
Natural convection	boiling water	particle movement from area to area
Radiation	Sun	electromagnetic waves

1. According to the table all of these types of heat transfer involve molecules in motion EXCEPT ___.
   A conduction   C natural convection
   B forced convection   D radiation
2. Rowena is studying outside on a sunny day. She notices she feels warmer. The Sun is most likely transferring heat to Rowena by ___.
   F forced convection   H natural convection
   G radiation   J conduction
3. According to the table, heating a pot of water on a stove until it boils would demonstrate ___.
   A conduction and forced convection
   B radiation and conduction
   C natural convection and conduction
   D natural convection and forced convection

L2

Teaching

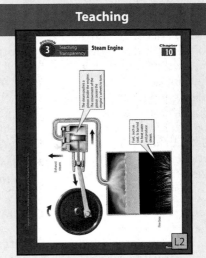

3 Teaching Transparency — **Steam Engine** — Chapter **10**

L2

Hands-on Activities

Student Text Lab Worksheet

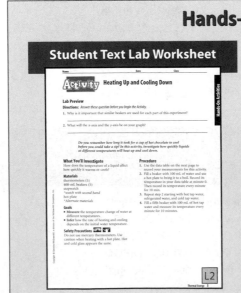

Name _____ Date _____ Class _____

Activity — **Heating Up and Cooling Down**

Lab Preview
Directions: Answer these question before you begin the Activity.
1. Why is it important that similar beakers are used for each part of this experiment?

2. What will the x-axis and the y-axis be on your graph?

Do you remember how long it took for a cup of hot chocolate to cool before you could take a sip? In this activity, investigate how quickly liquids at different temperatures will heat up and cool down.

What You'll Investigate
How does the temperature of a liquid affect how quickly it warms or cools?

Materials
thermometers (5)
400-mL beakers (5)
stopwatch
*watch with second hand
hot plate
*Alternate materials

Goals
• **Measure** the temperature change of water at different temperatures.
• **Infer** how the rate of heating and cooling depends on the initial water temperature.

Safety Precautions
Do not use mercury thermometers. Use caution when heating with a hot plate. Hot and cold glass appears the same.

Procedure
1. Use the data table on the next page to record your measurements for this activity.
2. Fill a beaker with 100 mL of water and use a hot plate to bring it to a boil. Record its temperature in your data table at minute 0. Then record its temperature every minute for 10 min.
3. Repeat step 2 starting with hot tap water, refrigerated water, and cold tap water.
4. Fill a fifth beaker with 100 mL of hot tap water and measure its temperature every minute for 10 minutes.

L2

Laboratory Activities

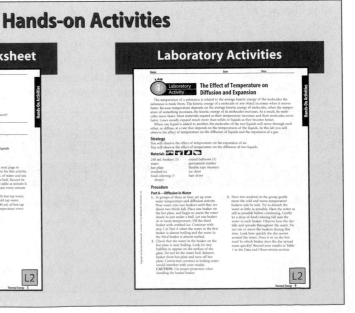

Name _____ Date _____ Class _____

LAB 1 Laboratory Activity — **The Effect of Temperature on Diffusion and Expansion**

The temperature of a substance is related to the average kinetic energy of the molecules the substance is made from. The kinetic energy of a molecule or are object increases when it moves faster. Because temperature depends on the average kinetic energy of molecules, when the temperature of something increases, the kinetic energy of its molecules increases. As a result, the molecules move faster. Most materials expand as their temperature increases and their molecules move faster. Gases usually expand much more than solids or liquids as they become hotter.
When one liquid is added to another, the molecules of the two liquids will move through each other, or diffuse, at a rate that depends on the temperatures of the liquids. In this lab you will observe the effect of temperature on the diffusion of liquids and the expansion of a gas.

Strategy
You will observe the effect of temperature on the expansion of air.
You will observe the effect of temperature on the diffusion of two liquids.

Materials
250 mL beakers (3)   round balloons (3)
water   permanent marker
hot plate   flexible tape measure
crushed ice   ice chest
food coloring (3   hair dryer
drops)

Procedure
Part A—Diffusion in Water
1. In groups of three or four, set up your water temperature and diffusion activity. Pour water into two beakers until they are about two thirds full. Place one beaker on the hot plate, and begin to warm the water slowly to just under a boil. Let one beaker sit at room temperature. Fill the third beaker with crushed ice. Continue with step 2 of Part A when the water in the first beaker is almost boiling and the water in the third beaker is almost melted.
2. Check that the water in the beaker on the hot plate is near boiling. Look for tiny bubbles to appear on the surface of the glass. Do not let the water boil. Remove beaker from hot plate and turn off hot plate. Convection currents in boiling water would interfere with your results.
CAUTION: Use proper protection when handling the heated beaker.
3. Have two students in the group gently move the cold and room-temperature beakers side by side. Try to disturb the water as little as possible. Have the water as still as possible before continuing. Gently let a drop of food coloring fall into the water in each beaker. Observe how the dye falls and spreads throughout the water. Do not stir or move the beakers during this time. Look how quickly the dye moves around the water. Does it sit on the bottom? In which beaker does the dye spread more quickly? Record your results in Table 1 in the Data and Observations section.

L2

Meeting Different Ability Levels

Content Outline

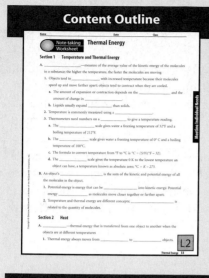

Note-taking Worksheet — Thermal Energy

Section 1 Temperature and Thermal Energy

A. _____—measure of the average value of the kinetic energy of the molecules in a substance; the higher the temperature, the faster the molecules are moving
  1. Objects tend to _____ with increased temperature because their molecules speed up and move farther apart; objects tend to contract when they are cooled.
    a. The amount of expansion or contraction depends on the _____ and the amount of change in _____.
    b. Liquids usually expand _____ than solids.
  2. Temperature is commonly measured using a _____.
  3. Thermometers need numbers on a _____ to give a temperature reading.
    a. The _____ scale gives water a freezing temperature of 32°F and a boiling temperature of 212°F.
    b. The _____ scale gives water a freezing temperature of 0° C and a boiling temperature of 100°C.
    c. The formula to convert temperature from °F to °C is °C = (5/9)(°F − 32).
    d. The _____ scale gives the temperature 0 K to the lowest temperature an object can have, a temperature known as absolute zero: °C = K − 273.
B. An object's _____ is the sum of the kinetic and potential energy of all the molecules in the object.
  1. Potential energy is energy that can be _____ into kinetic energy. Potential energy _____ as molecules move closer together or farther apart.
  2. Temperature and thermal energy are different concepts; _____ is related to the quantity of molecules.

Section 2 Heat

A. _____—thermal energy that is transferred from one object to another when the objects are at different temperatures
  1. Thermal energy always moves from _____ to _____ objects.

Thermal Energy 33 **L2**

Reinforcement

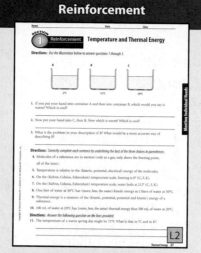

Section 1 Reinforcement — Temperature and Thermal Energy

Directions: *Use the illustration below to answer questions 1 through 3.*

A B C
2°C 15°C 30°C

1. If you put your hand into container A and then into container B, which would you say is warm? Which is cool?

2. Now put your hand into C, then B. Now which is warm? Which is cool?

3. What is the problem in your description of B? What would be a more accurate way of describing B?

Directions: *Correctly complete each sentence by underlining the best of the three choices in parentheses.*

4. Molecules of a substance are in motion (only as a gas, only above the freezing point, all of the time).
5. Temperature is relative to the (kinetic, potential, electrical) energy of the molecules.
6. On the (Kelvin, Celsius, Fahrenheit) temperature scale, freezing is 0° (C, F, K).
7. On the (Kelvin, Celsius, Fahrenheit) temperature scale, water boils at 212° (C, F, K).
8. One liter of water at 50°C has (more, less, the same) kinetic energy as 2 liters of water at 50°C.
9. Thermal energy is a measure of the (kinetic, potential and kinetic) energy of a substance.
10. 100 mL of water at 20°C has (more, less, the same) thermal energy than 500 mL of water at 20°C.

Directions: *Answer the following question on the lines provided.*

11. The temperature of a warm spring day might be 75°F. What is that in °C and in K?

Thermal Energy 27 **L2**

Enrichment

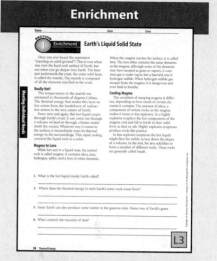

Section 1 Enrichment — Earth's Liquid Solid State

Have you ever heard the expression "standing on solid ground"? This is true when you view the hard rock surface of Earth, but not when you go deeper into Earth. The layer just underneath the crust, the outer solid layer, is called the mantle. The mantle is composed of all the elements you find in the crust.

Really Hot!

The temperatures in the mantle are estimated at thousands of degrees Celsius. The thermal energy that makes this layer so hot comes from the breakdown of radioactive atoms in the very center of Earth.

Every now and again, this hot liquid erupts through Earth's crust. It can come out through a volcano on land or through a fissure underneath the oceans. Whatever way it comes to the surface, it immediately loses its thermal energy to the surroundings. This rapid cooling converts the liquid rock to a solid.

Magma to Lava

While hot and in a liquid state, the melted rock is called magma. It contains silica, iron, hydrogen, sulfur, and a host of other elements.

When the magma reaches the surface, it is called lava. The lava often contains the same elements as the magma, although some of the elements may have escaped as gases or vapors. A common gas is water vapor, but a harmful one is hydrogen sulfide. When hydrogen sulfide gas escapes from the magma, it is dangerous and even fatal to breathe.

Cooling Magma

The condition of escaping magma is different, depending on how much of certain elements it contains. The amount of silica, a component of certain rocks, in the magma makes it more or less explosive. In a highly explosive eruption the hot components of the magma cool and fall to Earth in their solid form as dust or ash. Highly explosive eruptions produce rocks like pumice. In less explosive eruptions the liquid rock might flow for awhile as lava down the slopes of a volcano. In the end, the lava solidifies to form a number of different rocks. These rocks are generally called basalt.

1. What is the hot liquid inside Earth called?

2. Where does the thermal energy to melt Earth's inner rock come from?

3. Inner Earth can also produce some matter in the gaseous state. Name two of Earth's gases.

4. What controls the viscosity of lava?

30 Thermal Energy **L3**

Directed Reading (English/Spanish)

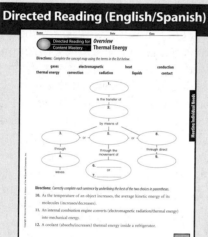

Directed Reading for Content Mastery — Overview — Thermal Energy

Directions: *Complete the concept map using the terms in the list below.*

gases electromagnetic heat conduction
thermal energy convection radiation liquids contact

1. _____
is the transfer of
2. _____
by means of
3. _____   5. _____   8. _____
 or or
through through the movement of through direct
4. _____   6. _____   9. _____
waves or
7. _____

Directions: *Correctly complete each sentence by underlining the best of the two choices in parentheses.*

10. As the temperature of an object increases, the average kinetic energy of its molecules (increases/decreases).
11. An internal combustion engine converts (electromagnetic radiation/thermal energy) into mechanical energy.
12. A coolant (absorbs/increases) thermal energy inside a refrigerator.

Thermal Energy 19 **L1**

Study Guide

Study Guide

Features
- Contains a study guide page for each section of the chapter
- Reviews key concepts
- Includes answer pages

L2

Reading Essentials

Reading Essentials for Glencoe Science
An Interactive Student Workbook

Features
- Condensed core content
- Actively involves students in reading

L1

Assessment

Test Practice Workbook

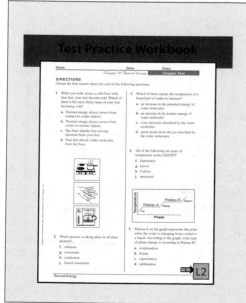

Chapter 10 Thermal Energy — Chapter Test

DIRECTIONS
Choose the best answer choice for each of the following questions.

1. When you walk across a cold floor with bare feet, your feet become cold. Which of these is the most likely cause of your feet becoming cold?
  a. Thermal energy always moves from warmer to cooler objects.
  b. Thermal energy always moves from cooler to warmer objects.
  c. The floor absorbs fast-moving electrons from your feet.
  d. Your feet absorb colder molecules from the floor.

2. Which process is taking place in all three pictures?
  f. radiation
  g. convection
  h. conduction
  j. forced convection

3. Which of these causes the temperature of a heated pot of water to increase?
  a. an increase in the potential energy of water molecules
  b. an increase in the kinetic energy of water molecules
  c. extra electrons absorbed by the water molecules
  d. metal atoms from the pot absorbed by the water molecules

4. All of the following are types of temperature scales EXCEPT
  f. Fahrenheit
  g. kelvin
  h. Celsius
  j. mercurial

5. Plateau A on the graph represents the point when the water is changing from a solid to a liquid. According to the graph, what type of phase change is occurring at Plateau B?
  a. condensation
  b. fusion
  c. vaporization
  d. sublimation

Temperature / Plateau B / Steam / Plateau A / Water / Phase

Thermal Energy **GO ON L2**

Chapter Review

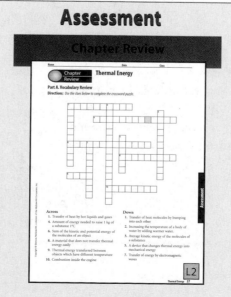

Chapter Review — Thermal Energy

Part A. Vocabulary Review
Directions: *Use the clues below to complete the crossword puzzle.*

Across
1. Transfer of heat by hot liquids and gases
4. Amount of energy needed to raise 1 kg of a substance 1°C
5. Sum of the kinetic and potential energy of the molecules of an object
8. A material that does not transfer thermal energy easily
9. Thermal energy transferred between objects which have different temperature
10. Combustion inside the engine

Down
1. Transfer of heat molecules by bumping into each other
2. Increasing the temperature of a body of water by adding warmer water.
3. Average kinetic energy of the molecules of a substance
6. A device that converts thermal energy into mechanical energy
7. Transfer of energy by electromagnetic waves

Thermal Energy 37 **L2**

Chapter Tests

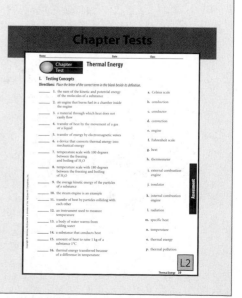

Chapter Test — Thermal Energy

I. Testing Concepts
Directions: *Place the letter of the correct term in the blank beside its definition.*

____ 1. the sum of the kinetic and potential energy of the molecules of a substance
____ 2. an engine that burns fuel in a chamber inside the engine
____ 3. a material through which heat does not easily flow
____ 4. transfer of heat by the movement of a gas or a liquid
____ 5. transfer of energy by electromagnetic waves
____ 6. a device that converts thermal energy into mechanical energy
____ 7. temperature scale with 100 degrees between the freezing and boiling of H_2O
____ 8. temperature scale with 180 degrees between the freezing and boiling of H_2O
____ 9. the average kinetic energy of the particles of a substance
____ 10. the steam engine is an example
____ 11. transfer of heat by particles colliding with each other
____ 12. an instrument used to measure temperature
____ 13. a body of water warms from adding water
____ 14. a substance that conducts heat
____ 15. amount of heat to raise 1 kg of a substance 1°C
____ 16. thermal energy transferred because of a difference in temperature

a. Celsius scale
b. conduction
c. conductor
d. convection
e. engine
f. Fahrenheit scale
g. heat
h. thermometer
i. external combustion engine
j. insulator
k. internal combustion engine
l. radiation
m. specific heat
n. temperature
o. thermal energy
p. thermal pollution

Thermal Energy 39 **L2**

Science Content Background

section 1

Temperature and Thermal Energy
What's hot? What's cold?

The atoms and molecules that make up all matter are in random motion, moving in all directions. It is this random motion that gives rise to the physical property of temperature. At room temperature, for example, the oxygen molecules in air are moving in all directions with an average speed of about 440 m/s. All the molecules in air are constantly colliding with each other and with the surfaces of the room. On average, a molecule in air travels about 10^{-5} cm, or about 1,000 times its diameter, before it collides with another molecule. Each molecule undergoes about five billion collisions each second.

Atoms and molecules in motion have kinetic energy. The temperature of an object is proportional to the average kinetic energy associated with the random motion of the atoms or molecules in the object. The faster the molecules are moving, the more kinetic energy they have, and the higher the temperature.

Temperature is related only to the random motion of the atoms or molecules. The organized motion of the molecules that occurs as an object moves does not affect the random molecular motion. Even though the kinetic energy of a falling ball increases as its speed increases, ignoring the effects of air resistance, the temperature of the ball doesn't change as it falls because the random motion of its molecules hasn't changed.

Thermal Energy

The thermal energy of a material or an object is the total energy of the atoms and molecules associated with their random motions. A molecule has kinetic energy as it moves through space. However, the molecule might be rotating like a top, and its atoms might be vibrating back and forth as if they were connected by springs. These rotational and vibrational motions also contribute to the total energy of a molecule.

Molecules in a substance also can exert intermolecular forces on each other. For example, as two molecules in a gas approach each other, the electric charges on each molecule exert forces

---

chapter content resources

Internet Resources
For additional content background, visit
ips.msscience.com to:
- access your book online
- find references to related articles in popular science magazines
- access Web links with related content background
- access current events with science journal topics

Print Resources
Introduction to Thermal Sciences: Thermodynamics, Fluid Dynamics, and Heat Transfer, Schmidt, Frank W., Henderson, Robert E., Wolgemuth, Carl H., Wiley, 1997
Encyclopedia of Applied Physics Volume 19: Storage of Energy to Thermal Processes, Trig, G.L. (Editor), Vera, E.S. (Editor), Ammergut, Emund H., John Wiley and Sons, 1997
Thermal Physics: Entropy and Free Energies, Lee, Joon Chang, World Scientific Publishing Co., Inc., 2002

that rearrange the charges on the other molecule. Even though the molecules are electrically neutral, this rearrangement of charge produces attractive electric forces between them.

Just as objects attracted to each other by the gravity have potential energy, molecules that are affected by intermolecular forces also have potential energy. If the electric force between molecules is attractive, a molecule's potential energy decreases as the molecules come closer. This potential energy also contributes to the thermal energy of an object.

As a result, the thermal energy of a substance is the sum of the kinetic energy associated with the random motion of its molecules through space, as well as the energy associated with rotational and vibrational motions, and the potential energy due to the electric forces between molecules.

Heat

Heat and Thermal Energy

Suppose two materials with different temperatures are brought into contact. At places where the materials are in contact, the molecules in the different materials can interact with each other. As these molecules collide with each other, kinetic energy is transferred from one molecule to another. The result of these collisions is the transfer of kinetic energy from the molecules in the warmer object to the molecules in the cooler object.

Because the kinetic energy of the molecules in the warmer object decreases, its thermal energy and its temperature decreases. At the same time, the thermal energy and the temperature of the cooler object increases as its molecules gain kinetic energy. Thermal energy has been transferred from the warmer object to the cooler object. This transfer of thermal energy is heat.

When a substance changes state, such as when ice melts or water boils, the temperature of the substance remains constant while the change in state is occurring. The average kinetic energy of the molecules doesn't change as the change in state occurs; instead, the potential energy of the molecules changes.

Thermal Expansion

Most substances expand when heated. As the temperature of a substance increases, its molecules move faster on average, and the distance between molecules increases. Water is unusual in that water is most dense at 4°C, so that water expands as it's cooled from 4°C to 0°C. One consequence is that an entire body of water must cool to 4°C before it can cool any further. So the temperature at the bottom of a pond or lake is above freezing as long as the lake isn't frozen solid. This means that aquatic life can survive at the bottom of large bodies of water during winter.

Teacher to Teacher

Steve Federman
Loveland Middle School
Loveland, Ohio

"To help students see that thermal energy is transferred from the Sun by radiation; we paint one plastic 2-liter bottle white and paint another one black. Next, place a small balloon over the mouth of each bottle, making sure they are airtight, and place both bottles in the sunlight. Within a few minutes the balloon on the black bottle will begin to expand and feel warm as the black bottle absorbs thermal energy, and the air inside expands. The balloon on the white bottle remains limp and the bottle remains cool to the touch, as it absorbs less of the Sun's radiant energy."

Steve Federman

Chapter Vocabulary

Science Journal Possible responses: fanning yourself, jumping into a pool, removing a jacket, putting on a jacket, jumping up and down, standing by a fire.

INTERACTIVE CHALKBOARD with Image Bank

PowerPoint® Presentations

This CD-ROM is an editable Microsoft® PowerPoint® presentation that includes:
• a pre-made presentation for every chapter
• interactive graphics
• animations
• audio clips
• image bank
• all new section and chapter questions
• Standardized Test Practice
• transparencies
• pre-lab questions for all labs
• Foldables directions
• links to ips.msscience.com

Thermal Energy

chapter preview

sections

1 Temperature and Thermal Energy

2 Heat
  Lab Heating Up and Cooling Down

3 Engines and Refrigerators
  Lab Comparing Thermal Insulators
  Virtual Lab How do the insulation properties of various materials compare?

Fastest to the Finish Line

In order to reach an extraordinary speed in a short distance, this dragster depends on more than an aerodynamic design. Its engine must transform the thermal energy produced by burning fuel to mechanical energy, which propels the dragster down the track.

Science Journal Describe five things that you do to make yourself feel warmer or cooler.

Theme Connection

Energy The thermal energy of a material is the sum of the kinetic and potential energy of its particles. Thermal energy can be converted into work in engines and refrigerators.

About the Photo

Dragsters Top fuel dragsters, like this one, can accelerate from 0 to 100 mph in less than one second. These machines have engines that produce over 6,000 horsepower—more than 40 times that of a typical car—and consume more than a gallon of fuel per second. The velocity of the exhaust gases is so high that even a slight variation in the exhaust angle will cause the dragster to veer sideways.

Start-Up Activities

Measuring Temperature

When you leave a glass of ice water on a kitchen table, the ice gradually melts and the temperature of the water increases. What is temperature, and why does the temperature of the ice water increase? In this lab you will explore one way of determining temperature.

1. Obtain three pans. Fill one pan with luke-warm water. Fill a second pan with cold water and crushed ice. Fill a third pan with very warm tap water. Label each pan.

2. Soak one of your hands in the warm water for one minute. Remove your hand from the warm water and put it in the luke-warm water. Does the lukewarm water feel cool or warm?

3. Now soak your hand in the cold water for one minute. Remove your hand from the cold water and place it in the lukewarm water. Does the lukewarm water feel cool or warm?

4. **Think Critically** Write a paragraph in your Science Journal discussing whether your sense of touch would make a useful thermometer.

FOLDABLES™
Study Organizer

Thermal Energy Make the following Foldable to help you identify how thermal energy, heat, and temperature are related.

STEP 1 **Fold** a vertical piece of paper into thirds.

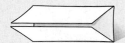

STEP 2 **Turn** the paper horizontally. **Unfold and label** the three columns as shown.

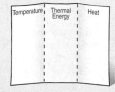

Read for Main Ideas Before you read the chapter, write down what you know about temperature, thermal energy, and heat on the appropriate tab. As you read, add to and correct what you wrote. Write what you have learned about the relationship between heat and thermal energy on the back of your Foldable.

Preview this chapter's content and activities at ips.msscience.com

---

434 CHAPTER 15 Thermal Energy

Bellringer

INTERACTIVE CHALKBOARD
PowerPoint® Presentations

Section Focus Transparencies also are available on the Interactive Chalkboard CD-ROM.

L2 **ELL**

SECTION
1 Section Focus Transparency **Coping with Winter**

Japanese macaques are one of the few species of primates that can live outside of the tropics. These macaques live on Honshu Island in Japan.

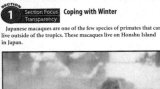

1. What do you think the air temperature is like in this photo? What is the water temperature like?
2. What do you think might explain the water's temperature?
3. If you were told that the temperature of the water was 40 degrees, would that be meaningful? Why or why not?

L2

Thermal Energy

Tie to Prior Knowledge

Daily Temperature Ask students what the temperature would be on a warm day. They will probably say about 85°F. Explain that 85°F is about 29° on the Celsius scale. In this section students will learn about temperature scales and how temperature is related to energy. L2

Temperature and Thermal Energy

as you read

What You'll Learn
- **Explain** how temperature is related to kinetic energy.
- **Describe** three scales used for measuring temperature.
- **Define** thermal energy.

Why It's Important
The movement of thermal energy toward or away from your body determines whether you feel too cold, too hot, or just right.

🔍 Review Vocabulary
kinetic energy: energy a moving object has that increases as the speed of the object increases

New Vocabulary
- temperature
- thermal energy

What is temperature?

Imagine it's a hot day and you jump into a swimming pool to cool off. When you first hit the water, you might think it feels cold. Perhaps someone else, who has been swimming for a few minutes, thinks the water feels warm. When you swim in water, touch a hot pan, or swallow a cold drink, your sense of touch tells you whether something is hot or cold. However, the words *cold, warm,* and *hot* can mean different things to different people.

Temperature How hot or cold something feels is related to its temperature. To understand temperature, think of a glass of water sitting on a table. The water might seem perfectly still, but water is made of molecules that are in constant, random motion. Because these molecules are always moving, they have energy of motion, or kinetic energy.

However, water molecules in random motion don't all move at the same speed. Some are moving faster and some are moving slower. **Temperature** is a measure of the average value of the kinetic energy of the molecules in random motion. The more kinetic energy the molecules have, the higher the temperature. Molecules have more kinetic energy when they are moving faster. So the higher the temperature, the faster the molecules are moving, as shown in **Figure 1.**

Figure 1 The temperature of a substance depends on how fast its molecules are moving. Water molecules are moving faster in the hot water on the left than in the cold water on the right.

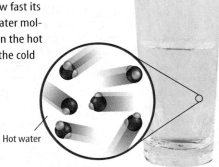

Cold water

Hot water

Section 1 Resource Manager

Chapter *FAST FILE* Resources

Transparency Activity, p. 44

Directed Reading for Content Mastery, pp. 19, 20

Note-taking Worksheets, pp. 33–35

Lab Activity, pp. 9–12

Enrichment, p. 30

Reinforcement, p. 27

Mathematics Skill Activities, p. 11

Thermal Expansion It wasn't an earthquake that caused the sidewalk to buckle in **Figure 2.** Hot weather caused the concrete to expand so much that it cracked, and the pieces squeezed each other upward. When the temperature of an object is increased, its molecules speed up and tend to move farther apart. This causes the object to expand. When the object is cooled, its molecules slow down and move closer together. This causes the object to shrink, or contract.

Almost all substances expand when they are heated and contract when they are cooled. The amount of expansion or contraction depends on the type of material and the change in temperature. For example, liquids usually expand more than solids. Also, the greater the change in temperature, the more an object expands or contracts.

 *Why do materials expand when their temperatures increase?*

Measuring Temperature

The temperature of an object depends on the average kinetic energy of all the molecules in an object. However, molecules are so small and objects contain so many of them, that it is impossible to measure the kinetic energy of all the individual molecules.

A more practical way to measure temperature is to use a thermometer. Thermometers usually use the expansion and contraction of materials to measure temperature. One common type of thermometer uses a glass tube containing a liquid. When the temperature of the liquid increases, it expands so that the height of the liquid in the tube depends on the temperature.

Temperature Scales To be able to give a number for the temperature, a thermometer has to have a temperature scale. Two common temperature scales are the Fahrenheit and Celsius scales, shown in **Figure 3.**

On the Fahrenheit scale, the freezing point of water is given the temperature 32°F and the boiling point 212°F. The space between the boiling point and the freezing point is divided into 180 equal degrees. The Fahrenheit scale is used mainly in the United States.

On the Celsius temperature scale, the freezing point of water is given the temperature 0°C and the boiling point is given the temperature 100°C. Because there are only 100 Celsius degrees between the boiling and freezing point of water, Celsius degrees are bigger than Fahrenheit degrees.

Figure 2 Most objects expand as their temperatures increase. Pieces of this concrete sidewalk forced each other upward when the concrete expanded on a hot day.

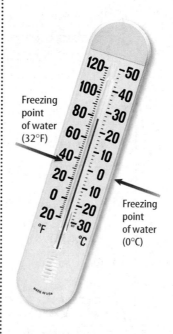

Freezing point of water (32°F)

Freezing point of water (0°C)

Figure 3 The Fahrenheit and Celsius scales are commonly used temperature scales.

Converting Fahrenheit and Celsius You can convert temperatures back and forth between the two temperature scales by using the following equations.

Temperature Conversion Equations

To convert temperature in °F to °C: $°C = (\frac{5}{9})(°F - 32)$

To convert temperature in °C to °F: $°F = (\frac{9}{5})(°C) + 32$

For example, to convert 68°F to degrees Celsius, first subtract 32, multiply by 5, then divide by 9. The result is 20°C.

The Kelvin Scale Another temperature scale that is sometimes used is the Kelvin scale. On this scale, 0 K is the lowest temperature an object can have. This temperature is known as absolute zero. The size of a degree on the Kelvin scale is the same as on the Celsius scale. You can change from Celsius degrees to Kelvin degrees by adding 273 to the Celsius temperature.

$$K = °C + 273$$

Applying Math Solving a Simple Equation

CONVERTING TO CELSIUS On a hot summer day, a Fahrenheit thermometer shows the temperature to be 86°F. What is this temperature on the Celsius scale?

Solution

1 *This is what you know:* Fahrenheit temperature: °F = 86

2 *This is what you need to find:* Celsius temperature: °C

3 *This is the procedure you need to use:* Substitute the Fahrenheit temperature into the equation that converts temperature in °F to °C.
$°C = (\frac{5}{9})(°F - 32) = \frac{5}{9}(86 - 32) = \frac{5}{9}(54) = 30°C$

4 *Check the answer:* Add 32 to your answer and multiply by 9/5. The result should be the given Fahrenheit temperature.

Practice Problems

1. A student's body temperature is 98.6°F. What is this temperature on the Celsius scale?

2. A temperature of 57°C was recorded in 1913 at Death Valley, California. What is this temperature on the Fahrenheit scale?

Science Online For more practice visit ips.msscience.com/ math_practice

Teacher FYI

Absolute Zero Sometimes the claim is made that at absolute zero all molecular motion stops. In fact, at absolute zero molecules still have vibrational energy known as zero point energy.

Differentiated Instruction

Learning Disabled To help learning disabled students understand the Celsius temperature scale, tell them that their clothing requirements will change every ten degrees Celsius from 0°C–30°C. At 0°C, they will need a winter coat. At 10°C, they will only need a jacket. At 20°C, a long sleeve shirt will be warm enough, and at 30°C, shorts and a t-shirt will be most comfortable.

Thermal Energy

The temperature of an object is related to the average kinetic energy of molecules in random motion. But molecules also have potential energy. Potential energy is energy that the molecules have that can be converted into kinetic energy. The sum of the kinetic and potential energy of all the molecules in an object is the **thermal energy** of the object.

The Potential Energy of Molecules When you hold a ball above the ground, it has potential energy. When you drop the ball, its potential energy is converted into kinetic energy as the ball falls toward Earth. It is the attractive force of gravity between Earth and the ball that gives the ball potential energy.

The molecules in a material also exert attractive forces on each other. As a result, the molecules in a material have potential energy. As the molecules get closer together or farther apart, their potential energy changes.

Increasing Thermal Energy Temperature and thermal energy are different. Suppose you have two glasses filled with the same amount of milk, and at the same temperature. If you pour both glasses of milk into a pitcher, as shown in **Figure 4,** the temperature of the milk won't change. However, because there are more molecules of milk in the pitcher than in either glass, the thermal energy of the milk in the pitcher is greater than the thermal energy of the milk in either glass.

Figure 4 At the same temperature, the larger volume of milk in the pitcher has more thermal energy than the smaller volumes of milk in either glass.

section 1 review

Summary

Temperature

- Temperature is related to the average kinetic energy of the molecules an object contains.
- Most materials expand when their temperatures increase.

Measuring Temperature

- On the Celsius scale the freezing point of water is 0°C and the boiling point is 100°C.
- On the Fahrenheit scale the freezing point of water is 32°F and the boiling point is 212°F.

Thermal Energy

- The thermal energy of an object is the sum of the kinetic and potential energy of all the molecules in an object.

Self Check

1. **Explain** the difference between temperature and thermal energy. How are they related?
2. **Determine** which temperature is always larger—an object's Celsius temperature or its Kelvin temperature.
3. **Explain** how kinetic energy and thermal energy are related.
4. **Describe** how a thermometer uses the thermal expansion of a material to measure temperature.

Applying Math

5. **Convert Temperatures** A turkey cooking in an oven will be ready when the internal temperature reaches 180°F. Convert this temperature to °C and K.

section 1 review

1. Temperature is the average kinetic energy of the particles in matter. Thermal energy is the total kinetic and potential energy of the particles.
2. The temperature on the Kelvin scale is always a larger number because 273 is added to the Celsius temperature.
3. The thermal energy of a material is the sum of the kinetic energy and the potential energy of all the molecules in the material. The thermal energy increases as the kinetic energy of the molecules increases.
4. As the temperature increases, molecules in a material move faster, causing the material to expand. As a result, the amount of expansion is related to the increase in temperature.
5. 82.2°C; 355.2 K

3 Assess

DAILY INTERVENTION

Check for Understanding

Logical-Mathematical If the temperature of a liquid is 8°C, what is its temperature on the Fahrenheit scale? 46.4°F On the Kelvin scale? 281 K L3

Reteach

Daytime Temperature Have students work in pairs using the Internet and other reference sources to determine the typical daytime temperature in your community for each season. Ask them to give the temperatures in Fahrenheit, Celsius, and kelvin. L2 LS **Naturalist**

Design a Temperature Scale Have students work in small groups to design a temperature scale based on something other than the boiling and freezing points of water. L3 LS **Logical-Mathematical**

Assessment

Oral Have small groups of students practice converting between Fahrenheit and Celsius. One student will say a Fahrenheit temperature and see which of the other students can first calculate the temperature in Celsius. Use **Performance Assessment in the Science Classroom,** p. 101. L2

Section Focus Transparencies also are available on the Interactive Chalkboard CD-ROM.

L2 ELL

Tie to Prior Knowledge

Heat Ask students to name some ways things are heated. They might mention heating food in a microwave, a furnace heating a home, or heat from the Sun on a summer day. This section explores heat and the ways thermal energy is transferred. L2

---

as you read

What You'll Learn
■ **Explain** the difference between thermal energy and heat.
■ **Describe** three ways heat is transferred.
■ **Identify** materials that are insulators or conductors.

Why It's Important
To keep you comfortable, the flow of heat into and out of your house must be controlled.

🔎 Review Vocabulary
electromagnetic wave: a wave produced by vibrating electric charges that can travel in matter and empty space

New Vocabulary
● heat
● conduction
● radiation
● convection
● conductor
● specific heat
● thermal pollution

Heat and Thermal Energy

It's the heat of the day. Heat the oven to 375°F. A heat wave has hit the Midwest. You've often heard the word *heat*, but what is it? Is it something you can see? Can an object have heat? Is heat anything like thermal energy? **Heat** is thermal energy that is transferred from one object to another when the objects are at different temperatures. The amount of heat that is transferred when two objects are brought into contact depends on the difference in temperature between the objects.

For example, no heat is transferred when two pots of boiling water are touching, because the water in both pots is at the same temperature. However, heat is transferred from the pot of hot water in **Figure 5** that is touching a pot of cold water. The hot water cools down and the cold water gets hotter. Heat continues to be transferred until both objects are the same temperature.

Transfer of Heat When heat is transferred, thermal energy always moves from warmer to cooler objects. Heat never flows from a cooler object to a warmer object. The warmer object loses thermal energy and becomes cooler as the cooler object gains thermal energy and becomes warmer. This process of heat transfer can occur in three ways—by conduction, radiation, or convection.

Figure 5 Heat is transferred only when two objects are at different temperatures. Heat always moves from the warmer object to the cooler object.

438 CHAPTER 15 Thermal Energy

Section 2 Resource Manager

Chapter *FAST FILE* Resources
Transparency Activity, p. 45
Directed Reading for Content Mastery, p. 20
MiniLAB, pp. 3, 4
Lab Activity, pp. 13–16

Enrichment, p. 31
Reinforcement, p. 28
Lab Worksheets, pp. 5–6
Reading and Writing Skill Activities, pp. 13, 33

Conduction

When you eat hot pizza, you experience conduction. As the hot pizza touches your mouth, heat moves from the pizza to your mouth. This transfer of heat by direct contact is called conduction. **Conduction** occurs when the particles in a material collide with neighboring particles.

Imagine holding an ice cube in your hand, as in **Figure 6.** The faster-moving molecules in your warm hand bump against the slower-moving molecules in the cold ice. In these collisions, energy is passed from molecule to molecule. Heat flows from your warmer hand to the colder ice, and the slow-moving molecules in the ice move faster. As a result, the ice becomes warmer and its temperature increases. Molecules in your hand move more slowly as they lose thermal energy, and your hand becomes cooler.

Conduction usually occurs most easily in solids and liquids, where atoms and molecules are close together. Then atoms and molecules need to move only a short distance before they bump into one another and transfer energy. As a result, heat is transferred more rapidly by conduction in solids and liquids than in gases.

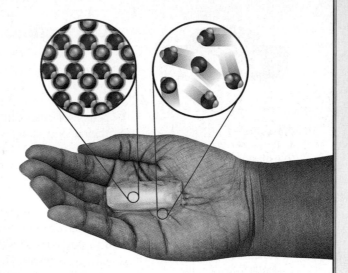

Figure 6 An ice cube in your hand melts because of conduction. The solid ice melts, becoming liquid water. Molecules in the water move faster than molecules in the ice.
Explain how the thermal energy of the ice cube changes.

> **Reading Check** Why does conduction occur more easily in solids and liquids than in gases?

Radiation

On a beautiful, clear day, you walk outside and notice the warmth of the Sun. You know that the Sun heats Earth, but how does this transfer of thermal energy occur? Heat transfer does not occur by conduction because almost no matter exists between the Sun and Earth. Instead, heat is transferred from the Sun to Earth by radiation. Heat transfer by **radiation** occurs when energy is transferred by electromagnetic waves. These waves carry energy through empty space, as well as through matter. The transfer of thermal energy by radiation can occur in empty space, as well as in solids, liquids, and gases.

The Sun is not the only source of radiation. All objects emit electromagnetic radiation, although warm objects emit more radiation than cool objects. The warmth you feel when you sit next to a fireplace is due to heat transferred by radiation from the fire to your skin.

SECTION 2 Heat **439**

Fun Fact

The radiation humans feel as heat has wavelengths in the infrared region of the electromagnetic spectrum.

Teacher FYI

Electromagnetic Radiation The wavelength of electromagnetic radiation an object emits is determined in part by its temperature. Objects at higher temperatures emit radiation with shorter wavelengths, and objects at lower temperatures emit radiation with longer wavelengths.

---

2 Teach

Activity

Passing Cards To demonstrate the difference between thermal energy and heat, cut out several large cardboard circles. On one side of each circle write "thermal energy," and on the other side write "heat." Have two groups of students stand near each other. Have one group hold cards with the "thermal energy" side showing. Then have the group pass the cards to the other group. During the transfer, the "heat" side should be showing. When the other group receives the cards, they should be turned again to show the "thermal energy" side. L2 **⬛ Kinesthetic**

Caption Answer

Figure 6 The thermal energy of the ice cube increases.

> **Reading Check**

Answer The atoms and molecules are closer to one another.

Inquiry Lab

Kinetic Energy and Diffusion

Purpose To explore and observe the effects of kinetic energy on the diffusion of molecules in a liquid, have students design experiments using water at various temperatures and food coloring. L2

Materials three containers, hot water, warm water, cold water, food coloring

Estimated Time half class session

Teaching Strategy Students should observe, summarize, and hypothesize about the rates of diffusion of food coloring through water samples of different temperatures.

For additional inquiry activities, see *Science Inquiry Labs.*

Mini LAB

Purpose Students observe the effect of ice water on melting ice. L2 **LS Kinesthetic**

Materials glass, ice, water, two coffee cups, timer

Teaching Strategy If possible, use clear cups so students can watch the ice melt.

Analysis

1. The ice cube in the ice water melted faster. Ice water is a poor insulator.
2. Air is a better insulator. The molecules in air are farther apart than those in water, so they don't collide as often and therefore they don't transfer thermal energy as fast.

Assessment

Process Have students write up their results as lab reports. Suggest they include illustrations. Use **Performance Assessment in the Science Classroom,** p. 119.

Try at Home

Discussion

Rising Air Why is it usually warmer near the ceiling of a room rather than near the floor? Warmer air is less dense than the cooler air around it, and is pushed upward by the denser, cooler air. L3 **LS Logical-Mathematical**

Mini LAB

Comparing Rates of Melting

Procedure

1. Prepare ice water by filling a **glass** with ice and then adding water. Let the glass sit until all the ice melts.
2. Place an ice cube in a **coffee cup.**
3. Place a similar-sized ice cube in another **coffee cup** and add ice water to a depth of about 1 cm.
4. Time how long it takes both ice cubes to melt.

Analysis

1. Which ice cube melted fastest? Why?
2. Is air or water a better insulator? Explain.

Try at Home

Figure 7 Wind movement near a lake or ocean can result from natural convection. Air is heated by the land and becomes less dense. Denser cool air rushes in, pushing the warm air up. The cooler air then is heated by the land and the cycle is repeated.

Convection

When you heat a pot of water on a stove, heat can be transferred through the water by a process other than conduction and radiation. In a gas or liquid, molecules can move much more easily than they can in a solid. As a result, the more energetic molecules can travel from one place to another, and carry their energy along with them. This transfer of thermal energy by the movement of molecules from one part of a material to another is called **convection.**

Transferring Heat by Convection As a pot of water is heated, heat is transferred by convection. First, thermal energy is transferred to the water molecules at the bottom of the pot from the stove. These water molecules move faster as their thermal energy increases. The faster-moving molecules tend to be farther apart than the slower-moving molecules in the cooler water above. Because the molecules are farther apart in the warm water, this water is less dense than the cooler water. As a result, the warm water rises and is replaced at the bottom of the pot by cooler water. The cooler water is heated, rises, and the cycle is repeated until all the water in the pan is at the same temperature.

Natural Convection Natural convection occurs when a warmer, less dense fluid is pushed away by a cooler, denser fluid. For example, imagine the shore of a lake. During the day, the water is cooler than the land. As shown in **Figure 7,** air above the warm land is heated by conduction. When the air gets hotter, its particles move faster and get farther from each other, making the air less dense. The cooler, denser air from over the lake flows in over the land, pushing the less dense air upward. You feel this movement of incoming cool air as wind. The cooler air then is heated by the land and also begins to rise.

Warm air

Cool air

Active Reading

Cause-and-Effect Chart This strategy is used to focus on cause-and-effect reasoning. In the center, students write the topic that they are trying to understand. On the left side, they write the apparent causes of the topic. On the right side, they write the apparent effects of the topic. Have students design a Cause-and-Effect chart for convection. P L2

Fluid is heated.		Warmer fluid is less dense.
Less dense fluid is pushed upward.	Convection	Rising fluid cools.
Fluid becomes more dense as it cools.		Cool fluid sinks.

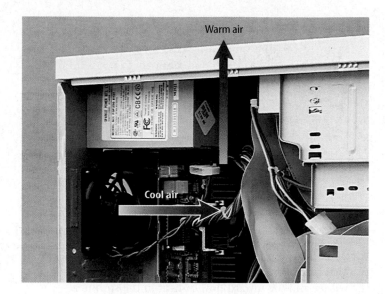

Warm air

Cool air

Figure 8 This computer uses forced convection to keep the electronic components surrounded by cooler air.
Identify *another example of forced convection.*

Forced Convection

Sometimes convection can be forced. Forced convection occurs when an outside force pushes a fluid, such as air or water, to make it move and transfer heat. A fan is one type of device that is used to move air. For example, computers use fans to keep their electronic components from getting too hot, which can damage them. The fan blows cool air onto the hot electronic components, as shown in **Figure 8.** Heat from the electronic components is transferred to the air around them by conduction. The warm air is pushed away as cool air rushes in. The hot components then continue to lose heat as the fan blows cool air over them.

Thermal Conductors

Why are cooking pans usually made of metal? Why does the handle of a metal spoon in a bowl of hot soup become warm? The answer to both questions is that metal is a good conductor. A **conductor** is any material that easily transfers heat. Some materials are good conductors because of the types of atoms or chemical compounds they are made up of.

Reading Check *What is a conductor?*

Remember that an atom has a nucleus surrounded by one or more electrons. Certain materials, such as metals, have some electrons that are not held tightly by the nucleus and are freer to move around. These loosely held electrons can bump into other atoms and help transfer thermal energy. The best conductors of heat are metals such as gold and copper.

Observing Convection

Procedure

1. Fill a **250-mL beaker** with room-temperature **water** and let it stand undisturbed for at least 1 min.
2. Using a **hot plate,** heat a small amount of water in a **50-mL beaker** until it is almost boiling. **WARNING:** *Do not touch the heated hot plate.*
3. Carefully drop a **penny** into the hot water and let it stand for about 1 min.
4. Take the penny out of the hot water with **metal tongs** and place it on a table. Immediately place the 250-mL beaker on the penny.
5. Using a **dropper,** gently place one drop of **food coloring** on the bottom of the 250-mL beaker of water.
6. Observe what happens in the beaker for several minutes.

Analysis
What happened when you placed the food coloring in the 250-mL beaker? Why?

Caption Answer
Figure 8 The use of an electric fan to make a person feel cooler.

Purpose Students observe convection. L2 LS **Kinesthetic**

Materials 250-mL beaker, hot plate, water, 50-mL beaker, penny, metal tongs, dropper, food coloring

Teaching Strategy Students should observe that the column of water directly above the penny (the heat source) is most affected by the convection currents.

Safety Precautions Remind students not to touch the hot plate.

Troubleshooting Be sure that the water is as still as possible when adding the food coloring.

Analysis
A column of colored water rose through the clear water, then fell on the sides. The hot water is less dense than the cool water, so the hot water was pushed upward.

Assessment

Process Ask students to predict what would happen to the water in the beaker if they continued to apply thermal energy only to the center part. The food coloring would be completely mixed in so that all of the water would become colored. Use **Performance Assessment in the Science Classroom,** p. 89.

Reading Check

Answer any material that easily transfers heat

Differentiated Instruction

English-Language Learners To help English Language Learners understand the distinction between convection and conduction, explain that conduction is like when you touch something hot, your hand is heated by conduction. Convection is like being heated up in a sauna. L2 **Linguistic**

Visual Learning

Figure 8 In order for forced convection to be possible, the computer must be designed to allow sufficient air flow. Have students describe how this is done in this picture. Ask students to suggest an alternate method for dissipating thermal energy in computers. Some computers are designed to use natural, rather than forced, convection. L2 LS **Visual-Spatial**

Animal Insulation A polar bear's long, outer "guard hairs" are hollow in order to trap heat from the Sun. A thick under-coat of fur provides insulation, and the bear's black skin absorbs heat from the guard hairs. Blubber is a layer of fat cells and connective tissue that serves as insulation to help retain body heat.

Make a Model

Energy Efficiency Have students work in small groups to make models of an energy-efficient room. Ceilings of the rooms should be removable so students can demonstrate and explain the design to the rest of the class. Students should be encouraged to use what they have learned about the transfer of thermal energy, insulators, and conductors in their designs. Models can be tested and compared by heating them with a lamp and measuring the change in temperature over a period of time. L3 ELL COOP LEARN LS **Kinesthetic**

Virtual Labs

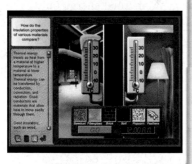

Insulation *How do the insulation properties of various materials compare?*

Animal Insulation
To survive in its arctic environment, a polar bear needs good insulation against the cold. Underneath its fur, a polar bear has 10 cm of insulating blubber. Research how animals in polar regions are able to keep themselves warm. Summarize the different ways in your Science Journal.

Figure 9 The insulation in houses and buildings helps reduce the transfer of heat between the air inside and air outside.

Thermal Insulators

If you're cooking food, you want the pan to conduct heat easily from the stove to your food, but you do not want the heat to move easily to the handle of the pan. An insulator is a material in which heat doesn't flow easily. Most pans have handles that are made from insulators. Liquids and gases are usually better insulators than solids are. Air is a good insulator, and many insulating materials contain air spaces that reduce the transfer of heat by conduction within the material. Materials that are good conductors, such as metals, are poor insulators, and poor conductors are good insulators.

Houses and buildings are made with insulating materials to reduce heat conduction between the inside and outside. Fluffy insulation like that shown in **Figure 9** is put in the walls. Some windows have double layers of glass that sandwich a layer of air or other insulating gas. This reduces the outward flow of heat in the winter and the inward flow of heat in the summer.

Heat Absorption

On a hot day, you can walk barefoot across the lawn, but the asphalt pavement of a street is too hot to walk on. Why is the pavement hotter than the grass? The change in temperature of an object as it absorbs heat depends on the material it is made of.

Specific Heat The amount of heat needed to change the temperature of a substance is related to its specific heat. The **specific heat** of a substance is the amount of heat needed to raise the temperature of 1 kg of that substance by 1°C.

More heat is needed to change the temperature of a material with a high specific heat than one with a low specific heat. For example, the sand on a beach has a lower specific heat than water. When you're at the beach during the day, the sand feels much warmer than the water does. Radiation from the Sun warms the sand and the water. Because of its lower specific heat, the sand heats up faster than the water. At night, however, the sand feels cool and the water feels warmer. The temperature of the water changes more slowly than the temperature of the sand as they both lose thermal energy to the cooler night air.

 LAB DEMONSTRATION

Purpose to observe how water conducts thermal energy away from a container so that it doesn't overheat and burn L2

Materials balloon; water; candle flame; sheet of paper cut, folded, and taped into a paper box with top open and all edges sealed with tape

Procedure Fill the balloon with water. Place the candle flame directly in contact with the balloon. You may hold it there for some time. Fill the paper box with water and hold the flame in contact with the box.

Expected Outcome The balloon and the box will get warm, but they will not ignite.

Assessment

The candle flame was very hot. Why didn't it catch the paper or balloon on fire? The water conducted the thermal energy away from the balloon and the paper. Water has a high specific heat, so it could absorb a large amount of thermal energy without a large temperature change.

Thermal Pollution

 Some electric power plants and factories that use water for cooling produce hot water as a by-product. If this hot water is released into an ocean, lake, or river, it will raise the temperature of the water nearby. This increase in the temperature of a body of water caused by adding warmer water is called **thermal pollution.** Rainwater that is heated after it falls on warm roads or parking lots also can cause thermal pollution if it runs off into a river or lake.

Effects of Thermal Pollution Increasing the water temperature causes fish and other aquatic organisms to use more oxygen. Because warmer water contains less dissolved oxygen than cooler water, some organisms can die due to a lack of oxygen. Also, in warmer water, many organisms become more sensitive to chemical pollutants, parasites, and diseases.

Reducing Thermal Pollution Thermal pollution can be reduced by cooling the warm water produced by factories, power plants, and runoff before it is released into a body of water. Cooling towers like the ones shown in **Figure 10** are used to cool the water used by some power plants and factories.

Figure 10 This power plant uses cooling towers to cool the warm water produced by the power plant.

---

section 2 review

Summary

Heat and Thermal Energy
- Heat is the transfer of thermal energy due to a temperature difference.
- Heat always moves from a higher temperature to a lower temperature.

Conduction, Radiation, and Convection
- Conduction is the transfer of thermal energy when substances are in direct contact.
- Radiation is the transfer of thermal energy by electromagnetic waves.
- Convection is the transfer of thermal energy by the movement of matter.

Thermal Conductors and Specific Heat
- A thermal conductor is a material in which heat moves easily.
- The specific heat of a substance is the amount of heat needed to raise the temperature of 1 kg of the substance by 1°C.

Self Check

1. **Explain** why materials such as plastic foam, feathers, and fur are poor conductors of heat.
2. **Explain** why the sand on a beach cools down at night more quickly than the ocean water.
3. **Infer** If a substance can contain thermal energy, can a substance also contain heat?
4. **Describe** how heat is transferred from one place to another by convection.
5. **Explain** why a blanket keeps you warm.
6. **Think Critically** In order to heat a room evenly, should heating vents be placed near the floor or near the ceiling of the room? Explain.

Applying Skills

7. **Design an Experiment** to determine whether wood or iron is a better thermal conductor. Identify the dependent and independent variables in your experiment.

---

section 2 review

1. They contain small pockets of air, which is a poor heat conductor. The trapped air prevents heat from moving easily through the material.
2. The sand on a beach has a lower specific heat than the water. As a result, its temperature changes more than the water temperature as the water and sand transfer heat to their surroundings.
3. No, heat is thermal energy that is transferred from one place to another.
4. As the temperature in one part of a fluid increases, the fluid becomes less dense and is pushed upward by the cooler surrounding fluid. As the warmer fluid moves upward, it transfers heat to the cooler fluid around, until it becomes cool enough to sink.
5. A blanket is an insulator that reduces the rate at which heat is transferred from your body to your surroundings.
6. near the floor, so that warm air rises and transfers thermal energy to the cooler air at all levels in the room
7. Place a piece of wax at one end of an iron rod and a wood rod of equal dimensions, then place the other end of each rod in a beaker of hot water. The wax will melt from the better conductor first. Independent variables: temperature of hot water, dimensions of rods; dependent variable: composition of rod.

Real-World Question

Purpose Students observe how the initial temperature of a liquid affects how quickly it warms or cools. L2

Process Skills observe, compare, measure in SI, make and use tables, record data, make and use graphs, infer

Time Required 45 min

Procedure

Safety Precautions Caution students to use oven mitts when removing hot beakers from the plate.

Teaching Strategies

- Remind students to fill each beaker to exactly the 100-mL line.
- Students should allow the hot plate to heat up before placing the first beaker of water on the hot plate. Remind students NOT to change the heat setting on the hot plate.
- Suggest students use different colored pencils to plot each of the five lines on the graph.

Conclude and Apply

1. Graphics may vary, but should indicate that the colder the initial temperature of the water, the lower its temperature will be after 10 min. The boiling water and the hot tap water will decrease in temperature over 10 minutes.
2. The rates of heating and cooling should be greater for the water with the greater difference between its initial temperature and the room temperature.
3. The greater the difference between room temperature and initial temperature, the greater the heating or cooling rate.

Heating Up and Cooling Down

Do you remember how long it took for a cup of hot chocolate to cool before you could take a sip? The hotter the chocolate, the longer it seemed to take to cool.

Real-World Question

How does the temperature of a liquid affect how quickly it warms or cools?

Goals

- Measure the temperature change of water at different temperatures.
- Infer how the rate of heating or cooling depends on the initial water temperature.

Materials

thermometers (5)
400-mL beakers (5)
stopwatch
*watch with second hand
hot plate
*Alternate materials

Safety Precautions

WARNING: *Do not use mercury thermometers. Use caution when heating with a hot plate. Hot and cold glass appears the same.*

Procedure

1. Make a data table to record the temperature of water in five beakers every minute from 0 to 10 min.
2. Fill one beaker with 100 mL of water. Place the beaker on a hot plate and bring the water to a boil. Carefully remove the hot beaker from the hot plate.

3. Record the water temperature at minute 0, and then every minute for 10 min.
4. Repeat step 3 starting with hot tap water, cold tap water, refrigerated water, and ice water with the ice removed.

Conclude and Apply

1. **Graph** your data. **Plot and label** lines for all five beakers on one graph.
2. **Calculate** the rate of heating or cooling for the water in each beaker by subtracting the initial temperature of the water from the final temperature and then dividing this answer by 10 min.
3. **Infer** from your results how the difference between room temperature and the initial temperature of the water affected the rate at which it heated up or cooled down.

Communicating Your Data

Share your data and graphs with other classmates and explain any differences among your data.

✓ Assessment

Process Ask students to hypothesize what happens to the rate of cooling or warming as the temperature of the water in the beakers becomes closer to room temperature. The rate of warming or cooling will slow as the difference in temperature between the water and room temperature becomes smaller. Use **Performance Assessment in the Science Classroom,** p. 93. L2

Communicating Your Data

Suggest students use a spreadsheet program to graph their results. Students should discuss why their data and graphs did or did not agree.

Engines and Refrigerators

Heat Engines

The engines used in cars, motorcycles, trucks, and other vehicles, like the one shown in **Figure 11,** are heat engines. A **heat engine** is a device that converts thermal energy into mechanical energy. Mechanical energy is the sum of the kinetic and potential energy of an object. The heat engine in a car converts thermal energy into mechanical energy when it makes the car move faster, causing the car's kinetic energy to increase.

Forms of Energy There are other forms of energy besides thermal energy and mechanical energy. For example, chemical energy is energy stored in the chemical bonds between atoms. Radiant energy is the energy carried by electromagnetic waves. Nuclear energy is energy stored in the nuclei of atoms. Electrical energy is the energy carried by electric charges as they move in a circuit. Devices such as heat engines convert one form of energy into other useful forms.

The Law of Conservation of Energy When energy is transformed from one form to another, the total amount of energy doesn't change. According to the law of conservation of energy, energy cannot be created or destroyed. Energy only can be transformed from one form to another. No device, including a heat engine, can produce energy or destroy energy.

as you read

What **You'll Learn**

- **Describe** what a heat engine does.
- **Explain** that energy can exist in different forms, but is never created or destroyed.
- **Describe** how an internal combustion engine works.
- **Explain** how refrigerators move heat.

Why **It's Important**

Heat engines enable you to travel long distances.

⊙ Review Vocabulary

work: a way of transferring energy by exerting a force over a distance

New Vocabulary

- heat engine
- internal combustion engine

Figure 11 The engine in this earth mover transforms thermal energy into mechanical energy that can perform useful work.

SECTION 3 Engines and Refrigerators **445**

Figure 12 Internal combustion engines are found in many tools and machines.

Internal Combustion Engines The heat engine you are probably most familiar with is the internal combustion engine. In **internal combustion engines**, the fuel burns in a combustion chamber inside the engine. Many machines, including cars, airplanes, buses, boats, trucks, and lawn mowers, use internal combustion engines, as shown in **Figure 12.**

Most cars have an engine with four or more combustion chambers, or cylinders. Usually the more cylinders an engine has, the more power it can produce. Each cylinder contains a piston that can move up and down. A mixture of fuel and air is injected into a combustion chamber and ignited by a spark. When the fuel mixture is ignited, it burns explosively and pushes the piston down. The up-and-down motion of the pistons turns a rod called a crankshaft, which turns the wheels of the car. **Figure 13** shows how an internal combustion engine converts thermal energy to mechanical energy in a process called the four-stroke cycle.

Several kinds of internal combustion engines have been designed. In diesel engines, the air in the cylinder is compressed to such a high pressure that the highly flammable fuel ignites without the need for a spark plug. Many lawn mowers use a two-stroke gasoline engine. The first stroke is a combination of intake and compression. The second stroke is a combination of power and exhaust.

✓ Reading Check *How does the burning of fuel mixture cause a piston to move?*

Science Journal

Steam Engines The earliest documented steam engine was produced by Heron of Alexandria in ancient Greece. Have students find out more about this engine and draw illustrations of it in their Science Journals. Ask them to include descriptions of how the engine worked. The recoil of steam from inside a ball made the ball rotate. ⌶L2⌶ **LS** **Visual-Spatial**

Differentiated Instruction

Challenge Have students research how a jet engine works and prepare a computer presentation about it. A jet engine is a gas turbine engine. As air rushes into the engine, a compressor increases its pressure and temperature. A fine spray of fuel is injected into the high-pressure air and burned. This causes the air to expand, so that it turns a turbine. Part of the energy from the turbine is used to power the compressor. The remainder leaves the system as exhaust to propel the plane forward. ⌶L3⌶ **LS** **Logical-Mathematical** ⌶P⌶

Figure 13

Most modern cars are powered by fuel-injected internal combustion engines that have a four-stroke combustion cycle. Inside the engine, thermal energy is converted into mechanical energy as gasoline is burned under pressure inside chambers known as cylinders. The steps in the four-stroke cycle are shown here.

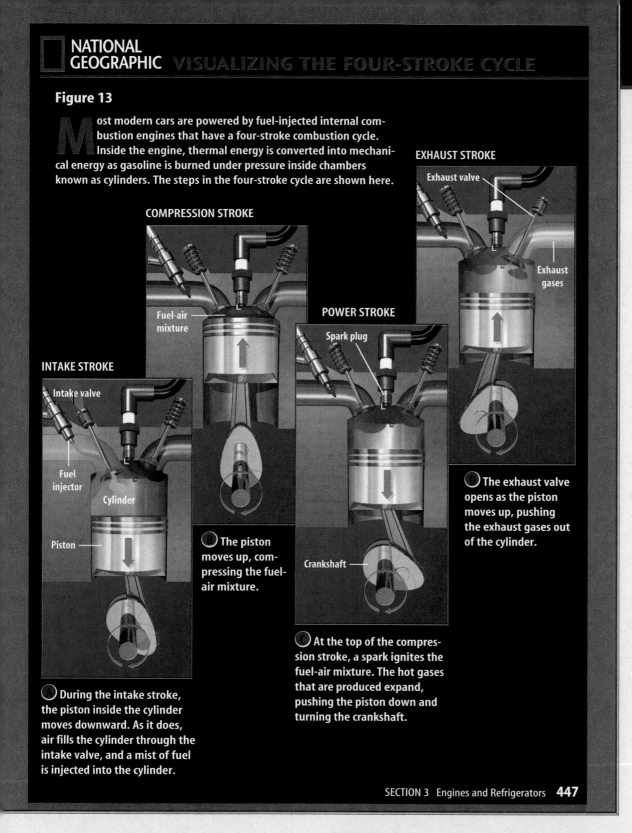

COMPRESSION STROKE

Fuel-air mixture

EXHAUST STROKE

Exhaust valve

Exhaust gases

POWER STROKE

Spark plug

INTAKE STROKE

Intake valve

Fuel injector

Cylinder

Piston

Crankshaft

Ⓑ The piston moves up, compressing the fuel-air mixture.

Ⓒ At the top of the compression stroke, a spark ignites the fuel-air mixture. The hot gases that are produced expand, pushing the piston down and turning the crankshaft.

Ⓓ The exhaust valve opens as the piston moves up, pushing the exhaust gases out of the cylinder.

Ⓐ During the intake stroke, the piston inside the cylinder moves downward. As it does, air fills the cylinder through the intake valve, and a mist of fuel is injected into the cylinder.

SECTION 3 Engines and Refrigerators **447**

Visualizing the Four-Stroke Cycle

Have students examine the pictures and read the captions. Then ask the following questions:

During the intake stroke, the volume of the cylinder is increased. How does this affect the pressure in the cylinder? The pressure decreases.

How does the density and pressure of the air/gas mixture change during the compression stroke? They all increase.

Does the thermal energy of the air/gas mixture increase or decrease during the power stroke? It decreases. What happens to this energy? The gas exerts a force on the piston, so the thermal energy is used to do work on the piston.

Activity

Diesel Engine Poster Ask students to work in pairs to make posters similar to this figure, but showing the operation of a typical diesel engine. When presenting their posters to the class, students should explain how the process differs from that of a four-stroke engine. L3 **IS** Visual-Spatial

Differentiated Instruction

Challenge Have students find out how a spark plug works and write a paragraph explaining what they find. Suggest students include illustrations with their paragraphs. L3 **IS** Logical-Mathematical

Mechanical Engineering Have students research a local university to find out what high-school classes are prerequisites for freshmen majoring in engineering.

Discussion

Spacing Food Is it better to have food in the refrigerator closely packed or spaced out? Why? It is better to have the food spaced out so that air can flow easily and carry heat from the food to the coils inside the refrigerator.
L2 LS **Logical-Mathematical**

Visual Learning

Figure 14 The arrows on the illustration show the flow of the refrigerant. Point out to students that the refrigerant must be pumped through the system to complete the cycle. Ask students why the refrigerant must go through the compressor. to raise the temperature so that heat can be transferred to the air surrounding the refrigerator L2 LS **Visual-Spatial**

Caption Answer

Figure 14 The coolant temperature decreases as it passes through the expansion valve, then increases as it absorbs heat from the interior of the refrigerator. Its temperature increases as it passes through the compressor, then decreases as it releases heat into the room and changes into a liquid.

Mechanical Engineering People who design engines and machines are mechanical engineers. Some mechanical engineers study ways to maximize the transformation of useful energy during combustion—the transformation of energy from chemical form to mechanical form.

Figure 14 A refrigerator uses a coolant to move thermal energy from inside to outside the refrigerator. The compressor supplies the energy that enables the coolant to transfer thermal energy to the room.
Diagram *how the temperature of the coolant changes as it moves in a refrigerator.*

Refrigerators

If thermal energy will only flow from something that is warm to something that is cool, how can a refrigerator be cooler inside than the air in the kitchen? A refrigerator is a heat mover. It absorbs thermal energy from the food inside the refrigerator. Then it carries the thermal energy to outside the refrigerator, where it is transferred to the surrounding air.

A refrigerator contains a material called a coolant that is pumped through pipes inside and outside the refrigerator. The coolant is the substance that carries thermal energy from the inside to the outside of the refrigerator.

Absorbing Thermal Energy Figure 14 shows how a refrigerator operates. Liquid coolant is forced up a pipe toward the freezer unit. The liquid passes through an expansion valve where it changes into a gas. When it changes into a gas, it becomes cold. The cold gas passes through pipes around the inside of the refrigerator. Because the coolant gas is so cold, it absorbs thermal energy from inside the refrigerator, and becomes warmer.

Releasing Thermal Energy However, the gas is still colder than the outside air. So, the thermal energy absorbed by the coolant cannot be transferred to the air. The coolant gas then passes through a compressor that compresses the gas. When the gas is compressed, it becomes warmer than room temperature. The gas then flows through the condenser coils, where thermal energy is transferred to the cooler air in the room. As the coolant gas cools, it changes into a liquid. The liquid is pumped through the expansion valve, changes into a gas, and the cycle is repeated.

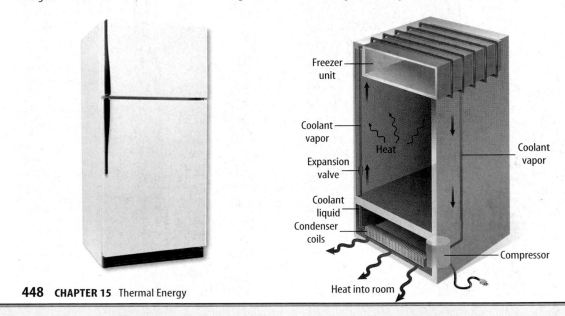

448 CHAPTER 15 Thermal Energy

Cultural Diversity

Refrigerated Trucks The first African American member of the American Society of Refrigeration Engineers was Frederick M. Jones. Jones invented a truck refrigeration system in 1939. Have students discuss how this invention has affected their lives. It made possible such things as the delivery of food from long distances and fresh fruit in winter.
L2 LS **Logical-Mathematical**

Air Conditioners Most air conditioners cool in the same way that a refrigerator does. You've probably seen air-conditioning units outside of many houses. As in a refrigerator, thermal energy from inside the house is absorbed by the coolant within pipes inside the air conditioner. The coolant then is compressed by a compressor, and becomes warmer. The warmed coolant travels through pipes that are exposed to the outside air. Here the thermal energy is transferred to the outside air.

Heat Pumps Some buildings use a heat pump for heating and cooling. Like an air conditioner or refrigerator, a heat pump moves thermal energy from one place to another. In heating mode, shown in **Figure 15,** the coolant absorbs thermal energy through the outside coils. The coolant is warmed when it is compressed and transfers thermal energy to the house through the inside coils. When a heat pump is used for cooling, it removes thermal energy from the indoor air and transfers it outdoors.

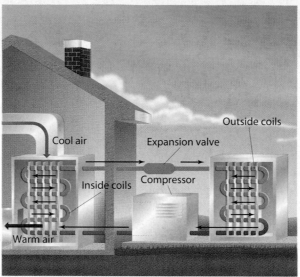
Cool air · Expansion valve · Outside coils · Inside coils · Compressor · Warm air

Figure 15 A heat pump heats a building by absorbing thermal energy from the outside air and transferring thermal energy to the cooler air inside.

DAILY INTERVENTION

Check for Understanding

Logical-Mathematical The efficiency of an ideal engine is given by the equation

Efficiency =
$$(T_2 - T_1)/T_2 \times 100\%$$

Here T_2 is the kelvin temperature of the heat source inside the engine. T_1 is the kelvin temperature of the surrounding air the exhaust gases are expelled into. Use this equation to determine what the temperature of the surrounding air must be for the engine to have 100% efficiency. An ideal engine would have an efficiency of 100% only if T_1 were 0 K, or absolute zero. L3 **LS** **Logical-Mathematical**

Reteach

Have students draw diagrams to help them see that a refrigerator is like an engine working in reverse. L2 **LS** **Visual-Spatial**

---

section 3 review

Summary

Heat Engines and Energy

- A heat engine is a device that converts thermal energy into mechanical energy.
- Energy cannot be created or destroyed. It only can be transformed from one form to another.
- An internal combustion engine is a heat engine that burns fuel in a combustion chamber inside the engine.

Refrigerators and Heat Pumps

- A refrigerator uses a coolant to transfer thermal energy to outside the refrigerator.
- The coolant gas absorbs thermal energy from inside the refrigerator.
- Compressing the coolant makes it warmer than the air outside the refrigerator.
- A heat pump heats by absorbing thermal energy from the air outside, and transferring it inside a building.

Self Check

1. **Diagram** the movement of coolant and the flow of heat when a heat pump is used to cool a building.
2. **Explain** why diesel engines don't use spark plugs.
3. **Identify** the source of thermal energy in an internal combustion engine.
4. **Determine** whether you could cool a kitchen by keeping the refrigerator door open.
5. **Describe** how a refrigerator uses a coolant to keep the food compartment cool.
6. **Think Critically** Explain how an air conditioner could also be used to heat a room.

Applying Skills

7. **Make a Concept Map** Make an events-chain concept map showing the sequence of steps in a four-stroke cycle.

☑ **Assessment**

Performance Have students design an engine that uses a heat source other than combustion to perform work. Use **Performance Assessment in the Science Classroom,** p. 117.

---

section 3 review

1. The coolant absorbs heat from the building interior, is warmed as it passes through the compressor, and releases the heat through the outside coils. It passes through the expansion valve and is cooled, and then passes through the inside coils.
2. The fuel-air mixture becomes so hot during the compression stroke that the mixture ignites.
3. the ignition of the fuel-air mixture
4. No. The heat extracted from the air in the room by having the door open is released back into the room by the condenser coils.
5. The coolant expands, changing to a gas and becoming cooler. It then absorbs heat from inside the refrigerator. The coolant is compressed and becomes warm, so that heat is transferred from the coolant to the outside air. The cycle repeats.
6. The air conditioner could be placed in the window so that the condenser coils were inside the room. Then the air conditioner would absorb heat from the outside air and release the heat into the room.
7. Answers should include fuel-air mixture being drawn into the cylinder, fuel-air mixture being ignited, hot gases expanding and pushing piston down, hot gases being forced out of the cylinder.

● Real-World Question

Purpose Students design an experiment to determine which type of beverage containers best insulate hot drinks. [L2] [LS] **Logical-Mathematical**

Process Skills design an experiment, form a hypothesis, observe, identify and control variables, make and use tables, measure in SI, make and use graphs, analyze results, draw conclusions

Time Required two 45-min periods

Materials a variety of disposable drink containers

Safety Precautions

● Form a Hypothesis

Possible Hypothesis Beverage containers made of polystyrene, plastic, and paper will block heat transfer from hot liquids better than containers made of glass, ceramic, or metal.

Data Table Data will vary, but the best insulators will show a slower decrease in temperature of liquid over time.

● Test Your Hypothesis

Possible Procedures Heat 500 mL of water to boiling. Measure and pour 100 mL of hot water into each of the five different beverage containers. Cover each container with aluminum foil. Insert a thermometer through the foil into each container. Measure and record the temperature of the liquid in each container at the beginning and each minute for ten min.

Goals
- **Predict** the temperature change of a hot drink in various types of containers over time.
- **Design** an experiment to test the hypothesis and collect data that can be graphed.
- **Interpret** the data.

Possible Materials
hot plate
large beaker
water
100-mL graduated cylinder
alcohol thermometers
various beverage
    containers
material to cover the
    containers
stopwatch
tongs
thermal gloves or mitts

Safety Precautions

WARNING: *Use caution when heating liquids. Use tongs or thermal gloves when handling hot materials. Hot and cold glass appear the same. Treat thermometers with care and keep them away from the edges of tables.*

Design Your Own

Comparing Thermal Insulators

● Real-World Question

Insulated beverage containers are used to reduce heat transfer. What kinds of containers do you most often drink from? Aluminum soda cans? Paper, plastic, or foam cups? Glass containers? In this investigation, compare how well several different containers block heat transfer. Which types of beverage containers are most effective at blocking heat transfer from a hot drink?

● Form a Hypothesis

Predict the temperature change of a hot liquid in several containers made of different materials over a time interval.

● Test Your Hypothesis

Make a Plan

1. **Decide** what types of containers you will test. Design an experiment to test your hypothesis. This is a group activity, so make certain that everyone gets to contribute to the discussion.

Temp. (°C)	foam	paper	plastic	glass	metal
Start					
1 min					
2 min					
3 min					
4 min					
5 min					
6 min					
7 min					
8 min					
9 min					
10 min					

2. **List** the materials you will use in your experiment. Describe exactly how you will use these materials. Which liquid will you test? At what temperature will the liquid begin? How will you cover the hot liquids in the container? What material will you use as a cover?

3. **Identify** the variables and controls in your experiment.

4. **Design** a data table in your Science Journal to record the observations you make.

Follow Your Plan

1. Ask your teacher to examine the steps of your experiment and your data table before you start.

2. To see the pattern of how well various containers retain heat, you will need to graph your data. What kind of graph will you use? Make certain you take enough measurements during the experiment to make your graph.

3. The time intervals between measurements should be the same. Be sure to keep track of time as the experiment goes along. For how long will you measure the temperature?

4. Carry out your investigation and record your observations.

● *Analyze Your Data*

1. **Graph** your data. Use one graph to show the data collected from all your containers. Label each line on your graph.

2. **Interpret Data** How can you tell by looking at your graphs which containers retain heat best?

3. **Evaluate** Did the water temperature change as you had predicted? Use your data and graph to explain your answers.

● *Conclude and Apply*

1. **Explain** why the rate of temperature change varies among the containers. Did the size of the containers affect the rate of cooling?

2. **Conclude** which containers were the best insulators.

*C*ommunicating
Your Data

Compare your data and graphs with other classmates and explain any differences in your results or conclusions.

LAB 451

✔ **Assessment**

Process Show students a picnic cooler. Remind them that people place food in picnic coolers to keep the food cold on a warm day. Ask them if a cooler really cools the food. If not, how does it work? The cooler slows heat transfer between the food and the outside (warm) environment. Use **Performance Assessment in the Science Classroom,** p. 89.

*C*ommunicating
Your Data

Students can use an electronic database to plot their data and graphs. Printouts of each group's data can be given to the other groups for easier comparison and discussion.

Teaching Strategies Suggest that students use different colored pencils to graph temperatures of beverages in different containers.

Troubleshooting Check students' procedures to be sure they have identified and controlled variables.

Expected Outcome Most results will show that a container made from plastic foam or plastic is best at blocking heat transfer.

● *Analyze Your Data*

1. Graphs should be consistent with data in the data table. The containers that are least effective at blocking heat transfer will show the steepest curves.

2. The containers that retain heat best show the least steep curves (the temperature will drop less over the same period of time).

3. Answers will vary depending on students' hypotheses.

Error Analysis Have students compare their results and their hypotheses and explain why differences occurred.

● *Conclude and Apply*

1. The rate of temperature change varied because some containers conducted heat more slowly than others. The size of the containers would not have much effect on the rate of cooling.

2. Answers will vary depending on containers chosen for testing. In general, cups made from plastic foam or other types of plastic are the best insulators.

Content Background

NASA scientists have used airplanes equipped with heat-sensitive cameras to generate thermal images of several cities. These images showed that darker colors and certain building materials, such as asphalt, absorb and retain far more heat than do lighter colors and materials like concrete. The images also identify areas that are cooler because of an abundance of foliage.

It is estimated that the additional air-conditioning used due to this urban heat-island effect accounts for as much as ten percent of electricity used during peak periods. In Los Angeles, this adds up to more than 100 million dollars per year.

Discussion

Planning Expansion What factors should be considered when planning expansion of cities? Possible answers include: use lighter colors and materials that reflect rather than absorb heat. Tracts of trees and other vegetation should be incorporated into urban and suburban design. Strategic planting of shade trees will reduce heat absorption by buildings. L2 LS **Logical-Mathematical**

Activity

Making Models Divide the class into two groups. Have them use simple materials such as shoeboxes or other cardboard materials to make models of buildings. Have the two groups decorate their models with colors that would make them hotter or cooler. Make other components of cities, such as streets, some dark, some light, to represent asphalt and concrete. Collect pictures of trees, of people who look comfortable, and of people who appear distressed in heat. Save these for construction of two model cities in the activity on the right.

The Heat Is On

You may live far from water, but still live on an island—a heat island

Think about all the things that are made of asphalt and concrete in a city. As far as the eye can see, there are buildings and parking lots, sidewalks and streets. The combined effect of these paved surfaces and towering structures can make a city sizzle in the summer. There's even a name for this effect. It's called the heat island effect.

Hot Times

You can think of a city as an island surrounded by an ocean of green trees and other vegetation. In the midst of those green trees, the air can be up to 8°C cooler than it is downtown. During the day in rural areas, the Sun's energy is absorbed by plants and soil. Some of this energy causes water to evaporate, so less energy is available to heat the surroundings. This keeps the temperature lower.

Higher temperatures aren't the only problems caused by heat islands. People crank up their air conditioners for relief, so the use of energy skyrockets. Also, the added heat speeds up the rates of chemical reactions in the atmosphere. Smog is due to chemical reactions caused by the interaction of sunlight and vehicle emissions. So hotter air means more smog. And more smog means more health problems.

Cool Cures

Several U.S. cities are working with NASA scientists to come up with a cure for the summertime blues. For instance, dark materials absorb heat more efficiently than light materials. So painting buildings, especially roofs, white can reduce heat and save on cooling bills.

Dark materials, such as asphalt, absorb more heat than light materials. In extreme heat, it's even possible to fry an egg on dark pavement!

Design and Research Visit the Web Site to the right to research NASA's Urban Heat Island Project. What actions are cities taking to reduce the heat-island effect? Design a city area that would help reduce this effect.

Science Online

For more information, visit ips.msscience.com/time

Design and Research Have students use the building models and collected pictures from the activity to construct two model cities. One should illustrate a city that absorbs a great deal of heat. The other should illustrate the benefits of a plan that includes the use of color, materials, trees, and parks to reduce the heat absorbed in the city.

Resources for Teachers and Students

Heat Islands—And How To Cool Them, Center For Building Science Newsletter, Spring 1994

"Cities trap heat, make their own weather, study indicates," *Seattle Times*, July 10, 2000

Reviewing Main Ideas

Section 1 Temperature and Thermal Energy

1. Molecules of matter are moving constantly. Temperature is related to the average value of the kinetic energy of the molecules.

2. Thermometers measure temperature. Three common temperature scales are the Celsius, Fahrenheit, and Kelvin scales.

3. Thermal energy is the total kinetic and potential energy of the particles in matter.

Section 2 Heat

1. Heat is thermal energy that is transferred from a warmer object to a colder object.

2. Heat can be transferred by conduction, convection, and radiation.

3. A material that easily transfers heat is called a conductor. A material that resists the flow of heat is an insulator.

4. The specific heat of a substance is the amount of heat needed to change the temperature of 1 kg of the substance 1°C.

5. Thermal pollution occurs when warm water is added to a body of water.

Section 3 Engines and Refrigerators

1. A device that converts thermal energy into mechanical energy is an engine.

2. In an internal combustion engine, fuel is burned in combustion chambers inside the engine using a four-stroke cycle.

3. Refrigerators and air conditioners use a coolant to move heat.

Visualizing Main Ideas

Copy and complete the following cycle map about the four-stroke cycle.

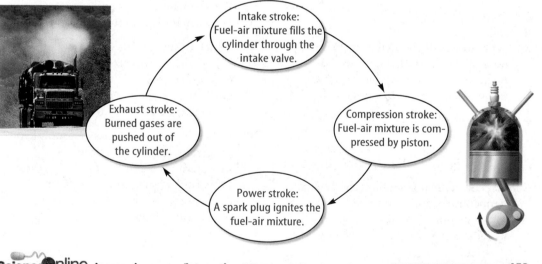

Intake stroke:
Fuel-air mixture fills the cylinder through the intake valve.

Compression stroke:
Fuel-air mixture is compressed by piston.

Power stroke:
A spark plug ignites the fuel-air mixture.

Exhaust stroke:
Burned gases are pushed out of the cylinder.

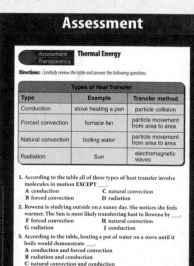

Science online ips.msscience.com/interactive_tutor

CHAPTER STUDY GUIDE **453**

Reviewing Main Ideas

Summary statements can be used by students to review the major concepts of the chapter.

Visualizing Main Ideas

See student page.

Science Online

Visit ips.msscience.com
/self_check_quiz
/interactive_tutor
/vocabulary_puzzlemaker
/chapter_review
/standardized_test

Assessment Transparency

For additional assessment questions, use the *Assessment Transparency* located in the transparency book.

Assessment

Assessment Transparency | Thermal Energy

Directions: *Carefully review the table and answer the following questions.*

Types of Heat Transfer		
Type	**Example**	**Transfer method**
Conduction	stove heating a pan	particle collision
Forced convection	furnace fan	particle movement from area to area
Natural convection	boiling water	particle movement from area to area
Radiation	Sun	electromagnetic waves

1. According to the table all of these types of heat transfer involve molecules in motion **EXCEPT** ___.
 A conduction   C natural convection
 B forced convection   D radiation

2. Rowena is studying outside on a sunny day. She notices she feels warmer. The Sun is most likely transferring heat to Rowena by ___.
 F forced convection   H natural convection
 G radiation   J conduction

3. According to the table, heating a pot of water on a stove until it boils would demonstrate ___.
 A conduction and forced convection
 B radiation and conduction
 C natural convection and conduction
 D natural convection and forced convection

L2

Thermal Energy

Using Vocabulary

1. An engine converts thermal energy to mechanical energy. In an internal combustion engine, fuel is burned in chambers inside the engine.

2. Temperature is the average value of the kinetic energy of the molecules in a material. Thermal energy is the sum of all the kinetic and potential energy of the molecules in the material.

3. Thermal energy is the sum of the kinetic and potential energy of the molecules in a material. Thermal pollution is an increase in the temperature of a natural body of water caused by adding warmer water.

4. Both are methods of transferring thermal energy. Conduction transfers thermal energy by direct contact. Convection transfers thermal energy by movement of fluids from one place to another.

5. Conduction is the transfer of thermal energy by direct contact. Heat is thermal energy transferred from warmer to cooler objects.

6. Heat is thermal energy transferred from one object to another. Specific heat is the amount of heat needed to change the temperature of 1 kg of a substance 1°C.

7. Both are methods of transferring thermal energy. Conduction transfers thermal energy by direct contact. Radiation transfers thermal energy by electromagnetic waves.

8. Both are methods of transferring thermal energy. Convection transfers thermal energy by movement of fluids from one place to another. Radiation transfers thermal energy by electromagnetic waves.

9. A conductor is any material that easily transfers thermal energy. Heat is thermal energy that is transferred from warmer to cooler objects.

Using Vocabulary

conduction p. 439	radiation p. 439
conductor p. 441	specific heat p. 442
convection p. 440	temperature p. 434
heat p. 438	thermal energy p. 437
heat engine p. 445	thermal pollution p. 443
internal combustion engine p. 446	

Explain the differences in the vocabulary words given below. Then explain how the words are related. Use complete sentences in your answers.

1. internal combustion engine—heat engine
2. temperature—thermal energy
3. thermal energy—thermal pollution
4. conduction—convection
5. conduction—heat
6. heat—specific heat
7. conduction—radiation
8. convection—radiation
9. conductor—heat

Checking Concepts

Choose the word or phrase that best answers the question.

10. What source of thermal energy does an internal combustion engine use?
    A) steam
    B) hot water
    C) burning fuel
    D) refrigerant

11. What happens to most materials when they become warmer?
    A) They contract.
    B) They float.
    C) They vaporize.
    D) They expand.

12. Which occurs if two objects at different temperatures are in contact?
    A) convection
    B) radiation
    C) condensation
    D) conduction

13. Which of the following describes the thermal energy of particles in a substance?
    A) average value of all kinetic energy
    B) total value of all kinetic energy
    C) total value of all kinetic and potential energy
    D) average value of all kinetic and potential energy

14. Heat being transferred from the Sun to Earth is an example of which process?
    A) convection
    B) expansion
    C) radiation
    D) conduction

15. Many insulating materials contain spaces filled with air because air is what type of material?
    A) conductor
    B) coolant
    C) radiator
    D) insulator

16. A recipe calls for a cake to be baked at a temperature of 350°F. What is this temperature on the Celsius scale?
    A) 162°C
    B) 177°C
    C) 194°C
    D) 212°C

17. Which of the following is true?
    A) Warm air is less dense than cool air.
    B) Warm air is as dense as cool air.
    C) Warm air has no density.
    D) Warm air is denser than cool air.

18. Which of these is the name for thermal energy that moves from a warmer object to a cooler one?
    A) kinetic energy
    B) specific heat
    C) heat
    D) temperature

19. Which of the following is an example of heat transfer by conduction?
    A) water moving in a pot of boiling water
    B) warm air rising from hot pavement
    C) the warmth you feel sitting near a fire
    D) the warmth you feel holding a cup of hot cocoa

Science Online ips.msscience.com/vocabulary_puzzlemaker

Checking Concepts

10. C	15. D
11. D	16. B
12. D	17. A
13. C	18. C
14. C	19. D

Use the Exam*View*® Pro Testmaker CD-ROM to:
- customize tests
- create multiple versions of tests
- generate tests in Spanish
- build tests aligned with state standards

Thinking Critically

20. Infer Water is a poor conductor of heat. Yet when you heat water in a pan, the surface gets hot quickly, even though you are applying heat to the bottom of the water. Explain.

21. Explain why several layers of clothing often keep you warmer than a single layer.

22. Identify The phrase "heat rises" is sometimes used to describe the movement of heat. For what type of materials is this phrase correct? Explain.

23. Describe When a lightbulb is turned on, the electric current in the filament causes the filament to become hot and glow. If the filament is surrounded by a gas, describe how thermal energy is transferred from the filament to the air outside the bulb.

24. Design an Experiment Some colors of clothing absorb heat better than other colors. Design an experiment that will test various colors by placing them in the hot Sun for a period of time. Explain your results.

25. Explain Concrete sidewalks usually are made of slabs of concrete. Why do the concrete slabs have a space between them?

26. Concept Map Copy and complete the following concept map on convection in a liquid.

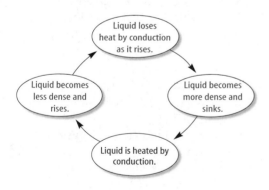

27. Explain A winter jacket is lined with insulating material that contains air spaces. How would the insulating properties of the jacket change if the insulating material in the jacket becomes wet? Explain.

28. Compare Two glasses of water are poured into a pitcher. If the temperature of the water in both glasses was the same before they were mixed, describe how the temperature and thermal energy of the water in the pitcher compares to the water in the glasses.

Performance Activities

29. Poll In the United States, the Fahrenheit temperature scale is used most often. Some people feel that Americans should switch to the Celsius scale. Take a poll of at least 20 people. Find out if they feel the switch to the Celsius scale should be made. Make a list of reasons people give for or against changing.

Applying Math

30. Temperature Order List the following temperatures from coldest to warmest: 80° C, 200 K, 50° F.

31. Temperature Change The high temperature on a summer day is 88°F and the low temperature is 61°F. What is the difference between these two temperatures in degrees Celsius?

32. Global Temperature The average global temperature is 286 K. Convert this temperature to degrees Celsius.

33. Body Temperature A doctor measures a patient's temperature at 38.4°C. Convert this temperature to degrees Fahrenheit.

 Science Online ips.msscience.com/chapter_review

Thinking Critically

20. Convection transfers heat from the bottom of the pan to the water at the surface.

21. Several layers of clothing enable more air to be trapped within and between layers, making the layers a better insulator than a single layer.

22. Fluid. Warm fluid is less dense and is forced upward when convection occurs.

23. Thermal energy is transferred to the glass bulb by convection in the gas and radiation. Thermal energy is then transferred to the air outside by conduction and radiation through the glass.

24. The darker colors will become warmer more quickly.

25. The space prevents the concrete from buckling when it expands in the summer.

26. See student answers.

27. Water fills the air spaces, and because water is a much better conductor of heat than air, the jacket is a better conductor.

28. The thermal energy of the water in the pitcher is the sum of the thermal energy of the water in the glasses. The temperature is the same as the water in the glasses.

Performance Activities

29. Some people might say that switching to Celsius would be too difficult and unnecessary. Others might say that Celsius is easier to use.

Applying Math

National Math Standards
1, 2, 4, 9
30. 200 K, 50°F, 80°C
31. 15°C
32. 13°C
33. 101.1°F

Assessment Resources

Reproducible Masters

Chapter *Fast File* Resources
Chapter Review, pp. 37–38
Chapter Tests, pp. 39–42
Assessment Transparency Activity, p. 49

Glencoe Science Web site
Chapter Review Test
Standardized Test Practice

Glencoe Technology
- Assessment Transparency
- Exam*View*® Pro Testmaker
- MindJogger Videoquiz
- Interactive Chalkboard

Answer Sheet A practice answer sheet can be found at ips.msscience.com/answer_sheet.

S A M P L E

Part 1 | Multiple Choice

1. D 5. C
2. A 6. B
3. C 7. A
4. C

Part 2 | Short Response

8. The water warms the ice. Heat always flows from warm materials to cool materials.

9. You would expect the warmer air mass to rise.

10. Because a diesel engine contains no spark plug, the fuel mixture must be flammable enough to ignite when it is compressed in the cylinder.

11. Air fills the cylinder through the intake valve, and a mist of fuel is injected into the cylinder.

12. Metal is a good heat conductor. The handle is made of a material that is not a good conductor.

13. thermal energy

Part 1 | Multiple Choice

Record your answers on the answer sheet provided by your teacher or on a sheet of paper.

Use the photo below to answer questions 1 and 2.

1. The temperatures of the two glasses of water shown in the photograph above are 30°C and 0°C. Which of the following is a correct statement about the two glasses of water?
   A. The cold water has a higher average kinetic energy.
   B. The warmer water has lower thermal energy.
   C. The molecules of the cold water move faster.
   D. The molecules of the warmer water have more kinetic energy.

2. The difference in temperature of the two glasses of water is 30°C. What is their difference in temperature on the Kelvin scale?
   A. 30 K   C. 243 K
   B. 86 K   D. 303 K

3. Which of the following describes a refrigerator?
   A. heat engine   C. heat mover
   B. heat pump   D. conductor

Test-Taking Tip

Avoid rushing on test day. Prepare your clothes and test supplies the night before. Wake up early and arrive at school on time on test day.

4. Which of the following is not a step in the four-stroke cycle of internal combustion engines?
   A. compression   C. idling
   B. exhaust   D. power

Use the table below to answer question 5.

Material	Specific Heat (J/kg °C)
aluminum	897
copper	385
lead	129
nickel	444
zinc	388

5. A sample of each of the metals in the table above is formed into a 50-g cube. If 100 J of heat are applied to each of the samples, which metal would change temperature by the greatest amount?
   A. aluminum   C. lead
   B. copper   D. nickel

6. An internal combustion engine converts thermal energy to which of the following forms of energy?
   A. chemical   C. radiant
   B. mechanical   D. electrical

7. Which of the following is a statement of the law of conservation of energy?
   A. Energy never can be created or destroyed.
   B. Energy can be created, but never destroyed.
   C. Energy can be destroyed, but never created.
   D. Energy can be created and destroyed when it changes form.

Part 3 | Open Ended

14. Coolant constantly flows through the coils that surround the freezer unit. This coolant has been cooled by passing it through the expansion valve. Although heat from the food compartment enters the freezer unit, the coolant in the pipes absorbs this heat, keeping the freezer unit very cold.

15. The expansion valve changes the coolant from a liquid to a vapor. This causes the coolant to expand. The compressor compresses the vapor, making it warmer. The condenser transfers heat from the warmed coolant to the cooler air in the room.

16. Convection is a method of thermal energy transfer by the movement of molecules from one part of a material to another. Natural convection occurs when a warmer, less dense fluid is pushed away by a cooler, denser fluid. An example is the way cooler denser air over a lake flows in over the land, pushing the warmer, less dense air

Part 2 | Short Response/Grid In

Record your answers on the answer sheet provided by your teacher or on a sheet of paper.

8. If you add ice to a glass of room-temperature ice, does the water warm the ice or does the ice cool the water? Explain.

9. Strong winds that occur during a thunderstorm are the result of temperature differences between neighboring air masses. Would you expect the warmer or the cooler air mass to rise above the other?

10. A diesel engine uses a different type of fuel than the fuel used in a gasoline engine. Explain why.

11. What are the two main events that occur while the cylinder moves downward during the intake stroke of an internal combustion engine's four-stroke cycle?

Use the photo below to answer questions 12 and 13.

12. Why are cooking pots like the one in the photograph above often made of metal? Why isn't the handle made of metal?

13. When heating water in the pot, electrical energy from the cooking unit is changed to what other type of energy?

Part 3 | Open Ended

Record your answers on a sheet of paper.

Use the illustration below to answer questions 14 and 15.

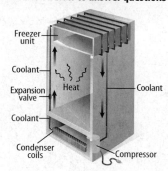

14. The illustration above shows the parts of a refrigerator and how coolant flows through the refrigerator. Explain how thermal energy is transferred to the coolant inside the refrigerator and then transferred from the coolant to the outside air.

15. What are the functions of the expansion valve, the condenser coils, and the compressor in the illustration?

16. Define convection. Explain the difference between natural and forced convection, and give an example of each.

17. Draw a sketch with arrows showing how conduction, convection, and radiation affect the movement and temperature of air near an ocean.

18. Define temperature and explain how it is related to the movement of molecules in a substance.

19. Explain what makes some materials good thermal conductors.

20. You place a cookie sheet in a hot oven. A few minutes later you hear a sound as the cookie sheet bends slightly. Explain what causes this.

ScienceOnline **ips.msscience.com/standardized_test**

STANDARDIZED TEST PRACTICE **457**

ecules in a substance. The more kinetic energy the molecules have, the higher the temperature. Molecules have more kinetic energy when they are moving faster. Thus the higher the temperature, the faster the molecules are moving.

19. Some materials, such as metals, have some electrons that are not held tightly by the nucleus and are freer to move around. These loosely held electrons can bump into each other. This bumping transfers thermal energy from one part of the material to another.

20. The cookie sheet makes a banging sound because of thermal expansion. Thermal expansion is the increase in length or volume of an object due to changes in temperature. When the temperature of the object increases, its molecules speed up and tend to move farther apart. This increases the size of the object slightly. The cookie sheet may bend when one side experiences more thermal expansion than the other size. Also, some cookie sheets are made of two different metals which experience different amounts of thermal expansion.

Rubrics

For more help evaluating open-ended assessment questions, see the rubric on p. 4T.

Part 3 | Open Ended

upward. Forced convection is when something other than a difference in temperature or density causes the movement of the molecules and transfer of heat. An example is when a fan inside a computer blows cool air onto hot electronic components, causing the warmer air to move away from the components.

17. Sketches should show heat traveling from the Sun to Earth by radiation. The Sun's energy heats the land and water. The air above the land and water are heated by conduction. Warmer air near the surface of the land rises during the day by convection. This causes cooler air over the ocean to flow toward land. This air becomes heated and rises also as the cycle is repeated.

18. Temperature is a measure of the average kinetic energy of the mol-

Unit Contents

WebQuest **Laser Eye Surgery** is a personal journey to investigate the new technology and procedures for corrective vision. Students will make an informed decision as to whether Lasik or PRK procedures are an option for patients with myopia. Students will study the advantages and disadvantages of surgery for this type of procedure and decide if they might be a candidate. A set of questions to guide them in their investigations is provided.

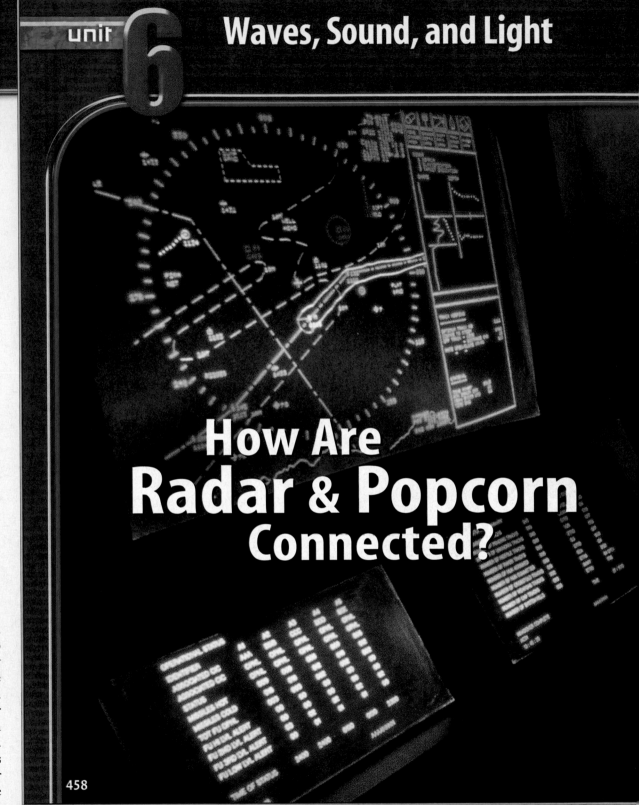

How Are Radar & Popcorn Connected?

458

PROJECT CRISS SM

Study Skills

Organize Information Concept mapping gives students a graphic means of organizing information as they read. Using each type of wave as a main topic, students use the wave's properties and behaviors as arms or branches. The arms can become topics on note cards for use in future study.

NATIONAL GEOGRAPHIC

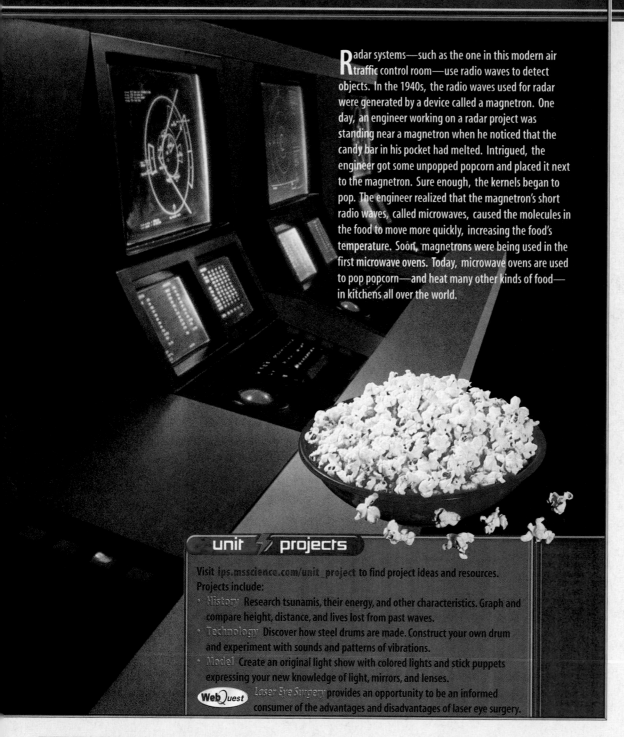

Radar systems—such as the one in this modern air traffic control room—use radio waves to detect objects. In the 1940s, the radio waves used for radar were generated by a device called a magnetron. One day, an engineer working on a radar project was standing near a magnetron when he noticed that the candy bar in his pocket had melted. Intrigued, the engineer got some unpopped popcorn and placed it next to the magnetron. Sure enough, the kernels began to pop. The engineer realized that the magnetron's short radio waves, called microwaves, caused the molecules in the food to move more quickly, increasing the food's temperature. Soon, magnetrons were being used in the first microwave ovens. Today, microwave ovens are used to pop popcorn—and heat many other kinds of food—in kitchens all over the world.

unit projects

Visit ips.msscience.com/unit_project to find project ideas and resources.
Projects include:

- **History** Research tsunamis, their energy, and other characteristics. Graph and compare height, distance, and lives lost from past waves.
- **Technology** Discover how steel drums are made. Construct your own drum and experiment with sounds and patterns of vibrations.
- **Model** Create an original light show with colored lights and stick puppets expressing your new knowledge of light, mirrors, and lenses.

WebQuest *Laser Eye Surgery* provides an opportunity to be an informed consumer of the advantages and disadvantages of laser eye surgery.

unit projects

History Have students research tsunamis, their energy and characteristics, how they are created, how they travel, and their effects on beach-front communities. Have students graph and compare the lives lost, the height of the waves, and the distance the waves moved inland.

Technology Ask students to investigate how steel drums are made. This instrument has a distinct sound that demonstrates different pitch in a simple and effective way. Students may experiment with balloons stretched across an empty can to produce a variety of pitches. Ask students to sprinkle pepper or sand on their drum head and then strike the drum. With the balloon-drum head at different tensions, have students make drawings of the pepper patterns that develop from the range of vibrations and pitch.

Model Have students create a light show using three different-colored incandescent light sources and stick puppets. Have students write a short shadow puppet play with a simple plot to demonstrate their knowledge of primary light colors, reflection and absorption, concave and convex mirrors, lenses, prisms, refraction, critical angle, and the uses of these concepts in science and science equipment.

Additional Resources For more information, resources, and assessment rubrics, visit ips.msscience.com/unit_project

NATIONAL GEOGRAPHIC   How Are Radar & Popcorn Connected?

Popcorn, like all matter, is composed of atoms in constant motion. Heating a substance is one way to increase an object's temperature. Microwaves also can be used to raise an object's temperature by harnessing electromagnetic waves that carry radiant energy.

Popcorn kernels, like most food, contain water. Inside a microwave oven, water molecules absorb the microwave energy, causing the water molecules to move faster until the water turns to steam. The pressure increases until the kernel explodes. The kernel is turned inside out. The end result is the familiar-looking, white puff of popcorn.

Section/Objectives	Standards		Labs/Features
	National	**State/Local**	
Chapter Opener See p. 16T–17T for a Key to Standards.			**Launch Lab:** How do waves carry energy?, p. 461 **Foldables,** p. 461
Section 1 What are waves? ● 1 session 🖥 0.5 block 1. **Explain** the relationship between waves, energy, and matter. 2. **Describe** the difference between transverse waves and compressional waves.	National Content Standards: UCP.1–UCP.3, UCP.5, A.1, A.2, B.2, B.3, D.1		**MiniLAB:** Comparing Sounds, p. 465 **Integrate Physics,** p. 466
Section 2 Wave Properties ● 2 sessions 🖥 1 block 3. **Describe** the relationship between the frequency and wavelength of a wave. 4. **Explain** why waves travel at different speeds.	National Content Standards: UCP.1–UCP.3, UCP.5, A.1, A.2, D.1		**Integrate Health,** p. 470 **Science Online,** p. 471 **Lab:** Waves on a Spring, p. 472
Section 3 Wave Behavior ● 4 sessions 🖥 2 blocks 5. **Explain** how waves can reflect from some surfaces. 6. **Explain** how waves change direction when they move from one material into another. 7. **Describe** how waves are able to bend around barriers.	National Content Standards: UCP.1–UCP.3, UCP.5, A.1, A.2, B.2, B.3, D.1		**MiniLAB:** Observing How Light Refracts, p. 474 **Science Online,** p. 477 **Applying Science:** Can you create destructive interference?, p. 477 **Visualizing Interference,** p. 478 **Lab:** Wave Speed, pp. 480–481 **Science Stats:** Waves, Waves, and More Waves, p. 482

Glencoe Exclusive!
Teacher Works™
All-In-One Planner and Resource Center

Lab Materials	Reproducible Resources	Section Assessment	Technology
Launch Lab: clear-plastic plate, a cork or straw, dropper, water	**Chapter *FAST FILE* Resources** Foldables Worksheet, p. 15 Directed Reading Overview, p. 17 Note-taking Worksheets, pp. 31–32	**GLENCOE'S ASSESSMENT ADVANTAGE**	TeacherWorks includes: • Interactive Teacher Edition • Lesson Planner with calendar • Access to all program blacklines • Correlations to standards • Web links
MiniLAB: wooden ruler	**Chapter *FAST FILE* Resources** Transparency Activity, p. 42 MiniLAB, p. 3 Enrichment, p. 28 Reinforcement, p. 25 Directed Reading, p. 18 Transparency Activity, pp. 45–46	**Portfolio** Activity, p. 464 **Performance** MiniLAB, p. 471 Applying Skills, p. 472 **Content** Section Review, p. 472	Section Focus Transparency Teaching Transparency Guided Reading Audio Program Interactive Chalkboard CD-ROM
Lab: long, coiled spring toy; 5 cm colored yarn; meterstick; stopwatch *Need materials?* Contact Science Kit at 1-800-828-7777 or www.sciencekit.com on the Internet.	**Chapter *FAST FILE* Resources** Transparency Activity, p. 43 Enrichment, p. 29 Reinforcement, p. 26 Directed Reading, p. 19 Lab Worksheets, pp. 5–6 Lab Activity, pp. 9–11 **Reading and Writing Skill Activities,** p. 33 **Home and Community Involvement,** p. 42	**Portfolio** Science Journal, p. 477 **Performance** Applying Math, p. 477 **Content** Section Review, p. 477	Section Focus Transparency Virtual Labs CD-ROM Guided Reading Audio Program Interactive Chalkboard CD-ROM Video Lab
MiniLAB: large, opaque drinking glass or cup of water; white soda straw **Lab:** long, coiled spring toy; stopwatch; meterstick; tape	**Chapter *FAST FILE* Resources** Transparency Activity, p. 44 Enrichment, p. 30 Reinforcement, p. 27 Directed Reading, pp. 19, 20 MiniLAB, p. 4 Lab Activity, pp. 13–14 Lab Worksheets, pp. 7–8 **Lab Management and Safety,** p. 65 **Mathematics Skill Activities,** p. 47	**Portfolio** Assessment, p. 479 **Performance** MiniLAB, p. 480 Applying Science, p. 483 Applying Skills, p. 485 **Content** Section Review, p. 485	Section Focus Transparency Guided Reading Audio Program Interactive Chalkboard CD-ROM

End of Chapter Assessment

GLENCOE'S ASSESSMENT ADVANTAGE

Blackline Masters	Technology	Professional Series
Chapter *FAST FILE* Resources Chapter Review, pp. 35–36 Chapter Tests, pp. 37–40 **Standardized Test Practice,** pp. 67–70	MindJogger Videoquiz Virtual Labs CD-ROM ExamView® Pro Testmaker TeacherWorks CD-ROM Interactive Chalkboard CD-ROM	**Performance Assessment in the Science Classroom (PASC)**

Transparencies

Section Focus

Section Focus Transparency 1 — Ride the Wave!

Surfing may seem like a fairly new sport, but it's not. In fact, people think there were surfers in Hawaii in the 1400s. When Captain Cook landed in the Hawaiian Islands in 1778, he was greeted by an islander on a surfboard!

1. Name some different kinds of waves.
2. What do you think creates waves on the ocean?
3. Describe the path of light from the Sun to the camera that took this picture.

L2

Section Focus Transparency 2 — The Sun's Radiant Energies

Visible light and ultraviolet (UV) radiation both come from the Sun. UV radiation causes eye damage, skin cancer, and burns skin. Visible light and UV radiation are both electromagnetic waves, but they have different properties.

1. How can you protect yourself from the harmful consequences of UV radiation?
2. What are some differences among water waves that you have noticed? How might electromagnetic waves be different, too?

L2

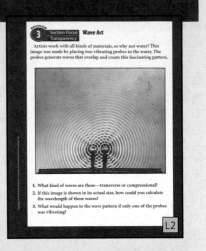

Section Focus Transparency 3 — Wave Art

Artists work with all kinds of materials, so why not water? This image was made by placing two vibrating probes in the water. The probes generate waves that overlap and create this fascinating pattern.

1. What kind of waves are these—transverse or compressional?
2. If this image is shown in its actual size, how could you calculate the wavelength of these waves?
3. What would happen to the wave pattern if only one of the probes was vibrating?

L2

This is a representation of key blackline masters available in the Teacher Classroom Resources. See Resource Manager boxes within the chapter for additional information.

Key to Teaching Strategies

The following designations will help you decide which activities are appropriate for your students.

L1 Level 1 activities should be appropriate for students with learning difficulties.

L2 Level 2 activities should be within the ability range of all students.

L3 Level 3 activities are designed for above-average students.

ELL ELL activities should be within the ability range of English Language Learners.

COOP LEARN Cooperative Learning activities are designed for small group work.

LS Multiple Learning Styles logos, as described on page 12T, are used throughout to indicate strategies that address different learning styles.

P These strategies represent student products that can be placed into a best-work portfolio.

PBL Problem-Based Learning activities apply real-world situations to learning.

Assessment

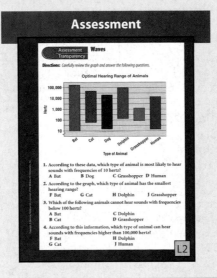

Assessment Transparency — Waves

Directions: Carefully review the graph and answer the following questions.

Optimal Hearing Range of Animals

1. According to these data, which type of animal is most likely to hear sounds with frequencies of 10 hertz?
   A Bat   B Dog   C Grasshopper   D Human
2. According to the graph, which type of animal has the smallest hearing range?
   F Bat   G Cat   H Dolphin   J Grasshopper
3. Which of the following animals cannot hear sounds with frequencies below 100 hertz?
   A Bat   C Dolphin
   B Cat   D Grasshopper
4. According to this information, which type of animal can hear sounds with frequencies higher than 100,000 hertz?
   F Bat   H Dolphin
   G Cat   J Human

L2

Teaching

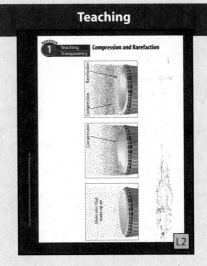

Teaching Transparency 1 — Compression and Rarefaction

L2

Hands-on Activities

Student Text Lab Worksheet

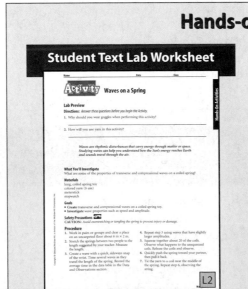

Activity — Waves on a Spring

Lab Preview

Directions: Answer these questions before you begin the Activity.

1. Why should you wear goggles when performing this activity?

2. How will you use yarn in this activity?

Waves are rhythmic disturbances that carry energy through matter or space. Studying waves can help you understand how the Sun's energy reaches Earth and sounds travel through the air.

What You'll Investigate
What are some of the properties of transverse and compressional waves on a coiled spring?

Materials
long, coiled spring toy
colored yarn (5 cm)
meterstick
stopwatch

Goals
• **Create** transverse and compressional waves on a coiled spring toy.
• **Investigate** wave properties such as speed and amplitude.

Safety Precautions
CAUTION: Avoid overstretching or tangling the spring to prevent injury or damage.

Procedure
1. Work in pairs or groups and clear a place on an uncarpeted floor about 6 m x 2 m.
2. Stretch the springs between two people to the length suggested by your teacher. Measure the length.
3. Create a wave with a quick, sideways snap of the wrist. Time several waves as they travel the length of the spring. Record the average time in the data table in the Data and Observations section.
4. Repeat step 3 using waves that have slightly larger amplitudes.
5. Squeeze together about 20 of the coils. Observe what happens to the unsqueezed coils. Release the coils and observe.
6. Quickly push the spring toward your partner, then pull it back.
7. Tie the yarn to a coil near the middle of the spring. Repeat step 6, observing the string.

L2

Laboratory Activities

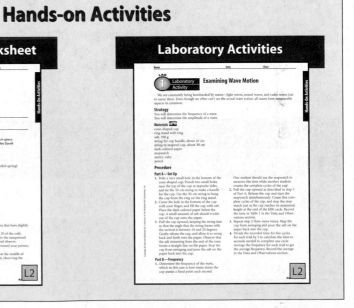

Laboratory Activity 1 — Examining Wave Motion

We are constantly being bombarded by waves—light waves, sound waves, and radio waves just to name three. Even though we often can't see the actual wave action, all waves have measurable aspects in common.

Strategy
You will determine the frequency of a wave.
You will determine the amplitude of a wave.

Materials
cone-shaped cup
ring stand with ring
salt, 100 g
string for cup handle, about 10 cm
string to suspend cup, about 30 cm
dark-colored paper
stopwatch
metric ruler
pencil

Procedure
Part A—Set Up
1. Poke a very small hole in the bottom of the cone-shaped cup. Punch two small holes near the top of the cup at opposite sides, and tie the 10-cm string to make a handle for the cup. Use the 30-cm string to hang the cup from the ring on the ring stand.
2. Cover the hole in the bottom of the cup with your finger, and fill the cup with salt. Place the dark-colored paper below the cup. A small amount of salt should trickle out of the cup onto the paper.
3. Pull the cup upward, keeping the string taut so that the angle that the string forms with the vertical is between 10 and 20 degrees. Gently release the cup, and allow it to swing back and forth over the paper. Observe that salt streaming from the end of the cone forms a straight line on the paper. Stop the cup from swinging and pour the salt on the paper back into the cup.

One student should use the stopwatch to measure the time while another student counts the complete cycles of the cup.
4. Pull the cup upward as described in step 3 of Part A. Release the cup and start the stopwatch simultaneously. Count the complete cycles of the cup, and stop the stopwatch just as the cup reaches its maximum height at the end of the fifth cycle. Record the time in Table 1 in the Data and Observations section.
5. Repeat step 4 two more times. Stop the cup from swinging and pour the salt on the paper back into the cup.
6. Divide the recorded time for five cycles for each trial by 5 to calculate the time in seconds needed to complete one cycle. Average the frequency for each trial to get the average frequency. Record the average in the Data and Observations section.

Part B—Frequency
1. Determine the frequency of the wave, which in this case is how many times the cup passes a fixed point each second.

L2

Meeting Different Ability Levels

Content Outline

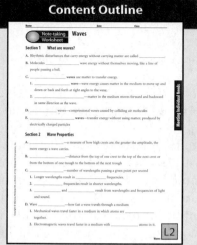

L2

Reinforcement

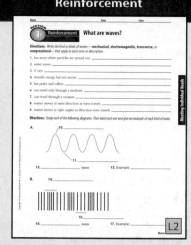

L2

Enrichment

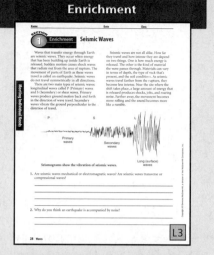

L3

Directed Reading (English/Spanish)

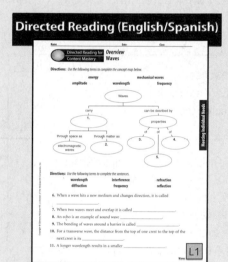

L1

Study Guide

L2

Reading Essentials

L2

Assessment

Test Practice Workbook

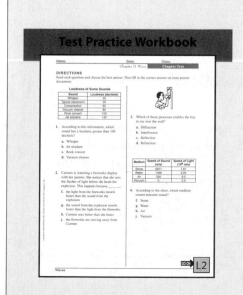

L2

Chapter Review

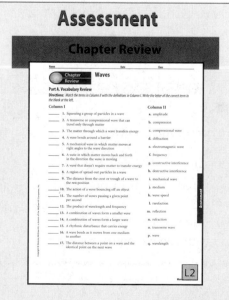

L2

Chapter Tests

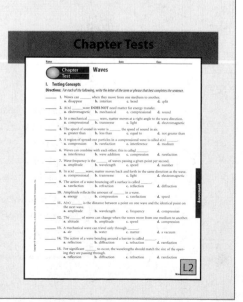

L2

Science Content Background

section 1 What are waves?

What is a wave?

A wave transfers energy from one place to another without transferring matter in the process. Mechanical waves need a material in which to travel. In the material, the bonds between atoms and molecules in some ways are similar to springs. When one of these particles is moved, the springlike bonds exert forces that move the particle back to its original position. At the same time, the particle exerts forces on neighboring particles, causing them to be displaced. In this way, the original disturbance is propagated through the material.

Mechanical waves that travel in a material are produced by something vibrating in the material. Electromagnetic waves don't need a material in which to travel. These waves consist of oscillating electric and magnetic fields. Light waves are electromagnetic waves with wavelenghts between 400 nm and 700 nm.

section 2 Wave Properties

Wave Movements

Waves travel outward from an energy source. If a rock is thrown into a pond, energy traveling outward from the center is seen as waves that decrease in amplitude as they move through the water. A wave will move through one complete cycle in one wavelength. The period (T) of a wave is the time it takes one wavelength to pass a fixed point. A wave's period is the reciprocal of its frequency.

The amplitude of a sound wave determines its sound intensity, or how loud it is. The more energy the sound wave carries the louder the sound is. Two or more sounds produced at the same time can be unpleasant (dissonant) or pleasant (harmonious). The ratios of the frequencies of the tones determine whether or not they sound pleasing to the ear.

Teacher to Teacher

Erin Peters, Lead Science Teacher
Williamsburg Middle School
Arlington, VA

"Long springs are helpful in demonstrating both transverse and compressional (longitudinal) waves. To demonstrate transverse waves, have a student hold one end of the spring and move the other end perpendicular to the spring. Compression waves can be demonstrated by gathering up part of the slack in the spring and letting go. Note how the compression wave travels down through the spring, parallel to the spring."

Erin Peters

chapter content resources

Internet Resources
For additional content background, visit
ips.msscience.com to:
- access your book online
- find references to related articles in popular science magazines
- access Web links with related content background
- access current events with science journal topics

Print Resources
The Physics of Waves, by William C. Elmore and Mark A. Heald, Dover Publications, New York, 1985
Wave Motion in Elastic Solids, by Karl F. Graff, Dove Publications, New York, 1991
Field Guide to Geology, by David Lambert and the Diagram Group. Diagram Visual Information LTD, 1998

section 3 Wave Behavior
Reflection

When reflection occurs, the angle of incidence (the incoming wave angle) equals the angle of reflection (the outgoing wave angle). This is known as the law of reflection. The angles of incidence and reflection are measured relative to a line drawn perpendicular to the reflecting surface. Diffuse reflection occurs as waves bounce at different angles from uneven surfaces. Diffuse reflection of light makes rough surfaces appear dull.

Refraction

Refraction occurs when a wave changes speed as it passes from one material to another. The waves change direction at the interface between the two materials. Light waves can travel with different speeds in different materials, and can change direction as they move from one material to another.

Eyeglasses and contact lenses correct vision by refracting light rays so that they focus properly on the retina of the eye. Binoculars, microscopes, and telescopes also utilize refraction to produce magnified images of small objects and objects at great distances.

Diffraction

The phenomenon called diffraction occurs as waves bend around barriers or spread through openings. Diffraction of light can produce fringes (a series of bright and dark lines) as light waves bend around the edges of objects such as razor blades, diffraction gratings, or the teeth of a comb. The fringes, which can be seen on a screen, are formed by constructive and destructive interference. As the light passes through the opening, each point within the opening can be considered a new point source of light, a concept known as Huygens's principle. The light waves reaching a particular point on the screen come from different points within the opening, and thus have traveled different distances to the screen. The interference patterns are produced because, at different points on the screen, the waves add constructively or destructively.

Wave Interference

Sound waves can be made to interfere constructively or destructively as they reflect from a curved wall or a curved backdrop in a concert hall. Much planning and great expense go into designing the acoustics in a fine performance hall.

Seismic waves are produced by energy traveling through the material medium of Earth. Seismic waves are of three types—S, P, and surface waves. S waves (secondary waves) are transverse or shear and cannot travel through fluids. These seismic waves reflect off the fluid outer core of Earth. P waves, or primary waves, are compressional, or longitudinal, waves. They may pass through all of Earth's materials and are detected first. Surface waves are seismic waves that occur along Earth's surface. They cause up-down and rolling motions on the surface and cause most of the destruction.

Barry L. Runk/Grant Heilman Photography, Inc.

chapter 16

Chapter Vocabulary

wave, p. 468
mechanical wave, p. 469
transverse wave, p. 470
compressional wave, p. 471
electromagnetic wave, p. 472
amplitude, p. 473
wavelength, p. 474
frequency, p. 475
reflection, p. 479
refraction, p. 480
diffraction, p. 481
interference, p. 483

Science Journal Student responses will vary, but may include references to any body of water, large or small, when disturbed.

PowerPoint® Presentations

This CD-ROM is an editable Microsoft® PowerPoint® presentation that includes:
• a pre-made presentation for every chapter
• interactive graphics
• animations
• audio clips
• image bank
• all new section and chapter questions
• Standardized Test Practice
• transparencies
• pre-lab questions for all labs
• Foldables directions
• links to ips.msscience.com

Waves

chapter preview

sections

1 **What are waves?**

2 **Wave Properties**
   Lab Waves on a Spring

3 **Wave Behavior**
   Lab Wave Speed

   Virtual Lab **What are some characteristics of waves?**

Catch A Wave

On a breezy day in Maui, Hawaii, wind-surfers ride the ocean waves. Waves carry energy. You can see the ocean waves in this picture, but there are other waves you cannot see, such as microwaves, radio waves, and sound waves.

Science Journal Write a paragraph about some places where you have seen water waves.

460

Theme Connection

Energy Waves are periodic disturbances that carry energy. The larger the amplitude of the wave, the more energy is transferred.

About the Photo

Energy in Waves In addition to the wind, wind-surfers rely on waves to move them. Like all mechanical waves, water waves carry energy and exert forces that can move objects. The bigger the waves, the more energy they have to give a wind-surfer a really exciting ride. Some islands and coastal areas are known for producing large waves when the wind and currents are just right.

Start-Up Activities

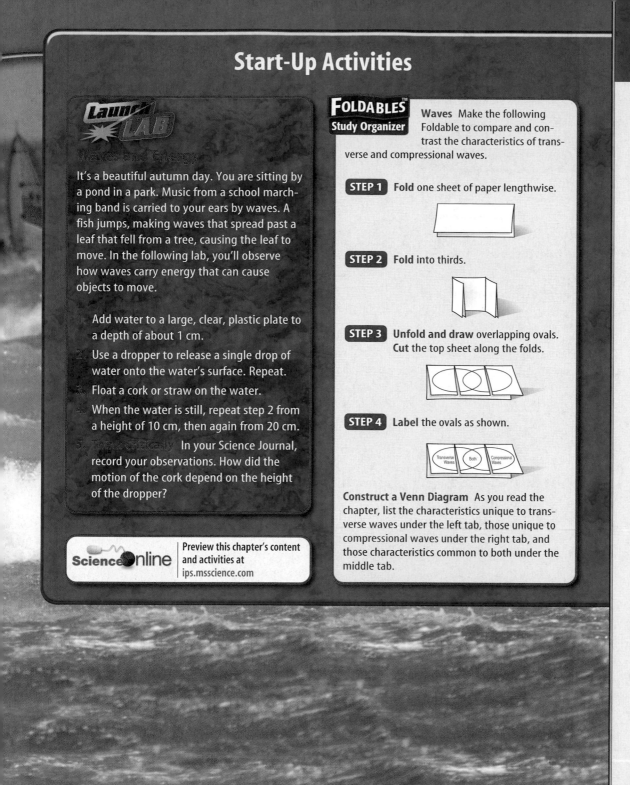

Waves and Energy

It's a beautiful autumn day. You are sitting by a pond in a park. Music from a school marching band is carried to your ears by waves. A fish jumps, making waves that spread past a leaf that fell from a tree, causing the leaf to move. In the following lab, you'll observe how waves carry energy that can cause objects to move.

1. Add water to a large, clear, plastic plate to a depth of about 1 cm.
2. Use a dropper to release a single drop of water onto the water's surface. Repeat.
3. Float a cork or straw on the water.
4. When the water is still, repeat step 2 from a height of 10 cm, then again from 20 cm.
5. **Think Critically** In your Science Journal, record your observations. How did the motion of the cork depend on the height of the dropper?

 Science Online Preview this chapter's content and activities at ips.msscience.com

FOLDABLES Study Organizer

Waves Make the following Foldable to compare and contrast the characteristics of transverse and compressional waves.

STEP 1 **Fold** one sheet of paper lengthwise.

STEP 2 **Fold** into thirds.

STEP 3 **Unfold and draw** overlapping ovals. **Cut** the top sheet along the folds.

STEP 4 **Label** the ovals as shown.

Transverse Waves | Both | Compressional Waves

Construct a Venn Diagram As you read the chapter, list the characteristics unique to transverse waves under the left tab, those unique to compressional waves under the right tab, and those characteristics common to both under the middle tab.

Purpose Use the Launch Lab to give students an opportunity to observe and describe wave behavior. **L2** **ELL** **COOP LEARN**

LS **Logical-Mathematical**

Materials large, clear-plastic plate; small cork or piece of a soda straw; dropper; water

Teaching Strategies

• Suggest that students observe closely because the waves will move quickly.
• Tell students to be sure the water is still before adding drops of water. They also should be careful not to disturb the water when adding the cork.

Think Critically

Circular waves travel outward from the point where the drops hit the water's surface. Drops released from a height of 20 cm cause larger waves and transfer more energy than do drops released from a height of 10 cm. The cork bobs up and down as the waves pass but does not move horizontally.

Assessment

Process Provide students with diagrams of transverse waves with different amplitudes. Ask them to identify which diagram shows waves generated by dropping water from a greater height. Use **Performance Assessment in the Science Classroom**, p. 89.

FOLDABLES Study Organizer **Dinah Zike Study Fold**

Student preparation materials for this Foldable are available in the Chapter *FAST FILE* Resources.

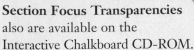

Bellringer

Section Focus Transparencies also are available on the Interactive Chalkboard CD-ROM.

L2 ELL

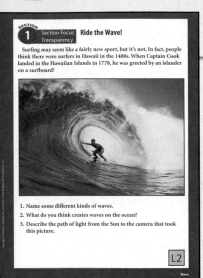

Section Focus Transparency Ride the Wave!

Surfing may seem like a fairly new sport, but it's not. In fact, people think there were surfers in Hawaii in the 1400s. When Captain Cook landed in the Hawaiian Islands in 1778, he was greeted by an islander on a surfboard!

1. Name some different kinds of waves.
2. What do you think creates waves on the ocean?
3. Describe the path of light from the Sun to the camera that took this picture.

L2

Tie to Prior Knowledge

Wave Discussion Ask students to describe any waves they know of. Discuss with them the form of energy transferred by each wave.

---

section 1

What are waves?

as you read

What You'll Learn
- **Explain** the relationship among waves, energy, and matter.
- **Describe** the difference between transverse waves and compressional waves.

Why It's Important
Waves enable you to see and hear the world around you.

Review Vocabulary
energy: the ability to cause change

New Vocabulary
- wave
- mechanical wave
- transverse wave
- compressional wave
- electromagnetic wave

What is a wave?

When you are relaxing on an air mattress in a pool and someone does a cannonball dive off the diving board, you suddenly find yourself bobbing up and down. You can make something move by giving it a push or pull, but the person jumping didn't touch your air mattress. How did the energy from the dive travel through the water and move your air mattress? The up-and-down motion was caused by the peaks and valleys of the ripples that moved from where the splash occurred. These peaks and valleys make up water waves.

Waves Carry Energy Rhythmic disturbances that carry energy without carrying matter are called waves. Water waves are shown in **Figure 1.** You can see the energy of the wave from a speedboat traveling outward, but the water only moves up and down. If you've ever felt a clap of thunder, you know that sound waves can carry large amounts of energy. You also transfer energy when you throw something to a friend, as in **Figure 1.** However, there is a difference between a moving ball and a wave. A ball is made of matter, and when it is thrown, the matter moves from one place to another. So, unlike the wave, throwing a ball involves the transport of matter as well as energy.

Figure 1 The wave and the thrown ball carry energy in different ways.

The waves created by a boat move mostly up and down, but the energy travels outward from the boat.

When the ball is thrown, the ball carries energy as it moves forward.

462 CHAPTER 16 Waves

Section 1 Resource Manager

Chapter FAST FILE Resources
Transparency Activity, pp. 42, 45–46
Enrichment, p. 28
Reinforcement, p. 25
MiniLAB, p. 3

Directed Reading for Content Mastery, pp. 17, 18
Note-taking Worksheets, pp. 31–32
Cultural Diversity, p. 63
Mathematics Skill Activities, p. 11

As the students pass the ball, the students' positions do not change—only the position of the ball changes.

In a water wave, water molecules bump each other and pass energy from molecule to molecule.

A Model for Waves

How does a wave carry energy without transporting matter? Imagine a line of people, as shown in **Figure 2.** The first person in line passes a ball to the second person, who passes the ball to the next person, and so on. Passing a ball down a line of people is a model for how waves can transport energy without transporting matter. Even though the ball has traveled, the people in line have not moved. In this model, you can think of the ball as representing energy. What do the people in line represent?

Think about the ripples on the surface of a pond. The energy carried by the ripples travels through the water. The water is made up of water molecules. It is the individual molecules of water that pass the wave energy, just as the people. The water molecules transport the energy in a water wave by colliding with the molecules around them, as shown in **Figure 2.**

Reading Check *What is carried by waves?*

Mechanical Waves

In the wave model, the ball could not be transferred if the line of people didn't exist. The energy of a water wave could not be transferred if no water molecules existed. These types of waves, which use matter to transfer energy, are called **mechanical waves.** The matter through which a mechanical wave travels is called a medium. For ripples on a pond, the medium is the water.

A mechanical wave travels as energy is transferred from particle to particle in the medium. For example, a sound wave is a mechanical wave that can travel through air, as well as solids, liquids, and other gases. Without a medium such as air, there would be no sound waves. In outer space sound waves can't travel because there is no air.

Figure 2 A wave transports energy without transporting matter from place to place.
Describe *other models that could be used to represent a mechanical wave.*

Differentiated Instruction

Challenge Ask students to investigate the behavior of surface waves near the seashore and make posters showing what they find. As the waves approach land, water molecules near the surface experience more elliptical movement, causing the waves to form high crests that eventually crash into land. L3 [LS] **Visual-Spatial**

Visual Learning

Figure 2 Tell students that the water molecules near the surface of a wave actually travel in small circles. Have students model this movement with a cork in water. L1 ELL [LS] **Kinesthetic**

2 Teach

Discussion

Energy Waves Ask students to describe how being near a source of deep, loud sounds, such as heavy machinery or the sub-woofer of a stereo, demonstrates that waves carry energy. You can feel the vibrations as well as hear the sound. L2 [LS] **Auditory-Musical**

Make a Model

Water Wave Have students duplicate the model described in the text. As they do this, emphasize that they are like the molecules of water through which a wave flows. Point out that the ball is made of matter, but in the model it represents energy. L1 ELL
COOP LEARN [LS] **Kinesthetic**

Reading Check

Answer energy

Caption Answer

Figure 2 Possible answers include a bucket brigade, bumping someone at one end of a line of people, whispering a message to someone in a line of people who pass the message from one to another.

IDENTIFYING Misconceptions

Mechanical Wave Students might be surprised that some waves are described as mechanical. The word *mechanical* comes from the Greek word *mechane*, meaning "a device." Based on this, have students discuss why *mechanical* is an appropriate term to use for waves that need matter to move. One definition of *machine* is a device that transmits energy. In a mechanical wave, matter transmits energy. L3 [LS] **Linguistic**

464 CHAPTER 16 Waves

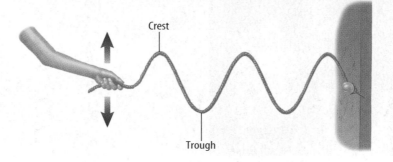

Crest

Trough

Figure 3 The high points on the wave are called crests and the low points are called troughs.

Use an Analogy

Stadium Wave Ask students to think of people "doing the wave" in a stadium. Point out that this wave is similar to a transverse mechanical wave because the people, like particles, move up and down at right angles to the direction the wave moves. L2

LS Visual-Spatial

Quick Demo

Floating on a Wave

Materials clear plate, colored water, overhead projector, small cork

Estimated Time five minutes

Procedure Put the clear plate on the overhead projector and add the colored water. Ask students to predict what will happen to a floating object as waves are generated in the water. Put the cork in the water and make small waves by moving a pencil or your finger in the water. The floating object will bob up and down because the water waves are very much like transverse waves.

✔ Reading Check

Answer crests

Activity

Describing Waves Ask students to list on chart paper examples of mechanical waves. Have them draw each type of wave, describe each wave as transverse or compressional, and label the different parts of each wave. L2

 COOP LEARN **LS Visual-Spatial** P

Transverse Waves In a mechanical transverse wave, the wave energy causes the matter in the medium to move up and down or back and forth at right angles to the direction the wave travels. You can make a model of a transverse wave. Stretch a long rope out on the ground. Hold one end in your hand. Now shake the end in your hand back and forth. As you shake the rope, you create a wave that seems to slide along the rope.

When you first started shaking the rope, it might have appeared that the rope itself was moving away from you. But it was only the wave that was moving away from your hand. The wave energy moves through the rope, but the matter in the rope doesn't travel. You can see that the wave has peaks and valleys at regular intervals. As shown in **Figure 3,** the high points of transverse waves are called crests. The low points are called troughs.

✔ Reading Check
What are the highest points of transverse waves called?

Figure 4 A compressional wave can travel through a coiled spring toy.

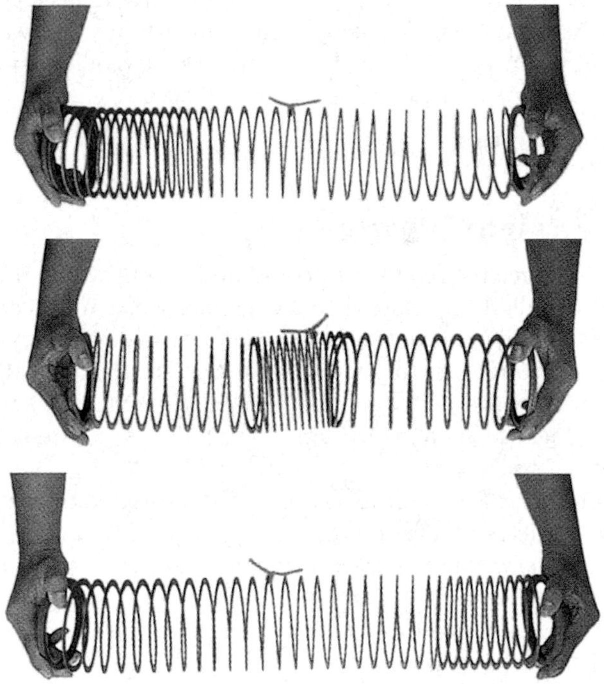

As the wave motion begins, the coils on the left are close together and the other coils are far apart.

The wave, seen in the squeezed and stretched coils, travels along the spring.

The string and coils did not travel with the wave. Each coil moved forward and then back to its original position.

464 CHAPTER 16 Waves

Teacher FYI

Seismic Waves There are three main types of seismic waves. Primary (P) waves oscillate back and forth along the direction the wave travels. Secondary (S) waves oscillate perpendicular to the direction of wave motion. Surface waves cause horizontal and, sometimes, vertical ground surface movement.

Active Reading

Bubble Map Using a Bubble Map helps students start ideas flowing about a given topic. Words are clustered to describe a concept. Students can use the bubble map for a prewrite, to generate ideas before writing in their Journals, or to review for a test. Have students design a Bubble Map for the different types of waves described in this section. L2

Compressional Waves Mechanical waves can be either transverse or compressional. In a **compressional wave,** matter in the medium moves forward and backward along the same direction that the wave travels. You can make a compressional wave by squeezing together and releasing several coils of a coiled spring toy, as shown in **Figure 4.**

The coils move only as the wave passes and then return to their original positions. So, like transverse waves, compressional waves carry only energy forward along the spring. In this example, the spring is the medium the wave moves through, but the spring does not move along with the wave.

Sound Waves Sound waves are compressional waves. How do you make sound waves when you talk or sing? If you hold your fingers against your throat while you hum, you can feel vibrations. These vibrations are the movements of your vocal cords. If you touch a stereo speaker while it's playing, you can feel it vibrating, too. All waves are produced by something that is vibrating.

Making Sound Waves

How do vibrating objects make sound waves? Look at the drum shown in **Figure 5.** When you hit the drumhead it starts vibrating up and down. As the drumhead moves upward, the molecules next to it are pushed closer together. This group of molecules that are closer together is a compression. As the compression is formed, it moves away from the drumhead, just as the squeezed coils move along the coiled spring toy in **Figure 4.**

When the drumhead moves downward, the molecules near it have more room and can spread farther apart. This group of molecules that are farther apart is a rarefaction. The rarefaction also moves away from the drumhead. As the drumhead vibrates up and down, it forms a series of compressions and rarefactions that move away and spread out in all directions. This series of compressions and rarefactions is a sound wave.

Figure 5 A vibrating drumhead makes compressions and rarefactions in the air.
Describe *how compressions and rarefactions are different.*

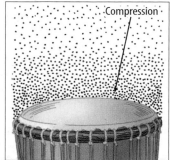
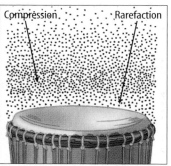

Molecules that make up air

Compression

Compression   Rarefaction

SECTION 1 What are waves? **465**

Global Positioning Systems There are 24 GPS satellites, and they orbit Earth at a height of about 20,000 km. Their electromagnetic radio waves can be received all over Earth, regardless of the weather. GPS was designed for and is operated by the U.S. Department of Defense and provides positioning information to military submarines, helicopters, ships, bombers, tanks, and missiles. However, since the signals can be received by an unlimited number of users, they are increasingly important in everyday civilian navigation.

Global Positioning Systems Maybe you've used a global positioning system (GPS) receiver to determine your location while driving, boating, or hiking. Earth-orbiting satellites send electromagnetic radio waves that transmit their exact locations and times of transmission. The GPS receiver uses information from four of these satellites to determine your location to within about 16 m.

Electromagnetic Waves

Waves that can travel through space where there is no matter are **electromagnetic waves**. There are different types of electromagnetic waves, including radio waves, infrared waves, visible light waves, ultraviolet waves, X rays, and gamma rays. These waves can travel in matter or in space. Radio waves from TV and radio stations travel through air, and may be reflected from a satellite in space. They then travel through air, through the walls of your house, and to your TV or radio.

Radiant Energy from the Sun The Sun emits electromagnetic waves that travel through space and reach Earth. The energy carried by electromagnetic waves is called radiant energy. Almost 92 percent of the radiant energy that reaches Earth from the Sun is carried by infrared and visible light waves. Infrared waves make you feel warm when you sit in sunlight, and visible light waves enable you to see. A small amount of the radiant energy that reaches Earth is carried by ultraviolet waves. These are the waves that can cause sunburn if you are exposed to sunlight for too long.

Check for Understanding

Logical-Mathematical Brainstorm with students to create a list of ways water waves display energy. Responses could include moving a surf board, depositing sand and debris along shorelines, or damage to piers and boats seen after a storm. L2

Reteach

Waves in a Spring Demonstrate compressional and transverse waves using a spring toy. Have students identify each type of wave and the parts of the waves. L2 LS **Visual-Spatial**

Process Have students draw diagrams of transverse and compressional waves, labeling the crests and troughs. Use **Performance Assessment in the Science Classroom**, p. 127. L2

---

section 1 review

Summary

What is a wave?
- Waves transfer energy, but do not transfer matter.

Mechanical Waves
- Mechanical waves require a medium in which to travel.
- When a transverse wave travels, particles of the medium move at right angles to the direction the wave is traveling.
- When a compressional wave travels, particles of the medium move back and forth along the same direction the wave is traveling.
- Sound is a compressional wave.

Electromagnetic Waves
- Electromagnetic waves can travel through empty space.
- The Sun emits different types of electromagnetic waves, including infrared, visible light, and ultraviolet waves.

Self Check

1. **Describe** the movement of a floating object on a pond when struck by a wave.
2. **Explain** why a sound wave can't travel from a satellite to Earth.
3. **Compare and contrast** a transverse wave and a compressional wave. How are they similar and different?
4. **Compare and contrast** a mechanical wave and an electromagnetic wave.
5. **Think Critically** How is it possible for a sound wave to transmit energy but not matter?

Applying Skills

6. **Concept Map** Create a concept map that shows the relationships among the following: *waves, mechanical waves, electromagnetic waves, compressional waves,* and *transverse waves.*
7. **Use a Word Processor** Use word-processing software to write short descriptions of the waves you encounter during a typical day.

Science Online ips.msscience.com/self_check_quiz

---

section 1 review

1. It bobs up and down.
2. It requires a medium through which to travel, and there is no medium in space.
3. Possible answer: Water waves are transverse waves. Sound waves are compressional waves. Compressional waves cause vibration in the direction of wave movement. Transverse waves cause vibration at right angles to the wave's direction. Both involve periodic motion and carry energy.
4. Mechanical waves use matter to transmit energy. Electromagnetic waves do not require matter to carry energy.
5. The wave causes molecules of matter to bump neighboring molecules.
6. Answers should show mechanical waves as compressional or transverse; electromagnetic waves are transverse.
7. Answers might include radio waves, sound waves, or waves in a bathtub.

Wave Properties

Amplitude

Can you describe a wave? For a water wave, one way might be to tell how high the wave rises above, or falls below, the normal level. This distance is called the wave's amplitude. The **amplitude** of a transverse wave is one-half the distance between a crest and a trough, as shown in **Figure 6.** In a compressional wave, the amplitude is greater when the particles of the medium are squeezed closer together in each compression and spread farther apart in each rarefaction.

Amplitude and Energy A wave's amplitude is related to the energy that the wave carries. For example, the electromagnetic waves that make up bright light have greater amplitudes than the waves that make up dim light. Waves of bright light carry more energy than the waves that make up dim light. In a similar way, loud sound waves have greater amplitudes than soft sound waves. Loud sounds carry more energy than soft sounds. If a sound is loud enough, it can carry enough energy to damage your hearing.

When a hurricane strikes a coastal area, the resulting water waves carry enough energy to damage almost anything that stands in their path. The large waves caused by a hurricane carry more energy than the small waves or ripples on a pond.

as you read

What You'll Learn

- **Describe** the relationship between the frequency and wavelength of a wave.
- **Explain** why waves travel at different speeds.

Why It's Important

The properties of a wave determine whether the wave is useful or dangerous.

Review Vocabulary
speed: the distance traveled divided by the time needed to travel the distance

New Vocabulary
- amplitude
- wavelength
- frequency

Figure 6 The energy carried by a wave increases as its amplitude increases.

A water wave of large amplitude carried the energy that caused this damage.

The amplitude of a transverse wave is a measure of how high the crests are or how deep the troughs are.

Inquiry Lab

Seismic Activity

Purpose to locate and evaluate areas of seismic activity around the world L2 PBL

Possible Materials library resource materials, encyclopedic computer programs, accessed from **ips.msscience.com/internet_lab**

Estimated Time 1 class period

Teaching Strategies

• Allow students to work in pairs or small groups.

• Present this as a Problem-Based Learning activity. Company XYZ is planning to build an amusement park. The company has secured the option to buy at several locations around the world. What recommendations would the students make to the company regarding site selection so that students their age get the most enjoyment out of the park?

• Students can investigate seismic activity as well as other science-based factors such as bedrock; impact upon land, air, and water; traffic flow, etc.

• Allow students to explore other questions that arise.

For additional inquiry activities, see *Science Inquiry Labs*.

For transverse waves, wavelength is the distance from crest to crest or trough to trough.

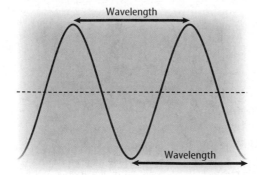

For compressional waves, wavelength is the distance from compression to compression or rarefaction to rarefaction.

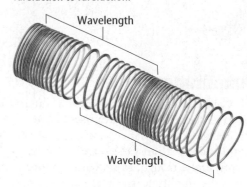

Figure 7 A transverse or a compressional wave has a wavelength.

Figure 8 The wavelengths and frequencies of electromagnetic waves vary.

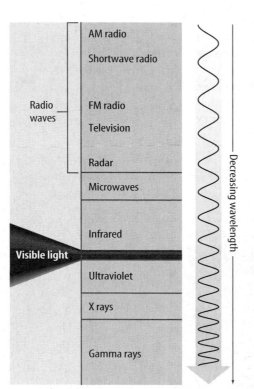

The devastating effect that a wave with large amplitude can have is seen in the aftermath of tsunamis. Tsunamis are huge sea waves that are caused by underwater earthquakes along faults on the seafloor. The movement of the seafloor along a fault produces the wave. As the wave moves toward shallow water and slows down, the amplitude of the wave grows. The tremendous amounts of energy tsunamis carry cause great damage when they move ashore.

Wavelength

Another way to describe a wave is by its wavelength. **Figure 7** shows the wavelength of a transverse wave and a compressional wave. For a transverse wave, **wavelength** is the distance from the top of one crest to the top of the next crest, or from the bottom of one trough to the bottom of the next trough. For a compressional wave, the wavelength is the distance between the center of one compression and the center of the next compression, or from the center of one rarefaction to the center of the next rarefaction.

Electromagnetic waves have wavelengths that range from kilometers, for radio waves, to less than the diameter of an atom, for X rays and gamma rays. This range is called the electromagnetic spectrum. **Figure 8** shows the names given to different parts of the electromagnetic spectrum. Visible light is only a small part of the electromagnetic spectrum. It is the wavelength of visible light waves that determines their color. For example, the wavelength of red light waves is longer than the wavelength of green light waves.

468 CHAPTER 16 Waves

Visual Learning

Figure 8 Electromagnetic waves sometimes behave as if they are particles called photons. Waves with a longer wavelength have lower energy per photon than waves with a shorter wavelength.

Teacher FYI

Decibels The threshold of human hearing for sound intensity (loudness) is 0 dB (10^{-12} watts/m^2). Hearing damage commences at sustained levels of about 85 dB. Normal conversation has an intensity of about 60 dB. A jet engine can generate noise levels of about 120 dB to 140 dB.

Frequency

The **frequency** of a wave is the number of wavelengths that pass a given point in 1 s. The unit of frequency is the number of wavelengths per second, or hertz (Hz). Recall that waves are produced by something that vibrates. The faster the vibration is, the higher the frequency is of the wave that is produced.

Reading Check *How is the frequency of a wave measured?*

A Sidewalk Model For waves that travel with the same speed, frequency and wavelength are related. To model this relationship, imagine people on two parallel moving sidewalks in an airport, as shown in **Figure 9.** One sidewalk has four travelers spaced 4 m apart. The other sidewalk has 16 travelers spaced 1 m apart.

Now imagine that both sidewalks are moving at the same speed and approaching a pillar between them. On which sidewalk will more people go past the pillar? On the sidewalk with the shorter distance between people, four people will pass the pillar for each one person on the other sidewalk. When four people pass the pillar on the first sidewalk, 16 people pass the pillar on the second sidewalk.

Figure 9 When people are farther apart on a moving sidewalk, fewer people pass the pillar every minute.
Infer *how the number of people passing the pillar each minute would change if the sidewalk moved slower.*

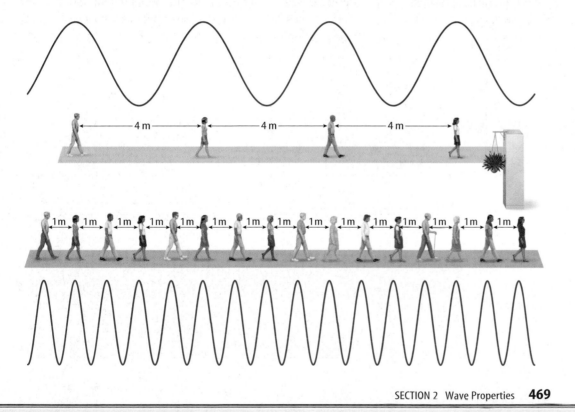

Use Science Words

Word Origin Have students investigate the origin of the word *hertz* and why it is used to describe frequency. The unit hertz was named after Heinrich Hertz, a German physicist who studied electromagnetic waves. L2 LS **Linguistic**

Reading Check

Answer in units of the number of wavelengths per second, or Hz

Discussion

String Music How does pressing a string on a guitar affect the frequency of the sound produced? It shortens the string, which increases the frequency of the sound the string produces when it is plucked. How does this relate to the sounds produced by a harp? On a harp, the short strings produce high frequency sounds and the long strings produce low frequency sounds. L2 LS **Auditory-Musical**

Caption Answer

Figure 9 The number would decrease.

Activity

Geographic Waves Ask students to bring in magazine and newspaper articles about tidal waves (tsunamis) and earthquakes around the world. Display the articles and discuss with students the relationship between energy, wave amplitude, and the amount of destruction caused. L2 LS **Interpersonal**

Differentiated Instruction

English-Language Learners Play music through speakers with their interior exposed. Students can see and feel the vibrations that result from changes in pitch (frequency) or volume (amplitude).

Curriculum Connection

Music Have students find out what quarter tones are and play recordings of music with quarter tones for the class. The difference in frequency between two adjacent pitches in some types of music, including Hindu music, is about half that between adjacent pitches in western music. These pitches are called quarter tones. L3 ELL LS **Auditory-Musical**

Activity

Making Waves Have each student fill a bowl with water and dip a pencil into and out of the water to form waves. They should notice that dipping the pencil with low frequency produces waves with longer wavelengths (greater distance between crests) than dipping the pencil with high frequency. Have students use a stopwatch to help calibrate the frequencies of their waves.
L1 ELL LS Kinesthetic

Quick Demo

Musical Sounds

Materials musical instruments, oscilloscope, microphone

Estimated Time 15 minutes

Procedure Have students who play instruments demonstrate compressional waves of high and low frequency by producing notes of varying pitch. If an oscilloscope is available connect it to a microphone to show students the wavelengths and amplitudes of the notes.

INTEGRATE Health

Ultrasonic Waves The wavelengths are much shorter than those of the sound waves we hear.

Research Have students research one of the medical uses of ultrasound mentioned. Students should present their findings to you or to the class in whatever format they choose. L2

Reading Check

Answer frequency increases as wavelength decreases

INTEGRATE Health

Ultrasonic Waves Sound waves with ultra-high frequencies cannot be heard by the human ear, but they are used by medical professionals in several ways. They are used to perform echocardiograms of the heart, produce ultrasound images of internal organs, break up blockages in arteries, and sterilize surgical instruments. Describe how the wavelengths of these sound waves compare to sound waves you can hear.

Figure 10 The frequency of the notes on a musical scale increases as the notes get higher in pitch, but the wavelength of the notes decreases.

Frequency and Wavelength Suppose that each person in **Figure 9** represents the crest of a wave. Then the movement of people on the first sidewalk is like a wave with a wavelength of 4 m. For the second sidewalk, the wavelength would be 1 m. On the first sidewalk, where the wavelength is longer, the people pass the pillar *less* frequently. Smaller frequencies result in longer wavelengths. On the second sidewalk, where the wavelength is shorter, the people pass the pillar *more* frequently. Higher frequencies result in shorter wavelengths. This is true for all waves that travel at the same speed. As the frequency of a wave increases, its wavelength decreases.

Reading Check *How are frequency and wavelength related?*

Color and Pitch Because frequency and wavelength are related, either the wavelength or frequency of a light wave determines the color of the light. For example, blue light has a larger frequency and shorter wavelength than red light.

Either the wavelength or frequency determines the pitch of a sound wave. Pitch is how high or low a sound seems to be. When you sing a musical scale, the pitch and frequency increase from note to note. Wavelength and frequency are also related for sound waves traveling in air. As the frequency of sound waves increases, their wavelength decreases. **Figure 10** shows how the frequency and wavelength change for notes on a musical scale.

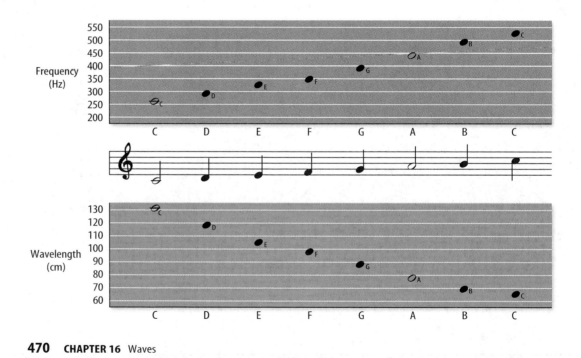

Science Journal

Musical Instruments Ask students to investigate various musical instruments and write in their Science Journals what vibrates on each instrument to make sound and how this produces certain pitches. Students might mention the reed of a clarinet or the lips of a trumpet player. Air inside the instrument also vibrates. The shape and material of the instrument affect pitch. L3 LS Linguistic

Differentiated Instruction

Challenge Compare the sound of a siren moving toward you with the sound of a siren moving away from you. When the siren is moving toward you, the wavelengths of the compressional waves decrease, resulting in a higher pitch. As the siren moves away from you, the wavelengths increase and the pitch gets lower. This is known as the Doppler effect. L3 LS Logical-Mathematical

Wave Speed

You've probably watched a distant thunderstorm approach on a hot summer day. You see a bolt of lightning flash between a dark cloud and the ground. If the thunderstorm is many kilometers away, several seconds will pass between when you see the lightning and when you hear the thunder. This happens because light travels much faster in air than sound does. Light travels through air at about 300 million m/s. Sound travels through air at about 340 m/s. The speed of any wave can be calculated from this equation:

> **Wave Speed Equation**
>
> **wave speed** (in m/s) = **frequency** (in Hz) × **wavelength** (m)
>
> $$v = f\lambda$$

In this equation, the wavelength is represented by the symbol λ, which is the Greek letter lambda.

When mechanical waves, such as sound, and electromagnetic waves, such as light, travel in different materials, they change speed. Mechanical waves usually travel fastest in solids, and slowest in gases. Electromagnetic waves travel fastest in gases and slowest in solids. For example, the speed of light is about 30 percent faster in air than in water.

Science Online

Topic: Wave Speed
Visit ips.msscience.com for Web links to information about wave speed in different materials.

Activity Make a chart showing the speed of light in different materials.

Check for Understanding

Visual-Spatial Have each student draw a wave at the top of a piece of paper. Below the first wave, draw an identical wave, but with a greater frequency. Next, draw a wave identical to the first, but with a smaller amplitude. Draw a wave identical to the first, but with a shorter wavelength. L2

Reteach

Parts of a Wave Have students use a spiral drawing toy to demonstrate the amplitude, wavelength, and frequency of a wave. L1 LS
Kinesthetic

---

section 2 review

Summary

Amplitude
- In a transverse wave, the amplitude is one-half the distance between a crest and a trough.
- The larger the amplitude, the greater the energy carried by the wave.

Wavelength
- For a transverse wave, wavelength is the distance from crest to crest, or from trough to trough.
- For a compressional wave, wavelength is the distance from compression to compression, or from rarefaction to rarefaction.

Frequency
- The frequency of a wave is the number of wavelengths that pass a given point in 1 s.
- For waves that travel at the same speed, as the frequency of the wave increases, its wavelength decreases.

Self Check

1. **Describe** how the frequency of a wave changes as its wavelength changes.
2. **Explain** why a sound wave with a large amplitude is more likely to damage your hearing than one with a small amplitude.
3. **State** what accounts for the time difference between seeing and hearing a fireworks display.
4. **Explain** why the statement "The speed of light is 300 million m/s" is not always correct.
5. **Think Critically** Explain the differences between the waves that make up bright, green light and dim, red light.

Applying Math

6. **Calculate Wave Speed** Find the speed of a wave with a wavelength of 5 m and a frequency of 68 Hz.
7. **Calculate Wavelength** Find the wavelength of a sound wave traveling in water with a speed of 1,470 m/s, and a frequency of 2,340 Hz.

Science Online Ips.msscience.com/self_check_quiz

SECTION 2 Wave Properties **471**

Assessment

Process Fill test tubes with different amounts of water and tap on them gently with a glass stirring rod. Have students explain the differences between the pitches produced. The more water in a tube, the shorter the wavelength of air that fits in the tube, so the higher the pitch produced when the glass is tapped. Use **Performance Assessment in the Science Classroom**, p. 89.

Virtual Labs

Waves *What are some characteristics of waves?*

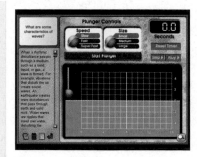

---

section 2 review

1. The frequency increases as the wavelength decreases.
2. Waves having large amplitudes carry more energy than waves with small amplitudes.
3. Light travels much faster than sound.
4. The speed of light varies, depending on the medium through which it travels. The speed of light is about 300 million m/s in air.
5. The waves that make up bright green light have shorter wavelengths, higher frequencies, and larger amplitudes.
6. 340 m/s
7. 0.63 m

Waves on a Spring

● **Real-World Question** ─────

Purpose Students make waves with a coiled-spring toy and observe the waves. **L2** **ELL**

COOP LEARN **LS** **Kinesthetic**

Process Skills observe and infer, compare and contrast, interpret data, classify, make and use tables

Time Required 45 minutes

● **Procedure** ─────

Safety Precautions Space student groups far enough apart that the coiled springs do not interfere with each other.

Teaching Strategies
• Help students compare the two types of waves they generate.
• Help students recognize the parts of a wave.

Troubleshooting Watch students to ensure that they do not tangle or overstretch the coiled springs.

● **Conclude and Apply** ─────

1. In steps 4 and 5, transverse waves were produced. In steps 6 to 8, compressional waves were produced.
2. rarefaction
3. The yarn moved back and forth from a fixed position, while the wave moved along the spring from one end to the other.

☑ Assessment

Process Have students draw and label the parts of each type of wave they generated in the activity. Use **Performance Assessment in the Science Classroom**, p. 127.

Waves are rhythmic disturbances that carry energy through matter or space. Studying waves can help you understand how the Sun's energy reaches Earth and sounds travel through the air.

● **Real-World Question**─────

What are some of the properties of transverse and compressional waves on a coiled spring?

Goals
■ **Create** transverse and compressional waves on a coiled spring toy.
■ **Investigate** wave properties such as speed and amplitude.

Materials
long, coiled spring toy
colored yarn (5 cm)
meterstick
stopwatch

Safety Precautions 🌀 🧤

WARNING: *Avoid overstretching or tangling the spring to prevent injury or damage.*

● **Procedure**─────

1. Prepare a data table such as the one shown.

Wave Data	
Length of stretched spring toy	4.20 m
Average time for a wave to travel from end to end—step 4	1.35 s
Average time for a wave to travel from end to end—step 5	1.25 s

2. Work in pairs or groups and clear a place on an uncarpeted floor about 6 m × 2 m.

3. Stretch the springs between two people to the length suggested by your teacher. Measure the length.

4. Create a wave with a quick, sideways snap of the wrist. Time several waves as they travel the length of the spring. Record the average time in your data table.

5. Repeat step 4 using waves that have slightly larger amplitudes.

6. Squeeze together about 20 of the coils. Observe what happens to the unsqueezed coils. Release the coils and observe.

7. Quickly push the spring toward your partner, then pull it back.

8. Tie the yarn to a coil near the middle of the spring. Repeat step 7, observing the string.

9. **Calculate** and compare the speeds of the waves in steps 4 and 5.

● **Conclude and Apply**─────

1. **Classify** the wave pulses you created in each step as compressional or transverse.
2. **Classify** the unsqueezed coils in step 6 as a compression or a rarefaction.
3. **Compare and contrast** the motion of the yarn in step 8 with the motion of the wave.

*C*ommunicating
Your Data

Write a summary paragraph of how this lab demonstrated any of the vocabulary words from the first two sections of the chapter. **For more help, refer to the Science Skill Handbook.**

*C*ommunicating
Your Data

Have students use a computer graphics program to create a display explaining the results of the activity.

Wave Behavior

Reflection

What causes the echo when you yell across an empty gymnasium or down a long, empty hallway? Why can you see your face when you look in a mirror? The echo of your voice and the face you see in the mirror are caused by wave reflection.

Reflection occurs when a wave strikes an object or surface and bounces off. An echo is reflected sound. Sound reflects from all surfaces. Your echo bounces off the walls, floor, ceiling, furniture, and people. You see your face in a mirror or a still pond, as shown in **Figure 11,** because of reflection. Light waves produced by a source of light such as the Sun or a lightbulb bounce off your face, strike the mirror, and reflect back to your eyes.

When a surface is smooth and even the reflected image is clear and sharp. However, **Figure 11** shows that when light reflects from an uneven or rough surface, you can't see a sharp image because the reflected light scatters in many different directions.

✓ Reading Check *What causes reflection?*

as you read

What You'll Learn

- **Explain** how waves can reflect from some surfaces.
- **Explain** how waves change direction when they move from one material into another.
- **Describe** how waves are able to bend around barriers.

Why It's Important

The reflection of waves enables you to see objects around you.

◉ Review Vocabulary

echo: the repetition of a sound caused by the reflection of sound waves

New Vocabulary

- reflection
- refraction
- diffraction
- interference

Bellringer

Section Focus Transparencies also are available on the Interactive Chalkboard CD-ROM.

L2 **ELL**

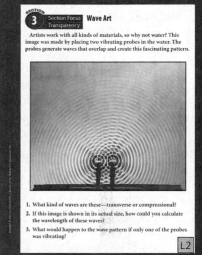

Section Focus Transparency **Wave Art**

Artists work with all kinds of materials, so why not water? This image was made by placing two vibrating probes in the water. The probes generate waves that overlap and create this fascinating pattern.

1. What kind of waves are these—transverse or compressional?
2. If this image is shown in its actual size, how could you calculate the wavelength of these waves?
3. What would happen to the wave pattern if only one of the probes was vibrating?

L2

Tie to Prior Knowledge

Visible Light Remind students that visible light rays are electromagnetic waves. Discuss whether they can see themselves in a mirror without light rays. Explain that in this section, they will learn how waves reflect and refract.

The smooth surface of a still pond enables you to see a sharp, clear image of yourself.

If the surface of the pond is rough and uneven, your reflected image is no longer clear and sharp.

Figure 11 The image formed by reflection depends on the smoothness of the surface.

Mini LAB

Purpose Students observe how light refracts. L1 ELL LS
Visual-Spatial

Materials white soda straw, opaque drinking glass or cup, water

Teaching Strategy The larger the diameter of the glass or cup, the easier it will be to see the refraction. Also, tell students to fill the glass or cup almost to the top.

Analysis
1. The straw appears to be straight.
2. The straw appears to bend at the water's surface. Light reflects from the straw and refracts as it passes from the water into the air.

Assessment

Performance Have students draw ray diagrams in their Science Journals that show how the light waves refract. Use **Performance Assessment in the Science Classroom,** p. 127.

Mini LAB

Observing How Light Refracts

Procedure 🥽
1. Fill a **large, opaque drinking glass or cup** with **water**.
2. Place a **white soda straw** in the water at an angle.
3. Looking directly down into the cup from above, observe the straw where it meets the water.
4. Placing yourself so that the straw angles to your left or right, slowly back away about 1 m. Observe the straw as it appears above, at, and below the surface of the water.

Analysis
1. Describe the straw's appearance from above.
2. Compare the straw's appearance above and below the water's surface in step 4.

Try at Home

Refraction

A wave changes direction when it reflects from a surface. Waves also can change direction in another way. Perhaps you have tried to grab a sinking object when you are in a swimming pool, only to come up empty-handed. Yet you were sure you grabbed right where you saw the object. You missed grabbing the object because the light rays from the object changed direction as they passed from the water into the air. The bending of a wave as it moves from one medium into another is called **refraction**.

Refraction and Wave Speed Remember that the speed of a wave can be different in different materials. For example, light waves travel faster in air than in water. Refraction occurs when the speed of a wave changes as it passes from one substance to another, as shown in **Figure 12**. A line that is perpendicular to the water's surface is called the normal. When a light ray passes from air into water, it slows down and bends toward the normal. When the ray passes from water into air, it speeds up and bends away from the normal. The larger the change in speed of the light wave is, the larger the change in direction is.

You notice refraction when you look down into a fishbowl. Refraction makes the fish appear to be closer to the surface and farther away from you than it really is, as shown in **Figure 13**. Light rays reflected from the fish are bent away from the normal as they pass from water to air. Your brain interprets the light that enters your eyes by assuming that light rays always travel in straight lines. As a result, the light rays seem to be coming from a fish that is closer to the surface.

Figure 12 A wave is refracted when it changes speed.
Explain *how the direction of the light ray changes if it doesn't change speed.*

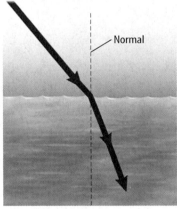

As the light ray passes from air to water, it bends toward the normal.

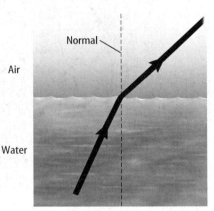

As the light ray passes from water to air, it bends away from the normal.

Cultural Diversity

An Advanced Warning System The Chinese used pottery jars to detect the sounds of an advancing enemy. Leather membranes were stretched over the mouths of empty 80-L pottery jars. The jars were lowered into deep shafts that were dug a few paces apart around the city, and men with good hearing were stationed nearby. Not only could they hear the sounds of an approaching army, but by listening to different sounds from the shafts, the watchers also could judge from which direction the enemy was coming and how far away the enemy was. Why do you think the jars were put in shafts deep underground? The thudding footsteps of the approaching army produced low-frequency, long-wavelength vibrations in the ground. Putting the jars deep in the ground filtered out higher frequency vibrations produced by other sources. L3 LS **Logical-Mathematical**

Color from Refraction Sunlight contains light of various wavelengths. When sunlight passes through a prism, refraction occurs twice: once when sunlight enters the prism and again when it leaves the prism and returns to the air. Violet light has the shortest wavelength and is bent the most. Red light has the longest wavelength and is bent the least. Each color has a different wavelength and is refracted a different amount. As a result, the colors of sunlight are separated when they emerge from the prism.

Figure 14 shows how refraction produces a rainbow when light waves from the Sun pass into and out of water droplets. The colors you see in a rainbow are in order of decreasing wavelength: red, orange, yellow, green, blue, indigo, and violet.

Diffraction

Why can you hear music from the band room when you are down the hall? You can hear the music because the sound waves bend as they pass through an open doorway. This bending isn't caused by refraction. Instead, the bending is caused by diffraction. **Diffraction** is the bending of waves around a barrier.

Light waves can diffract, too. You can hear your friends in the band room but you can't see them until you reach the open door. Therefore, you know that light waves do not diffract as much as sound waves do. Light waves do bend around the edges of an open door. However, for an opening as wide as a door, the amount the light bends is extremely small. As a result, the diffraction of light is far too small to allow you to see around a corner.

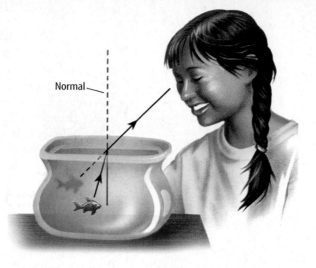

Figure 13 When you look at the goldfish in the water, the fish is in a different position than it appears.
Infer *how the location of the fish would change if light traveled faster in water than in air.*

Figure 14 Light rays refract as they enter and leave each water drop. Each color refracts at different angles because of their different wavelengths, so they separate into the colors of the visible spectrum.

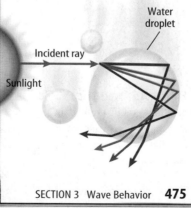

SECTION 3 Wave Behavior **475**

Overlapping Waves Have students consider what happens when three waves overlap. If three waves interfere at a given point and have amplitudes of +3 units, +2 units, and −5 units, what is the amplitude of the resultant wave at that point? 0 units L3 LS
Logical-Mathematical

Answer when the frequency of the wave and the barrier opening are similar in size

IDENTIFYING
Misconceptions

Wave Changes Students may think that as waves move from one medium to another and are refracted, the wavelength and frequency of the waves change. However, the frequency doesn't change. Because the wave speed changes and the frequency stays the same the wavelength changes.

Diffraction and Wavelength The reason that light waves don't diffract much when they pass through an open door is that the wavelengths of visible light are much smaller than the width of the door. Light waves have wavelengths between about 400 and 700 billionths of a meter, while the width of doorway is about one meter. Sound waves that you can hear have wavelengths between a few millimeters and about 10 m. They bend more easily around the corners of an open door. A wave is diffracted more when its wavelength is similar in size to the barrier or opening.

Reading Check *Under what conditions would more diffraction of a wave occur?*

Diffraction of Water Waves Perhaps you have noticed water waves bending around barriers. For example, when water waves strike obstacles such as the islands shown in **Figure 15,** they don't stop moving. Here the size and spacing of the islands is not too different from the wavelength of the water waves. So the water waves bend around the islands, and keep on moving. They also spread out after they pass through openings between the islands. If the islands were much larger than the water wavelength, less diffraction would occur.

What happens when waves meet?

Suppose you throw two pebbles into a still pond. Ripples spread from the impact of each pebble and travel toward each other. What happens when two of these ripples meet? Do they collide like billiard balls and change direction? Waves behave differently from billiard balls when they meet. Waves pass right through each other and continue moving.

Figure 15 Water waves bend or diffract around these islands. More diffraction occurs when the object is closer in size to the wavelength.

LAB DEMONSTRATION

Purpose to observe wave behavior

Materials 2 pencils; paper; large, rectangular glass baking dish; water

Preparation Fill the dish with water to a depth of 2 cm. Use several books on each side to suspend the pan over a sheet of white paper. Place a strong light about 40 cm above the pan. Dim all other lights.

Procedure To form waves, vibrate a vertical pencil up and down on one side of the pan. Show interference by vibrating two vertical pencils, about 10 cm apart, up and down at one end of the pan. Place an object in the path of the waves to show diffraction.

Expected Outcome Students observe reflection, diffraction, and interference.

Assessment

What would the waves have looked like if you had held the pencil horizontally instead of vertically when vibrating it? They would have formed a line of waves instead of circles. L2

Wave Interference While two waves overlap a new wave is formed by adding the two waves together. The ability of two waves to combine and form a new wave when they overlap is called **interference**. After they overlap, the individual waves continue to travel on in their original form.

The different ways waves can interfere are shown in **Figure 16** on the next page. Sometimes when the waves meet, the crest of one wave overlaps the crest of another wave. This is called constructive interference. The amplitudes of these combining waves add together to make a larger wave while they overlap. Destructive interference occurs when the crest of one wave overlaps the trough of another wave. Then, the amplitudes of the two waves combine to make a wave with a smaller amplitude. If the two waves have equal amplitudes and meet crest to trough, they cancel each other while the waves overlap.

Waves and Particles Like waves of water, when light travels through a small opening, such as a narrow slit, the light spreads out in all directions on the other side of the slit. If small particles, instead of waves, were sent through the slit, they would continue in a straight line without spreading. The spreading, or diffraction, is only a property of waves. Interference also doesn't occur with particles. If waves meet, they reinforce or cancel each other, then travel on. If particles approach each other, they either collide and scatter or miss each other completely. Interference, like diffraction, is a property of waves.

Science Online

Topic: Interference
Visit ips.msscience.com for Web links to information about wave interference.

Activity Write a paragraph about three kinds of interference you found in your research.

Applying Science

Can you create destructive interference?

Your brother is vacuuming and you can't hear the television. Is it possible to diminish the sound of the vacuum so you can hear the TV? Can you eliminate some sound waves and keep the sounds you do want to hear?

Identifying the Problem

It is possible to create a wave that will destructively interfere with one wave, but will not destructively interfere with another wave. The graph shows two waves with different wavelengths.

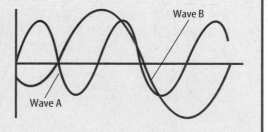
Wave B
Wave A

Solving the Problem

1. Create the graph of a wave that will eliminate wave A but not wave B.
2. Create the graph of a wave that would amplify wave A.

Fun Fact

The rainbow pattern seen on the back of compact disks is a diffraction pattern that results from the reflection of the different wavelengths of visible light.

Differentiated Instruction

Challenge Have pairs of students prepare posters showing the types of waves produced by a combination of (1) two transverse waves in which crests overlap, (2) two transverse waves in which crests and troughs overlap, (3) two compressional waves in which crests overlap, and (4) two compressional waves in which crests and troughs overlap. L3 COOP LEARN  **Visual-Spatial** P

Discussion

Music Halls How does interference affect the way music sounds in different concert halls? Constructive and destructive interference patterns in a concert hall determine whether sound waves produced by individual voices or instruments combine to form waves that are pleasant or displeasing to listeners' ears. L3 LS **Logical-Mathematical**

Applying Science

Answers

1. The wave must be out of phase with the vacuum wave. That is, it must have a trough when the vacuum wave has a crest, and vice versa.
2. Any wave that has crests and troughs in the same place will amplify the wave.

Quick Demo

Refracted White Light

Materials prism, flashlight, darkened room

Estimated Time five minutes

Procedure Shine an intense beam of white light through a prism in a darkened room to demonstrate that different colors in white light refract at different angles.

Visualizing Interference

Have students examine the pictures and read the captions. Then ask the following questions.

Two waves both with an amplitude of 2 m pass through each other. The maximum amplitude reached is 4 m. Is this constructive or destructive interference? constructive

Two waves both with an amplitude of 2 m approach each other and the peak of the crest of one wave passes through the bottom of the trough of the other wave. What is the amplitude of the resulting wave at that instant? zero

Activity

Rope Waves Have two students hold the ends of a long rope. Ask students to practice making waves with the rope by moving their hands vertically or horizontally in quick strokes. The students should then work together to set up constructive and destructive interference with the waves in their ropes. L3 **LS Kinesthetic**

Activity

Graphing Waves Help students understand how to graph the addition of waves by demonstrating it on an overhead projector. Overlap transparencies of drawings of waves as you add them together. L2 **LS Visual-Spatial**

Figure 16

Whether they are ripples on a pond or huge ocean swells, when water waves meet they can combine to form new waves in a process called interference. As shown below, wave interference can be constructive or destructive.

Constructive Interference

In constructive interference, a wave with greater amplitude is formed.

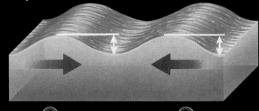

The crests of two waves—A and B—approach each other.

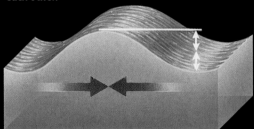

The two waves form a wave with a greater amplitude while the crests of both waves overlap.

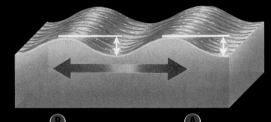

The original waves pass through each other and go on as they started.

Destructive Interference

In destructive interference, a wave with a smaller amplitude is formed.

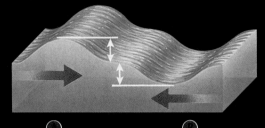

The crest of one wave approaches the trough of another.

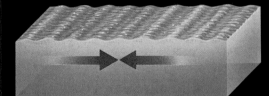

If the two waves have equal amplitude, they momentarily cancel when they meet.

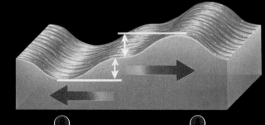

The original waves pass through each other and go on as they started.

478 CHAPTER 16 Waves

Reducing Noise You might have seen someone use a power lawn mower or a chain saw. In the past, many people who performed these tasks damaged their hearing because of the loud noises produced by these machines.

Loud sounds have waves with larger amplitudes and carry more energy than softer sounds. The energy carried by loud sounds can damage cells in the ear that vibrate and transmit signals to the brain. Damage to the ear from loud sounds can be prevented by reducing the energy that reaches the ear. Ear protectors contain materials that absorb some of the energy carried by sound waves, so that less sound energy reaches the ear.

Pilots of small planes have a more complicated problem. If they shut out all the noise of the plane's motor, the pilots wouldn't be able to hear instructions from air-traffic controllers. To solve this problem, ear protectors have been developed, as shown in **Figure 17,** that have electronic circuits. These circuits detect noise from the aircraft and produce sound frequencies that destructively interfere with the noise. They do not interfere with human voices, so people can hear normal conversation. Destructive interference can be a benefit.

Figure 17 Some airplane pilots use special ear protectors that cancel out engine noise but don't block human voices.

section 3 review

Summary

Reflection
- Reflected sound waves can produce echoes.
- Reflected light rays produce images in a mirror.

Refraction
- The bending of waves as they pass from one medium to another is refraction.
- Refraction occurs when the wave's speed changes.
- A prism separates sunlight into the colors of the visible spectrum.

Diffraction and Interference
- The bending of waves around barriers is diffraction.
- Interference occurs when waves combine to form a new wave while they overlap.
- Destructive interference can reduce noise.

Self Check

1. **Explain** why you don't see your reflection in a building made of rough, white stone.

2. **Explain** how you are able to hear the siren of an ambulance on the other side of a building.

3. **Describe** the behavior of light that enables magnifying lenses and contact lenses to bend light rays.

4. **Define** the term *diffraction*. How does the amount of diffraction depend on wavelength?

5. **Think Critically** Why don't light rays that stream through an open window into a darkened room spread evenly through the entire room?

Applying Skills

6. **Compare and Contrast** When light rays pass from water into a certain type of glass, the rays refract toward the normal. Compare and contrast the speed of light in water and in the glass.

section 3 review

1. The rough surface scatters light in all directions.
2. Sound diffracts easily around objects such as buildings.
3. refraction
4. bending of waves around a barrier; A wave is diffracted more when its wavelength is similar in size to the barrier or opening.
5. The light waves have very small wavelengths, so very little diffraction occurs as they move through a wide opening such as a window.
6. Because the light rays refract toward the normal, their speed must be lower in the glass than in water.

Real-World Question

Purpose Students will model the behavior of seismic waves by creating transverse standing waves on a demonstration spring or coiled toy spring. Factors such as length, type of spring, and frequency will be varied and controlled to determine how the speed of a wave within a coil depends upon such factors. By comparing their results with those of others, students can make generalizations about waves within a spring, and by analogy, seismic waves within Earth.

Process Skills measure, calculate, separate and control variables, predict

Time Required 45 minute class

Possible Materials Demonstration springs sold by educational supply companies create the best waves. The spring should be very long.

Alternate Materials If springs are not available, a length of hose or rope will make waves. A metric tape measure can replace a meterstick.

Safety Precautions Caution students not to use or swing the spring anywhere but on the floor.

Form a Hypothesis

Possible Hypothesis The hypotheses of most students will reflect that the speed of a wave is determined by dividing the distance the wave travels by the time it takes for the wave to travel one wavelength.

WAVE ≈ SPEED

Goals
- **Measure** the speed of a wave within a coiled spring toy.
- **Predict** whether the speed you measured will be different in other types of coiled spring toys.

Possible Materials
long, coiled spring toy
meterstick
stopwatch
tape
*clock with a second hand
*Alternate materials

Safety Precautions

Real-World Question

When an earthquake occurs, it produces waves that are recorded at points all over the world by instruments called seismographs. By comparing the data that they collected from these seismographs, scientists discovered that the interior of Earth must be made of layers of different materials. These data showed that the waves traveled at different speeds as they passed through different parts of Earth's interior. How can the speed of a wave be measured?

Form a Hypothesis

In some materials, waves travel too fast for their speeds to be measured directly. Think about what you know about the relationships among the frequency, wavelength, and speed of a wave in a medium. Make a hypothesis about how you can use this relationship to measure the speed of a wave within a medium. Explain why you think the experiment will support your hypothesis.

Test Your Hypothesis

Make a Plan

1. Make a data table in your Science Journal like the one shown.
2. In your Science Journal, write a detailed description of the coiled spring toy you are going to use. Be sure to include its mass and diameter, the width of a coil, and what it is made of.
3. **Decide** as a group how you will measure the frequency and length of waves in the spring toy. What are your variables? Which variables must be controlled? What variable do you want to measure?

Alternative Inquiry Lab

Wave Speed Suggest students explore the speed of a mechanical wave in another medium. Provide a tank of water, stopwatch, meter stick, and a coiled spring toy. Students can complete the same experiment under water. The speed of the wave can be calculated and a similar table created. Students can observe the effects of changing the medium on the wave. L2

4. Repeat your experiment three times.

Follow Your Plan

1. Make sure your teacher approves your plan before you start.

2. Carry out the experiment.

3. While you are doing the experiment, record your observations and measurements in your data table.

Wave Data			
	Trial 1	Trial 2	Trial 3
Length spring was stretched (m)	3.30	3.30	3.91
Number of crests	2	3	4
Wavelength (m)	3.30	2.20	1.96
# of vibrations timed	10	10	10
# of seconds vibrations were timed	5.49	3.60	6.01
Wave speed (m/s)	6.01	6.12	6.29

● Analyze Your Data

1. **Calculate** the frequency of the waves by dividing the number of vibrations you timed by the number of seconds you timed them. Record your results in your data table.

2. Use the following formula to calculate the speed of a wave in each trial.

   wavelength $\times$ frequency $=$ wave speed

3. Average the wave speeds from your trials to determine the average speed of a wave in your coiled spring toy.

● Conclude and Apply

1. **Infer** which variables affected the wave speed in spring toys the most. Which variables affected the speed the least? Was your hypothesis supported?

2. **Analyze** what factors caused the wave speed measured in each trial to be different.

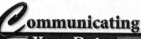
Communicating Your Data

Post a description of your coiled spring toy and the results of your experiment on a bulletin board in your classroom. **Compare and contrast** your results with other students in your class.

☑ Assessment

Oral Ask students how they might determine the speed of water waves that are crashing ashore at a beach. Time the waves coming ashore to determine the frequency. Estimate the distance between wave crests to determine wavelength. The product of these two numbers is the speed of the wave. Use **Performance Assessment in the Science Classroom,** p. 89 L2

Communicating Your Data

Encourage students to record their data in electronically designed spreadsheets.

● Test Your Hypothesis

Possible Procedures Help your student groups create standing waves. While a student holds one end of the coiled-spring toy stationary, have another student move the other end from side to side with a rhythm that produces a standing wave.

Tie to Prior Knowledge Most students will have observed waves moving through a medium such as ocean waves or ripples on a pond.

Expected Outcome Students will create standing transverse waves and measure their frequency, wavelengths, and speeds. From this data, they will predict the speed of waves in other types of coiled springs.

● Analyze Your Data

Answers to Questions

1. Based on the sample data in the table, frequencies were as follows: Trial 1, 1.82 Hz; Trial 2, 2.78 Hz; Trial 3, 3.21 Hz.

2. Based on the sample data in the table, speeds were as follows: Trial 1, 6.00 m/s; Trial 2, 6.12 m/s; Trial 3, 6.29 m/s.

3. Average wave speed is 6.14 m/s.

Error Analysis Ask student groups to compare data with other groups and explain any significant discrepancies.

● Conclude and Apply

1. Answers will vary.

2. Possible answer: how fast the spring toy was shaken

Content Background

Electromagnetic, ocean, and sound are different types of waves. Each of these waves propagate in a different manner. Electromagnetic waves do not require a medium for travel and can carry energy through the vacuum of space. Surface ocean waves are a mixture of longitudinal and transverse waves that carry energy through the water. Sound waves are longitudinal waves that can carry energy through solids, liquids, and gases. The velocity of waves can be determined by the equation velocity = wavelength × frequency.

Discussion

Wave Descriptions Waves are described by their frequency, wavelength, amplitude, and speed. What do the numbers represent in each of the examples? 34 meters, amplitude; 900 km/h, speed; 800 pulses per second, frequency
L3

Applying Math

Answer 5 hours

Graph It

Radio Waves Have students find the frequency of radio waves. Are these waves low-frequency or high-frequency waves in the electromagnetic spectrum? low

SCIENCE Stats

Waves, Waves, and More Waves

Did you know...

. . . Radio waves from space were discovered in 1932 by Karl G. Jansky, an American engineer. His discovery led to the creation of radio astronomy, a field that explores parts of the universe that can't be seen with telescopes.

. . . The highest recorded ocean wave was 34 meters high, which is comparable to the height of a ten-story building. This super wave was seen in the North Pacific Ocean and recorded by the crew of the naval ship *USS Ramapo* in 1933.

Applying Math A tsunami formed by an earthquake on the ocean floor travels at 900 km/h. How long will it take the tsunami to travel 4,500 km?

. . . Waves let dolphins see with their ears! A dolphin sends out ultrasonic pulses, or clicks, at rates of 800 pulses per second. These sound waves are reflected back to the dolphin after they hit an obstacle or a meal. This process is called echolocation.

Graph It

Go to ips.msscience.com/science_stats to learn about discoveries by radio astronomers. Make a time line showing some of these discoveries.

482 CHAPTER 16 Waves

Curriculum Connection

Geography Earthquakes produce seismic waves that travel through the ground and can do a great deal of damage. Have students research earthquakes around the world and mark the location on a map. Discuss locations that are more likely to experience earthquakes. L2

Reviewing Main Ideas

Section 1 What are waves?

1. Waves are rhythmic disturbances that carry energy but not matter.

2. Mechanical waves can travel only through matter. Electromagnetic waves can travel through matter and space.

3. In a mechanical transverse wave, matter in the medium moves back and forth at right angles to the direction the wave travels.

4. In a compressional wave, matter in the medium moves forward and backward in the same direction as the wave.

Section 2 Wave Properties

1. The amplitude of a transverse wave is the distance between the rest position and a crest or a trough.

2. The energy carried by a wave increases as the amplitude increases.

3. Wavelength is the distance between neighboring crests or neighboring troughs.

4. The frequency of a wave is the number of wavelengths that pass a given point in 1 s.

5. Waves travel through different materials at different speeds.

Section 3 Wave Behavior

1. Reflection occurs when a wave strikes an object or surface and bounces off.

2. The bending of a wave as it moves from one medium into another is called refraction. A wave changes direction, or refracts, when the speed of the wave changes.

3. The bending of waves around a barrier is called diffraction.

4. Interference occurs when two or more waves combine and form a new wave while they overlap.

Visualizing Main Ideas

Copy and complete the following spider map about waves.

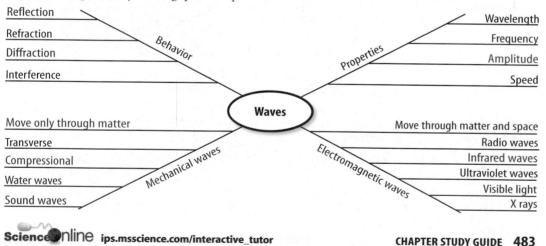

Reviewing Main Ideas

Summary statements can be used by students to review the major concepts of the chapter.

Visualizing Main Ideas

See student page.

Science Online

Visit ips.msscience.com
/self_check_quiz
/interactive_tutor
/vocabulary_puzzlemaker
/chapter_review
/standardized_test

Assessment Transparency

For additional assessment questions, use the *Assessment Transparency* located in the transparency book.

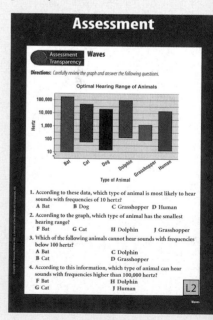

Using Vocabulary

1. Refraction
2. compressional wave
3. wavelength
4. amplitude
5. electromagnetic wave

Checking Concepts

6. D
7. C
8. B
9. B
10. A
11. D
12. A
13. C
14. D

Thinking Critically

15. Compressional; each car is pushed into the next. The cars then rebound. This is like a compressional wave.

16. Yes; yes; electromagnetic waves can travel through space and matter.

17. The frequency decreases because fewer wavelengths pass a given point in 1 s.

18. because the rough surface reflects the light rays in many different directions

19. Light travels much faster than sound, so the flash of the cannon will reach you before the sound will.

Using Vocabulary

amplitude p. 467	interference p. 477
compressional wave p. 465	mechanical wave p. 463
	reflection p. 473
diffraction p. 475	refraction p. 474
electromagnetic wave p. 466	transverse wave p. 464
	wave p. 462
frequency p. 469	wavelength p. 468

Fill in the blanks with the correct word or words.

1. _____ is the change in direction of a wave going from one medium to another.

2. The type of wave that has rarefactions is a _____.

3. The distance between two adjacent crests of a transverse wave is the _____.

4. The more energy a wave carries, the greater its _____ is.

5. A(n) _____ can travel through space without a medium.

Checking Concepts

Choose the word or phrase that best answers the question.

6. What is the material through which mechanical waves travel?
   A) charged particles
   B) space
   C) a vacuum
   D) a medium

7. What is carried from particle to particle in a water wave?
   A) speed   C) energy
   B) amplitude   D) matter

8. What are the lowest points on a transverse wave called?
   A) crests   C) compressions
   B) troughs   D) rarefactions

---

9. What determines the pitch of a sound wave?
   A) amplitude   C) speed
   B) frequency   D) refraction

10. What is the distance between adjacent wave compressions?
    A) one wavelength
    B) 1 km
    C) 1 m/s
    D) 1 Hz

11. What occurs when a wave strikes an object or surface and bounces off?
    A) diffraction
    B) refraction
    C) a transverse wave
    D) reflection

12. What is the name for a change in the direction of a wave when it passes from one medium into another?
    A) refraction   C) reflection
    B) interference   D) diffraction

Use the figure below to answer question 13.

13. What type of wave is a sound wave?
    A) transverse
    B) electromagnetic
    C) compressional
    D) refracted

14. What color light has the shortest wavelength and the highest frequency?
    A) red   C) Orange
    B) green   D) Blue

Science**Online** ips.msscience.com/vocabulary_puzzlemaker

Use the ExamView® Pro Testmaker CD-ROM to:
- create multiple versions of tests
- create modified tests with one mouse click for inclusion students
- edit existing questions and add your own questions
- build tests aligned with state standards using built-in State Curriculum Tags
- change English tests to Spanish with one mouse click and vice versa

Thinking Critically

15. Explain what kind of wave—transverse or compressional—is produced when an engine bumps into a string of coupled railroad cars on a track.

16. Infer Is it possible for an electromagnetic wave to travel through a vacuum? Through matter? Explain your answers.

17. Draw a Conclusion Why does the frequency of a wave decrease as the wavelength increases?

18. Explain why you don't see your reflected image when you look at a white, rough surface?

19. Infer If a cannon fires at a great distance from you, why do you see the flash before you hear the sound?

20. Form a Hypothesis Form a hypothesis that can explain this observation. Waves A and B travel away from Earth through Earth's atmosphere. Wave A continues on into space, but wave B does not.

Use the figure below to answer question 21.

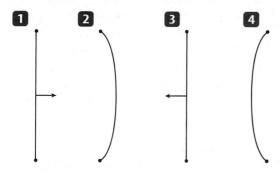

21. Explain how the object shown above causes compressions and rarefactions as it vibrates in air.

22. Explain why you can hear a person talking even if you can't see them.

23. Compare and Contrast AM radio waves have wavelengths between about 200 m and 600 m, and FM radio waves have wavelengths of about 3 m. Why can AM radio signals often be heard behind buildings and mountains but FM radio signals cannot?

24. Infer how the wavelength of a wave would change if the speed of the wave increased, but the frequency remained the same.

25. Explain You are motionless on a rubber raft in the middle of a pool. A friend sitting on the edge of the pool tries to make the float move to the other edge of the pool by slapping the water every second to form a wave. Explain whether the wave produced will cause you to move to the edge of the pool.

Performance Activities

26. Make Flashcards Work with a partner to make flashcards for the bold-faced terms in the chapter. Illustrate each term on the front of the cards. Write the term and its definition on the back of the card. Use the cards to review the terms with another team.

Applying Math

Use the following equation to answer questions 27–29.

$$\text{wave speed} = \text{wavelength} \times \text{frequency}$$

27. Wave Speed If a wave pool generates waves with a wavelength of 3.2 m and a frequency of 0.60 Hz, how fast are the waves moving?

28. Frequency An earthquake wave travels at 5000 m/s and has a wavelength of 417 m. What is its frequency?

29. Wavelength A wave travels at a velocity of 4 m/s. It has a frequency of 3.5 Hz. What is the wavelength of the wave?

Science Online ips.msscience.com/chapter_review

CHAPTER REVIEW 485

20. Wave A is an electromagnetic wave and wave B is a mechanical wave.

21. The vibrating object moves back and forth, colliding with the molecules in the air around it. As the object moves forward, it pushes molecules together to form a compression. As the object moves back toward its original position and beyond, it creates a rarefaction—a region in which molecules are spread farther apart.

22. Sound waves have longer wavelengths than light waves and will diffract around large objects, while light waves will not.

23. Because their longer wavelengths are closer to the size of buildings and mountains, AM radio waves diffract around them more than FM radio waves do.

24. The wavelength would increase.

25. No, the wave will cause you to move up and down, but you will not move forward.

Performance Activities

26. Use **Performance Assessment in the Science Classroom**, p. 127.

Applying Math

National Math Standards
1, 2, 9
27. 1.9 m/s
28. 12 Hz
29. 1.1 m

☑ Assessment Resources

📁 Reproducible Masters
Chapter *Fast File* Resources
 Chapter Review, pp. 35–36
 Chapter Tests, pp. 37–40
 Assessment Transparency Activity, p. 47
Glencoe Science Web site
 Chapter Review Test
 Standardized Test Practice

Glencoe Technology
 🔋 Assessment Transparency
 ⦿ Exam*View*® Pro Testmaker
 ▭ MindJogger Videoquiz
 ⦿ Interactive Chalkboard

chapter 16 Standardized Test Practice

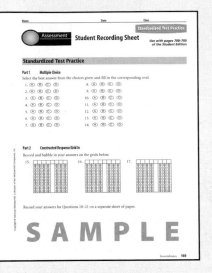

Answer Sheet A practice answer sheet can be found at ips.msscience.com/answer_sheet.

Part 1 | Multiple Choice

1. B   7. A
2. C   8. A
3. B   9. B
4. C   10. C
5. C   11. B
6. D

Part 2 | Short Response

12. No, the water does not travel with the wave. The waves only transfer energy, not matter. So the water that hits the island was already near the shore.

13. Wave A has a longer wavelength and a lower frequency than Wave B.

14. Both waves are traveling at the same speed because the speed is the same in a given medium.

15. To make waves of a longer wavelength, you would dip your hand into the water less often. To increase the amplitude of the waves, you could dip your hand in deeper with more force.

16. All electromagnetic waves are transverse waves that carry energy and can travel through outer space or through a vacuum where no matter exists. Different electromagnetic waves have different wavelengths and frequencies.

Part 1 | Multiple Choice

Record your answers on the answer sheet provided by your teacher or on a sheet of paper.

1. What do waves carry as they move?
   - A. matter
   - B. energy
   - C. matter and energy
   - D. particles and energy

Use the figure below to answer questions 2 and 3.

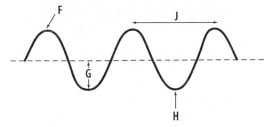

2. What property of the wave is shown at F?
   - A. amplitude
   - B. wavelength
   - C. crest
   - D. trough

3. What property of the wave is shown at J?
   - A. amplitude
   - B. wavelength
   - C. crest
   - D. trough

4. What kind of wave does NOT need a medium through which to travel?
   - A. mechanical
   - B. sound
   - C. light
   - D. refracted

5. What happens as a sound wave's energy decreases?
   - A. Wave frequency decreases.
   - B. Wavelength decreases.
   - C. Amplitude decreases.
   - D. Wave speed decreases.

6. What unit is used to measure frequency?
   - A. meters
   - B. meters/second
   - C. decibels
   - D. hertz

7. What properties of a light wave determines its color?
   - A. wavelength
   - B. amplitude
   - C. speed
   - D. interference

8. When two waves overlap and interfere constructively, what does the resulting wave have?
   - A. a greater amplitude
   - B. less energy
   - C. a change in frequency
   - D. a lower amplitude

9. What happens when light travels from air into glass?
   - A. It speeds up.
   - B. It slows down.
   - C. It travels at 300,000 km/s.
   - D. It travels at the speed of sound.

Use the figure below to answer questions 10 and 11.

10. What behavior of light waves lets you see a sharp, clear image of yourself?
    - A. refraction
    - B. diffraction
    - C. reflection
    - D. interference

11. Why can't you see a clear image of yourself if the water's surface is rough?
    - A. The light bounces off the surface in only one direction.
    - B. The light scatters in many different directions.
    - C. There is no light shining on the water's surface.
    - D. The light changes speed when it strikes the water.

486 STANDARDIZED TEST PRACTICE

Part 2 | Short Response/Grid In

Record your answers on the answer sheet provided by your teacher or on a sheet of paper.

12. An earthquake in the middle of the Indian Ocean produces a tsunami that hits an island. Is the water that hits the island the same water that was above the place where the earthquake occurred? Explain.

Use the figure below to answer questions 13 and 14.

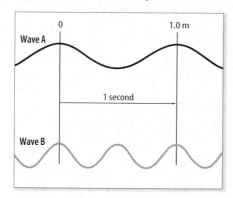

13. Compare the wavelengths and frequencies of the two waves shown.

14. If both waves are traveling through the same medium, how do their speeds compare? Explain.

15. Suppose you make waves in a pond by dipping your hand in the water with a frequency of 1 Hz. How could you make waves of a longer wavelength? How could you increase the amplitude of the waves?

16. How are all electromagnetic waves alike? How do they differ from one another?

Test-Taking Tip

Take Your Time Stay focused during the test and don't rush, even if you notice that other students are finishing the test early.

Part 3 | Open Ended

Record your answers on a sheet of paper.

Use the figure below to answer questions 17 and 18.

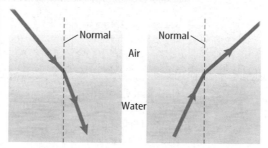

17. Why does the light ray bend toward the normal when is passes from air into water, but bend away from the normal as it passes from water into air?

18. A boy has caught a fish on his fishing line. He reels the fish in near the boat. How could the refraction of light waves affect him as he tries to net the fish while it is still in the water?

19. In a science fiction movie, a spaceship explodes. The people in a nearby spaceship see and hear the explosion. Is this realistic? Explain.

20. The speed of light in warm air is greater than its speed in cold air. The air just above a highway is warmer than the air a little higher. Will the light moving parallel to the highway be bent up or down? Explain.

21. You are standing outside a classroom with an open door. You know your friends are in the room because you can hear them talking. Explain why you can hear them talking but cannot see them.

22. How does the size of an obstacle affect the diffraction of a wave?

because light waves can travel through space.

20. The light will bend toward the region where light has a slower speed. This means that the light rays would be bent up.

21. You can hear the people talking because the sound waves bend as they pass through the open door. Sound waves are similar in size to the open door. Light waves have much smaller wavelengths than the size of the open door, so they are not diffracted as much. Therefore, you cannot see your friends.

22. More diffraction or bending of the wave occurs if the wavelength is similar to the size of the obstacle.

Rubrics

For more help evaluating open-ended assessment questions, see the rubric on p. 10T

Part 3 | Open Ended

17. Light waves travel faster in air than in water. When a light ray passes from air into water, it slows down and bends toward the normal. When the ray passes from water into air, it speeds up and bends away from the normal.

18. The boy is looking into the water

from air, so the light rays are refracted. But his brain interprets the light rays coming from the fish as traveling in a straight line. So the light rays seem to be coming from a fish that is in a different location than it really is. So the boy might miss the fish with the net.

19. No, sound needs a medium through which to travel. It cannot travel through outer space where there is no matter. So sound waves would not reach the nearby spaceship and the people would not hear the explosion. They would, however, see the explosion

Section/Objectives	Standards		Labs/Features
Chapter Opener	**National**	**State/Local**	**Launch Lab:** Making Human Sounds, p. 489 **Foldables,** p. 489
	See pp. 16T–17T for a Key to Standards.		
Section 1 What is sound? ● 3 sessions 📷 1.5 blocks 1. **Identify** the characteristics of sound waves. 2. **Explain** how sound travels. 3. **Describe** the Doppler effect.	National Content Standards: UCP.1, UCP.2, UCP.3, UCP.5, A.1, A.2, B.1, B.2, B.3		**MiniLAB:** Comparing and Contrasting Sounds, p. 492 **Science Online,** p. 495 **Integrate Astronomy,** p. 496 **Applying Science:** How does Doppler radar work?, p. 496 **Visualizing the Doppler Effect,** p. 497 **Lab:** Observe and Measure Reflection of Sound, p. 500
Section 2 Music ● 5 sessions 📷 2.5 blocks 4. **Explain** the difference between music and noise. 5. **Describe** how different instruments produce music. 6. **Explain** how you hear.	National Content Standards: UCP.1, UCP.2, UCP.3, UCP.5, A.1, A.2, B.1, B.2, B.3, F.3, G.3		**Integrate Social Studies,** p. 502 **MiniLAB:** Modeling a Stringed Instrument, p. 504 **Science Online,** p. 507 **Lab:** Music, pp. 510–511 **Science and Society:** It's a Wrap, p. 512

Lab Materials	Reproducible Resources	Section Assessment	Technology
Launch Lab: no materials needed	**Chapter *FAST FILE* Resources** Foldables Worksheet, p. 15 Directed Reading Overview, p. 17 Note-taking Worksheets, pp. 29–30	**GLENCOE'S ASSESSMENT ADVANTAGE**	**TeacherWorks** includes: • Interactive Teacher Edition • Lesson Planner with calendar • Access to all program blacklines • Correlations to standards • Web links
MiniLAB: block of wood, metal spoon, cotton string **Lab:** 20- to 30-cm long cardboard tubes (2), watch with a second hand that ticks audibly, protractor	**Chapter *FAST FILE* Resources** Transparency Activity, p. 40 MiniLAB, p. 3 Enrichment, p. 27 Reinforcement, p. 25 Directed Reading, p. 18 Lab Worksheet, pp. 5–6 Lab Activity, pp. 9–10 **Mathematics Skill Activities,** p. 9 **Reading and Writing Skill Activities,** p. 7	**Portfolio** MiniLAB Assessment, p. 492 **Performance** MiniLAB, p. 492 Applying Science, p. 496 Applying Math, p. 499 **Content** Section Review, p. 499	♪ Section Focus Transparency ∩ Guided Reading Audio Program ◉ Interactive Chalkboard CD-ROM ▭ Video Lab
MiniLAB: rubber band, shoe box **Lab:** musical instruments, measuring tape, tuning forks *Need materials?* Contact Science Kit at 1-800-828-7777 or www.sciencekit.com on the Internet.	**Chapter *FAST FILE* Resources** Transparency Activity, p. 41 MiniLAB, p. 4 Enrichment, p. 28 Reinforcement, p. 26 Directed Reading, pp. 19, 20 Lab Worksheet, pp. 7–8 Transparency Activity, pp. 43–44 Lab Activity, pp. 11–14 **Cultural Diversity,** p. 61 **Lab Management and Safety,** p. 64	**Portfolio** Assessment, p. 509 **Performance** MiniLAB, p. 504 Applying Math p. 509 **Content** Section Review, p. 509	♪ Section Focus Transparency ♪ Teaching Transparency ◉ Virtual Labs CD-ROM ∩ Guided Reading Audio Program ◉ Interactive Chalkboard CD-ROM

End of Chapter Assessment

GLENCOE'S ASSESSMENT ADVANTAGE

Blackline Masters	Technology	Professional Series
Chapter *FAST FILE* Resources Chapter Review, pp. 33–34 Chapter Tests, pp. 35–38 **Standardized Test Practice,** pp. 71–74	▭ MindJogger Videoquiz ◉ Virtual Labs CD-ROM ◉ Exam*View*® Pro Testmaker ◉ TeacherWorks CD-ROM ◉ Interactive Chalkboard CD-ROM	**Performance Assessment in the Science Classroom (PASC)**

chapter 17 Sound

Transparencies

Section Focus

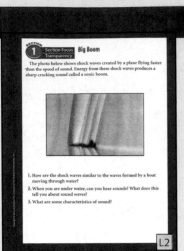

This is a representation of key blackline masters available in the Teacher Classroom Resources. See Resource Manager boxes within the chapter for additional information.

Key to Teaching Strategies

The following designations will help you decide which activities are appropriate for your students.

L1 Level 1 activities should be appropriate for students with learning difficulties.

L2 Level 2 activities should be within the ability range of all students.

L3 Level 3 activities are designed for above-average students.

ELL ELL activities should be within the ability range of English Language Learners.

COOP LEARN Cooperative Learning activities are designed for small group work.

LS Multiple Learning Styles logos, as described on page 12T, are used throughout to indicate strategies that address different learning styles.

P These strategies represent student products that can be placed into a best-work portfolio.

PBL Problem-Based Learning activities apply real-world situations to learning.

Assessment

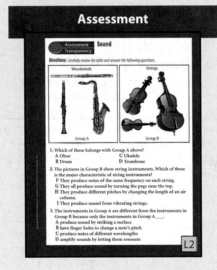

Teaching

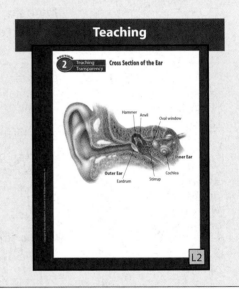

Hands-on Activities

Student Text Lab Worksheet

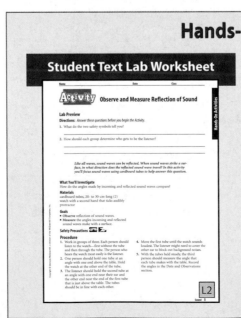

Laboratory Activities

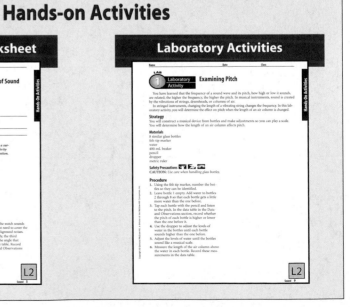

Meeting Different Ability Levels

Content Outline

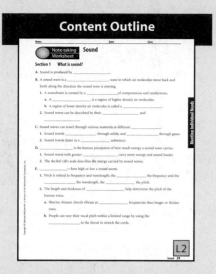

Reinforcement

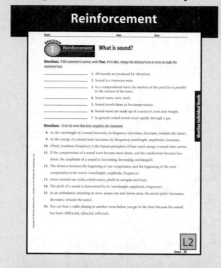

Enrichment

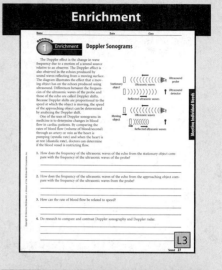

Directed Reading (English/Spanish)

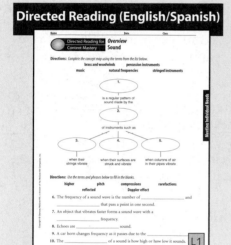

Study Guide

Reading Essentials

Assessment

Test Practice Workbook

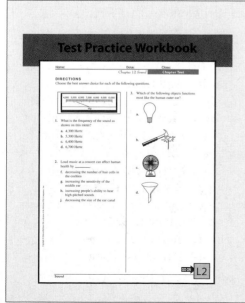

Chapter Review

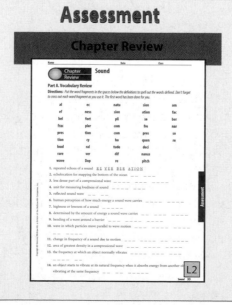

Chapter Tests

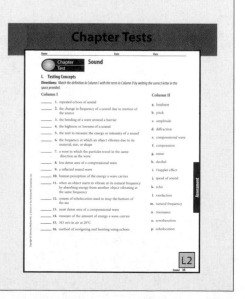

Science Content Background

section 1

What is sound?
Sound Waves

Sound waves are mechanical waves, which means they need a medium to travel through and they can't travel through a vacuum. It is the sound energy that travels through a medium, not the particles of the medium. The particles of the medium move back and forth as the sound wave passes, but then return to their original positions.

Sound waves are called *compressional* or *longitudinal* waves. The compressions and rarefractions produced by sound waves cause temporary changes in the pressure of the medium it travels through. Our ears respond to these pressure changes and interpret them as sound.

The Speed of Sound

The speed of sound is how fast the sound energy travels through the medium. Frequency is the rate at which the particles of the medium vibrate back and forth.

The approximate speed of sound through air at room temperature is 343 m/s. While this is fast, light travels about 900,000 times faster. This explains why we see lightning before we hear thunder. To calculate how far away lightning is, multiply the speed of sound by the number of seconds between seeing the lightning and hearing the thunder. If this is three seconds, then the lightning is 3 s × 343 m/s = 1,029 m away. For an approximate distance in miles, divide the time by five.

In any material, molecules are connected to their neighbors by springlike forces. In a gas, molecules are far apart and these forces are much weaker than in a solid. The speed of sound in a material is related to the strength of these forces. The weaker the forces between molecules in a material, the slower the speed of sound in the material. As a result, the speed of sound tends to be greater in solids than in liquids, and greater in liquids than in gases. The density of the substance also effects the speed of sound

waves traveling through it. As the density increases, the speed of sound decreases.

Amplitude and Loudness

Sound intensity is the amount of energy that passes through a given area in a given amount of time. Since sound spreads out as it travels, the intensity of the sound decreases as it travels and is proportional to the inverse square of the distance. This means that if the distance from the source doubles, the sound intensity is one-fourth as large.

Humans can detect very low levels of sound. This threshold is defined as 0 dB. A sound of 0 dB will move our eardrum as little as one-billionth of a centimeter, but we can still hear it.

Frequency and Pitch

The unit of frequency is the Hertz (Hz), which is equal to one cycle per second. The higher the frequency of a wave, the smaller is its wavelength. The velocity of a wave is equal to its frequency multiplied by its wavelength.

section 2

Music
What is music?

The sounds produced by different frequencies are referred to as *pitch*. People with well-trained ears can detect frequency differences of as little as 3 Hz.

Resonance plays an important role in the production of music. Resonance occurs when an object absorbs energy from something vibrating at a certain frequency, and then begins to vibrate at that frequency. Many objects can absorb energy from sound waves vibrating at a number of frequencies. These frequencies are the object's natural frequencies of vibration.

When musical instruments are made to vibrate, they produce sound waves corresponding to their natural frequencies. The sound you hear is the combination of the natural frequencies. This combination is different for each type of instrument and gives an instrument its distinctive sound.

Crandall/The Image Works

The Ear

The ear amplifies sound vibrations. Resonance in the ear canal can amplify sounds with frequencies between about 2,000 Hz and 5,500 Hz by up to 10 times. In the middle ear, some frequencies can be amplified by 20 to 30 times by the lever system formed by bones of the middle ear, and by the difference in area between the eardrum and the oval window. As a result, some sounds can be amplified by several hundred times.

Teacher to Teacher

Erin Peters, Lead Science Teacher
Williamsburg Middle School
Arlington, Virginia

"I use this demonstration to show that sound needs matter to travel through, since it is a compressional wave. Get the inside part of a music box (the wind up arm, the cylinder with the bumps and the metal teeth that make the sound). Some science shops sell them cheaply. In the air, wind the arm and listen carefully to the sound it makes. Dink...dink...dink... very quiet. Now put the apparatus on the desk and wind the arm. It sounds like the music box did. Sound travels better when the vibrating particles are closer together."

chapter content resources

Internet Resources
For additional content background, visit
ips.msscience.com to:
- access your book online
- find references to related articles in popular science magazines
- access Web links with related content background
- access current events with science journal topics

Print Resources
Great Experiments in Physics, First Hand Accounts from Galileo to Einstein, by Morris Shamos, Dover Publications, 1987

Mad About Physics, by Christopher P. Jargodzki and Franklin Potter, John Wiley and Sons, Inc., 2001

Science and Music, by Sir James Jeans, Dover Publications, 1968

Chapter Vocabulary

Science Journal Student responses will vary, but may include experiences in nature or being alone in a room.

INTERACTIVE CHALKBOARD
with Image Bank

PowerPoint® Presentations

This CD-ROM is an editable Microsoft® PowerPoint® presentation that includes:
- a pre-made presentation for every chapter
- interactive graphics
- animations
- audio clips
- image bank
- all new section and chapter questions
- Standardized Test Practice
- transparencies
- pre-lab questions for all labs
- Foldables directions
- links to ips.msscience.com

Sound

chapter preview

sections

1 What is sound?
Lab Observe and Measure Reflection of Sound

2 Music
Lab Music

Virtual Labs How is an oscilloscope used to tune a musical instrument?

An Eerie Silence

You probably have never experienced complete silence unless you've been in a room like this one. The room is lined with special materials that absorb sound waves and eliminate sound reflections.

Science Journal Write a paragraph about the quietest place you've ever been.

Theme Connection

Stability and Change Sound waves are produced by periodic changes in the motion, or vibration, of an object. Sound waves produce changes in air pressure that the ear detects as sound.

About the Photo

Reverberation This is an anechoic chamber, which means "without echo." The material lining the room is soft, porous, and irregular in shape to absorb reverberation. Such rooms are used to test sound equipment.

Start-Up Activities

When you speak or sing, you push air from your lungs past your vocal cords, which are two flaps of tissue inside your throat. When you tighten your vocal cords, you can make the sound have a higher pitch. Do this lab to explore how you change the shape of your throat to vary the pitch of sound.

1. Hold your fingers against the front of your throat and say *Aaaah*. Notice the vibration against your fingers.

2. Now vary the pitch of this sound from low to high and back again. How do the vibrations in your throat change? Record your observations.

3. Change the sound to an *Ooooh*. What do you notice as you listen? Record your observations.

4. **Think Critically** In your Science Journal, describe how the shape of your throat changed the pitch.

Science Online Preview this chapter's content and activities at ips.msscience.com

Sound Make the following Foldable to help you answer questions about sound.

STEP 1 Fold a vertical sheet of notebook paper from side to side.

STEP 2 Cut along every third line of only the top layer to form tabs.

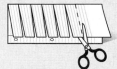

STEP 3 Write a question about sound on each tab.

Answer Questions Before you read the chapter, write some questions you have about sound on the front of the tabs. As you read the chapter, write the answer beneath the question. You may add questions as you read.

Purpose Use the Launch Lab to demonstrate how the throat changes as the voice changes in pitch. [L2] [ELL] [LS] Auditory-Musical

Teaching Strategies

- After they observe the tone (pitch) difference in a single sound, suggest students try holding their hands to their throats while speaking. Pitch varies with the emphasis given to different words. The last word of a question, for example, is usually at a higher pitch.

- If you have students who speak languages other than English, have them determine how the pitches vary when the same sentence is said in a different language. Some languages use different rules for pitch to indicate a question, statement, or exclamation. Others use changing pitch to alter the meanings of words.

Think Critically

Student answers will vary.

Assessment

Process Ask students to sing or speak for about 10 seconds while other students sketch a graph of how pitch varies, using dashes at different heights above a line. If students ask a question, the pitch would start on a mid-tone and end on a higher pitch. Use **Performance Assessment in the Science Classroom**, p. 111.

 Dinah Zike Study Fold

Student preparation materials for this Foldable are available in the **Chapter FAST FILE Resources.**

489

1 Motivate

Bellringer

Section Focus Transparencies also are available on the Interactive Chalkboard CD-ROM.

 L2 ELL

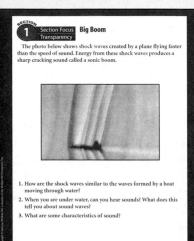

Tie to Prior Knowledge

Pond Ripples Ask students what happens when a rock is tossed into a body of water such as a pond or lake. Water waves move outward along the water's surface in all directions from the point where the object strikes the water. Explain that sound is a form of energy that also travels in waves. Sound waves, however, are compressional waves, while the waves in the water are transverse waves.

---

as you read

***What* You'll Learn**

- **Identify** the characteristics of sound waves.
- **Explain** how sound travels.
- **Describe** the Doppler effect.

***Why* It's Important**

Sound gives important information about the world around you.

Review Vocabulary

frequency: number of wavelengths that pass a given point in one second, measured in hertz (Hz)

New Vocabulary

- loudness
- pitch
- echo
- Doppler effect

Sound and Vibration

Think of all the sounds you've heard since you awoke this morning. Did you hear your alarm clock blaring, car horns honking, or locker doors slamming? Every sound has something in common with every other sound. Each is produced by something that vibrates.

Sound Waves How does an object that is vibrating produce sound? When you speak, the vocal cords in your throat vibrate. These vibrations cause other people to hear your voice. The vibrations produce sound waves that travel to their ears. The other person's ears interpret these sound waves.

A wave carries energy from one place to another without transferring matter. An object that is vibrating in air, such as your vocal cords, produces a sound wave. The vibrating object causes air molecules to move back and forth. As these air molecules collide with those nearby, they cause other air molecules to move back and forth. In this way, energy is transferred from one place to another. A sound wave is a compressional wave, like the wave moving through the coiled spring toy in **Figure 1.** In a compressional wave, particles in the material move back and forth along the direction the wave is moving. In a sound wave, air molecules move back and forth along the direction the sound wave is moving.

Figure 1 When the coils of a coiled spring toy are squeezed together, a compressional wave moves along the spring. The coils move back and forth as the compressional wave moves past them.

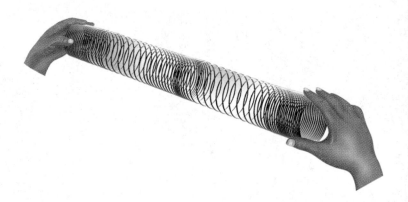

Section 1 Resource Manager

Chapter *FAST FILE* Resources

Transparency Activity, p. 40
Directed Reading for Content Mastery, pp. 17, 18
Note-taking Worksheets, pp. 29–30
MiniLAB, p. 3
Enrichment, p. 27
Reinforcement, p. 25

Lab Worksheet, pp. 5–6
Lab Activity, pp. 9–10
Home and Community Involvement, p. 29
Physical Science Critical Thinking/Problem Solving, p. 21
Mathematics Skill Activities, p. 9

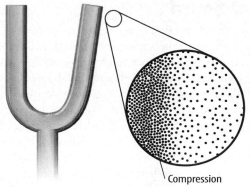

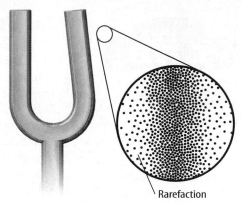

When the tuning fork vibrates outward, it forces molecules in the air next to it closer together, creating a region of compression.

When the tuning fork moves back, the molecules in the air next to it spread farther apart, creating a region of rarefaction.

Making Sound Waves

When an object vibrates, it exerts a force on the surrounding air. For example, as the end of the tuning fork moves outward into the air, it pushes the molecules in the air together, as shown on the left in **Figure 2.** As a result, a region where the molecules are closer together, or more dense, is created. This region of higher density is called a compression. When the end of the tuning fork moves back, it creates a region of lower density called a rarefaction, as shown on the right in **Figure 2.** As the tuning fork continues to vibrate, a series of compressions and rarefactions is formed. The compressions and rarefactions move away from the tuning fork as molecules in these regions collide with other nearby molecules.

Like other waves, a sound wave can be described by its wavelength and frequency. The wavelength of a sound wave is shown in **Figure 3.** The frequency of a sound wave is the number of compressions or rarefactions that pass by a given point in one second. An object that vibrates faster forms a sound wave with a higher frequency.

Figure 2 A tuning fork makes a sound wave as the ends of the fork vibrate in the air.
Explain *why a sound wave cannot travel in a vacuum.*

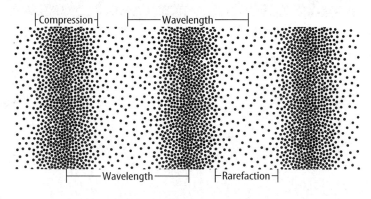

Figure 3 Wavelength is the distance from one compression to another or one rarefaction to another.

SECTION 1 What is sound? **491**

SECTION 1 What is sound? **491**

Purpose to observe that sound can travel through materials other than air L2 LS Auditory-Musical

Materials block of wood, metal spoon, about 2 m of cotton string

Teaching Strategy Ask students about other times they have heard sounds through materials other than air.

Analysis

1. Sound was transmitted through both the wood and the string. Answers will vary.
2. The sound was louder when transmitted through the wood than when transmitted through the string.

Assessment

Process Ask students to make an illustration of each part of the experiment, with labels showing how the sound of the metal striking something was transmitted to their ears. Use **Performance Assessment in the Science Classroom,** p. 127. P

Mini **LAB**

Comparing and Contrasting Sounds

Procedure

1. Strike a **block of wood** with a **spoon** and listen carefully to the sound. Then press the block of wood to your ear and strike it with the spoon again. Listen carefully to the sound.
2. Tie the middle of a length of **cotton string** to a metal spoon. Strike the spoon on something to hear it ring. Now press the ends of the string against your ears and repeat the experiment. What do you hear?

Analysis

1. Did you hear sounds transmitted through wood and through string? Describe the sounds.
2. Compare and contrast the sounds in wood and in air.

Try at Home

The Speed of Sound

Sound waves can travel through other materials besides air. In fact, sound waves travel in the same way through different materials as they do in air, although they might travel at different speeds. As a sound wave travels through a material, the particles in the material collide with each other. In a solid, molecules are closer together than in liquids or gases, so collisions between molecules occur more rapidly than in liquids or gases. The speed of sound is usually fastest in solids, where molecules are closest together, and slowest in gases, where molecules are farthest apart. **Table 1** shows the speed of sound through different materials.

The Speed of Sound and Temperature The temperature of the material that sound waves are traveling through also affects the speed of sound. As a substance heats up, its molecules move faster, so they collide more frequently. The more frequent the collisions are, the faster the speed of sound is in the material. For example, the speed of sound in air at 0°C is 331 m/s; at 20°C, it is 343 m/s.

Amplitude and Loudness

What's the difference between loud sounds and quiet sounds? When you play a song at high volume and low volume, you hear the same instruments and voices, but something is different. The difference is that loud sound waves generally carry more energy than soft sound waves do.

Loudness is the human perception of how much energy a sound wave carries. Not all sound waves with the same energy are as loud. Humans hear sounds with frequencies between 3,000 Hz and 4,000 Hz as being louder than other sound waves with the same energy.

Table 1 Speed of Sound Through Different Materials	
Material	**Speed (m/s)**
Air	343
Water	1,483
Steel	5,940
Glass	5,640

🔬 LAB DEMONSTRATION

Purpose to observe the transfer of energy in sound waves

Materials cardboard tube, balloon, rubber bands, candle, matches or lighter, scissors

Procedure Cut pieces from the balloon and stretch them over the two open ends of the cardboard tube. Secure them with the rub-ber bands. Poke a small hole in one end of the drum. Hold this end about 10 cm from a lighted candle, and tap the other end.

Expected Outcome The vibrations made at one end travel through the tube, forcing air through the hole at the other end. This blows out the candle.

Assessment

Does the strength of the tap on the drum affect the distance from which a candle could be blown out? Explain. Yes; the stronger the tap, the greater the energy in the sound wave. With more energy, the wave can travel farther.

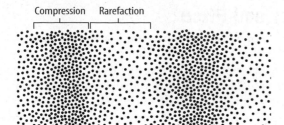

This sound wave has a lower amplitude.

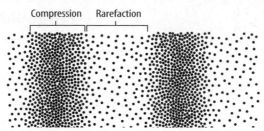

This sound wave has a higher amplitude. Particles in the material are more compressed in the compressions and more spread out in the rarefactions.

Amplitude and Energy The amount of energy a wave carries depends on its amplitude. For a compressional wave such as a sound wave, the amplitude is related to how spread out the molecules or particles are in the compressions and rarefactions, as **Figure 4** shows. The higher the amplitude of the wave is, the more compressed the particles in the compression are and the more spread out they are in the rarefactions. More energy had to be transferred by the vibrating object that created the wave to force the particles closer together or spread them farther apart. Sound waves with greater amplitude carry more energy and sound louder. Sound waves with smaller amplitude carry less energy and sound quieter.

 **Reading Check** *What determines the loudness of different sounds?*

The Decibel Scale Perhaps an adult has said to you, "Turn down your music, it's too loud! You're going to lose your hearing!" Although the perception of loudness varies from person to person, the energy carried by sound waves can be described by a scale called the decibel (dB) scale. **Figure 5** shows the decibel scale. An increase in the loudness of a sound of 10 dB means that the energy carried by the sound has increased ten times, but an increase of 20 dB means that the sound carries 100 times more energy.

Hearing damage begins to occur at sound levels of about 85 dB. The amount of damage depends on the frequencies of the sound and the length of time a person is exposed to the sound. Some music concerts produce sound levels as high as 120 dB. The energy carried by these sound waves is about 30 billion times greater than the energy carried by sound waves that are made by whispering.

Figure 4 The amplitude of a sound wave depends on how spread out the particles are in the compressions and rarefactions of the wave.

Figure 5 The loudness of sound is measured on the decibel scale.

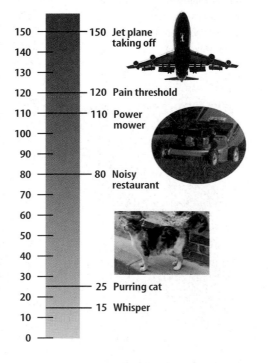

150	150 Jet plane taking off
140	
130	
120	120 Pain threshold
110	110 Power mower
100	
90	
80	80 Noisy restaurant
70	
60	
50	
40	
30	
25	25 Purring cat
20	
15	15 Whisper
10	
0	

SECTION 1 What is sound? **493**

Teacher FYI

Sound Intensity The loudness of sound decreases as it travels away from a source because the waves lose energy as particles of the medium collide with each other and because they radiate out from the source. Sound intensity decreases at $1/r^2$, where r is the distance from the source. For example, the intensity of a sound 100 m from its source is about one-fourth the intensity of the same sound 50 m from its source.

✓ **Reading Check**

Answer the energy of the sound waves

Activity

Whistles Have students bring in various whistles. Go outside and have them blow the whistles separately and rank them from loudest to softest. Afterward, have students examine the whistles to find out what produced the vibration and look for features that caused one whistle to be louder than another. L2 **ELL IS** Auditory-Musical

Visual Learning

Figure 5 Point out the pain threshold, at about 120 dB. What types of sounds exceed this threshold? Possible answers: loud music at a concert or a jet taking off L2 **IS** Logical-Mathematical

Differentiated Instruction

English-Language Learners Have students duplicate the decibel chart in this section, on poster board. Then have them cut pictures out of magazines of things that make sound and add the pictures to the chart, estimating where they should be placed. L1 **ELL**

Science Journal

Decibels Ask students to find out what the word *decibel* means and how it was coined. Have them write their responses in their Science Journals. A decibel is one-tenth of a bel, named in honor of Alexander Graham Bell. L2 **IS** Linguistic

Discussion

Animal Noises Have students think of noises that animals make when they fly: the high-pitched whine of a mosquito, the buzz of a fly, and the hum of a hummingbird. Explain that these sounds are caused by the animal's wings vibrating the air and that the pitch corresponds to the speed of vibration. What change in the movement of the animals' wings causes an increase in pitch? When pitch rises, the animal is beating its wings more rapidly. L2
LS **Logical-Mathematical**

Visual Learning

Figure 6 How do the wavelength and frequency of the two waves shown differ? The upper wave has one-half the wavelength and twice the frequency of the other. Because the frequency is greater, the pitch will be higher. L2 **LS** **Visual-Spatial**

Teacher FYI

Recorded Sound When sound is recorded, the frequencies and amplitudes of the sound waves are converted into varying voltage. When recorded sound is played back, these voltages are converted into vibrations in the speaker.

Caption Answer

Figure 6 the upper wave

Frequency and Pitch

The **pitch** of a sound is how high or low it sounds. For example, a piccolo produces a high-pitched sound or tone, and a tuba makes a low-pitched sound. Pitch corresponds to the frequency of the sound. The higher the pitch is, the higher the frequency is. A sound wave with a frequency of 440 Hz, for example, has a higher pitch than a sound wave with a frequency of 220 Hz.

The human ear can detect sound waves with frequencies between about 20 Hz and 20,000 Hz. However, some animals can detect even higher and lower frequencies. For example, dogs can hear frequencies up to almost 50,000 Hz. Dolphins and bats can hear frequencies as high as 150,000 Hz, and whales can hear frequencies higher than those heard by humans.

Recall that frequency and wavelength are related. If two sound waves are traveling at the same speed, the wave with the shorter wavelength has a higher frequency. If the wavelength is shorter, then more compressions and rarefactions will go past a given point every second than for a wave with a longer wavelength, as shown in **Figure 6.** Sound waves with a higher pitch have shorter wavelengths than those with a lower pitch.

The Human Voice When you make a sound, you exhale past your vocal cords, causing them to vibrate. The length and thickness of your vocal cords help determine the pitch of your voice. Shorter, thinner vocal cords vibrate at higher frequencies than longer or thicker ones. This explains why children, whose vocal cords are still growing, have higher voices than adults. Muscles in the throat can stretch the vocal cords tighter, letting people vary their pitch within a limited range.

Figure 6 The upper sound wave has a shorter wavelength than the lower wave. If these two sound waves are traveling at the same speed, the upper sound wave has a higher frequency than the lower one. For this wave, more compressions and rarefactions will go past a point every second than for the lower wave.
Identify the wave that has a higher pitch.

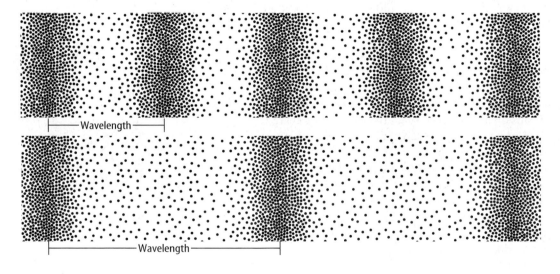

Wavelength

Wavelength

Cultural Diversity

Measuring Bells More than 2,000 years ago, the Chinese used tuned bells as the basis of their entire system of measurement. They divided the scale into twelve pitches, and had official sets of twelve bells. A stringed tuner about 2.1 m long called a chun was used to standardize the pitches of bells throughout China. The length of a chun would be varied until the pitch of the chun matched the pitch of a standard bell. The chun could then be used to determine the pitch of a bell in a distant city. Pitch pipes later replaced the bells.

Figure 7 Sonar uses reflected sound waves to determine the location and shape of an object.

Echoes

Sound reflects off of hard surfaces, just like a water wave bounces off the side of a bath tub. A reflected sound wave is called an echo. If the distance between you and a reflecting surface is great enough, you might hear the echo of your voice. This is because it might take a few seconds for the sound to travel to the reflecting surface and back to your ears.

Sonar systems use sound waves to map objects underwater, as shown in **Figure 7.** The amount of time it takes an echo to return depends on how far away the reflecting surface is. By measuring the length of time between emitting a pulse of sound and hearing its echo off the ocean floor, the distance to the ocean floor can be measured. Using this method, sonar can map the ocean floor and other undersea features. Sonar also can be used to detect submarines, schools of fish, and other objects.

 *How do sonar systems measure distance?*

Echolocation Some animals use a method called echolocation to navigate and hunt. Bats, for example, emit high-pitched squeaks and listen for the echoes. The type of echo it hears helps the bat determine exactly where an insect is, as shown in **Figure 8.** Dolphins also use a form of echolocation. Their high-pitched clicks bounce off of objects in the ocean, allowing them to navigate in the same way.

People with visual impairments also use echolocation. For example, they can interpret echoes to estimate the size and shape of a room by using their ears.

Science Online

Topic: Sonar
Visit ips.msscience.com for Web links to information about how sonar is used to detect objects underwater.

Activity List and explain how several underwater discoveries were made using sonar.

Figure 8 Bats use echolocation to hunt.
Explain *why this is a good technique for hunting at night.*

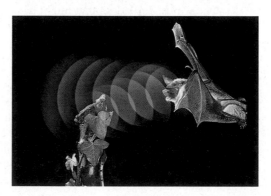

Curriculum Connection

History Ask students to find out how archaeologists use sonar mapping to learn about history. Archaeologists use sonar to map areas that were once above water level. For example, researchers have mapped the route early Siberian hunter-gatherers may have taken to North America. Using the map and samples collected from the area, they found that forests once grew along the now ice-covered coasts. [L2] [LS] **Linguistic**

Discussion

Echoes Have students think about situations in which they have heard echoes. What characteristics does a room that produces an echo have? It would be large and have mostly hard surfaces, which are better at reflecting sound waves than are soft surfaces. Point out that soft surfaces such as carpeting and upholstery tend to absorb sounds. Also, the room must be large enough for there to be a delay between the initial sound and the echo. [L2] [LS] **Auditory-Musical**

Caption Answer

Figure 8 There is little light, so it's difficult to see well at night.

Teacher **FYI**

Animal Sonar Some night-flying moths and butterflies can hear the ultrasonic frequencies used by hunting bats. Tiger moths make ultrasonic clicks when they detect a bat's sonar. This may act to jam the sonar, or it may signal that this insect is a bad-tasting tiger moth.

Fun Fact

When you inhale or exhale without making a sound, the vocal cords are separated at the edges of the windpipe. In this position they are not vibrated.

Reading Check

Answer They measure the time needed for sound waves to travel to an object and be reflected back to the sonar unit.

INTEGRATE Astronomy

Doppler Shift of Light
The frequency of light waves is also changed by the Doppler shift. If a light source is moving away from an observer, the frequencies of the emitted light waves decrease. Research how the Doppler shift is used by astronomers to determine how other objects in the universe are moving relative to Earth.

The Doppler Effect

Perhaps you've heard an ambulance siren as the ambulance speeds toward you, then goes past. You might have noticed that the pitch of the siren gets higher as the ambulance moves toward you. Then as the ambulance moves away, the pitch of the siren gets lower. The change in frequency that occurs when a source of sound is moving relative to a listener is called the **Doppler effect**. **Figure 9** shows why the Doppler effect occurs.

The Doppler effect occurs whether the sound source or the listener is moving. If you drive past a factory as its whistle blows, the whistle will sound higher pitched as you approach. As you move closer you encounter each sound wave a little earlier than you would if you were sitting still, so the whistle has a higher pitch. When you move away from the whistle, each sound wave takes a little longer to reach you. You hear fewer wavelengths per second, which makes the sound lower in pitch.

Radar guns that are used to measure the speed of cars and baseball pitches also use the Doppler effect. Instead of a sound wave, the radar gun sends out a radio wave. When the radio wave is reflected, its frequency changes depending on the speed of the object and whether it is moving toward the gun or away from it. The radar gun uses the change in frequency of the reflected wave to determine the object's speed.

Applying Science

How does Doppler radar work?

Doppler radar is used by the National Weather Service to detect areas of precipitation and to measure the speed at which a storm moves. Because the wind moves the rain, Doppler radar can "see" into a strong storm and expose the winds. Tornadoes that might be forming in the storm then can be identified.

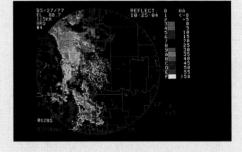

Identify the Problem

An antenna sends out pulses of radio waves as it rotates. The waves bounce off raindrops and return to the antenna at a different frequency, depending on whether the rain is moving toward the antenna or away from it. The change in frequency is due to the Doppler shift.

Solving the Problem

1. If the frequency of the reflected radio waves increases, how is the rain moving relative to the radar station?
2. In a tornado, winds are rotating. How would the radio waves reflected by rotating winds be Doppler-shifted?

Figure 9

You've probably heard the siren of an ambulance as it races through the streets. The sound of the siren seems to be higher in pitch as the ambulance approaches and lower in pitch as it moves away. This is the Doppler effect, which occurs when a listener and a source of sound waves are moving relative to each other.

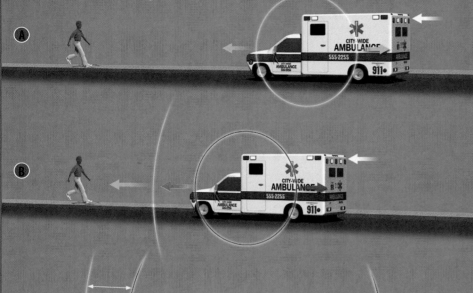

Ⓐ **As the ambulance speeds down the street, its siren emits sound waves. Suppose the siren emits the compression part of a sound wave as it goes past the girl.**

Ⓑ **As the ambulance continues moving, it emits another compression. Meanwhile, the first compression spreads out from the point from which it was emitted.**

Ⓒ **The waves traveling in the direction that the ambulance is moving have compressions closer together. As a result, the wavelength is shorter and the boy hears a higher frequency sound as the ambulance moves toward him. The waves traveling in the opposite direction have compressions that are farther apart. The wavelength is longer and the girl hears a lower frequency sound as the ambulance moves away from her.**

SECTION 1 What is sound? **497**

Visualizing the Doppler Effect

Have students examine the pictures and read the captions. Then ask the following questions.

If the source of sound begins to move faster, what will happen to the frequency? The frequency will be shifted even higher in front of the source, and even lower behind the source.

What would happen if the source moved as fast as the sound wave it creates? The waves would bunch up in front of the source. This would intensify the sound, creating a sonic boom like that created by a supersonic airplane.

Activity

Water Doppler Waves Have students work in pairs to demonstrate the Doppler effect in water waves. Have one student in each pair use a finger to make waves in a shallow glass baking dish. Once the waves are moving steadily, have the student move his or her finger toward one side of the dish, while maintaining a steady movement up and down to generate waves. Have the other student observe what happens to the waves. Tell students to switch roles so each will have an opportunity to observe the waves. L2 IS **Kinesthetic**

Seeing Around Corners Hearing sound from around a corner is so common you don't think about it. But what would happen if light, which is also a wave, diffracted around the corner of a doorway? You would be able to see what was going on in a room without being in the direct line of sight. The people in the room would also be able to see you. L3 **LS** Logical-Mathematical

Use Science Words

Word Meaning Have students find the meaning of the prefix *ultra-* and relate this meaning to the meaning of ultrasound. *Ultra-* means "beyond what is ordinary," or "super." Ultrasound is sound that is at high frequencies that are beyond ordinary frequencies. L2 **LS** Linguistic

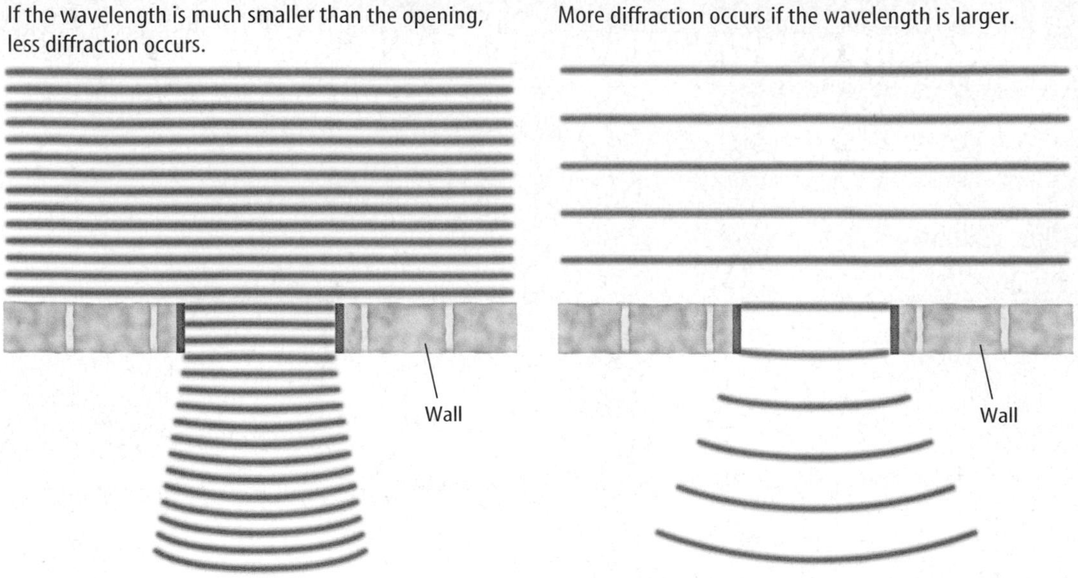

If the wavelength is much smaller than the opening, less diffraction occurs.

More diffraction occurs if the wavelength is larger.

Wall

Wall

Figure 10 The spreading of a wave by diffraction depends on the wavelength and the size of the opening.

Diffraction of Sound Waves

Like other waves, sound waves diffract. This means they can bend around obstacles or spread out after passing through narrow openings. The amount of diffraction depends on the wavelength of the sound wave compared to the size of the obstacle or opening. If the wavelength is much smaller than the obstacle, almost no diffraction occurs. As the wavelength becomes closer to the size of the obstacle, the amount of diffraction increases.

You can observe diffraction of sound waves by visiting the school band room during practice. If you stand in the doorway, you will hear the band normally. However, if you stand to one side outside the door or around a corner, you will hear the lower-pitched instruments better. **Figure 10** shows why this happens. The sound waves that are produced by the lower-pitched instruments have lower frequencies and longer wavelengths. These wavelengths are closer to the size of the door opening than the higher-pitched sound waves are. As a result, the longer wavelengths diffract more, and you can hear them even when you're not standing in the doorway.

The diffraction of lower frequencies in the human voice allows you to hear someone talking even when the person is around the corner. This is different from an echo. Echoes occur when sound waves bounce off a reflecting surface. Diffraction occurs when a wave spreads out after passing through an opening, or when a wave bends around an obstacle.

498 CHAPTER 17 Sound

Teacher FYI

Stereo Speakers Some stereo speakers or stereo systems account for differences in the diffraction of sound waves of different frequencies by usually having only one woofer for the low notes, but several tweeters, pointed in different directions, for the high notes.

Differentiated Instruction

Challenge As a train approaches, the Doppler effect causes the sound to be higher in pitch. Suppose you were rushing toward the oncoming train. Would you expect the Doppler shift in the frequency of sound to increase, stay the same, or disappear? Explain. Increase; because you and the train are coming together more quickly than if you were standing still. L3 **LS** Logical-Mathematical

Using Sound Waves

Sound waves can be used to treat certain medical problems. A process called ultrasound uses high-frequency sound waves as an alternative to some surgeries. For example, some people develop small, hard deposits in their kidneys or gallbladders. A doctor can focus ultrasound waves at the kidney or gallbladder. The ultrasound waves cause the deposits to vibrate rapidly until they break apart into small pieces. Then, the body can get rid of them.

Ultrasound can be used to make images of the inside of the body. One common use of ultrasound is to examine a developing fetus. Also, ultrasound along with the Doppler effect can be used to examine the functioning of the heart. An ultrasound image of the heart is shown in **Figure 11.** This technique can help determine if the heart valves and heart muscle are functioning properly, and how blood is flowing through the heart.

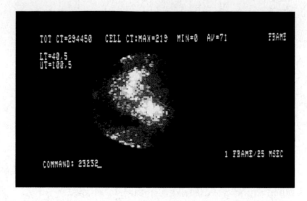

Figure 11 Ultrasound is used to make this image of the heart.
Describe *other ways ultrasound is used in medicine.*

section 1 review

Summary

Sound Waves

- Sound waves are compressional waves produced by vibrations.
- Sound travels fastest in solids and slowest in gases.
- Sound travels faster as the temperature of the medium increases.
- The energy carried by a sound wave increases as its amplitude increases.

Loudness and Pitch

- Loudness is the human perception of the energy carried by a sound wave.
- The pitch of a sound becomes higher as the frequency of the sound increases.

The Doppler Effect and Diffraction

- In the Doppler effect, the frequency of a sound wave changes if the source of the sound is moving relative to the listener.
- Diffraction occurs when sound waves bend around objects or spread out after passing through an opening.

Self Check

1. **Describe** how the loudness of a sound wave changes when the amplitude of the wave is increased.
2. **Explain** how the wavelength of a sound wave affects the diffraction of the sound wave through an open window.
3. **Describe** how echolocation could be used to measure the distance to the bottom of a lake.
4. **Discuss** how the spacing of particles in a sound wave changes as the amplitude of the wave decreases.
5. **Describe** how the wavelength of a sound wave changes if the frequency of the wave increases.
6. **Think Critically** You hear the pitch of the sound from an ambulance siren get lower, then get higher. Describe the motion of the ambulance relative to you.

Applying Math

7. **Calculate Distance** Sound travels through water at a speed of 1,483 m/s. Use the equation

    distance = speed × time

    to calculate how far a sound wave in water will travel in 5 s.

section 1 review

1. Loudness increases.
2. Sounds whose waves are about the same length as the opening are diffracted the most. Sound waves with frequencies of about 150 Hz have wavelengths similar in size to a window opening.
3. Using sonar, record the time it takes

for a sound wave to travel from the surface to the bottom of the lake and reflect back to the surface. Multiply one-half the time by the speed of sound in water to get the distance.
4. As the amplitude of a sound wave decreases, the space between the particles of the medium increases in

the compressions and decreases in the rarefactions.
5. If the frequency of a sound wave increases, the wavelength of the wave decreases.
6. lower—moving away from you; higher—moving toward you
7. 7,415 m

BENCH TESTED

● Real-World Question

Purpose Students observe that sound waves can be reflected and focused. L2 ELL COOP LEARN LS **Auditory-Musical**

Process Skills observe and infer, measure, draw conclusions

Time Required 30 minutes

● Procedure

Teaching Strategies

• Announce the lab at least the day before, so enough ticking watches can be located. Check to be sure students can hear the watches ticking.

• Smooth surfaces reflect sound; don't try the experiment on carpeting.

• Students should work quietly so that the ticking of the watch can be heard.

Troubleshooting The two tubes need to be in the same plane. You should be able to hold a piece of poster board up so that the sides of both tubes rest along the poster board. If the tubes are not in the same plane, students will not hear the watch.

● Conclude and Apply

1. The angles are approximately equal.
2. They are equal and less than 90°.
3. Yes

Observe and Measure Reflection of Sound

● Real-World Question

Like all waves, sound waves can be reflected. When sound waves strike a surface, in what direction does the reflected sound wave travel? In this activity, you'll focus sound waves using cardboard tubes to help answer this question. How are the angles made by incoming and reflected sound waves related?

Goals

■ **Observe** reflection of sound waves.
■ **Measure** the angles incoming and reflected sound waves make with a surface.

Materials

20-cm to 30-cm-long cardboard tubes (2)
watch that ticks audibly
protractor

Safety Precautions

● Procedure

1. Work in groups of three. Each person should listen to the watch—first without a tube and then through a tube. The person who hears the watch most easily is the listener.

2. One person should hold one tube at an angle with one end above a table. Hold the watch at the other end of the tube.

3. The listener should hold the second tube at an angle, with one end near his or her ear and the other end near the end of the first tube that is just above the table. The tubes should be in the same vertical plane.

4. Move the first tube until the watch sounds

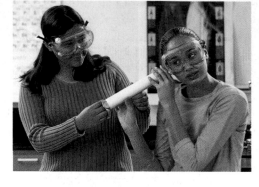

loudest. The listener might need to cover the other ear to block out background noises.

5. The third person should measure the angle that each tube makes with the table.

● Conclude and Apply

1. **Compare** the angles the incoming and reflected waves make with the table.

2. The normal is a line at 90 degrees to the table at the point where reflection occurs. Determine the angles the incoming and reflected waves make with the normal.

3. The law of reflection states that the angles the incoming and reflected waves make with the normal are equal. Do sound waves obey the law of reflection?

Communicating Your Data

Make a scientific illustration to show how the experiment was done. Describe your results using the illustration.

☑ Assessment

Process Compare and contrast the reflection of sound with the reflection of light. Have two students stand to either side of a mirror. Can they see themselves in the mirror? no Can they see each other? Yes; both are examples of reflection: the angle of incidence with the reflecting surface will be the same as the angle of reflection for both sound and light. Use **Performance Assessment in the Science Classroom**, p. 89.

Communicating Your Data

Students can view each other's illustrations. As they review the illustrations, they should ask themselves, "If I hadn't done the experiment myself, would I be able to do it based on the illustration?"

Music

What is music?

What do you like to listen to—rock 'n' roll, country, blues, jazz, rap, or classical? Music and noise are groups of sounds. Why do humans hear some sounds as music and other sounds as noise?

The answer involves patterns of sound. **Music** is a group of sounds that have been deliberately produced to make a regular pattern. Look at **Figure 12**. The sounds that make up music usually have a regular pattern of pitches, or notes. Some natural sounds such as the patter of rain on a roof, the sound of ocean waves splashing, or the songs of birds can sound musical. On the other hand, noise is usually a group of sounds with no regular pattern. Sounds you hear as noise are irregular and disorganized such as the sounds of traffic on a city street or the roar of a jet aircraft.

However, the difference between music and noise can vary from person to person. What one person considers to be music, another person might consider noise.

Natural Frequencies Music is created by vibrations. When you sing, your vocal cords vibrate. When you beat a drum, the drumhead vibrates. When you play a guitar, the strings vibrate.

If you tap on a bell with a hard object, the bell produces a sound. When you tap on a bell that is larger or smaller or has a different shape you hear a different sound. The bells sound different because each bell vibrates at different frequencies. A bell vibrates at frequencies that depend on its shape and the material it is made from. Every object will vibrate at certain frequencies called its **natural frequencies**.

as you read

What You'll Learn

- **Explain** the difference between music and noise.
- **Describe** how different instruments produce music.
- **Explain** how you hear.

Why It's Important

Music is made by people in every part of the world.

Review Vocabulary

compressional wave: a type of mechanical wave in which matter in the medium moves forward and backward in the same direction the wave travels

New Vocabulary

- music
- natural frequencies
- resonance
- fundamental frequency
- overtone
- reverberation
- eardrum

Figure 12 Music and noise have different types of sound patterns.

Noise has no specific or regular sound wave pattern.

Music is organized sound. Music has regular sound wave patterns and structures.

SECTION 2 Music **501**

1 Motivate

Bellringer

Section Focus Transparencies also are available on the Interactive Chalkboard CD-ROM.

L2 ELL

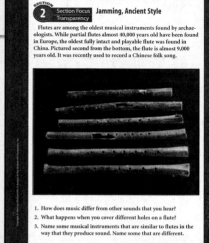

Tie to Prior Knowledge

Musical Instruments Ask students to name any musical instruments they play. Tell them that this section explains the science of music.

Section 2 Resource Manager

Chapter FAST FILE Resources

Transparency Activity, pp. 41, 43–44

Directed Reading for Content Mastery, pp. 19, 20

Lab Activity, pp. 11–14

MiniLAB, p. 4

Enrichment, p. 28

Reinforcement, p. 26

Lab Worksheet, pp. 7–8

Cultural Diversity, p. 61

Lab Management and Safety, p. 64

Discussion

Music v. Noise Discuss with students how music differs from noise. What natural sounds seem and do not seem musical? Possible answer: Sounds are musical when they make distinguishable pitches and have a regular pattern. [L2] [LS] **Auditory-Musical**

Reading Check

Answer size, shape, and material of the vibrating object

INTEGRATE Social Studies

Some newer buildings are supported by flexible moorings that are made from alternating layers of rubber and steel. In older buildings, steel rods are used to reinforce walls.

Quick Demo

Resonance

Materials plastic container with lid

Estimated Time five minutes

Procedure Tap the lid when it is not on the container. Then fit the lid over the empty container and tap it again. The second sound is louder because the container and the air inside also vibrate, an example of resonance.

INTEGRATE Social Studies

Reducing Earthquake Damage The shaking of the ground during an earthquake can cause buildings to resonate. The increased vibration of a building due to resonance could result in the collapse of the building, causing injuries and loss of life. To reduce damage during earthquakes, buildings are designed to resonate at frequencies different than those that occur during earthquakes. Research how buildings are designed to reduce damage caused by earthquakes.

Musical Instruments and Natural Frequencies Many objects vibrate at one or more natural frequencies when they are struck or disturbed. Like a bell, the natural frequencies of any object depend on the size and shape of the object and the material it is made from. Musical instruments use the natural frequencies of strings, drumheads, or columns of air contained in pipes to produce various musical notes.

Reading Check *What determines the natural frequencies?*

Resonance You may have seen the comedy routine in which a loud soprano sings high enough to shatter glass. Sometimes sound waves cause an object to vibrate. When a tuning fork is struck, it vibrates at its natural frequency and produces a sound wave with the same frequency. Suppose you have two tuning forks with the same natural frequency. You strike one tuning fork, and the sound waves it produces strike the other tuning fork. These sound waves would cause the tuning fork that wasn't struck to absorb energy and vibrate. This is an example of resonance. **Resonance** occurs when an object is made to vibrate at its natural frequencies by absorbing energy from a sound wave or another object vibrating at these frequencies.

Musical instruments use resonance to amplify their sounds. Look at **Figure 13.** The vibrating tuning fork might cause the table to vibrate at the same frequency, or resonate. The combined vibrations of the table and the tuning fork increase the loudness of the sound waves produced.

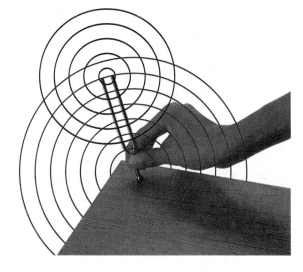

Figure 13 When a vibrating tuning fork is placed against a table, resonance might cause the table to vibrate.

Differentiated Instruction

Hearing Impaired Help these students sense the vibrations of sound waves. Have a student hold a balloon while you make a sound. The sound waves will vibrate the balloon, and the vibration will be passed to the student's fingers. Have students use balloons to help them sense sounds during all the sound-producing activities performed in this section. [L2]

Visual Learning

Figure 13 Discuss with students the effect touching the vibrating tuning fork to the table has on the sound made by the tuning fork. Vibrations from the tuning fork cause the table to resonate, which makes the sound louder. [L2] [LS] **Visual-Spatial**

Overtones

Before a concert, all orchestra musicians tune their instruments by playing the same note. Even though the note has the same pitch, it sounds different for each instrument. It also sounds different from a tuning fork that vibrates at the same frequency as the note.

A tuning fork produces a single frequency, called a pure tone. However, the notes produced by musical instruments are not pure tones. Most objects have more than one natural frequency at which they can vibrate. As a result, they produce sound waves of more than one frequency.

If you play a single note on a guitar, the pitch that you hear is the lowest frequency produced by the vibrating string. The lowest frequency produced by a vibrating object is the **fundamental frequency.** The vibrating string also produces higher frequencies. These higher frequencies are **overtones.** Overtones have frequencies that are multiples of the fundamental frequency, as in **Figure 14.** The number and intensity of the overtones produced by each instrument are different and give instruments their distinctive sound quality.

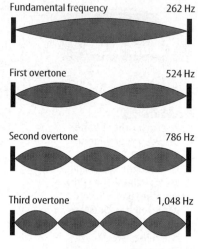

Fundamental frequency	262 Hz
First overtone	524 Hz
Second overtone	786 Hz
Third overtone	1,048 Hz

Figure 14 A string vibrates at a fundamental frequency, as well as at overtones. The overtones are multiples of that frequency.

Musical Scales

A musical instrument is a device that produces musical sounds. These sounds are usually part of a musical scale that is a sequence of notes with certain frequencies. For example, **Figure 15** shows the sequence of notes that belong to the musical scale of C. Notice that the frequency produced by the instrument doubles after eight successive notes of the scale are played. Other musical scales consist of a different sequence of frequencies.

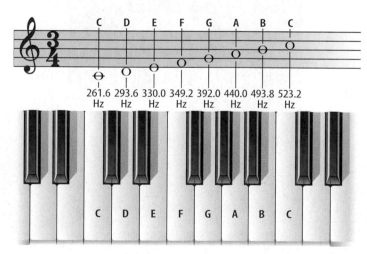

C D E F G A B C

261.6 293.6 330.0 349.2 392.0 440.0 493.8 523.2
Hz   Hz   Hz   Hz   Hz   Hz   Hz   Hz

C D E F G A B C

Figure 15 A piano produces a sequence of notes that are a part of a musical scale.
Describe *how the frequencies of the two C notes on this scale are related.*

SECTION 2 Music **503**

Stringed Instruments

Stringed instruments, like the cello shown in **Figure 16,** produce music by making strings vibrate. Different methods are used to make the strings vibrate—guitar strings are plucked, piano strings are struck, and a bow is slid across cello strings. The strings often are made of wire. The pitch of the note depends on the length, diameter, and tension of the string—if the string is shorter, narrower, or tighter, the pitch increases. For example, pressing down on a vibrating guitar string shortens its length and produces a note with a higher pitch. Similarly, the thinner guitar strings produce a higher pitch than the thicker strings.

Amplifying Vibrations The sound produced by a vibrating string usually is soft. To amplify the sound, stringed instruments usually have a hollow chamber, or box, called a resonator, which contains air. The resonator absorbs energy from the vibrating string and vibrates at its natural frequencies. For example, the body of a guitar is a resonator that amplifies the sound that is produced by the vibrating strings. The vibrating strings cause the guitar's body and the air inside it to resonate. As a result, the vibrating guitar strings sound louder, just as the tuning fork that was placed against the table sounded louder.

Purpose Students observe how changes in a vibrating string change the sound it produces. **L2 IS Auditory- Musical**

Materials rubber band, box

Teaching Strategy Have students use rubber bands of varying lengths and thicknesses.

Analysis

1. Stretching the rubber band increased the tension and increased the pitch. This matches the predictions for stringed instruments given in the text.
2. The sound became louder when the box was included. This agrees with the text's prediction about using a resonator with a string.

Assessment

Process Have each student make a small model harp using several rubber bands and a resonator box. Bands may be identical, with different amounts of tension, or they may vary in size. Students should be able to explain and demonstrate how the different conditions for each band affect the sound produced, and the role of the resonator. Use **Performance Assessment in the Science Classroom,** p. 123.

Use an Analogy

Calendar A musical scale can be compared to a calendar. Just as every week starts with a Sunday, every scale starts with Do. The sequence of days are the same every week, and when you get to Saturday the week starts again with Sunday. The same is true with a musical scale.

Modeling a Stringed Instrument

Procedure 🥽

1. Stretch a **rubber band** between your fingers.
2. Pluck the rubber band. Listen to the sound and observe the shape of the vibrating band. Record what you hear and see.
3. Stretch the band farther and repeat step 2.
4. Shorten the length of the band that can vibrate by holding your finger on one point. Repeat step 2.
5. Stretch the rubber band over an open box, such as a **shoe box.** Repeat step 2.

Analysis

1. How did the sound change when you stretched the rubber band? Was this what you expected? Explain.
2. How did the sound change when you stretched the band over the box? Did you expect this? Explain.

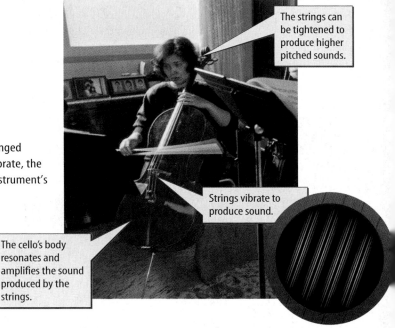

Figure 16 A cello is a stringed instrument. When strings vibrate, the natural frequencies of the instrument's body amplify the sound.

The strings can be tightened to produce higher pitched sounds.

Strings vibrate to produce sound.

The cello's body resonates and amplifies the sound produced by the strings.

Visual Learning

Figure 16 Point out the pegs at the end of the strings, which are used to adjust tension. Individual strings also have different thicknesses, which gives them different natural frequencies and pitches. Note the bridge supporting the strings. Ask what function the bridge performs. The bridge transfers the vibrations of the strings to the soundboard in the body of the instrument. **L2 IS Visual-Spatial**

Percussion

Percussion instruments, such as the drum shown in **Figure 17,** are struck to make a sound. Striking the top surface of the drum causes it to vibrate. The vibrating drumhead is attached to a chamber that resonates and amplifies the sound.

Drums and Pitch

Some drums have a fixed pitch, but some can be tuned to play different notes. For example, if the drumhead on a kettledrum is tightened, the natural frequency of the drumhead is increased. As a result, the pitches of the sounds produced by the kettledrum get higher. A steel drum, shown in **Figure 17,** plays different notes in the scale when different areas in the drum are struck. In a xylophone, wood or metal bars of different lengths are struck. The longer the bar is, the lower the note that it produces is.

Brass and Woodwinds

Just as the bars of a xylophone have different natural frequencies, so do the air columns in pipes of different lengths. Brass and woodwind instruments, such as those in **Figure 18,** are essentially pipes or tubes of different lengths that sometimes are twisted around to make them easier to hold and carry. To make music from these instruments, the air in the pipes is made to vibrate at various frequencies.

Different methods are used to make the air column vibrate. A musician playing a brass instrument, such as a trumpet, makes the air column vibrate by vibrating the lips and blowing into the mouthpiece. Woodwinds such as clarinets, saxophones, and oboes contain one or two reeds in the mouthpiece that vibrate the air column when the musician blows into the mouthpiece. Flutes also are woodwinds, but a flute player blows across a narrow opening to make the air column vibrate.

Figure 17 The sounds produced by drums depend on the material that is vibrating.

The vibrating drumhead of this drum is amplified by the resonating air in the body of the drum.

The vibrating steel surface in a steel drum produces loud sounds that don't need to be amplified by an air-filled chamber.

Figure 18 Brass and woodwind instruments produce sounds by causing a column of air to vibrate.

Figure 19 A flute changes pitch as holes are opened and closed.

By opening holes on a flute, the length of the vibrating air column is made shorter.

Quick Demo

Slide Whistle

Materials metal pipe, dowel that just fits into pipe, party whistle, or commercial slide whistle.

Estimated Time 10 minutes

Procedure Attach the end of the party whistle to the pipe containing the dowel. Blow into the mouthpiece while sliding the dowel up and down from the bottom. Have students explain what happens as you move the slide. As you vary the length of the vibrating air column, you vary the pitch. A shorter air column has a higher pitch.

Activity

Instrument Demonstration Have students who play wind or brass instruments demonstrate how the instruments work to the class. As part of their presentations, have students explain how they change the pitch of their instruments. L2 [IS] **Visual-Spatial**

Use Science Words

Word Meaning Acoustical engineers design buildings and other structures to enhance or reduce sound. Have students find the two meanings of the word *acoustics*. the scientific study of sound; the total effect of sound in a place, especially an enclosed space. L2 [IS] **Linguistic**

Virtual Labs

Fine Tuned *How is an oscilloscope used to tune a musical instrument?*

Changing Pitch in Woodwinds To change the note that is being played in a woodwind instrument, a musician changes the length of the resonating column of air. By making the length of the vibrating air column shorter, the pitch of the sound produced is made higher. In a woodwind such as a flute, saxophone, or clarinet, this is done by closing and opening finger holes along the length of the instrument, as shown in **Figure 19.**

Changing Pitch in Brass In brass instruments, musicians vary the pitch in other ways. One is by blowing harder to make the air resonate at a higher natural frequency. Another way is by pressing valves that change the length of the tube.

Beats

Recall that interference occurs when two waves overlap and combine to form a new wave. The new wave formed by interference can have a different frequency, wavelength, and amplitude than the two original waves.

Suppose two notes close in frequency are played at the same time. The two notes interfere to form a new sound whose loudness increases and decreases several times a second. If you were listening to the sound, you would hear a series of beats as the sound got louder and softer. The beat frequency, or the number of beats you would hear each second, is equal to the difference in the frequencies of the two notes.

For example, if the two notes have frequencies of 329 Hz and 332 Hz, the beat frequency would be 3 Hz. You would hear the sound get louder and softer—a beat—three times each second.

Figure 20 A piano can be tuned by using beats.

Curriculum Connection

History The earliest complete, playable instrument known is a flute from China, dating from about 9,000 years ago. This flute is made from a bird bone and has seven main holes. A tiny extra hole, drilled next to the final hole, appears to adjust a slight defect in the pitch, giving some idea of the practical musical knowledge of the flute's maker. Parts of bone flutes as much as 30,000 years old have been found in parts of Europe. Why might people have used bones for flutes? What other items would also work? Bird bones are hollow, and other bones can be hollowed. Hollow plants, such as reeds, can be used, but they would not survive as well in the archaeological record. L2 [IS] **Logical-Mathematical**

Beats Help Tune Instruments Beats are used to help tune instruments. For example, a piano tuner, like the one shown in **Figure 20,** might hit a tuning fork and then the corresponding key on the piano. Beats are heard when the difference in pitch is small. The piano string is tuned properly when the beats disappear. You might have heard beats while listening to an orchestra tune before a performance. You also can hear beats produced by two engines vibrating at slightly different frequencies.

Reverberation

Sound is reflected by hard surfaces. In an empty gymnasium, the sound of your voice can be reflected back and forth several times by the floor, walls, and ceiling. Repeated echoes of sound are called **reverberation.** In a gym, reverberation makes the sound of your voice linger before it dies out. Some reverberation can make voices or music sound bright and lively. Too little reverberation makes the sound flat and lifeless. However, reverberation can produce a confusing mess of noise if too many sounds linger for too long.

Concert halls and theaters, such as the one in **Figure 21,** are designed to produce the appropriate level of reverberation. Acoustical engineers use soft materials to reduce echoes. Special panels that are attached to the walls or suspended from the ceiling are designed to reflect sound toward the audience.

Science Online

Topic: Controlling Reverberation
Visit ips.msscience.com for Web Links to information about how acoustical engineers control reverberation.

Activity Make a list of the materials engineers use to reduce and enhance reverberation.

Figure 21 The shape of a concert hall and the materials it contains are designed to control the reflection of sound waves.

Teacher FYI

Reverberation Reverberation makes sound confusing because each echo takes a different amount of time to reach your ears. For example, if someone on stage shouts "One-two-three!" you might be hearing "Three!" while simultaneously hearing several slightly offset echoes of "Two!" and a few fainter, offset re-echoes of "One!" It is hard to pick meaning out of this collage of sound.

Quick Demo

Beats

Materials digital tuner, pairs of students who play the same type of instrument

Estimated Time 15 minutes

Procedure Ask students to use the digital tuner to tune their instruments to an A. One frequency should be 440 Hz and the other to 435 Hz. Play both instruments simultaneously and ask the other students in the class to count the beats. They should hear 5 beats per second.

Differentiated Instruction

Challenge Have students write reports describing what happens when two sound waves meet. When crests overlap, waves interfere constructively, and the amplitude of the wave increases. If the initial waves are identical, the amplitude of the wave doubles. If the crests in one meet the troughs in the other, the waves interfere destructively. If identical waves interfere exactly destructively, they cancel each other. L3

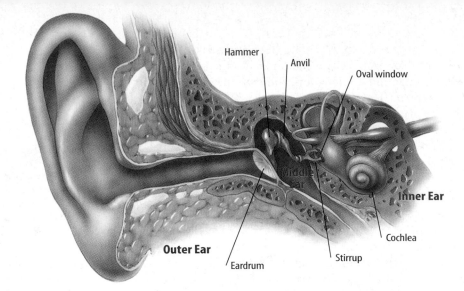

Visual Learning

Figure 22 Have students trace the path of sound as it moves through the ear. Sound moves through the outer ear, ear canal, middle ear, eardrum, hammer, anvil, and stirrup, oval window, and cochlea. Impulses are then carried to the brain where they are interpreted by the auditory nerve. L2 **LS** **Visual-Spatial**

Quick Demo
Two Ears
Materials none
Estimated Time five minutes
Procedure Ask students to close their eyes and listen to you speak to them from one point in the room. Have them point to you. Repeat the process with students covering one ear and your position changed. What happens? It should be more difficult to locate you using only one ear. Point out that having an ear on either side of your head make it easier to pinpoint the source of a sound.

Figure 22 The human ear has three different parts—the outer ear, the middle ear, and the inner ear.

Figure 23 Animals, such as rabbits and owls, have ears that are adapted to their different needs.

The Ear

You hear sounds with your ears. The ear is a complex organ that is able to detect a wide range of sounds. The ear can detect frequencies ranging from about 20 Hz to about 20,000 Hz. The ear also can detect a wide range of sound intensities. The faintest sounds you can hear carry about one trillionth the amount of energy as the loudest sounds you can hear. The human ear is illustrated in **Figure 22.** It has three parts—the outer ear, the middle ear, and the inner ear.

The Outer Ear—Sound Collector Your outer ear collects sound waves and directs them into the ear canal. Notice that your outer ear is shaped roughly like a funnel. This shape helps collect sound waves.

Animals that rely on hearing to locate predators or prey often have larger, more adjustable ears than humans, as shown in **Figure 23.** A barn owl, which relies on its excellent hearing for hunting at night, does not have outer ears made of flesh. Instead, the arrangement of its facial feathers helps direct sound to its ears. Some sea mammals, on the other hand, have only small holes for outer ears, even though their hearing is good.

The Middle Ear—Sound Amplifier When sound waves reach the middle ear, they vibrate the **eardrum,** which is a membrane that stretches across the ear canal like a drumhead. When the eardrum vibrates, it transmits vibrations to three small connected bones—the hammer, anvil, and stirrup. The bones amplify the vibrations, just as a lever can change a small movement at one end into a larger movement at the other.

508 CHAPTER 17 Sound

Teacher FYI
Popping Ears Why do your ears pop? Your middle ear has an air pocket between the eardrum and oval window membranes. When the pressure of the air on either side of the eardrum is unbalanced, your ears feel blocked. You need to swallow to equalize the pressure. This feels like a pop.

Differentiated Instruction
Challenge Western musical harmony is based on triad chords consisting of the notes *do, mi,* and *sol.* The overtones produced by a piano are called the overtone series and form the basis of Western harmony. Have students find out how this works. The first six overtones produced by a note on the piano include *do, do* an octave higher, *sol* an octave and a fifth above *do, do* two octaves higher, and *mi* two octaves and a third above *do.* L3 **LS** **Logical-Mathematical**

508 CHAPTER 17 Sound

The Inner Ear—Sound Interpreter The stirrup vibrates a second membrane called the oval window. This marks the start of the inner ear, which is filled with fluid. Vibrations in the fluid are transmitted to hair-tipped cells lining the cochlea, as shown in **Figure 24**. Different sounds vibrate the cells in different ways. The cells generate signals containing information about the frequency, intensity, and duration of the sound. The nerve impulses travel along the auditory nerve and are transmitted to the part of the brain that is responsible for hearing.

 **Reading Check** *Where are waves detected and interpreted in the ear?*

Hearing Loss

The ear can be damaged by disease, age, and exposure to loud sounds. For example, constant exposure to loud noise can damage hair cells in the cochlea. If damaged mammalian hair cells die, some loss of hearing results because mammals cannot make new hair cells. Also, some hair cells and nerve fibers in the inner ear degenerate and are lost as people age. It is estimated that about 30 percent of people over 65 have some hearing loss due to aging.

Figure 24 The inner ear contains tiny hair cells that convert vibrations into nerve impulses that travel to the brain.

Science**Online** ips.msscience.com/self_check_quiz

---

section ② review

Summary

What is music?

- Music is sound that is deliberately produced in a regular pattern.
- Objects vibrate at certain natural frequencies.
- The lowest frequency produced by a vibrating object is the object's fundamental frequency.
- The overtones produced by a vibrating object are multiples of the fundamental frequency.

Musical Instruments and Hearing

- In stringed instruments the sounds made by vibrating strings are amplified by a resonator.
- Percussion instruments produce sound by vibrating when they are struck.
- Brass and woodwind instruments produce sound by vibrating a column of air.
- The ear collects sound waves, amplifies the sound, and interprets the sound.

Self Check

1. **Describe** how music and noise are different.
2. **Infer** Two bars on a xylophone are 10 cm long and 14 cm long. Identify which bar produces a lower pitch when struck and explain why.
3. **Describe** the parts of the human ear and the function of each part in enabling you to hear sound.
4. **Predict** how the sound produced by a guitar string changes as the length of the string is made shorter.
5. **Diagram** the fundamental and the first two overtones for a vibrating string.
6. **Think Critically** How does reverberation explain why your voice sounds different in a gym than it does in your living room?

Applying Math

7. **Calculate Overtone Frequency** A guitar string has a fundamental frequency of 440 Hz. What is the frequency of the second overtone?

SECTION 2 Music **509**

---

section ② review

1. Music has a regular pattern but noise does not.
2. the 14-cm bar; the larger the vibrating object, usually the deeper the sound it produces.
3. The outer ear collects sound, the middle ear amplifies sound, and the inner ear generates nerve impulses.
4. As the vibrating length of a guitar string becomes shorter, the pitch gets higher.
5. Drawings should be similar to Figure 14.
6. A gym produces a lot of reverberation because of the large, flat, hard walls and floor. Your living room probably has carpeting, upholstered chairs and draperies, and other furniture that absorb sound.
7. 440 Hz × 3 = 786 Hz

Real-World Question

Purpose Students compare and contrast different instruments and observe how changes in the different instruments correspond to changes in the pitches produced. L2 ELL COOP LEARN LS **Auditory-Musical**

Process Skills observe, infer, compare and contrast, measure, recognize cause and effect, control variables, formulate hypotheses, make and use tables, interpret data

Time Required one class period to make measurements, one class period to analyze and check results

Possible Materials Make sure students are prepared in advance to bring in instruments that they know how to play.

Safety Precautions Warn students not to stand in the way of the musicians.

Form a Hypothesis

Possible Hypothesis To play a higher note, the vibrating part of the instrument (string, bar, column of air) must be shortened. To play G, for example, the vibrating part must be shortened to two-thirds the length it has when the C below it is played.

Design Your Own

LAB

Music

Goals
- **Design** an experiment to compare the changes that are needed in different instruments to produce a variety of different notes.
- **Observe** which changes are made when playing different notes.
- **Measure and record** these changes whenever possible.

Possible Materials
musical instruments
measuring tape
tuning forks

Safety Precautions
Properly clean the mouthpiece of any instrument before it is used by another student.

Real-World Question

The pitch of a note that is played on an instrument sometimes depends on the length of the string, the air column, or some other vibrating part. Exactly how does sound correspond to the size or length of the vibrating part? Is this true for different instruments? What causes different instruments to produce different notes?

Form a Hypothesis

Based on your reading and observations, make a hypothesis about what changes in an instrument to produce different notes.

Test Your Hypothesis

Make a Plan

1. You should do this lab as a class, using as many instruments as possible. You might want to go to the music room or invite friends and relatives who play an instrument to visit the class.

Alternative Inquiry Lab

Construct Instruments Suggest that students make their own instruments. Provide materials like string, rubber bands, cardboard cartons and tubes, tissue paper, tape, scissors, plastic containers and other materials of the student's choice. Encourage students to devise a way to change pitch and try to play a simple song. L2

2. As a group, decide how you will measure changes in instruments. For wind instruments, can you measure the length of the vibrating air column? For stringed instruments, can you measure the length and thickness of the vibrating string?

3. Refer to the table of wavelengths and frequencies for notes in the scale. Note that no measurements are given—if you measure C to correspond to a string length of 30 cm, for example, the note G will correspond to two thirds of that length.

4. Decide which musical notes you will compare. Prepare a table to collect your data. List the notes you have selected.

Ratios of Wavelengths and Frequencies of Musical Notes

Note	Wavelength	Frequency
C	1	1
D	8/9	9/8
E	4/5	5/4
F	3/4	4/3
G	2/3	3/2
A	3/5	5/3
B	8/15	15/8
C	1/2	2

Follow Your Plan

1. Make sure your teacher approves your plan before you start.

2. Carry out the experiment as planned.

3. While doing the experiment, record your observations and complete the data table.

Analyze Your Data

1. **Compare** the change in each instrument when the two notes are produced.

2. **Compare and contrast** the changes between instruments.

3. What were the controls in this experiment?

4. What were the variables in this experiment?

5. How did you eliminate bias?

Conclude and Apply

1. How does changing the length of the vibrating column of air in a wind instrument affect the note that is played?

2. Describe how you would modify an instrument to increase the pitch of a note that is played.

Communicating
Your Data

Demonstrate to another teacher or to family members how the change in the instrument produces a change in sound.

✔ Assessment

Oral Ask students how they would analyze an instrument they'd never seen before. How could they tell what kind of instrument it was? How could they determine how it varied its pitch? Use **Performance Assessment in the Science Classroom**, p. 89.

Communicating
Your Data

Have students make illustrated tables of their data that include pictures of the different instruments. Tables should include descriptions of how the instrument changes when the pitch is changed. L2

● Test Your Hypothesis

Possible Procedure Choose two notes and measure the length of the vibrating part of each instrument when the two notes are played. Record your results in a table.

Teaching Strategies
- Make sure that students note differences other than length.
- Suggest that students first determine how to measure.

Expected Outcome To play a higher note, the vibrating part of the instrument is shortened. If a string, it may also be tighter or thinner. If a brass instrument, the force of air blown may increase to make the air column vibrate in thirds rather than halves, for example.

● Analyze Your Data

Answers to Questions
1. Answers will depend on instruments used.
2. Answers will depend on instruments used.
3. playing the same notes or using the same instrument
4. playing different notes or using different instruments
5. Answers will vary.

Error Analysis If students get anomalous results, help them look for possible errors in their measurements.

● Conclude and Apply

1. Increasing the length of the vibrating column of air decreases the pitch of the note.
2. Reduce the length of the vibrating part of the instrument.

Content Background

Explain that sound waves are compressional waves that originate when there is a disturbance in the air. Vibrating objects or sudden movement in the air can cause a disturbance. In the case of candy wrappers, the sudden repositioning of the plastic wrapper causes sudden movement in the air molecules near the plastic wrap. As a result, areas where molecules are bunched together (compression) or spread apart (rarefaction) are formed. These compressional waves are transmitted through the air as sound waves.

Discussion

Definition Suggest students debate this question: If a tree falls in the forest and no one is there to hear it, is sound formed? The answer depends on how sound is defined. If sound is characterized as what the human ear perceives, then the answer is no. But if sound is defined as a wave of energy traveling through a medium, then the answer is yes. **LS** **Interpersonal**

Activity

Candy Divide the class into small groups, and then distribute one piece of wrapped hard candy to each student. Have students take turns trying to unwrap the candy as quietly as possible. Ask students to record the methods used to open the candy and the effectiveness of each. If time permits, have the quietest students from each group compete for quietest in the class. **LS** **Auditory-Musical**

TIME SCIENCE AND Society

SCIENCE ISSUES THAT AFFECT YOU!

It's a Wrap!

No matter how quickly or slowly you open a candy wrapper, it always will make a noise

snap! crackle! pop! crackle! pop! pop! snap! snap! crackle!

Y ou're at the movies and it's the most exciting part of the film. The audience is silent and intent on what is happening on the screen. At that moment, you decide to unwrap a piece of candy. CRACKLE! POP! SNAP! No matter how you do it, the candy wrapper makes a lot of noise.

Why can't you unwrap candy without making a racket? To test this plastics problem, researchers put some crinkly wrappers in a silent room. Then they stretched out the wrappers and recorded the sounds they made. Next, the sounds were analyzed by a computer. The research team discovered that the wrapper didn't make a continuous sound. Instead, it made many separate little popping noises, each taking only a thousandth of a second. They found that whether you open the wrapper quickly or slowly the amount of noise made by the pops will be the same. "And there's nothing you can do about it," said a member of the research team.

By understanding what makes a plastic wrapper snap when it changes shape, doctors can better understand molecules in the human body that also change shape.

The pop chart

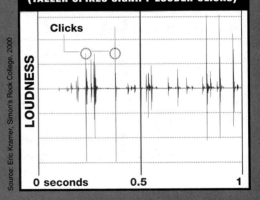

SOUND LEVEL OVER TIME
The sound that a candy wrapper makes is emitted as a series of pulses or clicks. So, opening a wrapper slowly only increases the length of time in between clicks, but the amount of noise remains the same.
(TALLER SPIKES SIGNIFY LOUDER CLICKS)

Clicks

LOUDNESS

0 seconds   0.5   1

Source: Eric Kramer, Simon's Rock College, 2000

Recall and Retell Have you ever opened a candy wrapper in a quiet place? Did it bother other people? If so, did you try to open it more slowly? What happened?

Science Online

For more information, visit ips.msscience.com/time

Recall & Retell Have students work in small groups to list different kinds of candies. Next, have them arrange their lists from the noisiest to open to the least noisy. Ask students to describe the outer wrappers of the noisiest and least noisy. Their descriptions should include the type of material used and how easy it is to open. Share conclusions with the class. **L2** **LS** **Interpersonal**

Resources for Teachers and Students

Sound: More Than What You Hear, Christopher F. Lampton, Enslow Publishers Inc., New Jersey, 1992

Sound Fundamentals Funtastic Science Activities for Kids, Robert W. Wood, McGraw-Hill Companies, Inc., 1997

Reviewing Main Ideas

Section 1 **What is sound?**

1. Sound is a compressional wave that travels through matter, such as air. Sound is produced by something that vibrates.

2. The speed of sound depends on the material in which it is traveling.

3. The larger the amplitude of a sound wave, the more energy it carries and the louder the sound.

4. The pitch of a sound wave becomes higher as its frequency increases. Sound waves can reflect and diffract.

5. The Doppler effect occurs when a source of sound and a listener are in motion relative to each other. The pitch of the sound heard by the listener changes.

Section 2 **Music**

1. Music is made of sounds that are used in a regular pattern. Noise is made of sounds that are irregular and disorganized.

2. Objects vibrate at their natural frequencies. These depend on the shape of the object and the material it's made of.

3. Resonance occurs when an object is made to vibrate by absorbing energy at one of its natural frequencies.

4. Musical instruments produce notes by vibrating at their natural frequencies.

5. Beats occur when two waves of nearly the same frequency interfere.

6. The ear collects sound waves and converts sound waves to nerve impulses.

Visualizing Main Ideas

Copy and complete the following concept map on sound.

Sound waves — are → Compressional waves — that have → Frequency — which corresponds to → Pitch; Amplitude — which corresponds to → Loudness

Sound waves — produced in a regular pattern create → Music — which arises from an instrument's → Natural frequencies — which are composed of → Fundamental frequency, Overtones

Science Online   ips.msscience.com/interactive_tutor

Reviewing Main Ideas

Summary statements can be used by students to review the major concepts of the chapter.

Visualizing Main Ideas

See student page.

Science Online

Visit ips.msscience.com
/self_check_quiz
/interactive_tutor
/vocabulary_puzzlemaker
/chapter_review
/standardized_test

Assessment Transparency

For additional assessment questions, use the *Assessment Transparency* located in the transparency book.

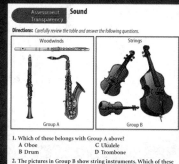

Assessment

Assessment Transparency — **Sound**

Directions: Carefully review the table and answer the following questions.

Woodwinds	Strings
Group A	Group B

1. Which of these belongs with Group A above?
   A Oboe   C Ukulele
   B Drum   D Trombone

2. The pictures in Group B show string instruments. Which of these is the major characteristic of string instruments?
   F They produce notes of the same frequency on each string.
   G They all produce sound by turning the pegs near the top.
   H They produce different pitches by changing the length of an air column.
   J They produce sound from vibrating strings.

3. The instruments in Group A are different from the instruments in Group B because only the instruments in Group A ___.
   A produce sound by striking a surface
   B have finger holes to change a note's pitch
   C produce notes of different wavelengths
   D amplify sounds by letting them resonate

Using Vocabulary

1. The lowest frequency produced by a vibrating object is the fundamental frequency. The higher frequencies at which it vibrates are overtones.

2. Pitch corresponds to the frequency of a sound wave.

3. The pitch of a sound wave gets higher if the source of the sound and the listener are approaching each other and gets lower if they are moving farther apart. This phenomenon is called the Doppler effect.

4. Loudness corresponds to the energy, or amplitude, of a sound wave. Resonance refers to the tendency of an object to vibrate at its natural frequencies.

5. The fundamental frequency is the lowest natural frequency of an object.

6. The loudness of a sound is related to the amplitude of the sound wave.

7. Natural frequencies produced by vibrating objects include the fundamental frequency, which is the lowest natural frequency the object produces, and the overtones, which are multiples of the fundamental frequency.

8. Resonance occurs when an object is made to vibrate at its natural frequency by absorbing energy from a sound wave produced by another vibrating object. Reverberation occurs when sound is reflected many times to produce repeated echoes.

Checking Concepts

9. A	13. A	17. D
10. B	14. A	18. C
11. D	15. A	
12. C	16. C	

Thinking Critically

19. Each pipe resonates at the pitch produced by the bar above it and amplifies it.

20. The shift in frequency is not large enough to be detected by your ear.

Using Vocabulary

Doppler effect p. 496	music p. 501
eardrum p. 508	natural frequency p. 501
echo p. 495	overtone p. 503
fundamental	pitch p. 494
frequency p. 503	resonance p. 502
loudness p. 492	reverberation p. 507

Distinguish between the terms in the following pairs

1. overtones—fundamental frequency

2. pitch—sound wave

3. pitch—Doppler effect

4. loudness—resonance

5. fundamental frequency— natural frequency

6. loudness—amplitude

7. natural frequency—overtone

8. reverberation—resonance

Checking Concepts

Choose the word or phrase that best answers the question.

9. A tone that is lower in pitch is lower in what characteristic?
   A) frequency   C) loudness
   B) wavelength   D) resonance

10. If the wave speed stays the same, which of the following decreases as the frequency increases?
    A) pitch   C) loudness
    B) wavelength   D) resonance

11. What part of the ear is damaged most easily by continued exposure to loud noise?
    A) eardrum   C) oval window
    B) stirrup   D) hair cells

12. What is an echo?
    A) diffracted sound
    B) resonating sound
    C) reflected sound
    D) an overtone

13. A trumpeter depresses keys to make the column of air resonating in the trumpet shorter. What happens to the note being played?
    A) Its pitch is higher.
    B) Its pitch is lower.
    C) It is quieter.
    D) It is louder.

14. When tuning a violin, a string is tightened. What happens to a note being played on the string?
    A) Its pitch is higher.
    B) Its pitch is lower.
    C) It is quieter.
    D) It is louder.

15. As air becomes warmer, how does the speed of sound in air change?
    A) It increases.   C) It doesn't change.
    B) It decreases.   D) It oscillates.

16. Sound waves are which type of wave?
    A) slow   C) compressional
    B) transverse   D) electromagnetic

17. What does the middle ear do?
    A) focuses sound
    B) interprets sound
    C) collects sound
    D) transmits and amplifies sound

18. An ambulance siren speeds away from you. What happens to the pitch of the siren?
    A) It becomes softer.
    B) It becomes louder.
    C) It decreases.
    D) It increases.

Science online ips.msscience.com/vocabulary_puzzlemaker

Use the Exam*View*® Pro Testmaker CD-ROM to:

- create multiple versions of tests
- create modified tests with one mouse click for inclusion students
- edit existing questions and add your own questions
- build tests aligned with state standards using built-in State Curriculum Tags
- change English tests to Spanish with one mouse click and vice versa

Thinking Critically

19. Explain Some xylophones have open pipes of different lengths hung under each bar. The longer a bar is, the longer the pipe beneath it. Explain how these pipes help amplify the sound of the xylophone.

20. Infer why you don't notice the Doppler effect for a slow moving train.

21. Predict Suppose the movement of the bones in the middle ear were reduced. Which would be more affected—the ability to hear quiet sounds or the ability to hear high frequencies? Explain your answer.

22. Explain The triangle is a percussion instrument consisting of an open metal triangle hanging from a string. A chiming sound is heard when the triangle is struck by a metal rod. If the triangle is held in the hand, a quiet dull sound is heard when it is struck. Why does holding the triangle make the sound quieter?

Use the table below to answer question 23.

Speed of Sound Through Different Materials	
Material	**Speed (m/s)**
Air	343
Water	1,483
Steel	5,940
Glass	5,640

23. Calculate Using the table above, determine the total amount of time needed for a sound wave to travel 3.5 km through air and then 100.0 m through water.

 nline ips.msscience.com/chapter_review

24. Predict If the holes of a flute are all covered while playing, then all uncovered, what happens to the length of the vibrating air column? What happens to the pitch of the note?

25. Identify Variables and Controls Describe an experiment to demonstrate that sound is diffracted.

26. Interpret Scientific Illustrations The picture below shows pan pipes. How are different notes produced by blowing on pan pipes?

Performance Activities

27. Recital Perform a short musical piece on an instrument. Explain how your actions changed the notes that were produced.

28. Pamphlet Make a pamphlet describing how a hearing aid works.

29. Interview Interview several people over 65 with some form of hearing loss. Create a table that shows the age of each person and how their hearing has changed with age.

Applying Math

30. Beats Two flutes are playing at the same time. One flute plays a note with a frequency of 524 Hz. If two beats per second are heard, what are the possible frequencies the other flute is playing?

31. Overtones Make a table showing the first three overtones of C, which has a frequency of 262 Hz, and G, which has a frequency of 392 Hz.

CHAPTER REVIEW **515**

---

21. Sound vibration would not be amplified and quiet sounds could be missed.

22. When you hold the triangle, you keep it from vibrating freely. Your fingers absorb the energy, so little sound is produced.

23. 10.3 s

24. When all holes are covered, the column is longer and the note is lower. When all holes are uncovered, the column is shorter and the note is higher.

25. Possible answer: set up a radio playing in a room. Leave the room, and stand to one side of the door. If you can hear the music, it must be diffracted around the edge of the door to reach your ears.

26. Air is blown across the top of each individual pipe, resonating the column of air. The longer the pipe, the deeper the note.

Performance Activities

27. Check students' explanations. Use **Performance Assessment in the Science Classroom,** p. 143.

28. Explanations should include information about how the device collects, transmits, and amplifies sound. Use **Performance Assessment in the Science Classroom,** p. 129.

29. Students' tables will vary.

Applying Math

National Math Standards

1, 9

30. Possible frequencies are 522 Hz and 526 Hz

31.

	C	G
Fundamental	262	392
First Overtone	524	784
Second Overtone	786	1,176
Third Overtone	1,048	1,568

☑ Assessment **Resources**

📁 **Reproducible Masters**
Chapter *Fast File* Resources
Chapter Review, pp. 33–34
Chapter Tests, pp. 35–38
Assessment Transparency Activity, p. 45
Glencoe Science Web site
Chapter Review Test
Standardized Test Practice

Glencoe Technology
🔋 Assessment Transparency
Ⓧ Exam*View*® Pro Testmaker
▭ MindJogger Videoquiz
Ⓒ Interactive Chalkboard

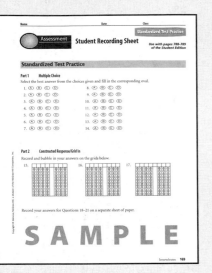

FAST FILE

Answer Sheet A practice answer sheet can be found at ips.msscience.com/answer_sheet.

SAMPLE

Part 1 Multiple Choice

1. D	**6.** A
2. C	**7.** A
3. B	**8.** C
4. C	**9.** C
5. B	

Part 2 Short Response

10. Echoes occur when sound waves bounce off a reflecting surface. Diffraction occurs when a wave spreads out after passing through an opening or a wave bends around an obstacle.

11. 0.022 s

12. 0.44 s

13. 4752 m

14. Each object vibrates at its natural frequencies. The natural frequencies of an object depends on its size, shape, and the material of which it is made.

15. The sound waves from the first tuning fork strike the other tuning fork. The sound waves would cause the tuning fork that wasn't struck to absorb energy and vibrate too. This

---

Part 1 Multiple Choice

Record your answers on the answer sheet provided by your teacher or on a sheet of paper.

1. In which of the following materials does sound travel the fastest?
  A. empty space   **C.** air
  B. water   **D.** steel

2. How can the pitch of the sound made by a guitar string be lowered?
  A. by shortening the part of the string that vibrates
  B. by tightening the string
  C. by replacing the string with a thicker string
  D. by plucking the string harder

Use the figure below to answer questions 3 and 4.

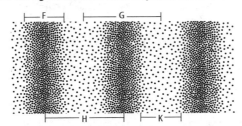

3. What part of the wave is shown at F?
  A. rarefaction   **C.** wavelength
  B. compression   **D.** amplitude

4. What part of the wave is shown at H?
  A. rarefaction   **C.** wavelength
  B. compression   **D.** amplitude

5. What happens to the particles of matter when a compressional wave moves through the matter?
  A. The particles do not move.
  B. The particles move back and forth along the wave direction.
  C. The particles move back and forth and are carried along with the wave.
  D. The particles move at right angles to the direction the wave travels.

516 STANDARDIZED TEST PRACTICE

---

6. If you were on a moving train, what would happen to the pitch of a bell at a crossing as you approached and then passed by the crossing?
  A. It would seem higher, then lower.
  B. It would remain the same.
  C. It would seem lower and then higher.
  D. It would keep getting lower.

Use the figure below to answer questions 7 and 8.

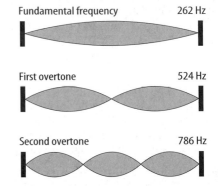

Fundamental frequency   262 Hz

First overtone   524 Hz

Second overtone   786 Hz

7. How are the overtone frequencies of any vibrating object related to the fundamental frequency of vibration?
  A. They are multiples of the fundamental.
  B. They are not related to the fundamental.
  C. They equal twice the fundamental.
  D. They are lower than the fundamental.

8. Which of the following is the frequency of the third overtone?
  A. 1,572 Hz   **C.** 1,048 Hz
  B. 1,000 Hz   **D.** 786 Hz

9. Which of the following is NOT related to the amplitude of a sound wave?
  A. energy carried by the wave
  B. loudness of a sound
  C. pitch of a sound
  D. how spread out the particles are in the compressions and rarefactions

---

Part 3 Open Ended

is an example of resonance.

16. Each instrument produces different numbers and intensities of overtones. This gives each instrument a different sound quality.

17. A drum produces sound when the top surface, or drumhead, is struck and vibrates. The body of the drum

and the air inside it are the resonator. A flute produces sound when a player blows a stream of air across a narrow opening. This causes the air inside the flute to vibrate. The metal tube containing the air is the resonator.

18. Sound waves traveling through the outer ear would be slower, since they are traveling through air. In

the inner ear, the vibrations are traveling through a fluid and sound travels faster through a fluid than through air.

19. Depth can be calculated using $d = st$ and by measuring the time required for a sound to travel to and from the ocean floor. Repeated measurements and calculations of depths could be used to create a

Part 2 | Short Response/Grid In

Record your answers on the answer sheet provided by your teacher or on a sheet of paper.

10. What is the difference between diffracted sound waves and echoes?

Use the figure below to answer questions 11–13.

Speed of Sound in Different Materials	
Material	**Speed of sound (m/s)**
Air	343
Water	1,483
Steel	5,940

11. A fish locator sends out a pulse of ultrasound and measures the time needed for the sound to travel to a school of fish and back to the boat. If the fish are 16 m below the boat, how long would it take sound to make the round trip in the water?

12. Suppose you are at a baseball game 150 m from home plate. How long after the batter hits the ball do you hear the sound?

13. A friend drops a stone on a steel railroad track. If the sound made by the stone hitting the track reaches you in 0.8 s, how far away is your friend?

14. Why do different objects produce different sounds when they are struck?

15. Explain how one vibrating tuning fork could make a second tuning fork also vibrate. What is this an example of?

Test-Taking Tip

Notice Units Read carefully and make note of the units used in any measurement.

Question 13 Notice the units used for time in the question and the units for speed given in the table.

Part 3 | Open Ended

Record your answers on a sheet of paper.

16. Why do different musical instruments sound different even when they play a note with the same pitch?

17. Compare the way a drum and a flute produce sound waves. What acts as a resonator in each instrument?

18. Would sound waves traveling through the outer ear travel faster or slower than those traveling through the inner ear? Explain.

Use the figure below to answer questions 19.

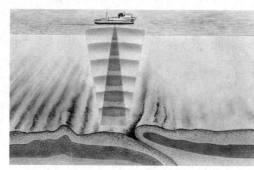

19. Describe how the process shown in the figure can be used to map the ocean floor.

20. When a sound wave passes through an opening, what does the amount of diffraction depend on?

21. Describe how a cello produces and amplifies sounds.

22. People who work on the ground near jet runways are required to wear ear protection. Explain why this is necessary.

23. Bats use ultrasound when they echolocate prey. If ultrasound waves bounce off an insect that is flying away from the bat, how would the frequency of the wave be affected? What is this effect called?

Rubrics

The following rubrics are sample scoring devices for short response and open-ended questions.

Short Response

Points	Description
2	The student demonstrates a thorough understanding of the science of the task. The response may contain minor flaws that do not detract from the demonstration of a thorough understanding.
1	The student has provided a response that is only partially correct.
0	The student has provided a completely incorrect solution or no response at all.

Open Ended

Points	Description
4	The student demonstrates a thorough understanding of the science of the task. The response may contain minor flaws that do not detract from the demonstration of a thorough understanding.
3	The student demonstrates an understanding of the science of the task. The response is essentially correct and demonstrates an essential but less than thorough understanding of the science.
2	The student demonstrates only a partial understanding of the science of the task. Although the student may have used the correct approach to a solution or may have provided a correct solution, the work lacks an essential understanding of the underlying science concepts.
1	The student demonstrates a very limited understanding of the science of the task. The response is incomplete and exhibits many flaws.
0	The student provides a completely incorrect solution or no response at all.

map of the ocean floor.

20. wavelength of the sound compared to the size of the obstacle or opening

21. The cello produces sound when the cellist draws a bow across tightly stretched strings to make them vibrate. The cello's body is a resonator that amplifies sound.

22. The noise level of a jet taking off is very loud and exposure to loud sounds can damage hair cells in the cochlea. This results in hearing loss. The sound insulator in the ear muffs decreases the intensity of the sound reaching the workers' ears and thus protects their hearing.

23. The frequency of the wave would be decreased because the source of the sound, the echo bouncing off the insect, is moving away. This change in frequency is the Doppler effect.

Section/Objectives	Standards		Labs/Features
	National	**State/Local**	
Chapter Opener	See pp. 16T–17T for a Key to Standards.		**Launch Lab:** Detecting Invisible Waves, p. 519 **Foldables,** p. 519
Section 1 The Nature of Electromagnetic Waves ⏱ 2 sessions 📷 1 block 1. **Explain** how electromagnetic waves are produced. 2. **Describe** the properties of electromagnetic waves.	National Content Standards: UCP.1–3, UCP.5, A.1–2, B.1–3		**Science Online,** p. 521 **MiniLAB:** Observing Electric Fields, p. 523
Section 2 The Electromagnetic Spectrum ⏱ 2 sessions 📷 1 block 3. **Explain** differences among kinds of electromagnetic waves. 4. **Identify** uses for different kinds of electromagnetic waves.	National Content Standards: UCP.1–3, UCP.5, A.1–2, B.1–3		**MiniLAB:** Observing the Focusing of Infrared Rays, p. 527 **Integrate Life Science,** p. 530 **Visualizing the Universe,** p. 532 **Lab:** Prisms of Light, p. 534
Section 3 Using Electromagnetic Waves ⏱ 3 sessions 📷 1.5 blocks 5. **Describe** different ways of using electromagnetic waves to communicate. 6. **Compare and contrast** AM and FM radio signals.	National Content Standards: UCP.1–3, UCP.5, A.1–2, B.1–3		**Integrate History,** p. 536 **Applying Math:** Wavelength of an FM Station, p. 537 **Science Online,** p. 538 **Lab:** Spectrum Inspection, p. 540 **Science and History:** Hopping the Frequencies, p. 542

Lab Materials	Reproducible Resources	Section Assessment	Technology
Launch Lab: sheet of black paper, glass prism, thermometers (2)	**Chapter FAST FILE Resources** Foldables Worksheet, p. 15 Directed Reading Overview p. 17 Note-taking Worksheets, pp. 31–33	GLENCOE'S **ASSESSMENT** ADVANTAGE	**TeacherWorks** includes: • Interactive Teacher Edition • Lesson Planner with calendar • Access to all program blacklines • Correlations to standards • Web links
MiniLAB: hard plastic comb, wool sweater or flannel shirt, water faucet	**Chapter FAST FILE Resources** Transparency Activity, p. 42 MiniLAB, p. 3 Enrichment, p. 28 Reinforcement, p. 25 Directed Reading, p. 18 **Cultural Diversity,** p. 61 **Science Inquiry Labs,** pp. 35–36	**Portfolio** Science Journal, p. 521 **Performance** MiniLAB, p. 523 Applying Math, p. 524 **Content** Section Review, p. 524	Section Focus Transparency Guided Reading Audio Program Interactive Chalkboard CD-ROM
MiniLAB: concave mirror, meterstick, electric heater **Lab:** microscope slides (3), transparent tape, clay, flashlight, water	**Chapter FAST FILE Resources** Transparency Activity, p. 43 MiniLAB, p. 4 Enrichment, p. 29 Reinforcement, p. 26 Directed Reading, p. 18 Lab Activity, pp. 9–11 Lab Worksheet, pp. 5–6 **Reading and Writing Skill Activities,** p. 25	**Portfolio** Reteach, p. 533 **Performance** MiniLAB, p. 527 Applying Skills, p. 533 **Content** Section Review, p. 533	Section Focus Transparency Virtual Labs CD-ROM Guided Reading Audio Program Interactive Chalkboard CD-ROM Video Lab
Lab: diffraction grating, clear tubular incandescent light with dimmer switch; red, yellow, and blue colored pencils *Need materials?* Contact Science Kit at 1-800-828-7777 or www.sciencekit.com on the Internet.	**Chapter FAST FILE Resources** Transparency Activity, p. 44 Enrichment, p. 30 Reinforcement, p. 27 Directed Reading, pp. 19, 20 Lab Activity, pp. 13–14 Transparency Activity, pp. 45–46 Lab Worksheet, pp. 7–8 **Mathematics Skill Activities,** p. 9 **Lab Management and Safety,** p. 73	**Portfolio** Curriculum Connection, p. 537 **Performance** Applying Math, p. 537 Applying Skills, p. 539 **Content** Section Review, p. 539	Section Focus Transparency Teaching Transparency Guided Reading Audio Program Interactive Chalkboard CD-ROM

End of Chapter Assessment

GLENCOE'S **ASSESSMENT** ADVANTAGE

Blackline Masters	Technology	Professional Series
Chapter FAST FILE Resources Chapter Review, pp. 35–36 Chapter Tests, pp. 37–40 **Standardized Test Practice,** pp. 75–78	MindJogger Videoquiz Virtual Labs CD-ROM ExamView® Pro Testmaker TeacherWorks CD-ROM Interactive Chalkboard CD-ROM	**Performance Assessment in the Science Classroom (PASC)**

Transparencies

Section Focus

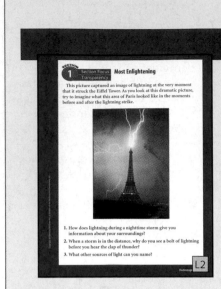

Section Focus Transparency 1 — Most Enlightening

This picture captured an image of lightning at the very moment that it struck the Eiffel Tower. As you look at this dramatic picture, try to imagine what this area of Paris looked like in the moments before and after the lightning strike.

1. How does lightning during a nighttime storm give you information about your surroundings?
2. When a storm is in the distance, why do you see a bolt of lightning before you hear the clap of thunder?
3. What other sources of light can you name?

L2

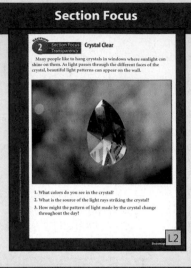

Section Focus Transparency 2 — Crystal Clear

Many people like to hang crystals in windows where sunlight can shine on them. As light passes through the different faces of the crystal, beautiful light patterns can appear on the wall.

1. What colors do you see in the crystal?
2. What is the source of the light rays striking the crystal?
3. How might the pattern of light made by the crystal change throughout the day?

L2

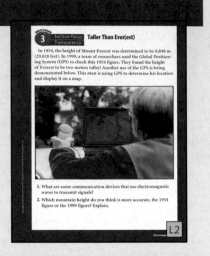

Section Focus Transparency 3 — Taller Than Ever(est)

In 1954, the height of Mount Everest was determined to be 8,848 m (29,028 feet). In 1999, a team of researchers used the Global Positioning System (GPS) to check this 1954 figure. They found the height of Everest to be two meters taller! Another use of the GPS is being demonstrated below. This man is using GPS to determine his location and display it on a map.

1. What are some communication devices that use electromagnetic waves to transmit signals?
2. Which mountain height do you think is more accurate, the 1954 figure or the 1999 figure? Explain.

L2

This is a representation of key blackline masters available in the Teacher Classroom Resources. See Resource Manager boxes within the chapter for additional information.

Key to Teaching Strategies

The following designations will help you decide which activities are appropriate for your students.

L1 Level 1 activities should be appropriate for students with learning difficulties.

L2 Level 2 activities should be within the ability range of all students.

L3 Level 3 activities are designed for above-average students.

ELL ELL activities should be within the ability range of English Language Learners.

COOP LEARN Cooperative Learning activities are designed for small group work.

LS Multiple Learning Styles logos, as described on page 12T, are used throughout to indicate strategies that address different learning styles.

P These strategies represent student products that can be placed into a best-work portfolio.

PBL Problem-Based Learning activities apply real-world situations to learning.

Assessment

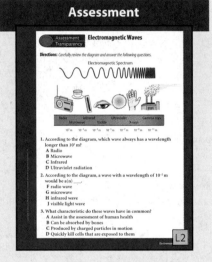

Assessment Transparency — Electromagnetic Waves

Directions: Carefully review the diagram and answer the following questions.

Electromagnetic Spectrum

1. According to the diagram, which wave always has a wavelength longer than 10^1 m?
   A Radio
   B Microwave
   C Infrared
   D Ultraviolet radiation
2. According to the diagram, a wave with a wavelength of 10^{-2} m would be a(n) ____.
   F radio wave
   G microwave
   H infrared wave
   J visible light wave
3. What characteristic do these waves have in common?
   A Assist in the assessment of human health
   B Can be absorbed by bones
   C Produced by charged particles in motion
   D Quickly kill cells that are exposed to them

L2

Teaching

Teaching Transparency 3 — Carrier Wave Modulation

L2

Hands-on Activities

Student Text Lab Worksheet

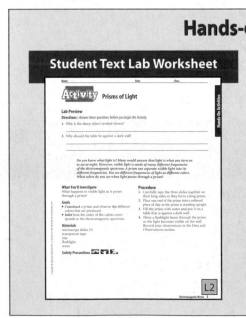

Activity — Prisms of Light

Lab Preview
Directions: Answer these questions before you begin the Activity.
1. Why is the sharp object symbol shown?

2. Why should the table be against a dark wall?

Do you know what light is? Many would answer that light is what you turn on to see at night. However, visible light is made of many different frequencies of the electromagnetic spectrum. A prism is used to separate visible light into its different frequencies. You see different frequencies of light as different colors. What colors do you see when light passes through a prism?

What You'll Investigate
What happens to visible light as it passes through a prism?

Goals
- **Construct** a prism and observe the different colors that are produced.
- **Infer** how the order of the colors corresponds to the electromagnetic spectrum.

Materials
microscope slides (3)
transparent tape
clay
flashlight
water

Safety Precautions

Procedure
1. Carefully tape the three slides together on their long sides so they form a long prism.
2. Place one end of the prism into a softened piece of clay so that the prism is standing vertical.
3. Fill the prism with water and put it on a table that is against a dark wall.
4. Shine a flashlight beam through the prism so the light becomes visible on the wall. Record your observations in the Data and Observations section.

L2

Laboratory Activities

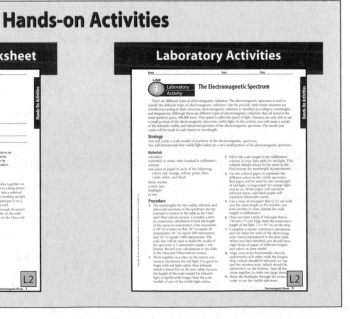

Laboratory Activity 1 — The Electromagnetic Spectrum

There are different types of electromagnetic radiation. The electromagnetic spectrum is used to classify the different types of electromagnetic radiation. Like the periodic table where elements are classified according to their structure, electromagnetic radiation is classified according to wavelengths and frequencies. Although they are different types of electromagnetic radiation, they all travel at the same speed in space, 300,000 km/s. This speed is called the speed of light. Humans are only able to see a small portion of the electromagnetic spectrum, visible light. In this activity, you will create a model of the infrared, visible, and ultraviolet portions of the electromagnetic spectrum. The model you create will be made to scale based on wavelength.

Strategy
You will create a scale model of portions of the electromagnetic spectrum.
You will demonstrate that visible light makes up a very small portion of the electromagnetic spectrum.

Materials
calculator
metric stick or metric ruler (marked in millimeters)
scissors
one piece of paper in each of the following colors: red, orange, yellow, green, blue, violet, white, and black
black marker
scotch tape
flashlight
prism

Procedure
1. The wavelengths for the visible, infrared, and ultraviolet portions of the spectrum are represented in meters in the table in the Data and Observations section. Complete a metric conversion calculation to find the length of the waves in nanometers. One nanometer is 10^{-9} of a meter so that 10^{-9} m equals 50 nanometers, 10^{-7} m equals 100 nanometers, and 10^{-6} m equals 1,000 nanometers. The scale that will be used to build the model of the spectrum is 1 nanometer equals 1 millimeter. Record your calculations in the table in the Data and Observations section.
2. Work together as a class on the metric conversion calculation for red light. It is good to begin with red light rather than infrared, which is listed first in the data table, because the length of the scale model for infrared light is significantly longer than the scale models of any of the visible light colors.

3. Fill in the scale length in the millimeters column in your data table for red light. This column should always be the same as the final answer for wavelength in nanometers.
4. Use the colored paper to represent the different colors in the visible spectrum. Red paper will be used for the wavelength of red light, orange paper for orange light, and so on. White paper will represent infrared waves, and black paper will represent ultraviolet waves.
5. Cut a strip of red paper that is 2.5 cm wide and the same length as the number you have written in your column for scale length in millimeters.
6. Once you have a strip of red paper that is 750 mm (75 cm) long, mark the actual wavelength of red light, 7.5×10^{-7} m, on the strip.
7. Complete a metric conversion calculation and cut strips for each of the electromagnetic waves represented in the data table. When you have finished, you should have eight strips of paper of different lengths and colors in your model.
8. Align your strips horizontally, directly underneath each other, with the longest strip (which should be infrared) on top and the shortest strip (which should be ultraviolet) on the bottom. Tape all the strips together to make one large sheet representing the entire spectrum.
9. Shine the flashlight through the prism in order to see the visible spectrum.

L2

Meeting Different Ability Levels

Content Outline

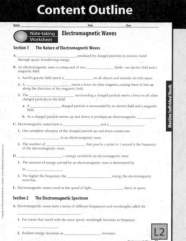

Note-taking Worksheet — **Electromagnetic Waves**

L2

Reinforcement

Section 1 Reinforcement — **The Nature of Electromagnetic Waves**

L2

Enrichment

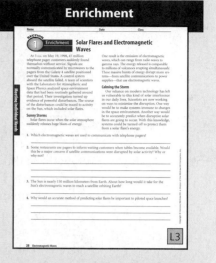

Section 1 Enrichment — **Solar Flares and Electromagnetic Waves**

L3

Directed Reading (English/Spanish)

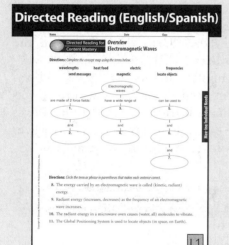

Directed Reading for Content Mastery — *Overview* **Electromagnetic Waves**

L1

Study Guide

Study Guide

Features
• Contains a study guide page for each section of the chapter
• Reviews key concepts
• Includes answer pages

L2

Reading Essentials

Reading Essentials for Glencoe Science
An Interactive Student Workbook

Features
• Condensed core content
• Actively involves students in reading
• Reinforces key vocabulary

L1

Assessment

Test Practice Workbook

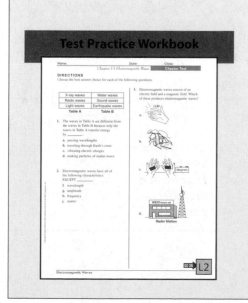

L2

Chapter Review

Electromagnetic Waves

Part A. Vocabulary Review

L2

Chapter Tests

Electromagnetic Waves

I. Testing Concepts

L2

Science Content Background

section 1 The Nature of Electromagnetic Waves

Waves in Space

For many years scientists thought that electromagnetic waves were mechanical waves, and needed a medium in which to travel. Space was thought to be filled with this hypothetical medium, called the *ether*. However, all attempts to detect the ether proved unsuccessful, and near the end of the nineteenth century, it was realized that the ether did not exist.

Properties of Electromagnetic Waves

An electromagnetic wave consists of an electric field and a magnetic field oscillating at right angles to each other and to the direction the wave is traveling. The wave can travel without a medium because of electromagnetic induction: an oscillating electric field creates an oscillating magnetic field; and an oscillating magnetic field creates an oscillating electric field.

section 2 The Electromagnetic Spectrum

Electromagnetic Waves

The electromagnetic spectrum is divided into a number of bands. Each band extends over a range of frequencies or wavelengths.

Infrared Waves

All objects emit electromagnetic waves. The higher the temperature of the object, the higher the frequencies of the emitted electromagnetic waves. Much of the electromagnetic radiation emitted by objects near room temperature is infrared radiation. The surface of the Sun is a temperature of about 6,000 K and much of the electromagnetic radiation it emits is visible light.

X Rays and Gamma Rays

Radiation detectors detect X rays and gamma rays by the tendency of these rays to ionize atoms. Workers who may be exposed to these types of radiation often wear radiation-sensitive badges that determine the amount of radiation the workers have received.

section 3 Using Electromagnetic Waves

Using Radio Waves

Guglielmo Marconi was given credit for inventing radio, but some credit should be given to Nikola Tesla. Tesla invented the means to turn electrical energy into radio waves.

On some nights you can pick up an AM station a few hundred miles from where it was broadcast. This is because the AM radio waves reflect off of the ionosphere. FM radio waves need to travel in a straight line to reach you.

chapter content resources

Internet Resources
For additional content background, visit
ips.msscience.com to:
- access your book online
- find references to related articles in popular science magazines
- access Web links with related content background
- access current events with science journal topics

Print Resources
An Introduction to Electromagnetic Wave Propagation and Antennas, by Shane R. Cloude, Springer Verlag, 1996
Electromagnetic Waves, by Umran S. Inan and Aziz S. Inan, Prentice Hall, 1999
Mad about Physics: Braintwisters, and Paradoxes, and Curiosities, by Christopher Jargodzki and Franklin Potter, John Wiley and Sons, 2000

IDENTIFYING Misconceptions

Find Out What Students Think

Students may think that . . .

Light is very different from other electromagnetic waves such as X rays.

Students can see light, but they cannot see other electromagnetic waves. Thus they may think of them as different entities. Additionally, some electromagnetic waves, such as X rays and ultraviolet rays, often are perceived as hazardous, while light is perceived as harmless.

Activity

Write the following on the board for the class to see. *Which of the following pairs of waves are most similar, "light and sound" or "light and X rays"? Explain your answer.* Ask students to write their answers in their Science Journals. Then have selected students read their answers. Have students try to convince others about their point of view.

Promote Understanding

Demonstration and Activity

Explain that sound waves and water waves need a medium to travel through, while electromagnetic waves can travel through a vacuum. Show students some other similarities among electromagnetic waves.

• Show light reflected by using a mirror and a flashlight.

• Show infrared reflection by using a mirror and a remote control to turn on a television or VCR.

• Show shadow formation by using the flashlight and a board eraser to cast a shadow on the wall.

• Shine an ultraviolet light on a fluorescent rock and then put the eraser in front of it to produce a shadow effect. You can also show developed X-ray film and explain how it shows the shadows of bones.

Explain that visible light, ultraviolet, infrared, and X-ray radiation are all types of electromagnetic radiation.

• Assign student groups one of the following types of waves: radio, microwaves, infrared, visible light, ultraviolet, X rays, and gamma rays. For their type of wave they should use the Internet or library to find the wavelength range, how to detect it, how it is used by people, and if it is harmful to people. If it is harmful to people, they should describe the dangers.

• Have students share their results with other groups until all students have received information about these seven types of electromagnetic waves. Point out to students that the types of electromagnetic waves may have some overlapping frequencies.

Assess

After completing the chapter, see *Identifying Misconceptions* in the Study Guide at the end of the chapter.

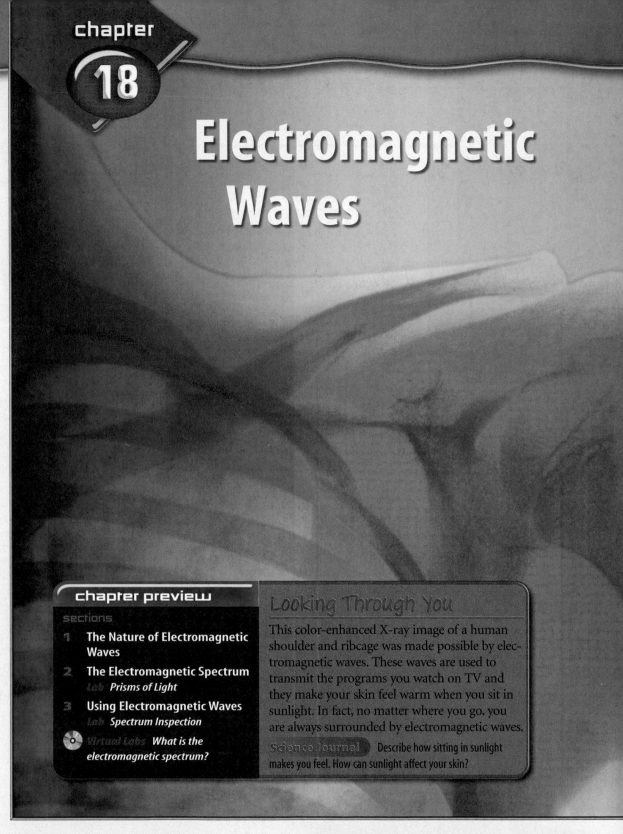

Electromagnetic Waves

Chapter Vocabulary

electromagnetic wave, p. 520
radiant energy, p. 524
electromagnetic spectrum, p. 525
radio wave, p. 526
infrared wave, p. 527
visible light, p. 528
ultraviolet radiation, p. 529
X ray, p. 530
gamma ray, p. 530
carrier wave, p. 536
Global Positioning System, p. 539

Science Journal Accept all reasonable answers.

PowerPoint® Presentations

This CD-ROM is an editable Microsoft® PowerPoint® presentation that includes:
• a pre-made presentation for every chapter
• interactive graphics
• animations
• audio clips
• image bank
• all new section and chapter questions
• Standardized Test Practice
• transparencies
• pre-lab questions for all labs
• Foldables directions
• links to ips.msscience.com

chapter preview

sections

1 The Nature of Electromagnetic Waves

2 The Electromagnetic Spectrum
   Lab Prisms of Light

3 Using Electromagnetic Waves
   Lab Spectrum Inspection

Virtual Labs What is the electromagnetic spectrum?

Looking Through You

This color-enhanced X-ray image of a human shoulder and ribcage was made possible by electromagnetic waves. These waves are used to transmit the programs you watch on TV and they make your skin feel warm when you sit in sunlight. In fact, no matter where you go, you are always surrounded by electromagnetic waves.

Science Journal Describe how sitting in sunlight makes you feel. How can sunlight affect your skin?

Theme Connection

Energy Visible light is only one of the many types of electromagnetic waves. This chapter identifies other types of electromagnetic waves and discusses the ways they are used.

About the Photo

X Rays Medical uses of X rays are well known, but there are other uses for X-ray imaging. Some production lines use X rays to inspect products on a production line to find defects. Fake gems can be detected with X rays and customs inspectors use X rays to detect smuggled goods. Security screening of luggage at commercial airports also uses X rays.

Start-Up Activities

Detecting Invisible Waves

Light is a type of wave called an electromagnetic wave. You see light every day, but visible light is only one type of electromagnetic wave. Other electromagnetic waves are all around you, but you cannot see them. How can you detect electromagnetic waves that can't be seen with your eyes?

1. Cut a slit 2 cm long and 0.25 cm wide in the center of a sheet of black paper.
2. Cover a window that is in direct sunlight with the paper.
3. Position a glass prism in front of the light coming through the slit so it makes a visible spectrum on the floor or table.
4. Place one thermometer in the spectrum and a second thermometer just beyond the red light.
5. Measure the temperature in each region after 5 min.
6. **Think Critically** Write a paragraph in your Science Journal comparing the temperatures of the two regions and offer an explanation for the observed temperatures.

FOLDABLES
Study Organizer

Electromagnetic Waves Make the following Foldable to help you understand the electromagnetic spectrum.

STEP 1 **Collect** 4 sheets of paper and layer them about 1 cm apart vertically. Keep the edges level.

STEP 2 **Fold** up the bottom edges of the paper to form 8 equal tabs.

STEP 3 **Fold** the papers and crease well to hold the tabs in place. Staple along the fold. **Label** each tab as indicated below.

Sequence Turn your Foldable so the staples are at the top. Label the tabs, in order from top to bottom, *Electromagnetic Spectrum, Radio Waves, Microwaves, Infrared Rays, Visible Light, Ultraviolet Light, X Rays,* and *Gamma Rays.* As you read, write facts you learn about each topic under the appropriate tab.

Science Online
Preview this chapter's content and activities at
ips.msscience.com

519

FOLDABLES
Study Organizer

Dinah Zike Study Fold

Student preparation materials for this Foldable are available in the **Chapter FAST FILE** Resources.

Purpose Use the Launch Lab to introduce students to the concept that electromagnetic radiation includes other waves besides light. L2 ELL LS **Kinesthetic**

Preparation Locate a window that gets direct sunlight at the time of day that you wish students to do this activity. Check the weather to make sure the day will be sunny.

Paint the bulbs of the thermometers black to increase the temperature rise for the thermometer placed below the red portion of the spectrum. A computer temperature probe may also be used.

Because some window glass absorbs infrared waves, this activity could also be performed outdoors. Place a piece of white paper in the bottom of a box. Tape the prism to the top edge of a box so the spectrum appears on the paper.

Materials black construction paper, tape, metric ruler, scissors, glass prism, two thermometers, watch

Teaching Strategy Explain to students that the visible light from the sun contains many different wavelengths of radiation, and that the prism spreads the wavelengths apart so they can be seen separately.

Think Critically

The electromagnetic waves from the Sun slightly raise the temperature of the thermometers in the visible spectrum and just below the red light. The thermometer in the infrared region is slightly warmer than the one in the visible region because it absorbs more energy.

Assessment

Oral Ask students which thermometer absorbs more energy: the one in the visible spectrum or the one just below the red light. the one below the red light

Tie to Prior Knowledge

Invisible Waves Ask students to name types of waves or rays that they know exist but that they cannot see. Explain that these waves, which share many of the features of visible light but are also different in some ways, are the subject of this chapter.

---

section 1

The Nature of Electromagnetic Waves

Waves in Space

On a clear day you feel the warmth in the Sun's rays, and you see the brightness of its light. Energy is being transferred from the Sun to your skin and eyes. Who would guess that the way in which this energy is transferred has anything to do with radios, televisions, microwave ovens, or the X-ray pictures that are taken by a doctor or dentist? Yet the Sun and the devices shown in **Figure 1** use the same type of wave to move energy from place to place.

Transferring Energy A wave transfers energy from one place to another without transferring matter. How do waves transfer energy? Waves, such as water waves and sound waves, transfer energy by making particles of matter move. The energy is passed along from particle to particle as they collide with their neighbors. Mechanical waves are the types of waves that use matter to transfer energy.

However, mechanical waves can't travel in the almost empty space between Earth and the Sun. So how can a wave transfer energy from the Sun to Earth? A different type of wave called an electromagnetic wave carries energy from the Sun to Earth. An **electromagnetic wave** is a wave that can travel through empty space or through matter and is produced by charged particles that are in motion.

Figure 1 Getting a dental X ray or talking on a cell phone uses energy carried by electromagnetic waves.

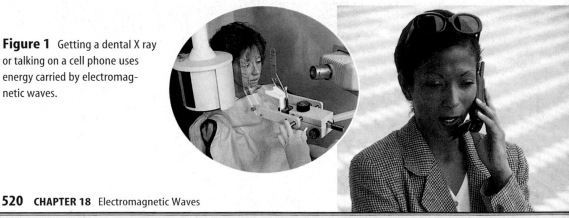

Section 1 Resource Manager

Chapter FAST FILE Resources

Transparency Activity, p. 42

Directed Reading for Content Mastery, pp. 17, 18

Note-taking Worksheets, pp. 31–33

MiniLAB, p. 3

Enrichment, p. 28

Reinforcement, p. 25

Science Inquiry Labs, pp. 35–36

Force due to gravity

Figure 2 A gravitational field surrounds all objects. When a ball is thrown, Earth's gravitational field exerts a downward force on the ball at every point along the ball's path.

Forces and Fields

An electromagnetic wave is made of two parts—an electric field and a magnetic field. These fields are force fields. A force field enables an object to exert forces on other objects, even though they are not touching. Earth is surrounded by a force field called the gravitational field. This field exerts the force of gravity on all objects that have mass.

Reading Check *What force field surrounds Earth?*

How does Earth's force field work? If you throw a ball in the air as high as you can, it always falls back to Earth. At every point along the ball's path, the force of gravity pulls down on the ball, as shown in **Figure 2.** In fact, at every point in space above or at Earth's surface, a ball is acted on by a downward force exerted by Earth's gravitational field. The force exerted by this field on a ball could be represented by a downward arrow at any point in space. The diagram above shows this force field that surrounds Earth and extends out into space. It is Earth's gravitational field that causes the Moon to orbit Earth.

Magnetic Fields You know that magnets repel and attract each other even when they aren't touching. Two magnets exert a force on each other when they are some distance apart because each magnet is surrounded by a force field called a magnetic field. Just as a gravitational field exerts a force on a mass, a magnetic field exerts a force on another magnet and on magnetic materials. Magnetic fields cause other magnets to line up along the direction of the magnetic field.

Earth's gravitational field extends out through space, exerting a force on all masses.
Determine *whether the forces exerted by Earth's gravitational field are attractive or repulsive.*

Topic: Force Fields
Visit to ips.msscience.com for Web links to information about Earth's gravitational and magnetic force fields.

Activity Write a paragraph comparing and contrasting the two force fields.

Quick Demo

Magnets

Materials two doughnut-shaped magnets, pencil

Estimated Time five minutes

Procedure Arrange the magnets so like poles face each other. Place a pencil through the holes and hold the pencil vertically. Observe the behavior of the magnet. The upper magnet seems to float in the air because of its repulsion for the lower magnet. Push the magnets together. Observe that when the pressure is released, the magnets spring apart again.

Reading Check

Answer a gravitational field

Caption Answer

Figure 2 attractive because it causes objects near Earth's surface to fall toward Earth

IDENTIFYING Misconceptions

Speed of Light Stress that the term *speed of light* refers to the speed at which all electromagnetic waves travel. At this speed, light given off by the Sun reaches Earth in about eight minutes.

Science Journal

Aurorae Have students write paragraphs describing how Earth's magnetic field contributes to the aurora borealis and the aurora australis. Earth's magnetic field is strongest near the poles and causes charged particles from space to be deflected toward the poles. There they collide with atoms in the atmosphere, causing them to emit light that is seen as the aurorae. L2 **LS** **Linguistic**
P

Differentiated Instruction

Challenge Light from the Sun takes about eight minutes to reach Earth. Use the speed of light to estimate the distance between Earth and the Sun.
$d = v \times t = (300{,}000 \text{ km/s}) \times (480 \text{ s}) = 144{,}000{,}000 \text{ km}$
L3 **LS** **Logical-Mathematical**

Make a Model

Electromagnetic Waves To help students visualize electromagnetic waves, have them make a model of one. Each student should draw or trace a sine wave on a piece of cardboard, and then draw or trace an identical sine wave on a second piece of cardboard. Have students cut the cardboard, following the outlines of the sine waves. Students should then cut one of the waves in half lengthwise and glue or tape the two halves to either side of the other wave at right angles to it. Make sure students position the waves so that the crest of a vertical wave corresponds to the crest of a horizontal wave.

L2 **IS** **Kinesthetic**

Misconceptions

Only Waves Travel Make sure students understand that as an electromagnetic wave travels, the moving charged particle does not go with it. Only the electric field and its associated magnetic field travel through space.

Figure 3 Force fields surround all magnets and electric charges.

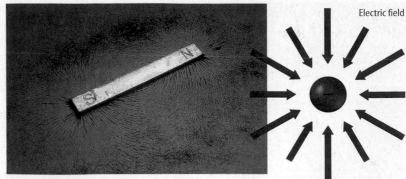

A magnetic field surrounds all magnets. The magnetic field exerts a force on iron filings, causing them to line up with the field.

Electric field

The electric field around an electric charge extends out through space, exerting forces on other charged particles.

Figure 4 Electrons moving in a wire produce a magnetic field in the surrounding space. This field causes iron filings to line up with the field.

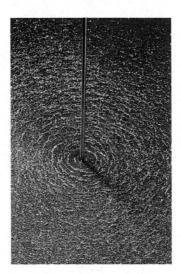

Electric Fields

Recall that atoms contain protons, neutrons, and electrons. Protons and electrons have a property called electric charge. The two types of electric charge are positive and negative. Protons have positive charge and electrons have negative charge.

Just as a magnet is surrounded by a magnetic field, a particle that has electric charge, such as a proton or an electron, is surrounded by an electric field, as shown in **Figure 3.** The electric field is a force field that exerts a force on all other charged particles that are in the field.

Making Electromagnetic Waves

An electromagnetic wave is made of electric and magnetic fields. How is such a wave produced? Think about a wave on a rope. You can make a wave on a rope by shaking one end of the rope up and down. Electromagnetic waves are produced by charged particles, such as electrons, that move back and forth or vibrate.

A charged particle always is surrounded by an electric field. But a charged particle that is moving also is surrounded by a magnetic field. For example, electrons are flowing in a wire that carries an electric current. As a result, the wire is surrounded by a magnetic field, as shown in **Figure 4.** So a moving charged particle is surrounded by an electric field and a magnetic field.

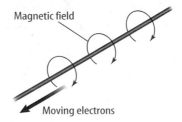

Magnetic field

Moving electrons

LAB DEMONSTRATION

Purpose to help students visualize the concept of a field

Materials magnet, glass or clear-plastic plate, iron filings

Procedure Sprinkle iron filings on the plate. Hold the magnet beneath the plate. Gently shake the plate and have students observe what happens.

Expected Outcome The iron filings align themselves with the magnetic field to produce a map of the field.

Assessment

Why do some of the filings point straight upward? The field is pointing directly upward, or out of the plane of the plate.

Producing Waves When you shake a rope up and down, you produce a wave that moves away from your hand. As a charged particle vibrates by moving up and down or back and forth, it produces changing electric and magnetic fields that move away from the vibrating charge in many directions. These changing fields traveling in many directions form an electromagnetic wave. **Figure 5** shows how the electric and magnetic fields change as they move along one direction.

Properties of Electromagnetic Waves

Like all waves, an electromagnetic wave has a frequency and a wavelength. You can create a wave on a rope when you move your hand up and down while holding the rope. Look at **Figure 5.** Frequency is how many times you move the rope through one complete up and down cycle in 1 s. Wavelength is the distance from one crest to the next or from one trough to the next.

Wavelength and Frequency An electromagnetic wave is produced by a vibrating charged particle. When the charge makes one complete vibration, one wavelength is created, as shown in **Figure 5.** Like a wave on a rope, the frequency of an electromagnetic wave is the number of wavelengths that pass by a point in 1 s. This is the same as the number of times in 1 s that the charged particle makes one complete vibration.

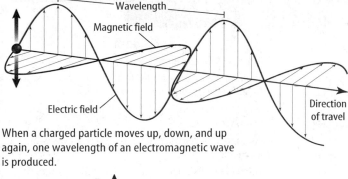

When a charged particle moves up, down, and up again, one wavelength of an electromagnetic wave is produced.

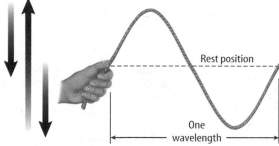

Figure 5 The vibrating motion of an electric charge produces an electromagnetic wave. One complete cycle of vibration produces one wavelength of a wave.
Determine *the magnetic field when the electric field is zero.*

By shaking the end of a rope down, up, and down again, you make one wavelength.

Mini LAB

Observing Electric Fields

Procedure
1. Rub a **hard, plastic comb** vigorously with a **wool sweater or wool flannel shirt.**
2. Turn on a **water faucet** to create the smallest possible continuous stream of water.
3. Hold the comb near the stream of water and observe.

Analysis
1. What happened to the stream of water when you held the comb near it?
2. Explain why the stream of water behaved this way.

Try at Home

Mini LAB

Purpose Students observe the effects of an electric field. ⬜L2
IS Kinesthetic
Materials hard plastic comb, wool sweater or wool flannel shirt, water faucet

Teaching Strategies
• Instruct students not to touch the stream of water with their combs.
• Instruct them to hold the comb near the water stream immediately after rubbing it with the wool.

Analysis
1. The stream of water bent toward the comb.
2. Rubbing the comb with the clothing gave it a charge and produced an electric field. The electric field of the comb attracted the water molecules.

Assessment

Oral Ask students to explain the difference between the electric field they created and the electric field of an electromagnetic wave. The electric field of an electromagnetic wave is changing and moving, but the electric field they generated was stationary.

Try at Home

Discussion

Speed of Light Wave speed = frequency × wavelength and the speed of an electromagnetic wave in space is a constant (300,000 km/s). Use this mathematical relationship to reinforce that when frequency increases, wavelength decreases, and vice versa.

Caption Answer

Figure 5 From the figure, the magnetic field is zero when the electric field is zero.

Differentiated Instruction

Learning Disabled Help students visualize wave properties by asking them to use chenille stems to make models of waves. Ask them to make a high-frequency wave and a low-frequency wave. What is the difference between the two waves? The crests and troughs of high-frequency waves are closer to each other than those of low-frequency waves. ⬜L1 **IS** **Kinesthetic**

Visual Learning

Figure 5 Review with students the locations of crests and troughs of a wave. Clarify that one wavelength is a complete vibration of one wave and can be measured from crest to crest, from trough to trough, or between any two corresponding points on a wave.

Figure 6 The light that reaches Earth today from Alpha Centauri left the star more than four years ago.

Radiant Energy The energy carried by an electromagnetic wave is called **radiant energy.** What happens if an electromagnetic wave strikes a charged particle? The electric field part of the wave exerts a force on this particle and causes it to move. Some of the radiant energy carried by the wave is transferred into the energy of motion of the particle.

Reading Check *What is radiant energy?*

The amount of energy that an electromagnetic wave carries is determined by the wave's frequency. The higher the frequency of the electromagnetic wave, the more energy it has.

The Speed of Light All electromagnetic waves travel through space at the same speed—about 300,000 km/s. This speed sometimes is called the speed of light. Even though light travels incredibly fast, stars other than the Sun are so far away that it takes years for the light they emit to reach Earth. **Figure 6** shows Alpha Centauri, one of the closest stars to our solar system. This star is more than 40 trillion km from Earth.

---

section ① review

Summary

Force Fields

- A charged particle is surrounded by an electric field that exerts forces on other charged particles.
- A magnet is surrounded by a magnetic field that exerts a force on other magnets.
- A moving charged particle is surrounded by electric and magnetic fields.

Electromagnetic Waves

- The changing electric and magnetic fields made by a vibrating electric charge form an electromagnetic wave.
- Electromagnetic waves carry radiant energy.
- All electromagnetic waves travel at the speed of light, which is about 300,000 km/s in empty space.

Self Check

1. **Describe** how electromagnetic waves are produced.
2. **Compare** the energy carried by high-frequency and low frequency electromagnetic waves.
3. **Identify** what determines the frequency of an electromagnetic wave.
4. **Compare and contrast** electromagnetic waves with mechanical waves.
5. **Think Critically** Unlike sound waves, electromagnetic waves can travel in empty space. What evidence supports this statement?

Applying Math

6. **Use Ratios** To go from Earth to Mars, light waves take four min and a spacecraft takes four months. To go to the nearest star, light takes four years. How long would it take the spacecraft to go to the nearest star?

Science Online ips.msscience.com/self_check_quiz

---

section ① review

1. by charged particles in motion
2. A high-frequency electromagnetic wave carries more energy than a low-frequency electromagnetic wave does.
3. the number of times in 1s that the charged particle makes one complete vibration
4. Both mechanical waves and electromagnetic waves carry energy. Mechanical waves require matter through which to travel, but electromagnetic waves don't.
5. Radiant energy reaches Earth from the Sun by traveling through empty space.
6. The following ratios are equal: (spacecraft time to star)/(light time to star) = (spacecraft time to Mars)/(light time to Mars). So: spacecraft time to star = (4 yr)(4 month)/(4 min) = (4 yr)(4 month)(30.5 days/month)(24 h/day)(60 min/h)/(4 min) = (4 yr)(43,920) = 175,687 yr.

The Electromagnetic Spectrum

Electromagnetic Waves

The room you are sitting in is bathed in a sea of electromagnetic waves. These electromagnetic waves have a wide range of wavelengths and frequencies. For example, TV and radio stations broadcast electromagnetic waves that pass through walls and windows. These waves have wavelengths from about 1 m to over 500 m. Light waves that you see are electromagnetic waves that have wavelengths more than a million times shorter than the waves broadcast by radio stations.

Classifying Electromagnetic Waves The wide range of electromagnetic waves with different frequencies and wavelengths forms the **electromagnetic spectrum**. The electromagnetic spectrum is divided into different parts. **Figure 7** shows the electromagnetic spectrum and the names given to the electromagnetic waves in different parts of the spectrum. Even though electromagnetic waves have different names, they all travel at the same speed in empty space—the speed of light. Remember that for waves that travel at the same speed, the frequency increases as the wavelength decreases. So as the frequency of electromagnetic waves increases, their wavelength decreases.

Figure 7 The electromagnetic spectrum consists of electromagnetic waves arranged in order of increasing frequency and decreasing wavelength.

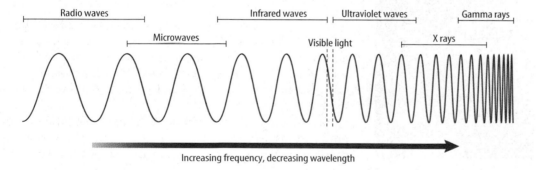

Radio waves · Microwaves · Infrared waves · Visible light · Ultraviolet waves · X rays · Gamma rays

Increasing frequency, decreasing wavelength

---

as you read

What You'll Learn
- **Explain** differences among kinds of electromagnetic waves.
- **Identify** uses for different kinds of electromagnetic waves.

Why It's Important
Electromagnetic waves are used to cook food, to send and receive information, and to diagnose medical problems.

Review Vocabulary
spectrum: a continuous series of waves arranged in order of increasing or decreasing wavelength or frequency

New Vocabulary
- electromagnetic spectrum
- radio wave
- infrared wave
- visible light
- ultraviolet radiation
- X ray
- gamma ray

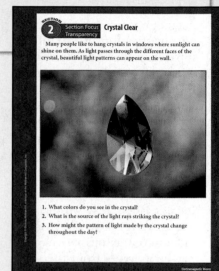

Caption Answer

Figure 8 Possible answers are cell phones, car radios and cordless phones. Remind students that some antennas are inside the device and not visible.

Inquiry Lab

Investigating Electromagnetic Waves

Purpose Students can deepen their understanding of electro-magnetic waves by conducting an investigation of one of the topics introduced in the chapter or another suitable topic of their own choosing.

Estimated Time 1 class period to 3 weeks

Teaching Strategies

• Possible research topics include: how bees and other insects use electromagnetic waves for navigation, how weather and atmospheric conditions affect radio wave transmission, electro-magnetic waves from the stars, ultraviolet rays and skin damage, the use of electromagnetic waves in medicine, the behavior of elec-tromagnetic waves as particles, and the use of electromagnetic waves in communication.

• If you assign this as a large research project, have students write up a proposal and review it with them before they begin.

For additional inquiry activities, see *Science Inquiry Labs.*

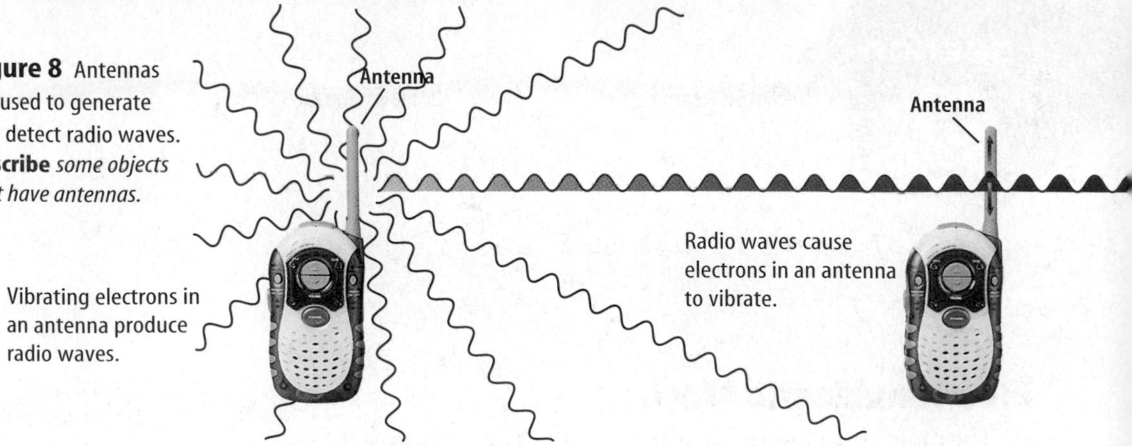

Figure 8 Antennas are used to generate and detect radio waves. **Describe** *some objects that have antennas.*

Antenna

Vibrating electrons in an antenna produce radio waves.

Radio waves cause electrons in an antenna to vibrate.

Antenna

Radio Waves

Electromagnetic waves with wavelengths longer than about 0.001 m are called radio waves. **Radio waves** have the lowest fre-quencies of all the electromagnetic waves and carry the least energy. Television signals, as well as AM and FM radio signals, are types of radio waves. Like all electromagnetic waves, radio waves are produced by moving charged particles. One way to make radio waves is to make electrons vibrate in a piece of metal, as shown in **Figure 8.** This piece of metal is called an antenna. By changing the rate at which the electrons vibrate, radio waves of different frequencies can be produced that travel outward from the antenna.

Detecting Radio Waves These radio waves can cause elec-trons in another piece of metal, such as another antenna, to vibrate, as shown in **Figure 8.** As the electrons in the receiving antenna vibrate, they form an alternating current. This alternat-ing current can be used to produce a picture on a TV screen and sound from a loudspeaker. Varying the frequency of the radio waves broadcast by the transmitting antenna changes the alter-nating current in the receiving antenna. This produces the dif-ferent pictures you see and sounds you hear on your TV.

Figure 9 Towers such as the one shown here are used to send and receive microwaves.

Microwaves Radio waves with wavelengths between about 0.3 m and 0.001 m are called microwaves. They have a higher fre-quency and a shorter wavelength than the waves that are used in your home radio. Microwaves are used to transmit some phone calls, especially from cellular and portable phones. **Figure 9** shows a microwave tower.

Microwave ovens use microwaves to heat food. Microwaves produced inside a microwave oven cause water molecules in your food to vibrate faster, which makes the food warmer.

526 CHAPTER 18 Electromagnetic Waves

Science Journal

Radio Frequencies Have students examine radios they have at home and record the range of fre-quencies spanned by AM and FM bands. Ask stu-dents to determine if AM and FM overlap anywhere, and have them record their findings in their Science Journals. AM stations broadcast in kilo-hertz (kHz) and FM stations broadcast in megahertz (MHz). The bands do not overlap. L2 **LS** **Intrapersonal**

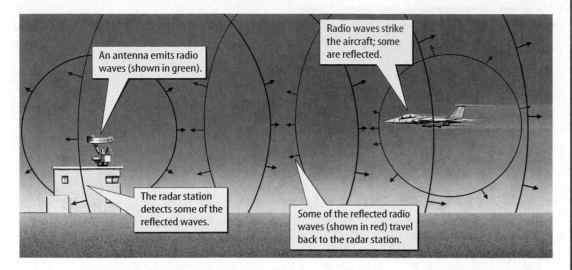

An antenna emits radio waves (shown in green).

Radio waves strike the aircraft; some are reflected.

The radar station detects some of the reflected waves.

Some of the reflected radio waves (shown in red) travel back to the radar station.

Radar

You might be familiar with echolocation, in which sound waves are reflected off an object to determine its size and location. Some bats and dolphins use echolocation to navigate and hunt. Radar, an acronym for RAdio Detecting And Ranging, uses electromagnetic waves to detect objects in the same way. Radar was first used during World War II to detect and warn of incoming enemy aircraft.

 **Reading Check** *What does radar do?*

A radar station sends out radio waves that bounce off an object such as an airplane. Electronic equipment measures the time it takes for the radio waves to travel to the plane, be reflected, and return. Because the speed of the radio waves is known, the distance to the airplane can be determined from the measured time.

An example of radar being used is shown in **Figure 10.** Because electromagnetic waves travel so quickly, the entire process takes only a fraction of a second.

Infrared Waves

You might know from experience that when you stand near the glowing coals of a barbecue or the red embers of a campfire, your skin senses the heat and becomes warm. Your skin may also feel warm near a hot object that is not glowing. The heat you are sensing with your skin is from electromagnetic waves. These electromagnetic waves are called **infrared waves** and have wavelengths between about one thousandth and 0.7 millionths of a meter.

Figure 10 Radar stations use radio waves to determine direction, distance, and speed of aircraft.

Mini LAB

Observing the Focusing of Infrared Rays

Procedure
1. Place a **concave mirror** 2 m to 3 m away from an **electric heater.** Turn on the heater.
2. Place the palm of your hand in front of the mirror and move it back until you feel heat on your palm. Note the location of the warm area.
3. Move the heater to a new location. How does the warm area move?

Analysis
1. Did you observe the warm area? Where?
2. Compare the location of the warm area to the location of the mirror.

Figure 11 A pit viper hunting in the dark can detect the infrared waves emitted from the warm body of its prey.

Figure 12 When objects are heated, their electrons vibrate faster. When the temperature is high enough, the vibrating electrons will emit visible light. **Describe** *an object that emits visible light when heated.*

Detecting Infrared Waves Electromagnetic waves are emitted by every object. In any material, the atoms and molecules are in constant motion. Electrons in the atoms and molecules also are vibrating, and so they emit electromagnetic waves. Most of the electromagnetic waves given off by an object at room temperature are infrared waves and have a wavelength of about 0.000 01 m, or one hundred thousandth of a meter.

Infrared detectors can detect objects that are warmer or cooler than their surroundings. For example, areas covered with vegetation, such as forests, tend to be cooler than their surroundings. Using infrared detectors on satellites, the areas covered by forests and other vegetation, as well as water, rock, and soil, can be mapped. Some types of night vision devices use infrared detectors that enable objects to be seen in nearly total darkness.

Animals and Infrared Waves Some animals also can detect infrared waves. Snakes called pit vipers, such as the one shown in **Figure 11,** have a pit located between the nostril and the eye that detects infrared waves. Rattlesnakes, copperheads, and water moccasins are pit vipers. These pits help pit vipers hunt at night by detecting the infrared waves their prey emits.

Visible Light

As the temperature of an object increases, the atoms and molecules in the object move faster. The electrons also vibrate faster, and produce electromagnetic waves of higher frequency and shorter wavelength. If the temperature is high enough, the object might glow, as in **Figure 12.** Some of the electromagnetic waves that the hot object is emitting are now detectable with your eyes. Electromagnetic waves you can detect with your eyes are called **visible light.** Visible light has wavelengths between about 0.7 and 0.4 millionths of a meter. What you see as different colors are electromagnetic waves of different wavelengths. Red light has the longest wavelength (lowest frequency), and blue light has the shortest wavelength (highest frequency).

Most objects that you see do not give off visible light. They simply reflect the visible light that is emitted by a source of light, such as the Sun or a lightbulb.

Differentiated Instruction

English-Language Learners Have students use magazines to find pictures of animals that hunt at night. Put the pictures on two pieces of poster board, one labeled warm-blooded and the other labeled cold-blooded.

Challenge Have students find out how different kinds of night vision systems work and present their findings to the class. Most night vision systems amplify the small amount of light that already exists. However, some systems make it possible to see infrared even when there is no visible light at all. Infrared light also can be used as an illuminator or flashlight to see objects in total darkness. L3 IS **Linguistic**

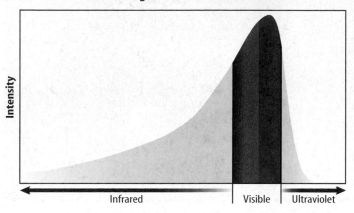

Electromagnetic Waves from the Sun

Intensity

Infrared • Visible • Ultraviolet

Figure 13 The Sun emits mainly infrared waves and visible light. Only about 8 percent of the electromagnetic waves emitted by the Sun are ultraviolet radiation. **Identify** *the electromagnetic waves emitted by the Sun that have the highest intensity.*

Ultraviolet Radiation

Ultraviolet radiation is higher in frequency than visible light and has even shorter wavelengths—between 0.4 millionths of a meter and about ten billionths of a meter. Ultraviolet radiation has higher frequencies than visible light and carries more energy. The radiant energy carried by an ultraviolet wave can be enough to damage the large, fragile molecules that make up living cells. Too much ultraviolet radiation can damage or kill healthy cells.

Figure 13 shows the intensity of electromagnetic waves emitted by the Sun. Too much exposure to the Sun's ultraviolet waves can cause sunburn. Exposure to these waves over a long period of time can lead to early aging of the skin and possibly skin cancer. You can reduce the amount of ultraviolet radiation you receive by wearing sunglasses and sunscreen, and staying out of the Sun when it is most intense.

Reading Check *Why can too much exposure to the Sun be harmful?*

Beneficial Uses of UV Radiation A few minutes of exposure each day to ultraviolet radiation from the Sun enables your body to produce the vitamin D it needs. Most people receive that amount during normal activity. The body's natural defense against too much ultraviolet radiation is to tan. However, a tan can be a sign that overexposure to ultraviolet radiation has occurred.

Because ultraviolet radiation can kill cells, it is used to disinfect surgical equipment in hospitals. In some chemistry labs, ultraviolet rays are used to sterilize goggles, as shown in **Figure 14.**

Figure 14 Sterilizing devices, such as this goggle sterilizer, use ultraviolet waves to kill organisms on the equipment.

Science Journal

Body Temperature Since warm-blooded animals generate their own body heat, they don't have to rely on their environment to maintain their temperature and can inhabit a wide range of climates. However, warm-blooded animals spend a large amount of energy maintaining their body temperatures, so they need to eat a large amount of food. Cold-blooded animals don't expend as much energy to heat their bodies, so they need to eat less food. Pit vipers would have an easier time detecting warm-blooded animals. Investigate the requirements for a career working with animals at the zoo.

Use an Analogy

Sunscreen and Ozone Compare the role of sunscreen to that of the ozone layer. Point out that just as sunscreen blocks some ultraviolet radiation from the skin and prevents burning, the ozone layer blocks some ultraviolet radiation from reaching Earth's surface, where it could be harmful to the cells of living things. Without the ozone shield, there probably would be very little life on Earth.

Quick Demo

Popcorn

Materials microwave popcorn, a few kernels of unpopped corn, microwave oven, napkins

Estimated Time 15 minutes

Procedure Prepare the popcorn just before needed or have a student do it. Examine the kernels of unpopped corn and compare them with some popped kernels. Discuss what happened and why. The energy carried by microwaves is absorbed by water in the popcorn kernel. The water in the kernel is heated until steam is formed. This is why the popcorn is warm. The pressure from the steam causes the kernel to explode and turn inside out.

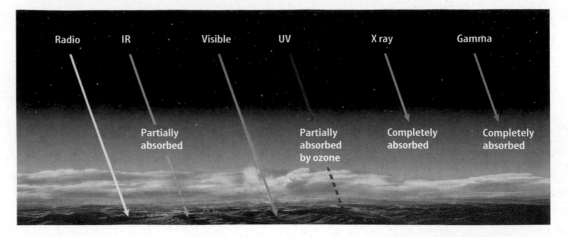

Figure 15 Earth's atmosphere serves as a shield to block some types of electromagnetic waves from reaching the surface.

The Ozone Layer Much of the ultraviolet radiation arriving at Earth is absorbed in the upper atmosphere by ozone, as shown in **Figure 15.** Ozone is a molecule that has three oxygen atoms and is formed high in Earth's atmosphere.

Chemical compounds called CFCs, which are used in air conditioners and refrigerators, can react with ozone molecules and break them apart. There is evidence that these reactions play a role in forming the seasonal reduction in ozone over Antarctica, known as the ozone hole. To prevent this, the use of CFC's is being phased out.

Ultraviolet radiation is not the only type of electromagnetic wave absorbed by Earth's atmosphere. Higher energy waves of X rays and gamma rays also are absorbed. The atmosphere is transparent to radio waves and visible light and partially transparent to infrared waves.

X Rays and Gamma Rays

Ultraviolet rays can penetrate the top layer of your skin. **X rays,** with an even higher frequency than ultraviolet rays, have enough energy to go right through skin and muscle. A shield made from a dense metal, such as lead, is required to stop X rays.

Gamma rays have the highest frequency and, therefore, carry the most energy. Gamma rays are the hardest to stop. They are produced by changes in the nuclei of atoms. When protons and neutrons bond together in nuclear fusion or break apart from each other in nuclear fission, enormous quantities of energy are released. Some of this energy is released as gamma rays.

Just as too much ultraviolet radiation can hurt or kill cells, too much X-ray or gamma radiation can have the same effect. Because the energy of X rays and gamma rays is greater, the exposure that is needed to cause damage is much less.

Curriculum Connection

Math X rays were discovered accidentally by Wilhelm Roentgen in 1895. Because they were a mystery and *x* is the usual symbol for an unknown in mathematics, they were named X rays. Have students find out what the unit named for Roentgen measures and what other units are used to make similar measurements. A *roentgen* is a unit for absorbed energy or dose from nuclear radiation. Other units for absorbed dose are the *gray* and the *rad*.

Using High-Energy Electromagnetic Radiation The fact that X rays can pass through the human body makes them useful for medical diagnosis, as shown in **Figure 16.** X rays pass through the less dense tissues in skin and other organs. These X rays strike a film, creating a shadow image of the denser tissues. X-ray images help doctors detect injuries and diseases, such as broken bones and cancer. A CT scanner uses X rays to produce images of the human body as if it had been sliced like a loaf of bread.

Although the radiation received from getting one medical or dental X ray is not harmful, the cumulative effect of numerous X rays can be dangerous. The operator of the X-ray machine usually stands behind a shield to avoid being exposed to X rays. Lead shields or aprons are used to protect the parts of the patient's body that are not receiving the X rays.

Using Gamma Rays Although gamma rays are dangerous, they also have beneficial uses, just as X rays do. A beam of gamma rays focused on a cancerous tumor can kill the tumor. Gamma radiation also can kill disease-causing bacteria in food. More than 1,000 Americans die each year from *Salmonella* bacteria in poultry and *E. coli* bacteria in meat. Although gamma radiation has been used since 1963 to kill bacteria in food, this method is not widely used in the food industry.

Figure 16 Dense tissues such as bone absorb more X rays than softer tissues do. Consequently, dense tissues leave a shadow on an X ray film that can be used to diagnose medical and dental conditions.

Astronomy with Different Wavelengths

Some astronomical objects produce no visible light and can be detected only through the infrared and radio waves they emit. Some galaxies emit X rays from regions that do not emit visible light. Studying stars and galaxies like these using only visible light would be like looking at only one color in a picture. **Figure 17** shows how different electromagnetic waves can be used to study the Sun.

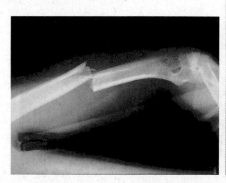
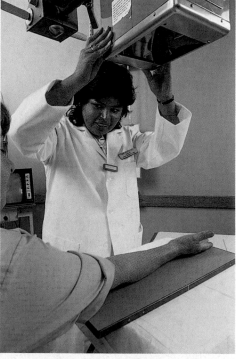

Active Reading

Jigsaw In this collaborative learning technique individuals become experts on a portion of a text and share their expertise with a small group, called their home group. Assign each person in each group an expert number (1 through 5, for example). Have students gather into the expert groups that correspond to the number they were assigned. Have them read, discuss, and master chapter concepts and determine how best to teach these concepts to their home groups. Have students return to their home groups and share the content they learned in their expert groups. Have students use the Jigsaw strategy as they learn about different types of electromagnetic waves.

Visualizing the Universe

Have students examine the pictures and read the captions. Then ask the following questions.

Why have astronomers only recently studied wavelengths other than visible light? Possible answer: Detecting these different types of waves requires technologies that were not always available.

Why might the Sun or other celestial objects look different when various types of waves are being detected? Possible answer: While an object may be a strong emitter of one type of wave, it may not emit another type as well. Dust, atmosphere, or other objects may block out certain wavelengths too.

Activity

Telescope Wavelength Have students look at photographs of various celestial objects from a variety of different types of telescopes. Have students locate the type of wavelength used for each photograph on the electromagnetic spectrum. L2 **LS** **Visual-Spatial**

Figure 17

For centuries, astronomers studied the universe using only the visible light coming from planets, moons, and stars. But many objects in space also emit X rays, ultraviolet and infrared radiation, and radio waves. Scientists now use telescopes that can detect these different types of electromagnetic waves. As these images of the Sun reveal, the new tools are providing more information of objects in the universe.

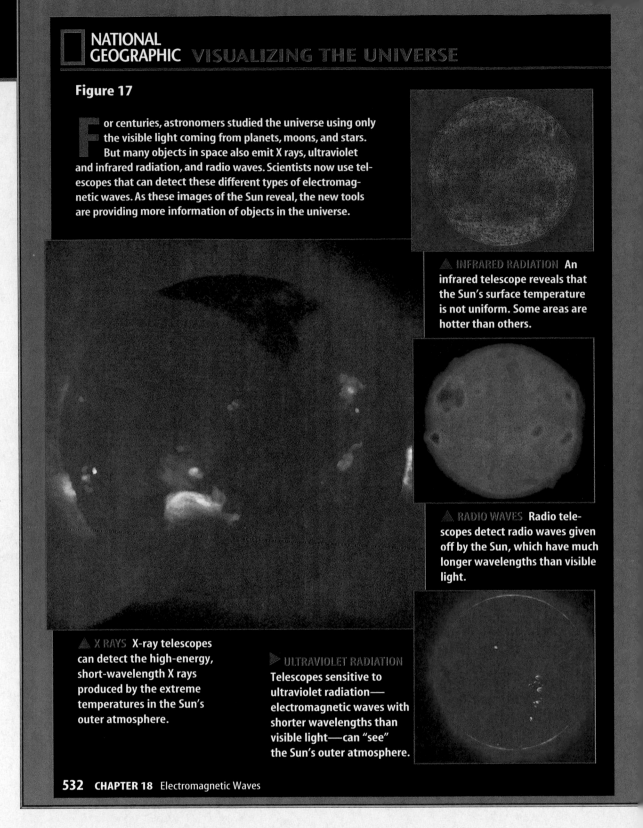

▲ **INFRARED RADIATION** An infrared telescope reveals that the Sun's surface temperature is not uniform. Some areas are hotter than others.

▲ **RADIO WAVES** Radio telescopes detect radio waves given off by the Sun, which have much longer wavelengths than visible light.

▲ **X RAYS** X-ray telescopes can detect the high-energy, short-wavelength X rays produced by the extreme temperatures in the Sun's outer atmosphere.

▶ **ULTRAVIOLET RADIATION** Telescopes sensitive to ultraviolet radiation—electromagnetic waves with shorter wavelengths than visible light—can "see" the Sun's outer atmosphere.

532 CHAPTER 18 Electromagnetic Waves

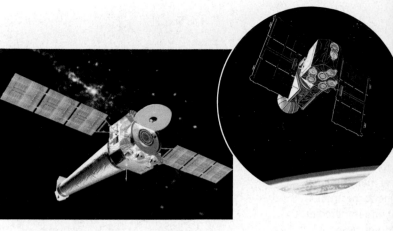

 **Satellite Observations** Recall from **Figure 15** that Earth's atmosphere blocks X rays, gamma rays, most ultraviolet rays, and some infrared rays. However, telescopes in orbit above Earth's atmosphere can detect the electromagnetic waves that can't pass through the atmosphere. **Figure 18** shows three such satellites—the Extreme Ultraviolet Explorer (EUVE), the Chandra X-Ray Observatory, and the Infrared Space Observatory (ISO).

Figure 18 Launching satellite observatories above Earth's atmosphere is the only way to see the universe at electromagnetic wavelengths that are absorbed by Earth's atmosphere.

section 2 review

Summary

Radio Waves

- Radio waves have wavelengths longer than about 0.3 m.

Infrared Waves and Visible Light

- Infrared waves have wavelengths between about one thousandth and 0.7 millionths of a meter.

- The wavelengths of infrared waves emitted by an object get shorter as the object's temperature increases.

- Visible light waves have wavelengths between about 0.7 and 0.4 millionths of a meter.

Ultraviolet Waves, X Rays, and Gamma Rays

- Ultraviolet radiation has wavelengths between about 0.4 millionths of a meter and 10 billionths of a meter.

- Prolonged exposure to ultraviolet waves from the Sun can cause skin damage.

- X rays and gamma rays are the most energetic electromagnetic waves.

Self Check

1. **Explain** why ultraviolet radiation is more damaging to living cells than infrared waves.

2. **Compare and contrast** X rays and gamma rays.

3. **Describe** how infrared detectors on satellites can be used to obtain information about the location of vegetation on Earth's surface.

4. **Explain** why X rays and gamma rays coming from space do not reach Earth's surface.

5. **Explain** how the energy of electromagnetic waves change as the wavelength of the waves increase.

6. **Think Critically** Why does the Sun emit mostly infrared waves and visible light, and Earth emits infrared waves?

Applying Skills

7. **Make a table** listing five objects in your home that produce electromagnetic waves. In another column, list next to each object the type of electromagnetic wave or waves produced. In a third column describe each object's use.

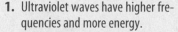 ips.msscience.com/self_check_quiz

SECTION 2 The Electromagnetic Spectrum **533**

section 2 review

1. Ultraviolet waves have higher frequencies and more energy.
2. Gamma rays have a higher frequencies, shorter wavelengths, and more energy than X rays do.
3. Vegetation tends to be cooler than its surroundings and will look darker on an image from an infrared detector.
4. They are absorbed by Earth's atmosphere.
5. As the wavelength increases, the frequency and the energy of the wave decreases.
6. The frequencies of the electromagnetic waves emitted by an object increase as the temperature increases. The Sun is much hotter than Earth, and so it emits more higher-frequency electromagnetic radiation than Earth emits.
7. Possible answers include TV, radio, lights and stove. Check students work.

SECTION 2 The Electromagnetic Spectrum **533**

Real-World Question

Purpose Students observe that light is composed of various colors or frequencies. L2 LS **Visual-Spatial**

Process Skills observe, infer, recognize cause and effect, formulate models

Time Required 40 minutes

Procedure

Safety Precautions Caution students to be careful not to break the glass slides.

Teaching Strategy The prism may need to be moved around to produce a spectrum.

Conclude and Apply

1. red, orange, yellow, green, blue, violet
2. Raising the flashlight so it is above the prism causes the colors to shift downward. Lowering the flashlight shifts the colors upward.
3. The order of the colors doesn't change.
4. Red light waves have been bent the least and violet light waves have been bent the most.
5. The amount of bending increases as the wavelength decreases and the frequency increases.

✔ Assessment

Process Have students hypothesize about the role of the water in the prism. Then have them test their hypotheses by removing the water and seeing the effect this has on the spectrum. The water makes the different colors separate more. Without the water, the spectrum is harder to see. Use **PASC**, p. 93.

Prisms Of Light

Do you know what light is? Many would answer that light is what you turn on to see at night. However, white light is made of many different frequencies of the electromagnetic spectrum. A prism can separate white light into its different frequencies. You see different frequencies of light as different colors. What colors do you see when light passes through a prism?

Real-World Question

What happens to visible light as it passes through a prism?

Goals

■ **Construct** a prism and observe the different colors that are produced.
■ **Infer** how the bending of light waves depends on their wavelength.

Materials

microscope slides (3)	flashlight
transparent tape	water
clay	*prism

*Alternate materials

Safety Precautions

Procedure

1. Carefully tape the three slides together on their long sides so they form a long prism.
2. Place one end of the prism into a softened piece of clay so the prism is standing upright.
3. Fill the prism with water and put it on a table that is against a dark wall.
4. Shine a flashlight beam through the prism so the light becomes visible on the wall.

534 CHAPTER 18 Electromagnetic Waves

Conclude and Apply

1. **List** the order of the colors you saw on the wall.
2. **Describe** how the position of the colors on the wall changes as you change the direction of the flashlight beam.
3. **Describe** how the order of colors on the wall changes as you change the direction of the flashlight beam.
4. **Infer** which color light waves have changed direction, or have been bent, the most after passing through the prism. Which color has been bent the least?
5. **Infer** how the bending of a light wave depends on its wavelength.

Communicating Your Data

Compare your conclusions with those of other students in your class. **For more help, refer to the Science Skill Handbook.**

Communicating Your Data

Have each student make a labeled diagram that illustrates the procedure and results of the experiment.

Using Electromagnetic Waves

Telecommunications

In the past week, have you spoken on the phone, watched television, done research on the Internet, or listened to the radio? Today you can talk to someone far away or transmit and receive information over long distances almost instantly. Thanks to telecommunications, the world is becoming increasingly connected through the use of electromagnetic waves.

Using Radio Waves

Radio waves usually are used to send and receive information over long distances. Using radio waves to communicate has several advantages. For example, radio waves pass through walls and windows easily. Radio waves do not interact with humans, so they are not harmful to people like ultraviolet rays or X rays are. So most telecommunication devices, such as TVs, radios, and telephones, use radio waves to transmit information such as images and sounds. **Figure 19** shows how radio waves can be used to transmit information—in this case transmitting information that enables sounds to be reproduced at a location far away.

as you read

What You'll Learn

■ **Describe** different ways of using electromagnetic waves to communicate.
■ **Compare and contrast** AM and FM radio signals.

Why It's Important

Using electromagnetic waves to communicate enables you to contact others worldwide.

Review Vocabulary
satellite: a natural or artificial object that orbits a planet

New Vocabulary
● carrier wave
● Global Positioning System

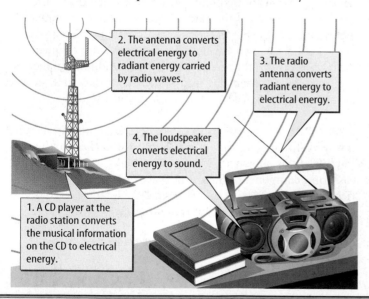

2. The antenna converts electrical energy to radiant energy carried by radio waves.

3. The radio antenna converts radiant energy to electrical energy.

4. The loudspeaker converts electrical energy to sound.

1. A CD player at the radio station converts the musical information on the CD to electrical energy.

Figure 19 Radio waves are used to transmit information that can be converted to other forms of energy, such as electrical energy and sound.

535

---

1 Motivate

Bellringer

Section Focus Transparencies also are available on the Interactive Chalkboard CD-ROM.
L2 ELL

3 Section Focus Transparency — **Taller Than Ever(est)**

In 1954, the height of Mount Everest was determined to be 8,848 m (29,028 feet). In 1999, a team of researchers used the Global Positioning System (GPS) to check this 1954 figure. They found the height of Everest to be two meters taller! Another use of the GPS is being demonstrated below. This man is using GPS to determine his location and display it on a map.

1. What are some communication devices that use electromagnetic waves to transmit signals?
2. Which mountain height do you think is more accurate, the 1954 figure or the 1999 figure? Explain.

Tie to Prior Knowledge

Phones Ask students whether they have ever used a cordless, cellular, or digital phone. Point out that all of these communication devices work using electromagnetic waves.

Visual Learning

Figure 19 Review with students the generation of an electromagnetic wave in an antenna shown in this figure. What determines the frequency of the wave? how fast the charge moves up and down in the antenna What determines the wavelength of the wave? The wavelength is determined by the frequency and the speed of the waves. L2 LS Visual-Spatial

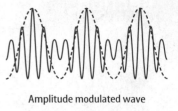

Figure 20 A signal can be carried by a carrier wave in two ways—amplitude modulation or frequency modulation.

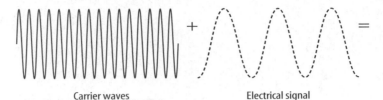

Carrier waves + Electrical signal =

Amplitude modulated wave

or

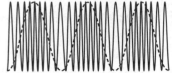

Frequency modulated wave

Pulsars Bell-Burnell was a graduate student working for Hewish. Bell-Burnell was responsible for collecting the data and observing the pulses of radio waves. Pulsars are small, heavy, collapsed stars called neutron stars that rotate about once per second. They have enormous magnetic fields. They emit beams of radio waves once per rotation. If Earth happens to be on the path of the beam, we detect a regular periodic radio signal. Because it is so regular, it is easy to understand how it may have been interpreted as a signal from an alien civilization.

Research Have students research other types of radio waves from space and their sources.

Reading Check

Answer in radio transmission, the variation of the frequency of a carrier wave to carry information

INTEGRATE Astronomy

Pulsars and Little Green Men A type of collapsed star called a pulsar emits pulses of radio waves at extremely regular intervals. Pulsars were first discovered by Jocelyn Bell-Burnell and Anthony Hewish in 1967. Puzzled by a regular sequence of radio pulses they detected, they considered the possibility that the pulses might be coming from an alien civilization. They jokingly labeled the pulses LGMs, for "little green men". Soon other signals were detected that proved the pulses were coming from collapsed stars. Research the role Jocelyn Bell-Burnell played in the discovery of pulsars.

Radio Transmission How is information, such as images or sounds, broadcast by radio waves? Each radio and television station is assigned a particular frequency at which it broadcasts radio waves. The radio waves broadcast by a station at its assigned frequency are the carrier waves for that station. To listen to a station you tune your radio or television to the frequency of the station's carrier waves. To carry information on the carrier wave, either the amplitude or the frequency of the carrier wave is changed, or modulated.

Amplitude Modulation The letters *AM* in AM radio stand for amplitude modulation, which means that the amplitude of the carrier wave is changed to transmit information. The original sound is transformed into an electrical signal that is used to vary the amplitude of the carrier wave, as shown in **Figure 20.** Note that the frequency of the carrier wave doesn't change—only the amplitude changes. An AM receiver tunes to the frequency of the carrier wave. In the receiver, the varying amplitude of the carrier waves produces an electrical signal. The radio's loudspeaker uses this electric signal to produce the original sound.

Frequency Modulation FM radio works in much the same way as AM radio, but the frequency instead of the amplitude is modulated, as shown in **Figure 20.** An FM receiver contains electronic components that use the varying frequency of the carrier wave to produce an electric signal. As in an AM radio, this electric signal is converted into sound waves by a loudspeaker.

Reading Check   *What is frequency modulation?*

Science Journal

Early Communication Have students write about how they think information was spread before any type of electronic communication existed. Challenge them to describe the speed and accuracy of such communication and compare it with ways they communicate today. L1 LS **Linguistic**

Cultural Diversity

Early Observations in Astronomy In 1054, Chinese astronomers observed a massive supernova explosion where the Crab Nebula now exists. A pulsar now can be detected at the heart of this nebula. Have students calculate how many years ago the supernova exploded and how many times their age this is. L2 LS **Logical-Mathematical**

Telephones

A telephone contains a microphone in the mouthpiece that converts a sound wave into an electric signal. The electric signal is carried through a wire to the telephone switching systems. There, the signal might be sent through other wires or be converted into a radio or microwave signal for transmission through the air. The electric signal also can be converted into a light wave for transmission through fiber-optic cables.

At the receiving end, the signal is converted back to an electric signal. A speaker in the earpiece of the phone changes the electric signal into a sound wave.

Reading Check *What device converts sound into an electric signal?*

Applying Math   Solve a Simple Equation

WAVELENGTH OF AN FM STATION You are listening to an FM radio station with a frequency of 94.9 MHz, which equals 94,900,000 Hz. What is the wavelength of these radio waves. Use the wave speed equation $v = \lambda f$, and assume the waves travel at the speed of light, 300,000.0 km/s.

Solution

1 *This is what you know:*
- frequency: $f = 94,900,000$ Hz
- wave speed: $v = 300,000.0$ km/s

2 *This is what you need to find:*
- wavelength: $\lambda = ?$ m

3 *This is the procedure you need to use:*

Solve the wave equation for wavelength, λ, by dividing each side by the frequency, f. Then substitute the known values for frequency and wave speed into the equation you derived:

$$\lambda = \frac{v}{f} = \frac{300,000.0 \text{ km/s}}{94,900,000 \text{ Hz}} = \frac{300,000.0 \text{ km } 1/\text{s}}{94,900,000 \text{ } 1/\text{s}}$$

$$= 0.00316 \text{ km} = 0.00316 \text{ km} \times (1,000 \text{ m/km})$$

$$= 3.16 \text{ m}$$

4 *Check your answer:*

Multiply your answer by the given frequency. The result should be the given wave speed.

Practice Problems

1. Your friend is listening to an AM station with a frequency of 1,520 kHz. What is the wavelength of these radio waves?

2. What is the frequency of the radio waves broadcast by an AM station if the wave length of the radio waves is 500.0 m?

 Science Online | For more practice, visit ips.msscience.com/math_practice

SECTION 3   Using Electromagnetic Waves   **537**

Activity

Signal Flowchart Encourage students to make flowcharts detailing the transmission of a signal from one telephone to another, using the text description as a guide. L1 IS **Visual-Spatial**

Teacher FYI

Fiber-Optic Cables Fiber-optic cables have several advantages over copper wires. They are much smaller, will never rust or corrode, and aren't susceptible to electronic interference. A single pair of fiber-optic cables can carry more than 1,000 conversations simultaneously. Several of these cables could fit through the eye of a needle.

Reading Check

Answer a microphone

Applying Math

National Math Standards
Correlation to Mathematics Objectives
1, 2, 9

Answers to Practice Problems
1. 197.4 m
2. 600.0 kHz or 600,000 Hz

A A cordless phone can be used more than 0.5 km from its base station.

B Cell phones communicate with a base station that can be several kilometers away, or more.

Use Science Words

Word Meaning Ask students to find the origin of the term *cell phone*. The term *cell phone* refers to the cell, or the area that one tower can serve. A cell tower can cover up to a 15 km radius. Tower cells overlap so that coverage isn't lost. L2 **LS** **Linguistic**

Discussion

Cell Phone Limits Why is there a limit to the number of people who can talk on cell phones in a particular cell at the same time? Each phone uses a different frequency. If all of the assigned frequencies are being used, no other phones can be used at that time. L3 **LS** **Logical-Mathematical**

Make a Model

Geosynchronous Satellites Have students find the locations of two or three geosynchronous communications satellites above Earth and make models showing their positions. Geosynchronous satellites orbit Earth directly above the equator once every 24 hours, so that each is always above the same point on the equator. They maintain an altitude of about 35,800 km. L2 **LS** **Visual-Spatial**

Science Online

Topic: Satellite Communications
Visit ips.msscience.com for Web links to information about how satellites are used in around-the-world communications.

Activity Create a table listing satellites from several countries, their names and their communications function.

Remote Phones A telephone does not have to transmit its signal through wires. In a cordless phone, the electrical signal produced by the microphone is transmitted through an antenna in the phone to the base station. **Figure 21A** shows how incoming signals are transmitted from the base station to the phone. A cellular phone communicates with a base station that can be many kilometers away. The base station uses a large antenna, as shown in **Figure 21B,** to communicate with the cell phone and with other base stations in the cell phone network.

Pagers The base station also is used in a pager system. When you dial a pager, the signal is sent to a base station. From there, an electromagnetic signal is sent to the pager. The pager beeps or vibrates to indicate that someone has called. With a touch-tone phone, you can transmit numeric information, such as your phone number, which the pager will receive and display.

Communications Satellites

How do you send information to the other side of the world? Radio waves can't be sent directly through Earth. Instead, radio signals are sent to satellites. The satellites can communicate with other satellites or with ground stations. Some communications satellites are in geosynchronous orbit, meaning each satellite remains above the same point on the ground.

538 **CHAPTER 18** Electromagnetic Waves

Curriculum Connection

Astronomy The color of a star is an indication of its temperature. The coolest stars are reddish, and the hottest stars are slightly blue. Encourage students to look outside at night and attempt to identify different colors of stars. L2 **LS** **Naturalist**

Differentiated Instruction

Challenge Ask students to find the difference between a digital signal and analog signal. A digital signal is composed of combinations of 1's and 0's that carry information. An analog signal transmits information as a continually varying waveform. L3 **LS** **Linguistic**

The Global Positioning System

Satellites also are used as part of the **Global Positioning System,** or GPS. GPS is used to locate objects on Earth. The system consists of satellites, ground-based stations, and portable units with receivers, as illustrated in **Figure 22.**

A GPS receiver measures the time it takes for radio waves to travel from several satellites to the receiver. This determines the distance to each satellite. The receiver then uses this information to calculate its latitude, longitude, and elevation. The accuracy of GPS receivers ranges from a few hundred meters for handheld units, to several centimeters for units that are used to measure the movements of Earth's crust.

Figure 22 The signals broadcast by GPS satellites enable portable, handheld receivers to determine the position of an object or person.

---

section 3 review

Summary

Using Radio Waves

- Radio waves are used for communication because they can pass through most objects.
- Amplitude modulation transmits information by modifying the amplitude of a carrier wave.
- Frequency modulation transmits information by modifying the frequency of a carrier wave.

Cordless Phones and Cell Phones

- Cordless phones use radio waves to transmit signals between the base and the handset.
- Cellular phones use radio waves to transmit signals between the phone and cell phone radio towers.

Communications Satellites

- Communications satellites in geosynchronous orbits relay radio signals from one part of the world to another.
- The Global Positioning System uses radio waves to enable a user to accurately determine their position on Earth's surface.

Self Check

1. **Describe** how a cordless phone is different from a cell phone.
2. **Explain** how a communications satellite is used.
3. **Describe** the types of information a GPS receiver provides.
4. **Describe** how an AM radio signal is used to transmit information.
5. **Think Critically** Explain why ultraviolet waves are not used to transmit signals to and from communications satellites.

Applying Skills

6. **Make an events chain** showing the sequence of energy transformations that occur when live music is broadcast by a radio station and played by a radio.
7. **Make a Diagram** showing how geosynchronous satellites and ground stations could be used to send information from you to someone on the other side of Earth.

---

section 3 review

1. A cordless phone sends and receives radio signals to and from a base unit that relays the signals through a phone line. A cell phone sends and receives radio signals to and from a broadcasting tower or cell.
2. Ground stations broadcast radio waves to a satellite that re-broadcasts the signals to another ground station.
3. latitude, longitude, and elevation
4. The amplitude of the carrier wave broadcast by the station is varied.
5. The ozone layer absorbs ultraviolet waves.
6. microphone converts sound waves to a varying electric current, varying current in antenna produces radio waves, radio antenna converts radio waves to varying current, speaker converts current to sound waves
7. Diagrams should show radio waves going from ground stations to satellites back to ground stations.

Real-World Question

Purpose Students identify the color spectrum of a light source and relate the wavelength of the colors to the temperature of the light source. **L2** **IS** **Logical-Mathematical**

Process Skills observe, interpret data, infer, communicate, compare and contrast, recognize cause and effect, form operational definitions, form a hypothesis, design an experiment

Time Required 40 minutes

Materials Dimmer switches which can be obtained at local hardware or discount stores.

Alternate Materials Use clear 4-, 15-, 25-, 60-, and 100-watt lightbulbs if a dimmer is not available.

Safety Precautions Caution students that current from a 120-V AC wall socket can be lethal. Remind students that lightbulbs can become hot.

Design Your Own

Spectrum Inspection

Goals
- **Design** an experiment that determines the relationship between brightness and the wavelengths emitted by a lightbulb.
- **Observe** the wavelengths of light emitted by a lightbulb as its brightness changes.

Possible Materials
diffraction grating
power supply with variable resistor switch
clear, tubular lightbulb and socket
red, yellow, and blue colored pencils

Safety Precautions

WARNING: *Be sure all electrical cords and connections are intact and that you have a dry working area. Do not touch the bulbs as they may be hot.*

Real-World Question

You've heard the term "red-hot" used to describe something that is unusually hot. When a piece of metal is heated it may give off a red glow or even a yellow glow. All objects emit electromagnetic waves. How do the wavelengths of these waves depend on the temperature of the object?

Form a Hypothesis

The brightness of a lightbulb increases as its temperature increases. Form a hypothesis describing how the wavelengths emitted by a lightbulb will change as the brightness of a lightbulb changes.

Test Your Hypothesis

Make a Plan

1. **Decide** how you will determine the effect of lightbulb brightness on the colors of light that are emitted.

2. As shown in the photo at the right, you will look toward the light through the diffraction grating to detect the colors of light emitted by the bulb. The color spectrum will appear to the right and to the left of the bulb.

3. **List** the specific steps you will need to take to test your hypothesis. Describe precisely what you will do in each step. Will you first test the bulb at a bright or dim setting? How many settings will you test? (Try at least three.) How will you record your observations in an organized way?

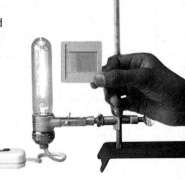

Alternative Inquiry Lab

Extend the Experience What do the spectrums of different types of lightbulbs look like? Have students extend their experiment by testing and observing the spectrums produced by a variety of other types of lightbulbs. Students can also observe the spectrums created by different wattages of lightbulbs. Students can hold different colored cellophane in front of an incandescent bulb and compare the spectrums produced as the light passes through the colored filter.

4. **List** the materials you will need for your experiment. Describe exactly how and in which order you will use these materials.

5. **Identify** any constants and variables in your experiment.

Follow Your Plan

1. Make sure your teacher approves your plan before you start.

2. **Perform** your experiment as planned.

3. While doing your experiment, write down any observations you make in your Science Journal.

● Analyze Your Data

1. Use the colored pencils to draw the color spectrum emitted by the bulb at each brightness.

2. Which colors appeared as the bulb became brighter? Did any colors disappear?

3. How did the wavelengths emitted by the bulb change as the bulb became brighter?

4. **Infer** how the frequencies emitted by the lightbulb changed as it became hotter.

● Conclude and Apply

1. **Infer** If an object becomes hotter, what happens to the wavelengths it emits?

2. How do the wavelengths that the bulb emits change if it is turned off?

3. **Infer** from your results whether red stars or yellow stars are hotter.

Compare your results with others in your class. How many different colors were seen?

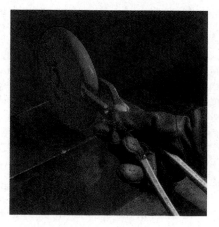

LAB 541

✔ Assessment

Process Predict how the spectrum you see in the diffraction grating would differ if you looked at different types of bulbs, such as a colored lightbulb, neon light, or fluorescent bulb. Test your predictions. The spectrum will vary with the nature of the light source and its temperature. Use **Performance Assessment in the Science Classroom**, p. 93.

Communicating Your Data

Have students compare the drawings they made of the spectrum for the different settings of the dimmer switch.

● Form a Hypothesis

Students may hypothesize that the spectra remain the same regardless of the brightness of the light source.

● Test Your Hypothesis

Possible Procedures Align the grating with the filament and observe the spectrum. Vary power to the lamp and observe the spectrum again.

Teaching Strategy Students should hold the diffraction grating near their eyes for best observations.

Expected Outcome Students should observe all colors from bright light but decreased blue from dimmer light.

● Analyze Your Data

1. Drawings should show all colors present from bright lights, but less blue as the brightness decreases.
2. All colors are visible when the bulb is bright. Bluish colors fade in dimmer light.
3. Short wavelengths are visible from brighter light.
4. Short wavelengths are visible from a hotter bulb.

● Conclude and Apply

1. It emits shorter wavelengths.
2. The bulb cools off, so the wavelengths emitted shift toward the red and infrared end of the spectrum.
3. yellow stars

TIME SCIENCE AND HISTORY

SCIENCE CAN CHANGE THE COURSE OF HISTORY!

Hedy Lamarr, actor and inventor

Hopping the Frequencies

Ringggg. There it is—that familiar beep! Out come all the cellular phones. At any given moment, a million wireless signals are flying through the air—and not just cell phone signals. With radio and television signals, Internet data, and even Global Positioning System information, the air seems like a pretty crowded place. How does a cellular phone pick out its own signal from among the clutter? The answer lies in a concept developed in 1940 by Hedy Lamarr.

Lamarr was born in Vienna, Austria. In 1937, she left Austria to escape Hitler's invading Nazi army. She also left to pursue a career as an actor. And she became a famous movie star.

In 1940, Lamarr came up with an idea to keep radio signals that guided torpedoes from being jammed. Her idea, called frequency hopping, involved breaking the radio signal that was guiding the torpedo into tiny parts and rapidly changing their frequency. The enemy would not be able to keep up with the frequency changes and thus would not be able to divert the torpedo from its target.

Spread Spectrum

Lamarr's idea was ahead of its time. The digital technology that allowed efficient operation of her system wasn't invented until decades later. However, after 1962, frequency hopping was adopted and used in U.S. military communications. It was the development of wireless phones, however, that benefited the most from Lamarr's concept.

Cordless phones and other wireless technologies operate by breaking their signals into smaller parts, called packets. The frequency of the packets switches rapidly, preventing interference with other calls and enabling millions of callers to use the same narrow band of frequencies.

A torpedo is launched during World War II.

Brainstorm How are you using wireless technology in your life right now? List ways it makes your life easier. Are there drawbacks to some of the uses for wireless technology? What are they?

Science online

For more information, visit ips.msscience.com/time

Reviewing Main Ideas

Section 1 The Nature of Electromagnetic Waves

1. Vibrating charges generate vibrating electric and magnetic fields. These vibrating fields travel through space and are called electromagnetic waves.

2. Electromagnetic waves have wavelength, frequency, amplitude, and carry energy.

Section 2 The Electromagnetic Spectrum

1. Radio waves have the longest wavelength and lowest energy. Radar uses radio waves to locate objects.

2. All objects emit infrared waves. Most objects you see reflect the visible light emitted by a source of light.

3. Ultraviolet waves have a higher frequency and carry more energy than visible light.

4. X rays and gamma rays are highly penetrating and can be dangerous to living organisms.

Section 3 Using Electromagnetic Waves

1. Communications systems use electromagnetic waves to transmit information.

2. Radio and TV stations use modulated carrier waves to transmit information.

3. Cordless and cell phones use radio waves to communicate between the mobile phone and a base station.

4. Radio waves are used to send information between communications satellites and ground stations on Earth.

Reviewing Main Ideas

Summary statements can be used by students to review the major concepts of the chapter.

Visualizing Main Ideas

See student page.

Science Online

Visit ips.msscience.com
 /self_check_quiz
 /interactive_tutor
 /vocabulary_puzzlemaker
 /chapter_review
 /standardized_test

Assessment Transparency

For additional assessment questions, use the *Assessment Transparency* located in the transparency book.

Visualizing Main Ideas

Copy and complete the following spider map about electromagnetic waves.

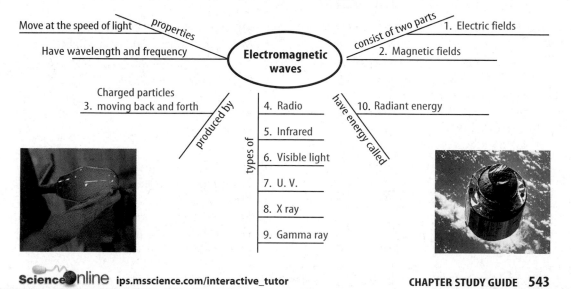

Move at the speed of light — properties
Have wavelength and frequency

Electromagnetic waves

consist of two parts
1. Electric fields
2. Magnetic fields

produced by
Charged particles
3. moving back and forth

types of
4. Radio
5. Infrared
6. Visible light
7. U. V.
8. X ray
9. Gamma ray

have energy called
10. Radiant energy

Science Online ips.msscience.com/interactive_tutor

CHAPTER STUDY GUIDE 543

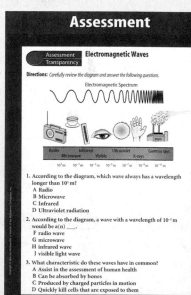

Assessment

Assessment Transparency Electromagnetic Waves

Directions: *Carefully review the diagram and answer the following questions.*

Electromagnetic Spectrum

Radio Infrared Ultraviolet Gamma rays
 Microwave Visible X-rays
10^1 m 10^{-1} m 10^{-3} m 10^{-5} m 10^{-7} m 10^{-9} m 10^{-11} m

1. According to the diagram, which wave always has a wavelength longer than 10^1 m?
 A Radio
 B Microwave
 C Infrared
 D Ultraviolet radiation

2. According to the diagram, a wave with a wavelength of 10^{-2} m would be a(n) ____.
 F radio wave
 G microwave
 H infrared wave
 J visible light wave

3. What characteristic do these waves have in common?
 A Assist in the assessment of human health
 B Can be absorbed by bones
 C Produced by charged particles in motion
 D Quickly kill cells that are exposed to them

Electromagnetic Waves

Identifying Misconceptions   **Assess**

Use the assessment as follow-up to the identifying misconceptions activity at the beginning of the chapter.

Procedure Have students compare and contrast visible light with any two other types of electromagnetic waves by completing charts giving the wavelength range, means of detection, and uses of the three types of electromagnetic waves.

Expected Outcome Students should realize that light is similar to electromagnetic radiation of other wavelengths.

chapter **18** **Review**

Using Vocabulary

1. Infrared waves have higher frequencies and more energy than radio waves do.

2. In radio communication, a carrier wave is a radio wave of a particular frequency that is modulated in either amplitude or frequency to carry information.

3. A communications satellite is a geosynchronous satellite used to transfer communication signals. GPS is a system of satellites and receivers used to determine locations on Earth.

4. Visible light is the section of the electromagnetic spectrum that we see with our eyes. Ultraviolet radiation is electromagnetic radiation at a slightly higher frequency than visible light.

5. Gamma rays have a higher frequency and more energy than X rays do and can cause more harm to living things.

6. An electromagnetic wave consists of oscillating electric and magnetic fields. The energy carried by an electromagnetic wave is called radiant energy.

7. Radio stations broadcast information using carrier waves. An AM radio signal carries information by changing or modulating the amplitude of the carrier wave.

8. An infrared wave has a slightly lower frequency than red light, and an ultraviolet wave has a slightly higher frequency than violet light.

Checking Concepts

9. B	14. C
10. D	15. B
11. B	16. C
12. C	17. A
13. A	18. A

Thinking Critically

19. Radio waves are not absorbed by the atmosphere and many common materials.

544 CHAPTER REVIEW

Using Vocabulary

carrier wave p. 536	infrared wave p. 527
electromagnetic spectrum p. 525	radiant energy p. 524
	radio wave p. 526
electromagnetic wave p. 520	ultraviolet radiation p. 529
	visible light p. 528
gamma ray p. 530	X ray p. 530
Global Positioning System p. 539	

Explain the difference between the terms in each of the following pairs.

1. infrared wave—radio wave

2. radio wave—carrier wave

3. communications satellite—Global Positioning System

4. visible light—ultraviolet radiation

5. X ray, gamma ray

6. electromagnetic wave—radiant energy

7. carrier wave—AM radio signal

8. infrared wave—ultraviolet wave

Checking Concepts

Choose the word or phrase that best answers the question.

9. Which of the following transformations can occur in a radio antenna?
   A) radio waves to sound waves
   B) radio waves to an electric signal
   C) radio waves to infrared waves
   D) sound waves to radio waves

10. Electromagnetic waves with wavelengths between about 0.7 millionths of a meter and 0.4 millionths of a meter are which of the following?
    A) gamma rays   C) radio waves
    B) microwaves   D) visible light

---

11. Which of the following is the speed of light in space?
    A) 186,000 km/s   C) 3,000,000 km/s
    B) 300,000 km/s   D) 30,000 km/s

12. Which of the following types of electromagnetic waves has the lowest frequency?
    A) infrared waves   C) radio waves
    B) visible light   D) gamma rays

13. Compared to an electric charge that is not moving, a moving electric charge is surrounded by which of the following additional fields?
    A) magnetic   C) electric
    B) microwave   D) gravitational

14. Most of the electromagnetic waves emitted by an object at room temperature are which of the following?
    A) visible light   C) infrared waves
    B) radio waves   D) X rays

15. Which of the following color of visible light has the highest frequency?
    A) green   C) yellow
    B) blue   D) red

16. Which type of electromagnetic waves are completely absorbed by Earth's atmosphere?
    A) radio waves   C) gamma rays
    B) infrared waves   D) visible light

17. Sunburn is caused by excessive exposure to which of the following?
    A) ultraviolet waves
    B) infrared waves
    C) visible light
    D) gamma rays

18. How does the frequency of a gamma ray change as its wavelength decreases?
    A) It increases.
    B) It decreases.
    C) It doesn't change.
    D) The frequency depends on the speed.

Science Online ips.msscience.com/vocabulary_puzzlemaker

Use the ExamView® Pro Testmaker CD-ROM to:

- create multiple versions of tests
- create modified tests with one mouse click for inclusion students
- edit existing questions and add your own questions
- build tests aligned with state standards using built-in State Curriculum Tags
- change English tests to Spanish with one mouse click and vice versa

Thinking Critically

19. Infer why communications systems usually use radio waves to transmit information.

20. Classify List the colors of the visible light spectrum in order of increasing frequency.

21. Compare and contrast an electromagnetic wave with a transverse wave traveling along a rope.

22. Explain Some stars form black holes when they collapse. These black holes sometimes can be found by detecting X rays and gamma rays that are emitted as matter falls into the black hole. Explain why it would be difficult to detect these X rays and gamma rays using detectors at Earth's surface.

Use the table below to answer question 23.

Speed of Light in Various Materials

Materials	Speed (km/s)
Air	300,000
Water	226,000
Polystyrene Plastic	189,000
Diamond	124,000

23. Calculate A radio wave has a frequency of 500,000 Hz. If the radio wave has the same frequency in air as in water, what is the ratio of the wavelength of the radio wave in air to its wavelength in water?

24. Explain how you could determine if there are electromagnetic waves traveling in a closed, completely dark room in a building.

25. Infer Light waves from a distant galaxy take 300 million years to reach Earth. How does the age of the galaxy when it emitted the light waves compare with the age of the galaxy when we see the light waves?

 Science Online ips.msscience.com/chapter_review

26. Concept Map Electromagnetic waves are grouped according to their frequencies. In the following concept map, write each frequency group and one way humans make use of the electromagnetic waves in that group. For example, in the second set of ovals, you might write *X rays* and *to see inside the body*.

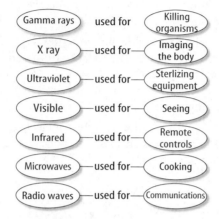

Performance Activities

27. Oral Presentation Explain to the class how a radio signal is generated, transmitted, and received.

28. Poster Make a poster showing the parts of the electromagnetic spectrum. Show how frequency, wavelength, and energy change throughout the spectrum. How is each wave generated? What are some uses of each?

Applying Math

29. Distance How long would it take a radio signal to travel from Earth to the Moon, a distance of 384,000 km?

30. Wavelength The frequency of a popular AM radio station is 720 kHz. What is the wavelength of the radio waves broadcast by this station?

CHAPTER REVIEW **545**

20. red, orange, yellow, green, blue, violet

21. Both carry energy and are transverse waves, but an electromagnetic wave can travel without a medium and a transverse wave on a rope must have a medium in which to travel.

22. The Earth's atmosphere absorbs gamma rays and X rays before they reach the surface.

23. Use $v = f\lambda$, then because the frequencies are equal $(\lambda_{air}/\lambda_{water}) = (v_{air}/v_{water}) = (300,000 \text{ km/s})/(226,000 \text{ km/s}) = 1.3$.

24. Accept all reasonable responses such as all objects in the room that contain atoms and molecules give off infrared waves at room temperature, see if you can send or receive a cell phone call, or see if a portable radio works in the room.

25. the galaxy will be 300 million years older

26. See student page.

Performance Activities

27. Students should show or explain sound being converted into electrical signals and these signals being transmitted as electromagnetic waves, received, and reconverted into sound waves. Use **PASC**, p. 143.

28. The spectrum should cover electromagnetic waves from radio to gamma rays. Use **PASC**, p. 145.

Applying Math

National Math Standards
1, 2, 9

29. $d = st$, so $t = d/s = (384,000 \text{ km})/(300,000 \text{ km/s}) = 1.3$ s.

30. $\lambda = v/f = (300,000 \text{ km/s})/(720,000 \text{ Hz}) = 0.42$ km.

☑ Assessment Resources

📂 **Reproducible Masters**

Chapter *Fast File* Resources
Chapter Review, pp. 35–36
Chapter Tests, pp. 37–40
Assessment Transparency Activity, p. 47

Glencoe Science Web site
Chapter Review Test
Standardized Test Practice

Glencoe Technology
🔧 Assessment Transparency
🔵 Exam*View*® Pro Testmaker
💿 MindJogger Videoquiz
🔵 Interactive Chalkboard

Answer Sheet A practice answer sheet can be found at ips.msscience.com/answer_sheet.

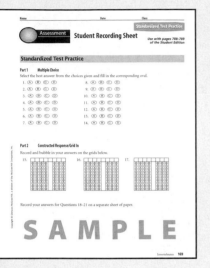

Part 1 | Multiple Choice

1. C	**6.** B
2. D	**7.** C
3. B	**8.** B
4. A	**9.** D
5. A	

Part 2 | Short Response

10. 0.12 m

11. Yes, a charged particle that is moving is surrounded by a magnetic field. An electric current consisting of moving electrons flows in the wire.

12. 100,000,000 Hz or 100 MHz

13. As the temperature increases, the charged particles in the object vibrate and move faster. As a result, the frequency of vibration of the charged particles increases. This causes the frequency of the electromagnetic waves produced to increase and their wavelength to decrease.

Part 1 | Multiple Choice

Record your answers on the answer sheet provided by your teacher or on a sheet of paper.

1. Which of the following types of electromagnetic waves has a frequency greater than visible light?
  A. infrared waves   **C.** ultraviolet waves
  B. radio waves   **D.** microwaves

2. Which of the following properties of a transverse wave is the distance from one crest to the next?
  A. intensity   **C.** frequency
  B. amplitude   **D.** wavelength

3. Which of the following types of electromagnetic waves enables your body to produce vitamin D?
  A. gamma rays
  B. ultraviolet waves
  C. visible light
  D. infrared waves

Use the illustration below to answer question 4.

Electromagnetic Waves from the Sun

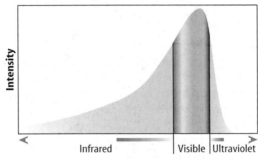

4. How does the intensity of ultraviolet waves emitted by the Sun change as the wavelength of the ultraviolet waves decreases?
  A. The intensity increases.
  B. The intensity decreases.
  C. The intensity doesn't change.
  D. The intensity increases, then decreases.

---

5. The color of visible light waves depends on which of the following wave properties?
  A. wavelength   **C.** direction
  B. amplitude   **D.** speed

6. Which of the following is NOT true about electromagnetic waves?
  A. They can travel through matter.
  B. They move by transferring matter.
  C. They are produced by vibrating charges.
  D. They can travel through empty space.

Use the illustration below to answer question 7.

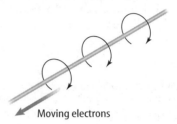

Moving electrons

7. Which of the following is represented by the circular lines around the current-carrying wire?
  A. direction of current
  B. electric and magnetic field lines
  C. magnetic field lines
  D. electric field lines

8. How are gamma rays produced?
  A. by vibrating electric fields
  B. by vibrating magnetic fields
  C. by the absorption of infrared waves
  D. by nuclear fission or fusion

9. Earth's atmosphere is transparent to which type of electromagnetic waves?
  A. gamma rays
  B. ultraviolet waves
  C. infrared waves
  D. radio waves

---

14. X rays pass through soft tissue such as organs and muscles. The X rays do not pass through hard tissue which creates a shadow image on the X ray film.

15. $t = d/s = (80,000,000 \text{ km})/(300,000 \text{ km/s}) = 267 \text{ s}$

Part 3 | Open Ended

16. The radar station sends out radio waves. The radio waves strike an airplane and are reflected back. The radar unit determines the time it took for the wave to travel back to the detector after it was reflected. Using the equation $d = st$, the distance of the airplane to the detector can be calculated.

17. Areas covered by vegetation tend to be cooler than the surrounding area. Areas of vegetation and the surrounding warmer areas can be mapped using emitted infrared waves.

18. Use **Figure 20** to check student's drawings.

Part 2 | Short Response/Grid In

Record your answers on the answer sheet provided by your teacher or on a sheet of paper.

Use the photograph below to answer question 10.

10. If the microwaves produced in a microwave oven have a frequency of 2,450 MHz, what is the wavelength of the microwaves?

11. You turn on a lamp that is plugged into an electric outlet. Does a magnetic field surround the wire that connects the lamp to the outlet? Explain.

12. A carrier wave broadcast by a radio station has a wavelength of 3.0 m. What is the frequency of the carrier wave?

13. Explain how the wavelengths of the electromagnetic waves emitted by an object change as the temperature of the object increases.

14. Explain why X rays can form images of dense tissues in the human body.

15. If the planet Mars is 80,000,000 km from Earth, how long will it take an electromagnetic wave to travel from Earth to Mars?

Test-Taking Tip

Recheck Answers Double check your answers before turning in the test.

Part 3 | Open Ended

Record your answers on a sheet of paper.

16. Describe the sequence of events that occur when a radar station detects an airplane and determines the distance to the plane.

17. Explain why infrared detectors on satellites can detect regions covered by vegetation.

18. The carrier waves broadcast by a radio station are altered in order to transmit information. The two ways of altering a carrier wave are amplitude modulation (AM) and frequency modulation (FM). Draw a carrier wave, an AM wave, and an FM wave.

19. Describe the effect of the ozone layer on electromagnetic waves that strike Earth's atmosphere.

20. List the energy conversions that occur when a song recorded on a CD is broadcast as radio waves and then reproduced as sound.

Use the illustration below to answer questions 21 and 22.

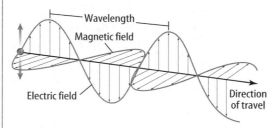

21. Explain how the vibrating electric and magnetic fields are produced.

22. Infer how the directions of the electric field and the magnetic field are related to the direction that the electromagnetic wave travels.

Rubrics

The following rubrics are sample scoring devices for short response and open-ended questions.

Short Response

Points	Description
2	The student demonstrates a thorough understanding of the science of the task. The response may contain minor flaws that do not detract from the demonstration of a thorough understanding.
1	The student has provided a response that is only partially correct.
0	The student has provided a completely incorrect solution or no response at all.

Open Ended

Points	Description
4	The student demonstrates a thorough understanding of the science of the task. The response may contain minor flaws that do not detract from the demonstration of a thorough understanding.
3	The student demonstrates an understanding of the science of the task. The response is essentially correct and demonstrates an essential but less than thorough understanding of the science.
2	The student demonstrates only a partial understanding of the science of the task. Although the student may have used the correct approach to a solution or may have provided a correct solution, the work lacks an essential understanding of the underlying science concepts.
1	The student demonstrates a very limited understanding of the science of the task. The response is incomplete and exhibits many flaws.
0	The student provides a completely incorrect solution or no response at all.

---

19. The ozone layer absorbs most of the ultraviolet waves that strike Earth's atmosphere.

20. 1. information on CD is converted to electrical energy; 2. antenna at radio station converts electrical energy to radiant energy; 3. receiving radio antenna converts radio waves (radiant energy) to electrical energy; 4. electrical energy converted to mechanical energy that creates sound waves

21. A charged particle is surrounded by an electric field. The movement of the charged particle creates a magnetic field. The vibrating charge produces vibrating electric and magnetic fields that travel outward from the charge and generate each other as they travel outward.

22. The wave travels at a right angle to the electric and magnetic fields.

Section/Objectives	Standards		Labs/Features
Chapter Opener	**National**	**State/Local**	**Launch Lab:** Bending Light, p. 549 **Foldables,** p. 549
	See pp. 16T–17T for a Key to Standards.		
Section 1 Properties of Light 🕐 2 sessions 📷 1 block 1. **Describe** the wave nature of light. 2. **Explain** how light interacts with materials. 3. **Determine** why objects appear to have color.	National Content Standards: UCP.2, UCP.3, UCP.5, A.1, A.2, B.1, B.2		**MiniLAB:** Observing Colors in the Dark, p. 551
Section 2 Reflection and Mirrors 🕐 2 sessions 📷 1 block 4. **Explain** how light is reflected from rough and smooth surfaces. 5. **Determine** how mirrors form an image. 6. **Describe** how concave and convex mirrors form an image.	National Content Standards: UCP.2, UCP.3, UCP.5, A.1, A.2, B.2		**Integrate Physics,** p. 557 **Science Online,** p. 558 **Visualizing Reflections in Concave Mirrors,** p. 559 **Lab:** Reflection from a Plane Mirror, p. 561
Section 3 Refraction and Lenses 🕐 3 sessions 📷 1.5 blocks 7. **Determine** why light rays refract. 8. **Explain** how convex and concave lenses form images.	National Content Standards: UCP.2, UCP.3, UCP.5, A.1, A.2, B.2		
Section 4 Using Mirrors and Lenses 🕐 4 sessions 📷 2 blocks 9. **Explain** how microscopes magnify objects. 10. **Explain** how telescopes make distant objects visible. 11. **Describe** how a camera works.	National Content Standards: UCP.2, UCP.3, UCP.5, A.1, A.2, B.2, G.3		**MiniLAB:** Forming an Image with a Lens, p. 568 **Integrate History,** p. 569 **Science Online,** p. 570 **Lab:** Image Formation by a Convex Lens, p. 572 **Oops! Accidents in Science:** Eyeglasses: Inventor Unknown, p. 574

Lab Materials	Reproducible Resources	Section Assessment	Technology
Launch Lab: 2 paper cups, 2 pennies, water	**Chapter FAST FILE Resources** Foldables Worksheet, p. 17 Directed Reading Overview, p. 19 Note-taking Worksheets, pp. 35–38	GLENCOE'S ASSESSMENT ADVANTAGE	**TeacherWorks** includes: • Interactive Teacher Edition • Lesson Planner with calendar • Access to all program blacklines • Correlations to standards • Web links
MiniLAB: 6 pieces of paper of different colors (10 cm × 10 cm each), pencil, darkened room	**Chapter FAST FILE Resources** Transparency Activity, p. 48 MiniLAB, p. 3 Lab Activities, pp. 9–12, 13–16 Enrichment, p. 31 Reinforcement, p. 27 Directed Reading, p. 20	**Portfolio** Assessment, p. 554 **Performance** MiniLAB, p. 551 Applying Skills, p. 554 **Content** Section Review, p. 554	Section Focus Transparency Guided Reading Audio Program Interactive Chalkboard CD-ROM
Lab: flashlight, protractor, metric ruler, scissors, tape, small plane mirror (at least 10 cm per side), black construction paper, modeling clay, white unlined paper	**Chapter FAST FILE Resources** Transparency Activity, p. 49 Enrichment, p. 32 Reinforcement, p. 28 Directed Reading, p. 20 Lab Worksheet, pp. 5–6 **Mathematics Skill Activities,** p. 47	**Portfolio** Visual Learning, p. 556 **Performance** Applying Skills, p. 560 **Content** Section Review, p. 560	Section Focus Transparency Guided Reading Audio Program Interactive Chalkboard CD-ROM
Need materials? Contact Science Kit at 1-800-828-7777 or www.sciencekit.com on the Internet.	**Chapter FAST FILE Resources** Transparency Activity, p. 50 Enrichment, p. 33 Reinforcement, p. 29 Directed Reading, p. 21 Transparency Activity, pp. 53–54	**Portfolio** Cultural Diversity, p. 563 Science Journal, p. 565 **Performance** Applying Math, p. 566 **Content** Section Review, p. 566	Section Focus Transparency Teaching Transparency Virtual Labs CD-ROM Guided Reading Audio Program Interactive Chalkboard CD-ROM
MiniLAB: glass test tube filled with water and sealed with stopper, card (10 cm × 10 cm), pencil **Lab:** convex lens, modeling clay, meterstick, flashlight, masking tape, cardboard with a white surface (20 cm square)	**Chapter FAST FILE Resources** Transparency Activity, p. 51 MiniLAB, p. 4 Enrichment, p. 34 Reinforcement, p. 30 Directed Reading, pp. 21, 22 Lab Worksheet, pp. 7–8 **Lab Management and Safety,** p. 64 **Science Inquiry Labs,** pp. 39–40	**Portfolio** Assessment, p. 571 **Performance** MiniLAB, p. 568 Applying Math, p. 571 **Content** Section Review, p. 571	Section Focus Transparency Guided Reading Audio Program Interactive Chalkboard CD-ROM Video Lab

End of Chapter Assessment

GLENCOE'S ASSESSMENT ADVANTAGE

Blackline Masters	Technology	Professional Series
Chapter FAST FILE Resources Chapter Review, pp. 41–42 Chapter Tests, pp. 43–46 **Standardized Test Practice,** pp. 79–82	MindJogger Videoquiz Virtual Labs CD-ROM ExamView® Pro Testmaker TeacherWorks CD-ROM Interactive Chalkboard CD-ROM	**Performance Assessment in the Science Classroom (PASC)**

Transparencies

Section Focus

Section Focus Transparency 1 — Wavelength — Chapter 23

These are water lilies floating in a pond on a sunny day. How would these lilies appear at night or on an overcast day? The French painter Claude Monet was very fascinated by light, and he often painted water lilies like these.

1. Describe the colors you see in this picture. How might they differ if the picture were taken at night?
2. What happens to light that strikes the water? What happens when it strikes the lilies?
3. Give some examples of the effects of the Sun's energy on Earth.

L2

Section Focus Transparency 2 — Just Popped up for a Shave

This large mirror is going to be used in a reflecting telescope. Astronomers use reflecting telescopes to view faint stars and galaxies. According to the company that helped make this mirror, it is "so smooth that if it were expanded to the size of the U.S., there would be no bumps higher than a speed bump."

1. Why is it important that the mirror is very smooth?
2. The technician is applying a thin coat of aluminum. Why?
3. How can a mirror make something appear larger or smaller?

L2

Section Focus Transparency 3 — Sea View

This view comes to you through the bottom of a glass-bottom boat. Glass-bottom boat tours are fun ways to get a glimpse of the underwater world. As you look at this picture, think about why you might get a better underwater view with a glass-bottom boat than you could looking over the side of an ordinary boat.

1. Beginning at the Sun, describe the different mediums that light traveled through to reach the camera's film.
2. If you are wading, can you look into the ocean and see the bottom? Explain.
3. Sunlight travels hundreds of miles through the atmosphere, but it can only travel a fraction of that into the ocean. Why is this?

L2

This is a representation of key blackline masters available in the Teacher Classroom Resources. See Resource Manager boxes within the chapter for additional information.

Key to Teaching Strategies

The following designations will help you decide which activities are appropriate for your students.

L1 Level 1 activities should be appropriate for students with learning difficulties.

L2 Level 2 activities should be within the ability range of all students.

L3 Level 3 activities are designed for above-average students.

ELL ELL activities should be within the ability range of English Language Learners.

COOP LEARN Cooperative Learning activities are designed for small group work.

LS Multiple Learning Styles logos, as described on page 12T, are used throughout to indicate strategies that address different learning styles.

P These strategies represent student products that can be placed into a best-work portfolio.

PBL Problem-Based Learning activities apply real-world situations to learning.

Assessment

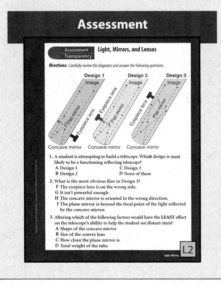

Assessment Transparency — Light, Mirrors, and Lenses

Directions: Carefully review the diagrams and answer the following questions.

Design 1 — Image
Design 2 — Image
Design 3 — Image

1. A student is attempting to build a telescope. Which design is most likely to be a functioning reflecting telescope?
   A Design 1   C Design 3
   B Design 2   D None of these
2. What is the most obvious flaw in Design 3?
   F The eyepiece lens is on the wrong side.
   G It isn't powerful enough.
   H The concave mirror is oriented in the wrong direction.
   J The plane mirror is beyond the focal point of the light reflected by the concave mirror.
3. Altering which of the following factors would have the LEAST effect on the telescope's ability to help the student see distant stars?
   A Shape of the concave mirror
   B Size of the convex lens
   C How clean the plane mirror is
   D Total weight of the tube

L2

Teaching

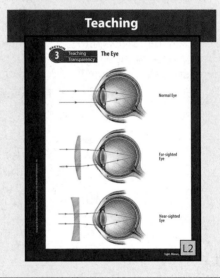

Teaching Transparency 3 — The Eye

Normal Eye

Far-sighted Eye

Near-sighted Eye

L2

Hands-on Activities

Student Text Lab Worksheet

Activity — Reflection from a Plane Mirror

Lab Preview
Directions: Answer these questions before you begin the Activity.
1. Which objects in this activity require careful use to avoid cuts and punctures?

2. What is a plane mirror?

A light ray strikes the surface of a plane mirror and is reflected. Does a relationship exist between the direction of the incoming light ray and the direction of the reflected light ray?

What You'll Investigate
How does the angle of incidence compare with the angle of reflection for a plane mirror?

Materials
flashlight
protractor
metric ruler
scissors
tape
small plane mirror, at least 10 cm on a side
black construction paper
modeling clay
white unlined paper

Goals
■ Measure the angle of incidence and the angle of reflection of a light ray reflected from a plane mirror.

Safety Precautions

Procedure
1. With the scissors, cut a slit in the construction paper and tape it over the flashlight lens.
2. Place the mirror at one end of the unlined paper. Push the mirror into the lump of clay so it stands vertically, and tilt the mirror so it leans slightly toward the table.
3. Measure with the ruler to find the center of the bottom edge of the mirror and mark it. Then use the protractor and the ruler to draw a line on the paper perpendicular to the mirror from the mark. Label this line P.
4. ...at the center of the mirror at angles of 45°, and 60° to line P.

L2

Light, Mirrors, and Lenses 5

Laboratory Activities

Laboratory Activity 1 — Distance and Light Intensity

The energy carried by a wave that passes across a small area is the intensity of the wave. As the source of the wave gets closer or farther away, the intensity of the wave changes. For example, a flashlight becomes less bright as you move farther away, or the signal from a radio station becomes weaker as you move away from the transmitting tower. What is the relationship between the intensity of a wave and the distance from the source of the wave?

In this experiment, you will use a photo resistor, which is a device that reacts to the intensity of the light striking it. This reaction, called resistance, can be measured by a multimeter or an ohmmeter. If an ohmmeter is connected to a photo resistor, the needle on the ohmmeter will move as the photo resistor reacts. The resistance is given in units called ohms (Ω).

Strategy
You will measure the effect of distance and direction on light intensity.
You will interpret a graph relating light intensity and distance.

Materials
pencil
photo resistor
tape (black)
meterstick
25-W lightbulb and lamp socket
utility clamp
ring stand
multimeter or ohmmeter
pencils (colored)

Procedure
1. In the Data and Observations section, write hypotheses explaining the relationships between light intensity and distance.
2. Mount the photo resistor on a pencil with tape. See Figure 1.
3. Lay the meterstick on a flat, hard surface. Place small pieces of black tape at 10-cm intervals along the meterstick.
4. Set the lightbulb and socket on a smooth, flat surface.
5. Clamp the meterstick to the ring stand with the utility clamp. Arrange the meterstick so that the lightbulb is at the 0-cm marker. See Figure 2.
6. Attach the wires of the photo resistor to the ohmmeter. If using a multimeter, set the meter to measure resistance and attach the wires to the appropriate terminals. Darken the room before any measurements are taken.

Figure 1

Figure 2

L2

Light, Mirrors, and Lenses 9

Meeting Different Ability Levels

Content Outline

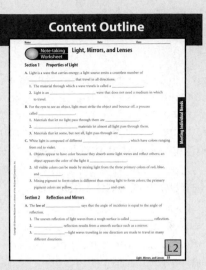

Reinforcement

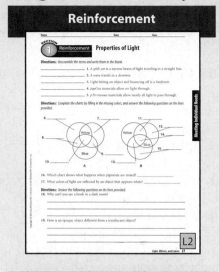

Enrichment

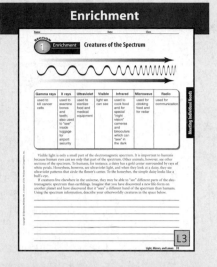

Directed Reading (English/Spanish)

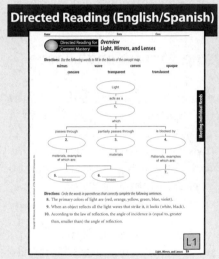

Study Guide

Reading Essentials

Assessment

Test Practice Workbook

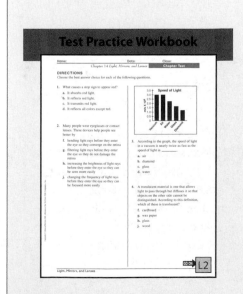

Chapter Review

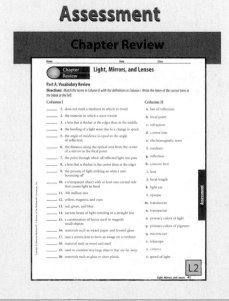

Chapter Tests

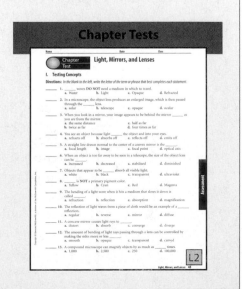

Science Content Background

section 1 Properties of Light
Light and Matter

Light is an electromagnetic wave made of oscillating magnetic and electric fields. When a light wave strikes an object, some of the energy carried by the light wave is absorbed, and some is reemitted. The reemitted wave results when the oscillating electric field of the light wave causes electrons in the object to oscillate. These oscillating electrons then emit electromagnetic waves. The frequencies of the reemitted waves depend on the types of atoms in the object and the bonding between atoms in the material.

As the light wave penetrates into the object it becomes less intense. Light waves cannot travel completely through an opaque object before all of their energy is absorbed. If an object is transparent, very little energy is absorbed. Some objects that are opaque become translucent or transparent if they are made thin enough.

section 2 Reflection and Mirrors
Reflection and Surfaces

Mirrors form two types of images. The image formed by a plane mirror, a convex mirror, or a concave mirror with the object inside the focal point is called a virtual image. A virtual image forms because no light waves emanate from where the image seems to be.

A concave mirror forms a real image when the object is outside the focal point. In this case, light waves from the object are brought to focus at the location of the image, and the image can be projected onto a surface placed at this location.

section 3 Refraction and Lenses
Concave and Convex Lenses

Lenses also form real and virtual images. Images formed when a lens or mirror causes light waves to diverge are virtual images. Images formed by converging light waves are real images.

section 4 Using Mirrors and Lenses
Microscopes

As an image is magnified, the light from the image is spread over a much larger area, causing the image to appear dim. A high-powered microscope usually illuminates the object with bright light so that the magnified image is as bright as possible.

Telescopes

The large size of a telescope's objective lens or mirror enables it to gather much more light than the human eye can alone. A bright, more detailed image can be formed if more of the light from the object is collected, and the image is further magnified.

chapter content resources

Internet Resources
For additional content background, visit **ips.msscience.com** to:
- access your book online
- find references to related articles in popular science magazines
- access Web links with related content background
- access current events with science journal topics

Print Resources
Visual Perception, by Steven H. Schwartz, McGraw-Hill/Appleton and Lange, 1998
Geometric, Physical, and Visual Optics, by Michael Keating, Butterworth-Heinemann, 2002
Seeing the Light, by David Falk, Dieter Brill, David Stork, John Wiley and Sons, 1985
Optics, by Eugene Hecht, Pearson Addison Wesley, 2001

IDENTIFYING Misconceptions

Find Out What Students Think

Students may think that . . .

light comes from a source and produces an effect, but light does not travel through matter or vacuums as rays having a finite speed.

Language and perception play a large role in people's conceptions about the world. People often use the term *light* to refer to illuminating electrical devices. Phrases such as "turn on the light" and "the light is broken" illustrate these uses. The effects of light are constantly and directly observed. For example, some things are lit up and others are in shadows. Further, when a lightbulb has been turned on it seems to light up the room immediately, masking the fact that the light took time to travel. Thinking of light as a source or an effect may interfere with an important foundation for optics—learning the concept of light as a traveling entity that moves at finite speeds.

Demonstration

Set up a flashlight on a stack of books. Have the flashlight point to a screen. Turn off the room lights and turn on the flashlight. Have students write down where there is light. They may initially say there is light only (a) at the bulb and (b) at the screen and not realize that light exists between the bulb and the screen as it travels.

Telegraph Colour Library/FPG International

Promote Understanding

Activity

Divide the class into groups.

- Give each group of students a flashlight and a paper screen.

- Have students in each group set their flashlight on books so it shines directly on the paper screen.

- Turn off the classroom lights.

- Ask students to observe the light from the flashlight.

- Ask students if there is light between the flashlight bulb and the paper screen. Have students in each group discuss the question and agree on an answer.

- Turn on the lights and have groups share their thoughts.

- Turn off the lights and then clap chalk erasers above each group's light beam so students can see the dust particles illuminated in the beam.

- Have students discuss again where there is light. Make sure they understand that light exists everywhere along the path from the bulb to the screen.

Assess

After completing the chapter, see *Identifying Misconceptions* in the Study Guide at the end of the chapter.

Chapter Vocabulary

light ray, p. 550
medium, p. 551
law of reflection, p. 555
focal point, p. 558
focal length, p. 558
refraction, p. 563
lens, p. 563
convex lens, p. 564
concave lens, p. 565
refracting telescope, p. 568
reflecting telescope, p. 569

Science Journal Possible answers include: lightbulb, concave mirror, lenses, prisms, panes of glass, and a motor to spin the beam of light.

INTERACTIVE CHALKBOARD
with Image Bank

PowerPoint® Presentations

This CD-ROM is an editable Microsoft® PowerPoint® presentation that includes:
- a pre-made presentation for every chapter
- interactive graphics
- animations
- audio clips
- image bank
- all new section and chapter questions
- Standardized Test Practice
- transparencies
- pre-lab questions for all labs
- Foldables directions
- links to ips.msscience.com

Light, Mirrors, and Lenses

chapter preview

sections

1 **Properties of Light**

2 **Reflection and Mirrors**
   Lab *Reflection from a Plane Mirror*

3 **Refraction and Lenses**

4 **Using Mirrors and Lenses**
   Lab *Image Formation by a Convex Lens*

   Virtual Lab *How are lenses used to correct vision?*

Seeing the Light

This lighthouse at Pigeon Point, California, produces beams of light that can be seen for many miles. These intense light beams are formed in the same way as a flashlight beam. The key ingredient is a curved mirror that reflects the light from a bright source.

Science Journal Describe how you use mirrors and lenses during a typical day.

Theme Connection

Energy Light waves carry energy. This energy can pass through materials, be absorbed by materials, and be reflected by materials.

About the Photo

Lighthouses Today, many lighthouses, such as the one shown here, use beacons that originally were developed for airports. These beacons contain a metal halide bulb positioned at the focal point of a precision parabolic reflector that is two or three feet in diameter. The bulb is designed to burn continuously for over two years.

Start-Up Activities

Bending Light

Everything you see results from light waves entering your eyes. These light waves are either given off by objects, such as the Sun and lightbulbs, or reflected by objects, such as trees, books, and people. Lenses and mirrors can cause light to change direction and make objects seem larger or smaller.

1. Place two paper cups next to each other and put a penny in the bottom of each cup.
2. Fill one of the cups with water and observe how the penny looks.
3. Looking straight down at the cups, slide the cup with no water away from you just until you can no longer see the penny.
4. Pour water into this cup and observe what seems to happen to the penny.
5. **Think Critically** In your Science Journal, record your observations. Did adding water make the cup look deeper or shallower?

 **Science Online**
Preview this chapter's content and activities at ips.msscience.com

---

 Light, Mirrors, and Lenses
Make the following Foldable to help you understand the properties of and the relationship between light, mirrors, and lenses.

STEP 1 **Fold** a sheet of pape in half lengthwise. Make the back edge about 5 cm longer than the front edge.

STEP 2 **Turn** the paper so the fold is on the bottom. Then **fold** it into thirds.

STEP 3 **Unfold and cut** only the top layer along folds to make three tabs.

STEP 4 **Label** the Foldable as shown.

Light, Mirrors, and Lenses		
Light	Mirrors	Lenses

Summarize in a Table As you read the chapter, summarize the information you find about light, mirrors, lenses.

549

1 Motivate

Bellringer

Section Focus Transparencies also are available on the Interactive Chalkboard CD-ROM.

Tie to Prior Knowledge

Waves Have students list types of waves with which they are familiar, such as ocean waves or sound waves. Discuss how these waves are similar to one another and how they are different. Explain that in this section they will learn about light waves.

---

as you read

What You'll Learn

- **Describe** the wave nature of light.
- **Explain** how light interacts with materials.
- **Determine** why objects appear to have color.

Why It's Important

Everything you see comes from information carried by light waves.

Review Vocabulary
electromagnetic waves: waves created by vibrating electric charges that can travel through space or through matter

New Vocabulary
- light ray
- medium

Figure 1 Light moves away in all directions from a light source, just as ripples spread out on the surface of water.

What is light?

Drop a rock on the smooth surface of a pond and you'll see ripples spread outward from the spot where the rock struck. The rock produced a wave much like the one in **Figure 1.** A wave is a disturbance that carries energy through matter or space. The matter in this case is the water, and the energy originally comes from the impact of the rock. As the ripples spread out, they carry some of that energy.

Light is another type of wave that carries energy. A source of light such as the Sun or a lightbulb gives off light waves into space, just as the rock hitting the pond causes waves to form in the water. But while the water waves spread out only on the surface of the pond, light waves spread out in all directions from the light source. **Figure 1** shows how light waves travel.

Sometimes, however, it is easier to think of light in a different way. A **light ray** is a narrow beam of light that travels in a straight line. You can think of a source of light as giving off, or emitting, a countless number of light rays that are traveling away from the source in all directions.

A source of light, such as a lightbulb, gives off light rays that travel away from the light source in all directions.

Ripples on the surface of a pond are produced by an object hitting the water. The ripples spread out from the point of impact.

550 CHAPTER 19 Light, Mirrors, and Lenses

Section 1 Resource Manager

Chapter FAST FILE Resources
Transparency Activity, p. 48
MiniLAB, p. 3
Lab Activity, pp. 9–12, 13–16
Directed Reading for Content Mastery, pp. 19, 20

Note-taking Worksheets, pp. 35–38
Enrichment, p. 31
Reinforcement, p. 27

Light Travels Through Space There is, however, one important difference between light waves and the water wave ripples on a pond. If the pond dried up and had no water, ripples could not form. Waves on a pond need a material—water—in which to travel. The material through which a wave travels is called a **medium**. Light is an electromagnetic wave and doesn't need a medium in which to travel. Electromagnetic waves can travel in a vacuum, as well as through materials such as air, water, and glass.

Light and Matter

What can you see when you are in a closed room with no windows and the lights out? You can see nothing until you turn on a light or open a door to let in light from outside the room. Most objects around you do not give off light on their own. They can be seen only if light waves from another source bounce off them and into your eyes, as shown in **Figure 2.** The process of light striking an object and bouncing off is called reflection. Right now, you can see these words because light emitted by a source of light is reflecting from the page and into your eyes. Not all the light rays reflected from the page strike your eyes. Light rays striking the page are reflected in many directions, and only some of these rays enter your eyes.

Reading Check *What must happen for you to see most objects?*

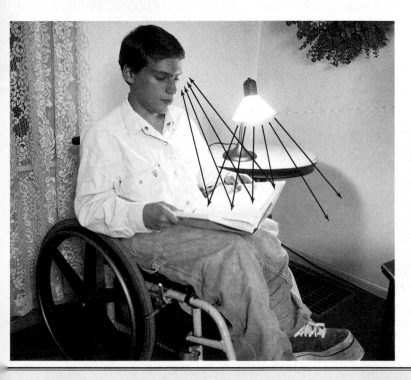

Figure 2 Light waves are given off by the lightbulb. Some of these light waves hit the page and are reflected. The student sees the page when some of these reflected waves enter the student's eyes.

Mini LAB

Observing Colors in the Dark

Procedure
1. Get six pieces of **paper** that are different colors and about 10 cm × 10 cm.
2. Darken a room and wait 10 min for your eyes to adjust to the darkness.
3. Write on each paper what color you think the paper is.
4. Turn on the lights and see if your night vision correctly detected the colors.

Analysis
1. If the room were perfectly dark, what would you see? Explain.
2. Your eyes contain rod cells and cone cells. Rod cells enable you to see in dim light, but don't detect color. Cone cells enable you to see color, but do not work in dim light. Which type of cell was working in the darkened room? Explain.

IDENTIFYING Misconceptions

Traveling Light Students may think that light produces an effect but does not travel through matter or space. See page F at the beginning of this chapter for teaching strategies related to this misconception.

Mini LAB

Purpose Students will investigate how their eyes respond to dim light. L2 ELL LS Visual-Spatial

Materials six pieces of construction paper, pen or pencil

Teaching Strategy Suggest students try the experiment in rooms with different levels of darkness.

Analysis
1. Nothing; seeing depends on light bouncing off an object.
2. Since some color could be seen, both rods and cones were working.

Assessment

Process Have students work in small groups to design an experiment to test which colors are easiest to distinguish in dim light. Use **Performance Assessment in the Science Classroom,** p. 95.

Reading Check

Answer Light must reflect off the objects and go into your eyes.

Differentiated Instruction

Visually Impaired Have sighted students work with visually impaired students for the minilab. The sighted students should tell the visually impaired students the lighting conditions and what they are seeing under the different lighting conditions.

Teacher FYI

Electromagnetic Spectrum Visible light is part of the electromagnetic spectrum. It also includes radio waves, microwaves, X rays, infrared waves, gamma rays, and ultraviolet waves. The frequency and wavelength of an electromagnetic wave determines which type of wave it is.

An opaque object allows no light to pass through it.

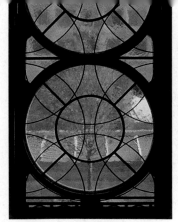

A translucent object allows some light to pass through it.

A transparent object allows almost all light to pass through it.

Figure 3 Materials are opaque, translucent, or transparent, depending on how much light passes through them.
Infer *which type of material reflects the least amount of light.*

Figure 4 A beam of white light passing through a prism is separated into many colors.
Describe *the colors you see emerging from the prism.*

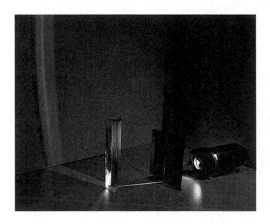

Opaque, Translucent, and Transparent When light waves strike an object, some of the waves are absorbed by the object, some are reflected by it, and some might pass through it. What happens to light when it strikes the object depends on the material that the object is made of.

All objects reflect and absorb some light waves. Materials that let no light pass through them are opaque (oh PAYK). You cannot see other objects through opaque materials. On the other hand, you clearly can see other objects through materials such as glass and clear plastic that allow nearly all the light that strikes them to pass through. These materials are transparent. A third type of material allows only some light to pass through. Although objects behind these materials are visible, they are not clear. These materials, such as waxed paper and frosted glass, are translucent (trans LEW sent). Examples of opaque, translucent, and transparent objects are shown in **Figure 3.**

Color

The light from the Sun might look white, but it is a mixture of colors. Each different color of light is a light wave with a different wavelength. Red light waves have the longest wavelengths and violet light waves have the shortest wavelengths. As shown in **Figure 4,** white light is separated into different colors when it passes through a prism. The colors in white light range from red to violet. When light waves from all these colors enter the eye at the same time, the brain interprets the mixture as being white.

552 CHAPTER 19 Light, Mirrors, and Lenses

Curriculum Connection

Math The intensity of light striking a surface decreases as the surface gets farther from the source. This decrease is given by the formula $I = P/d^2$, where I is the light intensity, d is the distance to the source, and P is related to the power emitted by the light source. If P remains constant, what will be the difference in the intensity of light striking a card 1 m from a lightbulb and light striking a card 4 m from the bulb? The light striking the card 4 m from the lightbulb will have 1/16 less intensity than will the light striking the card 1 m from the lightbulb. L3 **LS** Logical-Mathematical

A pair of gym shoes and socks as seen under white light.

The same shoes and socks photographed through a red filter.

Why do objects have color? Why does grass look green or a rose look red? When a mixture of light waves strikes an object that is not transparent, the object absorbs some of the light waves. Some of the light waves that are not absorbed are reflected. If an object reflects red waves and absorbs all the other waves, it looks red. Similarly, if an object looks blue, it reflects only blue light waves and absorbs all the others. An object that reflects all the light waves that strike it looks white, while one that reflects none of the light waves that strike it looks black. **Figure 5** shows gym shoes and socks as seen under white light and as seen when viewed through a red filter that allows only red light to pass through it.

Primary Light Colors How many colors exist? People often say white light is made up of red, orange, yellow, green, blue, and violet light. This isn't completely true, though. Many more colors than this exist. In reality, most humans can distinguish thousands of colors, including some such as brown, pink, and purple, that are not found among the colors of the rainbow.

Light of almost any color can be made by mixing different amounts of red, green, and blue light. Red, green, and blue are known as the primary colors. Look at **Figure 6.** White light is produced where beams of red, green, and blue light overlap. Yellow light is produced where red and green light overlap. You see the color yellow because of the way your brain interprets the combination of the red and green light striking your eye. This combination of light waves looks the same as yellow light produced by a prism, even though these light waves have only a single wavelength.

Figure 5 The color of an object depends on the light waves it reflects.
Infer *why the blue socks look black when viewed under red light.*

Figure 6 By mixing light from the three primary colors—red, blue, and green—almost all of the visible colors can be made.

SECTION 1 Properties of Light **553**

DAILY INTERVENTION

Check for Understanding

Visual-Spatial Have students create different colors using flashlights with red, green, and blue cellophane over the top in a darkened room.

Reteach

Color Combinations Quiz students on combining colors. What are the primary colors of light? red, green, and blue What are the primary pigment colors? yellow, cyan, and magenta What color is formed when red light and blue light combine? magenta What color is formed when yellow pigment and cyan pigment combine? green L2

 Visual-Spatial

☑ Assessment

Content Ask students to draw diagrams illustrating the difference between light waves and a light ray. A light source produces a wave that travels away from the source in all directions, like a ripple spreading on a pond. A light ray is the part of the light wave that travels in one direction and can be represented by an arrow. Use **Performance Assessment in the Science Classroom,** p. 127.

P

Figure 7 The three primary color pigments—yellow, magenta, and cyan—can form almost all the visible colors when mixed together in various amounts.

Primary Pigment Colors Materials like paint that are used to change the color of other objects, such as the walls of a room or an artist's canvas, are called pigments. Mixing pigments together forms colors in a different way than mixing colored lights does.

Like all materials that appear to be colored, pigments absorb some light waves and reflect others. The color of the pigment you see is the color of the light waves that are reflected from it. However, the primary pigment colors are not red, blue, and green—they are yellow, magenta, and cyan. You can make almost any color by mixing different amounts of these primary pigment colors, as shown in **Figure 7.**

Although primary pigment colors are not the same as the primary light colors, they are related. Each primary pigment color results when a pigment absorbs a primary light color. For example, a yellow pigment absorbs blue light and it reflects red and green light, which you see as yellow. A magenta pigment, on the other hand, absorbs green light and reflects red and blue light, which you see as magenta. Each of the primary pigment colors is the same color as white light with one primary color removed.

---

section 1 review

Summary

Light and Matter

- Light is an electromagnetic wave that can travel in a vacuum as well as through matter.
- When light waves strike an object some light waves might be absorbed by the object, some waves might be reflected from the object, and some waves might pass through the object.
- Materials can be opaque, translucent, or transparent, depending on how much light passes through the material.

Color

- Light waves with different wavelengths have different colors.
- White light is a combination of all the colors ranging from red to violet.
- The color of an object is the color of the light waves that it reflects.
- The primary light colors are red, green, and blue. The primary pigment colors are yellow, magenta and cyan.

Self Check

1. **Diagram** the path followed by a light ray that enters one of your eyes when you are reading at night in a room.

2. **Determine** the colors that are reflected from an object that appears black.

3. **Compare and contrast** primary light colors and primary pigment colors.

4. **Describe** the difference between an opaque object and a transparent object.

5. **Think Critically** A white shirt is viewed through a filter that allows only blue light to pass through the filter. What color will the shirt appear to be?

Applying Skills

6. **Draw Conclusions** A black plastic bowl and a white plastic bowl are placed in sunlight. After 15 minutes, the temperature of the black bowl is higher than the temperature of the white bowl. Which bowl absorbs more light waves and which bowl reflects more light waves?

Science Online ips.msscience.com/self_check_quiz

---

section 1 review

1. Light from a lamp reflects off the book to your eyes.
2. No colors are reflected by an object that appears black.
3. Primary light colors can be mixed to produce any other color of light.

Primary pigment colors result when a pigment absorbs a primary light color.
4. No light passes through an opaque object. Nearly all light passes through a transparent object.
5. The shirt will appear blue.

6. The black bowl absorbs more sunlight, and the white bowl reflects more sunlight.

Reflection and Mirrors

The Law of Reflection

You've probably noticed your image on the surface of a pool or lake. If the surface of the water was smooth, you could see your face clearly. If the surface of the water was wavy, however, your face might have seemed distorted. The image you saw was the result of light reflecting from the surface and traveling to your eyes. How the light was reflected determined the sharpness of the image you saw.

When a light ray strikes a surface and is reflected, as in **Figure 8,** the reflected ray obeys the law of reflection. Imagine a line that is drawn perpendicular to the surface where the light ray strikes. This line is called the normal to the surface. The incoming ray and the normal form an angle called the angle of incidence. The reflected light ray forms an angle with the normal called the angle of reflection. According to the law of reflection, the angle of incidence is equal to the angle of reflection. This is true for any surface, no matter what material it is made of.

Reflection from Surfaces

Why can you see your reflection in some surfaces and not others? Why does a piece of shiny metal make a good mirror, but a piece of paper does not? The answers have to do with the smoothness of each surface.

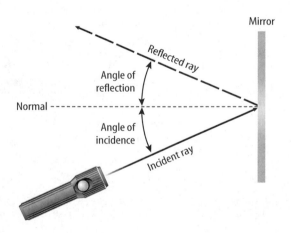

Figure 8 A light ray strikes a surface and is reflected. The angle of incidence is always equal to the angle of reflection. This is the law of reflection.

as you read

What You'll Learn
- **Explain** how light is reflected from rough and smooth surfaces.
- **Determine** how mirrors form an image.
- **Describe** how concave and convex mirrors form an image.

Why It's Important
Mirrors can change the direction of light waves and enable you to see images, such as your own face.

⟳ **Review Vocabulary**
normal: a line drawn perpendicular to a surface or line

New Vocabulary
- law of reflection
- focal point
- focal length

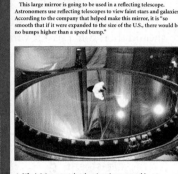

Aluminum Foil Provide students with pieces of new aluminum foil. Have them first look at their reflections in the smooth foil, then crumple the foil and observe their reflections again.
L2 LS **Visual-Spatial**

Make a Model

Ball Rolling Have students work in small groups to model the law of reflection. First, students should use chalk to draw a line normal to a wall. One student should then roll a ball toward the wall at a pre-determined angle to the normal. Another student will determine the angle of reflection that the ball makes as it bounces off the wall. Students should be able to relate this to the way light reflects off a flat surface.
L2 LS **Kinesthetic**

Teacher FYI

Valleys and Hills In order for a mirror to form a regular reflection, the hills and valleys on the surface must be smaller than the wavelengths of visible light, or smaller than about 400-billionths of a meter.

✔ Reading Check

Answer The rough surface causes light to be reflected in many different directions.

Caption Answer

Figure 11 Your image seems to be coming from behind the mirror and is reversed.

Figure 9 A highly magnified view of the surface of a sheet of paper shows that the paper is made of many cellulose wood fibers that make the surface rough and uneven.

Magnification: 80×

Regular and Diffuse Reflection Even though the surface of the paper might seem smooth, it's not as smooth as the surface of a mirror. **Figure 9** shows how rough the surface of a piece of paper looks when it is viewed under a microscope. The rough surface causes light rays to be reflected from it in many directions, as shown in **Figure 10.** This uneven reflection of light waves from a rough surface is diffuse reflection. The smoother surfaces of mirrors, as shown in **Figure 10,** reflect light waves in a much more regular way. For example, parallel rays remain parallel after they are reflected from a mirror. Reflection from mirrors is known as regular reflection. Light waves that are regularly reflected from a surface form the image you see in a mirror or any other smooth surface. Whether a surface is smooth or rough, every light ray that strikes it obeys the law of reflection.

✔ **Reading Check** *Why does a rough surface cause a diffuse reflection?*

Scattering of Light When diffuse reflection occurs, light waves that were traveling in a single direction are reflected and then travel in many different directions. Scattering occurs when light waves traveling in one direction are made to travel in many different directions. Scattering also can occur when light waves strike small particles, such as dust. You may have seen dust particles floating in a beam of sunlight. When the light waves in the sunbeam strike a dust particle, they are scattered in all directions. You see the dust particles as bright specks of light when some of these scattered light waves enter your eye.

Figure 10 The roughness of a surface determines whether it looks like a mirror.

A rough surface causes parallel light rays to be reflected in many different directions.

A smooth surface causes parallel light rays to be reflected in a single direction. This type of surface looks like a mirror.

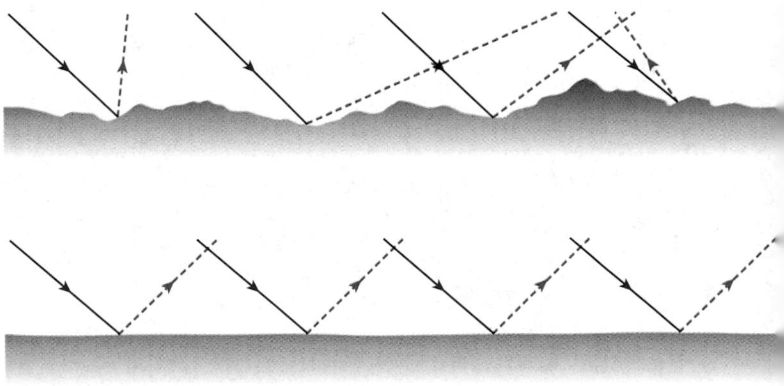

556 CHAPTER 19 Light, Mirrors, and Lenses

Visual Learning

Figure 10 Review with students the reflection of light from a rough surface shown in the top illustration of **Figure 10** and the reflection of light from a smooth surface shown in bottom illustration of **Figure 10.** Ask students to draw diagrams showing how light is reflected from a piece of crumpled aluminum foil. The surface of the crumpled foil is rougher than a mirror but less rough than the surface shown in the top illustration of **Figure 10.** Therefore the light would be reflected to form many different little images as from many little mirrors. L2 LS **Visual-Spatial** P

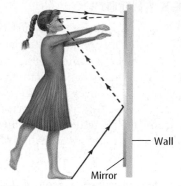

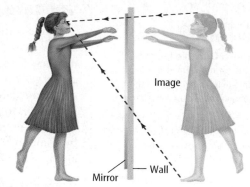

A Light rays that bounce off a person strike the mirror. Some these light rays are reflected into the person's eye.

B The light rays that are shown entering the person's eye seem to be coming from a person behind the mirror.

Reflection by Plane Mirrors
Did you glance in the mirror before leaving for school this morning? If you did, you probably looked at your reflection in a plane mirror. A plane mirror is a mirror with a flat reflecting surface. In a plane mirror, your image looks much the same as it would in a photograph. However, you and your image are facing in opposite directions. This causes your left side and your right side to switch places on your mirror image. Also, your image seems to be coming from behind the mirror. How does a plane mirror form an image?

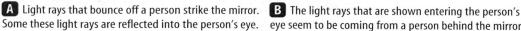 **Reading Check** *What is a plane mirror?*

Figure 11 shows a person looking into a plane mirror. Light waves from the Sun or another source of light strike each part of the person. These light rays bounce off the person according to the law of reflection, and some of them strike the mirror. The rays that strike the mirror also are reflected according to the law of reflection. **Figure 11A** shows the path traveled by a few of the rays that have been reflected off the person and reflected back to the person's eye by the mirror.

The Image in a Plane Mirror
Why does the image you see in a plane mirror seem to be behind the mirror? This is a result of how your brain processes the light rays that enter your eyes. Although the light rays bounced off the mirror's surface, your brain interprets them as having followed the path shown by the dashed lines in **Figure 11B.** In other words, your brain always assumes that light rays travel in straight lines without changing direction. This makes the reflected light rays look as if they are coming from behind the mirror, even though no source of light is there. The image also seems to be the same distance behind the mirror as the person is in front of the mirror.

Figure 11 A plane mirror forms an image by changing the direction of light rays.
Describe *how you and your image in a plane mirror are different.*

Light Waves and Photons
When an object like a marble or a basketball bounces off a surface, it obeys the law of reflection. Because light also obeys the law of reflection, people once thought that light must be a stream of particles. Today, experiments have shown that light can behave as though it were both a wave and a stream of energy bundles called photons. Read an article about photons and write a description in your Science Journal.

Differentiated Instruction

English-Language Learners At the beginning of this section have students who speak a different language translate the words *regular, diffuse, plane, concave,* and *convex,* by picture or description, into their native language. Have the students practice at home using these words in English.

Light Waves and Photons Many properties of light, such as diffraction and interference, are explained most easily by thinking of light as a wave. However, other properties, such as the ability of light to produce a current by ejecting electrons from a metal (the photoelectric effect), seem to indicate that light has a particulate nature. The packets of light energy that behave as particles are called photons.

Research Have students research the properties of electrons that are both particle-like and wave-like. Then research the properties of photons that are particle-like and wave-like. Have them compare and contrast these properties.

Quick Demo
Mirror Reversals
Materials hand mirror
Estimated Time five minutes
Procedure Pass a hand mirror around the classroom. Ask students to look at their textbooks in the mirror. They will see that left and right are reversed in the mirror. L2 **ELL** **LS** Visual-Spatial

Activity
Drawing Diagrams Students will be better able to interpret light ray diagrams if they actually draw them. On the board, draw a simple sketch of an object such as a house. Next, draw rays of light bouncing off the top, middle, and bottom part of the object and striking a plane mirror. Let student volunteers draw in the reflected rays. This will show them how the left-to-right reversal occurs. Have students then draw similar diagrams of their own. L2 **ELL** **LS** Visual-Spatial

Inquiry Lab

Exploring Mirrors

Purpose Students learn how to direct light using convex and plane mirrors.

Possible Materials flashlight, tape, several convex and plane mirrors

Estimated Time 30 minutes

Teaching Strategies Tape a flashlight to a table, and make a target on a wall not facing the students. Darken the room. Using several convex and plane mirrors, have the students hold the mirrors such that the beam of light is focused on the target.

For additional inquiry activities, see *Science Inquiry Labs.*

Quick Demo

Concave Mirror Images

Materials concave mirror

Estimated Time 15 minutes

Procedure You can demonstrate the focal point of a concave mirror by slowly walking up to students, one at a time, with the mirror facing them. Students can watch their images disappear and then turn right-side up in the mirror when they are between the mirror and the focal point.

Science Online

Topic: Concave Mirrors
Visit ips.msscience.com for Web links to information about the concave mirrors used in telescopes.

Activity Make a chart showing the five largest telescope mirrors and where they are located.

Concave and Convex Mirrors

Some mirrors are not flat. A concave mirror has a surface that is curved inward, like the bowl of a spoon. Unlike plane mirrors, concave mirrors cause light rays to come together, or converge. A convex mirror, on the other hand, has a surface that curves outward, like the back of a spoon. Convex mirrors cause light waves to spread out, or diverge. These two types of mirrors form images that are different from the images that are formed by plane mirrors. Examples of a concave and a convex mirror are shown in **Figure 12.**

Reading Check *What's the difference between a concave and convex mirror?*

Concave Mirrors The way in which a concave mirror forms an image is shown in **Figure 13.** A straight line drawn perpendicular to the center of a concave or convex mirror is called the optical axis. Light rays that travel parallel to the optical axis and strike the mirror are reflected so that they pass through a single point on the optical axis called the **focal point.** The distance along the optical axis from the center of the mirror to the focal point is called the **focal length.**

The image formed by a concave mirror depends on the position of the object relative to its focal point. If the object is farther from the mirror than the focal point, the image appears to be upside down, or inverted. The size of the image decreases as the object is moved farther away from the mirror. If the object is closer to the mirror than one focal length, the image is upright and gets smaller as the object moves closer to the mirror.

A concave mirror can produce a focused beam of light if a source of light is placed at the mirror's focal point, as shown in **Figure 13.** Flashlights and automobile headlights use concave mirrors to produce directed beams of light.

Figure 12 Convex and concave mirrors have curved surfaces.

A concave mirror has a surface that's curved inward.

A convex mirror has a surface that's curved outward.

558   CHAPTER 19 Light, Mirrors, and Lenses

Curriculum Connection

Art The artist M.C. Escher is well known for his ability to use shadows and lighting to make the impossible look real. In his painting *Convex and Concave*, he uses curved surfaces to create an optical illusion. Show students a copy of this painting and have them discuss Escher's use of lighting on the convex and concave surfaces.

Differentiated Instruction

Challenge If students have trouble remembering which type of curved surface is concave and which is convex, tell them to remember that a concave surface is curved inward like a cave. To practice using this mnemonic, have them name some curved surfaces and identify them as concave or convex. L3

Figure 13

Glance into a flat plane mirror and you'll see an upright image of yourself. But look into a concave mirror, and you might see yourself larger than life, right side up, or upside down—or not at all! This is because the way a concave mirror forms an image depends on the position of an object in front of the mirror, as shown here.

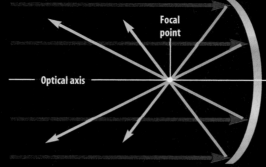

A concave mirror reflects all light rays traveling parallel to the optical axis so that they pass through the focal point.

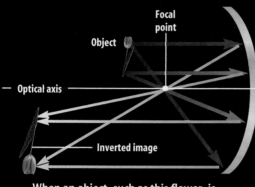

When an object, such as this flower, is placed beyond the focal point, the mirror forms an image that is inverted.

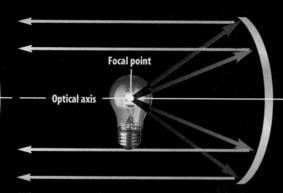

When a source of light is placed at the focal point, a beam of parallel light rays is formed. The concave mirror in a flashlight, for example, creates a beam of parallel light rays.

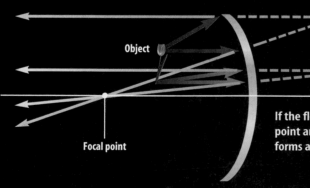

If the flower is between the focal point and the mirror, the mirror forms an upright, enlarged image.

Visualizing Reflections in Concave Mirrors

Have students examine the pictures and read the captions. Then ask the following questions.

How could the focal point of a concave mirror be used? Possible answer: since it concentrates all the light that comes in parallel to the optical axis, it could be used to heat something, start a fire, or cook food.

Where might you find a concave mirror? Possible answers: flashlight, car headlight, spotlight, telescope

Activity

Concave Spoons Pass out shiny metal spoons to students. Have students look into the concave side of the spoons. Point out how the image is inverted as shown in the diagrams. Since the curvature of the spoon puts the focal point very near the spoon, it is usually impossible to put your eye inside the focal length and get an enlarged upright image. L2 **LS** **Visual-Spatial**

560 **CHAPTER 19** Light, Mirrors, and Lenses

Discussion

Meeting Light Rays If the light rays reflected from a convex mirror spread apart, why is the image formed smaller than the reflected object? The image is formed as if the light rays met behind the mirror. Because the mirror is convex, if the light rays went through it, they would be bent toward the mirror's optical axis, making the image smaller. L3

LS Logical-Mathematical

DAILY INTERVENTION

Check for Understanding

Visual-Spatial Draw on the board a diagram showing a surface, and a line normal to that surface. Have the students copy your diagram on a piece of paper and label the parts of the diagram. Then have your students draw and label an incident and reflected ray on their diagram. Make sure the incident and reflected-ray angles are the same.

Reteach

Reversible Light Rays The directions of light rays given by the law of reflection are reversible. Students may think that if they can see someone in a mirror, that person cannot see them. Use a large plane mirror to show students that this is not true. L2 **LS**
Visual-Spatial

✓ Assessment

Performance Have students examine their images in both sides of shiny spoons while they move the spoons closer and then farther away. Ask them to form hypotheses about which side of the spoon would serve best as a rearview mirror. the back side Use **Performance Assessment in the Science Classroom,** p. 93.

Figure 14 A convex mirror is a mirror that curves outward.

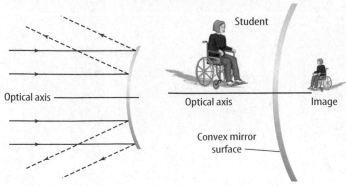

Optical axis
Student
Optical axis
Image
Convex mirror surface

A convex mirror causes light rays that are traveling parallel to the optical axis to spread apart after they are reflected.

No matter how far an object is from a convex mirror, the image is always upright and smaller than the object.

Convex Mirrors A convex mirror has a reflecting surface that curves outward and causes light rays to spread apart, or diverge, as shown in **Figure 14.** Like the image formed by plane mirror, the image formed by a convex mirror seems to be behind the mirror. **Figure 14** shows that the image always is upright and smaller than the object.

Convex mirrors often are used as security mirrors in stores and as outside rearview mirrors on cars and other vehicles. You can see a larger area reflected in a convex mirror than in other mirrors.

section 2 review

Summary

Reflection and Plane Mirrors

- The law of reflection states that the angle of incidence equals the angle of reflection.
- A regular reflection is produced by a smooth surface, such as a mirror. A rough surface forms a diffuse reflection.
- Scattering occurs when light rays traveling in one direction are made to travel in many directions.
- A plane mirror forms a image that is reversed left to right and seems to be behind the mirror.

Concave and Convex Mirrors

- Concave mirrors curve inward and make light rays converge.
- Images formed by a concave mirror can be either upright or inverted and can vary from larger to smaller than the object.
- Convex mirrors curve outward and make light rays diverge.
- Images formed by a convex mirror are always upright and smaller than the object.

Self Check

1. **Describe** the image formed by a concave mirror when an object is less than one focal length from the mirror.

2. **Explain** why concave mirrors are used in flashlights and automobile headlights.

3. **Describe** If an object is more than one focal length from a concave mirror, how does the image formed by the mirror change as the object moves farther from the mirror?

4. **Determine** which light rays striking a concave mirror are reflected so that they pass through the focal point.

5. **Think Critically** After you wash and wax a car, you can see your reflection in the car's surface. Before you washed and waxed the car, no reflection could be seen. Explain.

Applying Skills

6. **Use a Spreadsheet** Make a table using a spreadsheet comparing the images formed by plane, concave, and convex mirrors. Include in your table how the images depend on the distance of the object from the mirror.

560 **CHAPTER 19** Light, Mirrors, and Lenses

Science Online ips.msscience.com/self_check_quiz

section 2 review

1. The image is upright and larger.
2. They focus the light into a narrow beam.
3. The image gets smaller as the distance of the object from the mirror increases.
4. Light waves traveling parallel to the optical axis are reflected through the focal point.
5. With the car cleaned and the wax filling in irregularities in the surface, the surface is smoother. This causes regular reflection to occur.
6. Check students' spreadsheets for accuracy.

Figure 13

G lance into a flat plane mirror and you'll see an upright image of yourself. But look into a concave mirror, and you might see yourself larger than life, right side up, or upside down—or not at all! This is because the way a concave mirror forms an image depends on the position of an object in front of the mirror, as shown here.

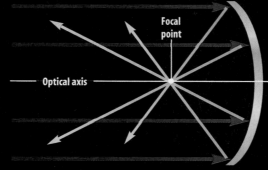

A concave mirror reflects all light rays traveling parallel to the optical axis so that they pass through the focal point.

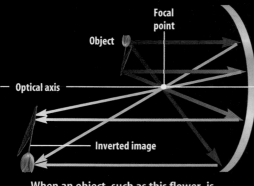

When an object, such as this flower, is placed beyond the focal point, the mirror forms an image that is inverted.

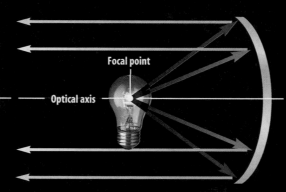

When a source of light is placed at the focal point, a beam of parallel light rays is formed. The concave mirror in a flashlight, for example, creates a beam of parallel light rays.

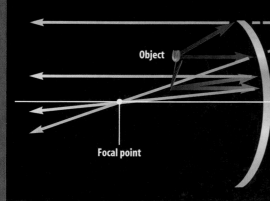

If the flower is between the focal point and the mirror, the mirror forms an upright, enlarged image.

Visualizing Reflections in Concave Mirrors

Have students examine the pictures and read the captions. Then ask the following questions.

How could the focal point of a concave mirror be used? Possible answer: since it concentrates all the light that comes in parallel to the optical axis, it could be used to heat something, start a fire, or cook food.

Where might you find a concave mirror? Possible answers: flashlight, car headlight, spotlight, telescope

Activity

Concave Spoons Pass out shiny metal spoons to students. Have students look into the concave side of the spoons. Point out how the image is inverted as shown in the diagrams. Since the curvature of the spoon puts the focal point very near the spoon, it is usually impossible to put your eye inside the focal length and get an enlarged upright image. L2 LS **Visual-Spatial**

Meeting Light Rays If the light rays reflected from a convex mirror spread apart, why is the image formed smaller than the reflected object? The image is formed as if the light rays met behind the mirror. Because the mirror is convex, if the light rays went through it, they would be bent toward the mirror's optical axis, making the image smaller. L3

LS Logical-Mathematical

3 Assess

DAILY INTERVENTION

Check for Understanding

Visual-Spatial Draw on the board a diagram showing a surface, and a line normal to that surface. Have the students copy your diagram on a piece of paper and label the parts of the diagram. Then have your students draw and label an incident and reflected ray on their diagram. Make sure the incident and reflected-ray angles are the same.

Reteach

Reversible Light Rays The directions of light rays given by the law of reflection are reversible. Students may think that if they can see someone in a mirror, that person cannot see them. Use a large plane mirror to show students that this is not true. L2 **LS**
Visual-Spatial

✓ Assessment

Performance Have students examine their images in both sides of shiny spoons while they move the spoons closer and then farther away. Ask them to form hypotheses about which side of the spoon would serve best as a rearview mirror. the back side Use **Performance Assessment in the Science Classroom,** p. 93.

Figure 14 A convex mirror is a mirror that curves outward.

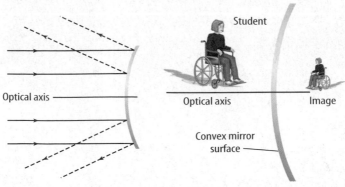

Optical axis

Student

Optical axis

Image

Convex mirror surface

A convex mirror causes light rays that are traveling parallel to the optical axis to spread apart after they are reflected.

No matter how far an object is from a convex mirror, the image is always upright and smaller than the object.

Convex Mirrors A convex mirror has a reflecting surface that curves outward and causes light rays to spread apart, or diverge, as shown in **Figure 14.** Like the image formed by plane mirror, the image formed by a convex mirror seems to be behind the mirror. **Figure 14** shows that the image always is upright and smaller than the object.

Convex mirrors often are used as security mirrors in stores and as outside rearview mirrors on cars and other vehicles. You can see a larger area reflected in a convex mirror than in other mirrors.

section 2 review

Summary

Reflection and Plane Mirrors

- The law of reflection states that the angle of incidence equals the angle of reflection.
- A regular reflection is produced by a smooth surface, such as a mirror. A rough surface forms a diffuse reflection.
- Scattering occurs when light rays traveling in one direction are made to travel in many directions.
- A plane mirror forms a image that is reversed left to right and seems to be behind the mirror.

Concave and Convex Mirrors

- Concave mirrors curve inward and make light rays converge.
- Images formed by a concave mirror can be either upright or inverted and can vary from larger to smaller than the object.
- Convex mirrors curve outward and make light rays diverge.
- Images formed by a convex mirror are always upright and smaller than the object.

Self Check

1. **Describe** the image formed by a concave mirror when an object is less than one focal length from the mirror.

2. **Explain** why concave mirrors are used in flashlights and automobile headlights.

3. **Describe** If an object is more than one focal length from a concave mirror, how does the image formed by the mirror change as the object moves farther from the mirror?

4. **Determine** which light rays striking a concave mirror are reflected so that they pass through the focal point.

5. **Think Critically** After you wash and wax a car, you can see your reflection in the car's surface. Before you washed and waxed the car, no reflection could be seen. Explain.

Applying Skills

6. **Use a Spreadsheet** Make a table using a spreadsheet comparing the images formed by plane, concave, and convex mirrors. Include in your table how the images depend on the distance of the object from the mirror.

560 CHAPTER 19 Light, Mirrors, and Lenses

Science Online ips.msscience.com/self_check_quiz

section 2 review

1. The image is upright and larger.
2. They focus the light into a narrow beam.
3. The image gets smaller as the distance of the object from the mirror increases.

4. Light waves traveling parallel to the optical axis are reflected through the focal point.
5. With the car cleaned and the wax filling in irregularities in the surface,

the surface is smoother. This causes regular reflection to occur.
6. Check students' spreadsheets for accuracy.

Reflection from a Plane Mirror

A light ray strikes the surface of a plane mirror and is reflected. Does a relationship exist between the direction of the incoming light ray and the direction of the reflected light ray?

● Real-World Question

How does the angle of incidence compare with the angle of reflection for a plane mirror?

Goals

■ **Measure** the angle of incidence and the angle of reflection for a light ray reflected from a plane mirror.

Materials

flashlight	small plane mirror,
protractor	at least 10 cm on a side
metric ruler	black construction paper
scissors	modeling clay
tape	white unlined paper

Safety Precautions

● Procedure

1. With the scissors, cut a slit in the construction paper and tape it over the flashlight lens.

2. Place the mirror at one end of the unlined paper. Push the mirror into lumps of clay so it stands vertically, and tilt the mirror so it leans slightly toward the table.

3. **Measure** with the ruler to find the center of the bottom edge of the mirror, and mark it. Then use the protractor and the ruler to draw a line on the paper perpendicular to the mirror from the mark. Label this line *P*.

4. Draw lines on the paper from the center mark at angles of 30°, 45°, and 60° to line *P*.

5. Turn on the flashlight and place it so the beam is along the 60° line. This is the angle of incidence. Measure and record the angle that the reflected beam makes with line *P*. This is the angle of reflection. If you cannot see the reflected beam, slightly increase the tilt of the mirror.

6. Repeat step 5 for the 30°, 45°, and *P* lines.

● Conclude and Apply

Infer from your results the relationship between the angle of incidence and the angle of reflection.

*C*ommunicating
Your Data

Make a poster that shows your measured angles of reflection for angles of incidence of 30°, 45°, and 60°. Write the relationship between the angles of incidence and reflection at the bottom.

☑ Assessment

Performance Have students work in small groups to examine what happens if a second mirror is placed in the path of the light reflected from the first mirror. Use **Performance Assessment in the Science Classroom,** p. 97.

*C*ommunicating
Your Data

Students can prepare a computer presentation of their data by using graphics software to make the posters.

BENCH TESTED

Purpose Students will investigate light reflection from a plane mirror by comparing the angle of incidence to the angle of reflection. L2 ELL COOP LEARN LS Kinesthetic

Process Skills observe and infer, compare and contrast, recognize cause and effect, measure, communicate

Time Required 50 minutes

Alternate Materials A laser pointer can be used instead of a flashlight.

Safety Precautions Caution students that the edge of the mirror may be sharp. If using a laser pointer, warn students not to look directly into the beam or point the beam toward another person.

● Procedure

Teaching Strategies

• The protractor should be held against the mirror when measuring the angles.

• The slit in the construction paper should be very thin and the construction paper should be held against the face of the flashlight.

Troubleshooting Students may have trouble seeing the beam before and after it reflects off the mirror. Suggest that they experiment with holding the flashlight closer to or farther from the mirror until the beam is clear.

● Conclude and Apply

The angle of incidence equals the angle of reflection.

Refraction and Lenses

as you read

What You'll Learn

- **Determine** why light rays refract.
- **Explain** how convex and concave lenses form images.

Why It's Important

Many of the images you see every day in photographs, on TV, and in movies are made using lenses.

Review Vocabulary

refraction: bending of a wave as it changes speed, moving from one medium to another

New Vocabulary

- lens
- convex lens
- concave lens

Bending of Light Rays

Objects that are in water can sometimes look strange. A pencil in a glass of water sometimes looks as if it's bent, or as if the part of the pencil in air is shifted compared to the part in water. A penny that can't be seen at the bottom of a cup suddenly appears as you add water to the cup. Illusions such as these are due to the bending of light rays as they pass from one material to another. What causes light rays to change direction?

The Speeds of Light The speed of light in empty space is about 300 million m/s. Light passing through a material such as air, water, or glass, however, travels more slowly than this. This is because the atoms that make up the material interact with the light waves and slow them down. **Figure 15** compares the speed of light in some different materials.

Figure 15 Light travels at different speeds in different materials.

Air

The speed of light through air is about 300 million m/s.

Water

The speed of light through water is about 227 million m/s.

Glass

The speed of light through glass is about 197 million m/s.

Diamond

The speed of light through diamond is about 125 million m/s.

The Refraction of Light Waves

Light rays from the part of a pencil that is underwater travel through water, glass, and then air before they reach your eye. The speed of light is different in each of these mediums. What happens when a light wave travels from one medium into another in which its speed is different? If the wave is traveling at an angle to the boundary between the two media, it changes direction, or bends. This bending is due to the change in speed the light wave undergoes as it moves from one medium into the other. The bending of light waves due to a change in speed is called refraction. **Figure 16** shows an example of refraction. The greater the change in speed is, the more the light wave bends, or refracts.

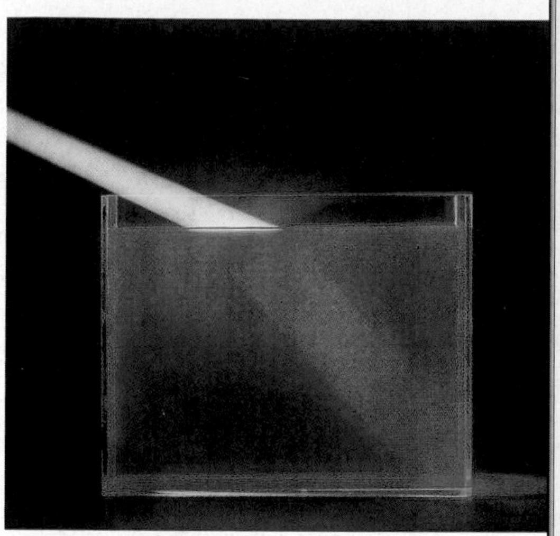

Figure 16 A light ray is bent as it slows down traveling from air into water.

Reading Check *What causes light to bend?*

Why does a change in speed cause the light wave to bend? Think about what happens to the wheels of a car as they move from pavement to mud at an angle, as in **Figure 17.** The wheels slip a little in the mud and don't move forward as fast as they do on the pavement. The wheel that enters the mud first gets slowed down a little, but the other wheel on that axle continues at the original speed. The difference in speed between the two wheels then causes the wheel axle to turn, so the car turns a little. Light waves behave in the same way.

Imagine again a light wave traveling at an angle from air into water. The first part of the wave to enter the water is slowed, just as the car wheel that first hit the mud was slowed. The rest of the wave keeps slowing down as it moves from the air into the water. As long as one part of the light wave is moving faster than the rest of the wave, the wave continues to bend.

Figure 17 An axle turns as the wheels cross the boundary between pavement and mud. **Predict** *how the axle would turn if the wheels were going from mud to pavement.*

Convex and Concave Lenses

Do you like photographing your friends and family? Have you ever watched a bird through binoculars or peered at something tiny through a magnifying glass? All of these activities involve the use of lenses. A **lens** is a transparent object with at least one curved side that causes light to bend. The amount of bending can be controlled by making the sides of the lenses more or less curved. The more curved the sides of a lens are, the more light will be bent after it enters the lens.

2 Teach

Quick Demo

Toy Cars

Materials toy car, pamphlet

Estimated Time five minutes

Procedure Use a toy car to model how light bends when it moves from one medium to another. Place a thin pamphlet on a desk or table. Roll the toy car toward the pamphlet at a 90° angle, and then at a 45° angle. Ask students to observe what happens as the car encounters the pamphlet. L2 LS **Visual-Spatial**

Teacher FYI

Albert Michelson The speed of light in air was measured accurately by Albert Michelson, who won the Nobel Prize in 1907 for his work. Michelson later refined his measurements by using a rotating eight-sided mirror and measuring the time light took to make a round-trip between mountaintops that were a known distance apart.

Fun Fact

Rainbows are formed when sunlight is refracted by water droplets in the air. If light traveled at the same speed in water and air, there would be no rainbows.

Reading Check

Answer a change of speed when the wave moves from one medium to another

Differentiated Instruction

Visually Impaired For these students, make ray diagrams using yarn wrapped around pushpins pushed into cardboard, polystyrene, or plastic foam board. Pushpins should mark the locations of the lens and the light rays. For convex and concave lenses, include pushpins that mark the focal point and focal length of the mirrors. L2 LS **Kinesthetic**

Cultural Diversity

Ibn al-Haytham The Arab scientist Ibn al-Haytham (born A.D. 965) was the first to recognize that refraction occurs because light travels at different speeds through different substances. Have students present reports on other things al-Haytham learned about light. He was possibly the first to use the term *ray of light,* and he developed the idea that vision occurs in response to light hitting the eye. L2 LS **Linguistic** P

Caption Answer

Figure 17 The motion of the axle would look the same as shown in the figure, except that the axle would be moving in the opposite direction—from the mud to the pavement instead of from the pavement to the mud.

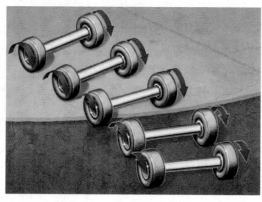

Word Origins Have students find the origin of the word *lens*. It comes from the Latin word *lens* meaning "lentil." Draw a lentil on the board. What type of lens does a lentil resemble? A lens with two convex sides.

IDENTIFYING
Misconceptions

Magnifying Objects Students believe that holding a magnifying glass closer to their eyes will magnify the object more. Make sure they understand that moving the convex lens away from the object makes the image larger.

✓ Reading Check

Answer The focal length is less.

Virtual Labs

Corrective Lenses *How are lenses used to correct vision?*

Figure 18 A convex lens forms an image that depends on the distance from the object to the lens.

Focal point

Optical axis ----

Focal length

A Light rays that are parallel to the optical axis are bent so they pass through the focal point.

Object

Optical axis ----

Image

Image   Object

Optical axis ----

One focal length

One focal length

Two focal lengths

B If the object is more than two focal lengths from the lens, the image formed is smaller than the object and inverted.

C If the object is closer to the lens than one focal length, the image formed is enlarged and upright.

Convex Lenses A lens that is thicker in the center than at the edges is a **convex lens.** In a convex lens, light rays traveling parallel to the optical axis are bent so they pass through the focal point, as shown in **Figure 18A.** The more curved the lens is, the closer the focal point is to the lens, and so the shorter the focal length of the lens is. Because convex lenses cause light waves to meet, they also are called converging lenses.

The image formed by a convex lens is similar to the image formed by a concave mirror. For both, the type of image depends on how far the object is from the mirror or lens. Look at **Figure 18B.** If the object is farther than two focal lengths from the lens, the image seen through the lens is inverted and smaller than the object.

✓ Reading Check
How does the focal length of a convex lens change if the lens becomes more curved?

If the object is closer to the lens than one focal length, then the image formed is right-side up and larger than the object, as shown in **Figure 18C.** A magnifying glass forms an image in this way. As long as the magnifying glass is less than one focal length from the object, you can make the image appear larger by moving the magnifying glass away from the object.

564 CHAPTER 19 Light, Mirrors, and Lenses

LAB DEMONSTRATION

Purpose to show how different materials refract light

Materials dropper, bottle, microscope immersion oil

Preparation The demonstration will not work with Pyrex glass.

Procedure Fill the bottle almost to the top with immersion oil. Put the dropper into the oil. Show the bottle to the students. Squeeze the dropper top and release. Show the bottle again.

Expected Outcome When the dropper filled with air is first put into the bottle, it is vis-

ible. When it is filled with immersion oil, it becomes invisible.

Assessment

Why did the dropper disappear after the oil was added? The glass of the dropper bends light in nearly the same way as the immersion oil does.

Concave Lenses

A lens that is thicker at the edges than in the middle is a **concave lens**. A concave lens also is called a diverging lens. **Figure 19** shows how light rays traveling parallel to the optical axis are bent after passing through a concave lens.

A concave lens causes light rays to diverge, so light rays are not brought to a focus. The type of image that is formed by a concave lens is similar to one that is formed by a convex mirror. The image is upright and smaller than the object.

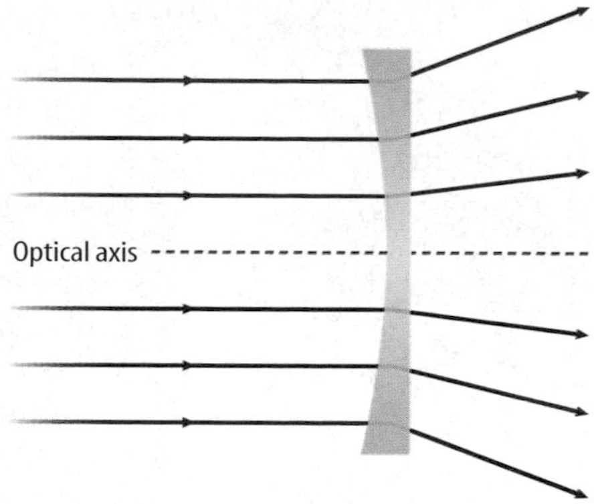

Total Internal Reflection

When you look at a glass window, you sometimes can see your reflection. You see a reflection because some of the light waves reflected from you are reflected back to your eyes when they strike the window. This is an example of a partial reflection—only some of the light waves striking the window are reflected. However, sometimes all the light waves that strike the boundary between two transparent materials can be reflected. This process is called total internal reflection.

The Critical Angle To see how total internal reflection occurs, look at **Figure 20.** Light travels faster in air than in water, and the refracted beam is bent away from the normal. As the angle between the incident beam and the normal increases, the refracted beam bends closer to the air-water boundary. At the same time, more of the light energy striking the boundary is reflected and less light energy passes into the air.

If a light beam in water strikes the boundary so that the angle with the normal is greater than an angle called the critical angle, total internal reflection occurs. Then all the light waves are reflected at the air-water boundary, just as if a mirror were there. The size of the critical angle depends on the two materials involved. For light passing from water to air, the critical angle is about 48 degrees.

Optical axis -

Figure 19 A concave lens causes light rays traveling parallel to the optical axis to diverge.

Figure 20 When a light beam passes from one medium to another, some of its energy is reflected (red) and some is refracted (blue).

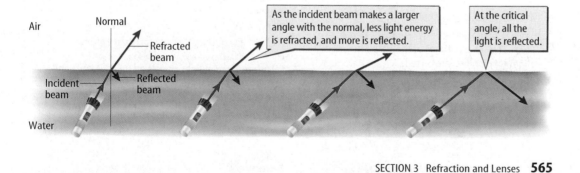

Air Normal

Refracted beam

Incident beam   Reflected beam

Water

As the incident beam makes a larger angle with the normal, less light energy is refracted, and more is reflected.

At the critical angle, all the light is reflected.

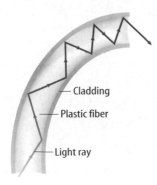

Figure 21 An optical fiber is made of materials that cause total internal reflection to occur. A light beam can travel for many kilometers through an optical fiber and lose almost no energy.

- Cladding
- Plastic fiber
- Light ray

Optical Fibers Optical fibers are thin, flexible, transparent fibers. An optical fiber is like a light pipe. Even if the fiber is bent, light that enters one end of the fiber comes out the other end.

Total internal reflection makes light transmission in optical fibers possible. A thin fiber of glass or plastic is covered with another material called cladding in which light travels faster. When light strikes the boundary between the fiber and the cladding, total internal reflection can occur. In this way, the beam bounces along inside the fiber as shown in **Figure 21.**

Optical fibers are used most commonly in the communications industry. For example, television programs, computer information, and phone conversations can be coded into light signals. These signals then can be sent from one place to another using optical fibers. Because of total internal reflection, signals can't leak from one fiber to another and interfere with others. As a result, the signal is transmitted clearly. One optical fiber the thickness of a human hair can carry thousands of phone conversations.

section 3 review

Summary

The Refraction of Light

- Light travels at different speeds in different materials.
- Refraction occurs when light changes speed as it travels from one material into another.

Convex and Concave Lenses

- A lens is a transparent object with at least one curved side that causes light to bend.
- A convex lens is thicker in the center than at the edges and causes light waves to converge.
- A concave lens is thinner in the center than at the edges and causes light waves to diverge.

Total Internal Reflection

- Total internal reflection occurs at the boundary between two transparent materials when light is completely reflected.
- Optical fibers use total internal reflection to transmit information over long distances with light waves.

Self Check

1. **Compare** the image formed by a concave lens and the image formed by a convex mirror.
2. **Explain** whether you would use a convex lens or a concave lens to magnify an object.
3. **Describe** the image formed by convex lens if an object is less than one focal length from the lens.
4. **Describe** how light rays traveling parallel to the optical axis are bent after they pass through a convex lens.
5. **Infer** If the speed of light were the same in all materials, would a lens cause light rays to bend?
6. **Think Critically** A light wave is bent more when it travels from air to glass than when it travels from air to water. Is the speed of light greater in water or in glass? Explain.

Applying Math

7. **Calculate Time** If light travels at 300,000 km/s and Earth is 150 million km from the Sun, how long does it take light to travel form the Sun to Earth?

Science Online ips.msscience.com/self_check_quiz

section 3 review

1. They are both upright and smaller than the object.
2. convex lens
3. The image is enlarged and upright.
4. They are bent so they pass through the focal point.
5. No, waves would not be bent if they didn't change speed.
6. The speed of light is greater in water. The greater the change in speed, the more the wave is bent. Since the wave is bent less as it travels from air to water, light must slow down less as it moves from air to water.
7. time = distance ÷ speed = 150,000,000 km ÷ 300,000 km/s = 500 s = 8.3 min

Using Mirrors and Lenses

Microscopes

For almost 500 years, lenses have been used to observe objects that are too small to be seen with the unaided eye. The first microscopes were simple and magnified less than 100 times. Today, a compound microscope like the one in **Figure 22** uses a combination of lenses to magnify objects by as much as 2,500 times.

Figure 22 also shows how a microscope forms an image. An object, such as an insect or a drop of water from a pond, is placed close to a convex lens called the objective lens. This lens produces an enlarged image inside the microscope tube. The light rays from that image then pass through a second convex lens called the eyepiece lens. This lens further magnifies the image formed by the objective lens. By using two lenses, a much larger image is formed than a single lens can produce.

Figure 22 A compound microscope uses lenses to magnify objects.

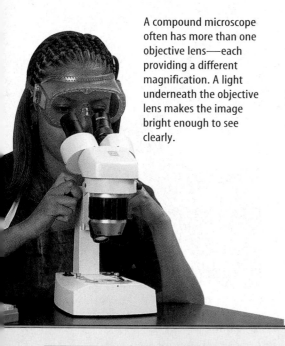

A compound microscope often has more than one objective lens—each providing a different magnification. A light underneath the objective lens makes the image bright enough to see clearly.

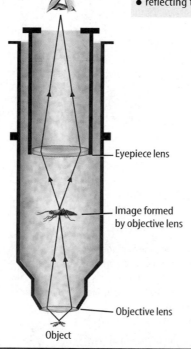

Eyepiece lens

Image formed by objective lens

Objective lens

Object

The objective lens in a compound microscope forms an enlarged image, which is then magnified by the eyepiece lens.

1 Motivate

Bellringer

Section Focus Transparencies also are available on the Interactive Chalkboard CD-ROM.

L2 ELL

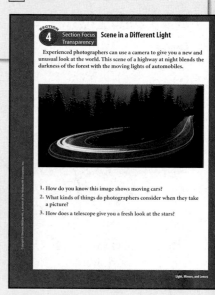

Tie to Prior Knowledge

Lenses and Images Discuss with students situations in which they may have seen objects reduced or enlarged by lenses. Ask them how they think the image on a movie screen becomes so large. The image on the film is enlarged using convex lenses.

567

Section 4 Resource Manager

Chapter *FAST FILE* Resources

Transparency Activity, p. 51

Directed Reading for Content Mastery, pp. 21, 22

MiniLAB, p. 4

Enrichment, p. 34

Reinforcement, p. 30

Lab Worksheet, pp. 7–8

Lab Management and Safety, p. 64

Cultural Diversity, pp. 51, 57

Physical Science Critical Thinking/Problem Solving, p. 22

Science Inquiry Labs, pp. 39–40

Use an Analogy

Collecting Rainwater Ask students how they might collect as much rainwater as possible. One way would be to use large containers that collect many raindrops. Explain that using a large container to collect raindrops is similar to using a large objective lens in a telescope to collect light.

☑ Reading Check

Answer It gathers light from objects to form images that are enlarged by the eyepiece.

Purpose Students will investigate how a water lens affects images.

Materials test tube with stopper, index card, water

Teaching Strategy Have students try the experiment with various liquids of differing indices of refraction.

Troubleshooting If an air bubble enters the test tube as students fill it, have them hold the tube slightly slanted so the bubble stays at one end.

Analysis

1. a convex lens
2. Close to the card, the image was magnified; far from the card, the image was reduced and inverted.

Assessment

Process Ask students to predict how the image would be affected if the test tube was held so that its axis was perpendicular to the line along which the name is written. Have them test their predictions. Use **Performance Assessment in the Science Classroom,** p. 103.

Forming an Image with a Lens

Procedure
1. Fill a **glass test tube** with **water** and seal it with a **stopper.**
2. Write your name on a **10-cm × 10-cm card.** Lay the test tube on the card and observe the appearance of your name.
3. Hold the test tube about 1 cm above the card and observe the appearance of your name through it again.
4. Observe what happens to your name as you slowly move the test tube away from the card.

Analysis
1. Is the water-filled test tube a concave or a convex lens?
2. Compare the images formed when the test tube was close to the card and far from the card.

Telescopes

Just as microscopes are used to magnify very small objects, telescopes are used to examine objects that are very far away. The first telescopes were made at about the same time as the first microscopes. Much of what is known about the Moon, the solar system, and the distant universe has come from images and other information gathered by telescopes.

Refracting Telescopes The simplest **refracting telescopes** use two convex lenses to form an image of a distant object. Just as in a compound microscope, light passes through an objective lens that forms an image. That image is then magnified by an eyepiece, as shown in **Figure 23.**

An important difference between a telescope and a microscope is the size of the objective lens. The main purpose of a telescope is not to magnify an image. A telescope's main purpose is to gather as much light as possible from distant objects. The larger an objective lens is, the more light can enter it. This makes images of faraway objects look brighter and more detailed when they are magnified by the eyepiece. With a large enough objective lens, it's possible to see stars and galaxies that are many trillions of kilometers away. **Figure 23** also shows the largest refracting telescope ever made.

☑ Reading Check

How does a telescope's objective lens enable distant objects to be seen?

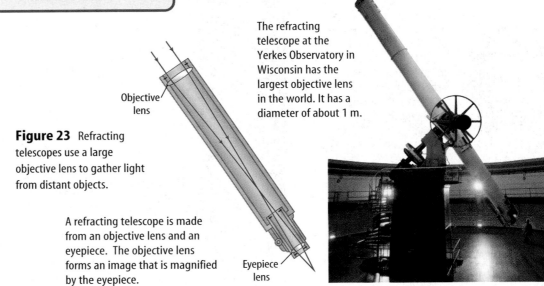

The refracting telescope at the Yerkes Observatory in Wisconsin has the largest objective lens in the world. It has a diameter of about 1 m.

Objective lens

Figure 23 Refracting telescopes use a large objective lens to gather light from distant objects.

A refracting telescope is made from an objective lens and an eyepiece. The objective lens forms an image that is magnified by the eyepiece.

Eyepiece lens

Figure 24 Reflecting telescopes gather light by using a concave mirror.

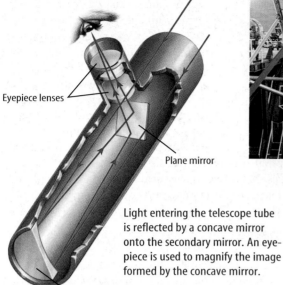

Eyepiece lenses

Plane mirror

Light entering the telescope tube is reflected by a concave mirror onto the secondary mirror. An eyepiece is used to magnify the image formed by the concave mirror.

Concave mirror

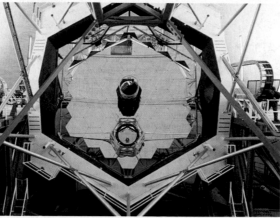

The Keck telescope in Mauna Kea, Hawaii, is the largest reflecting telescope in the world.

Reflecting Telescopes Refracting telescopes have size limitations. One problem is that the objective lens can be supported only around its edges. If the lens is extremely large, it cannot be supported enough to keep the glass from sagging slightly under its own weight. This causes the image that the lens forms to become distorted.

Reflecting telescopes can be made much larger than refracting telescopes. **Reflecting telescopes** have a concave mirror instead of a concave objective lens to gather the light from distant objects. As shown in **Figure 24**, the large concave mirror focuses light onto a secondary mirror that directs it to the eyepiece, which magnifies the image.

Because only the one reflecting surface on the mirror needs to be made carefully and kept clean, telescope mirrors are less expensive to make and maintain than lenses of a similar size. Also, mirrors can be supported not only at their edges but also on their backsides. They can be made much larger without sagging under their own weight. The Keck telescope in Hawaii, shown in **Figure 24,** is the largest reflecting telescope in the world. Its large concave mirror is 10 m in diameter, and is made of 36 six-sided segments. Each segment is 1.8 m in size and the segments are pieced together to form the mirror.

INTEGRATE History

The First Telescopes
A Dutch eyeglass maker, Hans Lippershey, constructed a refracting telescope in 1608 that had a magnification of 3. In 1609 Galileo built a refracting telescope with a magnification of 20. By 1668, the first reflecting telescope was built by Isaac Newton that had a metal concave mirror with a diameter of about 5 cm. More than a century later, William Herschel built the first large reflecting telescopes with mirrors as large as 50 cm. Research the history of the telescope and make a timeline showing important events.

Reading Check

Answer a convex lens

Make a Model

Pinhole Camera A pinhole camera produces an inverted image without a lens. The simplest form of a pinhole camera is just a box with a tiny hole at one end covered by a simple shutter. Light entering the hole is focused onto film in the box to produce an image. Have students work in pairs to research and make their own pinhole cameras. Ask students why long exposure times are necessary to take a picture with a pinhole camera. Only a small amount of light can pass through the pinhole, so that the image formed is very dim. [L2] [LS] **Kinesthetic**

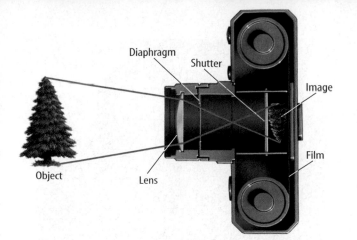

Figure 25 A camera uses a convex lens to form an image on a piece of light-sensitive film. The image formed by a camera lens is smaller than the object and is inverted.

Science Online

Topic: Lasers
Visit ips.msscience.com for Web links to information about uses for lasers.

Activity Make a table listing different types of lasers and how they are used.

Cameras

You probably see photographs taken by cameras almost every day. A typical camera uses a convex lens to form an image on a section of film, just as your eye's lens focuses an image on your retina. The convex lens has a short focal length, so it forms an image that is smaller than the object and inverted on the film. Look at the camera shown in **Figure 25.** When the shutter is open, the convex lens focuses an image on a piece of film that is sensitive to light. Light-sensitive film contains chemicals that undergo chemical reactions when light hits it. The brighter parts of the image affect the film more than the darker parts do.

Reading Check *What type of lens does a camera use?*

If too much light strikes the film, the image formed on the film is overexposed and looks washed out. On the other hand, if too little light reaches the film, the photograph might be too dark. To control how much light reaches the film, many cameras have a device called a diaphragm. The diaphragm is opened to let more light onto the film and closed to reduce the amount of light that strikes the film.

Lasers

Perhaps you've seen the narrow, intense beams of laser light used in a laser light show. Intense laser beams are also used for different kinds of surgery. Why can laser beams be so intense? One reason is that a laser beam doesn't spread out as much as ordinary light as it travels.

Spreading Light Beams Suppose you shine a flashlight on a wall in a darkened room. The size of the spot of light on the wall depends on the distance between the flashlight and the wall. As the flashlight moves farther from the wall, the spot of light gets larger. This is because the beam of light produced by the flashlight spreads out as it travels. As a result, the energy carried by the light beam is spread over an increasingly larger area as the distance from the flashlight gets larger. As the energy is spread over a larger area, the energy becomes less concentrated and the intensity of the beam decreases.

570 CHAPTER 19 Light, Mirrors, and Lenses

Differentiated Instruction

Visually Impaired Suggest that visually impaired students work with sighted partners for the Challenge Activity. The sighted student should allow the visually impaired student to feel the parts inside the camera while the sighted student describes them.

Challenge Obtain a disposable camera. Discharge the capacitor by taking a picture and removing the battery. Have the students take the camera apart and remove the plastic lens assembly. Ask students why multiple lenses are necessary. The second convex lens also causes light rays to converge, shortening the focal length of the first lens. This creates a lens with a longer focal length in a shorter space. [L3]

Using Laser Light Laser light is different from the light produced by the flashlight in several ways, as shown in **Figure 26.** One difference is that in a beam of laser light, the crests and troughs of the light waves overlap, so the waves are in phase.

Because a laser beam doesn't spread out as much as ordinary light, a large amount of energy can be applied to a very small area. This property enables lasers to be used for cutting and welding materials and as a replacement for scalpels in surgery. Less intense laser light is used for such applications as reading and writing to CDs or in grocery store bar-code readers. Surveyors and builders use lasers to measure distances, angles, and heights. Laser beams also are used to transmit information through space or through optical fibers.

Figure 26 Laser light is different from the light produced by a lightbulb.

The light from a bulb contains waves with many different wavelengths that are out of phase and traveling in different directions.

The light from a laser contains waves with only one wavelength that are in phase and traveling in the same direction.

---

section 4 review

Summary

Microscopes, Telescopes, and Cameras

- A compound microscope uses an objective lens and an eyepiece lens to form an enlarged image of an object.
- A refracting telescope contains a large objective lens to gather light and a smaller eyepiece lens to magnify the image.
- A reflecting telescope uses a large concave mirror to gather light and an eyepiece lens to magnify the image.
- The image formed by a telescope becomes brighter and more detailed as the size of the objective lens or concave mirror increases.
- A camera uses a convex lens to form an image on light-sensitive film.

Laser Light

- Light from a laser contains light waves that are in phase, have only one wavelength, and travel in the same direction.
- Because laser light does not spread out much as it travels the energy it carries can be applied over a very small area.

Self Check

1. **Explain** why the concave mirror of a reflecting telescope can be made much larger than the objective lens of a refracting telescope.
2. **Describe** how a beam of laser light is different than the beam of light produced by a flashlight.
3. **Explain** why the objective lens of a refracting telescope is much larger than the objective lens of a compound microscope.
4. **Infer** how the image produced by a compound microscope would be different if the eyepiece lens were removed from the microscope.
5. **Think Critically** Explain why the intensity of the light in a flashlight beam decreases as the flashlight moves farther away.

Applying Math

6. **Calculate Image Size** The size of an image is related to the magnification of an optical instrument by the following formula:

   Image size = magnification × object size

   A blood cell has a diameter of 0.001 cm. How large is the image formed by a microscope with a magnification of 1,000?

Activity

Photography Have students identify the variables in a camera that can be controlled to gain desired effects in a photograph. Variables include aperture, shutter speed, lenses, film speed, and flashes.

Quick Demo

Camera Lenses

Materials regular camera lens from a 35 mm camera, a telephoto lens, and a wide angle lens

Estimated Time 15 minutes

Procedure Hold lenses up in front of students. Point out that most camera lenses actually contain more than one lens. Organize the class into groups, and give students in each group the opportunity to look through the lenses.

3 Assess

DAILY INTERVENTION

Check for Understanding

Oral Have students list to a partner the optical tools discussed in this section and take turns describing how they work.

Reteach

Photography Have students hypothesize why photographs may not come out as perfectly as they expect. Why would a photograph be too dark? Possible answer: The diaphram let in too little light. Why would a photograph be out of focus? Possible answer: The lens was in the wrong position and didn't focus the image exactly on the film. L2 LS
Logical-Mathematical

---

section 4 review

1. The objective lens of a refracting telescope can be supported only around its edges, and the lens's weight can cause it to bend slightly if it is too large. A reflecting telescope uses a mirror that can be supported on its nonreflecting surface.

2. A flashlight beam spreads out as it travels from the flashlight and contains waves of many wavelengths. A laser beam contains waves of only one wavelength and does not spread out as it travels from the laser light source.

3. The lens is large so it can collect a large amount of light.
4. The image would be smaller.
5. As the distance from the flashlight increases, the light in the beam is spread over a larger area.
6. image size = 0.001 cm × 1,000 = 1 cm

Assessment

Portfolio Have each student make a drawing that shows how a radio telescope collects radio waves. Use **Performance Assessment in the Science Classroom,** p. 127. P

Real-World Question

Purpose Students investigate the images formed by a convex lens and observe how the image is affected when the distance between the lens and the light source is altered. L2 LS **Kinesthetic**

Process Skills observe and infer, recognize cause and effect, measure in SI, predict, communicate, make and use tables

Time Required one hour

Procedure

Materials The flashlight should have a narrow, intense beam to produce a clear image. If possible, you should be able to adjust the collimation of the beam. To help students clearly see how the image size has changed, you may wish to have them mark off a centimeter or millimeter scale on the cardboard ahead of time. You could also print these out on cardstock using a computer.

Alternate Materials Inexpensive lens supports are available from science supply companies. These can be attached to a meterstick to provide a clean, secure support. Similar supports are available for holding the cards.

Image Formation by a Convex Lens

Real-World Question

The type of image formed by a convex lens, also called a converging lens, is related to the distance of the object from the lens. This distance is called the object distance. The location of the image also is related to the distance of the object from the lens. The distance from the lens to the image is called the image distance. How are the image distance and object distance related for a convex lens?

Goals

- **Measure** the image distance as the object distance changes.
- **Observe** the type of image formed as the object distance changes.

Possible Materials

convex lens
modeling clay
meterstick
flashlight
masking tape
20-cm square piece of cardboard with a white surface

Safety Precautions

Procedure

1. **Design** a data table to record your data. Make three columns in your table —one column for the object distance, another for the image distance, and the third for the type of image.

Convex Lens Data

Object Distance (m)	Image Distance (m)	Image Type
1.00	0.43	inverted, smaller
0.50	0.75	inverted, larger
0.25	1.50	upright, larger

2. Use the modeling clay to make the lens stand upright on the lab table.
3. Form the letter F on the glass surface of the flashlight with masking tape.

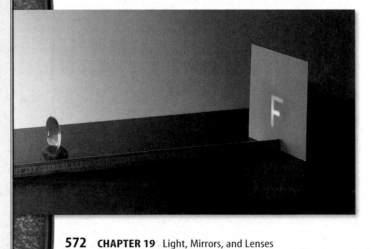

4. Turn on the flashlight and place it 1 m from the lens. Position the flashlight so the flashlight beam is shining through the lens.
5. **Record** the distance from the flashlight to the lens in the object distance column in your data table.
6. Hold the cardboard vertically upright on the other side of the lens, and move it back and forth until a sharp image of the letter F is obtained.

572 **CHAPTER 19** Light, Mirrors, and Lenses

Alternative Inquiry Lab

Provide students with flashlights, convex lenses, and metersticks. Have them devise a way to see if the flashlight beam is focused by the convex lens. Then have the students determine the focal length of two different convex lenses. Check their focal lengths against the lenses' known focal length.

Curriculum Connection

Art Artists must have a basic understanding of optics when painting a picture that shows light reflected by surfaces or transmitted through objects. Have students use what they have learned about light shining through convex lenses to make paintings or drawings showing sunlight shining through a glass of water.

7. **Measure** the distance of the card from the lens using the meterstick, and record this distance in the Image Distance column in your data table.

8. **Record** in the third column of your data table whether the image is upright or inverted, and smaller or larger.

9. Repeat steps 4 through 8 for object distances of 0.50 m and 0.25 m and record your data in your data table.

● *Analyze Your Data*

1. **Describe** any observed relationship between the object distance, and the image type.

2. **Identify** the variables involved in determining the image type for a convex lens.

● *Conclude and Apply*

1. **Explain** how the image distance changed as the object distance decreased.

2. **Identify** how the image changed as the object distance decreased.

3. **Predict** what would happen to the size of the image if the flashlight were much farther away than 1 m.

Communicating
Your Data

Demonstrate this lab to a third-grade class and explain how it works. **For more help, refer to the Science Skill Handbook.**

LAB 573

Teaching Strategies

- Slightly darkening the room will make the images easier to observe.
- The data obtained by students will depend on the type of lens and the focal length of the lens. The data in the data table are for a convex lens with a focal length of 30 cm.

● *Analyze Your Data*

Answers to Questions

1. Decreasing the object distance increases the image distance and increases the size of the image. If the object distance is less than the focal length of the lens, the image is virtual and can't be projected on the cardboard.
2. focal length of lens and object distance

Error Analysis Discuss with students how the image would be affected if the flashlight beam were too spread out.

● *Conclude and Apply*

1. It increased.
2. It became larger. When the object distance was less than the focal length of the lens, the image could no longer be seen on the cardboard.
3. It would be too small to see.

☑ Assessment

Oral How would the data obtained for the image distance and the image type differ if a double convex lens were used instead of a plano-convex lens? The lens would bend the light more so the image distance and the image would be smaller. Use **Performance Assessment in the Science Classroom,** p. 89.

Communicating
Your Data

When demonstrating the lab to the third-grade class, have students make simple drawings that show how the curve of the lens redirects the light to cause the image inversion and the increase or decrease in size.

Oops! Accidents in SCIENCE
SOMETIMES GREAT DISCOVERIES HAPPEN BY ACCIDENT!

Eyeglasses
Inventor Unknown

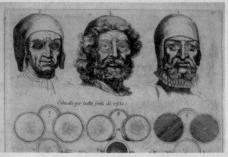

This Italian engraving from the 1600s shows some different types of glasses.

"It is not yet twenty years since the art of making spectacles, one of the most useful arts on Earth, was discovered. I, myself, have seen and conversed with the man who made them first."

This quote from an Italian monk dates back to 1306 and is one of the first historical records to refer to eyeglasses. Unfortunately, the monk, Giordano, never actually named the man he met. Thus, the inventor of eyeglasses remains unknown.

The mystery exists, in part, because different cultures in different places used some type of magnifying tool to improve their vision. For example, a rock-crystal lens, made by early Assyrians who lived 3,500 years ago in what is now Iraq, may have been used to improve vision. About 2,000 years ago, the Roman writer Seneca looked through a glass globe of water to make the letters appear bigger in the books he read. By the tenth century, glasses had been invented in China, but they were used to keep away bad luck, not to improve vision.

In the mid 1400s in Europe, eyeglasses began to appear in paintings of scholars, clergy, and the upper classes—eyeglasses were so expensive that only the rich could afford them. In the early 1700s, for example, glasses cost roughly $200, which is comparable to thousands of dollars today. By the mid-1800s, improvements in manufacturing techniques made eyeglasses much less expensive to make, and thus this important invention became widely available to people of all walks of life.

How Eyeglasses Work
Eyeglasses are used to correct farsightedness and nearsightedness, as well as other vision problems. The eye focuses light rays to form an image on a region called the retina on the back of the eye. Farsighted people have difficulty seeing things close up because light rays from nearby objects do not converge enough to form an image on the retina. This problem can be corrected by using convex lenses that cause light rays to converge before they enter the eye. Nearsighted people have problems seeing distant objects because light rays from far-away objects are focused in front of the retina. Concave lenses that cause light rays to diverge are used to correct this vision problem.

Research In many parts of the world, people have no vision care, and eye diseases and poor vision go untreated. Research the work of groups that bring eye care to people.

Science Online
For more information, visit
ips.msscience.com/oops

Resources for Teachers and Students
Samuele Mazza, *Spectacles*, San Francisco, Chronical Books, 1996

Margery Nichelason, "What's Old and New in Eyewear," in *Cricket*, May 1995, pp. 42–44

Anne Harding, "A Closer Look at Eye Surgery," in *Harvard Health Letter*, June 1996, Vol. 21 Issue 8, p. 4

Reviewing Main Ideas

Section 1 Properties of Light

1. Light waves can be absorbed, reflected, or transmitted when they strike an object.

2. The color of an object depends on the wavelengths of light reflected by the object.

Section 2 Reflection and Mirrors

1. Light reflected from the surface of an object obeys the law of reflection—the angle of incidence equals the angle of reflection.

2. Concave mirrors cause light waves to converge, or meet. Convex mirrors cause light waves to diverge, or spread apart.

Section 3 Refraction and Lenses

1. Light waves bend, or refract, when they change speed in traveling from one medium to another.

2. A convex lens causes light waves to converge, and a concave lens causes light waves to diverge.

Section 4 Using Mirrors and Lenses

1. A compound microscope uses a convex objective lens to form an enlarged image that is further enlarged by an eyepiece.

2. A refracting telescope uses a large objective lens and an eyepiece lens to form an image of a distant object.

3. A reflecting telescope uses a large concave mirror that gathers light and an eyepiece lens to form an image of a distant object.

4. Cameras use a convex lens to form an image on light-sensitive film.

Visualizing Main Ideas

Copy and complete the following concept map.

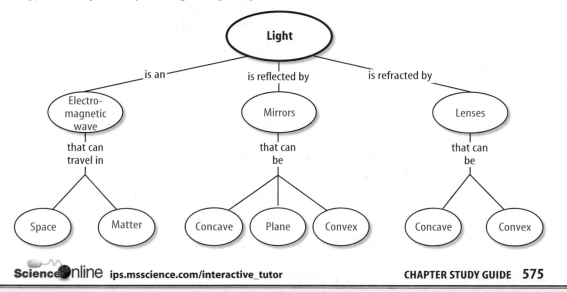

Reviewing Main Ideas

Summary statements can be used by students to review the major concepts of the chapter.

Visualizing Main Ideas

See student page.

Science Online

Visit ips.msscience.com
/self_check_quiz
/interactive_tutor
/vocabulary_puzzlemaker
/chapter_review
/standardized_test

Assessment Transparency

For additional assessment questions, use the *Assessment Transparency* located in the transparency book.

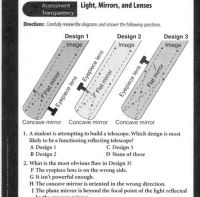

Identifying Misconceptions

Assess

Use the assessment as follow-up to page F after students have completed the chapter.

Procedure Ask students to imagine that at exactly 1:15 P.M. our Sun was magically turned off. Given that Earth is about 150,000,000 km from the Sun, at what time would Earth go dark? Pluto is about 40 times farther from the Sun than Earth is. At what time would someone on Pluto see the Sun go dark? Have students write, then discuss their answers.

Expected Outcome Darkness would fall on Earth at 1:23 P.M. On Pluto it would get dark at 6:35 P.M.

Using Vocabulary

1. medium
2. light ray
3. focal length
4. focal point
5. lens
6. convex
7. reflecting telescope

Checking Concepts

8. D	14. B
9. C	15. D
10. A	16. D
11. C	17. C
12. A	18. B
13. C	

Using Vocabulary

concave lens p. 565	lens p. 563
convex lens p. 564	light ray p. 550
focal length p. 558	medium p. 551
focal point p. 558	reflecting telescope p. 569
law of reflection p. 555	refracting telescope p. 568

Complete each statement using a word or words from the vocabulary list above.

1. A _____ is the material in which a light wave travels.

2. A narrow beam of light that travels in a straight line is a _____.

3. The _____ is the distance from a lens or a mirror to the focal point.

4. Light rays traveling parallel to the optical axis of a convex lens are bent so they pass through the _____.

5. A transparent object with at least one curved surface that causes light waves to bend is a _____.

6. A _____ is thicker in the center than it is at the edges.

7. A _____ uses a large concave mirror to gather light from distant objects.

Checking Concepts

Choose the word or phrase that best answers the question.

8. Light waves travel the fastest through which of the following?
   A) air
   B) diamond
   C) water
   D) a vacuum

9. Which of the following determines the color of light?
   A) a prism
   B) its refraction
   C) its wavelength
   D) its incidence

10. If an object reflects red and green light, what color does the object appear to be?
    A) yellow
    B) red
    C) green
    D) purple

11. If an object absorbs all the light that hits it, what color is it?
    A) white
    B) blue
    C) black
    D) green

12. What type of image is formed by a plane mirror?
    A) upright
    B) inverted
    C) magnified
    D) all of these

13. How is the angle of incidence related to the angle of reflection?
    A) It's greater.
    B) It's smaller.
    C) It's the same.
    D) It's not focused.

14. Which of the following can be used to magnify objects?
    A) a concave lens
    B) a convex lens
    C) a convex mirror
    D) all of these

15. Which of the following describes the light waves that make up laser light?
    A) same wavelength
    B) same direction
    C) in phase
    D) all of these

16. What is an object that reflects some light and transmits some light called?
    A) colored
    B) diffuse
    C) opaque
    D) translucent

17. What is the main purpose of the objective lens or concave mirror in a telescope?
    A) invert images
    B) reduce images
    C) gather light
    D) magnify images

18. Which of the following types of mirror can form an image larger than the object?
    A) convex
    B) concave
    C) plane
    D) all of these

Science Online ips.msscience.com/vocabulary_puzzlemaker

Use the Exam*View*® Pro Testmaker CD-ROM to:

- create multiple versions of tests
- create modified tests with one mouse click for inclusion students
- edit existing questions and add your own questions
- build tests aligned with state standards using built-in State Curriculum Tags
- change English tests to Spanish with one mouse click and vice versa

Thinking Critically

19. Diagram Suppose you can see a person's eyes in a mirror. Draw a diagram to determine whether or not that person can see you.

20. Determine A singer is wearing a blue outfit. What color spotlights could be used to make the outfit appear to be black?

21. Form a hypothesis to explain why sometimes you can see two images of yourself reflected from a window at night.

22. Explain why a rough surface, such as a road, becomes shiny in appearance and a better reflector when it is wet.

23. Infer An optical fiber is made of a material that forms the fiber and a different material that forms the outer covering. For total internal reflection to occur, how does the speed of light in the fiber compare with the speed of light in the outer covering?

Use the table below to answer question 24.

Magnification by a Convex Lens

Object Distance (cm)	Magnification
25	4.00
30	2.00
40	1.00
60	0.50
100	0.25

24. Use a Table In the table above, the object distance is the distance of the object from the lens. The magnification is the image size divided by the object size. If the focal length of the lens is 20 cm, how does the size of the image change as the object gets farther from the focal point?

25. Calculate What is the ratio of the distance at which the magnification equals 1.00 to the focal length of the lens?

 ips.msscience.com/chapter_review

Performance Activities

26. Oral Presentation Investigate the types of mirrors used in fun houses. Explain how these mirrors are formed, and why they produce distorted images. Demonstrate your findings to your class.

27. Reverse Writing Images are reversed left to right in a plane mirror. Write a note to a friend that can be read only in a plane mirror.

28. Design an experiment to determine the focal length of a convex lens. Write a report describing your experiment, including a diagram.

Applying Math

Use the graph below to answer questions 29 and 30.

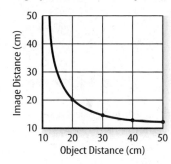

29. Image Position The graph shows how the distance of an image from a convex lens is related to the distance of the object from the lens. How does the position of the image change as the object gets closer to the lens?

30. Magnification The magnification of the image equals the image distance divided by the object distance. At what object distance does the magnification equal 2?

CHAPTER REVIEW **577**

Thinking Critically

19. Yes. Light rays bouncing off your eyes will be reflected by the mirror into the other person's eyes.

20. Red or green spotlights would make the outfit appear black. These spotlights do not contain any blue light that the outfit could reflect.

21. One image is caused by a reflection from the inside surface of the glass, and one is caused by reflection from the outside surface of glass.

22. The water fills in irregularities in the surface, making it smooth.

23. For internal reflection to occur, the speed of light in the fiber must be less than the speed of light in the outer covering.

24. The size of the image decreases as the object moves farther from the focal point.

25. The ratio is (40 cm)/(20 cm) = 2.

Performance Activities

26. Funhouse mirrors are plane mirrors that are bent so that different sections of the mirror are concave or convex. The convex parts make the object appear shorter, and the concave parts make the object appear longer.

27. Check students' notes; they should be upright and reversed left to right. Use **PASC,** p. 139.

28. One possible experiment is to use the setup in the 2-page lab. Determine location of flashlight where image produced goes from being inverted to upright. The distance from this location to the lens is close to the focal length.

Applying Math

National Math Standards

1, 5, 6, 9

29. As the object gets closer to the lens, the image gets farther.

30. 15 cm

Assessment Resources

▼ **Reproducible Masters**
Chapter *Fast File* Resources
Chapter Review, pp. 41–42
Chapter Tests, pp. 43–46
Assessment Transparency Activity, p. 55
Glencoe Science Web site
Chapter Review Test
Standardized Test Practice

Glencoe Technology
Assessment Transparency
Exam*View*® Pro Testmaker
MindJogger Videoquiz
Interactive Chalkboard

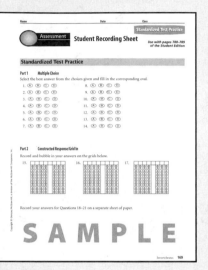

Answer Sheet A practice answer sheet can be found at ips.msscience.com/answer_sheet.

Part 1 ❚Multiple Choice

1. C   **6.** A
2. D   **7.** B
3. B   **8.** C
4. A   **9.** B
5. A   **10.** D

Part 2 ❚Short Response

11. Yes, because it will speed up when traveling from the diamond into air.

12. convex; upright and smaller

13. paper—red; print—black

14. 60°

15. Both are light that travel in waves in one direction. Flashlight beams have many different wavelengths that are out of phase, while laser light contains waves with only one wavelength that are in phase.

16. Since magenta light is a mixture of red and blue light, the outfit could reflect both these colors of light. In red light, the outfit would look red. In blue light, the outfit would look blue. In green light it would look black.

Part 1 ❚Multiple Choice

Record your answers on the answer sheet provided by your teacher or on a sheet of paper.

1. Which of the following describes an object that allows no light to pass through it?
  A. transparent   **C.** opaque
  B. translucent   **D.** diffuse

2. Which statement is always true about the image formed by a concave lens?
  A. It is upside down and larger than the object.
  B. It is upside down and smaller than the object.
  C. It is upright and larger than the object.
  D. It is upright and smaller than the object.

Use the figure below to answer questions 3 and 4.

3. Which of the following describes the process occurring in the upper panel of the figure?
  A. refraction
  B. diffuse reflection
  C. regular reflection
  D. total internal reflection

4. The surface in the lower panel of the figure would be like which of the following?
  A. a mirror   **C.** a sheet of paper
  B. waxed paper   **D.** a painted wall

5. Why does a leaf look green?
  A. It reflects green light.
  B. It absorbs green light.
  C. It reflects all colors of light.
  D. It reflects all colors except green.

6. What does a refracting telescope use to form an image of a distant object?
  A. two convex lenses
  B. a concave mirror and a plane mirror
  C. two concave lenses
  D. two concave mirrors

7. Through which of the following does light travel the slowest?
  A. air   **C.** water
  B. diamond   **D.** vacuum

8. What is the bending of a light wave due to a change in speed?
  A. reflection   **C.** refraction
  B. diffraction   **D.** transmission

Use the figure below to answer questions 9 and 10.

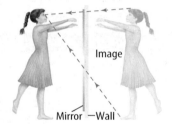

Image

Mirror —Wall

9. If the girl is standing 1 m from the mirror, where will her image seem to be located?
  A. 2 m behind the mirror
  B. 1 m behind the mirror
  C. 2 m in front of the mirror
  D. 1 m in front of the mirror

10. Which of the following describes the image of the girl formed by the plane mirror?
  A. It will be upside down.
  B. It will be in front of the mirror.
  C. It will be larger than the girl.
  D. It will be reversed left to right.

578 STANDARDIZED TEST PRACTICE

17. less than one focal length from the lens

Part 3 ❚Open Ended

18. On a calm day, the water has a smooth surface that would produce a sharp image. On a windy day, the water's surface is uneven.

19. A thin fiber of glass or plastic is covered with another material in which light travels faster, so total internal reflection can occur. So the beam of light bounces along inside the fiber. Optical fibers are used to send television, computer, or telephone information.

20. When the light source is placed at the focal point, a beam of parallel rays is formed. Flashlights and car headlights use concave mirrors to produce directed beams of light.

21. The focal point is farther from the lens.

Part 2 | Short Response/Grid In

Record your answers on the answer sheet provided by your teacher or on a sheet of paper.

11. Light travels slower in diamond than in air. Explain whether total internal reflection could occur for a light wave traveling in the diamond toward the diamond's surface.

Use the figure below to answer question 12.

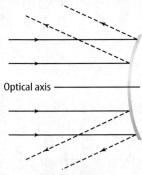

Optical axis

12. Identify the type of mirror shown in the figure and describe the image this mirror forms.

13. Under white light the paper of this page looks white and the print looks black. What color would the paper and the print appear to be under red light?

14. A light ray strikes a plane mirror such that the angle of incidence is 30°. What is the angle between the light ray and the surface of the mirror?

15. Contrast the light beam from a flashlight and a laser light beam.

16. An actor on stage is wearing a magenta outfit. Explain what color the outfit would appear in red light, in blue light, and in green light.

17. To use a convex lens as a magnifying lens, where must the object be located?

Part 3 | Open Ended

Record your answers on a sheet of paper.

18. Explain why you can see the reflection of trees in the water of a lake on a calm day, but not a very windy day.

19. Describe how total internal reflection enables optical fibers to transmit light over long distances.

20. What happens when a source of light is placed at the focal point of a concave mirror? Give an example.

Use the illustration below to answer question 21.

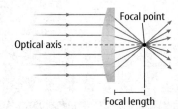

Focal point

Optical axis

Focal length

21. Describe how the position of the focal point changes as the lens becomes flatter and less curved.

22. Compare the images formed by a concave mirror when an object is between the focal point and the mirror and when an object is beyond the focal point.

23. Explain why increasing the size of the concave mirror in a reflecting telescope improves the images formed.

Test-Taking Tip

Organize Your Main Points For essay questions, spend a few minutes listing and organizing the main points that you plan to discuss. Make sure to do all of this work on your scratch paper, not your answer sheet.

Question 19 Organize your discussion points by first listing what you know about optical fibers and total internal reflection.

Rubrics

The following rubrics are sample scoring devices for short response and open-ended questions.

Short Response

Points	Description
2	The student demonstrates a thorough understanding of the science of the task. The response may contain minor flaws that do not detract from the demonstration of a thorough understanding.
1	The student has provided a response that is only partially correct.
0	The student has provided a completely incorrect solution or no response at all.

Open Ended

Points	Description
4	The student demonstrates a thorough understanding of the science of the task. The response may contain minor flaws that do not detract from the demonstration of a thorough understanding.
3	The student demonstrates an understanding of the science of the task. The response is essentially correct and demonstrates an essential but less than thorough understanding of the science.
2	The student demonstrates only a partial understanding of the science of the task. Although the student may have used the correct approach to a solution or may have provided a correct solution, the work lacks an essential understanding of the underlying science concepts.
1	The student demonstrates a very limited understanding of the science of the task. The response is incomplete and exhibits many flaws.
0	The student provides a completely incorrect solution or no response at all.

---

22. When the object is between the focal point and the mirror, the image formed is upright and enlarged. When the object is beyond the focal point, the image formed is inverted.

23. the greater the amount of light gathered by a concave mirror, the brighter the image

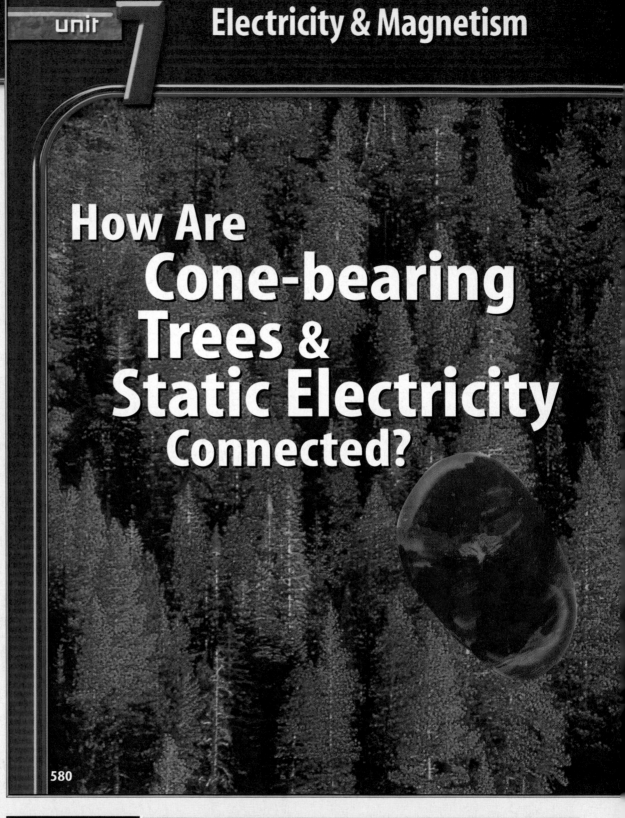

Electricity & Magnetism

Unit Contents

WebQuest **Hybrid Vehicles** is an investigation into the new technology being designed and produced by car manufacturers. Students will research the different uses of hybrid vehicles, how they work, and the reasons manufacturers are producing them. Students will assess the advantages and disadvantages of each type of hybrid vehicle and answer a set of questions.

How Are Cone-bearing Trees & Static Electricity Connected?

580

PROJECT

CRISS℠

Study Skills

Read—Recall—Check—Summarize Have students use the following strategy to strengthen their recall abilities, focus on main ideas, and summarize important information. Have the entire class *read* a particularly challenging section in this unit. Then have them *recall* the main ideas of that section as a group. Ask them to go back into the reading to *check* the details they brainstormed to make sure they are accurate. Then have them use the brainstorming notes to *summarize* what they have read. This technique can be used for each topic presented in the unit for better understanding of difficult concepts.

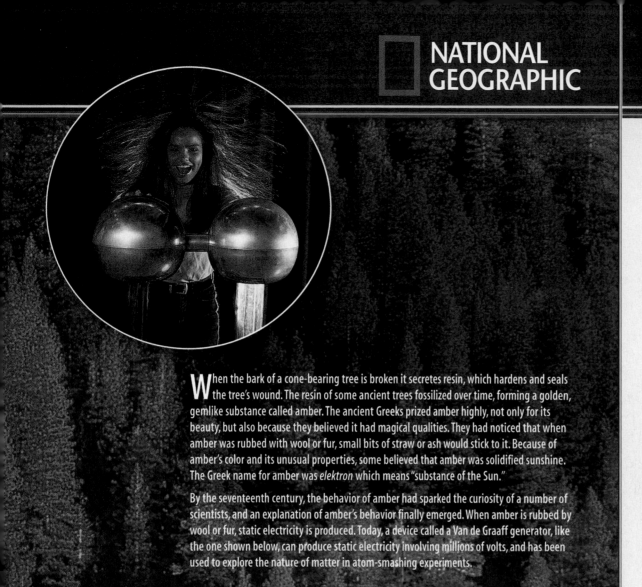

NATIONAL GEOGRAPHIC

When the bark of a cone-bearing tree is broken it secretes resin, which hardens and seals the tree's wound. The resin of some ancient trees fossilized over time, forming a golden, gemlike substance called amber. The ancient Greeks prized amber highly, not only for its beauty, but also because they believed it had magical qualities. They had noticed that when amber was rubbed with wool or fur, small bits of straw or ash would stick to it. Because of amber's color and its unusual properties, some believed that amber was solidified sunshine. The Greek name for amber was *elektron* which means "substance of the Sun."

By the seventeenth century, the behavior of amber had sparked the curiosity of a number of scientists, and an explanation of amber's behavior finally emerged. When amber is rubbed by wool or fur, static electricity is produced. Today, a device called a Van de Graaff generator, like the one shown below, can produce static electricity involving millions of volts, and has been used to explore the nature of matter in atom-smashing experiments.

unit projects

Visit ips.msscience.com/unit_project to find project ideas and resources.
Projects include:

- **History** Design a creative bookmark depicting a variety of aspects of Ben Franklin's contributions to science and his country.
- **Career** Discover how magnetic-resonance imaging is used in the medical field and how it compares to traditional X rays.
- **Model** Design an electrifying review game demonstrating your new understanding of electricity and magnetism.

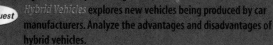 *Hybrid Vehicles* explores new vehicles being produced by car manufacturers. Analyze the advantages and disadvantages of hybrid vehicles.

NATIONAL GEOGRAPHIC
How Are Cone-Bearing Trees & Static Electricity Connected?

The electrical properties of amber were known to the Greeks. The philosopher Thales of Miletus thought that amber's ability to attract feathers and other light objects when the amber was rubbed was evidence of a soul.

In 1600, William Gilbert invented the term *electrica*, from the Latin name for amber, electrum, for any material that could be made to act like amber and hold a static charge.

In 1660, Otto Von Guericke built the first static generator from a glass sphere turned by a handle against woolen cloth. By placing a little mercury in the sphere and evacuating the air, Francis Hauksbee in 1705 was able to make the sphere glow brightly enough to read by.

Section/Objectives	Standards		Labs/Features
Chapter Opener	**National**	**State/Local**	**Launch Lab:** Observing Electric Forces, p. 583 **Foldables:** p. 583
	See pp. 16T–17T for a Key to Standards.		
Section 1 Electric Charge ● 2 sessions 📖 1 block 1. **Describe** how objects can become electrically charged. 2. **Explain** how an electric charge affects other electric charges. 3. **Distinguish** between electric conductors and insulators. 4. **Describe** how electric discharges such as lightning occur.	National Content Standards: UCP.1–UCP.3, UCP.5, A.1, A.2, B.1–B.3		**Visualizing Nerve Impulses,** p. 586 **Science Online,** p. 588
Section 2 Electric Current ● 2 sessions 📖 1 block 5. **Relate** voltage to the electrical energy carried by an electric current. 6. **Describe** a battery and how it produces an electric current. 7. **Explain** electrical resistance.	National Content Standards: UCP.1–UCP.3, UCP.5, A.1, A.2, B.1–B.3		**MiniLAB:** Investigating the Electric Force, p. 592 **Integrate Chemistry,** p. 593 **Integrate History,** p. 594
Section 3 Electric Circuits ● 4 sessions 📖 2 blocks 8. **Explain** how voltage, current, and resistance are related in an electric circuit. 9. **Investigate** the difference between series and parallel circuits. 10. **Determine** the electric power used in a circuit. 11. **Describe** how to avoid dangerous electric shock.	National Content Standards: UCP.1–UCP.3, UCP.5, A.1, A.2, B.1–B.3, F.3, G.3		**Applying Math:** Voltage from a Wall Outlet, p. 597 **MiniLAB:** Identifying Simple Circuits, p. 598 **Applying Math:** Electric Power Used by a Lightbulb, p. 600 **Science Online,** p. 601 **Integrate Life Science,** p. 602 **Lab:** Current in a Parallel Circuit, p. 603 **Lab:** A Model for Voltage and Current, pp. 604–605 **Science and Society:** Fire in the Forest, p. 606

Lab Materials	Reproducible Resources	Section Assessment	Technology
Launch Lab: rubber balloons (2), small bits of paper, piece of wool	**Chapter FAST FILE Resources** Foldables Worksheet, p. 17 Directed Reading Overview, p. 19 Note-taking Worksheets, pp. 33–35	GLENCOE'S ASSESSMENT ADVANTAGE	**TeacherWorks** includes: • Interactive Teacher Edition • Lesson Planner with calendar • Access to all program blacklines • Correlations to standards • Web links
Need materials? Contact Science Kit at 1-800-828-7777 or www.sciencekit.com on the Internet.	**Chapter FAST FILE Resources** Transparency Activity, p. 44 Enrichment, p. 30 Reinforcement, p. 27 Directed Reading, p. 20 Lab Activity, pp. 9–12 **Life Science Critical Thinking/Problem Solving,** p. 2	**Portfolio** Assessment, p. 590 **Performance** Applying Skills, p. 590 **Content** Section Review, p. 590	Section Focus Transparency Teaching Transparency Virtual Labs CD-ROM Guided Reading Audio Program Interactive Chalkboard CD-ROM
MiniLAB: salt, plate, pepper, rubber or plastic comb, wool cloth	**Chapter FAST FILE Resources** Transparency Activity, p. 45 MiniLAB, p. 3 Enrichment, p. 31 Reinforcement, p. 28 Directed Reading, p. 21 Transparency Activity, pp. 47–48 Lab Activity, pp. 13–15	**Portfolio** Assessment, p. 595 **Performance** MiniLAB, p. 592 Applying Skills, p. 595 **Content** Section Review, p. 595	Section Focus Transparency Virtual Labs CD-ROM Guided Reading Audio Program Interactive Chalkboard CD-ROM
MiniLAB: flashlight bulb, wire, battery **Lab:** 1.5-V lightbulbs (4), 1.5-V batteries (2), 10-cm-long pieces of insulated wire (8), battery holders (2), minibulb sockets (4) **Lab:** plastic funnel, 1-m lengths of rubber or plastic tubing of different diameters, meterstick, ring stand with ring, stopwatch, hose clamp, 500-mL beakers (2)	**Chapter FAST FILE Resources** Transparency Activity, p. 46 MiniLAB, p. 4 Enrichment, p. 32 Reinforcement, p. 29 Directed Reading, pp. 21, 22 Lab Worksheets, pp. 5–6, 7–8 **Physical Science Critical Thinking/Problem Solving,** p. 8	**Portfolio** Science Journal, p. 600 **Performance** Applying Math, p. 597 MiniLAB, p. 598 Applying Math, p. 600 Applying Math, p. 602 **Content** Section Review, p. 602	Section Focus Transparency Virtual Labs CD-ROM Guided Reading Audio Program Interactive Chalkboard CD-ROM Video Lab

End of Chapter Assessment

GLENCOE'S ASSESSMENT ADVANTAGE

Blackline Masters	Technology	Professional Series
Chapter FAST FILE Resources Chapter Review, pp. 37–38 Chapter Tests, pp. 39–42 **Standardized Test Practice,** pp. 83–86	MindJogger Videoquiz Virtual Labs CD-ROM ExamView® Pro Testmaker TeacherWorks CD-ROM Interactive Chalkboard CD-ROM	**Performance Assessment in the Science Classroom (PASC)**

Transparencies

Section Focus

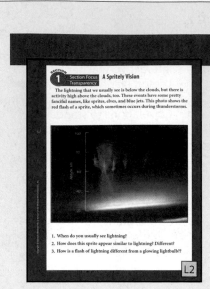

1 Section Focus Transparency — **A Spritely Vision**

The lightning that we usually see is below the clouds, but there is activity high above the clouds, too. These events have some pretty fanciful names, like sprites, elves, and blue jets. This photo shows the red flash of a sprite, which sometimes occurs during thunderstorms.

1. When do you usually see lightning?
2. How does this sprite appear similar to lightning? Different?
3. How is a flash of lightning different from a glowing lightbulb??

L2

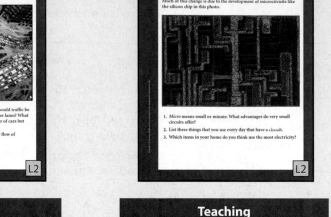

2 Section Focus Transparency — **Go with the Flow!**

Highways in heavily used areas are designed with many lanes to keep traffic moving, but sometimes it doesn't work.

1. Describe what is happening in the picture. What would traffic be like if there were the same number of cars but fewer lanes? What would traffic be like if there were the same number of cars but twice as many lanes?
2. How might the flow of traffic on a road be like the flow of electricity in a wire?

L2

3 Section Focus Transparency — **In the Chips**

A few decades ago, a single computer was the size of a classroom. Today's laptops, however, are smaller, faster, and have more memory. Much of this change is due to the development of microcircuits like the silicon chip in this photo.

1. *Micro* means small or minute. What advantages do very small circuits offer?
2. List three things that you use every day that have a circuit.
3. Which items in your home do you think use the most electricity?

L2

This is a representation of key blackline masters available in the Teacher Classroom Resources. See Resource Manager boxes within the chapter for additional information.

Key to Teaching Strategies

The following designations will help you decide which activities are appropriate for your students.

L1 Level 1 activities should be appropriate for students with learning difficulties.

L2 Level 2 activities should be within the ability range of all students.

L3 Level 3 activities are designed for above-average students.

ELL ELL activities should be within the ability range of English Language Learners.

COOP LEARN Cooperative Learning activities are designed for small group work.

LS Multiple Learning Styles logos, as described on page 12T, are used throughout to indicate strategies that address different learning styles.

P These strategies represent student products that can be placed into a best-work portfolio.

PBL Problem-Based Learning activities apply real-world situations to learning.

Assessment

Assessment Transparency — **Electricity**

Directions: *Carefully review the table and answer the following questions.*

Approximate Cost of Electricity for Some Appliances

Appliance	Wattage	Average daily use (hours)	Approximate cost per month
Air cleaner	35	24	$2.00
Box fan	100	24	$5.75
Clothes dryer	5,000	1/2	$6.00
Color TV (19 inch)	70	6	$1.05
Personal computer	150	8	$2.90
Laser printer	70	2	$0.30

1. Which of the listed appliances costs the most to operate each month?
   A Box fan   C Clothes dryer
   B Personal computer   D Color TV
2. According to the table, if two appliances are used for the same number of hours, the one with higher wattage will cost ___.
   F more to operate   H the same to operate
   G less to operate   J can't answer from table
3. The color TV costs more to operate than the laser printer because ___.
   A the wattage of the color TV is higher
   B the color TV is on longer
   C the color TV is bigger
   D the power company charges more for TVs

L2

Teaching

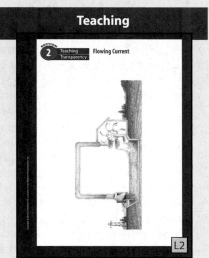

2 Teaching Transparency — **Flowing Current**

L2

Hands-on Activities

Student Text Lab Worksheet

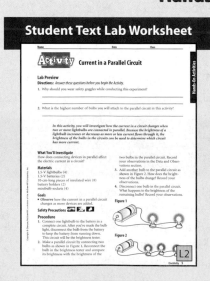

Activity — **Current in a Parallel Circuit**

Lab Preview
Directions: *Answer these questions before you begin the Activity.*
1. Why should you wear safety goggles while conducting this experiment?

2. What is the highest number of bulbs you will attach to the parallel circuit in this activity?

In this activity, you will investigate how the current in a circuit changes when two or more lightbulbs are connected in parallel. Because the brightness of a lightbulb increases or decreases as more or less current flows through it, the brightness of the bulbs in the circuits can be used to determine which circuit has more current.

What You'll Investigate
How does connecting devices in parallel affect the electric current in a circuit?

Materials
1.5-V lightbulbs (4)
1.5-V battery holders (2)
10-cm-long pieces of insulated wire (8)
battery holders (2)
minibulb sockets (4)

Goals
• **Observe** how the current in a parallel circuit changes as more devices are added.

Safety Precautions

Procedure
1. Connect one lightbulb to the battery in a complete circuit. After you've made the bulb light, disconnect the bulb from the battery to keep the battery from running down. This circuit will be the brightness tester.
2. Make a parallel circuit by connecting two bulbs as shown in Figure 1. Reconnect the bulb in the brightness tester and compare its brightness with the brightness of the

two bulbs in the parallel circuit. Record your observations in the Data and Observations section.
3. Add another bulb to the parallel circuit as shown in Figure 2. How does the brightness of the bulbs change? Record your observations.
4. Disconnect one bulb in the parallel circuit. What happens to the brightness of the remaining bulbs? Record your observations.

Figure 1

Figure 2

L2

Laboratory Activities

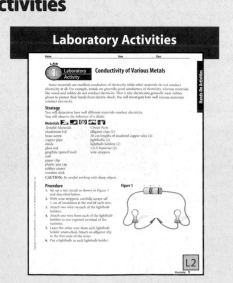

1 Laboratory Activity — **Conductivity of Various Metals**

Some materials are excellent conductors of electricity, while other materials do not conduct electricity at all. For example, metals are generally good conductors of electricity, whereas materials like wood and rubber do not conduct electricity. That is why electricians generally wear rubber gloves to protect their hands from electric shock. You will investigate how well various materials conduct electricity.

Strategy
You will determine how well different materials conduct electricity.
You will observe the behavior of a diode.

Materials
Testable Materials   *Circuit Parts*
aluminum foil   alligator clips (2)
brass screw   20-cm lengths of insulated copper wire (4)
copper pipe   lightbulbs (2)
diode   lightbulb holders (2)
glass rod   1.5-V batteries (2)
graphite (pencil lead)   wire strippers
nail
paper clip
plastic pen cap
rubber eraser
wooden stick
CAUTION: *Be careful working with sharp objects.*

Procedure   **Figure 1**
1. Set up a test circuit as shown in Figure 1 and described below.
2. With wire strippers, carefully scrape off 1 cm of insulation at the end of each wire.
3. Attach two wires to each of the lightbulb holders.
4. Attach one wire from each of the lightbulb holders to one exposed terminal of the batteries.
5. Leave the other wire loose on each lightbulb holder unattached. Attach an alligator clip to the free ends of the wires.
6. Put a lightbulb in each lightbulb holder.

L2

Meeting Different Ability Levels

Content Outline

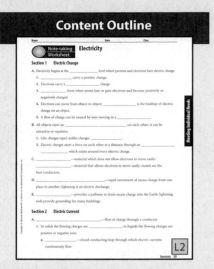

Note-taking Worksheet — Electricity

Section 1 — Electric Charge

L2

Reinforcement

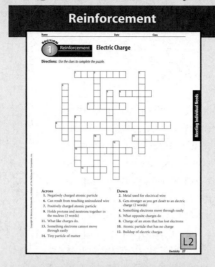

Reinforcement — Electric Charge

Directions: Use the clues to complete the puzzle.

L2

Enrichment

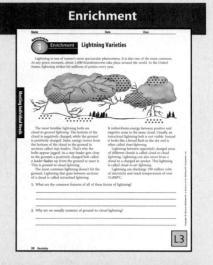

Enrichment — Lightning Varieties

L3

Directed Reading (English/Spanish)

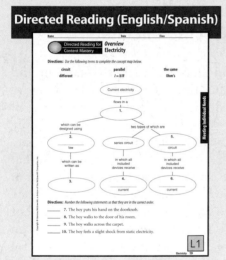

Directed Reading for Content Mastery — Overview Electricity

L1

Study Guide

Study Guide

Features
- Contains a study guide page for each section of the chapter
- Reviews key concepts
- Includes answer pages

L2

Reading Essentials

Reading Essentials for Glencoe Science — An Interactive Student Workbook

Features
- Condensed core content
- Actively involves students in reading
- Reinforces key vocabulary

L1

Assessment

Test Practice Workbook

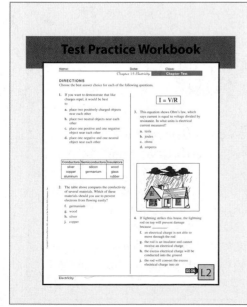

Chapter 15 Electricity — Chapter Test

L2

Chapter Review

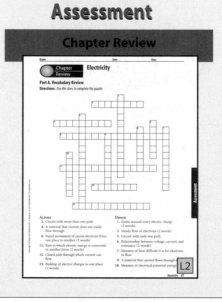

Chapter Review — Electricity

Part A. Vocabulary Review
Directions: Use the clues to complete the puzzle.

L2

Chapter Tests

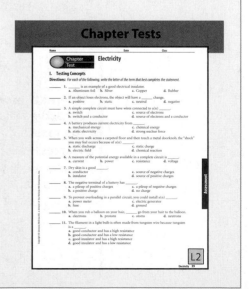

Chapter Test — Electricity

I. Testing Concepts

L2

Science Content Background

section 1 Electric Charge
Electricity

Charge is an abstract idea and is not a substance. Charge is the name given to a property acquired by objects, a property that seems to leak away, can be restored by rubbing, can move between objects, is highly mobile on metals, and so on. From observing the interactions between objects, we can infer the existence of a property called charge, but we cannot observe the charge itself, only the interactions it produces. In all of science, the appropriate starting point is not the model but the observation. The concept of charge was invented to provide a plausible explanation for scientists' observations.

section 2 Electric Current
Flow of Charge

Benjamin Franklin's charge model of positive and negative, with conventional current going from positive to negative, is still used today. Electrons were discovered almost 150 years later and exhibit the characteristics of negative charge. Franklin defined objects repelled by rubber rods stroked with rabbit fur as negative. They could easily have been defined as positive. Because rubber rods that have been stroked with rabbit fur repel electrons, we consider electrons to be negative.

When a wire is used as the conductor, the electrons in the metal carry negative charge through the wire. In a fluid conductor, such as the electrolyte inside a battery, positive and negative charges (ions) are free to move.

Students may wonder about the names of batteries. There are AA, AAA, C, and D; why are there no A or B batteries? In the 1920s, there were A and B batteries, which were used to power crank telephones and early radios. They are no longer produced today.

section 3 Electric Circuits
Electrical Safety

In electric shock, the amount and duration of electric current moving through the body determines the extent of the damage it does. Low voltage does not imply low hazard. A wall voltage of 120 V is not a particularly high voltage, yet it can be lethal because of the large current that can flow out of the wall socket. An example of the importance of current is to consider the balloon experiment in the opening Launch Lab. Rubbing a balloon on your hair can charge the balloon to several thousand volts. Even if you touch such a balloon, you will feel no shock because the current is so small.

chapter content resources

Internet Resources
For additional content background, visit **ips.msscience.com** to:
- access your book online
- find references to related articles in popular science magazines
- access Web links with related content background
- access current events with science journal topics

Print Resources
Fleet Fire: Thomas Edison and the Pioneers of the Electric Revolution, by L.J. Davis, Arcade Books, 2003

Electricity: Principles and Applications, Experiments Manual, by Richard J. Fowler, McGraw-Hill Science/Engineering/Math, 1998

TAB Guide to Understanding Electricity and Electronics, by G. Randy Slone, McGraw-Hill/TAB Electronics, 2000

Misconceptions

Find Out What Students Think

Students may think that . . .

Electricity travels from a battery to a lightbulb and stops there.

Most students have little experience with simple electric circuits. It might seem to students that electricity flows into appliances connected to an electric outlet just as gasoline flows into a car connected by a hose to a gas pump. In fact, an electric current will flow only if there is a closed path for the charges to follow.

Demonstration

Hold up a flashlight and turn it on. Ask students to write down their predictions about what would happen if you left the flashlight on for a couple of days. Ask them to write down why they think their predictions would happen. Hold up one D battery, one flashlight bulb, and one wire with the insulation stripped off both ends. Ask students to draw one way they could make the bulb light using only these materials.

Promote Understanding

Activity

Give each pair of students one wire, one flashlight bulb, and one D battery and ask them to do the following:

- Connect the items as shown in your drawings and see if the bulb lights.

- Try other ways to get the bulb to light.

- Draw all the arrangements you attempt—both those that don't work and those that do work.

After 25 minutes some pairs probably will have determined how to complete the circuit to get the bulb to light. Possible ways to make the bulb light include touching the bulb to one side of the battery while touching one end of the wire to the other side of the bulb, and touching the other end of the wire to the other side of the battery.

On one side of the board, have students draw ways that the materials were connected so that the bulbs did not light up. On the other side of the board, have students draw ways the materials were connected to produce a lit bulb.

Ask how the drawings on one side of the board are different from the drawings on the other side.

Based on the drawings, what is necessary to get a bulb to light? Establish that a complete circuit gives electrons a closed path through which to travel, while an energy source, such as the battery, gives electrons the energy needed to move through the circuit. L2

Assess

After completing the chapter, see *Identifying Misconceptions* in the Study Guide at the end of the chapter.

Chapter Vocabulary

ion, p. 584
static charge, p. 585
electric force, p. 587
electric field, p. 587
insulator, p. 588
conductor, p. 588
electric discharge, p. 589
electric current, p. 591
circuit, p. 591
voltage, p. 592
resistance, p. 594
Ohm's law, p. 597
series circuit, p. 598
parallel circuit, p. 599
electric power, p. 600

Science Journal Student answers will vary. Student responses regarding the weather conditions should include a reference to rain or rain clouds.

INTERACTIVE CHALKBOARD with Image Bank

PowerPoint® Presentations

This CD-ROM is an editable Microsoft® PowerPoint® presentation that includes:

- a pre-made presentation for every chapter
- interactive graphics
- animations
- audio clips
- image bank
- all new section and chapter questions
- Standardized Test Practice
- transparencies
- pre-lab questions for all labs
- Foldables directions
- links to ips.msscience.com

Electricity

chapter preview

sections

1 Electric Charge
2 Electric Current
3 Electric Circuits
   Lab Current in a Parallel Circuit
   Lab A Model for Voltage and Current
   Virtual Lab How are voltage, current, and resistance related?

A Blast of Energy
This flash of lightning is an electric spark that releases an enormous amount of electrical energy in an instant. However, in homes and other buildings, electrical energy is released in a controlled way by the flow of electric currents.

Science Journal Write a paragraph describing a lightning flash you have seen. Include information about the weather conditions at the time.

582

Theme Connection

Systems and Interactions Electric charges interact in observable ways with their environment. Electric circuits are systems of moving electric charges. The movement of electric charges in a circuit is controlled by interactions between parts of the circuit.

About the Photo

Lightning Lightning is an electric discharge that occurs between rain clouds or between rain clouds and Earth. The discharge is seen in the form of a visible arc between the discharge points. It is not fully understood why rain clouds become charged, but most rain clouds are negatively charged at the base and positively charged at the top. This polarization leads to the electric discharge.

Start-Up Activities

Observing Electric Forces

No computers? No CD players? No video games? Can you imagine life without electricity? Electricity also provides energy that heats and cools homes and produces light. The electrical energy that you use every day is produced by the forces that electric charges exert on each other.

1. Inflate a rubber balloon.

2. Place small bits of paper on your desktop and bring the balloon close to the bits of paper. Record your observations.

3. Charge the balloon by holding it by the knot and rubbing it on your hair or a piece of wool.

4. Bring the balloon close to the bits of paper. Record your observations.

5. Charge two balloons using the procedure in step 3. Hold each balloon by its knot and bring the balloons close to each other. Record your observations.

6. **Think Critically** Compare and contrast the force exerted on the bits of paper by the charged balloon and the force exerted by the two charged balloons on each other.

FOLDABLES™
Study Organizer

Electricity Make the following Foldable to help you understand the terms *electric charge, electric current,* and *electric circuit.*

STEP 1 **Fold** the top of a vertical piece of paper down and the bottom up to divide the paper into thirds.

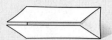

STEP 2 **Turn** the paper horizontally; **unfold and label** the three columns as shown.

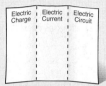

Read and Write Before you read the chapter, write a definition of electric charge, electric current, and electric circuit in the appropriate column. As you read the chapter, correct your definition and add additional information about each term.

Preview this chapter's content and activities at
ips.msscience.com

Purpose Use the Launch Lab to introduce the concept of electric charge. The moving paper in this activity is evidence that a force is being applied and that work is being done. **L2** **ELL** **LS**
Visual Spatial

Preparation To save time, inflate balloons before class.

Materials balloons, tissue paper, wool cloth

Teaching Strategies After students charge the balloon using their hair, ask whether their hair acts differently or feels odd. Have students describe the connection between charging the balloon and the behavior of their hair.

Think Critically

In step 2 the balloon has no effect on the paper. In step 4 the balloon attracts the pieces of paper. In step 5 the balloons repel each other.

Assessment

Performance Have students develop lists of questions about their observations. Questions should focus on the science concepts being explored; for example, why might the balloon and paper attract and why might they repel? Use **Performance Assessment in the Science Classroom,** p. 91.

FOLDABLES™
Study Organizer
Dinah Zike
Study Fold

Student preparation materials for this Foldable are available in the **Chapter FAST FILE** Resources.

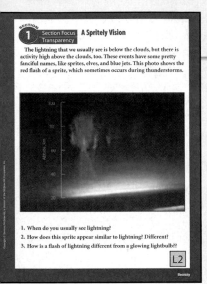
as you read

What You'll Learn
- **Describe** how objects can become electrically charged.
- **Explain** how an electric charge affects other electric charges.
- **Distinguish** between electric conductors and insulators.
- **Describe** how electric discharges such as lightning occur.

Why It's Important
All electric phenomena result from the forces electric charges exert on each other.

⊙ Review Vocabulary
force: the push or pull one object exerts on another

New Vocabulary
- ion
- static charge
- electric force
- electric field
- insulator
- conductor
- electric discharge

Electricity

You can't see, smell, or taste electricity, so it might seem mysterious. However, electricity is not so hard to understand when you start by thinking small—very small. All solids, liquids, and gases are made of tiny particles called atoms. Atoms, as shown in **Figure 1,** are made of even smaller particles called protons, neutrons, and electrons. Protons and neutrons are held together tightly in the nucleus at the center of an atom, but electrons swarm around the nucleus in all directions. Protons and electrons have electric charge, but neutrons have no electric charge.

Positive and Negative Charge There are two types of electric charge—positive and negative. Protons have a positive charge, and electrons have a negative charge. The amount of negative charge on an electron is exactly equal to the amount of positive charge on a proton. Because atoms have equal numbers of protons and electrons, the amount of positive charge on all the protons in the nucleus of an atom is balanced by the negative charge on all the electrons moving around the nucleus. Therefore, atoms are electrically neutral, which means they have no overall electric charge.

An atom becomes negatively charged when it gains extra electrons. If an atom loses electrons it becomes positively charged. A positively or negatively charged atom is called an **ion** (I ahn).

Figure 1 An atom is made of positively charged protons (orange), negatively charged electrons (red), and neutrons (blue) with no electric charge.
Identify *where the protons and neutrons are located in an atom.*

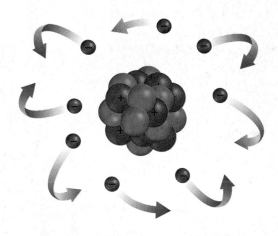

Electrons Move in Solids Electrons can move from atom to atom and from object to object. Rubbing is one way that electrons can be transferred. If you have ever taken clinging clothes from a clothes dryer, you have seen what happens when electrons are transferred from one object to another.

Suppose you rub a balloon on your hair. The atoms in your hair hold their electrons more loosely than the atoms on the balloon hold theirs. As a result, electrons are transferred from the atoms in your hair to the atoms on the surface of the balloon, as shown in **Figure 2.** Because your hair loses electrons, it becomes positively charged. The balloon gains electrons and becomes negatively charged. Your hair and the balloon become attracted to one another and make your hair stand on end. This imbalance of electric charge on an object is called a **static charge.** In solids, static charge is due to the transfer of electrons between objects. Protons cannot be removed easily from the nucleus of an atom and usually do not move from one object to another.

✔ Reading Check *How does an object become electrically charged?*

Ions Move in Solutions Sometimes, the movement of charge can be caused by the movement of ions instead of the movement of electrons. Table salt—sodium chloride—is made of sodium ions and chloride ions that are fixed in place and cannot move through the solid. However, when salt is dissolved in water, the sodium and chloride ions break apart and spread out evenly in the water, forming a solution, as shown in **Figure 3.** Now the positive and negative ions are free to move. Solutions containing ions play an important role in enabling different parts of your body to communicate with each other. **Figure 4** shows how a nerve cell uses ions to transmit signals. These signals moving throughout your body enable you to sense, move, and even think.

Figure 3 When table salt (NaCl) dissolves in water, the sodium ions and chloride ions break apart. These ions now are able to carry electric energy.

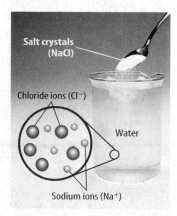

Salt crystals (NaCl)

Chloride ions (Cl⁻)

Water

Sodium ions (Na⁺)

Caption Answer
Figure 2 balloon, negative; hair, positive

Quick Demo
Attraction and Repulsion
Materials glass rod, 2 pieces of silk cloth, wooden surface
Estimated Time 10 minutes
Procedure Rub a glass rod with a piece of silk. Quickly separate the rod from the silk. With the silk sitting on a wooden surface, bring the rod near it.

Ask the students what effects they see. They should see the silk attracted to the rod.

Next, rub two pieces of silk with a glass rod and bring them together.

Ask the students what effects they see. They should see the two pieces repel each other.

Ask the students why these effects occur. When the silk was rubbed against the glass rod, one object lost electrons and one object gained electrons. The glass and silk attracted each other because they had different charges. The two pieces of silk repelled each other because they had the same charge.

✔ Reading Check

Answer by gaining or losing electrons

Teacher FYI

Humidity Activities involving the production of static electricity work better when the humidity in the room is low. Humid air is a better electrical conductor than dry air. As a result, an object will lose excess electric charge more rapidly in humid air than in dry air.

Cultural Diversity

Electric Amber The word *electricity* comes from the Greek word for amber, *elektron.* Ancient Greeks found that when amber was rubbed with fur, the amber attracted small pieces of straw.

Differentiated Instruction

Challenge Have students research and report on how fabric softeners prevent excess electric charge on clothes. Fabric softeners contain compounds that lubricate fabrics to reduce friction as clothes rub against each other in a dryer. Fabric softeners also attract water molecules, enabling fabrics to retain moisture. This makes clothes weakly conducting and allows excess charge to dissipate. L3
LS Linguistic

NATIONAL GEOGRAPHIC

Visualizing Nerve Impulses

Have students examine the pictures and read the captions. Then ask the following questions.

How are the outside and inside of a nerve-cell membrane charged when the cell is not transmitting an impulse? The outside of the membrane is positively charged and the inside is negatively charged.

What happens to the charge on the inside of the cell membrane as the nerve impulse moves along the cell? The inside of the membrane becomes positively charged as sodium ions move from the outside to the inside of the membrane.

Inquiry Lab

Nerve Impulse Failure

Purpose Various diseases interrupt the process by which nerve cells transmit impulses. Have students research to find examples of these diseases. Have students build a model showing how the disease interrupts nerve function.

Possible Materials encyclopedias, reference books, newspapers, journals, construction paper, poster board, color markers, modeling clay

Estimated Time 1 week, outside of class

Teaching Strategies Encourage students to find out why the nervous system fails in these diseases. Encourage them to report on any medical procedures that are used for treatment.

For additional inquiry activities, see
Science Inquiry Labs.

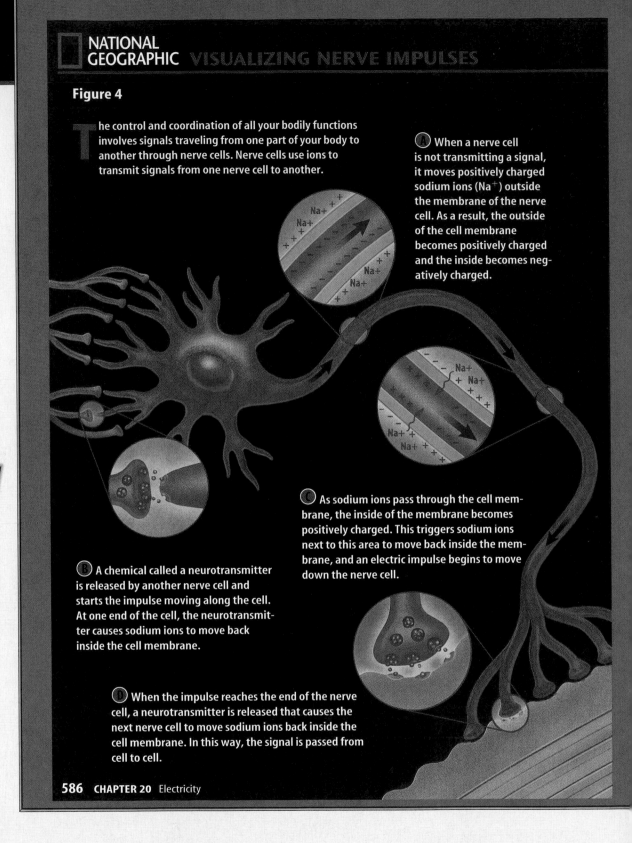

NATIONAL GEOGRAPHIC VISUALIZING NERVE IMPULSES

Figure 4

The control and coordination of all your bodily functions involves signals traveling from one part of your body to another through nerve cells. Nerve cells use ions to transmit signals from one nerve cell to another.

A When a nerve cell is not transmitting a signal, it moves positively charged sodium ions (Na^+) outside the membrane of the nerve cell. As a result, the outside of the cell membrane becomes positively charged and the inside becomes negatively charged.

C As sodium ions pass through the cell membrane, the inside of the membrane becomes positively charged. This triggers sodium ions next to this area to move back inside the membrane, and an electric impulse begins to move down the nerve cell.

B A chemical called a neurotransmitter is released by another nerve cell and starts the impulse moving along the cell. At one end of the cell, the neurotransmitter causes sodium ions to move back inside the cell membrane.

D When the impulse reaches the end of the nerve cell, a neurotransmitter is released that causes the next nerve cell to move sodium ions back inside the cell membrane. In this way, the signal is passed from cell to cell.

586 CHAPTER 20 Electricity

Unlike charges attract.

Like charges repel.   Like charges repel.

Figure 5 A positive charge and a negative charge attract each other. Two positive charges repel each other, as do two negative charges.

Electric Forces

The electrons in an atom swarm around the nucleus. What keeps these electrons close to the nucleus? The positively charged protons in the nucleus exert an attractive electric force on the negatively charged electrons. All charged objects exert an **electric force** on each other. The electric force between two charges can be attractive or repulsive, as shown in **Figure 5.** Objects with the same type of charge repel one another and objects with opposite charges attract one another. This rule is often stated as "like charges repel, and unlike charges attract."

The electric force between two charged objects depends on the distance between them and the amount of charge on each object. The electric force between two electric charges gets stronger as the charges get closer together. A positive and a negative charge are attracted to each other more strongly if they are closer together. Two like charges are pushed away more strongly from each other the closer they are. The electric force between two objects that are charged, such as two balloons that have been rubbed on wool, increases if the amount of charge on at least one of the objects increases.

☑ **Reading Check** *How does the electric force between two charged objects depend on the distance between them?*

Electric Fields You might have noticed examples of how charged objects don't have to be touching to exert an electric force on each other. For instance, two charged balloons push each other apart even though they are not touching. How are charged objects able to exert forces on each other without touching?

Electric charges exert a force on each other at a distance through an **electric field** that exists around every electric charge. **Figure 6** shows the electric field around a positive and a negative charge. An electric field gets stronger as you get closer to a charge, just as the electric force between two charges becomes greater as the charges get closer together.

Figure 6 The lines with arrowheads represent the electric field around charges. The direction of each arrow is the direction a positive charge would move if it were placed in the field.

The electric field arrows point away from a positive charge.

The electric field arrows point toward a negative charge.

Explain *why the electric field arrows around a negative charge are in the opposite direction of the arrows around a positive charge.*

Quick Demo
Electric Discharge

Materials balloon, foam cup or other piece of foam, dark room, fluorescent light bulb

Estimated Time five minutes

Procedure To show how an electric charge can build up on a balloon, rub a balloon vigorously with a foam cup or a piece of plastic foam. In a dark room, quickly bring the charged balloon near a fluorescent lightbulb. A small spark will jump, making the lightbulb flash. This works best on a cold, dry day.

Caption Answer
Figure 6 The direction of each arrow is the direction a positive charge would move if it were placed in the field. A positive charge would be attracted to the negative charge and repelled by the positive charge.

☑ **Reading Check**

Answer The electric force between two electric charges gets stronger as the charges get closer together.

☑ Active Reading

Metacognition Journal In this strategy, each student analyzes his or her own thought processes. Have students divide a piece of paper in half down the center. On the left, have them record what they have learned about electric charges. On the right, have them record the reason they learned it.

Differentiated Instruction

Learning Disabled Magnetism can be used to provide a visual on fields. Sprinkle iron filings on a piece of paper. Bring a bar magnet near the iron filings. The iron filings will line up with the magnetic field. Explain to students that a magnetic field is similar to an electric field. You cannot see it, but the forces are present.

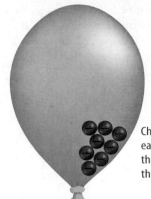

Charges placed on an insulator repel each other but cannot move easily on the surface of the insulator. As a result, the charges remain in one place.

Figure 7 Electric charges move more easily through conductors than through insulators.

The three wires in this electric cable are made of copper, which is a conductor. The wires are covered with plastic insulation that keeps the copper wires from touching each other.

Insulators and Conductors

Rubbing a balloon on your hair transfers electrons from your hair to the balloon. However, only the part of the balloon that was rubbed on your hair becomes charged, because electrons cannot move easily through rubber. As a result, the electrons that were rubbed onto the balloon tend to stay in one place, as shown in **Figure 7.** A material in which electrons cannot move easily from place to place is called an **insulator.** Examples of insulators are plastic, wood, glass, and rubber.

Materials that are **conductors** contain electrons that can move more easily in the material. The electric wire in **Figure 7** is made from a conductor coated with an insulator such as plastic. Electrons move easily in the conductor but do not move easily through the plastic insulation. This prevents electrons from moving through the insulation and causing an electric shock if someone touches the wire.

Metals as Conductors The best conductors are metals such as copper, gold, and aluminum. In a metal atom, a few electrons are not attracted as strongly to the nucleus as the other electrons, and are loosely bound to the atom. When metal atoms form a solid, the metal atoms can move only short distances. However, the electrons that are loosely bound to the atoms can move easily in the solid piece of metal. In an insulator, the electrons are bound tightly in the atoms that make up the insulator and therefore cannot move easily.

Science Online

Topic: Superconductors
Visit ips.msscience.com for Web links to information about materials that are superconductors.

Activity Make a table listing five materials that can become superconductors and the critical temperature for each material.

Induced Charge

Has this ever happened to you? You walk across a carpet and as you reach for a metal doorknob, you feel an electric shock. Maybe you even see a spark jump between your fingertip and the doorknob. To find out what happened, look at **Figure 8.**

As you walk, electrons are rubbed off the rug by your shoes. The electrons then spread over the surface of your skin. As you bring your hand close to the doorknob, the electric field around the excess electrons on your hand repels the electrons in the doorknob. Because the doorknob is a good conductor, its electrons move easily away from your hand. The part of the doorknob closest to your hand then becomes positively charged. This separation of positive and negative charges due to an electric field is called an induced charge.

If the electric field between your hand and the knob is strong enough, charge can be pulled from your hand to the doorknob, as shown in **Figure 8.** This rapid movement of excess charge from one place to another is an **electric discharge.** Lightning is an example of an electric discharge. In a storm cloud, air currents sometimes cause the bottom of the cloud to become negatively charged. This negative charge induces a positive charge in the ground below the cloud. A cloud-to-ground lightning stroke occurs when electric charge moves between the cloud and the ground.

As you walk across the floor, you rub electrons from the carpet onto the bottom of your shoes. These electrons then spread out over your skin, including your hands.

As you bring your hand close to the metal doorknob, electrons on the doorknob move as far away from your hand as possible. The part of the doorknob closest to your hand is left with a positive charge.

The attractive electric force between the electrons on your hand and the induced positive charge on the doorknob might be strong enough to pull electrons from your hand to the doorknob. You might see this as a spark and feel a mild electric shock.

Figure 8 A spark that jumps between your fingers and a metal doorknob starts at your feet.
Identify *another example of an electric discharge.*

SECTION 1 Electric Charge **589**

Check for Understanding

Visual-Spatial Have students draw a diagram showing the electric charge distribution when a hairbrush becomes charged and hair is attracted to it. L2

Reteach

Static Electricity Ask students to look up the word *static* and tell one reason this word is appropriate for the term *static electricity* and one reason the word is misleading. The word *static* means "not moving." It is true that static electricity is not in continual motion like current electricity. However, a static discharge is far from motionless; it is a very rapid, though noncontinuous, transfer of charge. L2 **LS Linguistic**

☑ Assessment

Portfolio Have students draw pictures representing the charging of a balloon and the subsequent attraction of bits of paper. Encourage students to use symbols to represent positive and negative charge. Use **Performance Assessment in the Science Classroom,** p. 127. P L2

Figure 9 A lightning rod can protect a building from being damaged by a lightning strike.

Grounding

Lightning is an electric discharge that can cause damage and injury because a lightning bolt releases an extremely large amount of electric energy. Even electric discharges that release small amounts of energy can damage delicate circuitry in devices such as computers. One way to avoid the damage caused by electric discharges is to make the excess charges flow harmlessly into Earth's surface. Earth can be a conductor, and because it is so large, it can absorb an enormous quantity of excess charge.

The process of providing a pathway to drain excess charge into Earth is called grounding. The pathway is usually a conductor such as a wire or a pipe. You might have noticed lightning rods at the top of buildings and towers, as shown in **Figure 9.** These rods are made of metal and are connected to metal cables that conduct electric charge into the ground if the rod is struck by lightning.

---

section 1 review

Summary

Electric Charges
- There are two types of electric charge—positive charge and negative charge.
- The amount of negative charge on an electron is equal to the amount of positive charge on a proton.
- Objects that are electrically neutral become negatively charged when they gain electrons and positively charged when they lose electrons.

Electric Forces
- Like charges repel and unlike charges attract.
- The force between two charged objects increases as they get closer together.
- A charged object is surrounded by an electric field that exerts a force on other charged objects.

Insulators and Conductors
- Electrons cannot move easily in an insulator but can move easily in a conductor.

Self Check

1. **Explain** why when objects become charged it is electrons that are transferred from one object to another rather than protons.
2. **Compare and contrast** the movement of electric charge in a solution with the transfer of electric charge between solid objects.
3. **Explain** why metals are good conductors.
4. **Compare and contrast** the electric field around a negative charge and the electric field around a positive charge.
5. **Explain** why an electric discharge occurs.
6. **Think Critically** A cat becomes negatively charged when it is brushed. How does the electric charge on the brush compare to the charge on the cat?

Applying Skills

7. **Analyze** You slide out of a car seat and as you touch the metal car door, a spark jumps between your hand and the door. Describe how the spark was formed.

Science online ips.msscience.com/self_check_quiz

---

section 1 review

1. It requires less energy to remove an electron from an atom than to remove a proton from the nucleus.
2. In a solution, both positive ions and negative ions can move. When charge is transferred between objects, only negatively charged electrons move.
3. Metals contain electrons that are not bound tightly to atoms, and can easily move in the metal.
4. The direction of the electric field is away from a positive charge and toward a negative charge.
5. The attractive electric force between the excess negative charge on one object and the excess positive charge on the other object is strong enough to make electrons move through air between the objects.
6. The excess negative charge on the cat equals the excess positive charge on the brush.
7. Sliding transferred electrons from the car seat that spread over your skin. The excess charge on your hand induced an opposite charge on the door nearest your hand. A spark jumped when the electric force caused electrons to move between the door and your hand.

Electric Current

Flow of Charge

An electric discharge, such as a lightning bolt, can release a huge amount of energy in an instant. However, electric lights, refrigerators, TVs, and stereos need a steady source of electrical energy that can be controlled. This source of electrical energy comes from an **electric current,** which is the flow of electric charge. In solids, the flowing charges are electrons. In liquids, the flowing charges are ions, which can be positively or negatively charged. Electric current is measured in units of amperes (A). A model for electric current is flowing water. Water flows downhill because a gravitational force acts on it. Similarly, electrons flow because an electric force acts on them.

A Model for a Simple Circuit How does a flow of water provide energy? If the water is separated from Earth by using a pump, the higher water now has gravitational potential energy, as shown in **Figure 10.** As the water falls and does work on the waterwheel, the water loses potential energy and the waterwheel gains kinetic energy. For the water to flow continuously, it must flow through a closed loop. Electric charges will flow continuously only through a closed conducting loop called a **circuit.**

What You'll Learn
- **Relate** voltage to the electrical energy carried by an electric current.
- **Describe** a battery and how it produces an electric current.
- **Explain** electrical resistance.

Why It's Important
Electric current provides a steady source of electrical energy that powers the electric appliances you use every day.

⊙ **Review Vocabulary**
gravitational potential energy: the energy stored in an object due to its position above Earth's surface

New Vocabulary
- electric current
- voltage
- circuit
- resistance

Figure 10 The gravitational potential energy of water is increased when a pump raises the water above Earth.

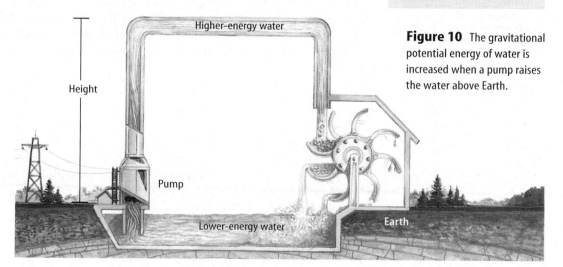

Higher-energy water

Height

Pump

Lower-energy water

Earth

---

 1 Motivate

Bellringer

Section Focus Transparencies also are available on the Interactive Chalkboard CD-ROM.
L2 ELL

Tie to Prior Knowledge

Batteries Ask students what happens to devices like tape players when the batteries get old. They either run more slowly or stop working. Explain that this occurs because the batteries no longer produce adequate electric current.

Section 2 Resource Manager

Chapter *FAST FILE* Resources
Transparency Activity, pp. 45, 47–48
Directed Reading for Content Mastery, p. 21
MiniLAB, p. 3

Lab Activity, pp. 13–15
Enrichment, p. 31
Reinforcement, p. 28

Mini LAB

Purpose Students observe static electricity with a comb. L2

ELL **LS** **Kinesthetic**

Materials plate, salt, pepper, plastic comb, wool clothing

Teaching Strategy Instruct students to rub the comb on the wool vigorously for several seconds and then comb through the particles immediately.

Analysis

1. The comb attracted the pepper flakes and some small crystals of salt.

2. Salt crystals are larger and heavier than pepper flakes, and the electric force is only strong enough to lift the smaller crystals.

Assessment

Performance Ask students to perform this activity for their family or friends as a "magic" trick. Have them explain how the trick works using static electricity. Use **Performance Assessment in the Science Classroom,** p. 97.

Activity

Simple Circuit Have students construct a simple circuit like the one shown in **Figure 11.**

Figure 11 As long as there is a closed path for electrons to follow, electrons can flow in a circuit. They move away from the negative battery terminal and toward the positive terminal.

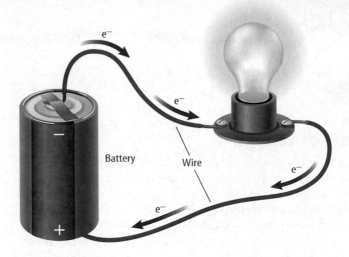

Mini LAB

Investigating the Electric Force

Procedure

1. Pour a layer of **salt** on a **plate.**
2. Sparingly sprinkle grains of **pepper** on top of the salt. Do not use too much pepper.
3. Rub a **rubber** or **plastic comb** on an article of **wool clothing.**
4. Slowly drag the comb through the salt and observe.

Analysis

1. How did the salt and pepper react to the comb?
2. Explain why the pepper reacted differently than the salt.

Electric Circuits The simplest electric circuit contains a source of electrical energy, such as a battery, and an electric conductor, such as a wire, connected to the battery. For the simple circuit shown in **Figure 11,** a closed path is formed by wires connected to a lightbulb and to a battery. Electric current flows in the circuit as long as none of the wires, including the glowing filament wire in the lightbulb, is disconnected or broken.

Voltage In a water circuit, a pump increases the gravitational potential energy of the water by raising the water from a lower level to a higher level. In an electric circuit, a battery increases the electrical potential energy of electrons. This electrical potential energy can be transformed into other forms of energy. The **voltage** of a battery is a measure of how much electrical potential energy each electron can gain. As voltage increases, more electrical potential energy is available to be transformed into other forms of energy. Voltage is measured in volts (V).

How a Current Flows You may think that when an electric current flows in a circuit, electrons travel completely around the circuit. Actually, individual electrons move slowly in an electric circuit. When the ends of a wire are connected to a battery, the battery produces an electric field in the wire. The electric field forces electrons to move toward the positive battery terminal. As an electron moves, it collides with other electric charges in the wire and is deflected in a different direction. After each collision, the electron again starts moving toward the positive terminal. A single electron may undergo more than ten trillion collisions each second. As a result, it may take several minutes for an electron in the wire to travel one centimeter.

Cultural Diversity

Lewis Latimer Thomas Edison's first successful electric lamp had treated paper filaments that burned out quickly. In 1881, African American inventor Lewis Latimer patented carbon-based filament that lasted much longer. Latimer also improved the lightbulb's socket. As part of Edison's team, Latimer helped supervise the installation of electric lights in New York, Philadelphia, Montreal, and London.

Differentiated Instruction

Learning Disabled Have students trace the movement of the electrons with their fingers. Show the students that the electrons exit the negative end of the battery and enter through the positive end of the battery.

Batteries

A battery supplies energy to an electric circuit. When the positive and negative terminals in a battery are connected in a circuit, the electric potential energy of the electrons in the circuit is increased. As these electrons move toward the positive battery terminal, this electric potential energy is transformed into other forms of energy, just as gravitational potential energy is converted into kinetic energy as water falls.

A battery supplies energy to an electric circuit by converting chemical energy to electric potential energy. For the alkaline battery shown in **Figure 12,** the two terminals are separated by a moist paste. Chemical reactions in the moist paste cause electrons to be transferred to the negative terminal from the atoms in the positive terminal. As a result, the negative terminal becomes negatively charged and the positive terminal becomes positively charged. This produces the electric field in the circuit that causes electrons to move away from the negative terminal and toward the positive terminal.

Battery Life

Batteries don't supply energy forever. Maybe you know someone whose car wouldn't start after the lights had been left on overnight. Why do batteries run down? Batteries contain only a limited amount of the chemicals that react to produce chemical energy. These reactions go on as the battery is used and the chemicals are changed into other compounds. Once the original chemicals are used up, the chemical reactions stop and the battery is "dead."

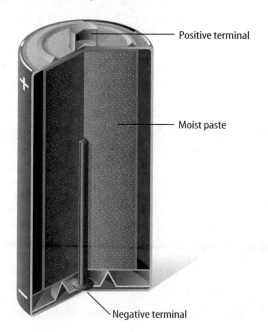

Positive terminal

Moist paste

Negative terminal

INTEGRATE
Chemistry

Alkaline Batteries Several chemicals are used to make an alkaline battery. Zinc is a source of electrons at the negative terminal, and manganese dioxide combines with electrons at the positive terminal. The moist paste contains potassium hydroxide that helps transport electrons from the positive terminal to the negative terminal. Research dry-cell batteries and lead-acid batteries. Make a table listing the chemicals used in these batteries and their purpose.

Figure 12 When this alkaline battery is connected in an electric circuit, chemical reactions occur in the moist paste of the battery that move electrons from the positive terminal to the negative terminal.

INTEGRATE
Chemistry

Alkaline Batteries The students' tables should contain the following information:

Dry cell—positive terminal, carbon and manganese dioxide; negative terminal, zinc; electrolyte (transports electrons), ammonium chloride and zinc chloride

Lead-acid—positive terminal, lead dioxide; negative terminal, lead; electrolyte, dilute sulfuric acid

Research Have students research the latest developments in battery technology. Have students share their information with the class.

Virtual Labs

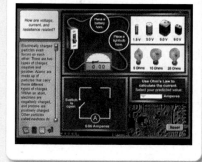

Relationships *How are voltage, current, and resistance related?*

LAB DEMONSTRATION

Purpose to show how a battery works

Materials ten pennies, ten nickels, salt, water, paper towel, voltmeter

Alternate Materials ten pieces of aluminum foil, ten dimes

Procedure Add as much salt to a cup of water as will dissolve. Soak a paper towel in the salt water. Make a stack by alternating pennies and nickels with pieces of the wet paper towel between them. Connect the voltmeter to each end of the stack and measure the voltage.

Expected Outcome The voltmeter should move when the wires are connected.

Assessment

What is happening in the stack of pennies and nickels? Chemical reactions are sending electrons to one end of the stack, making it negative and the other end positive. How might this battery wear out? The towel might dry out. [L2]

Household Wiring Why is household wiring usually made of copper? It has little resistance to electron flow. Resistance in wiring produces heat. Wiring with a high resistance would be a fire hazard.

The Ohm The unit for electrical resistance is named Ohm honoring this German physicist. He was born in 1787 in Erlangen, Bavaria (now Germany). He became a professor of mathematics at the Jesuits' College at Cologne in 1817. He was the director of the Polytechnic Institute of Nüremberg from 1833 to 1849 and a professor of experimental physics at the University of Munich from 1852 until his death in 1854. He was recognized by the Royal Society for his achievements in 1841.

Use an Analogy

Crowded Movement Electrons encounter atoms and other electrons as they move through a wire in a way that is similar to the way you bump into other people and objects as you move through a crowded hallway. You can't move as fast as you'd like because you must zigzag to avoid other people and objects.

IDENTIFYING
Misconceptions

Current Movement Students may think that electricity travels from a battery to a lightbulb and stops there. See page F at the beginning of this chapter for teaching strategies that address this misconception.

Caption Answer

Figure 13 heat and sometimes light

The Ohm The unit for electrical resistance was named in honor of the German physicist Georg Simon Ohm (1787–1854). Ohm is credited for discovering the relationship between current flow, voltage, and resistance. Research and find out more about Georg Ohm. Write a brief biography of him to share with the class.

Figure 13 As electrons flow through a wire, they travel in a zigzag path as they collide with atoms and other electrons. In these collisions, electrical energy is converted into other forms of energy. **Identify** *the other forms of energy that electrical energy is converted into.*

Resistance

Electrons can move much more easily through conductors than through insulators, but even conductors interfere somewhat with the flow of electrons. The measure of how difficult it is for electrons to flow through a material is called **resistance.** The unit of resistance is the ohm (Ω). Insulators generally have much higher resistance than conductors.

As electrons flow through a circuit, they collide with the atoms and other electric charges in the materials that make up the circuit. Look at **Figure 13.** These collisions cause some of the electrons' electrical energy to be converted into thermal energy—heat—and sometimes into light. The amount of electrical energy that is converted into heat and light depends on the resistance of the materials in the circuit.

Buildings Use Copper Wires The amount of electrical energy that is converted into thermal energy increases as the resistance of the wire increases. Copper has low resistance and is one of the best electric conductors. Because copper is a good conductor, less heat is produced as electric current flows in copper wires, compared to wires made of other materials. As a result, copper wire is used in household wiring because the wires usually don't become hot enough to cause fires.

Resistance of Wires The electric resistance of a wire also depends on the length and thickness of the wire, as well as the material it is made from. When water flows through a hose, the water flow decreases as the hose becomes narrower or longer, as shown in **Figure 14** on the next page. The electric resistance of a wire increases as the wire becomes longer or as it becomes narrower.

594 CHAPTER 20 Electricity

Differentiated Instruction

Challenge Have students research and find how current flows through a gas. Have students create a poster or other visual presentation to explain this process to the class. L3

Teacher FYI

No Resistance Some substances lose all resistance and become superconductors when they are cooled to temperatures approaching absolute zero (0 K). Scientists theorize that at these low temperatures electrons travel in connected groups or pairs. This enables them to move through the material without being scattered by collisions.

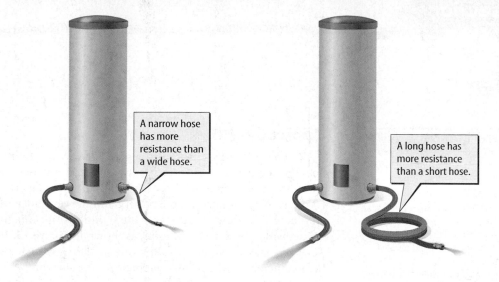

A narrow hose has more resistance than a wide hose.

A long hose has more resistance than a short hose.

Lightbulb Filaments In a lightbulb, the filament is made of wire so narrow that it has a high resistance. When electric current flows in the filament, it becomes hot enough to emit light. The filament is made of tungsten metal, which has a much higher melting point than most other metals. This keeps the filament from melting at the high temperatures needed to produce light.

Figure 14 The resistance of a hose to the flow of water depends on the diameter and length of the hose used.

Compare and contrast *water flowing in a hose and electric current flowing in a wire.*

---

section 2 review

Flow of Charge

- Electric current is the flow of electric charges.
- Electric charges will flow continuously only through a closed conducting loop, called a circuit.
- The voltage in a circuit is a measure of the electrical potential energy of the electrons in the circuit.
- A battery supplies energy to an electric circuit by increasing the electric potential energy of electrons in the circuit.

Resistance

- Electric resistance is the measure of how difficult it is for electrons to flow through a material.
- Electric resistance is due to collisions between flowing electrons and the atoms in a material.
- Electric resistance in a circuit converts electrical energy into thermal energy and light.

Self Check

1. **Compare and contrast** an electric discharge with an electric current.
2. **Describe** how a battery causes electrons to move in a circuit.
3. **Describe** how the electric resistance of a wire changes as the wire becomes longer. How does the resistance change as the wire becomes thicker?
4. **Explain** why the electric wires in houses are usually made of copper.
5. **Think Critically** In an electric circuit, where do the electrons come from that flow in the circuit?

Applying Skills

6. **Infer** Find the voltage of various batteries such as a watch battery, a camera battery, a flashlight battery, and an automobile battery. Infer whether the voltage produced by a battery is related to its size.

Science Online ips.msscience.com/self_check_quiz

SECTION 2 Electric Current **595**

---

section 2 review

1. Both involve the movement of electrons. Electric discharge is rapid, discontinuous movement of excess charge. Electric current is a continuous flow of electric charge.

2. A battery has a positive terminal that attracts electrons and a negative terminal that repels electrons.

These forces cause electrons to flow in a circuit.

3. A longer wire has more resistance. A wire has less resistance as it becomes wider.

4. Copper is a good conductor of electricity and has a low resistance. Less heat is produced when current

flows in copper wires.

5. The electrons are in the atoms of the elements that make up the wire in the circuit.

6. The voltage of a battery is not related to size. A car battery is 12 V. A D-cell battery is 1.5 V. A smaller camera battery is 6 V.

DAILY INTERVENTION

Check for Understanding

Logical-Mathematical Ask students to infer why rechargeable batteries recharge when a current passes through them. The current makes the chemical reaction run the opposite way. Once the battery is recharged, the original chemicals are again present. [L3]

Reteach

Voltage and Flow Ask students to relate current and voltage in a wire to the flow of water in a pipe. Water will flow through a pipe if the pressure at one end of the pipe is different from the pressure at the other end. Likewise, current flows through a wire if there is a voltage difference between the ends of the wire. [L2] **LS** Linguistic

---

✓ Assessment

Portfolio Have students make detailed posters of a particular type of battery. Labels should indicate the chemical reactions taking place and which way the charges will flow. Use **Performance Assessment in the Science Classroom,** p. 145. [P] [L2]

Caption Answer

Figure 14 The flow of water in a hose decreases as the hose becomes longer or narrower. The current in a wire decreases as the wire becomes longer or narrower.

Electric Circuits

1 Motivate

Bellringer

Section Focus Transparencies also are available on the Interactive Chalkboard CD-ROM.

 L2 ELL

SECTION 3 Section Focus Transparency — **In the Chips**

A few decades ago, a single computer was the size of a classroom. Today's laptops, however, are smaller, faster, and have more memory. Much of this change is due to the development of microcircuits like the silicon chip in this photo.

1. *Micro* means small or minute. What advantages do very small circuits offer?
2. List three things that you use every day that have a circuit.
3. Which items in your home do you think use the most electricity?

L2

Tie to Prior Knowledge

Water Hose What happens to the water flowing from a hose that has been perforated with holes? Water flows out of all the holes, making the flow at the end of the hose weaker. Tell students that in this section they will learn how voltage and current can be modified as electric charge flows through a wire.

---

as you read

What You'll Learn
- **Explain** how voltage, current, and resistance are related in an electric circuit.
- **Investigate** the difference between series and parallel circuits.
- **Determine** the electric power used in a circuit.
- **Describe** how to avoid dangerous electric shock.

Why It's Important
Electric circuits control the flow of electric current in all electrical devices.

Review Vocabulary
power: the rate at which energy is transferred; power equals the amount of energy transferred divided by the time over which the transfer occurs

New Vocabulary
- Ohm's law
- series circuit
- parallel circuit
- electric power

Controlling the Current

When you connect a conductor, such as a wire or a lightbulb, between the positive and negative terminals of a battery, electrons flow in the circuit. The amount of current is determined by the voltage supplied by the battery and the resistance of the conductor. To help understand this relationship, imagine a bucket with a hose at the bottom, as shown in **Figure 15.** If the bucket is raised, water will flow out of the hose faster than before. Increasing the height will increase the current.

Voltage and Resistance Think back to the pump and waterwheel in **Figure 10.** Recall that the raised water has energy that is lost when the water falls. Increasing the height from which the water falls increases the energy of the water. Increasing the height of the water is similar to increasing the voltage of the battery. Just as the water current increases when the height of the water increases, the electric current in a circuit increases as voltage increases.

If the diameter of the tube in **Figure 15** is decreased, resistance is greater and the flow of the water decreases. In the same way, as the resistance in an electric circuit increases, the current in the circuit decreases.

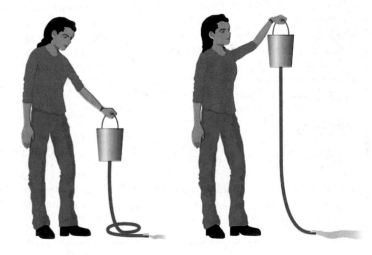

Figure 15 Raising the bucket higher increases the potential energy of the water in the bucket. This causes the water to flow out of the hose faster.

Section 3 Resource Manager

Chapter *FAST FILE* Resources
Directed Reading for Content Mastery, pp. 21, 22
Transparency Activity, p. 46
MiniLAB, p. 4

Enrichment, p. 32
Reinforcement, p. 29
Lab Worksheets, pp. 5–6, 7–8
Lab Management and Safety, p. 71

Ohm's Law A nineteenth-century German physicist, Georg Simon Ohm, carried out experiments that measured how changing the voltage in a circuit affected the current. He found a simple relationship among voltage, current, and resistance in a circuit that is now known as **Ohm's law**. In equation form, Ohm's law often is written as follows.

> **Ohm's Law**
> Voltage (in volts) = **current** (in amperes) × **resistance** (in ohms)
> $$V = IR$$

According to Ohm's law, when the voltage in a circuit increases the current increases, just as water flows faster from a bucket that is raised higher. However, if the voltage in the circuit doesn't change, then the current in the circuit decreases when the resistance is increased.

Applying Math Solving a Simple Equation

VOLTAGE FROM A WALL OUTLET A lightbulb is plugged into a wall outlet. If the lightbulb has a resistance of 220 Ω and the current in the lightbulb is 0.5 A, what is the voltage provided by the outlet?

Solution

1 *This is what you know:*
- current: $I = 0.5$ A
- resistance: $R = 220$ Ω

2 *This is what you need to find:* voltage: V

3 *This is the procedure you need to use:* Substitute the known values for current and resistance into Ohm's law to calculate the voltage:
$V = IR = (0.5$ A$) (220$ Ω$) = 110$ V

4 *Check your answer:* Divide your answer by the resistance 220 Ω. The result should be the given current 0.5 A.

Practice Problems

1. An electric iron plugged into a wall socket has a resistance of 24 Ω. If the current in the iron is 5.0 A, what is the voltage provided by the wall socket?

2. What is the current in a flashlight bulb with a resistance of 30 Ω if the voltage provided by the flashlight batteries is 3.0 V?

3. What is the resistance of a lightbulb connected to a 110-V wall outlet if the current in the lightbulb is 1.0 A?

Science Online For more practice, visit ips.msscience.com/ math_practice

---

Discussion

Current Flow The text states that narrowing a tube will increase the resistance to the flow of water through the tube. This is similar to using a thinner wire to conduct charge. In what other ways could you increase resistance to the flow of water in a tube, and what would be similar ways to increase resistance to electric current in a conductor? Making the tube longer would be similar to making the current path in a circuit longer. Adding material in the tube to reduce the flow at various places would be similar to putting resistors in a circuit. L2 **LS** Logical-Mathematical

Make a Model

Mechanical Circuit Have interested students make a mechanical model of an electric circuit. Students might rig a small motor to lift marbles to a height. These marbles would be dropped into a tube filled with marbles, pushing some marbles out the other end, and then returning them to the lift mechanism. Have students present their models to the class, describing how each segment represents one aspect of an electric circuit. L3 **LS** Kinesthetic

Applying Math

National Math Standards
Correlation to Mathematics Objectives
1, 2, 9

Answers to Practice Problems
1. 120 V
2. 0.1 A
3. 110 Ω

Curriculum Connection

History Ask students to find out about Thomas Alva Edison, the inventor of the modern lightbulb. Thomas Edison lived from 1847 to 1931. He patented over 1,000 inventions including the electric lightbulb, phonograph, and the motion-picture camera. L2 **LS** Linguistic

Mini LAB

Purpose Students make a complete circuit. L2 **LS** Logical-Mathematical

Materials 5-inch piece of wire, D-cell battery, flashlight bulb

Teaching Strategies Have students diagram the ways that did and the ways that didn't work.

Analysis
In one possible circuit, the wire is attached to the negative terminal of the battery and to the side of the light-bulb. When the base of the lightbulb touches the positive terminal of the battery, the bulb lights.

Assessment

Performance Have each student draw a cross section of a flashlight that shows the path of the current. After everyone has a design on paper, pass out flashlights for students to inspect and check the accuracy of their drawings. Use **Performance Assessment in the Science Classroom,** p. 127.

Reading Check

Answer Current has only one path through a series circuit.

Caption Answer

Figure 16 It stops.

Mini LAB

Identifying Simple Circuits

Procedure
1. The filament in a lightbulb is a piece of wire. For the bulb to light, an electric current must flow through the filament in a complete circuit. Examine the base of a **flashlight bulb** carefully. Where are the ends of the filament connected to the base?
2. Connect one piece of **wire,** a **battery,** and a flashlight bulb to make the bulb light. (There are four possible ways to do this.)

Analysis
Draw and label a diagram showing the path that is followed by the electrons in your circuit. Explain your diagram.

Figure 16 This circuit is an example of a series circuit. A series circuit has only one path for electric current to follow.
Predict *what will happen to the current in this circuit if any of the connecting wires are removed.*

Series and Parallel Circuits

Circuits control the movement of electric current by providing paths for electrons to follow. For current to flow, the circuit must provide an unbroken path for current to follow. Have you ever been putting up holiday lights and had a string that would not light because a single bulb was missing or had burned out and you couldn't figure out which one it was? Maybe you've noticed that some strings of lights don't go out no matter how many bulbs burn out or are removed. These two strings of holiday lights are examples of the two kinds of basic circuits—series and parallel.

Wired in a Line A series circuit is a circuit that has only one path for the electric current to follow, as shown in **Figure 16.** If this path is broken, then the current no longer will flow and all the devices in the circuit stop working. If the entire string of lights went out when only one bulb burned out, then the lights in the string were wired as a series circuit. When the bulb burned out, the filament in the bulb broke and the current path through the entire string was broken.

Reading Check
How many different paths can electric current follow in a series circuit?

In a series circuit, electrical devices are connected along the same current path. As a result, the current is the same through every device. However, each new device that is added to the circuit decreases the current throughout the circuit. This is because each device has electrical resistance, and in a series circuit, the total resistance to the flow of electrons increases as each additional device is added to the circuit. By Ohm's law, if the voltage doesn't change, the current decreases as the resistance increases.

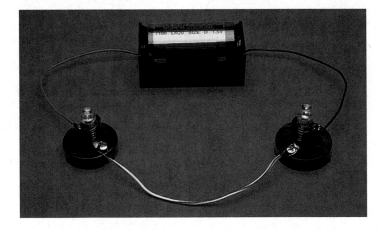

Visual Learning

Figures 16 and 17 Have students draw the two circuits with one device removed and show why current will still flow in the parallel circuit but not in the series circuit. L2 **LS** Visual-Spatial

Branched Wiring What if you wanted to watch TV and had to turn on all the lights, a hair dryer, and every other electrical appliance in the house to do so? That's what it would be like if all the electrical appliances in your house were connected in a series circuit.

Instead, houses, schools, and other buildings are wired using parallel circuits. A **parallel circuit** is a circuit that has more than one path for the electric current to follow, as shown in **Figure 17.** The current branches so that electrons flow through each of the paths. If one path is broken, electrons continue to flow through the other paths. Adding or removing additional devices in one branch does not break the current path in the other branches, so the devices on those branches continue to work normally.

In a parallel circuit, the resistance in each branch can be different, depending on the devices in the branch. The lower the resistance is in a branch, the more current flows in the branch. So the current in each branch of a parallel circuit can be different.

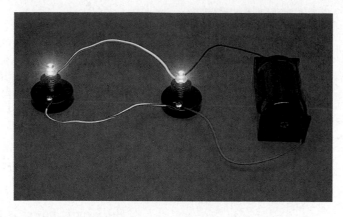

Figure 17 This circuit is an example of a parallel circuit. A parallel circuit has more than one path for electric current to follow.
Predict *what will happen to the current in the circuit if either of the wires connecting the two lightbulbs is removed.*

Protecting Electric Circuits

In a parallel circuit, the current that flows out of the battery or electric outlet increases as more devices are added to the circuit. As the current through the circuit increases, the wires heat up.

To keep the wire from becoming hot enough to cause a fire, the circuits in houses and other buildings have fuses or circuit breakers like those shown in **Figure 18** that limit the amount of current in the wiring. When the current becomes larger than 15 A or 20 A, a piece of metal in the fuse melts or a switch in the circuit breaker opens, stopping the current. The cause of the overload can then be removed, and the circuit can be used again by replacing the fuse or resetting the circuit breaker.

Fuse
In some buildings, each circuit is connected to a fuse. The fuses are usually located in a fuse box.

Figure 18 You might have fuses in your home that prevent electric wires from overheating.

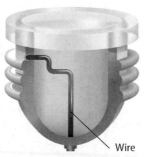

Wire
A fuse contains a piece of wire that melts and breaks when the current flowing through the fuse becomes too large.

Differentiated Instruction

English-Language Learners If possible, pair up students with the same native language. Try to pair students with limited English skills with someone that has better English skills. Allow the students to discuss the concepts in the chapter in both languages. Encourage the students to quiz each other to make sure that both students understand the concepts. Answer any questions that the students may have.

Table 1 Have students identify the appliances that use the most power. hair dryer, microwave Why do these use the most power? They have circuits that have low resistance and so draw a large current. L2 LS **Logical-Mathematical**

Make a Model

Circuit Diagram Explain to students that a circuit diagram is a model of an electric circuit. It shows the source of electric power, the arrangement of the wiring, and all of the devices that use electric power. Have students draw circuit diagrams of the wiring in one or two rooms in a house. Ask them to include in their diagrams at least three devices that use electricity. Students may use standard electrical symbols, or they may make up their own. Make sure they include a key to the symbols they use. L2 LS **Visual-Spatial**

Applying Math

National Math Standards
Correlation to Mathematics Objectives
1, 2, 9

Answers to Practice Problems
1. 3.0 W
2. 10 A
3. 220 V

Table 1 Power Used by Common Appliances	
Appliance	**Power (W)**
Computer	350
Color TV	200
Stereo	250
Refrigerator	450
Microwave	700–1,500
Hair dryer	1,000

Electric Power

When you use an appliance such as a toaster or a hair dryer, electrical energy is converted into other forms of energy. The rate at which electrical energy is converted into other forms of energy is **electric power.** In an electric appliance or in any electric circuit, the electric power that is used can be calculated from the electric power equation.

Electric Power Equation

Power (in watts) = **current** (in amperes) × **voltage** (in volts)
$$P = IV$$

The electric power is equal to the voltage provided to the appliance times the current that flows into the appliance. In the electric power equation, the SI unit of power is the watt. **Table 1** lists the electric power used by some common appliances.

Applying Math — Solving a Simple Equation

ELECTRIC POWER USED BY A LIGHTBULB A lightbulb is plugged into a 110-V wall outlet. How much electric power does the lightbulb use if the current in the bulb is 0.55 A?

Solution

1 *This is what you know:*
- voltage: $V = 110$ V
- current: $I = 0.55$ A

2 *This is what you need to find:*
power: P

3 *This is the procedure you need to use:*
To calculate electric power, substitute the known values for voltage and current into the equation for electric power:
$P = IV = (0.55\text{ A})(110\text{ V}) = 60\text{ W}$

4 *Check your answer:*
Divide your answer by the current 0.55 A. The result should be the given voltage 110 V.

Practice Problems

1. The batteries in a portable CD player provide 6.0 V. If the current in the CD player is 0.5 A, how much power does the CD player use?

2. What is the current in a toaster if the toaster uses 1,100 W of power when plugged into a 110-V wall outlet?

3. An electric clothes dryer uses 4,400 W of electric power. If the current in the dryer is 20.0 A, what is the voltage?

 For more practice, visit ips.msscience.com/ math_practice

600 CHAPTER 20 Electricity

Science Journal

Power in the Home Have students collect the power information from some of the appliances in their homes. Have them calculate how much power each device uses in a month and write their findings in their Science Journals. L2 LS **Logical-Mathematical** P

Fun Fact

Today, many electrical devices have various types of circuit breakers of their own. The large plugs on many hair dryers and the buttons on the sides of power strips are circuit breakers that prevent these devices from drawing too much current or overheating.

Cost of Electric Energy Power is the rate at which energy is used, or the amount of energy that is used per second. When you use a hair dryer, the amount of electrical energy that is used depends on the power of the hair dryer and the amount of time you use it. If you used it for 5 min yesterday and 10 min today, you used twice as much energy today as yesterday.

Using electrical energy costs money. Electric companies generate electrical energy and sell it in units of kilowatt-hours to homes, schools, and businesses. One kilowatt-hour, kWh, is an amount of electrical energy equal to using 1 kW of power continuously for 1 h. This would be the amount of energy needed to light ten 100-W lightbulbs for 1 h, or one 100-W lightbulb for 10 h.

 **Reading Check** *What does kWh stand for and what does it measure?*

An electric company usually charges its customers for the number of kilowatt-hours they use every month. The number of kilowatt-hours used in a building such as a house or a school is measured by an electric meter, which usually is attached to the outside of the building, as shown in **Figure 19.**

Electrical Safety

 Have you ever had a mild electric shock? You probably felt only a mild tingling sensation, but electricity can have much more dangerous effects. In 1997, electric shocks killed an estimated 490 people in the United States. **Table 2** lists a few safety tips to help prevent electrical accidents.

Table 2 Preventing Electric Shock
Never use appliances with frayed or damaged electric cords.
Unplug appliances before working on them, such as when prying toast out of a jammed toaster.
Avoid all water when using plugged-in appliances.
Never touch power lines with anything, including kite string and ladders.
Always respect warning signs and labels.

Figure 19 Electric meters measure the amount of electrical energy used in kilowatt-hours. **Identify** *the electric meter attached to your house.*

Science Online

Topic: Cost of Electrical Energy
Visit ips.msscience.com for Web links to information about the cost of electrical energy in various parts of the world.

Activity Make a bar graph showing the cost of electrical energy for several countries on different continents.

Reading Check

Answer kWh stands for kilowatt-hours. A kWh is the amount of electric energy equal to using 1 kW of power continuously for an hour.

Teacher FYI

Cardiac Danger A current from an electric shock that flows from the left hand to either foot poses the greatest threat of causing cardiac arrest. The damage caused by the electric shock depends on the amount of electric current and the length of time of the shock. For the average adult, a 200 mA jolt that flows from the left hand to either foot will induce muscular contractions that causes breathing difficulties in approximately 50 ms. In approximately 400 ms, the heart will experience ventricular fibrillation or rapid irregular heart beats.

SECTION 3 Electric Circuits **601**

Differentiated Instruction

Challenge Have students learn more about electrical safety. Have students create an informational brochure about electrical safety to share with their class. L2

Curriculum Connection

Math Have students read the electric meters for their homes at the beginning of the week and at the end of the week. Find the price per kilowatt-hour for electricity and have them calculate the cost of the week's electric usage. L2 **LS Logical-Mathematical**

Current's Effects Have students investigate the first-aid procedures for treating electric shock. What first-aid procedures should you be aware of? Possible answer: CPR to restart the heart and treatment for shock L2 **LS Kinesthetic**

3 Assess

DAILY INTERVENTION

Check for Understanding

Visual-Spatial With students, do an electrical safety check of the classroom. Identify electrical hazards, such as frayed cords or too many appliances running from a single outlet. Also check the placement of appliances and consider whether any might be in a dangerous spot. L2

Reteach

Energy Ratings Bring an energy-rating label from a new appliance to class. Have students use the energy specifications of the appliance to determine the energy it will use and its power. Have them estimate the cost to run the appliance for one year. L2 **LS Logical-Mathematical**

✓ Assessment

Process Provide students with basic circuit diagrams. Have them describe which devices are in series and which devices are in parallel. Have them predict the changes that occur when one device is turned off or removed. Use **Performance Assessment in the Science Classroom,** p. 89. L2

Current's Effects The scale below shows how the effect of electric current on the human body depends on the amount of current that flows into the body.

0.0005 A	Tingle
0.001 A	Pain threshold
0.01 A	Inability to let go
0.025 A	
0.05 A	Difficulty breathing
0.10 A	
0.25 A	
0.50 A	Heart failure
1.00 A	

Electric Shock You experience an electric shock when an electric current enters your body. In some ways your body is like a piece of insulated wire. The fluids inside your body are good conductors of current. The electrical resistance of dry skin is much higher. Skin insulates the body like the plastic insulation around a copper wire. Your skin helps keep electric current from entering your body.

A current can enter your body when you accidentally become part of an electric circuit. Whether you receive a deadly shock depends on the amount of current that flows into your body. The current that flows through the wires connected to a 60-W light-bulb is about 0.5 A. This amount of current entering your body could be deadly. Even a current as small as 0.001 A can be painful.

Lightning Safety On average, more people are killed every year by lightning in the United States than by hurricanes or tornadoes. Most lightning deaths and injuries occur outdoors. If you are outside and can see lightning or hear thunder, take shelter indoors immediately. If you cannot go indoors, you should take these precautions: avoid high places and open fields; stay away from tall objects such as trees, flag poles, or light towers; and avoid objects that conduct current such as bodies of water, metal fences, picnic shelters, and metal bleachers.

---

section 3 review

Summary

Electric Circuits

- In an electric circuit, voltage, resistance, and current are related. According to Ohm's law, this relationship can be written as $V = IR$.
- A series circuit has only one path for electric current to follow.
- A parallel circuit has more than one path for current to follow.

Electric Power and Energy

- The electric power used by an appliance is the rate at which the appliance converts electrical energy to other forms of energy.
- The electric power used by an appliance can be calculated using the equation $P = IV$.
- The electrical energy used by an appliance depends on the power of the appliance and the length of time it is used. Electrical energy usually is measured in kWh.

Self Check

1. **Compare** the current in two lightbulbs wired in a series circuit.
2. **Describe** how the current in a circuit changes if the resistance increases and the voltage remains constant.
3. **Explain** why buildings are wired using parallel circuits rather than series circuits.
4. **Identify** what determines the damage caused to the human body by an electric shock.
5. **Think Critically** What determines whether a 100-W lightbulb costs more to use than a 1,200-W hair dryer costs to use?

Applying Math

6. **Calculate Energy** A typical household uses 1,000 kWh of electrical energy every month. If a power company supplies electrical energy to 1,000 households, how much electrical energy must it supply every year?

Science Online ips.msscience.com/self_check_quiz

---

section 3 review

1. The current is the same.
2. The current must decrease.
3. So current will continue to flow in appliances after another appliance or device is turned off or disconnected.
4. the amount of current that flows into the body, the length of time the current flows, and whether or not your heart stops beating
5. time that each is used
6. 1,000 kWh/month × 12 months = 12,000 kWh; 12,000 kWh/household × 1,000 households = 12,000,000 kWh

Current in a Parallel Circuit

The brightness of a lightbulb increases as the current in the bulb increases. In this lab you'll use the brightness of a lightbulb to compare the amount of current that flows in parallel circuits.

● *Real-World Question*

How does connecting devices in parallel affect the electric current in a circuit?

Goal

■ **Observe** how the current in a parallel circuit changes as more devices are added.

Materials

1.5-V lightbulbs (4)   battery holders (2)
1.5-V batteries (2)   minibulb sockets (4)
10-cm-long pieces of
    insulated wire (8)

Safety Precautions

● *Procedure*

1. Connect one lightbulb to the battery in a complete circuit. After you've made the bulb light, disconnect the bulb from the battery to keep the battery from running down. This circuit will be the brightness tester.

2. Make a parallel circuit by connecting two bulbs as shown in the diagram. Reconnect the bulb in the brightness tester and compare its brightness with the brightness of the two bulbs in the parallel circuit. Record your observations.

3. Add another bulb to the parallel circuit as shown in the figure. How does the brightness of the bulbs change?

4. Disconnect one bulb in the parallel circuit. Record your observations.

● *Conclude and Apply*

1. **Describe** how the brightness of each bulb depends on the number of bulbs in the circuit.
2. **Infer** how the current in each bulb depends on the number of bulbs in the circuit.

𝒞ommunicating
Your Data

Compare your conclusions with those of other students in your class. **For more help, refer to the Science Skill Handbook.**

𝒞ommunicating
Your Data

Have students use a computer drawing program to draw the circuits they made in this lab. Encourage them to devise symbols for the different elements in the circuits (i.e., batteries and bulbs). L2

● *Real-World Question*

Purpose Students determine how adding and removing devices affects parallel circuits. L2 **IS** Kinesthetic

Process Skills observe, compare and contrast, classify, form operational definitions, experiment

Time Required 30 minutes

● *Procedure*

Safety Precautions The wires can become hot, especially if the wires short-circuit the battery. Rechargeable batteries are particularly susceptible to becoming hot when short-circuited. Bulbs can break. Be sure students are aware of classroom safety procedures for taking care of broken glass.

Troubleshooting If repeated trials fail to light the bulb, replace each element of the circuit with a component known to be in working order so as to isolate the defective circuit element.

● *Conclude and Apply*

1. The brightness of each bulb didn't change as more bulbs were added.
2. The current is each bulb didn't change as more bulbs were added.

☑ Assessment

Performance Have each student design and make a circuit. Have students place construction paper over their circuits and cut holes where the bulbs are. By only unscrewing and rescrewing lightbulbs, have other students try to determine the hidden wiring pattern. Use **Performance Assessment in the Science Classroom,** p. 97. L2

A Model for Voltage and Current

Real-World Question (Teacher notes)

Purpose Students investigate how the height of a water source and width of a tube affect the flow of water and relate the results to current, voltage, and resistance in electric circuits. L2

ELL **IS** **Kinesthetic**

Process Skills measure, experiment, make a model, make and use a table, recognize cause and effect

Time Required 50 minutes

Procedure (Teacher notes)

Teaching Strategies
- Discuss with students how to measure the tubing's diameter.
- To help students calculate rate, present *rate = volume ÷ time* on the board.

Tie to Prior Knowledge Before the experiment, have students discuss potential energy. What does gravitational potential energy depend upon? mass, gravity, and height What variable is manipulated in the experiment? height

Troubleshooting Demonstrate the proper way to connect tubing of different diameters to the funnels.

Analyze Your Data

Expected Outcome The flow rate is lower with the smaller diameter tubing and when the funnel is lower.

Goal
- **Model** the flow of current in a simple circuit.

Materials
plastic funnel
rubber or plastic tubing
   of different diameters
   (1 m each)
meterstick
ring stand with ring
stopwatch
*clock displaying seconds
hose clamp
*binder clip
500-mL beakers (2)
*Alternate materials

Safety Precautions

Real-World Question

The flow of electrons in an electric circuit is something like the flow of water in a tube connected to a water tank. By raising or lowering the height of the tank, you can increase or decrease the potential energy of the water. How does the flow of water in a tube depend on the diameter of the tube and the height the water falls?

Procedure

1. **Design** a data table in which to record your data. It should be similar to the table below.

2. Connect the tubing to the bottom of the funnel and place the funnel in the ring of the ring stand.

3. **Measure** the inside diameter of the rubber tubing. Record your data.

4. Place a 500-mL beaker at the bottom of the ring stand and lower the ring so the open end of the tubing is in the beaker.

5. Use the meterstick to measure the height from the top of the funnel to the bottom of the ring stand.

Flow Rate Data

Trial	Height (cm)	Diameter (mm)	Time (s)	Flow Rate (mL/s)
1	40	0.5	4	25
2	40	0.25	15	6.7
3	30	0.5	5	20
4	20	0.5	6	17

Alternative Inquiry Lab

Voltage and Current To make this Lab an Inquiry Lab, give students an assortment of electrical components. Have them design circuits and test the voltage and current in each of their designs. Students should experiment with various voltages and various arrangements of resistance components. Have them take measurements and record their data. Have students look for trends in their data and make predictions using their data.

6. Working with a classmate, pour water into the funnel fast enough to keep the funnel full but not overflowing. Measure and record the time needed for 100 mL of water to flow into the beaker. Use the hose clamp to start and stop the flow of water.

7. Connect tubing with a different diameter to the funnel and repeat steps 2 through 6.

8. Reconnect the original piece of tubing and repeat steps 4 through 6 for several lower positions of the funnel, lowering the height by 10 cm each time.

● Analyze Your Data

1. **Calculate** the rate of flow for each trial by dividing 100 mL by the time measured for 100 mL of water to flow into the beaker.

2. **Make a graph** that shows how the rate of flow depends on the funnel height.

● Conclude and Apply

1. **Infer** from your graph how the rate of flow depends on the height of the funnel.

2. **Explain** how the rate of flow depends on the diameter of the tubing. Is this what you expected to happen?

3. **Identify** which of the variables you changed in your trials that corresponds to the voltage in a circuit.

4. **Identify** which of the variables you changed in your trials that corresponds to the resistance in a circuit.

5. **Infer** from your results how the current in a circuit would depend on the voltage.

6. **Infer** from your results how the current in a circuit would depend on the resistance in the circuit.

Communicating
Your Data

Share your graph with other students in your class. Did other students draw the same conclusions as you? **For more help, refer to the** Science Skill Handbook.

LAB 605

Communicating
Your Data

Suggest that students use pencil and paper or computer drawing software to design other systems of tubing for water to flow through. Have them identify the areas of their designs that offer the greatest resistance to the flow of water. L2

Answers to Questions
1. Check student's calculations.
2. Check student's graphs.

● Conclude and Apply

1. Student graphs should indicate that flow rate increases as height increases.
2. As the diameter of the tube decreases, the rate of flow of the water decreases.
3. The height of the funnel corresponds to voltage.
4. The diameter of the tube corresponds to resistance.
5. As voltage increases, the current increases.
6. As resistance increases, the current decreases.

Error Analysis Ask students whether their answers make intuitive sense. Have them explain why they did or didn't expect their results. Have students work with their lab partners to brainstorm possible errors that might have occurred in the experiment, including using different pouring techniques and errors in measuring tube diameter, funnel height, and time.

☑ Assessment

Oral This lab uses an analogy between voltage and gravitational potential energy. Ask students to explain the real difference between these two quantities. Use **Performance Assessment in the Science Classroom,** p. 89. L2

TIME

Content Background

Fuel, oxygen, and heat must be present for a fire to continue burning. Therefore, modern firefighting tactics concentrate on removing one or more of these elements to suppress or contain forest fires.

Typically, the initial attack effort involves making a fuel break. To do this, hand crews and bulldozers remove unburned fuel from the path of a fire. Backfires are another, riskier technique used to remove unburned fuel. Backfires are purposely set between a fuel break and the front of a forest fire.

Helicopters and airplanes are also used to fight fires. Helicopters shuttle firefighting crews and supplies and also may be used to transport and drop water on a fire.

Discussion

Fires Scientists have determined that some fires may be beneficial to forests. What are some positive effects caused by forest fires? Possible responses: Clearing away diseased trees gives healthy trees greater access to the remaining water and nutrients; removing dead trees and underbrush creates space for new vegetation; regular removal of fuels helps prevent large, uncontrollable fires; burned vegetation returns some nutrients to the soil quicker than rotting vegetation; heat is needed for some seeds to germinate. L2

IS Logical-Mathematical

Activity

Current Events Have students search the newspaper or link shown on the student page for articles related to controlling forest fires. Suggest each student summarize the article in three sentences and then share the information with the class. L2

IS Logical-Mathematical

TIME

SCIENCE AND Society

SCIENCE ISSUES THAT AFFECT YOU!

Fire in the Forest

Plant life returns after a forest fire in Yellowstone National Park.

Fires started by lightning may not be all bad

When lightning strikes a tree, the intense heat of the lightning bolt can set the tree on fire. The fire then can spread to other trees in the forest. Though lightning is responsible for only about ten percent of forest fires, it causes about one-half of all fire damage. For example, in 2000, fires set by lightning raged in 12 states at the same time, burning a total area roughly the size of the state of Massachusetts.

Fires sparked by lightning often start in remote, difficult-to-reach areas, such as national parks and range lands. Burning undetected for days, these fires can spread out of control. In addition to threatening lives, the fires can destroy millions of dollars worth of homes and property. Smoke from forest fires also can have harmful effects on people, especially for those with preexisting conditions, such as asthma.

People aren't the only victims of forest fires. The fires kill animals as well. Those who survive the blaze often perish because their habitats have been destroyed. Monster blazes spew carbon dioxide and other gases into the atmosphere. Some of these gases may contribute to the greenhouse effect that warms the planet. Moreover, fires cause soil erosion and loss of water reserves.

But fires caused by lightning also have some positive effects. In old, dense forests, trees often become diseased and insect-ridden. By removing these unhealthy trees, fires allow healthy trees greater access to water and nutrients. Fires also clear away a forest's dead trees, underbrush, and needles, providing space for new vegetation. Nutrients are returned to the ground as dead organic matter decays, but it can take a century for dead logs to rot completely. A fire enables nutrients to be returned to soil much more quickly. Also, the removal of these highly combustible materials prevents more widespread fires from occurring.

Research Find out more about the job of putting out forest fires. What training is needed? What gear do firefighters wear? Why would people risk their lives to save a forest? Use the media center at your school to learn more about forest firefighters and their careers.

For more information, visit
ips.msscience.com/time

Research Large fires require a number of support personnel to perform a variety of tasks, including setting up and maintaining communications, supplying provisions and fuel, coordinating crews and equipment, monitoring the weather, and catering food. Ask each student to find information on a task provided by a member of a fire support team and prepare a report for the class. L3

Resources for Teachers and Students

Fire: Friend or Foe, Dorothy Hinshaw Patent, Clarion Books, 1998

Smoke Jumper, Keith Elliot Greenberg, Blackbirch Press, Inc., 1995

Reviewing Main Ideas

Section 1 Electric Charge

1. The two types of electric charge are positive and negative. Like charges repel and unlike charges attract.

2. An object becomes negatively charged if it gains electrons and positively charged if it loses electrons.

3. Electrically charged objects have an electric field surrounding them and exert electric forces on one another.

4. Electrons can move easily in conductors, but not so easily in insulators.

Section 2 Electric Current

1. Electric current is the flow of charges—usually either electrons or ions.

2. The energy carried by the current in a circuit increases as the voltage in the circuit increases.

3. In a battery, chemical reactions provide the energy that causes electrons to flow in a circuit.

4. As electrons flow in a circuit, some of their electrical energy is lost due to resistance in the circuit.

Section 3 Electric Circuits

1. In an electric circuit, the voltage, current, and resistance are related by Ohm's law.

2. The two basic kinds of electric circuits are parallel circuits and series circuits.

3. The rate at which electric devices use electrical energy is the electric power used by the device.

Reviewing Main Ideas

Summary statements can be used by students to review the major concepts of the chapter.

Visualizing Main Ideas

See student page.

Science Online

Visit ips.msscience.com
/self_check_quiz
/interactive_tutor
/vocabulary_puzzlemaker
/chapter_review
/standardized_test

Visualizing Main Ideas

Copy and complete the following concept map about electricity.

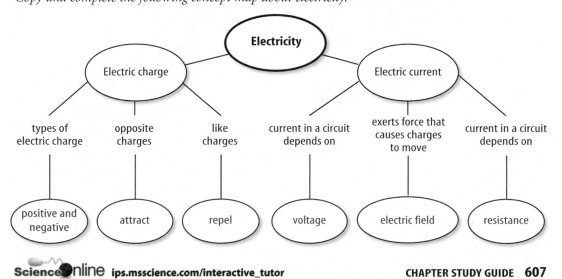

◆ Identifying Misconceptions

Use the assessment as follow-up after students have completed the chapter.
Materials 2 ammeters, circuit with battery and bulb, **Figure 1**
Procedure Show students **Figure 1**. Ask if the number of electrons passing through point A is the same as the number of electrons passing through point B. Place ammeters in the circuit at points A and B.
Expected Outcome The two points have the same current and therefore the same number of electrons passing through them.

Assess

Figure 1

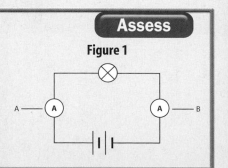

Using Vocabulary

1. electric current
2. Ohm's law
3. conductor
4. circuit
5. static charge
6. ion
7. parallel circuit
8. electric discharge

Checking Concepts

9. B
10. A
11. D
12. A
13. C
14. B

Assessment Transparency

For additional assessment questions, use the *Assessment Transparency* located in the transparency book.

Assessment

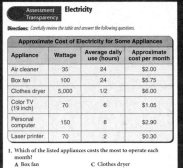

Assessment Transparency	**Electricity**

Directions: *Carefully review the table and answer the following questions.*

Approximate Cost of Electricity for Some Appliances

Appliance	Wattage	Average daily use (hours)	Approximate cost per month
Air cleaner	35	24	$2.00
Box fan	100	24	$5.75
Clothes dryer	5,000	1/2	$6.00
Color TV (19 inch)	70	6	$1.05
Personal computer	150	8	$2.90
Laser printer	70	2	$0.30

1. Which of the listed appliances costs the most to operate each month?
   A Box fan   C Clothes dryer
   B Personal computer   D Color TV
2. According to the table, if two appliances are used for the same number of hours, the one with higher wattage will cost ___.
   F more to operate   H the same to operate
   G less to operate   J can't answer from table
3. The color TV costs more to operate than the laser printer because ___.
   A the wattage of the color TV is higher
   B the color TV is on longer
   C the color TV is bigger
   D the power company charges more for TVs

L2

Electricity

Using Vocabulary

circuit p. 591	ion p. 584
conductor p. 588	Ohm's law p. 597
electric current p. 591	parallel circuit p. 599
electric discharge p. 589	resistance p. 594
electric field p. 587	series circuit p. 598
electric force p. 587	static charge p. 585
electric power p. 600	voltage p. 592
insulator p. 588	

Answer the following questions using complete sentences.

1. What is the term for the flow of electric charge?

2. What is the relationship among voltage, current, and resistance in a circuit?

3. In what type of material do electrons move easily?

4. What is the name for the unbroken path that current follows?

5. What is an excess of electric charge on an object?

6. What is an atom that has gained or lost electrons called?

7. Which type of circuit has more than one path for electrons to follow?

8. What is the rapid movement of excess charge known as?

Checking Concepts

Choose the word or phrase that best answers the question.

9. Which of the following describes an object that is positively charged?
   A) has more neutrons than protons
   B) has more protons than electrons
   C) has more electrons than protons
   D) has more electrons than neutrons

10. Which of the following is true about the electric field around an electric charge?
    A) It exerts a force on other charges.
    B) It increases the resistance of the charge.
    C) It increases farther from the charge.
    D) It produces protons.

11. What is the force between two electrons?
    A) frictional   C) attractive
    B) neutral   D) repulsive

12. What property of a wire increases when it is made thinner?
    A) resistance
    B) voltage
    C) current
    D) static charge

13. What property does Earth have that enables grounding to drain static charges?
    A) It has a high static charge.
    B) It has a high resistance.
    C) It is a large conductor.
    D) It is like a battery.

Use the graph below to answer question 14.

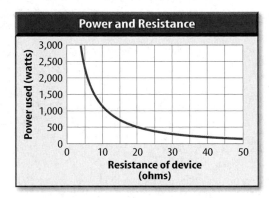

Power and Resistance

14. How does the resistance change if the power decreases from 2,500 W to 500 W?
    A) It increases four times.
    B) It decreases four times.
    C) It doubles.
    D) It doesn't change.

Science Online ips.msscience.com/vocabulary_puzzlemaker

Use the ExamView® Pro Testmaker CD-ROM to:

- create multiple versions of tests
- create modified tests with one mouse click for inclusion students
- edit existing questions and add your own questions
- build tests aligned with state standards using built-in State Curriculum Tags
- change English tests to Spanish with one mouse click and vice versa

Thinking Critically

15. Determine A metal wire is made thinner. How would you change the length of the wire to keep the electric resistance of the wire from changing?

The tables below show how the voltage and current vary in a portable radio and a portable CD player. Use these tables to answer questions 16 through 19.

Portable Radio		Portable CD Player	
Voltage (V)	Current (A)	Voltage (V)	Current (A)
2.0	1.0	2.0	0.5
4.0	2.0	4.0	1.0
6.0	3.0	6.0	1.5

16. Make a graph with current plotted on the horizontal axis and voltage plotted on the vertical axis. Plot the data in the above tables for both devices on your graph.

17. Identify from your graph which line is more horizontal—the line for the portable radio or the line for the portable CD player.

18. Calculate the electric resistance using Ohm's law for each value of the current and voltage in the tables above. What is the resistance of each device?

19. Determine For which device is the line plotted on your graph more horizontal—the device with higher or lower resistance?

20. Explain why a balloon that has a static electric charge will stick to a wall.

21. Describe how you can tell whether the type of charge on two charged objects is the same or different.

22. Infer Measurements show that Earth is surrounded by a weak electric field. If the direction of this field points toward Earth, what is the type of charge on Earth's surface?

Performance Activities

23. Design a board game about a series or parallel circuit. The rules of the game could be based on opening or closing the circuit, adding more devices to the circuit, blowing fuses or circuit breakers, replacing fuses, or resetting circuit breakers.

Applying Math

24. Calculate Resistance A toaster is plugged into a 110-V outlet. What is the resistance of the toaster if the current in the toaster is 10 A?

25. Calculate Current A hair dryer uses 1,000 W when it is plugged into a 110-V outlet. What is the current in the hair dryer?

26. Calculate Voltage A lightbulb with a resistance of 30 Ω is connected to a battery. If the current in the lightbulb is 0.10 A, what is the voltage of the battery?

Use the table below to answer question 27.

Average Standby Power Used	
Appliance	Power (W)
Computer	7.0
VCR	6.0
TV	5.0

27. Calculate Cost The table above shows the power used by several appliances when they are turned off. Calculate the cost of the electrical energy used by each appliance in a month if the cost of electrical energy is \$0.08/kWh, and each appliance is in standby mode for 600 h each month.

Thinking Critically

15. You would make the wire shorter.

16. Check students' graphs.

17. radio

18. $R = V/I$; for the radio $R = (2\,V)/(1\,A) = 2\,\Omega$; for the CD player $R = (2\,V)/(0.5\,A) = 4\,\Omega$

19. the device with the lower resistance

20. The balloon has a negative charge and the wall has an induced positive charge. Opposites attract so the balloon sticks to the wall.

21. Bring the two objects together. If they move toward each other, they are of opposite charge. If they move away from each other, they have the same charge.

22. negative

Performance Activities

23. Check student's games.

Applying Math

National Math Standards
1, 2, 5, 9

24. $R = V/I = 110\,V/10\,A = 11\,\Omega$

25. $P = IV; I = P/V = \frac{1,000\,W}{110\,V} = 9\,A$

26. $V = IR = (0.01\,A)(30\,\Omega) = 3\,V$

27. computer, (0.007 kW)(600 h) (\$0.08/kWh) = \$0.34; VCR, \$0.29; TV, \$0.24

☑ Assessment Resources

📁 Reproducible Masters
Chapter *Fast File* Resources
  Chapter Review, pp. 37–88
  Chapter Tests, pp. 39–42
  Assessment Transparency Activity, p. 49
Glencoe Science Web site
  Chapter Review Test
  Standardized Test Practice

Glencoe Technology
  🔋 Assessment Transparency
  💿 Exam*View*® Pro Testmaker
  📺 MindJogger Videoquiz
  🖥 Interactive Chalkboard

SAMPLE

Part 1 Multiple Choice

1. C
2. A
3. C
4. D
5. C
6. B
7. B
8. D
9. D
10. B
11. B

Part 2 Short Response

12. The lightbulb will stay lit because the circuit has more than one path for the electric current to flow.

13. No, the resistance in each branch can be different, depending on the devices in the branch. The lower the resistance is in a branch, the more current that flows in that branch.

14. The refrigerator because the energy used depends on the power rating and on how long the appliance is used.

Part 1 Multiple Choice

Record your answers on the answer sheet provided by your teacher or on a sheet of paper.

1. What happens when two materials are charged by rubbing against each other?
   A. both lose electrons
   B. both gain electrons
   C. one loses electrons
   D. no movement of electrons

Use the table below to answer questions 2–4.

Power Ratings of Some Appliances	
Appliance	**Power (W)**
Computer	350
Color TV	200
Stereo	250
Toaster	1,100
Microwave	900
Hair dryer	1,000

2. Which appliance will use the most energy if it is run for 15 minutes?
   A. microwave   C. stereo
   B. computer   D. color TV

3. What is the current in the hair dryer if it is plugged into a 110-V outlet?
   A. 110 A   C. 9 A
   B. 130,000 A   D. 1,100 A

4. Suppose using 1,000 W for 1 h costs $0.10. How much would it cost to run the color TV for 8 hours?
   A. $1.00   C. $1.60
   B. $10.00   D. $0.16

5. How does the current in a circuit change if the voltage is doubled and the resistance remains unchanged?
   A. no change   C. doubles
   B. triples   D. reduced by half

6. Which statement does NOT describe how electric changes affect each other?
   A. positive and negative charges attract
   B. positive and negative charges repel
   C. two positive charges repel
   D. two negative charges repel

Use the illustration below to answer questions 7 and 8.

7. What is the device on the chimney called?
   A. circuit breaker   C. fuse
   B. lightning rod   D. circuit

8. What is the device designed to do?
   A. stop electricity from flowing
   B. repel an electric charge
   C. turn the chimney into an insulator
   D. to provide grounding for the house

9. Which of the following is a material through which charge cannot move easily?
   A. conductor   C. wire
   B. circuit   D. insulator

10. What property of a wire increases when it is made longer?
    A. charge   C. voltage
    B. resistance   D. current

11. Which of the following materials are good insulators?
    A. copper and gold
    B. wood and glass
    C. gold and aluminum
    D. plastic and copper

15. 0.75 A

16. The lights would not come on because the circuit is broken.

17. Too large a current was present in the circuit. A safety device—a fuse or circuit breaker—opened the circuit.

18. Electrons move easily through the copper wire, but they cannot move easily through the plastic or rubber because they are insulators. This prevents someone who touches the wire from getting an electric shock.

Part 3 Open Ended

19. The 30-A fuse would allow too much current to flow through the circuit, possibly causing a fire.

20. The water pump provides the energy that enables water to flow in the water circuit. A battery provides the energy that enables current to flow in an electric circuit.

Part 2 | Short Response/Grid In

Record your answers on the answer sheet provided by your teacher or on a sheet of paper.

Use the illustration below to answer questions 12 and 13.

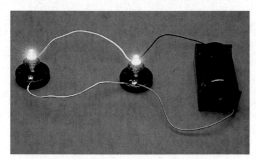

12. In this circuit, if one lightbulb is unscrewed, what happens to the current in the other lightbulb? Explain.

13. In this circuit, is the resistance and the current in each branch of the circuit always the same? Explain.

14. A 1,100-W toaster may be used for five minutes each day. A 400-W refrigerator runs all the time. Which appliance uses more electrical energy? Explain.

15. How much current does a 75-W bulb require in a 100-V circuit?

16. A series circuit containing mini-lightbulbs is opened and some of the lightbulbs are removed. What happens when the circuit is closed?

17. Suppose you plug an electric heater into the wall outlet. As soon as you turn it on, all the lights in the room go out. Explain what must have happened.

18. Explain why copper wires used in appliances or electric circuits are covered with plastic or rubber.

Part 3 | Open Ended

Record your answers on a sheet of paper.

19. Why is it dangerous to use a fuse that is rated 30 A in a circuit calling for a 15-A fuse?

Use the illustration below to answer question 20.

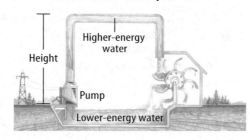

20. Compare the water pump in the water circuit above with the battery in an electric circuit.

21. Explain what causes the lightning that is associated with a thunderstorm.

22. Explain why two charged balloons push each other apart even if they are not touching.

23. Explain what can happen when you rub your feet on a carpet and then touch a metal doorknob.

24. Why does the fact that tungsten wire has a high melting point make it useful in the filaments of lightbulbs?

Test-Taking Tip

Recall Experiences Recall any hands-on experience as you read the question. Base your answer on the information given on the test.

Question 23 Recall from your personal experience the jolt you feel when you touch a doorknob after walking across a carpet.

Rubrics

The following rubrics are sample scoring devices for short response and open-ended questions.

Short Response

Points	Description
2	The student demonstrates a thorough understanding of the science of the task. The response may contain minor flaws that do not detract from the demonstration of a thorough understanding.
1	The student has provided a response that is only partially correct.
0	The student has provided a completely incorrect solution or no response at all.

Open Ended

Points	Description
4	The student demonstrates a thorough understanding of the science of the task. The response may contain minor flaws that do not detract from the demonstration of a thorough understanding.
3	The student demonstrates an understanding of the science of the task. The response is essentially correct and demonstrates an essential but less than thorough understanding of the science.
2	The student demonstrates only a partial understanding of the science of the task. Although the student may have used the correct approach to a solution or may have provided a correct solution, the work lacks an essential understanding of the underlying science concepts.
1	The student demonstrates a very limited understanding of the science of the task. The response is incomplete and exhibits many flaws.
0	The student provides a completely incorrect solution or no response at all.

---

21. In a storm cloud, the bottom of the cloud becomes negatively charged. This negative charge induces a positive charge in the ground below the cloud. The electric discharge is lightning.

22. Each balloon is surrounded by an electric field that extends into space. The electric field around each balloon exerts a force on the other balloon even though they are not touching.

23. Electrons are transferred from the rug to your shoes and then spread over your skin. The excess electrons on your hand induce a positive charge on the doorknob. The attractive electric force between the electrons on your hand and the doorknob can cause them to move to the doorknob, producing a spark.

24. A tungsten filament can become hot enough so that it glows, without the filament melting.

Section/Objectives	Standards		Labs/Features
Chapter Opener	**National**	**State/Local**	**Launch Lab:** Magnetic Forces, p. 613 **Foldables,** p. 613
	See pp. 16T–17T for a Key to Standards.		
Section 1 What is magnetism? ● 3 sessions ▥ 1.5 blocks 1. **Describe** the behavior of magnets. 2. **Relate** the behavior of magnets to magnetic fields. 3. **Explain** why some materials are magnetic.	National Content Standards: UCP.1, UCP.2, UCP.3, UCP.5, A.1, A.2, B.1, B.2, D.2		**Applying Science:** Finding the Magnetic Declination, p. 617 **MiniLAB:** Observing Magnetic Fields, p. 618 **Science Online,** p. 619 **Lab:** Make a Compass, p. 620
Section 2 Electricity and Magnetism ● 4 sessions ▥ 2 blocks 4. **Explain** how electricity can produce motion. 5. **Explain** how motion can produce electricity.	National Content Standards: UCP.1, UCP.2, UCP.3, UCP.5, A.1, A.2, B.1, B.2, D.2		**MiniLAB:** Assembling an Electromagnet, p. 622 **Visualizing Voltmeters and Ammeters,** p. 623 **Science Online,** p. 627 **Integrate History,** p. 629 **Lab:** How does an electric motor work?, pp. 632–633 **Science and Language Arts:** Aagjuuk and Sivulliit, p. 634

Lab Materials	Reproducible Resources	Section Assessment	Technology
Launch Lab: 2 bar magnets, sheet of paper, metric ruler	**Chapter FAST FILE Resources** Foldables Worksheet, p. 13 Directed Reading Overview, p. 15 Note-taking Worksheets, pp. 27–28	GLENCOE'S ADVANTAGE **ASSESSMENT**	**TeacherWorks** includes: • Interactive Teacher Edition • Lesson Planner with calendar • Access to all program blacklines • Correlations to standards • Web links
MiniLAB: iron filings, plastic petri dish, tape, several magnets **Lab:** petri dish, water, sewing needle, magnet, tape, marker, paper, plastic spoon *Need materials?* Contact Science Kit at 1-800-828-7777 or www.sciencekit.com on the Internet.	**Chapter FAST FILE Resources** Transparency Activity, p. 38 MiniLAB, p. 3 Enrichment, p. 25 Reinforcement, p. 23 Directed Reading, p. 16 Lab Activity, pp. 9–10 Lab Worksheets, pp. 5–6 **Earth Science Critical Thinking/Problem Solving,** p. 8	**Portfolio** Assessment, p. 618 **Performance** Applying Science, p. 617 MiniLAB, p. 618 Applying Science, p. 619 **Content** Section Review, p. 619	Section Focus Transparency Teaching Transparency Guided Reading Audio Program Interactive Chalkboard CD-ROM Video Lab
MiniLAB: wire, 16-penny steel nail, D-cell battery, paper clips **Lab:** 22-gauge enameled wire (4 m), steel knitting needle, 4 nails, hammer, 2 ceramic magnets, 18-gauge insulated wire (60 cm), masking tape, fine sandpaper, 15-cm wooden board, 6-V battery, wire cutters, 2 wooden blocks	**Chapter FAST FILE Resources** Transparency Activity, p. 39 MiniLAB, p. 4 Enrichment, p. 26 Reinforcement, p. 24 Directed Reading, pp. 17, 18 Lab Activity, pp. 11–12 Transparency Activity, pp. 41–42 Lab Worksheets, pp. 7–8 **Lab Management and Safety,** p. 64 **Physical Science Critical Thinking/Problem Solving,** p. 20	**Portfolio** Visual Learning, p. 622 Cultural Diversity, p. 625 **Performance** Assessment, p. 631 Applying Math, p. 631 **Content** Section Review, p. 631	Section Focus Transparency Virtual Labs CD-ROM Guided Reading Audio Program Interactive Chalkboard CD-ROM

End of Chapter Assessment

GLENCOE'S ADVANTAGE **ASSESSMENT**

Blackline Masters	Technology	Professional Series
Chapter Fast File Resources Chapter Review, pp. 31–32 Chapter Tests, pp. 33–36 **Standardized Test Practice** pp. 87–90	MindJogger Videoquiz Virtual Labs CD-ROM ExamView® Pro Testmaker TeacherWorks CD-ROM Interactive Chalkboard CD-ROM	**Performance Assessment in the Science Classroom (PASC)**

Transparencies

Section Focus

Section Focus Transparency 1 — Will he stick to the refrigerator?

These fish are rainbow trout. Recently, scientists discovered that rainbow trout have tiny amounts of magnetic material in cells in their noses. The researchers don't know exactly how the trout use the magnetic material, but they think it might help the trout navigate.

1. Do you think the magnetic material in the trout's nose makes a strong magnet? Why or why not?
2. What kind of material does a magnet stick to?
3. Where do you encounter magnets in your everyday life?

L2

Section Focus Transparency 2 — Heavy Duty

In a salvage yard it is necessary to move large amounts of scrap material. One way to do this is with a powerful magnet such as the magnet shown in the picture.

1. What does all the scrap material that the magnet can pick up have in common?
2. Would the magnet also be able to pick up old car seats or wind-shield glass? Explain.
3. How do you think the crane operator releases the scrap material from the large magnet?

L2

This is a representation of key blackline masters available in the Teacher Classroom Resources. See Resource Manager boxes within the chapter for additional information.

Key to Teaching Strategies

The following designations will help you decide which activities are appropriate for your students.

L1 Level 1 activities should be appropriate for students with learning difficulties.

L2 Level 2 activities should be within the ability range of all students.

L3 Level 3 activities are designed for above-average students.

ELL ELL activities should be within the ability range of English Language Learners.

COOP LEARN Cooperative Learning activities are designed for small group work.

LS Multiple Learning Styles logos, as described on page 12T, are used throughout to indicate strategies that address different learning styles.

P These strategies represent student products that can be placed into a best-work portfolio.

PBL Problem-Based Learning activities apply real-world situations to learning.

Assessment

Assessment Transparency — Magnetism

Directions: Carefully review the graph and answer the following questions.

Sunspot Activity

1. According to the graph, what year had the greatest number of sunspots?
   A 1948   C 1965
   B 1958   D 1980
2. Which year experienced the fewest sunspots?
   F 1954   H 1976
   G 1964   J 1983
3. What is the approximate length of time between points of low sunspot activity?
   A 1 year   C 11 years
   B 5 years   D 20 years

L2

Teaching

Teaching Transparency 2 — Principle of an Electric Generator

L2

Hands-on Activities

Student Text Lab Worksheet

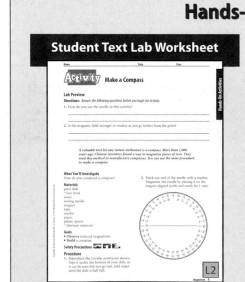

Activity — Make a Compass

Lab Preview
Directions: Answer the following questions before you begin the Activity.
1. How do you use the needle in this activity?

2. Is the magnetic field stronger or weaker as you go farther from the poles?

A valuable tool for any nature enthusiast is a compass. More than 1,000 years ago, Chinese inventors found a way to magnetize pieces of iron. They used this method to manufacture compasses. You can use the same procedure to make a compass.

What You'll Investigate
How do you construct a compass?

Materials
petri dish
*clear bowl
water
sewing needle
magnet
tape
marker
paper
plastic spoon
*Alternate materials

Goals
• Observe induced magnetism.
• Build a compass.

Safety Precautions

Procedure
1. Reproduce the circular protractor shown. Tape it under the bottom of your dish, so it can be seen but not get wet. Add water until the dish is half full.

2. Mark one end of the needle with a marker. Magnetize the needle by placing it on the magnet aligned north and south for 1 min.

L2

Laboratory Activities

Laboratory Activity 1 — Earth's Magnetism

Earth is surrounded by a magnetic field that is similar to the magnetic field around a bar magnet. Magnets have a north magnetic pole and a south magnetic pole. Earth's south magnetic pole is near the north geographic pole, and its north magnetic pole is near the south geographic pole.

You usually do not notice Earth's magnetic field because it is weak. In your classroom, wires carrying electric current also produce magnetic fields that add to Earth's magnetic field and can change its direction. A compass can show the direction of the magnetic field. A compass needle is a small bar magnet that aligns itself along the magnetic field lines around the compass. You can use a compass to map the magnetic field in your classroom.

Strategy
You will use a compass.
You will map the magnetic field in your classroom.

Materials
compass
graph paper

Procedure
1. Draw a floor plan of the classroom on the graph paper. (The floor plan does not have to be to scale.) Indicate north, south, east, and west on the floor plan.
2. Mark the desk locations on the floor plan with a small circle and a number.
3. Take a compass reading at each numbered location. Note the compass needle's direction. See Figure 1. Draw it neatly on the floor plan. Record each angle in Table 1.

Figure 1

Data and Observations
Table 1

Location	Angle
1	
2	
3	
4	
5	
6	
7	

L2

Meeting Different Ability Levels

Content Outline

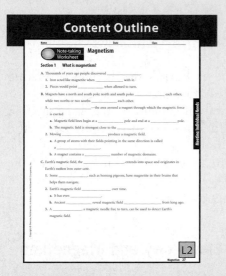

L2

Reinforcement

L2

Enrichment

L3

Directed Reading (English/Spanish)

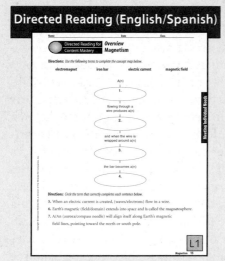

L1

Study Guide

L2

Reading Essentials

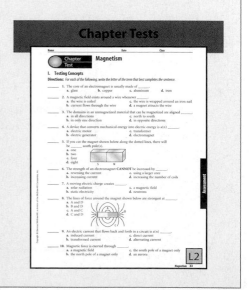

L1

Assessment

Test Practice Workbook

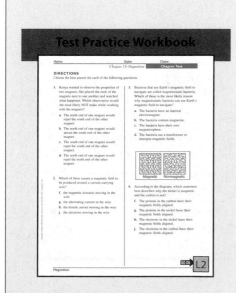

L2

Chapter Review

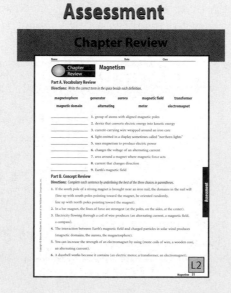

L2

Chapter Tests

L2

Science Content Background

section 1

What is magnetism?
Magnets

Electrons spin as they move around the nucleus of an atom. Because the electron has charge, its motion around the nucleus and its spin both produce magnetic fields. In most elements these magnetic fields cancel. But in a few elements, such as iron, cobalt, and nickel, the magnetic fields produced by the electron spins add together. These elements can be made into permanent magnets.

The lines that represent magnetic fields are called magnetic field lines. By convention, the lines are shown going from north poles to south poles. These lines can be used to describe any magnetic fields: the field around a magnet, the field between two or more magnets, the field around celestial objects such as Earth, or the field produced by a changing electric field.

Earth's Magnetic Field

The naming of a magnet's poles can cause some confusion. By convention we call one pole of a magnet north and the other part south. The part of a freely turning magnet that faces geographic north is called the north pole of the magnet. Like poles repel and unlike poles attract. Thus, Earth's north pole is really a south magnetic pole because it attracts the north end of magnets. If you picture Earth's magnetic field as being produced by a large bar magnet, the magnet's south pole would be at Earth's north pole, attracting the north poles of compass needles.

Another way of explaining this is to say that magnetic field lines go into south poles and come out of north poles. Compasses show the direction of the magnetic field lines. Thus if the north end of a compass points at something it must be a magnetic south pole.

section 2

Electricity and Magnetism
Moving Charge Forms a Magnet

In 1820, Hans Christian Oersted discovered that an electric current could deflect a magnetic compass needle. Michael Faraday's experimental work and James Clerk Maxwell's mathematical development of Faraday's ideas established electricity and magnetism as two aspects of one force, electromagnetism. Electromagnetism is one of the four fundamental forces known. Gravity, the strong nuclear force, and the weak nuclear force are the other three. These fundamental forces all act at a distance through a field. They are fundamental because they explain other forces. Familiar contact forces, such as friction between a book and a table, the normal force of the table holding up the book, or your ability to push a book with your hand, are due to the electromagnetic force of the atoms in the books, your hand, and the tabletop.

chapter content resources

Internet Resources
For additional content background, visit
ips.msscience.com to:
- access your book online
- find references to related articles in popular science magazines
- access Web links with related content background
- access current events with science journal topics

Print Resources
Electric Power: Motors, Controls, Generators, Transformers, by Joe Kaiser, Goodheart-Wilcox, 1998
Electricity and Magnetism, by E. Humberstone, Paul-Francis Law, and Peter Adamczyk, EDCP, 1999
Science Projects about Electricity and Magnetism, by Robert Gardner, Enslow Publishers, 1994

 **IDENTIFYING**

Misconceptions

Find Out What Students Think

Students may think that . . .

Earth's north and south geographic poles are corresponding north and south magnetic poles.
Most people assume that we call the north pole "north" because it is close to a magnetic north pole. This is logical reasoning. However, opposite magnetic poles attract, so Earth's geographic north pole is actually close to its magnetic south pole because it attracts the north end of a magnet. The convention for naming north and south came about in a logical way. The part of a magnet that pointed to the north was called the north magnetic pole. Later, people realized that the north pointing part of a magnet is actually attracted to a south magnetic pole. Since the convention naming north and south on Earth was already established it has been kept, even though it causes confusion.

Demonstration

Give each group sheets of paper, a strip of masking tape, and a bar magnet that is labeled N (north) and S (south). Ask them to use the bar magnet as the center of Earth and to draw around the magnet to make a model of Earth. Direct students to label the equator, the northern hemisphere, and the southern hemisphere. Then have them decide whether the N or the S end of the magnet should be in the Northern Hemisphere.

Promote Understanding

Activity

- Give each group of students a compass.

- Review with students that the north end of the compass needle points to the northern part of our planet.

- Ask students to check their models using the compass to make sure the north end of the compass needle points toward the Northern Hemisphere of their models.

- If the compass needle points the wrong way, have students rearrange their models to make the compass needle point to the Northern Hemisphere.

Many students will have made models of Earth with the north pole of the magnet in the Northern Hemisphere. They will see that the north end of the compass needle points away

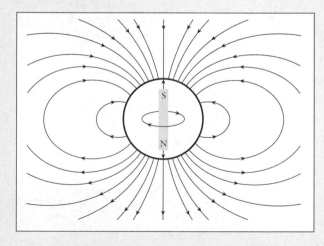

from this rather than towards it. In their models, the south pole of the magnet should be in the Northern Hemisphere.

Assess

After completing the chapter, see *Identifying Misconceptions* in the Study Guide at the end of the chapter.

chapter 21

Chapter Vocabulary

magnetic field, p. 615
magnetic domain, p. 616
magnetosphere, p. 617
electromagnet, p. 621
motor, p. 624
aurora, p. 625
generator, p. 626
alternating current, p. 626
direct current, p. 627
transformer, p. 628

Science Journal Student answers may include: to stick messages on a refrigerator, to pick up metal pieces, or to find nails (studs) in walls to hang up pictures.

PowerPoint® Presentations

This CD-ROM is an editable Microsoft® PowerPoint® presentation that includes:
- a pre-made presentation for every chapter
- interactive graphics
- animations
- audio clips
- image bank
- all new section and chapter questions
- Standardized Test Practice
- transparencies
- pre-lab questions for all labs
- Foldables directions
- links to ips.msscience.com

chapter 21

Magnetism

chapter preview

sections

1 What is magnetism?
  Lab Make a Compass

2 Electricity and Magnetism
  Lab How does an electric motor work?

  Virtual Lab How does a transformer work?

612

Magnetic Suspension

This experimental train can travel at speeds as high as 500 km/h—without even touching the track! It uses magnetic levitation, or maglev, to reach these high speeds. Magnetic forces lift the train above the track, and propel it forward at high speeds.

Science Journal List three ways that you have seen magnets used.

Theme Connection

Systems and Interactions Changing electric and magnetic fields form a system in which one of the fields produces the other.

About the Photo

Maglev Transportation With airports getting more and more crowded, and with airplane security issues, some people are looking to maglevs as a transportation alternative. Because maglevs travel on a cushion of air, reducing friction, they can travel at high speeds, almost as fast as an airplane.

Start-Up Activities

Magnetic Forces

A maglev is moved along at high speeds by magnetic forces. How can a magnet get something to move? The following lab will demonstrate how a magnet is able to exert forces.

1. Place two bar magnets on opposite ends of a sheet of paper.

2. Slowly slide one magnet toward the other until it moves. Measure the distance between the magnets.

3. Turn one magnet around 180°. Repeat Step 2. Then turn the other magnet and repeat Step 2 again.

4. Repeat Step 2 with one magnet perpendicular to the other, in a T shape.

5. **Think Critically** In your Science Journal, record your results. In each case, how close did the magnets have to be to affect each other? Did the magnets move together or apart? How did the forces exerted by the magnets change as the magnets were moved closer together? Explain.

Science Online Preview this chapter's content and activities at ips.msscience.com

---

FOLDABLES™ Study Organizer

Magnetic Forces and Fields Make the following Foldable to help you see how magnetic forces and magnetic fields are similar and different.

STEP 1 **Draw** a mark at the midpoint of a vertical sheet of paper along the side edge.

STEP 2 **Turn** the paper horizontally and **fold** the outside edges in to touch at the midpoint mark.

Magnetic Force | Magnetic Field

STEP 3 **Label** the flaps *Magnetic Force* and *Magnetic Field*.

Compare and Contrast As you read the chapter, write information about each topic on the inside of the appropriate flap. After you read the chapter, compare and contrast the terms *magnetic force* and *magnetic field*. Write your observations under the flaps.

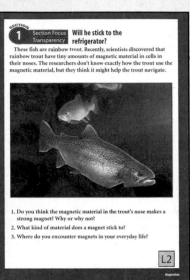
section 1

What is magnetism?

as you read

What You'll Learn

- **Describe** the behavior of magnets.
- **Relate** the behavior of magnets to magnetic fields.
- **Explain** why some materials are magnetic.

Why It's Important

Magnetism is one of the basic forces of nature.

Review Vocabulary

compass: a device which uses a magnetic needle that can turn freely to determine direction

New Vocabulary

- magnetic field
- magnetic domain
- magnetosphere

Early Uses

Do you use magnets to attach papers to a metal surface such as a refrigerator? Have you ever wondered why magnets and some metals attract? Thousands of years ago, people noticed that a mineral called magnetite attracted other pieces of magnetite and bits of iron. They discovered that when they rubbed small pieces of iron with magnetite, the iron began to act like magnetite. When these pieces were free to turn, one end pointed north. These might have been the first compasses. The compass was an important development for navigation and exploration, especially at sea. Before compasses, sailors had to depend on the Sun or the stars to know in which direction they were going.

Magnets

A piece of magnetite is a magnet. Magnets attract objects made of iron or steel, such as nails and paper clips. Magnets also can attract or repel other magnets. Every magnet has two ends, or poles. One end is called the north pole and the other is the south pole. As shown in **Figure 1,** a north magnetic pole always repels other north poles and always attracts south poles. Likewise, a south pole always repels other south poles and attracts north poles.

Two north poles repel   Two south poles repel

Figure 1 Two north poles or two south poles repel each other. North and south magnetic poles are attracted to each other.

Opposite poles attract

614 CHAPTER 21 Magnetism

The Magnetic Field You have to handle a pair of magnets for only a short time before you can feel that magnets attract or repel without touching each other. How can a magnet cause an object to move without touching it? Recall that a force is a push or a pull that can cause an object to move. Just like gravitational and electric forces, a magnetic force can be exerted even when objects are not touching. And like these forces, the magnetic force becomes weaker as the magnets get farther apart.

This magnetic force is exerted through a **magnetic field.** Magnetic fields surround all magnets. If you sprinkle iron filings near a magnet, the iron filings will outline the magnetic field around the magnet. Take a look at **Figure 2.** The iron filings form a pattern of curved lines that start on one pole and end on the other. These curved lines are called magnetic field lines. Magnetic field lines help show the direction of the magnetic field.

Iron filings show the magnetic field lines around a bar magnet.

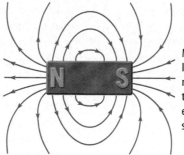
Magnetic field lines start at the north pole of the magnet and end on the south pole.

Reading Check *What is the evidence that a magnetic field exists?*

Magnetic field lines begin at a magnet's north pole and end on the south pole, as shown in **Figure 2.** The field lines are close together where the field is strong and get farther apart as the field gets weaker. As you can see in the figures, the magnetic field is strongest close to the magnetic poles and grows weaker farther from the poles.

Field lines that curve toward each other show attraction. Field lines that curve away from each other show repulsion. **Figure 3** illustrates the magnetic field lines between a north and a south pole and the field lines between two north poles.

Figure 2 A magnetic field surrounds a magnet. Where the magnetic field lines are close together, the field is strong.
Determine *for this magnet where the strongest field is.*

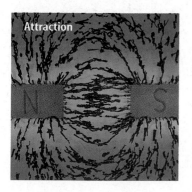
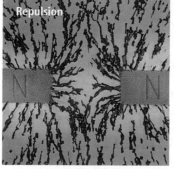

Figure 3 Magnetic field lines show attraction and repulsion.
Explain *what the field between two south poles would look like.*

SECTION 1 What is magnetism? **615**

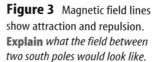

Differentiated Instruction

Challenge Students can use small metal objects such as BBs to get an idea of the strength of a magnetic field. Have them place the objects in a cup and count how many are picked up by a magnet held above the objects at heights of 1 cm, 2 cm, and so on. Ask students to use a spreadsheet program to organize their findings. L3

Caption Answer
Figure 2 near the poles

Reading Check

Answer Magnets exert a force on objects they don't touch.

Visual Learning

Figure 3 Iron filings in the presence of a magnetic field show where the field is strongest and where it is weakest. What similarities would you expect to see in the magnetic field for magnets of different shapes? The field will always be strongest at the poles. Magnetic field lines extend from one pole to the other, and are spaced farther apart as the distance from the magnet increases. L2 **LS** **Visual-Spatial**

Caption Answer

Figure 3 The field lines would curve away from each other, as in the picture with two north poles.

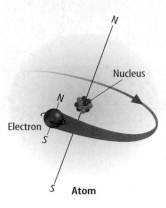

Figure 4 Movement of electrons produces magnetic fields. **Describe** what two types of motion are shown in the illustration.

Figure 5 Some materials can become temporary magnets.

Making Magnetic Fields Only certain materials, such as iron, can be made into magnets that are surrounded by a magnetic field. How are magnetic fields made? A moving electric charge, such as a moving electron, creates a magnetic field.

Inside every magnet are moving charges. All atoms contain negatively charged particles called electrons. Not only do these electrons swarm around the nucleus of an atom, they also spin, as shown in **Figure 4.** Because of its movement, each electron produces a magnetic field. The atoms that make up magnets have their electrons arranged so that each atom is like a small magnet. In a material such as iron, a large number of atoms will have their magnetic fields pointing in the same direction. This group of atoms, with their fields pointing in the same direction, is called a **magnetic domain.**

A material that can become magnetized, such as iron or steel, contains many magnetic domains. When the material is not magnetized, these domains are oriented in different directions, as shown in **Figure 5A.** The magnetic fields created by the domains cancel, so the material does not act like a magnet.

A magnet contains a large number of magnetic domains that are lined up and pointing in the same direction. Suppose a strong magnet is held close to a material such as iron or steel. The magnet causes the magnetic field in many magnetic domains to line up with the magnet's field, as shown in **Figure 5B.** As you can see in **Figure 5C** this process magnetizes paper clips.

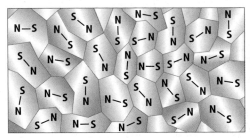

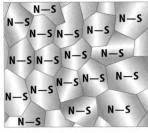

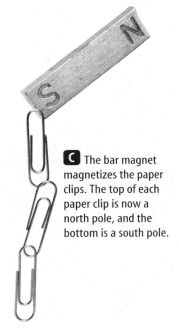

A Microscopic sections of iron and steel act as tiny magnets. Normally, these domains are oriented randomly and their magnetic fields cancel each other.

B When a strong magnet is brought near the material, the domains line up, and their magnetic fields add together.

C The bar magnet magnetizes the paper clips. The top of each paper clip is now a north pole, and the bottom is a south pole.

616 **CHAPTER 21** Magnetism

Earth's Magnetic Field

Magnetism isn't limited to bar magnets. Earth has a magnetic field, as shown in **Figure 6.** The region of space affected by Earth's magnetic field is called the **magnetosphere** (mag NEE tuh sfihr). This deflects most of the charged particles from the Sun. The origin of Earth's magnetic field is thought to be deep within Earth in the outer core layer. One theory is that movement of molten iron in the outer core is responsible for generating Earth's magnetic field. The shape of Earth's magnetic field is similar to that of a huge bar magnet tilted about 11° from Earth's geographic north and south poles.

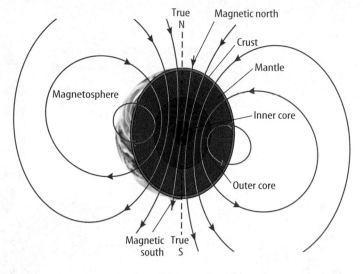

Figure 6 Earth has a magnetic field similar to the field of a bar magnet.

Applying Science

Finding the Magnetic Declination

The north pole of a compass points toward the magnetic pole, rather than true north. Imagine drawing a line between your location and the north pole, and a line between your location and the magnetic pole. The angle between these two lines is called the magnetic declination. Magnetic declination must be known if you need to know the direction to true north. However, the magnetic declination changes depending on your position.

Identifying the Problem

Suppose your location is at 50° N and 110° W. The location of the north pole is at 90° N and 110° W, and the location of the magnetic pole is at about 80° N and 105° W. What is the magnetic declination angle at your location?

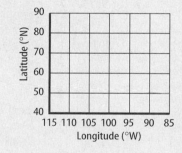

Solving the Problem

1. Draw and label a graph like the one shown above.
2. On the graph, plot your location, the location of the magnetic pole, and the location of the north pole.
3. Draw a line from your location to the north pole, and a line from your location to the magnetic pole.
4. Using a protractor, measure the angle between the two lines.

Mini LAB

Purpose Students observe magnetic fields. L2 **IS** **Kinesthetic**

Materials iron filings, plastic petri dish, tape, magnets

Safety Precaution Make sure to use iron *filings* only. DO NOT use iron *powder*, as it may contain ultrafine particles that present a serious risk of fire and explosion.

Troubleshooting Seal the petri dish with tape or glue to keep the filings off the magnets. Filings can be hard to remove.

Teaching Strategies Field lines around magnets can be illustrated with an overhead projector, using a clear petri dish containing iron filings and magnets of different shapes and strengths.

Analysis

1. Filings are densest at the poles. They are less dense farther away from the poles.
2. The stronger the magnet, the denser the filings.

Assessment

Performance Have students use iron filings to design an experiment to show whether flexible magnetic strips are a single magnet or a series of magnets, each with a north and south pole. Use **Performance Assessment in the Science Classroom,** p. 95. P

Mini LAB

Observing Magnetic Fields

Procedure

1. Place **iron filings** in a **plastic petri dish.** Cover the dish and seal it with **clear tape.**
2. Collect **several magnets.** Place the magnets on the table and hold the dish over each one. Draw a diagram of what happens to the filings in each case.
3. Arrange two or more magnets under the dish. Observe the pattern of the filings.

Analysis

1. What happens to the filings close to the poles? Far from the poles?
2. Compare the fields of the individual magnets. How can you tell which magnet is strongest? Weakest?

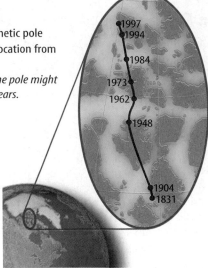

Figure 7 Earth's magnetic pole does not remain in one location from year to year.
Predict *how you think the pole might move over the next few years.*

Nature's Magnets Honeybees, rainbow trout, and homing pigeons have something in common with sailors and hikers. They take advantage of magnetism to find their way. Instead of using compasses, these animals and others have tiny pieces of magnetite in their bodies. These pieces are so small that they may contain a single magnetic domain. Scientists have shown that some animals use these natural magnets to detect Earth's magnetic field. They appear to use Earth's magnetic field, along with other clues like the position of the Sun or stars, to help them navigate.

Earth's Changing Magnetic Field Earth's magnetic poles do not stay in one place. The magnetic pole in the north today, as shown in **Figure 7,** is in a different place from where it was 20 years ago. In fact, not only does the position of the magnetic poles move, but Earth's magnetic field sometimes reverses direction. For example, 700 thousand years ago, a compass needle that now points north would point south. During the past 20 million years, Earth's magnetic field has reversed direction more than 70 times. The magnetism of ancient rocks contains a record of these magnetic field changes. When some types of molten rock cool, magnetic domains of iron in the rock line up with Earth's magnetic field. After the rock cools, the orientation of these domains is frozen into position. Consequently, these old rocks preserve the orientation of Earth's magnetic field as it was long ago.

618   CHAPTER 21 Magnetism

Visual Learning

Figure 7 The illustration shows that Earth's magnetic field is changing. What does this suggest is going on inside Earth? If the magnetic field arises from Earth's molten-iron core, it suggests that the processes in the core are changing, also. L3 **IS** **Logical-Mathematical**

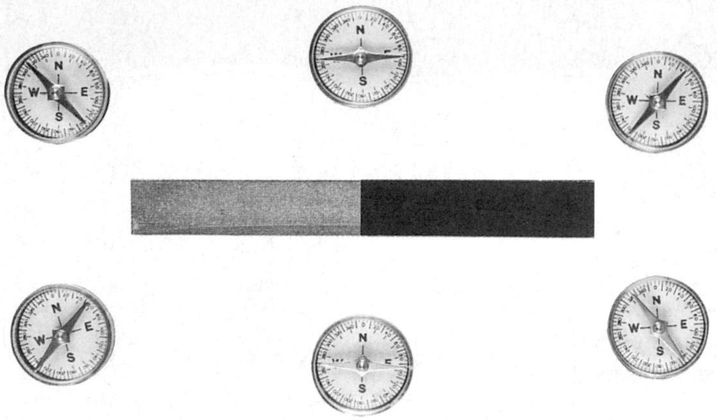

Figure 8 The compass needles align with the magnetic field lines around the magnet.
Explain *what happens to the compass needles when the bar magnet is removed.*

The Compass A compass needle is a small bar magnet with a north and south magnetic pole. In a magnetic field, a compass needle rotates until it is aligned with the magnetic field line at its location. **Figure 8** shows how the orientation of a compass needle depends on its location around a bar magnet.

Earth's magnetic field also causes a compass needle to rotate. The north pole of the compass needle points toward Earth's magnetic pole that is in the north. This magnetic pole is actually a magnetic south pole. Earth's magnetic field is like that of a bar magnet with the magnet's south pole near Earth's north pole.

> **Science Online**
> **Topic: Compasses**
> Visit ips.msscience.com for Web links to information about different types of compasses.
> **Activity** Find out how far from true north a compass points in your location.

section 1 review

Summary

Magnets

- A magnet has a north pole and a south pole.
- Like magnetic poles repel each other; unlike poles attract each other.
- A magnet is surrounded by a magnetic field that exerts forces on other magnets.
- Some materials are magnetic because their atoms behave like magnets.

Earth's Magnetic Field

- Earth is surrounded by a magnetic field similar to the field around a bar magnet.
- Earth's magnetic poles move slowly, and sometimes change places. Earth's magnetic poles now are close to Earth's geographic poles.

Self Check

1. **Explain** why atoms behave like magnets.
2. **Explain** why magnets attract iron but do not attract paper.
3. **Describe** how the behavior of electric charges is similar to that of magnetic poles.
4. **Determine** where the field around a magnet is the strongest and where it is the weakest.
5. **Think Critically** A horseshoe magnet is a bar magnet bent into the shape of the letter U. When would two horseshoe magnets attract each other? Repel? Have little effect?

Applying Skills

6. **Communicate** Ancient sailors navigated by using the Sun, stars, and following a coastline. Explain how the development of the compass would affect the ability of sailors to navigate.

Science Online ips.msscience.com/self_check_quiz

Caption Answer

Figure 8 They align with Earth's magnetic field.

3 Assess

DAILY INTERVENTION

Check for Understanding

Kinesthetic Have the students pretend a pencil or pen is a compass needle with the point as the north and the other end as the south. Take a ruler with one end marked north and the other marked south and pretend it is a magnet. Have the students point the pen or pencil where the compass would point as the magnet is moved around the room.

Reteach

Display Magnetic Fields Use iron filings to display the magnetic fields surrounding a variety of magnets. Have students identify where the fields are strongest and weakest. **LS Visual-Spatial**

Assessment

Performance Have students use a paper clip, a magnet, and materials such as paper or aluminum foil to determine whether materials can shield magnetic forces. Use **Performance Assessment in the Science Classroom,** p. 97.

section 1 review

1. They contain moving electrons.
2. Some metals have magnetic domains in which atoms are oriented in the same direction. Paper does not.
3. Like poles repel, like charges repel; unlike poles attract, unlike charges attract.
4. The field is strongest near the magnet's poles and weakest far from the poles.
5. If like poles face each other, the magnets will repel each other. If opposite poles face each other, the magnets will attract each other. If the bends face each other, the magnets will have little effect on each other.
6. It would tell you the direction in which you were traveling, even if you could not see the Sun or stars.

SECTION 1 What is magnetism? **619**

Real-World Question

Purpose Students discover how magnetism can be used to find direction on Earth. L2
ELL **IS** **Kinesthetic**

Process Skills observe, infer, compare and contrast, interpret data

Time Required 45 minutes

Procedure

Safety Precautions Caution students about responsible and careful handling of the needles. Collect and count needles before and at the end of class.

Teaching Strategies Needles can be difficult to handle; help students place them on the water.

Troubleshooting Caution students about disturbing the water and needle as little as possible when moving the dish.

Conclude and Apply

1. The needle always aligns itself north-south.
2. The compass needle moved to align itself with the magnet's field.
3. Answers will vary. If the marked end points to the north pole of the bar magnet, it is a south pole. If it points to the south pole of the bar magnet, it is a north pole. This is because opposite poles attract.

Make a Compass

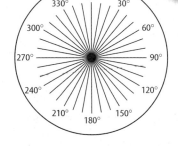

A valuable tool for hikers and campers is a compass. Almost 1,000 years ago, Chinese inventors found a way to magnetize pieces of iron. They used this method to manufacture compasses. You can use the same procedure to make a compass.

Real-World Question

How do you construct a compass?

Goals
■ **Observe** induced magnetism.
■ **Build** a compass.

Materials
petri dish	tape
*clear bowl	marker
water	paper
sewing needle	plastic spoon
magnet	*Alternate material

Safety Precautions 🥽 👕 🧤

Procedure

1. Reproduce the circular protractor shown. Tape it under the bottom of your dish so it can be seen but not get wet. Add water until the dish is half full.

2. Mark one end of the needle with a marker. Magnetize a needle by placing it on the magnet aligned north and south for 1 min.

3. Float the needle in the dish using a plastic spoon to lower the needle carefully onto the water. Turn the dish so the marked part of the needle is above the 0° mark. This is your compass.

4. Bring the magnet near your compass. Observe how the needle reacts. Measure the angle the needle turns.

Conclude and Apply

1. **Explain** why the marked end of the needle always pointed the same way in step 3, even though you rotated the dish.

2. **Describe** the behavior of the compass when the magnet was brought close.

3. **Observe** the marked end of your needle. Does it point to the north or south pole of the bar magnet? **Infer** whether the marked end of your needle is a north or a south pole. How do you know?

Communicating Your Data

Make a half-page insert that will go into a wilderness survival guide to describe the procedure for making a compass. Share your half-page insert with your classmates. **For more help, refer to the Science Skill Handbook.**

Performance Have students find out what orienteering is. Have them learn how to find places using only a compass and directions. Ask them to write about what they find. Use **Performance Assessment in the Science Classroom,** p. 157.

Communicating Your Data

Students can use a word processing program and a scanner to help them produce their directions for making a compass. Scanned photos could show how to magnetize a needle and how to mount it.

Electricity and Magnetism

Current Can Make a Magnet

Magnetic fields are produced by moving electric charges. Electrons moving around the nuclei of atoms produce magnetic fields. The motion of these electrons causes some materials, such as iron, to be magnetic. You cause electric charges to move when you flip a light switch or turn on a portable CD player. When electric current flows in a wire, electric charges move in the wire. As a result, a wire that contains an electric current also is surrounded by a magnetic field. **Figure 9A** shows the magnetic field produced around a wire that carries an electric current.

Electromagnets Look at the magnetic field lines around the coils of wire in **Figure 9B.** The magnetic fields around each coil of wire add together to form a stronger magnetic field inside the coil. When the coils are wrapped around an iron core, the magnetic field of the coils magnetizes the iron. The iron then becomes a magnet, which adds to the strength of the magnetic field inside the coil. A current-carrying wire wrapped around an iron core is called an **electromagnet,** as shown in **Figure 9C.**

Figure 9 A current-carrying wire produces a magnetic field.

as you read

What You'll Learn
- **Explain** how electricity can produce motion.
- **Explain** how motion can produce electricity.

Why It's Important
Electricity and magnetism enable electric motors and generators to operate.

Review Vocabulary
electric current: the flow of electric charge

New Vocabulary
- electromagnet
- motor
- aurora
- generator
- alternating current
- direct current
- transformer

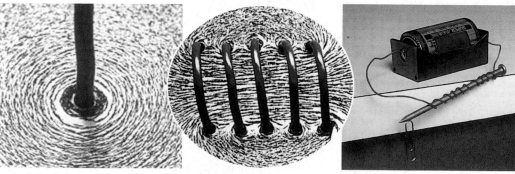

A Iron particles show the magnetic field lines around a current-carrying wire.

B When a wire is wrapped in a coil, the field inside the coil is made stronger.

C An iron core inside the coils increases the magnetic field because the core becomes magnetized.

SECTION 2 Electricity and Magnetism **621**

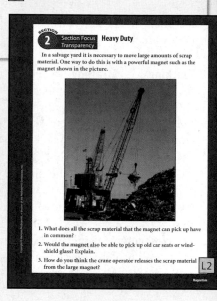

Section 2 Resource Manager

Chapter FAST FILE Resources
Transparency Activity, pp. 39, 41–42
Directed Reading for Content Mastery, pp. 17, 18
MiniLAB, p. 4
Enrichment, p. 26
Lab Activity, pp. 11–12

Reinforcement, p. 24
Lab Worksheets, pp. 7–8
Mathematics Skill Activities, p. 1
Home and Community Involvement, p. 49
Lab Management and Safety, p. 64

Caption Answer

Figure 10 The hammer striking the bell opens the circuit, which turns off the electromagnet.

Mini LAB

Purpose Students build an electromagnet. **L2** **LS** **Kinesthetic**

Materials insulated wire, 16-penny steel nail, D-cell battery, paper clips

Teaching Strategy Provide sealed iron filings or compasses so students can investigate the fields produced by their electromagnets.

Safety Precautions Make sure students do not leave the electromagnets connected to the battery for long periods of time.

Troubleshooting Make sure students use insulated wire and do not short the batteries by wiring directly across the terminals.

Analysis

1. The more coils on the electromagnet, the more paper clips it picked up.
2. The five-coil electromagnet should pick up about half as many paper clips as the ten-coil electromagnet.

Assessment

Oral Have students summarize the relationship between the number of coils and the number of paper clips an electromagnet can pick up. The more coils, the greater the number of paper clips that can be picked up.

Try at Home

Mini LAB

Assembling an Electromagnet

Procedure 🥽 ♒ ✋

1. Wrap a **wire** around a **16-penny steel nail** ten times. Connect one end of the wire to a **D-cell battery,** as shown in **Figure 9C.** Leave the other end loose until you use the electromagnet. **WARNING:** *When current is flowing in the wire, it can become hot over time.*
2. Connect the wire. Observe how many **paper clips** you can pick up with the magnet.
3. Disconnect the wire and rewrap the nail with 20 coils. Connect the wire and observe how many paper clips you can pick up. Disconnect the wire again.

Analysis

1. How many paper clips did you pick up each time? Did more coils make the electromagnet stronger or weaker?
2. Graph the number of coils versus number of paper clips attracted. Predict how many paper clips would be picked up with five coils of wire. Check your prediction.

Try at Home

622 **CHAPTER 21** Magnetism

Figure 10 An electric doorbell uses an electromagnet. Each time the electromagnet is turned on, the hammer strikes the bell. **Explain** *how the electromagnet is turned off.*

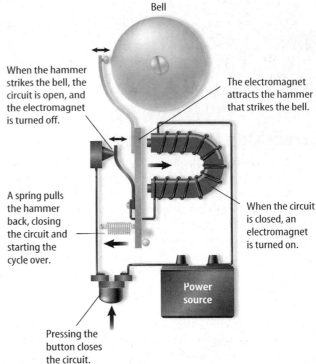

When the hammer strikes the bell, the circuit is open, and the electromagnet is turned off.

A spring pulls the hammer back, closing the circuit and starting the cycle over.

Pressing the button closes the circuit.

The electromagnet attracts the hammer that strikes the bell.

When the circuit is closed, an electromagnet is turned on.

Bell

Power source

Using Electromagnets The magnetic field of an electromagnet is turned on or off when the electric current is turned on or off. By changing the current, the strength and direction of the magnetic field of an electromagnet can be changed. This has led to a number of practical uses for electromagnets. A doorbell, as shown in **Figure 10,** is a familiar use of an electromagnet. When you press the button by the door, you close a switch in a circuit that includes an electromagnet. The magnet attracts an iron bar attached to a hammer. The hammer strikes the bell. When the hammer strikes the bell, the hammer has moved far enough to open the circuit again. The electromagnet loses its magnetic field, and a spring pulls the iron bar and hammer back into place. This movement closes the circuit, and the cycle is repeated as long as the button is pushed.

Some gauges, such as the gas gauge in a car, use a galvanometer to move the gauge pointer. **Figure 11** shows how a galvanometer makes a pointer move. Ammeters and voltmeters used to measure current and voltage in electric circuits also use galvanometers, as shown in **Figure 11.**

Differentiated Instruction

Physically Challenged An electromagnet can be made with larger equipment that will make the manipulation easier. A tall metal cylinder can be used in place of the nail and a spray-painted metal spring toy can be used in place of the wire. **LS** **Kinesthetic**

Visual Learning

Figure 10 Have students use the illustration and text description to make a flowchart that traces the sequence of events that results in a doorbell ringing. Possible answer: Pushing the button closes the circuit, which activates the electromagnet and causes an iron bar to move a hammer that strikes a bell. The bell rings, and the hammer movement opens the circuit again, shutting off the current. **L2** **LS** **Visual-Spatial** **P**

Figure 11

The gas gauge in a car uses a device called a galvanometer to make the needle of the gauge move. Galvanometers are also used in other measuring devices. A voltmeter uses a galvanometer to measure the voltage in a electric circuit. An ammeter uses a galvanometer to measure electric current. Multimeters can be used as an ammeter or voltmeter by turning a switch.

A galvanometer has a pointer attached to a coil that can rotate between the poles of a permanent magnet. When a current flows through the coil, it becomes an electromagnet. Attraction and repulsion between the magnetic poles of the electromagnet and the poles of the permanent magnet makes the coil rotate. The amount of rotation depends on the amount of current in the coil.

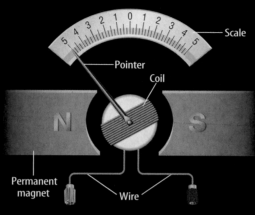

Scale
Pointer
Coil
Permanent magnet
Wire

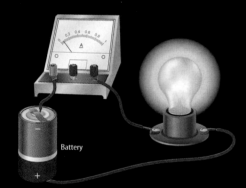

To measure the current in a circuit an ammeter is used. An ammeter contains a galvanometer and has low resistance. To measure current, an ammeter is connected in series in the circuit, so all the current in the circuit flows through it. The greater the current in the circuit, the more the needle moves.

Battery

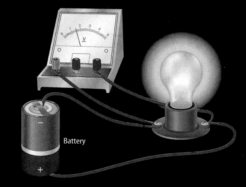

To measure the voltage in a circuit a voltmeter is used. A voltmeter also contains a galvanometer and has high resistance. To measure voltage, a voltmeter is connected in parallel in the circuit, so almost no current flows through it. The higher the voltage in the circuit, the more the needle moves.

Battery

SECTION 2 Electricity and Magnetism **623**

Visualizing Voltmeters and Ammeters

Have students examine the pictures and read the captions. Then ask the following questions.

Why is it important that the resistance of an ammeter be small compared to the other resistance in a circuit? If it weren't, the meter would change the amount of current flowing in the circuit that it is measuring.

Why must a direct current meter be hooked up so that the portion of the circuit going to the positive of the battery is connected to the positive side of the meter? If the meter connections were reversed, the current through the coil would force the pointer to rotate in the wrong direction, farther past the lowest reading on the scale.

Activity

Battery Connections Have students diagram how they would connect an ammeter to find the current flowing when a motor is connected to a battery. Then have them diagram how they would connect a voltmeter to find the voltage in a circuit with a motor connected to a battery. **LS** Visual-Spatial

Differentiated Instruction

Challenge Challenge students to research the differences between a microammeter, a milliammeter, and an ammeter. Have them prepare posters with labeled diagrams that explain the differences in the meters. [L3]

Connect Electricity and Magnetism

Materials DC circuit (battery, wire), compass

Estimated Time 10 minutes

Procedure Set up a DC circuit and show how the needle of a compass is deflected in opposite directions when the compass is held over and under the wire. If possible, set this up on an over-head projector so students can see it better. Ask students to describe a way to move the wire that will keep the compass spinning. L3 **LS** **Logical-Mathematical**

Visual Learning

Figure 13 The illustration shows that the current loop spins because of the force exerted on it by the magnetic field. Help students see that to keep the loop spinning, some mechanism must be in place that changes the direction of the current each half-turn. This is done by two split rings connected to the ends of the loop. These establish connections with the battery terminals. When the loop spins, the rings also spin and come in contact with the opposite terminals. This changes the direction of the current and keeps the motor operating. L2 **LS** **Visual-Spatial**

Fun Fact

The relationship between electricity and magnetism was discovered by Hans Oersted in 1820, when he saw that an electric current in a wire could deflect a compass needle. In 1825, an English electrical engineer named William Sturgeon developed the first practical electromagnet.

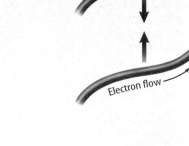

Figure 12 Two wires carrying current in the same direction attract each other, just as unlike magnetic poles do.

Figure 13 In an electric motor, the force a magnet exerts on a current-carrying wire transforms electric energy into kinetic energy.

Magnets Push and Pull Currents

Look around for electric appliances that produce motion, such as a fan. How does the electric energy entering the fan become transformed into the kinetic energy of the moving fan blades? Recall that current-carrying wires produce a magnetic field. This magnetic field behaves the same way as the magnetic field that a magnet produces. Two current-carrying wires can attract each other as if they were two magnets, as shown in **Figure 12.**

Electric Motor Just as two magnets exert a force on each other, a magnet and a current-carrying wire exert forces on each other. The magnetic field around a current-carrying wire will cause it to be pushed or pulled by a magnet, depending on the direction the current is flowing in the wire. As a result, some of the electric energy carried by the current is converted into kinetic energy of the moving wire, as shown on the left in **Figure 13.** Any device that converts electric energy into kinetic energy is a **motor.** To keep a motor running, the current-carrying wire is formed into a loop so the magnetic field can force the wire to spin continually, as shown on the right in **Figure 13.**

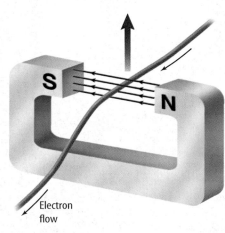
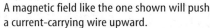

A magnetic field like the one shown will push a current-carrying wire upward.

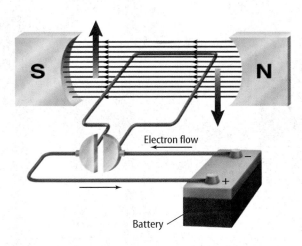

The magnetic field exerts a force on the wire loop, causing it to spin as long as current flows in the loop.

Teacher FYI

Electromagnetism Electromagnetic interactions are important in the operation of television sets. Magnets control the beam of electrons that forms the television picture. Some laboratory balances measure mass by determining the current needed in an electromagnet to produce a magnetic force that balances the object's weight.

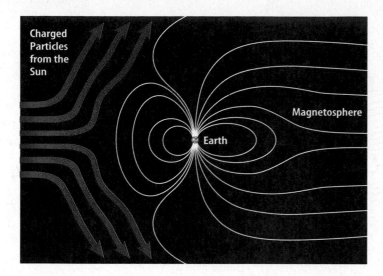

Charged
Particles
from the
Sun

Magnetosphere

Earth

Figure 14 Earth's magneto-sphere deflects most of the charged particles streaming from the Sun.
Explain why the magnetosphere is stretched away from the Sun.

Earth's Magnetosphere The Sun emits charged particles that stream through the solar system like an enormous electric current. Just like a current-carrying wire is pushed or pulled by a magnetic field, Earth's magnetic field pushes and pulls on the electric current generated by the Sun. This causes most of the charged particles in this current to be deflected so they never strike Earth, as shown in **Figure 14.** As a result, living things on Earth are protected from damage that might be caused by these charged particles. At the same time, the solar current pushes on Earth's magnetosphere so it is stretched away from the Sun.

The Aurora Sometimes the Sun ejects a large number of charged parti-cles all at once. Most of these charged particles are deflected by Earth's mag-netosphere. However, some of the ejected particles from the Sun produce other charged particles in Earth's outer atmosphere. These charged particles spiral along Earth's magnetic field lines toward Earth's magnetic poles. There they collide with atoms in the atmos-phere. These collisions cause the atoms to emit light. The light emitted causes a display known as the **aurora** (uh ROR uh), as shown in **Figure 15.** In north-ern latitudes, the aurora sometimes is called the northern lights.

Figure 15 An aurora is a natural light show that occurs far north and far south.

SECTION 2 Electricity and Magnetism **625**

Use Science Words

Word Meaning Tell students that scientists often use the word *induce* to describe what happens between electricity and magnets. Have students use a dictionary to find the meaning of the word *induce*. *Induce* means "to bring about by some influence." Ask students to relate this meaning to what happens in a generator. Possible answer: In a generator, a magnetic field is used to bring about an electric current.
L2 LS **Linguistic**

Fun Fact

The frequency of alternating current in Europe is 50 cycles per second.

Quick Demo

AC/DC Differences
Materials AC power source, DC power source, light bulb, ammeter
Estimated Time 10 minutes
Procedure Make a circuit with an AC power source, a lightbulb, and an ammeter. Have students note how the needle fluctuates between positive and negative values. Next, connect the ammeter to a DC power source, and have students note the constant positive value. L2 LS **Visual-Spatial**

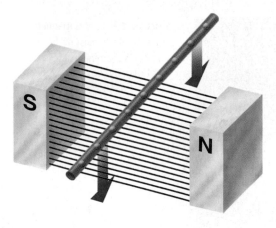

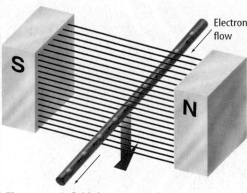

If a wire is pulled through a magnetic field, the electrons in the wire also move downward.

The magnetic field then exerts a force on the moving electrons, causing them to move along the wire.

Figure 16 When a wire is made to move through a magnetic field, an electric current can be produced in the wire.

Figure 17 In a generator, a power source spins a wire loop in a magnetic field. Every half turn, the current will reverse direction. This type of generator supplies alternating current to the lightbulb.

Using Magnets to Create Current

In an electric motor, a magnetic field turns electricity into motion. A device called a **generator** uses a magnetic field to turn motion into electricity. Electric motors and electric generators both involve conversions between electric energy and kinetic energy. In a motor, electric energy is changed into kinetic energy. In a generator, kinetic energy is changed into electric energy. **Figure 16** shows how a current can be produced in a wire that moves in a magnetic field. As the wire moves, the electrons in the wire also move in the same direction, as shown on the left. The magnetic field exerts a force on the moving electrons that pushes them along the wire on the right, creating an electric current.

Electric Generators To produce electric current, the wire is fashioned into a loop, as in **Figure 17.** A power source provides the kinetic energy to spin the wire loop. With each half turn, the current in the loop changes direction. This causes the current to alternate from positive to negative. Such a current is called an **alternating current** (AC). In the United States, electric currents change from positive to negative to positive 60 times each second.

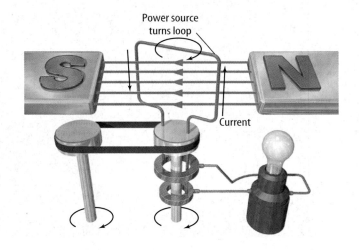

626 CHAPTER 21 Magnetism

LAB DEMONSTRATION

Purpose to build an electric generator
Materials four small bar magnets, 70 m #30 wire, holiday lightbulb, small cardboard box, long nail, tape
Procedure Poke holes in the long sides of the box. Insert the nail so that it spans the box opening and spins freely. Tape the magnets to the nail, 2 on each side, so that the north poles point in the same direction. Wrap wire around the sides of the box. Use tape to keep the wire away from the nail holes. Attach each wire end to one wire of the bulb. Hand spin the nail vigorously.
Expected Outcome The bulb glows dimly.

To increase brightness, clamp the nail into the chuck of a hand drill. (brace and bit)
Assessment
Why does the bulb light only dimly? Not much current is produced. Why is the bulb brighter when the nail is turned faster? The faster the magnets rotate, the more current generated.

Types of Current A battery produces direct current instead of alternating current. In a **direct current** (DC) electrons flow in one direction. In an alternating current, electrons change their direction of movement many times each second. Some generators are built to produce direct current instead of alternating current.

✓ **Reading Check** *What type of currents can be produced by a generator?*

Power Plants Electric generators produce almost all of the electric energy used all over the world. Small generators can produce energy for one household, and large generators in electric power plants can provide electric energy for thousands of homes. Different energy sources such as gas, coal, and water are used to provide the kinetic energy to rotate coils of wire in a magnetic field. Coal-burning power plants, like the one pictured in **Figure 18,** are the most common. More than half of the electric energy generated by power plants in the United States comes from burning coal.

Voltage The electric energy produced at a power plant is carried to your home in wires. Recall that voltage is a measure of how much energy the electric charges in a current are carrying. The electric transmission lines from electric power plants transmit electric energy at a high voltage of about 700,000 V. Transmitting electric energy at a low voltage is less efficient because more electric energy is converted into heat in the wires. However, high voltage is not safe for use in homes and businesses. A device is needed to reduce the voltage.

Science Online

Topic: Power Plants
Visit ips.msscience.com for Web links to more information about the different types of power plants used in your region of the country.

Activity Describe the different types of power plants.

Figure 18 Coal-burning power plants supply much of the electric energy for the world.

627

Science Journal

Providing Power Have students research in more detail how power gets from the power plant to their homes. Ask them to outline the steps in their Science Journals, paying particular attention to those steps that in some way involve magnetism. L2 **LS** **Linguistic**

✓ **Reading Check**

Answer direct current and alternating current

Inquiry Lab

Electromagnets

Purpose Students will explore different cores and shapes for electromagnets

Possible Materials wires (copper, nickel, aluminum, etc.), batteries, core materials (carbon, plastic, or metal rods; donuts or spheres; toilet paper tube, etc.), iron filings or small nuts to pick up

Estimated Time 1 class session

Teaching Strategies

• Invite students to explore the strength of electromagnets made from different core materials and in different shapes. Encourage them to bring different core materials from home.

• Students can create electromagnets out of different types of wire, cores, and shapes. Have them make diagrams of each magnet they make, and record its strength. It may be better to use small nuts instead of filings, if available, so they can quantitatively compare the magnets.

• Ask students which shape they think worked best. What purposes could the other shapes be used for?

• Have students research electromagnets in industry. What shapes of electromagnets are used in car wrecking yards? How about in manufacturing plants or factories? What materials are used for these magnets, and what strength of voltage is supplied?

For additional inquiry activities, see *Science Inquiry Labs.*

Transformers Collect several discarded transformers from used or broken appliances and break open their outer, plastic casings. Organize the class into groups and give each a transformer and its casing. Describe the power-converting specifications of each transformer. If possible, tell students what device each transformer was used to operate. Have students identify the input coil, output coil, and iron core. Have them try to determine from the windings to what voltage the transformer converts the 120 V from an outlet and whether their findings match the rating stated on the case. L3 LS **Logical-Mathematical**

IDENTIFYING
Misconceptions

Working Transformers Make sure students understand that transformers work only with alternating current and not with direct current. This is because the constant electrical field of direct current induces a constant magnetic field that cannot induce an electrical field in the secondary winding.

☑ Reading Check

Answer It can increase or decrease voltage of an alternating current.

Caption Answer
Figure 20 180 V

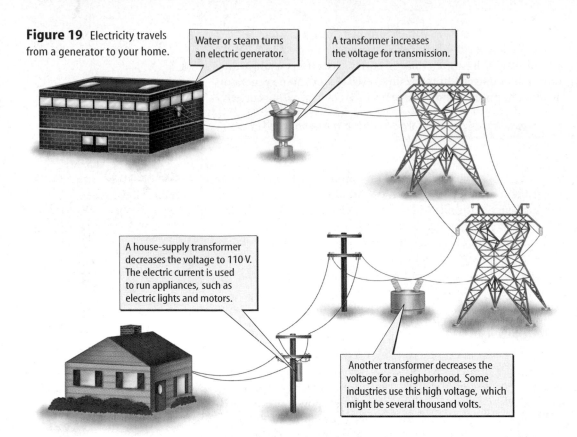

Figure 19 Electricity travels from a generator to your home.

Water or steam turns an electric generator.

A transformer increases the voltage for transmission.

A house-supply transformer decreases the voltage to 110 V. The electric current is used to run appliances, such as electric lights and motors.

Another transformer decreases the voltage for a neighborhood. Some industries use this high voltage, which might be several thousand volts.

Figure 20 A transformer can increase or decrease voltage. The ratio of input coils to output coils equals the ratio of input voltage to output voltage.
Determine *the output voltage if the input voltage is 60 V.*

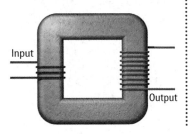

Input

Output

Changing Voltage

A **transformer** is a device that changes the voltage of an alternating current with little loss of energy. Transformers are used to increase the voltage before transmitting an electric current through the power lines. Other transformers are used to decrease the voltage to the level needed for home or industrial use. Such a power system is shown in **Figure 19.** Transformers also are used in power adaptors. For battery-operated devices, a power adaptor must change the 120 V from the wall outlet to the same voltage produced by the device's batteries.

☑ Reading Check   *What does a transformer do?*

A transformer usually has two coils of wire wrapped around an iron core, as shown in **Figure 20.** One coil is connected to an alternating current source. The current creates a magnetic field in the iron core, just like in an electromagnet. Because the current is alternating, the magnetic field it produces also switches direction. This alternating magnetic field in the core then causes an alternating current in the other wire coil.

Science Journal

AC v. DC When Thomas Edison first installed his electric lamps, he powered them with direct current. Have students find out and write in their Science Journals why alternating current became the preferred electrical current. Alternating current could be transmitted at a high voltage that could be stepped down by transformers for household use. L2 LS **Linguistic**

The Transformer Ratio Whether a transformer increases or decreases the input voltage depends on the number of coils on each side of the transformer. The ratio of the number of coils on the input side to the number of coils on the output side is the same as the ratio of the input voltage to the output voltage. For the transformer in **Figure 20,** the ratio of the number of coils on the input side to the number of coils on the output side is three to nine, or one to three. If the input voltage is 60 V, the output voltage will be 180 V.

In a transformer the voltage is greater on the side with more coils. If the number of coils on the input side is greater than the number of coils on the output side, the voltage is decreased. If the number of coils on the input side is less than the number on the output side, the voltage is increased.

Superconductors

Electric current can flow easily through materials, such as metals, that are electrical conductors. However, even in conductors, there is some resistance to this flow and heat is produced as electrons collide with atoms in the material.

Unlike an electrical conductor, a material known as a superconductor has no resistance to the flow of electrons. Superconductors are formed when certain materials are cooled to low temperatures. For example, aluminum becomes a superconductor at about $-272°C$. When an electric current flows through a superconductor, no heat is produced and no electric energy is converted into heat.

Superconductors and Magnets Superconductors also have other unusual properties. For example, a magnet is repelled by a superconductor. As the magnet gets close to the superconductor, the superconductor creates a magnetic field that is opposite to the field of the magnet. The field created by the superconductor can cause the magnet to float above it, as shown in **Figure 21.**

SECTION 2 Electricity and Magnetism **629**

The Currents War In the late 1800s, electric power was being transmitted using a direct-current transmission system developed by Thomas Edison. To preserve his monopoly, Edison launched a public-relations war against the use of alternating-current power transmission, developed by George Westinghouse and Nikola Tesla. However, by 1893, alternating current transmission had been shown to be more efficient and economical, and quickly became the standard.

Figure 21 A small magnet floats above a superconductor. The magnet causes the superconductor to produce a magnetic field that repels the magnet.

Make a Model
Model Transformers Have students roll cardboard into a tube and wind different colors of string around it to make a model of a transformer. Give them several different voltage conversions to model, such as 60 V to 120 V, 120 V to 3 V, and 120 V to 220 V. L2 **LS** Kinesthetic

Activity
Transformer Voltage Draw simple transformers similar to the one that appears in the section on the board. Write the following information beside each transformer and have the students determine whether the transformer is increasing or decreasing the voltage and determine the new voltage:

- Transformer #1:
  Input: 5 turns, 50 volts
  Output: 15 turns, ? volts
  Increasing the voltage, 150 volts
- Transformer #2:
  Input: 50 turns, 300 volts
  Output: 5 turns, ? volts
  Decreasing the voltage, 30 volts
- Transformer #3:
  Input: 150 turns, 600 volts
  Output: 30 turns, ? volts
  Decreasing the voltage, 120 volts

The Current Wars Despite Edison's campaign against it, Westinghouse and Tesla were gaining ground with their alternating current. The Westinghouse Corporation was given the contract for the lighting of The Chicago World's Fair, the world's first all-electric fair. Westinghouse was able to underbid the General Electric Company (which had taken over the Edison Company), because most of General Electric's costs were due to the large amounts of copper wire necessary to use direct current. Westinghouse could do the job for less money with his efficient, cost-effective alternating current system.

Cultural Diversity

Japan's Maglev Japanese engineers have built a maglev that can travel more than 500 km/h. This vehicle is levitated above the track by magnets, hence the name *maglev*. Levitation is achieved by the magnetic repulsion of helium-cooled, superconducting magnets on the vehicle and electromagnets of the same polarity in the guideway track. Have students research how these maglevs work in detail. Students should prepare a poster explaining the procedure. Germany has built maglevs using different technology. For comparison, part of the class can research Germany's version of the maglev and report their results.

MRIs Compare and contrast magnetic resonance imaging and X-ray imaging. Both types of imaging give images inside the human body without surgery. MRI gives detailed images of soft tissue. X rays give images of bones and dense tissues. X-ray radiation can damage tissue, but apparently there is no damage from the radio waves and magnetic fields that are used in an MRI.

What are the benefits of MRI imaging compared to exploratory surgery? Possible answer: There are no risks from infection, excessive bleeding, and anesthesia when using a MRI.

Use Science Words

Word Usage Have students use the word *superconductor* in a sentence describing characteristics of these materials.

Figure 22 The particle accelerator at Fermi National Accelerator Laboratory near Batavia, Illinois, accelerates atomic particles to nearly the speed of light. The particles travel in a beam only a few millimeters in diameter. Magnets made of superconductors keep the beam moving in a circular path about 2 km in diameter.

Figure 23 A patient is being placed inside an MRI machine. The strong magnetic field inside the machine enables images of tissues inside the patient's body to be made.

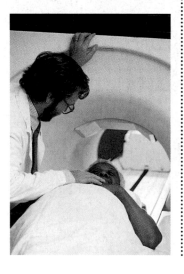

Using Superconductors Large electric currents can flow through electromagnets made from superconducting wire and can produce extremely strong magnetic fields. The particle accelerator shown in **Figure 22** uses more than 1,000 superconducting electromagnets to help accelerate subatomic particles to nearly the speed of light.

Other uses for superconductors are being developed. Transmission lines made from a superconductor could transmit electric power over long distances without having any electric energy converted to heat. It also may be possible to construct extremely fast computers using microchips made from superconductor materials.

Magnetic Resonance Imaging

INTEGRATE Health A method called magnetic resonance imaging, or MRI, uses magnetic fields to create images of the inside of a human body. MRI images can show if tissue is damaged or diseased, and can detect the presence of tumors.

Unlike X-ray imaging, which uses X-ray radiation that can damage tissue, MRI uses a strong magnetic field and radio waves. The patient is placed inside a machine like the one shown in **Figure 23.** Inside the machine an electromagnet made from superconductor materials produces a magnetic field more than 20,000 times stronger than Earth's magnetic field.

630 CHAPTER 21 Magnetism

Curriculum Connection

Chemistry Atoms are composed of protons, neutrons, and electrons. Protons and neutrons are classified as hadrons. Quarks are thought to be elementary particles that form hadrons. Scientists theorized that there were six quarks. Scientists discovered the first five quarks, but the sixth quark eluded them for some time. Finally, confirmation of the existence of the sixth or *top* quark was made at the Fermi National Accelerator Laboratory in March of 1995. Challenge students to research more about quarks and report to their class what they have learned.

Producing MRI Images About 63 percent of all the atoms in your body are hydrogen atoms. The nucleus of a hydrogen atom is a proton, which behaves like a tiny magnet. The strong magnetic field inside the MRI tube causes these protons to line up along the direction of the field. Radio waves are then applied to the part of the body being examined. The protons absorb some of the energy in the radio waves, and change the direction of their alignment.

When the radio waves are turned off, the protons realign themselves with the magnetic field and emit the energy they absorbed. The amount of energy emitted depends on the type of tissue in the body. This energy emitted is detected and a computer uses this information to form an image, like the one shown in **Figure 24.**

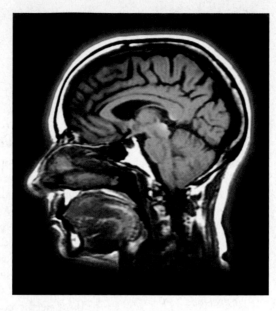

Figure 24 This MRI image shows a side view of the brain.

Connecting Electricity and Magnetism Electric charges and magnets are related to each other. Moving electric charges produce magnetic fields, and magnetic fields exert forces on moving electric charges. It is this connection that enables electric motors and generators to operate.

---

section 2 review

Summary

Electromagnets

- A current-carrying wire is surrounded by a magnetic field.
- An electromagnet is made by wrapping a current-carrying wire around an iron core.

Motors, Generators, and Transformers

- An electric motor transforms electrical energy into kinetic energy. An electric motor rotates when current flows in a wire loop that is surrounded by a magnetic field.
- An electric generator transforms kinetic energy into electrical energy. A generator produces current when a wire loop is rotated in a magnetic field.
- A transformer changes the voltage of an alternating current.

Self-Check

1. **Describe** how the magnetic field of an electromagnet depends on the current and the number of coils.
2. **Explain** how a transformer works.
3. **Describe** how a magnetic field affects a current-carrying wire.
4. **Describe** how alternating current is produced.
5. **Think Critically** What are some advantages and disadvantages to using superconductors as electric transmission lines?

Applying Math

6. **Calculate Ratios** A transformer has ten turns of wire on the input side and 50 turns of wire on the output side. If the input voltage is 120 V, what will the output voltage be?

Science Online ips.msscience.com/self_check_quiz

SECTION 2 Electricity and Magnetism **631**

Check for Understanding

Logical-Mathematical The color of the aurora depends on the atoms that are struck (nitrogen or oxygen) and the height at which the charged particles strike them. The colors for oxygen and nitrogen vary as follows:

green—oxygen up to 240 km

red—oxygen more than 240 km

blue—nitrogen up to 95 km

purple/violet—nitrogen more than 95 km

Have students obtain color photos of the auroras and use the information above to identify the atoms producing the colors and the heights at which they were struck.

Reteach

Transformer Ratios Ask students to predict how various electromagnets with different numbers of windings compare. Then give students sample transformer ratios and ask them whether each will increase or decrease voltage.

L2 **IS** **Logical-Mathematical**

☑ Assessment

Performance Have students take an inventory of their homes and list all the items that make use of an electric motor. Have them summarize their findings in a spreadsheet or table. Use **Performance Assessment in the Science Classroom**, p. 109.

---

section 2 review

1. The magnetic field increases as the current in the coils increases and as the number of coils increases.
2. An alternating current in the input coil induces a magnetic field in the core. This induces an alternating current in the output coil.
3. It exerts a force on the wire.
4. One way is for a power source to spin a wire loop surrounded by a magnet. The movement of the wire relative to the magnetic field induces current in the wire.
5. advantage: reduces the amount of electrical energy converted into heat; disadvantage: difficult to keep wires cold enough to remain superconducting
6. (50 turns ÷ 10 turns) × 120 V = 600 V

LAB

How does an electric m⚡tor work?

Real-World Question

Purpose Students build an electric motor. L2 ELL LS Kinesthetic

Process Skills observe and infer, recognize cause and effect, interpret scientific illustrations, formulate models

Time Required 1 class period

Procedure

Materials You can obtain wood blocks from your school's wood shop or from a lumber yard's scraps.

Safety Precautions Caution students to hold only the insulated part of each wire when wires are attached to the battery.

Teaching Strategy Show students how to use sandpaper to strip the insulation off the wire without cutting the wire itself. Make certain all batteries are charged.

Analyze Your Data

Tie to Prior Knowledge Ask students whether they have ever seen a tiny, electric motor in a toy or model. Did they notice that there were magnets in it?

Troubleshooting Be sure students attach the wire securely to the battery terminals and to the knitting needles.

Goals

■ **Assemble** a small electric motor.

■ **Observe** how the motor works.

Materials

22-gauge enameled wire (4 m)
steel knitting needle
*steel rod
nails (4)
hammer
ceramic magnets (2)
18-gauge insulated wire (60 cm)
masking tape
fine sandpaper
approximately 15-cm square wooden board
wooden blocks (2)
6-V battery
*1.5-V batteries connected in a series (4)
wire cutters
*scissors
*Alternate materials

Safety Precautions

WARNING: *Hold only the insulated part of a wire when it is attached to the battery. Use care when hammering nails. After cutting the wire, the ends will be sharp.*

Real-World Question

Electric motors are used in many appliances. For example, a computer contains a cooling fan and motors to spin the hard drive. A CD player contains electric motors to spin the CD. Some cars contain electric motors that move windows up and down, change the position of the seats, and blow warm or cold air into the car's interior. All these electric motors consist of an electromagnet and a permanent magnet. In this activity you will build a simple electric motor that will work for you. How can you change electric energy into motion?

Differentiated Instruction

Physically Challenged Pair physically challenged students with others who work well in the lab. Have the physically challenged student read the instructions aloud as the other student builds the model. Have both students evaluate the setup to make sure the needle is as close to the magnets as possible.

Alternative Inquiry Lab

Extend the Experience Have students examine the magnetic field around the motor, using a compass or iron filings. Ask students to figure out how to make the motor spin the other way, spin faster, and spin slower. How could the motor be turned into a generator? How could they make the motor consume less power? Have them explore other questions that arise. Finally, students might research how these issues are handled by industry.

Procedure

1. Use sandpaper to strip the enamel from about 4 cm of each end of the 22-gauge wire.

2. Leaving the stripped ends free, make this wire into a tight coil of at least 30 turns. A D-cell battery or a film canister will help in forming the coil. Tape the coil so it doesn't unravel.

3. Insert the knitting needle through the coil. Center the coil on the needle. Pull the wire's two ends to one end of the needle.

4. Near the ends of the wire, wrap masking tape around the needle to act as insulation. Then tape one bare wire to each side of the needle at the spot where the masking tape is.

5. Tape a ceramic magnet to each block so that a north pole extends from one and a south pole from the other.

6. Make the motor. Tap the nails into the wood block as shown in the figure. Try to cross the nails at the same height as the magnets so the coil will be suspended between them.

7. Place the needle on the nails. Use bits of wood or folded paper to adjust the positions of the magnets until the coil is directly between the magnets. The magnets should be as close to the coil as possible without touching it.

8. Cut two 30-cm lengths of 18-gauge wire. Use sandpaper to strip the ends of both wires. Attach one wire to each terminal of the battery. Holding only the insulated part of each wire, place one wire against each of the bare wires taped to the needle to close the circuit. Observe what happens.

Conclude and Apply

1. **Describe** what happens when you close the circuit by connecting the wires. Were the results expected?

2. **Describe** what happens when you open the circuit.

3. **Predict** what would happen if you used twice as many coils of wire.

Communicating Your Data

Compare your conclusions with other students in your class. **For more help, refer to the Science Skill Handbook.**

Expected Outcome The wire coil will spin when the current is turned on and stop when the current stops.

Error Analysis If the motor doesn't turn, have students move the magnet closer to the coil. Also, have students make sure the knitting needle is centered between the magnets.

Conclude and Apply

1. The coil starts to spin.
2. The coil stops spinning.
3. A larger magnetic field would be induced by the coil, so the coil would spin faster.

✓ Assessment

Performance Have students design machines that could use this motor. They should consider how much force this motor can apply. Possibilities include using the motor as a fan, to spin an artistic design, or to lift a small object. Use **Performance Assessment in the Science Classroom,** p. 117.

✓ Active Reading

Synthesis Journal In this strategy, students reflect on a project, a paper, or a performance in light of their own experiences and plan for personal application. Have each student divide a piece of paper into three sections. Have them record *What I did*, *What I learned*, and *How I can use it*. Have students write a Synthesis Journal entry for this activity.

Communicating Your Data

Have students make diagrams of their motors including explanations of how the parts worked, what worked well, and what didn't work.

"Aagjuuk[1] and Sivulliit[2]"
from Intellectual Culture of the Copper Eskimos
by Knud Rasmussen, told by Tatilgak

Understanding Literature

Ethnography Ethnographers have recorded Inuit stories about stars and constellations and other links to navigation. The Inuit must be skilled at navigation because they often travel over vast areas of frozen ground that have few landmarks.

Respond to the Reading

1. The verse mentions the names of two constellations and includes phrases such as "By which way."

2. In winter it is dark in the morning in the arctic region where the Inuit live.

3. **Linking Science and Writing** Students could make a map of the constellations before they write about their northward trip.

 **Magnetic North Pole**

At high northern latitudes, a compass needle still points toward Earth's magnetic north pole. However, because the compass is close to the magnetic pole, the direction the compass needle points changes as the position of the compass changes. As a result, a compass needle at high northern latitudes doesn't point in a single direction. Instead the direction depends on the location. This makes a compass more difficult to use for determining direction. In 1993, the magnetic pole was located in northern Canada, at about 78°27' N, 104°24' W.

The following are "magic words" that are spoken before the Inuit (IH noo wut) people go seal hunting. Inuit are native people that live in the arctic region. Because the Inuit live in relative darkness for much of the winter, they have learned to find their way by looking at the stars to guide them. The poem is about two constellations that are important to the Inuit people because their appearance marks the end of winter when the Sun begins to appear in the sky again.

By which way, I wonder the mornings—
You dear morning, get up!
See I am up!
By which way, I wonder,
the constellation *Aagjuuk* rises up in the sky?
By this way—perhaps—by the morning
It rises up!

Morning, you dear morning, get up!
See I am up!
By which way, I wonder,
the constellation *Sivulliit*
Has risen to the sky?
By this way—perhaps—by the morning.
It rises up!

[1] Inuit name for the constellation of stars called Aquila (A kwuh luh)
[2] Inuit name for the constellation of stars called Bootes (boh OH teez)

Understanding Literature

Ethnography Ethnography is a description of a culture. To write an ethnography, an ethnographer collects cultural stories, poems, or other oral tales from the culture that he or she is studying. Why must the Inuit be skilled in navigation?

Respond to the Reading

1. How can you tell the importance of constellations to the Inuit for telling direction?
2. How is it possible that the Inuit could see the constellations in the morning sky?
3. **Linking Science and Writing** Research the constellations in the summer sky in North America and write a paragraph describing the constellations that would help you navigate from south to north.

 Earth's magnetic field causes the north pole of a compass needle to point in a northerly direction. Using a compass helps a person to navigate and find his or her way. However, at the far northern latitudes where the Inuit live, a compass becomes more difficult to use. Some Inuit live north of Earth's northern magnetic pole. In these locations a compass needle points in a southerly direction. As a result, the Inuit developed other ways to navigate.

Resources for Teachers and Students

A Walk Through the Heavens: A Guide to Stars and Constellations and Their Legends, by Milton D. Heifetz and Wil Tirion, Cambridge University Press, 1998

The Starlore Handbook: An Essential Guide to the Night Sky, by Geoffrey Cornelius, Chronicle Books, 1997

Exploring the Night Sky: The Equinox Astronomy Guide for Beginners, by Terrence Dickinson and John Bianchi (Illustrator), Firefly Books, 1988

Reviewing Main Ideas

Section 1 What is magnetism?

1. All magnets have two poles—north and south. Like poles repel each other and unlike poles attract.

2. A magnet is surrounded by a magnetic field that exerts forces on other magnets.

3. Atoms in magnetic materials are magnets. These materials contain magnetic domains which are groups of atoms whose magnetic poles are aligned.

4. Earth is surrounded by a magnetic field similar to the field around a bar magnet.

Section 2 Electricity and Magnetism

1. Electric current creates a magnetic field. Electromagnets are made from a coil of wire that carries a current, wrapped around an iron core.

2. A magnetic field exerts a force on a moving charge or a current-carrying wire.

3. Motors transform electric energy into kinetic energy. Generators transform kinetic energy into electric energy.

4. Transformers are used to increase and decrease voltage in AC circuits.

Visualizing Main Ideas

Copy and complete the following concept map on magnets.

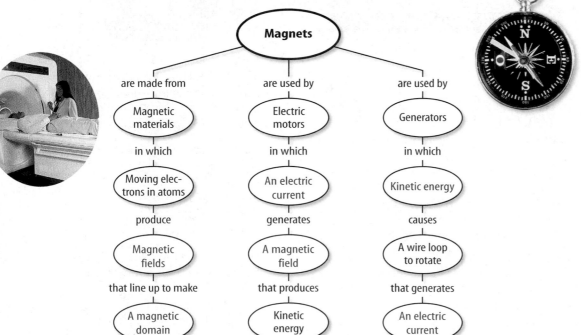

Magnets

- are made from → **Magnetic materials** → in which → **Moving electrons in atoms** → produce → **Magnetic fields** → that line up to make → **A magnetic domain**

- are used by → **Electric motors** → in which → **An electric current** → generates → **A magnetic field** → that produces → **Kinetic energy**

- are used by → **Generators** → in which → **Kinetic energy** → causes → **A wire loop to rotate** → that generates → **An electric current**

Science online ips.msscience.com/interactive_tutor

CHAPTER STUDY GUIDE 635

Reviewing Main Ideas

Summary statements can be used by students to review the major concepts of the chapter.

Visualizing Main Ideas

See student page.

Science Online

Visit ips.msscience.com
/self_check_quiz
/interactive_tutor
/vocabulary_puzzlemaker
/chapter_review
/standardized_test

Assessment Transparency

For additional assessment questions, use the *Assessment Transparency* located in the transparency book.

Assessment

| Assessment Transparency | Magnetism |

Directions: *Carefully review the graph and answer the following questions.*

Sunspot Activity

Number of Sunspots vs *Year* (1945–1985)

1. According to the graph, what year had the greatest number of sunspots?
   A 1948   C 1965
   B 1958   D 1980

2. Which year experienced the fewest sunspots?
   F 1954   H 1976
   G 1964   J 1983

3. What is the approximate length of time between points of low sunspot activity?
   A 1 year   C 11 years
   B 5 years   D 20 years

L2

Magnetism

◆Identifying Misconceptions   Assess

Use the assessment as follow-up to page F at the beginning of this chapter.

Materials bar magnets on which the N and S labels have been covered with masking tape, compasses

Procedure Use the compasses to determine which end of each magnet is the north pole and which end is the south pole. Write the labels N and S on the tape, exchange magnets with another student, and determine if the other magnet is labeled correctly. Tell the other student what you think and return the magnet. Take off the tape to see which end is actually N and which is S.

Expected Outcome The north end of a compass needle points toward a magnet's south pole.

Using Vocabulary

1. A generator produces an electric current; a transformer can change the voltage of that current.

2. A magnetic field is the space in which a magnetic force acts.

3. Alternating current changes direction while direct current does not.

4. Electric current induces magnetism in an electromagnet.

5. A motor changes electrical energy to kinetic energy, while a generator reverses the process to change kinetic energy to electrical energy.

6. Moving electrons cause magnetism.

7. Charged particles from the Sun are deflected to the poles by Earth's magnetosphere. There they cause atoms in Earth's atmosphere to emit light that is seen as the aurora.

8. Magnetic domains are groups of atoms with aligned magnetic poles that are present in magnets and magnetic materials.

Checking Concepts

9. A
10. D
11. C
12. B
13. B
14. B
15. C
16. A
17. B

Using Vocabulary

alternating current p. 626	magnetic domain p. 616
aurora p. 625	magnetic field p. 615
direct current p. 627	magnetosphere p. 617
electromagnet p. 621	motor p. 624
generator p. 626	transformer p. 628

Explain the relationship that exists between each set of vocabulary words below.

1. generator—transformer
2. magnetic force—magnetic field
3. alternating current—direct current
4. current—electromagnet
5. motor—generator
6. electron—magnetism
7. magnetosphere—aurora
8. magnet—magnetic domain

Checking Concepts

Choose the word or phrase that best answers the question.

9. What can iron filings be used to show?
   A) magnetic field   C) gravitational field
   B) electric field   D) none of these

10. Why does the needle of a compass point to magnetic north?
    A) Earth's north pole is strongest.
    B) Earth's north pole is closest.
    C) Only the north pole attracts compasses.
    D) The compass needle aligns itself with Earth's magnetic field.

11. What will the north poles of two bar magnets do when brought together?
    A) attract
    B) create an electric current
    C) repel
    D) not interact

12. How many poles do all magnets have?
    A) one   C) three
    B) two   D) one or two

13. When a current-carrying wire is wrapped around an iron core, what can it create?
    A) an aurora   C) a generator
    B) a magnet   D) a motor

14. What does a transformer between utility wires and your house do?
    A) increases voltage
    B) decreases voltage
    C) leaves voltage the same
    D) changes DC to AC

Use the figure below to answer question 15.

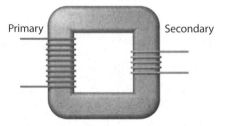

Primary   Secondary

15. For this transformer which of the following describes how the output voltage compares with the input voltage?
    A) larger   C) smaller
    B) the same D) zero voltage

16. Which energy transformation occurs in an electric motor?
    A) electrical to kinetic
    B) electrical to thermal
    C) potential to kinetic
    D) kinetic to electrical

17. What prevents most charged particles from the Sun from hitting Earth?
    A) the aurora
    B) Earth's magnetic field
    C) high-altitude electric fields
    D) Earth's atmosphere

Science⬤nline ips.msscience.com/vocabulary_puzzlemaker

Use the Exam*View*® Pro Testmaker CD-ROM to:

- create multiple versions of tests
- create modified tests with one mouse click for inclusion students
- edit existing questions and add your own questions
- build tests aligned with state standards using built-in State Curriculum Tags
- change English tests to Spanish with one mouse click and vice versa

Thinking Critically

18. Concept Map Explain how a doorbell uses an electromagnet by placing the following phrases in the cycle concept map: *circuit open, circuit closed, electromagnet turned on, electromagnet turned off, hammer attracted to magnet and strikes bell,* and *hammer pulled back by a spring.*

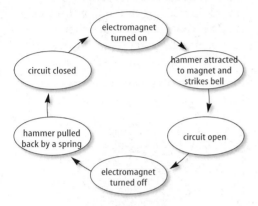

19. Infer A nail is magnetized by holding the south pole of a magnet against the head of the nail. Does the point of the nail become a north pole or a south pole? Include a diagram with your explanation.

20. Explain why an ordinary bar magnet doesn't rotate and align itself with Earth's magnetic field when you place it on a table.

21. Determine Suppose you were given two bar magnets. One magnet has the north and south poles labeled, and on the other magnet the magnetic poles are not labeled. Describe how you could use the labeled magnet to identify the poles of the unlabeled magnet.

22. Explain A bar magnet touches a paper clip that contains iron. Explain why the paper clip becomes a magnet that can attract other paper clips.

Science online ips.msscience.com/chapter_review

23. Explain why the magnetic field produced by an electromagnet becomes stronger when the wire coils are wrapped around an iron core.

24. Predict Magnet A has a magnetic field that is three times as strong as the field around magnet B. If magnet A repels magnet B with a force of 10 N, what is the force that magnet B exerts on magnet A?

25. Predict Two wires carrying electric current in the same direction are side by side and are attracted to each other. Predict how the force between the wires changes if the current in both wires changes direction.

Performance Activities

26. Multimedia Presentation Prepare a multimedia presentation to inform your classmates on the possible uses of superconductors.

Applying Math

Use the table below to answer questions 27 and 28.

Transformer Properties

Transformer	Number of Input Coils	Number of Output Coils
R	4	12
S	10	2
T	3	6
U	5	10

27. Input and Output Coils According to this table, what is the ratio of the number of input coils to the number of output coils on transformer T?

28. Input and Output Voltage If the input voltage is 60 V, which transformer gives an output voltage of 12 V?

Thinking Critically

18. See student page.
19. The head of the nail becomes a north pole, and the point of the nail becomes a south pole.
20. The magnetic force acting on the bar magnet is not strong enough to overcome the forces of gravity and static friction that are acting on the magnet.
21. Use another magnet that is already marked to see which end is attracted and which is repelled by a given pole.
22. The magnetic domains in the paper clip become aligned so that the like poles of the domains point in the same direction. As a result, the paper clip becomes a temporary magnet.
23. The magnetic field produced by the current in the coil causes the magnetic domains in the iron core to become aligned. The iron core becomes a temporary magnet, and its magnetic field adds to the field produced by the current in the coils.
24. 10 N; By Newton's third law of motion, the force magnet A exerts on magnet B is equal and opposite to the force B exerts on A.
25. The force between the wires will still be attractive. The force is attractive if the current in both wires is in the same direction.

Performance Activities

26. Ask students to note the sources of their information. Use **Performance Assessment in the Science Classroom,** p. 149.

Applying Math

National Math Standards
1, 5

27. 1 to 2 or 0.5.
28. The ratio of input to out coils equals the ratio of input voltage to output voltage. This ratio is 5, so the transformer must be S.

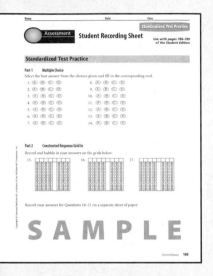

FAST FILE

Answer Sheet A practice answer sheet can be found at ips.msscience.com/answer_sheet.

SAMPLE

Part 1 | Multiple Choice

1. C	3. C	5. C	7. B
2. A	4. C	6. B	8. C

Part 2 | Short Response

9. The compass needles align with the magnetic field lines around the bar magnet. Each compass needle rotates until it is aligned with the magnet field line that passes through the compass.

10. All the compass needles will point in the same north-south direction, because they will rotate until they align with Earth's magnetic field.

11. The current produces a magnetic field around the wire. A force in the magnetic field causes the compass needle to line up with the magnetic field lines.

12. Increase the current and increase the number of turns in the coil of wire.

13. The ratio of the number of turns on the input coil to the number of turns on the output coil equals the ratio of the input voltage to the output voltage = (100 V)/(50 V) = 2.

Part 1 | Multiple Choice

Record your answers on the answer sheet provided by your teacher or on a sheet of paper.

Use the figure below to answer questions 1 and 2.

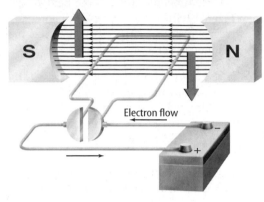

Electron flow

1. What is the device shown?
   A. electromagnet   C. electric motor
   B. generator   D. transformer

2. Which of the following best describes the function of this device?
   A. It transforms electrical energy into kinetic energy.
   B. It transforms kinetic energy into electrical energy.
   C. It increases voltage.
   D. It produces an alternating current.

3. How is an electromagnet different from a permanent magnet?
   A. It has north and south poles.
   B. It attracts magnetic substances.
   C. Its magnetic field can be turned off.
   D. Its poles cannot be reversed.

Test-Taking Tip

Check the Question Number For each question, double check that you are filling in the correct answer bubble for the question number you are working on.

---

4. Which of the following produces alternating current?
   A. electromagnet   C. generator
   B. superconductor   D. motor

5. Which statement about the domains in a magnetized substance is true?
   A. Their poles are in random directions.
   B. Their poles cancel each other.
   C. Their poles point in one direction.
   D. Their orientation cannot change.

Use the figure below to answer questions 6–8.

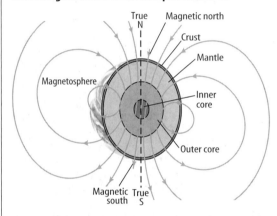

6. What is the region of space affected by Earth's magnetic field called?
   A. declination   C. aurora
   B. magnetosphere   D. outer core

7. What is the shape of Earth's magnetic field similar to?
   A. that of a horseshoe magnet
   B. that of a bar magnet
   C. that of a disk magnet
   D. that of a superconductor

8. In which of Earth's layers is Earth's magnetic field generated?
   A. crust   C. outer core
   B. mantle   D. inner core

---

14. You could rub the screwdriver in one direction with a permanent magnet in one direction.

15. Each half of the magnet will have its own north and south poles. Like poles of the two halves will attract each other, while unlike poles will repel each other.

16. The core of an electromagnet should be able to be easily magnet- ized or demagnetized because it should respond quickly to the turning on and off of the current. So alnico would not be a good choice.

Part 2 | Short Response/Grid In

Record your answers on the answer sheet provided by your teacher or on a sheet of paper.

Use the figure below to answer questions 9 and 10.

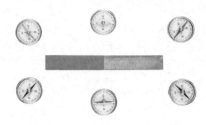

9. Explain why the compass needles are pointed in different directions.

10. What will happen to the compass needles when the bar magnet is removed? Explain why this happens.

11. Describe the interaction between a compass needle and a wire in which an electric current is flowing.

12. What are two ways to make the magnetic field of an electromagnet stronger?

13. The input voltage in a transformer is 100 V and the output voltage is 50 V. Find the ratio of the number of wire turns on the input coil to the number of turns on the output coil.

14. Explain how you could magnetize a steel screwdriver.

15. Suppose you break a bar magnet in two. How many magnetic poles does each of the pieces have?

16. Alnico is a mixture of steel, aluminum, nickel, and cobalt. It is very hard to magnetize. However, once magnetized, it remains magnetic for a long time. Explain why it would not be a good choice for the core of an electromagnet.

Part 3 | Open Ended

Record your answers on a sheet of paper.

17. Explain why the aurora occurs only near Earth's north and south poles.

18. Why does a magnet attract an iron nail to either of its poles, but attracts another magnet to only one of its poles?

19. A battery is connected to the input coil of a step-up transformer. Describe what happens when a lightbulb is connected to the output coil of the transformer.

20. Explain how electric forces and magnetic forces are similar.

Use the figure below to answer questions 21 and 22.

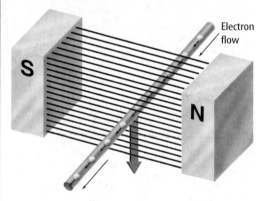

Electron flow

21. Describe the force that is causing the electrons to flow in the wire.

22. Infer how electrons would flow in the wire if the wire were pulled upward.

23. Explain why a nail containing iron can be magnetized, but a copper penny that contains no iron cannot be magnetized.

24. Every magnet has a north pole and a south pole. Where would the poles of a magnet that is in the shape of a disc be located?

19. The lightbulb doesn't glow. No current flows in the output coil because a direct current, not an alternating current, flows in the input coil.

20. Like electric charges repel each other and like magnetic pole repel each other. Unlike electric charges attract each other and unlike magnetic poles attract each other. Moving electric charges produce magnetic fields, and magnetic fields exert forces on moving electric charges.

21. The magnetic field is exerting a magnetic force on the electrons in the wire that causes them to flow.

22. The magnetic force would be in the opposite direction and the electrons would flow in the opposite direction.

23. Iron is a magnetic material that contains magnetic domains that can be aligned to form a magnet. Copper is not a magnetic material and contains no magnetic domains, so it can't be magnetized.

24. at the top surface and the bottom surface of the disk

Rubrics

For more help evaluating open-ended assessment questions, see the rubric on p. 10T.

Part 3 | Open Ended

17. When the Sun ejects a large number of charged particles all at once, most of the particles are deflected by Earth's magnetosphere. But some of the ejected particles produce other charged particles in Earth's outer atmosphere. These charged particles spiral along Earth's magnetic field lines toward Earth's magnetic poles. There they collide with atoms in the atmosphere. These collisions cause the atoms to emit light called the aurora.

18. The nail is a magnetic substance, but not a magnet, so the magnetic domains in the nail line up with their opposite poles closest to the designated pole of the magnet. An attractive force results between opposite poles on the nail and the magnet. Only the opposite pole of another magnet will be attracted to the first magnet.

Section/Objectives	Standards		Labs/Features
Chapter Opener	**National**	**State/Local**	**Launch Lab:** Student and Electronic Calculators, p. 641 **Foldables,** p. 641
	See pp. 16T–17T for a Key to Standards.		
Section 1 Electronics ● 3 sessions ▭ 1.5 blocks 1. **Compare and contrast** analog and digital signals. 2. **Explain** how semiconductors are used in electronic devices.	National Content Standards: UCP.1, UCP.2, UCP.3, UCP.5, A.1, A.2, E.2, F.5		**Science Online,** p. 645 **Lab:** Investigating Diodes, p. 648
Section 2 Computers ● 5 sessions ▭ 2.5 blocks 3. **Describe** the different parts of a computer. 4. **Compare** computer hardware with computer software. 5. **Discuss** the different types of memory and storage in a computer.	National Content Standards: UCP.1, UCP.2, UCP.3, UCP.5, A.1, A.2, E.2, F.5, G.3		**MiniLAB:** Using Binary Numbers, p. 650 **Applying Science:** How much information can be stored?, p. 651 **Science Online,** p. 652 **MiniLAB:** Observing Memory, p. 653 **Integrate Career,** p. 654 **Integrate Environment,** p. 656 **Science Online,** p. 656 **Visualizing a Hard Disk,** p. 657 **Science Online,** p. 658 **Lab:** Does your computer have a virus?, pp. 660–661 **Science and Society:** E-Lectrifying E-Books, p. 662

Lab Materials	Reproducible Resources	Section Assessment	Technology
Launch Lab: stopwatch, calculator, pencil and paper	**Chapter *FAST FILE* Resources** Foldables Worksheet, p. 17 Directed Reading Overview, p. 19 Note-taking Worksheets, pp. 31–32	**GLENCOE'S ASSESSMENT ADVANTAGE**	**TeacherWorks** includes: • Interactive Teacher Edition • Lesson Planner with calendar • Access to all program blacklines • Correlations to standards • Web links
Lab: light-emitting diode, lightbulb and holder, D-cell battery and holder, wire *Need materials?* Contact Science Kit at 1-800-828-7777 or www.sciencekit.com on the Internet.	**Chapter *FAST FILE* Resources** Transparency Activity, p. 42 Lab Activity, pp. 9–11 Enrichment, p. 29 Reinforcement, p. 27 Directed Reading, p. 20 Lab Worksheet, pp. 5–6 **Lab Management and Safety,** p. 76	**Portfolio** Reteach, p. 647 **Performance** Applying Math, p. 647 **Content** Section Review, p. 647	Section Focus Transparency Guided Reading Audio Program Interactive Chalkboard CD-ROM
MiniLAB: 8 small paper squares **MiniLAB:** 3-in × 5-in cards (6) **Lab:** paper and pencil	**Chapter *FAST FILE* Resources** Transparency Activity, p. 43 MiniLAB, pp. 3, 4 Transparency Activity, pp. 45–46 Lab Activity, pp. 13–16 Enrichment, p. 30 Reinforcement, p. 28 Directed Reading, pp. 21, 22 Lab Worksheet, pp. 7–8 **Cultural Diversity,** p. 27	**Portfolio** Differentiated Instruction, p. 655 **Performance** MiniLAB, p. 650 Applying Science, p. 651 MiniLAB, p. 653 Applying Skills, p. 659 **Content** Section Review, p. 659	Section Focus Transparency Teaching Transparency Virtual Labs CD-ROM Guided Reading Audio Program Interactive Chalkboard CD-ROM Video Lab

End of Chapter Assessment

GLENCOE'S ASSESSMENT ADVANTAGE

Blackline Masters	Technology	Professional Series
Chapter *FAST FILE* Resources Chapter Review, pp. 35–36 Chapter Tests, pp. 37–40 **Standardized Test Practice,** pp. 91–94	MindJogger Videoquiz Virtual Labs CD-ROM ExamView® Pro Testmaker TeacherWorks CD-ROM Interactive Chalkboard CD-ROM	**Performance Assessment in the Science Classroom (PASC)**

Transparencies

Section Focus

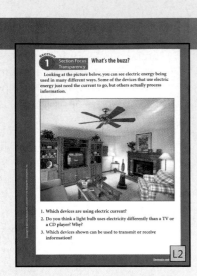

SECTION 1 Section Focus Transparency — **What's the buzz?**

Looking at the picture below, you can see electric energy being used in many different ways. Some of the devices that use electric energy just need the current to go, but others actually process information.

1. Which devices are using electric current?
2. Do you think a light bulb uses electricity differently than a TV or a CD player? Why?
3. Which devices shown can be used to transmit or receive information?

L2

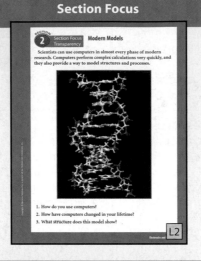

SECTION 2 Section Focus Transparency — **Modern Models**

Scientists can use computers in almost every phase of modern research. Computers perform complex calculations very quickly, and they also provide a way to model structures and processes.

1. How do you use computers?
2. How have computers changed in your lifetime?
3. What structure does this model show?

L2

This is a representation of key blackline masters available in the Teacher Classroom Resources. See Resource Manager boxes within the chapter for additional information.

Key to Teaching Strategies

The following designations will help you decide which activities are appropriate for your students.

L1 Level 1 activities should be appropriate for students with learning difficulties.

L2 Level 2 activities should be within the ability range of all students.

L3 Level 3 activities are designed for above-average students.

ELL ELL activities should be within the ability range of English Language Learners.

COOP LEARN Cooperative Learning activities are designed for small group work.

LS Multiple Learning Styles logos, as described on page 12T, are used throughout to indicate strategies that address different learning styles.

P These strategies represent student products that can be placed into a best-work portfolio.

PBL Problem-Based Learning activities apply real-world situations to learning.

Assessment

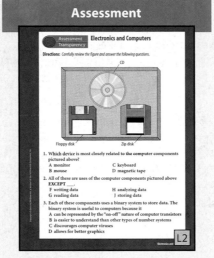

Assessment Transparency — **Electronics and Computers**

Directions: Carefully review the figure and answer the following questions.

CD
Floppy disk   Zip disk

1. Which device is most closely related to the computer components pictured above?
   A monitor   C keyboard
   B mouse   D magnetic tape
2. All of these are uses of the computer components pictured above EXCEPT ____.
   F writing data   H analyzing data
   G reading data   J storing data
3. Each of these components uses a binary system to store data. The binary system is useful to computers because it
   A can be represented by the "on-off" nature of computer transistors
   B is easier to understand than other types of number systems
   C discourages computer viruses
   D allows for better graphics

L2

Teaching

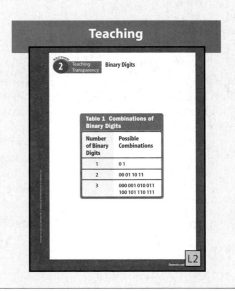

SECTION 2 Teaching Transparency — **Binary Digits**

Table 1 Combinations of Binary Digits

Number of Binary Digits	Possible Combinations
1	0 1
2	00 01 10 11
3	000 001 010 011 100 101 110 111

L2

Hands-on Activities

Student Text Lab Worksheet

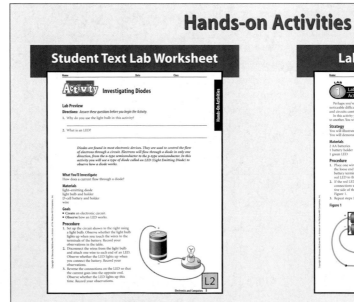

Activity Investigating Diodes

Lab Preview
Directions: Answer these questions before you begin the Activity.

1. Why do you use the light bulb in this activity?

2. What is an LED?

Diodes are found in most electronic devices. They are used to control the flow of electrons through a circuit. Electrons will flow through a diode in only one direction, from the n-type semiconductor to the p-type semiconductor. In this activity you will use a type of diode called an LED (Light Emitting Diode) to observe how a diode works.

What You'll Investigate
How does a current flow through a diode?

Materials
light-emitting diode
light bulb and holder
D-cell battery and holder
wire

Goals
• Create an electronic circuit.
• Observe how an LED works.

Procedure
1. Set up the circuit shown to the right using a light bulb. Observe whether the light bulb lights up when you touch the wires to the terminals of the battery. Record your observations in the table.
2. Disconnect the wires from the light bulb and attach one wire to each end of an LED. Observe whether LED lights up when you connect the battery. Record your observations.
3. Reverse the connections on the LED so that the current goes into the opposite end. Observe whether the LED lights up this time. Record your observations.

L2

Laboratory Activities

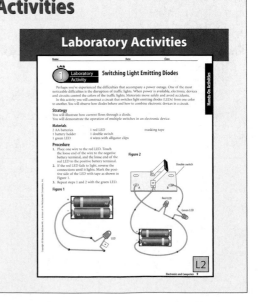

LAB 1 Laboratory Activity — **Switching Light Emitting Diodes**

Perhaps you've experienced the difficulties that accompany a power outage. One of the most noticeable difficulties is the disruption of traffic lights. When power is available, electronic devices and circuits control the colors of the traffic lights. Motorists move safely and avoid accidents.
In this activity you will construct a circuit that switches light emitting diodes (LEDs) from one color to another. You will observe how diodes behave and how to combine electronic devices in a circuit.

Strategy
You will illustrate how current flows through a diode.
You will demonstrate the operation of multiple switches in an electronic device.

Materials
2 AA batteries   1 red LED   masking tape
1 battery holder   1 double switch
1 green LED   4 wires with alligator clips

Procedure
1. Place one wire to the red LED. Touch the loose end of the wire to the negative battery terminal, and the loose end of the red LED to the positive battery terminal.
2. If the red LED fails to light, reverse the connections until it lights. Mark the positive side of the LED with tape as shown in Figure 1.
3. Repeat steps 1 and 2 with the green LED.

Figure 1
Figure 2

L2

Meeting Different Ability Levels

Content Outline

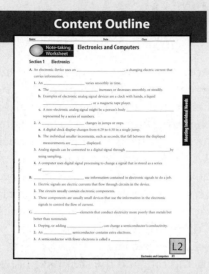

L2

Reinforcement

L2

Enrichment

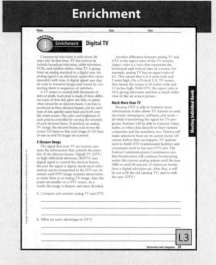

L3

Directed Reading (English/Spanish)

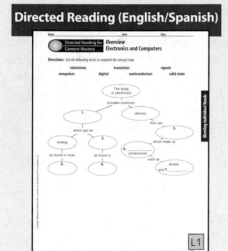

L1

Study Guide

L2

Reading Essentials

L1

Assessment

Test Practice Workbook

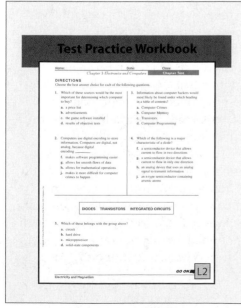

L2

Chapter Review

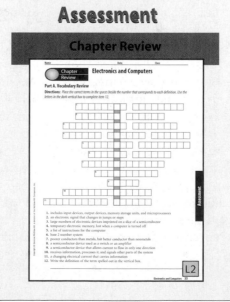

L2

Chapter Tests

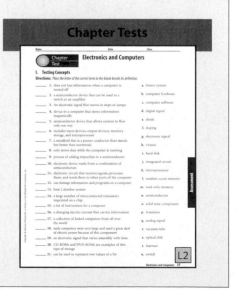

L2

Science Content Background

section 1 **Electronics**
Electronic Signals

Information can be transmitted by an electric current. However, the electric current doesn't carry the information directly. Rather, it is the changes in the current that contain the information. For example, a song is the result of variations in air pressure. These air pressure variations are information that your ears and brain use to produce the sensation of hearing the song.

Teacher to Teacher

Deborah Peters Huffine
Noblesville Intermediate School
Noblesville, IN

"I have groups of six to eight students create a human circuit by holding hands. The class identifies the circuit as a series or parallel and predicts whether it will work. Using a set of electrical equipment, have another group create the demonstrated circuit."

Deborah Peters Huffine

A microphone converts the variations in air pressure into a varying electric current. It does this in such a way that there is a relationship between the variations in air pressure and changes in the current. As a result, the varying current contains nearly the same information as the air pressure variations. A loudspeaker then can convert the information in the varying electric current, or electronic signal, into air pressure variations that you interpret as the song.

The electronic signal produced by a microphone is an example of an analog signal. Here the word *analog* means the electric current varies smoothly. In contrast, a *digital* signal varies in jumps, with each jump giving the value of the signal over some time interval. As a result, a digital signal can be represented as a collection of numbers.

Music is stored as a digital signal on a CD. The analog signal originally produced by the musicians is converted into a digital signal by *sampling*. In the sampling process, the analog signal is measured at a fixed time interval, such as every 0.001 s. The number of samples measured per second is the *sampling rate*. The measured value is converted into a number that can vary only in steps or have only certain values. The number of possible measured values or steps is the *sampling precision*.

As the sampling rate and the sampling precision increase, the digital signal more closely resembles the analog signal being sampled. However, more numbers must be stored. A stereo digital signal on a CD is recorded at a sampling rate of 44,100 samples per second for each channel, and a sampling precision of 65,536, or 2^{16}. Each sample requires 16 bits, or 2 bytes of storage. So one minute of stereo music on a CD requires 44,100 samples $\times$ 60 s $\times$ 2 bytes/sample $\times$ 2 channels = 10,584,000 bytes.

Semiconductors

Most electronic devices contain integrated circuits that usually consist of a number of layers of semiconductor material, and can contain thousands or millions of electronic components, such as transistors. These electronic components are formed by etching away regions of certain layers, and can be made microscopic in size.

The electrical conductivity of metals usually is only slightly affected if the metal contains small amounts of impurities, However, the electrical behavior of semiconductor elements, such as silicon, can be altered greatly by the addition of small amounts of impurities, a process called *doping*.

For example, a silicon atom has four outer electrons, and an arsenic atom has five outer electrons. When a small amount of arsenic is added to a silicon crystal, the arsenic atoms supply extra electrons that are free to move through the crystal. A doped semiconductor with extra electrons is an n-type semiconductor. An alu-

minum atom has only three outer electrons, so a silicon crystal doped with aluminum has an electron deficit. A doped semiconductor with an electron deficiency is a p-type semiconductor.

Electronic components can be made simply by joining an n-type and a p-type semiconductor to form a p-n junction. A diode contains a single p-n junction, and transistors are made from several p-n junctions.

Unlike metals, the electrical resistance of semiconductors decreases with increasing temperature. By measuring the resistance of a semiconductor device called a thermistor, temperatures can be determined. The electrical properties of some semiconductors vary, depending on the amount of light that shines on them. These semiconductors are used in light meters, in photo cells that are used as switches, and in photovoltaic cells.

section 2 Computers
What are computers?

Some people consider the 5,000-year-old abacus to be the first computer. Others consider Pascal's wheel calculator, created in 1642, to be the first. The impetus for the development of the first modern computer came from the U.S. census in 1880, when it took seven years to tally the information. It was realized that as the U.S. population grew, it would be impossible to tally all the census information in the ten-year period prior to the next census. Herman Hollerith invented a machine to store the information on punched cards. He got the idea from watching a train conductor punch train tickets. The 1890 census was done using this machine, and the data was processed in only six weeks. Hollerith formed a business to market his machines, which eventually became known as International Business Machines, or IBM.

In the 1950s and 1960s the development of transistors and integrated circuits allowed computers to shrink in size and energy usage. An early computer had 18,000 vacuum tubes, which took up a lot of space, produced a great deal of heat, and consumed a large amount of energy. Later, vacuum tubes were replaced with transistors and other solid-state components packed tightly together on an integrated circuit.

chapter content resources

Internet Resources
For additional content background, visit
ips.msscience.com to:
- access your book online
- find references to related articles in popular science magazines
- access Web links with related content background
- access current events with science journal topics

Print Resources
Teach Yourself Electricity and Electronics, by Stan Bigilisco, McGraw-Hill Companies, 2001
Techno-Matter: The Materials Behind the Marvels, by Alfred B. Bortz, Millbrook Press, 2001
Computers, by Brian K. Williams and Brian Williams, Heinemann Library, 2001
How Computers Work, by Ron White, Timothy Downs, Timothy Edward Downs, Pearson Education, 2001

Chapter Vocabulary

analog signal, p. 642
electronic signal, p. 642
digital signal, p. 643
semiconductor, p. 645
diode, p. 646
transistor, p. 647
integrated circuit, p. 647
binary system, p. 650
random-access memory, p. 652
read-only memory, p. 652
computer software, p. 653
microprocessor, p. 655

Science Journal Student responses will vary, but could include playing games, word processing, surfing the web.

INTERACTIVE
CHALKBOARD
with Image Bank

PowerPoint® Presentations

This CD-ROM is an editable Microsoft® PowerPoint® presentation that includes:
• a pre-made presentation for every chapter
• interactive graphics
• animations
• audio clips
• image bank
• all new section and chapter questions
• Standardized Test Practice
• transparencies
• pre-lab questions for all labs
• Foldables directions
• links to ips.msscience.com

Electronics and Computers

chapter preview

sections

1 Electronics
Lab **Investigating Diodes**

2 Computers
Lab **Does your computer have a virus?**

Virtual Lab **How can a decision tree be used to generate binary numbers?**

Deep in Thought?

You are looking at a brain—the brain of a computer. This is a microprocessor—a device that controls a computer. Even though this microprocessor is only a few centimeters on a side, it contains over a million microscopic circuits that enable it to store and process information very quickly.

Science Journal Describe three activities that you do using a computer.

Theme Connection

Systems and Interactions A study of electronics provides the basis for understanding computers. Computers are complex systems of interacting components.

About the Photo

Microprocessor This is a scanning electron microscope photo of a CX486 microprocessor at a magnification of $50\times$ for the original image size of 6×7 cm. The gold microwires at the edge of the microprocessor connect it to pins that plug into a socket on the computer motherboard. In this way the microprocessor is connected to the rest of the computer.

Start-Up Activities

Electronic and Human Calculators

Imagine how your life would be different if you had been born before the invention of electronic devices. You could not watch television or use a computer. Besides providing entertainment, electronic devices and computers can make many tasks easier. For example, how much quicker is an electronic calculator than a human calculator?

1. Use a stopwatch to time how long it takes a volunteer to add the numbers 423, 21, 84, and 1,098.

2. Time how long it takes another volunteer to add these numbers using a calculator.

3. Repeat steps 1 and 2 this time asking the competitors to multiply 149 and 876.

4. Divide the time needed by the student calculator by the time needed by the calculator to solve each problem. How many times faster is the calculator?

5. **Think Critically** Write a paragraph describing which step in each calculation takes the most time.

Preview this chapter's content and activities at
ips.msscience.com

Electronics and Computers Make the following Foldable to help you identify what you already know and what you want to learn about electronics and computers.

STEP 1 Fold a vertical sheet of paper from side to side. Make the front edge about 1 cm shorter than the back edge.

STEP 2 Turn lengthwise and fold into thirds.

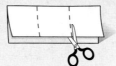

STEP 3 Unfold and cut only the top layer along both folds to make three tabs.

STEP 4 Label the tabs as shown.

| Know | Want | Learned |

Identify Questions Before you read the chapter, write what you know under the left tab and what you want to know under the middle tab. As you read the chapter, add to and correct what you have written. After you read the chapter, write what you have learned under the right tab of your Foldable.

641

Purpose
Use the Launch Lab to introduce students to ways electronic devices can make some tasks easier and faster. L2 ELL
Kinesthetic

Preparation Make sure there are enough calculators and stopwatches for the class.

Materials calculator, stopwatch

Teaching Strategy In addition to measuring the time required to perform the calculations, volunteers can compete against one another to demonstrate how fast they can do the calculations with and without the calculator.

Think Critically
When doing the calculations on the calculator, punching in the numbers takes the most time. When doing the calculations by hand most of the time is taken in performing the mental additions and multiplications.

Assessment
Process Have students repeat the lab by comparing the times required to add two low numbers, such as 6 + 5. Ask them why simple computations like this are more easily done in your mind than on a calculator. For simple calculations, you can state the answer from memory. On a calculator, you must first type in the numbers. Use **Performance Assessment in the Science Classroom**, p. 89.

 Dinah Zike Study Fold

Student preparation materials for this Foldable are available in the Chapter **FAST FILE** Resources.

Electronics

Electronic Signals

You've popped some popcorn, put a video in the VCR, and turned off the lights. Now you're ready to watch a movie. The VCR, television, and lamp shown in **Figure 1** use electricity to operate. However, unlike the lamp, the VCR and the TV are electronic devices. An electronic device uses electricity to store, process, and transfer information.

The VCR and the TV use information recorded on the videotape to produce the images and sounds you see as a movie. As the videotape moves inside the VCR, it produces a changing electric current. This changing electric current is the information the VCR uses to send signals to the TV. The TV then uses these signals to produce the images you see and the sounds you hear.

A changing electric current that carries information is an **electronic signal.** The information can be used to produce sounds, images, printed words, numbers, or other data. For example, a changing electric current causes a loudspeaker to produce sound. If the electric current didn't change, no sound would be produced by the loudspeaker. There are two types of electronic signals—analog and digital.

Analog Signals Most TVs, VCRs, radios, and telephones process and transmit information that is in the form of analog electronic signals. An **analog signal** is a signal that varies smoothly in time. In an analog electronic signal the electric current increases or decreases smoothly in time, just as your hand can move smoothly up and down.

Electronic signals are not the only types of analog signals. An analog signal can be produced by something that varies in a smooth, continuous way and contains information. For example, a person's temperature changes smoothly and contains information about a person's health.

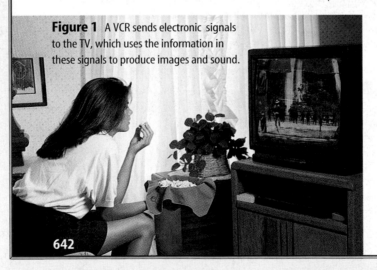

Figure 1 A VCR sends electronic signals to the TV, which uses the information in these signals to produce images and sound.

642

Figure 2 Clocks can be analog or digital devices.

The information displayed on an analog device such as this clock changes continuously.

On this digital clock, the displayed time jumps from one number to another.

Analog Devices The clock with hands shown in **Figure 2** is an example of an analog device. The hands move smoothly from one number to the next to represent the time of day. Fluid-filled and dial thermometers also are analog devices. In a fluid-filled thermometer, the height of the fluid column smoothly rises or falls as the temperature changes. In a dial thermometer, a spring smoothly expands or contracts as the temperature changes.

You have used another analog device if you ever have made a recording on a magnetic tape recorder. When voices or music are recorded on magnetic tape, the tape stores an analog signal of the sounds. When you play the tape, the tape recorder converts the analog signal to an electric current. This current changes smoothly with time and causes a loudspeaker to vibrate, recreating the sounds for you to hear.

Digital Signals Some devices, such as CD players, use a different kind of electronic signal called a digital signal. Unlike an analog signal, a **digital signal** does not vary smoothly, but changes in jumps or steps. If each jump is represented by a number, a digital signal can be represented by a series of numbers.

☑ **Reading Check** *How is a digital signal different from an analog signal?*

You might have a digital clock or watch similar to the one shown on the right in **Figure 2** that displays the time as numbers. The display changes from 6:29 to 6:30 in a single jump, rather than sweeping smoothly from second to second. You might have seen digital thermometers that display temperature as a number. Some digital thermometers display temperature to the nearest whole degree, such as 23°C. The displayed temperature changes by jumps of 1°C. As a result, temperatures between two whole degrees, such as 22.7°C, are not displayed.

SECTION 1 Electronics **643**

Differentiated Instruction

Learning Disabled Students may benefit from a review of atoms, electrons, and electrical circuits. Remind them that electrons will only flow in a closed circuit.

IDENTIFYING Misconceptions

Direction of Current Flow Students may not understand the correct way to refer to the direction of current flow in a circuit. On the board, draw a picture of a circuit containing a battery and a lamp. Label the battery terminals negative and positive. Remind students that negative means the terminal is a source of electrons, and positive means the terminal accepts electrons. Explain that although electrons flow from the negative to the positive terminal, the direction of current is conventionally taken to be the direction in which positive charge would flow. So in a circuit containing a battery, conventional current would flow from the positive terminal to the negative terminal.

☑ **Reading Check**

Answer An analog signal varies smoothly. A digital signal can have only certain values.

Discussion

Watches Bring to class a digital watch and an analog watch (a watch with hands that mark the time). Display both watches. What are some advantages of each type of watch? Possible answer: It is easier to tell the time to the minute on a digital watch, but an analog watch shows not only the present time, but also how far past one hour it is and how long until the next hour. L2 LS
Visual-Spatial

Figure 3 Point out that in the graph the temperature seems to change in steps, although in reality the temperature changes smoothly. The height of the bars on the graph would be different if the temperature were recorded more often or less often. Ask students how the graph would differ if the temperature had been recorded every thirty minutes instead of every hour. The bars would be narrower and the change in height from one bar to the next would be less, making the graph smoother. L2 LS **Visual-Spatial**

Quick Demo
Analog v. Digital

Materials digital thermometer, analog thermometer, container of ice water, container of warm water

Estimated Time ten minutes

Procedure Place digital and analog thermometers in ice water. Have students note readings. Place digital and analog thermometers in warm water. Have students note readings. Have students discuss which thermometer is more accurate, and which thermometer is easier to use. L2 ELL LS **Visual-Spatial**

Misconceptions

Electronic and Electric Students may confuse an electronic device with an electrical device. Explain that an electronic device produces or uses a varying electric current that represents information. An electrical device uses the current only to provide energy to the device.

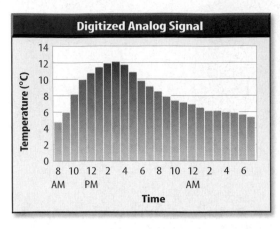

Figure 3 A temperature record made by recording the temperature every hour changes in steps and is a digital signal.

Figure 4 An analog signal can be converted to a digital signal. At a fixed time interval, the strength of the analog signal is measured and recorded. The resulting digital signal changes in steps.

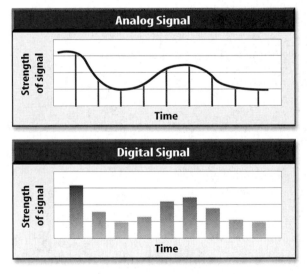

Making Digital Signals A smoothly varying analog signal can be converted to a digital signal. For example, suppose you wish to create a record of how the temperature outside changed over a day. One way to do this would be read an outdoor thermometer every hour and record the temperature and time. At the end of the day your temperature record would be a series of numbers. If you used these numbers to make a graph of the temperature record, it might look like the one shown in **Figure 3.** The temperature information shown by the graph changes in steps and is a digital signal.

Sampling an Analog Signal By recording the temperature every hour, you have sampled the smoothly varying outdoor temperature. When an analog signal is sampled, a value of the signal is read and recorded at some time interval, such as every hour or every second. An example is shown in **Figure 4.** As a result, a smoothly changing analog signal is converted to a series of numbers. This series of numbers is a digital signal.

The process of converting an analog signal to a digital signal is called digitization. The analog signal on a magnetic tape can be converted to a digital signal by sampling. In this way, a song can be represented by a series of numbers.

Using Digital Signals It might seem that analog signals would be more useful than digital signals. After all, when an analog signal is converted to a digital signal, some information is lost. However, think about how analog and digital signals might be stored. Suppose a song that is stored as an analog signal on a small cassette tape were digitized and converted into a series of numbers. It might take millions of numbers to digitize a song, so how could these numbers be stored? As you will see later in this chapter, there is one electronic device that can store these numbers easily—a computer.

Once a digital signal is stored on a computer as a series of numbers, the computer can change these numbers using mathematical formulas. This process changes the signal and is called signal processing. For example, background noise can be removed from a digitized song using signal processing.

Curriculum Connection

Music Using signal processing, even musicians with minimal experience can produce professional quality music. Have students discuss the differences between hearing music produced by nonmusicians using advanced technology and music performed by a professional musician. Students might debate quality of sound or the emotional impact of the sound. L2 LS **Auditory-Musical**

Active Reading

Write-Draw-Discuss This strategy encourages students to actively participate in reading and lectures, assimilating content creatively. Have students write about an idea, clarify it, then make an illustration or drawing. Ask students to share responses with the class and display several examples. Have students Write-Draw-Discuss about analog and digital electronic signals.

Early Television

Vacuum Tube

Modern Television

Electronic Devices

An electronic device, such as a calculator or a CD player, uses the information contained in electronic signals to do a job. For example, the job can be adding two numbers together or making sounds and images. The electronic signals are electric currents that flow through circuits in the electronic device. An electronic device, such as a calculator or a VCR, may contain hundreds or thousands of complex electric circuits.

Electronic Components The electric circuits in an electronic device usually contain electronic components. These electronic components are small devices that use the information in the electronic signals to control the flow of current in the circuits.

Early electronic devices, such as the early television shown in **Figure 5,** used electronic components called vacuum tubes, such as the one shown in the middle of **Figure 5,** to help create sounds and images. Vacuum tubes were bulky and generated a great deal of heat. As a result, early electronic devices used more electric power and were less dependable than those used today, such as the modern television shown in **Figure 5.** Today, televisions and radios no longer use vacuum tubes. Instead, they contain electronic components made from semiconductors.

Semiconductors

On the periodic table, the small number of elements found between the metals and nonmetals are called metalloids. Some metalloids, such as silicon and germanium, are semiconductors. A **semiconductor** is an element that is a poorer conductor of electricity than metals but a better conductor than nonmetals. However, semiconductors have a special property that ordinary conductors and insulators lack—their electrical conductivity can be controlled by adding impurities.

Figure 5 Because early televisions used vacuum tubes, they used more electrical power and were less reliable than their modern versions.

Science Online

Topic: Semiconductor Devices
Visit ips.msscience.com for Web links to information about semiconductor devices.

Activity Choose one semiconductor device and write a paragraph explaining one way that it is used.

Teacher FYI

Digital Sound Sound, such as music, is naturally analog. To convert a sound to a digital signal, the intensity of the sound is measured thousands of times per second. Each of these measurements is assigned a number value that depends on the amplitude of the sound waves. This process is known as digital sound recording.

Inquiry Lab

Analog and Digital Analogies in Real Life

Purpose To have students deepen their understanding of the concepts of analog and digital signal by drawing parallels with things they see in everyday life.

Possible Materials graph paper, poster paper

Estimated Time 1 class session for discussion and presentations.

Teaching Strategies
• Ask students to think of examples of analog and digital situations in real life and how to present these to the class.
• Give students about a week to research their examples and plan their presentations.
• Students' answers will depend on their experience. Try to give credit for innovative thought, even if it is not entirely accurate.

For additional inquiry activities, see *Science Inquiry Labs.*

Quick Demo
Vacuum Tubes

Materials one vacuum tube (available from electronics stores)

Estimated Time five minutes

Procedure Explain that the vacuum tube is almost completely free of air so that electrons can flow through it freely. Vacuum tubes were used as switches in early computers. The vacuum tubes generated so much heat that computers using them had to be kept in air-conditioned rooms. L2 LS Visual-Spatial

Activity
Periodic Table Display a large copy of the periodic table. Ask students to point out silicon and germanium and to tell the number of outer electrons they have. four Show students that nearby atoms, such as gallium and arsenic, have one more or one less outer electron. L2 LS Visual-Spatial

Make a Model

Doped Semiconductors Have students work in pairs using modeling clay, colored beads, construction paper, or other materials to create two models of doped semiconductors. One model should be an n-type semiconductor and the other should be a p-type semiconductor. Students should use the models to demonstrate how adding impurities to the semiconductor alters its conductivity so that it either donates or accepts electrons. L2

COOP LEARN LS **Kinesthetic**

Use an Analogy

One-Way Doors Ask students if they have ever gone into a building that had an in door that could only be pushed inward and an out door that could only be pushed outward. Explain that a diode is similar to these one-way doors. Electrons can only travel one way through the diode.

Quick Demo

Electronic Components

Materials diodes, LEDs, transistors, integrated circuits

Estimated Time five minutes

Procedure Remind students that an integrated circuit can contain thousands of miniature transistors and diodes. L2 ELL LS

Visual-Spatial

Reading Check

The n-type semiconductor gives electrons and the p-type superconductor takes electrons.

Fun Fact

While diodes are usually used to provide one-way paths for current, some contain materials that allow them to emit light. These are called Light-Emitting Diodes or LEDs and they are used in many technologies, including digital clocks.

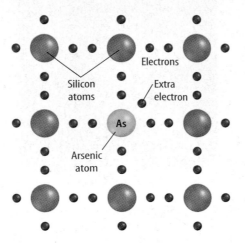

Figure 6 When arsenic atoms are added to a silicon crystal, they add extra electrons that are free to move about. This causes the electrical conductivity of the silicon crystal to increase.

Figure 7 Diodes like these allow current to flow in only one direction.

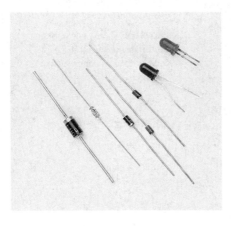

INTEGRATE Chemistry

Adding Impurities Adding even a single atom of an element such as gallium or arsenic to a million silicon atoms significantly changes the conductivity. This process of adding impurities is called doping.

Doping can produce two different kinds of semiconductors. One type of semiconductor can be created by adding atoms like arsenic to a silicon crystal, as shown in **Figure 6.** Then the silicon crystal contains extra electrons. A semiconductor with extra electrons is an n-type semiconductor.

A p-type semiconductor is produced when atoms like gallium are added to a silicon crystal. Then the silicon crystal has fewer electrons than it had before. An n-type semiconductor can give, or donate, electrons and a p-type semiconductor can take, or accept, electrons.

Reading Check

How are n-type and p-type semiconductors different?

Solid-State Components

The two types of semiconductors can be put together to form electronic components that can control the flow of electric current in a circuit. Combinations of n-type and p-type semiconductors can form components that behave like switches that can be turned off and on. Other combinations can form components that can increase, or amplify, the change in an electric current or voltage. Electronic components that are made from combinations of semiconductors are called solid-state components. Diodes and transistors are examples of solid-state components that often are used in electric circuits.

Diodes A **diode** is a solid-state component that, like a one-way street, allows current to flow only in one direction. In a diode, a p-type semiconductor is connected to an n-type semiconductor. Because an n-type semiconductor gives electrons and a p-type semiconductor accepts electrons, current can flow from the n-type to the p-type semiconductor, but not in the opposite direction. **Figure 7** shows common types of diodes. Diodes are useful for converting alternating current (AC) to direct current (DC). Recall that an alternating current constantly changes direction. When an alternating current reaches a diode, the diode allows the current to flow in only one direction. The result is direct current.

Visual Learning

Figure 6 Point out that silicon atoms have four electrons available for sharing (outer electrons), and arsenic atoms have five. The extra electron moves freely. Gallium has three electrons for sharing. Doping with it creates a "hole" that seems to move as nearby electrons fill the hole. Have students draw the figure using gallium instead of arsenic. L3 LS **Visual-Spatial**

Differentiated Instruction

Challenge An integrated circuit is often referred to simply as a chip. Ask students to find out why this is an appropriate name. A chip is a thin, flat piece of something. An integrated circuit is made of a thin slice of semiconductor material. L3 LS **Linguistic**

Transistors A **transistor** is a solid-state component that can be used to amplify signals in an electric circuit. A transistor also is used as an electronic switch. Electronic signals can cause a transistor to allow current to pass through it or to block the flow of current. **Figure 8** shows examples of transistors that are used in many electronic devices. Unlike a diode, a transistor is made from three layers of n-type and p-type semiconductor material sandwiched together.

Figure 8 Transistors such as these are used in electric circuits to amplify signals or to act as switches.

Integrated Circuits Personal computers usually contain millions of transistors, and would be many times larger if they used transistors the size of those shown in **Figure 8.** Instead, computers and other electronic devices use integrated circuits. An **integrated circuit** contains large numbers of interconnected solid-state components and is made from a single chip of semiconductor material such as silicon. An integrated circuit, like the one shown in **Figure 9,** may be smaller than 1 mm on each side and still can contain millions of transistors, diodes, and other components.

Figure 9 This tiny integrated circuit contains thousands of diodes and transistors.

Science Online ips.msscience.com/self_check_quiz

SECTION 1 Electronics **647**

3 Assess

DAILY INTERVENTION

Check for Understanding

Linguistic Have students research and report on different ways integrated circuits are fabricated. Students might discuss photolithography (writing on the chips with beams of light), chemical etching (using chemicals to imprint the circuits), or diffusion (adding chemical impurities to the silicon by diffusing). L3 LS

Reteach

Electronic Components Have students use colored pencils to draw a layer of p-type semiconductor on a layer of n-type semiconductor and label the drawing "Diode." Have them make similar drawings for n-p-n and p-n-p transistors. For each of these, students should draw arrows to represent the direction of electron flow. L2 LS **Visual-Spatial** P

✔ Assessment

Process Ask students to write paragraphs comparing and contrasting diodes and transistors. Both are solid state components based on doped semiconductors. A diode has an n-type and a p-type semiconductor and allows current to flow in only one direction. A transistor is a layer of three semiconductors. It is used as a switch or to amplify signals. Use **Performance Assessment in the Science Classroom,** p. 159.

---

section 1 review

1. The electric current in a lamp is steady and does not carry information.
2. Integrated circuits are smaller, lighter, and more reliable than vacuum tubes. Integrated circuits do not generate as much heat as vacuum tubes and do not use as much electricity. Vacuum tubes also break easily.

3. Digital signals can be stored as numbers.
4. Diodes allow current to flow in only one direction. A diode is a p-type semiconductor connected to an n-type semiconductor. A diode converts alternate current to direct current. A transistor can amplify a

signal and can be used as an electronic switch. It contains 3 semiconductors joined together (an n-p-n transistor or a p-n-p transistor).
5. Decreasing the time interval increases the number of signal samples. This enables the analog signal to be converted more accurately to a digital sig-

nal, but increases the amount of information that must be stored.
6. 3×60 s $= 180$ s; 180 s $+ 20$ s $= 200$ s; $200/.1 = 2000$ numbers.

Investigating Diodes

Diodes are found in most electronic devices. They are used to control the flow of electrons through a circuit. Electrons will flow through a diode in only one direction, from the n-type semiconductor to the p-type semiconductor. In this lab you will use a type of diode called an LED (light-emitting diode) to observe how a diode works.

● Real-World Question ——

How does electric current flow through a diode?

Goals
■ **Create** an electronic circuit.
■ **Observe** how an LED works.

Materials
light-emitting diode   D-cell battery and holder
lightbulb and holder   wire

Safety Precautions
🥽 🧤

● Procedure ——

1. Set up the circuit shown below. Record your observations. Then reverse the connections so each wire is connected to the other battery terminals. Record your observations.

2. Disconnect the wires from the lightbulb and attach one wire to each end of an LED. Observe whether the LED lights up when you connect the battery.

1.5V
Battery
Lightbulb

3. Reverse the connections on the LED so the current goes into the opposite end. Observe whether the LED lights up this time. Record your observation.

● Conclude and Apply ——

1. **Explain** why the bulb did or did not light up each time.
2. **Explain** why the LED did or did not light up each time.
3. **Describe** how the behavior of the lightbulb is different from that of the LED.
4. **Infer** which wire on the LED is connected to the n-type semiconductor and which is connected to the p-type semiconductor based on your observations.

𝒞ommunicating Your Data

Discuss your results with other students in your class. Did their LEDs behave in the same way? **For more help, refer to the Science Skill Handbook.**

𝒞ommunicating Your Data

Have each student prepare a chart explaining the results they obtained in the lab. When comparing their results with those of other students, students should refer to the charts and discuss any differences.

☑ Assessment

Process Ask students to hypothesize what would happen if they had two LEDs connected in series in the circuit. Have students test their hypotheses. In order for the LEDs to light up, both must be positioned so that the electrons can flow from the n-type to the p-type semiconductor. Use **Performance Assessment in the Science Classroom**, p. 93.

Computers

What are computers?

When was the last time you used a computer? Computers are found in libraries, grocery stores, banks, and gas stations. Computers seem to be everywhere. A computer is an electronic device that can carry out a set of instructions, or a program. By changing the program, the same computer can be made to do a different job.

Compared to today's desktop and laptop computers, the first electronic computers, like the one shown in **Figure 10,** were much bigger and slower. Several of the first electronic computers were built in the United States between 1946 and 1951. Solid-state components and the integrated circuit had not been developed yet. So these early computers contained thousands of vacuum tubes that used a great deal of electric power and produced large amounts of heat.

Computers became much smaller, faster, and more efficient after integrated circuits became available in the 1960s. Today, even a game system, like the one in **Figure 10,** can carry out many more operations each second than the early computers.

Figure 10 One of the first electronic computers was ENIAC, which was built in 1946 and weighed more than 30 tons. ENIAC could do 5,000 additions per second.

This handheld game system can do millions of operations per second.

---

as you read

What You'll Learn

- **Describe** the different parts of a computer.
- **Compare** computer hardware with computer software.
- **Discuss** the different types of memory and storage in a computer.

Why It's Important

You can do more with computers if you understand how they work.

⊙ Review Vocabulary

laser: a device that produces a concentrated beam of light

New Vocabulary

- binary system
- random-access memory
- read-only memory
- computer software
- microprocessor

---

1 Motivate

Bellringer

Section Focus Transparencies also are available on the Interactive Chalkboard CD-ROM.
L2 ELL

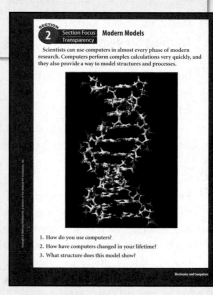

Section Focus Transparency — Modern Models

Scientists can use computers in almost every phase of modern research. Computers perform complex calculations very quickly, and they also provide a way to model structures and processes.

1. How do you use computers?
2. How have computers changed in your lifetime?
3. What structure does this model show?

Tie to Prior Knowledge

Using Computers Have students discuss the many ways they use computers. They might mention word processing, video games, accessing the Internet, and graphics.

Section 2 Resource Manager

Chapter *FAST FILE* Resources
Transparency Activity, pp. 43, 45–46
Directed Reading for Content Mastery, pp. 21, 22
MiniLAB, pp. 3, 4

Enrichment, p. 30
Reinforcement, p. 28
Lab Worksheet, pp. 7–8
Lab Activity, pp. 13–16

✔ Reading Check

Answer 0 and 1

Mini LAB

Purpose Students investigate binary numbers. L1 ELL LS

Kinesthetic

Materials paper, scissors

Teaching Strategy Students are most likely to discover all combinations if they make changes in an orderly way.

Analysis

1. It doubles.
2. 32

Assessment

Process Have the class produce their own binary code by assigning a letter of the alphabet to each of the five-bit combinations. Have students decide what other characters, such as blank space or a period, could be assigned to the remaining six combinations, and then use their code to send and decipher short messages. Use **Performance Assessment in the Science Classroom,** p 169.

Try at Home

Text Question Answer

no

Mini LAB

Using Binary Numbers

Procedure

1. Cut out **8 small paper squares.**
2. On four of the squares, draw the number zero, and on the other four, draw the number one.
3. Use the numbered squares to help determine the number of different combinations possible from four binary digits. List the combinations.

Analysis

1. From **Table 1** and your results from this MiniLAB, what happens to the number of combinations each time the number of binary digits is increased by one?
2. Infer how many combinations would be possible using five binary digits.

Try at Home

Table 1 Combinations of Binary Digits	
Number of of Binary Digits	**Possible Combinations**
1	0 1
2	00 01 10 11
3	000 001 010 011 100 101 110 111

Computer Information

How does a computer display images, generate sounds, and manipulate numbers and words? Every piece of information that is stored in or used by a computer must be converted to a series of numbers. The words you write with a word processor, or the numbers in a spreadsheet are stored in the computer's memory as numbers. An image or a sound file also is stored as a series of numbers. Information stored in this way is sometimes called digital information.

Binary Numbers Imagine what it would be like if you had to communicate with just two words—on and off. Could you use these words to describe your favorite music or to read a book out loud? Communication with just two words seems impossible, but that's exactly what a computer does.

All the digital information in a computer is converted to a type of number that is expressed using only two digits—0 and 1. This type of number is called a binary (BI nuh ree) number. Each 0 or 1 is called a binary digit, or bit. Because this number system uses only two digits, it is called the **binary system,** or base-2 number system.

✔ Reading Check *Which digits are used in the binary system?*

Combining Binary Digits You might think that using only two digits would limit the amount of information you can represent. However, a small number of binary digits can be used to generate a large number of combinations, as shown in **Table 1.**

While one binary digit has only two possible combinations—0 or 1—there are four possible combinations for a group of two binary digits, as shown in **Table 1.** By using just one more binary digit the possible number of combinations is increased to eight. The number of combinations increases quickly as more binary digits are added to the group. For example, there are 65,536 combinations possible for a group of 16 binary digits.

Representing Information with Binary Digits

Combinations of binary digits can be used to represent information. For example, the English alphabet has 26 letters. Suppose each letter was represented by one combination of binary digits. To represent both lowercase and uppercase letters would require a total of 52 different combinations of binary digits. Would a group of five binary digits have enough possible combinations?

LAB DEMONSTRATION

Purpose demonstrate how electronic switches can represent binary code

Materials four D-cell batteries in holders, four 1.5-V light bulbs with sockets, four switches, insulated wire

Preparation Connect a battery, a light bulb, and a switch four times.

Procedure Start with all switches in the circuits open. This represents the binary code 0000. Close only the second switch. This represents the binary code 0010. Demonstrate other combinations.

Expected Outcome Students will be able to determine the possible number of combi-

nations that four bits can make.

Assessment

Oral Ask students how many bits are represented by these four lightbulbs. 4 Ask students how many possible unique combinations can be made with four bits. 16

Representing Letters and Numbers A common system that is used by computers represents each letter, number, or other text character by eight binary digits, or one byte. There are 256 combinations possible for a group of eight binary digits. In this system, the letter "A" is represented by the byte 01000001, while the letter "a" is represented by the byte 01100001, and a question mark is represented by 00111111.

Computer Memory

Why are digital signals stored in a computer as binary numbers? A binary number is a series of bits that can have only one of two values—0 and 1. A switch, such as a light switch on a wall, can have two positions: on or off. A switch could be used to represent the two values of a bit. A switch in the "off" position could represent a 0, and a switch in the "on" position could represent a 1. **Table 2** shows how switches could be used to represent combinations of binary digits.

Table 2 Representing Binary Digits	
Binary Number	**Switches**
0000	⌐ ⌐ ⌐ ⌐
0001	⌐ ⌐ ⌐ ⌐
0010	⌐ ⌐ ⌐ ⌐
0011	⌐ ⌐ ⌐ ⌐
0100	⌐ ⌐ ⌐ ⌐
1010	⌐ ⌐ ⌐ ⌐

Applying Science

How much information can be stored?

Information can be stored in a computer's memory or in storage devices such as hard disks or CDs. The amount of information that can be stored is so large that special units, shown in the table on the right, are used. Desktop computers often have hard disks that can store many gigabytes of information. How much information can be stored in one gigabyte of storage?

Identifying the Problem

When words are stored on a computer, every letter, punctuation mark, and space between words is represented by one byte. A page of text, such as this page, might contain as many as 2,900 characters. So to store a page of text on a computer might require 2,900 bytes.

If you write a page of text using a word-processing program, more bytes

Size of Information Storage Units	
Information Storage Unit	**Number of Bytes**
kilobyte	1,024
megabyte	1,048,576
gigabyte	1,073,741,824

might be needed to store the page. This is because when the page is stored, some word-processing programs include other information along with the text.

Solving the Problem

1. If it takes 2,900 bytes to store one page of text on a computer, how many pages can be stored in 1 gigabyte of storage?
2. Suppose a book contains 400 pages of text. How many books could be stored on a 1-gigabyte hard disk?
3. A CD can hold 650 megabytes of information. How many 400-page books could be stored on a CD?

Curriculum Connection

Language Arts Have students find ways the word *binary* is used in other branches of science. Possible answers: In chemistry, a binary compound is composed of two elements. In astronomy, a binary star is two stars revolving about a common center of mass. L2 LS **Linguistic**

Activity

ASCII ASCII (American Standard Code for Information Interchange) is a code used in computers to represent digits, letters, and symbols. For example, the letters *d o g* are assigned the ASCII numbers 100, 111, and 103. These can be represented by the binary numbers 01100100, 01101111, and 01100111. Display a copy of the ASCII table on an overhead projector. Have students use the table to write the letters of their first name in binary numbers. L2 ELL LS **Logical-Mathematical** P

Misconceptions

Microscopic Switches Students may think of switches in a computer as mechanical objects that can be flipped one way or the other like a wall switch. Point out that the smallest imaginable mechanical switch would be far too large to use in a computer. Remind students that switches in computer memory are microscopic in size and are made by combining microscopic layers of semiconductor materials. The switch is turned on or off by the movement of electrons.

Applying Science

Answers

1. 1,073,741,824/2,900 = about 370,255 pages
2. 370,255/400 = about 926 books
3. 650 × 1,048,576 = 681,574,400; 681,574,400/2,900/400 = about 588 books

Pencil v. Pen Compare RAM and ROM to writing with a pencil and writing with an ink pen. Storing information in RAM is like writing with a pencil. You can erase and rewrite the information repeatedly. ROM is like information written in ink. Once it is written, it can't be erased.

Reading Check

Answer It is lost.

Teacher FYI

Computer Booting Turning on a computer is typically called booting the computer. The name for this procedure comes from the term bootstrap, meaning able to function independently of outside direction. When the computer is turned on, the bootstrap program, contained in ROM, transfers the computer's operating system to RAM.

IDENTIFYING
Misconceptions

Computer Chips Students may not realize that many devices they use every day, such as calculators, televisions, and microwaves, are controlled by tiny computer chips. Explain that computers used this way are known as embedded or hidden computers.

Figure 11 Computer memory is made of integrated circuits like this one. This integrated circuit can contain millions of microscopic circuits, shown here under high magnification.

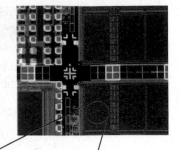

Science Online

Topic: Computer Software
Visit ips.msscience.com for Web links to information about types of computer software.

Activity Choose one type of software application and write a paragraph explaining why it is useful. Create a chart that summarizes what the software does.

Storing Information The memory in a computer is an integrated circuit that contains millions of tiny electronic circuits, as shown in **Figure 11.** In the most commonly used type of computer memory, each circuit is able to store electric charge and can be either charged or uncharged. If the circuit is charged, it represents the bit 1 and if it is uncharged it represents the bit 0. Because computer memory contains millions of these circuits, it can store tremendous amounts of information using only the numbers 1 and 0.

What is your earliest memory? When you remember something from long ago, you use your long-term memory. On the other hand, when you work on a math problem, you may keep the numbers in your head long enough to find the answer. Like you, a computer has a long-term memory and a short-term memory that are used for different purposes.

Random-Access Memory A computer's **random-access memory,** or RAM, is short-term memory that stores documents, programs, and data while they are being used. Program instructions and data are temporarily stored in RAM while you are using a program or changing the data.

For example, a computer game is kept in RAM while you are playing it. If you are using a word-processing program to write a report, the report is temporarily held in RAM while you are working on it. Because information stored in RAM is lost when the computer is turned off, this type of memory cannot store anything that you want to use later.

The amount of RAM depends on the number of binary digits it can store. Recall that eight bits is called a byte. A megabyte is more than one million bytes. A computer that has 128 megabytes of memory can store more than 128 million bytes of information in its RAM, or nearly one billion bits.

Reading Check *What happens to information in RAM when the computer is turned off?*

Read-Only Memory Some information that is needed to enable the computer to operate is stored in its permanent memory. The computer can read this memory, but it cannot be changed. Memory that can't be changed and is permanently stored inside the computer is called **read-only memory,** or ROM. ROM is not lost when the computer is turned off.

Visual Learning

Figure 11 Point out to students that integrated circuits, such as the one shown here, are much too small to contain large transistors like those shown in **Figure 8.** This figure shows thin strips of metal imprinted onto a small silicon chip. The metal connects microscopic layers of doped silicon that form the transistors and other electronic components. L2 LS **Visual-Spatial**

Computer Programs

It's your mother's birthday and you decide to surprise her by baking a chocolate cake. You find a recipe for chocolate cake in a cookbook and follow the directions in the order the recipe tells you to. However, if the person who wrote the recipe left out any steps or put them in the wrong order, the cake probably will not turn out the way you expected. A computer program is like a recipe. A program is a series of instructions that tell the computer how to do a job. Unlike the recipe for a cake, some computer programs contain millions of instructions that tell the computer how to do many different jobs.

All the functions of a computer, such as displaying an image on the computer monitor or doing a math calculation, are controlled by programs. These instructions tell the computer how to add two numbers, how to display a word, or how to change an image on the monitor when you move a joystick. Many different programs can be stored in a computer's memory.

Computer Software When you type a report, play a video game, draw a picture, or look through an encyclopedia on a computer, you are using computer software. **Computer software** is any list of instructions for the computer. The instructions that are part of the software tell the computer what to display on the monitor. If you respond to what you see, for example by moving the mouse, the software instructions tell the computer how to respond to your action.

Computer Programming

The process of writing computer software is called computer programming. To write a computer program, you must decide what you want the computer to do, plan the best way to organize the instructions, write the instructions, and test the program to be sure it works. A person who writes computer programs is called a computer programmer. Computer programmers write software in computer languages such as Basic, C++, and Java.

Figure 12 shows part of a computer program. After the program is written, it is converted into binary digits to enable it to be stored in the computer's memory. Then the computer can carry out the program's instructions.

Mini LAB

Observing Memory

Procedure

1. Write a different five-digit number on six **3 × 5 cards.**
2. Show a card to a partner for 3 s. Turn the card over and ask your partner to repeat the number. Repeat with two other cards.
3. Repeat this procedure with the last three cards, but wait 20 s before asking your partner to repeat each number.

Analysis

Is your partner's memory of the five-digit numbers more like computer RAM or ROM? Explain.

Try at Home

Figure 12 The text below is part of a computer program that directs the operation of a computer.

```
int request_dma(unsigned int dmanr, const char * device_id)
{
      if (dmanr > = MAX_DMA_CHANNELS)
            return -EINVAL;

      if (xchg(&dma_chan_busy[dmanr].lock, 1) != 0)
            return -EBUSY;

      dma_chan_busy[dmanr].device_id = device_id;

      /* old flag was 0, now contains 1 to indicate busy */
      return 0;
} /* request_dma */

void free_dma(unsigned int dmanr)
{
      if (dmanr > = MAX_DMA_CHANNELS) {
            printk("Trying to free DMA%d\n", dmanr);
            return;
      }
```


Mini LAB

Purpose Students observe memory. L2 LS **Auditory-Musical**

Materials six index cards

Teaching Strategy Some students will easily remember the numbers. Have them use 6-digit numbers instead.

Analysis

It is more like RAM because the student is only asked to remember the numbers for a short time and they are not permanently stored like ROM.

Assessment

Process Have students describe what might happen to them if human memory worked like computer ROM. Use **Performance Assessment in the Science Classroom,** p. 89.

Quick Demo

Types of Software

Materials Computer with various types of software installed

Estimated Time 15 minutes

Procedure Most students are familiar with games and word processors, but they may not have experience with other computer programs. Demonstrate various types, such as graphics programs, desktop publishing, and spreadsheets. L2 LS **Visual-Spatial**

Activity

Programming Languages Have students with programming experience demonstrate programs in various languages. L2 LS **Logical-Mathematical**

Teacher FYI

CPU The central processing unit in a computer can understand instructions only if they are in machine language. Because the instructions in machine language are strings of binary numbers, programs are almost never written in machine language. Instead, programs are written in languages that are easier to use, such as C++. These programs are then translated by the computer into machine language.

Computer Hardware

When you press a key on a computer's keyboard, a letter appears on the screen. This seems to occur all at once, but actually three steps are involved. In the first step, the computer receives information from an input device, such as a keyboard or mouse. For example, when you press a key on the keyboard, the computer receives and stores an electronic signal from the keyboard.

The next step is to process the input signal from the keyboard. This means to change the input signal into an electronic signal that can be understood by the computer monitor. The computer does this by following instructions contained in the programs stored in the computer's memory. The third step is to send the processed signal to the monitor.

All three steps can be carried out with a combination of hardware and software components. Computer hardware consists of input devices, output devices, storage devices, and integrated circuits for storing information. A keyboard and a mouse are examples of input devices, while a monitor, a printer, and loudspeakers are examples of output devices. Storage devices, such as floppy disks, hard disks, and CDs, are used to store information outside of the computer memory. A computer also contains a microprocessor that controls the computer hardware. Examples of computer hardware are shown in **Figure 13.**

Figure 13 Computer hardware includes input devices, output devices, and storage devices.

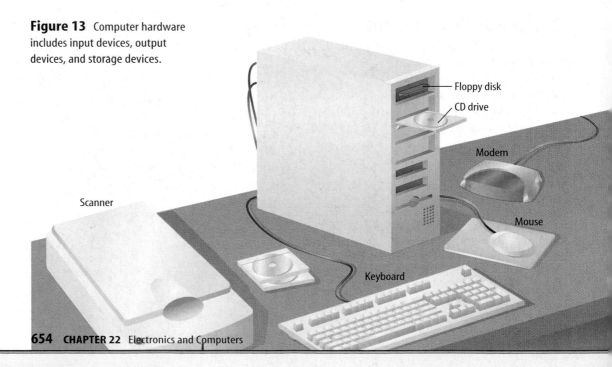

Scanner
Floppy disk
CD drive
Modem
Mouse
Keyboard

The Microprocessor Modern computers contain a microprocessor, like the one shown in **Figure 14,** that serves as the brain of the computer. A **microprocessor,** which is also called the central processing unit, or CPU, is an integrated circuit that controls the flow of information between different parts of the computer. A microprocessor can contain millions of interconnected transistors and other components. The microprocessor receives electronic signals from various parts of the computer, processes these signals, and sends electronic signals to other parts of the computer. For example, the microprocessor might tell the hard-disk drive to write data to the hard disk or the monitor to change the image on the screen. The microprocessor does this by carrying out instructions that are contained in computer programs stored in the computer's memory.

The microprocessor was developed in the late 1970s as the result of a process that made it possible to fit thousands of electronic components on a silicon chip. In the 1980s, the number of components on a silicon chip increased to hundreds of thousands. In the 1990s, microprocessors were developed that contained several million components on a single chip.

Figure 14 The pencil points to the microprocessor in the photo above. This microprocessor has dimensions of about one centimeter on a side, but contains millions of transistors and other solid-state components.

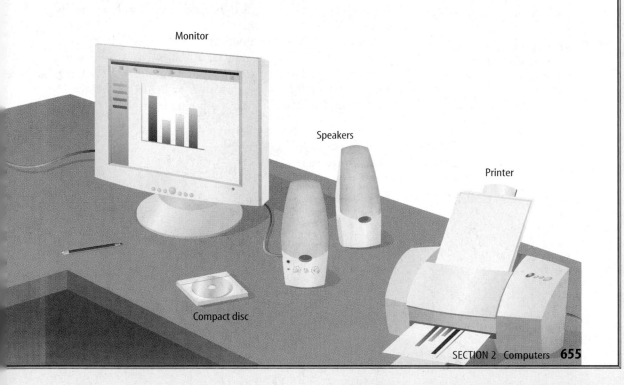

Monitor

Speakers

Printer

Compact disc

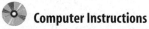

Recycling Computers The glass in computer monitors contains lead to shield the user from electromagnetic radiation emitted by the cathode ray tube. The amount of lead and other toxic substances in computers is so high that some states ban them from landfills. Donating old computers to charity or schools is a possibility, but the need for up-to-date technology often makes this difficult. Some states send computers to computer recycling companies where the metal, plastic, and lead glass parts are recycled.

Research Have students research where they can bring computer parts for recycling in their communities.

Activity

Hard Drives To show students how information is organized on a hard disk, have them draw about ten concentric circles on a piece of paper. Next, have them draw lines through the center of the circles so that they are divided into eight equal parts. Explain that the concentric circles represent the platter's tracks where information is stored. The slices formed by the diameters split the tracks into sectors. The hard disk is able to retrieve information by labeling these tracks and sectors and remembering the location where information is stored. L2 ELL LS
Visual-Spatial

Discussion

Pocket of Air Explain to students that the heads of the hard disk don't actually touch the platters. The heads and platters are kept apart by a pocket of air formed as the platters spin. Why is this necessary? The platter would have to be extremely smooth to allow the head to slide over it smoothly. Also, if they touched, the head and the platter would wear out easily. L2 LS **Logical-Mathematical**

Recycling Computers Changes in computer technology occur so rapidly that computers are often replaced after being used for only a few years. What happens to old computers? Some computer parts contain lead, mercury, and other toxic substances. Research how toxic materials can be recovered from old computers, and disposed of safely. Summarize your findings in your Science Journal.

Science Online

Topic: Magnetic Disks
Visit ips.msscience.com for Web links to information about storing data on magnetic disks.

Activity Write a paragraph explaining why hard disks can store more information than floppy disks.

Storing Information

You have decided to type your homework assignment on a computer. The resulting paper is quite long and you make many changes to it each time you read it. How does the computer make it possible for you to store your information and make changes to it?

Both RAM and ROM are integrated circuits inside the computer. You might wonder, then, why other types of information storage are needed. Information stored in RAM is lost when the computer is turned off, and information stored in ROM can only be read—it can't be changed. If you want to store information that can be changed but isn't lost when the computer is off, you must store that information on a storage device, such as a disk. Several different types of disks are available.

Hard Disks A hard disk is a device that stores computer information magnetically. A hard disk is usually located inside a computer. **Figure 15** shows the inside of a hard disk, and **Figure 16** shows how a hard disk stores data. The hard disk contains one or more metal disks that have magnetic particles on one surface. When you save information on a hard disk, a device called a read/write head inside the disk drive changes the orientation of the magnetic particles on the disk's surface. Orientation in one direction represents 0 and orientation in the opposite direction represents 1. When a magnetized disk is read, the read/write head converts the digital information on the disk to pulses of electric current.

Information stored magnetically cannot be read by the computer as quickly as information stored on RAM and ROM. However, because the information on a hard disk is stored magnetically rather than with electronic switches like RAM, the information isn't lost when the computer is turned off.

Figure 15 A hard disk contains a disk or platter that is coated with magnetic particles. A read/write head moves over the surface of the disk.

Science Journal

The Information Age The age we live in is sometimes referred to as the Information Age because so much information is available to everyone. Have each student write a paragraph in his or her Science Journal discussing the relationship between the development of digital computers and the increase in the amount of information available to people. L2 LS **Linguistic**

Fun Fact

Modern hard drives may have platters with more than 60,000 tracks per inch. Some platters spin more than 10,000 times per second.

Figure 16

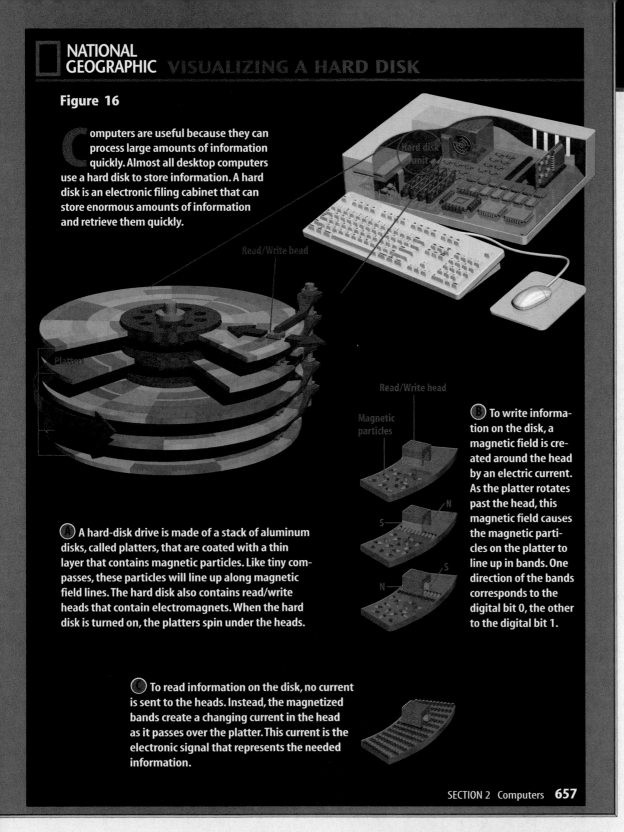

Computers are useful because they can process large amounts of information quickly. Almost all desktop computers use a hard disk to store information. A hard disk is an electronic filing cabinet that can store enormous amounts of information and retrieve them quickly.

Read/Write head

Platters

A A hard-disk drive is made of a stack of aluminum disks, called platters, that are coated with a thin layer that contains magnetic particles. Like tiny compasses, these particles will line up along magnetic field lines. The hard disk also contains read/write heads that contain electromagnets. When the hard disk is turned on, the platters spin under the heads.

Read/Write head

Magnetic particles

B To write information on the disk, a magnetic field is created around the head by an electric current. As the platter rotates past the head, this magnetic field causes the magnetic particles on the platter to line up in bands. One direction of the bands corresponds to the digital bit 0, the other to the digital bit 1.

C To read information on the disk, no current is sent to the heads. Instead, the magnetized bands create a changing current in the head as it passes over the platter. This current is the electronic signal that represents the needed information.

SECTION 2 Computers **657**

Visualizing a Hard Disk

Have students examine the pictures and read the captions. Then ask the following questions.

Why is it important for hard drives to be enclosed in a metal casing? The metal casing keeps out dust that could get in the space between a head and a platter, preventing it from working properly.

Why is more than one platter used in most hard drives? to increase the amount of information that can be stored on the hard drive

Activity

Investigate Hard Drives Obtain an old hard drive from a computer repair store. Open it and allow students to identify the platters, read/write heads, and actuator arms. Point out that each platter has a head on either side of it. Explain that when the hard drive is off, the heads rest on the platters. When the platters spin, the air flow forces the heads slightly away from the surface.

Teacher FYI

Capacitors Each bit of information is stored on RAM in a capacitor. A charged capacitor has a value of 1, and a capacitor without charge has a value of 0. Capacitors must be read and recharged hundreds of times every second. This is why information stored on RAM is lost when the computer is turned off.

Quick Demo

Floppy Disks

Materials old 5.25″ and 3.5″ floppy disks

Estimated Time five minutes

Procedure Cut apart one of the 5.25″ disks so that students can see the film inside. The soft white material inside the disk removes dust that would interfere with the performance of the disk. **L2** **LS** **Visual-Spatial**

Discussion

Magnetic Storage Why should floppy disks never be exposed to a magnetic field, and why is this not a problem for CDs and DVDs? Exposing floppy disks to a magnetic field will demagnetize them and destroy the information stored magnetically on them. Information is not stored magnetically on CDs and DVDs. Exposure to a magnetic field will not affect these disks. Would exposure to a magnetic field harm a computer? Yes; although critical magnetic components are shielded, they can be harmed by exposure to a strong magnet. The monitor can be distorted by exposure to a magnetic field. **L2** **LS** **Logical-Mathematical**

Use Science Words

Word Origin The word optical comes from the Greek word *ops*, meaning "eye." Ask students to find words with this root and explain their meaning. optic—relating to the eye or to lenses, optician—a maker of eyeglasses, ophthalmologist—eye doctor

Caption Answer

Figure 17 A read-only disk is permanently marked so that the information cannot be erased or changed. The information on a reusable disk can be erased or changed.

Science Online

Topic: Optical Disks
Visit ips.msscience.com for Web links to information about storing data on optical disks.

Activity Make a table that shows the similarities and differences between CDs and DVDs.

Figure 17 An optical storage disk stores information that is read by a laser.
Explain *the difference between a read-only disk and a reusable disk.*

Information is stored on an optical disk by a series of pits and flat spots, representing a binary 1 or 0.

Floppy Disks Storing information on a hard disk is convenient, but sometimes you might want to store information that you can carry with you. The original storage device of this type was the floppy disk. A floppy disk is a thin, flexible, plastic disk. You might be confused by the term *floppy* if you have heard it used to describe disks that seem quite rigid. That is because you don't actually hold the floppy disk. Instead, you hold the harder plastic case in which the floppy disk is encased. Just as for a hard disk, the floppy disk is coated with a magnetic material that is magnetized and read by a read/write head. Floppy disks have lower storage capacity than hard disks. Also, compared to hard disks, information is read from and written to floppy disks much more slowly.

Optical Disks An optical storage disk, such as a CD, is a thin, plastic disk that has information digitally stored on it. The disk contains a series of microscopic pits and flat spots as shown on the left in **Figure 17.** A tiny laser beam shines on the surface of the disk. The information on the disk is read by measuring the intensity of the laser light reflected from the surface of the disk. This intensity will depend on whether the laser beam strikes a pit or a flat spot. The original optical storage disks, laser discs, CD-ROMs, and DVD-ROMs, were read-only. Several of these are shown on the right in **Figure 17.** However, CD-RW disks can be erased and rewritten many times. Information is written by a CD burner that causes a metal alloy in the disk to change form when heated by a laser. When the disk is read, the intensity of reflected laser light depends on which form of the alloy the beam strikes.

CDs, laser disks, and DVDs are all examples of optical storage disks.

Teacher FYI

WWW Inventor The World Wide Web was developed in 1990 by a computer scientist named Tim Berners-Lee at CERN, the European Organization for Nuclear Research. The Web was originally intended to provide high-speed information transfer between high-energy physics groups.

Computer Networks

People can communicate using a computer if it is part of a computer network. A computer network is two or more computers that are connected to share files or other information. The computers might be linked by cables, telephone lines, or radio signals.

The Internet is a collection of computer networks from all over the world. The Internet is linked together by cable or satellite. The Internet itself has no information. No documents or files exist on the Internet, but you can use the Internet to access a tremendous amount of information by linking to other computers.

The World Wide Web is part of the Internet. The World Wide Web is the ever-changing collection of information (text, graphics, audio, and video) on computers all over the world. The computers that store these documents are called servers. When you connect with a server through the Internet, you can view any of the Web documents that are stored there, like the Web page shown in **Figure 18.** A particular collection of information that is stored in one place is known as a Web site.

Figure 18 When you connect to the Internet, you can be linked with other computers that are part of the World Wide Web. Then you can have access to the information stored at millions of Web sites.

---

section 2 review

Summary

Computer Information
- A binary digit can be a 0 or a 1.
- Computers store information as groups of binary digits.
- Computers use tiny electronic circuits to represent binary digits and store information.

Computer Software and Hardware
- Computer software and computer programs are lists of instructions for a computer.
- Computer programs are written in special computer languages.
- Computer hardware, such as keyboards and hard disks, is controlled by a microprocessor.

Storing Information
- Hard disks and floppy disks store information on disks coated with magnetic particles.
- Optical disks store information as a series of pits and flat spots that is read by a laser.

Self Check

1. **Explain** why the binary number system is used for storing information in computers.
2. **Compare and contrast** the Internet and the World Wide Web.
3. **Describe** what a microprocessor does with the signals it receives from various parts of a computer.
4. **Compare and contrast** three different computer information storage devices.
5. **Think Critically** Why can't computer information be stored only in RAM and ROM, making storage devices such as hard disks and optical disks unnecessary?

Applying Skills

6. **Make a Concept Map** Develop a spider map about computers. Include the following terms in your spider map: *keyboard, monitor, microprocessor, software, printer, RAM, ROM, floppy disk, hard disk, CD, Internet,* and *World Wide Web*.

Real-World Question

Purpose

Internet Students use Internet sites that can be accessed through **ips.msscience.com/internet_lab**.

Students can post their findings on the site and get information from other schools around the country.

Non-Internet Sources Students can obtain library books that describe computer viruses and discuss the problem with network administrators at schools, libraries, or businesses.

Time Required one week

Make a Plan

Preparation

Internet Use the Internet site on the student text to run through the steps that the students will follow.

Non-Internet Bring books to class about computers that contain information on computer viruses.

Virus Protection Computer viruses can be avoided by being aware of the problem and taking proper precautions.

Follow Your Plan

Teaching Strategy You might also want to have students research other harmful computer programs that are similar to viruses (*i.e.*, Trojan horses, logic bombs, and worms). Have students find out how each of these affects a computer.

Does your c🖥mputer have a virus?

Goals
- **Understand** what a computer virus is.
- **Identify** different types of computer viruses.
- **Describe** how a computer virus is spread.
- **Create** a plan for protecting electronic files and computers from computer viruses.

Data Source

Science Online

Visit **ips.msscience.com/internet_lab** to get more information about computer viruses and for data collected by other students.

Real-World Question

The Internet has provided many ways to share information and become connected with people near and far. People can communicate ideas and information quickly and easily. Unfortunately, some people use computers and the Internet as an opportunity to create and spread computer viruses. Many new viruses are created each year that can damage information and programs on a computer. Viruses create problems for computers in homes and schools. Computer problems caused by viruses can be costly for business and government computers, as well. How can acquiring and transmitting computer viruses be prevented?

Make a Plan

People share information and ideas by exchanging electronic files with one another. Perhaps you send email to your friends and family. Many people send word processing or spreadsheet files to friends and associates. What happens if a computer file is infected with a virus? How is that virus spread among different users? How can you protect your computer and your information from being attacked by a virus?

Differentiated Instruction

Learning Disabled Students who are not as capable or experienced with using a computer for Internet searches can be paired with students who can provide guidance.

Alternative Inquiry Lab

Other Viruses To extend this Lab into an Inquiry Lab, have students make a biology connection by researching how biological viruses work, and drawing an analogy to computer viruses. Exploring the exponential growth patterns of biological viruses in cells will help them understand how they propagate so quickly through computer systems. Students may write a paragraph to explain their analogy.

Follow Your Plan

1. Do research to find out what a computer virus is and the difference between various types of viruses. Also research the ways that a computer virus can damage computer files and programs.

2. After you know what a computer virus is, make a list of different types of viruses and how they are passed from computer to computer. For example, some viruses can be passed through attachments to email. Others can be passed by sharing spreadsheet files. Be specific about how a virus is passed.

3. Discover how you can protect yourself from viruses that attack your computer. Make a list of steps to follow to avoid infection.

4. Make sure your teacher approves your plan before you start.

5. Visit the link below to post your data.

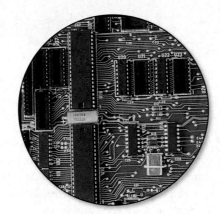

Analyze Your Data

1. **Explain** how computer viruses are transferred from one computer to another.

2. **Explain** how you can prevent your computer from becoming infected by a virus.

3. **Explain** how you can prevent other people from getting computer viruses.

4. **Describe** the different ways computer viruses can damage computer files and programs.

Conclude and Apply

1. **List** five to eight steps a computer user should follow to prevent getting a computer virus or passing a computer virus to another computer.

2. **Discuss** how antivirus software can keep viruses from spreading. Could antivirus software always prevent you from getting a computer virus? Why or why not?

*C*ommunicating Your Data

Find this lab using the link below. Post your data in the table that is provided. **Compare** your data on types of viruses and how they infect computers with that of other students.

Science Online

ips.msscience.com/internet_lab

☑ Assessment

Pamphlets Have groups of students design and produce pamphlets about computer viruses and security measures. Some of the best pamphlets can be copied and distributed to other students in the school. Use **Performance Assessment in the Science Classroom,** p. 129.

*C*ommunicating Your Data

Have students use their data and the data they find at the link in the lab to prepare posters about the types of viruses and ways to protect against them. The posters can be displayed at various places throughout the school for other students to see. L2 **LS Visual-Spatial**

Analyze Your Data

1. Possible answer: by opening infected e-mail attachments, copying or downloading infected files

2. Possible answers: Install virus protection. Don't open unknown e-mail attachments or copy programs unless you know they are not infected. Obtain software only from legitimate sources; use scanning or monitoring software on your computer; use only write-protected disks.

3. Possible answers: Don't share suspicious files without checking them. Be sure that files sent with e-mail don't contain viruses.

4. Possible answers: They can make your hard disk unusable, make files unreadable, alter programs so they cannot be run, and mail themselves to addresses on your e-mail address list.

5. Viruses can damage files and programs so that they are no longer useable. They also can alter programs so that the programs transmit the virus to other files and programs on different computers. Some viruses can erase the programs and files on a hard disk.

Conclude and Apply

1. Possible answers: Don't open unknown e-mail attachments. Use up-to-date anti-virus software. Don't copy unknown files. Don't download Internet files unless they are checked by anti-virus software. See if your software provider has software security patches. Use write-protected disks. Obtain software only from legitimate sources.

2. It identifies a virus and deletes it. It compares files with known viruses. It checks to see if an unknown program is trying to alter the operating system on your computer. A virus could still infect your operating system if anti-virus software is not up-to-date or if the type of virus is unknown.

TIME

TIME SCIENCE AND Society

SCIENCE ISSUES THAT AFFECT YOU!

E-Lectrifying E-Books

Here's a look at how computers and the Internet are changing what—and how—you read

All of these stacked books can fit into one e-book.

In recent years, people have been using their computers to order books from online bookstores. That's no big deal. What might become a big deal is the ordering of electronic books—books that you download to your own computer and read on the screen or print out to read later. Some famous authors are writing books just for that purpose. Some of the books are published only online—you can't find them anywhere else.

Many other Web sites, however, are selling any book anybody wishes to write—including students like you. In fact, you could start your own online bookstore with your own stories and reports. It will be up to readers to pick and choose what's good from the huge number of e-books that will be on the Web.

Curling Up with a Good Disk

Downloading books to your home computer is just one way to get an e-book. You can also buy versions of books to read on hand-held devices that are about the size of a paperback book. With one device, the books come on CD-ROM disks. With another, the books download to the device over a modem.

Current e-book devices are expensive, heavy, and awkward, and the number of books you can get for them is small. But if improvements come quickly, it might not be long before you check out of the library with a pocketful of disks instead of a heavy armload of books!

Will Traditional Books Disappear?

Most people think that the traditional printed book will never disappear. Publishers will still be printing books on paper with soft and hard covers. But publishers also predict there will be more and more kinds of formats for books. E-books, for example, might be best for interactive works that blend video, sound, and words the way many Web sites already do. For example, an e-book biography might allow the reader to click on photos and videos of the subject, and even provide links to other sources of information.

Interview Talk to a bookstore employee to find out how book publishing and selling has changed in the last five years. Can he or she predict how people will read books in the future? Report to the class.

For more information, visit ips.msscience.com/time

Reviewing Main Ideas

Section 1 Electronics

1. A changing electric current used to carry information is an electronic signal. Electronic signals can be either analog or digital.

2. Semiconductor elements, such as silicon and germanium, conduct electricity better than nonmetals but not as well as metals. If a small amount of some impurities is added to a semiconductor, its conductivity can be controlled.

3. Diodes and transistors are solid-state components. Diodes allow current to flow in one direction only. Transistors are used as switches or amplifiers.

Section 2 Computers

1. The binary system consists of two digits, 0 and 1. Switches within electronic devices such as computers can store information by turning on (1) and off (0).

2. Electronic memory within a computer can be random-access (RAM) or read-only (ROM).

3. Computer hardware consists of the physical parts of a computer. Computer software is a list of instructions for a computer.

4. A microprocessor is a complex integrated circuit that receives signals from various parts of the computer, processes these signals, and then sends instructions to various parts of the computer.

5. Floppy disks, hard disks, and optical disks are types of computer information storage devices.

6. The Internet is a collection of linked computer networks from all over the world. The World Wide Web is part of the Internet.

Visualizing Main Ideas

Copy and complete the following concept map on computers.

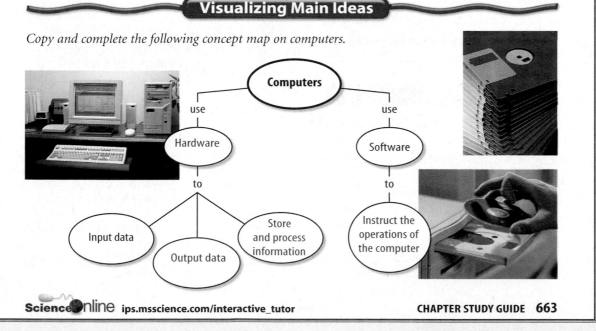

Science Online ips.msscience.com/interactive_tutor

CHAPTER STUDY GUIDE 663

Reviewing Main Ideas

Summary statements can be used by students to review the major concepts of the chapter.

Visualizing Main Ideas

See student page.

Science Online

Visit ips.msscience.com
/self_check_quiz
/interactive_tutor
/vocabulary_puzzlemaker
/chapter_review
/standardized_test

Assessment Transparency

For additional assessment questions, use the *Assessment Transparency* located in the transparency book.

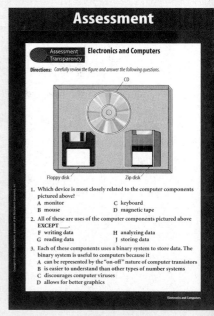

Using Vocabulary

1. binary system
2. diode
3. integrated circuit
4. RAM
5. transistor
6. microprocessor
7. analog signal

Checking Concepts

8. D   12. D
9. C   13. A
10. C   14. B
11. B   15. C

Thinking Critically

16. Possible answer: A liquid thermometer is analog and displays temperature variations smoothly as liquid expands and contracts. A digital camera has sensors that convert light into an electrical signal that is stored in digital form.

17. A diode has two semiconductors, one n-type and one p-type. It can be used to change AC to DC. A transistor has three semiconductor layers. It is used as a switch or to amplify signals. An integrated circuit has many interconnected solid-state components on a semiconductor chip. Integrated circuits can be used as microprocessors and to electronically control devices such as video cameras.

18. Binary has two digits rather than ten. On/off switches in a computer can be used to represent information using the binary system.

19. See student page.

20. Before integrated circuits were developed, computers were larger, used more power, and were less reliable.

Using Vocabulary

analog signal p. 642
binary system p. 650
computer software p. 653
digital signal p. 643
diode p. 646
electronic signal p. 642
integrated circuit p. 647
microprocessor p. 655
random access memory p. 652
read-only memory p. 652
semiconductor p. 645
transistor p. 647

Fill in the blanks with the correct vocabulary word or words.

1. _____ is a base-2 number system.

2. A(n) _____ can change AC current to DC current.

3. A(n) _____ is made from a single piece of semiconductor material and can contain thousands of solid-state components.

4. The information in a computer's _____ changes each time the computer is used.

5. An electronic device that can be used as a switch or to amplify electronic signals is a(n) _____.

6. A(n) _____ is also called a CPU.

7. An electronic signal that varies smoothly with time is a(n) _____.

Checking Concepts

Choose the word or phrase that best answers the question.

8. Which of the following best describes integrated circuits?
   A) They can be read with a laser.
   B) They use vacuum tubes as transistors and diodes.
   C) They contain pits and flat areas.
   D) They can be small and contain a large number of solid-state components.

9. Which type of elements are semiconductors?
   A) metals   C) metalloids
   B) nonmetals   D) gases

10. How is a digital signal different from an analog signal?
    A) It uses electric current.
    B) It varies continuously.
    C) It changes in steps.
    D) It is used as a switch.

11. Which of the following uses magnetic materials to store digital information.
    A) DVD   C) RAM
    B) hard disk   D) compact disk

12. Which part of a computer carries out the instructions contained in computer programs and software?
    A) RAM   C) hard disk
    B) ROM   D) microprocessor

13. Which type of computer memory is used when a computer is first turned on?
    A) ROM   C) DVD
    B) RAM   D) floppy disk

14. The instructions contained in a computer program are stored in which type of computer memory while the program is being used?
    A) ROM   C) CD
    B) RAM   D) floppy disk

Use the figure below to answer question 15.

15. What binary number is represented by the positions of the switches?
    A) 1110   C) 0101
    B) 0010   D) 0001

 Science online   ips.msscience.com/vocabulary_puzzlemaker

Use the Exam*View*® Pro Testmaker CD-ROM to:
- create multiple versions of tests
- create modified tests with one mouse click for inclusion students
- edit existing questions and add your own questions
- build tests aligned with state standards using built-in State Curriculum Tags
- change English tests to Spanish with one mouse click and vice versa

Thinking Critically

16. Compare and contrast an analog device and a digital device.

17. Make and Use Tables Copy and complete the following table that describes solid-state components.

Solid-State Components		
Component	Description	Use
Diode		
Transistor		
Integrated circuit		

18. Explain why the binary number system is used to store digital information in computers, instead of the decimal number system you use every day.

19. Concept Map Copy and complete the following events-chain map showing the sequence of events that occurs when a computer mouse is moved.

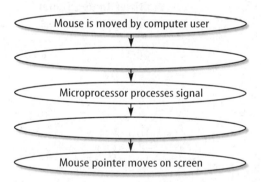

Mouse is moved by computer user

↓

↓

Microprocessor processes signal

↓

↓

Mouse pointer moves on screen

20. Discuss how the development of solid-state components and integrated circuits affected devices such as TVs and computers.

21. Make a table to classify the different types of internal and external computer memory and storage.

Performance Activities

22. Make a Poster Microprocessors continue to be developed that are more complex and contain an ever-increasing number of solid state components. Visit **msscience.com** for links to information about different microprocessors and how they have changed. Make a poster that summarizes what you have learned.

Applying Math

Students at a middle school researched the storage capacity of different computer storage devices. The information is summarized in the table below. The storage capacity is listed in units of gigabytes. A gigabyte is 1,074,000,000 bytes.

Use the table below to answer questions 23–25.

Computer Storage Devices	
Device	Capacity (Gb)
Floppy disk	0.00144
Compact disc	0.650
DVD	4.7
Hard Disk A	8.60
Hard Disk B	120.2

23. Music Files Storage In a certain format, to store 1 min of music as a digital signal requires 10,584,000 bytes. How many minutes of music in this format can be stored on the compact disc?

24. Digital Pictures Storage A certain digital camera produces digital images that require 921,600 bytes to store. How many of these images could be stored on hard disk A?

25. Documents Storage Seven documents produced by word processing software are stored on a floppy disk. If there are 40,000 bytes of storage still available on the disk, what is the average amount of storage used by each of the documents?

---

21. ROM (read-only) and RAM (random access) are internal electronic memory. Floppy disks are external magnetic memory. Optical disks are external and store information as pits and flat spots on disks. Hard disks are magnetic and usually internal.

Performance Activities

22. Students could investigate how the newest microprocessors are used as well as their speed and performance abilities. They could also research state-of-the-art techniques for producing microprocessors. Use **PASC,** p. 91.

Applying Math

National Math Standards
1, 2, 9

23. 65.95 minutes

24. 10,022

25. 215,222 bytes

☑ **Assessment** **Resources**

📁 **Reproducible Masters**
Chapter *Fast File* Resources
 Chapter Review, pp. 35–36
 Chapter Tests, pp. 37–40
 Assessment Transparency Activity, p. 47
Glencoe Science Web site
 Chapter Review Test
 Standardized Test Practice

Glencoe Technology
 🔔 Assessment Transparency
 🌐 Exam*View*® Pro Testmaker
 💻 MindJogger Videoquiz
 ⚫ Interactive Chalkboard

Answer Sheet A practice answer sheet can be found at ips.msscience.com/answer_sheet.

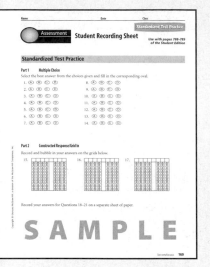

Part 1 | Multiple Choice

1. A	**6.** D
2. B	**7.** D
3. B	**8.** A
4. A	**9.** D
5. B	**10.** D

Part 2 | Short Response

11. A binary zero is a microscopic section of the platter whose magnetic poles point in a certain direction. A binary one is a microscopic region whose poles point in the opposite direction.

12. This is an arsenic-doped silicon semiconductor that contains extra electrons. As a result it is a n-type semiconductor.

13. Atoms of other elements are added to semiconductors to change the conductivity. The extra electrons are free to move about. This causes the electrical conductivity to increase. This process is called doping.

14. In a diode, current flows from the n-type semiconductor to the p-type semiconductor.

Part 1 | Multiple Choice

Record your answers on the answer sheet provided by your teacher or on a sheet of paper.

1. What kinds of materials are used to make solid-state components?
  A. semiconductors
  B. superconductors
  C. conductors
  D. insulators

2. Which of the following are not contained in integrated circuits?
  A. semiconductors   **C.** diodes
  B. vacuum tubes   **D.** transistors

Use the table below to answer questions 3 and 4.

Number of Binary Digit Combinations	
Number of Binary Digits	**Total Number of Combinations**
1	2
2	4
3	8
4	?
5	32

3. Which of the following is the total number of combinations of four binary digits?
  A. 64   **C.** 32
  B. 16   **D.** 8

4. Based on the data table, which of the following is the total number of combinations of six binary digits?
  A. 64   **C.** 32
  B. 16   **D.** 8

5. Which of the following best describes computer software?
  A. It is a type of temporary storage.
  B. It is a list of instructions.
  C. It contains analog information.
  D. It cannot be stored magnetically.

6. Which of the following is a computer input device?
  A. printer   **C.** monitor
  B. loudspeakers   **D.** keyboard

7. Which of the following is an optical storage device?
  A. hard disk   **C.** floppy disk
  B. RAM   **D.** CD

8. Where are elements that are semiconductors located on the periodic table?
  A. between metals and nonmetals
  B. on the right column
  C. on the left column
  D. at the bottom

9. Which of the following is not an electronic device?
  A. calculator   **C.** CD player
  B. television   **D.** light bulb

Use the figure below to answer question 10.

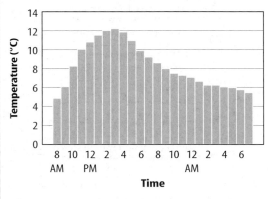

10. Which of the following is a process that produces this digital signal from an analog signal?
  A. doping   **C.** switching
  B. programming   **D.** sampling

666 STANDARDIZED TEST PRACTICE

15. This process is called signal processing.

Part 3 | Open Ended

16. It is an analog device because it smoothly records the rise and fall of the air pressure over a period of time as the drum rotates.

17. A monitor is an output device that lets the computer communicate with the operator. It lets you see what you have typed into the computer. A keyboard is an input device. It lets you type in the report. The hard drive is a storage device. It stores the word-processing program you are using, and file that the word-processing program produces.

18. A floppy disk is a thin, flexible, plastic disk. It is coated with a magnetic material that is magnetized and read by a read/write head. An optical disk is a thin plastic disk. It has a series of microscopic pits and flat spots. The information on the disk is read by measuring the intensity of laser light reflected from the disk's surface. Optical disks also can

Part 2 | Short Response/Grid In

Record your answers on the answer sheet provided by your teacher or on a sheet of paper.

11. What is the difference between a binary 1 or 0 that is stored on a platter of a hard disk?

Use the figure below to answer questions 12 and 13.

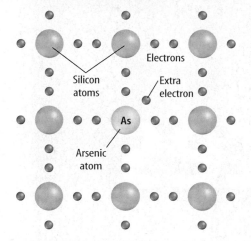

12. Describe the type of semiconductor material that is shown in the figure above.

13. Explain why atoms of other elements are added to a semiconductor material.

14. In a diode, which way does current flow between the n-type semiconductor and the p-type semiconductor?

15. Identify the process that enables background noise to be removed from a digitized music file that is stored on a hard disk.

Test-Taking Tip

Some Questions Have Qualifiers Look for qualifiers in a question. Such questions are not looking for absolute answers. Qualifiers could be words such as *most likely, most common,* or *least common.*

Part 3 | Open Ended

Record your answers on a sheet of paper.

16. A barograph is a device that measures and records air pressure. A barograph contains a pen that moves up and down as the pressure changes. The pen continuously draws a line on paper attached to a drum that slowly rotates. Infer whether the barograph is an analog or digital device. Explain.

17. Classify each of the following as an input, output, or storages device: monitor, keyboard, printer, hard disk. Explain the function of each device if you are using a word processing program to write a report.

18. Compare and contrast a floppy disk with an optical disk, such as a CD.

19. Explain why electric circuits that can be charged or uncharged are used as the components of computer memory.

Use the figure below to answer questions 20 and 21.

20. Describe how the read/write heads write information on a platter.

21. Describe how the read/write heads read information that is stored on the platters.

Rubrics

The following rubrics are sample scoring devices for short response and open-ended questions.

Short Response

Points	Description
2	The student demonstrates a thorough understanding of the science of the task. The response may contain minor flaws that do not detract from the demonstration of a thorough understanding.
1	The student has provided a response that is only partially correct.
0	The student has provided a completely incorrect solution or no response at all.

Open Ended

Points	Description
4	The student demonstrates a thorough understanding of the science of the task. The response may contain minor flaws that do not detract from the demonstration of a thorough understanding.
3	The student demonstrates an understanding of the science of the task. The response is essentially correct and demonstrates an essential but less than thorough understanding of the science.
2	The student demonstrates only a partial understanding of the science of the task. Although the student may have used the correct approach to a solution or may have provided a correct solution, the work lacks an essential understanding of the underlying science concepts.
1	The student demonstrates a very limited understanding of the science of the task. The response is incomplete and exhibits many flaws.
0	The student provides a completely incorrect solution or no response at all.

be written to by a CD burner that uses a laser.

19. The memory in a computer is an integrated circuit that consists of millions of tiny electrical circuits. Each circuit can be either charged, which corresponds to a binary one, or uncharged, which corresponds to a binary zero. In this way, binary numbers can be stored in memory

as groups of microcircuits that are charged and uncharged.

20. To write information, an electric current in read/write head produces a magnetic field around the head. This magnetic field causes magnetic particles on the platter to line up in bands. The direction of the bands corresponds to a binary zero or one.

21. To read information, the magnetic bands on the platter produce an electric current in the head as the platter rotates past the head. This electric current changes as different bands move past the head. The changing current is the electronic signal corresponding to the information stored on the disk.

Student Resources

CONTENTS

Scientific Methods

Scientists use an orderly approach called the scientific method to solve problems. This includes organizing and recording data so others can understand them. Scientists use many variations in this method when they solve problems.

Identify a Question

The first step in a scientific investigation or experiment is to identify a question to be answered or a problem to be solved. For example, you might ask which gasoline is the most efficient.

Figure 1 The Internet can be a valuable research tool.

Gather and Organize Information

After you have identified your question, begin gathering and organizing information. There are many ways to gather information, such as researching in a library, interviewing those knowledgeable about the subject, testing and working in the laboratory and field. Fieldwork is investigations and observations done outside of a laboratory.

Researching Information Before moving in a new direction, it is important to gather the information that already is known about the subject. Start by asking yourself questions to determine exactly what you need to know. Then you will look for the information in various reference sources, like the student is doing in **Figure 1.** Some sources may include textbooks, encyclopedias, government documents, professional journals, science magazines, and the Internet. Always list the sources of your information.

Evaluate Sources of Information Not all sources of information are reliable. You should evaluate all of your sources of information, and use only those you know to be dependable. For example, if you are researching ways to make homes more energy efficient, a site written by the U.S. Department of Energy would be more reliable than a site written by a company that is trying to sell a new type of weatherproofing material. Also, remember that research always is changing. Consult the most current resources available to you. For example, a 1985 resource about saving energy would not reflect the most recent findings.

Sometimes scientists use data that they did not collect themselves, or conclusions drawn by other researchers. This data must be evaluated carefully. Ask questions about how the data were obtained, if the investigation was carried out properly, and if it has been duplicated exactly with the same results. Would you reach the same conclusion from the data? Only when you have confidence in the data can you believe it is true and feel comfortable using it.

Interpret Scientific Illustrations As you research a topic in science, you will see drawings, diagrams, and photographs to help you understand what you read. Some illustrations are included to help you understand an idea that you can't see easily by yourself, like the tiny particles in an atom in **Figure 2.** A drawing helps many people to remember details more easily and provides examples that clarify difficult concepts or give additional information about the topic you are studying. Most illustrations have labels or a caption to identify or to provide more information.

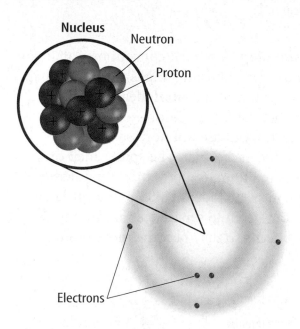

Figure 2 This drawing shows an atom of carbon with its six protons, six neutrons, and six electrons.

Concept Maps One way to organize data is to draw a diagram that shows relationships among ideas (or concepts). A concept map can help make the meanings of ideas and terms more clear, and help you understand and remember what you are studying. Concept maps are useful for breaking large concepts down into smaller parts, making learning easier.

Network Tree A type of concept map that not only shows a relationship, but how the concepts are related is a network tree, shown in **Figure 3.** In a network tree, the words are written in the ovals, while the description of the type of relationship is written across the connecting lines.

When constructing a network tree, write down the topic and all major topics on separate pieces of paper or notecards. Then arrange them in order from general to specific. Branch the related concepts from the major concept and describe the relationship on the connecting line. Continue to more specific concepts until finished.

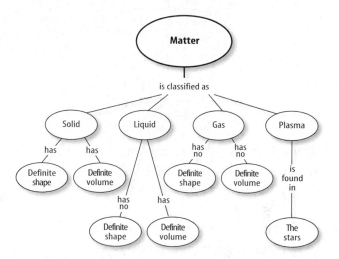

Figure 3 A network tree shows how concepts or objects are related.

Events Chain Another type of concept map is an events chain. Sometimes called a flow chart, it models the order or sequence of items. An events chain can be used to describe a sequence of events, the steps in a procedure, or the stages of a process.

When making an events chain, first find the one event that starts the chain. This event is called the initiating event. Then, find the next event and continue until the outcome is reached, as shown in **Figure 4.**

Initiating Event

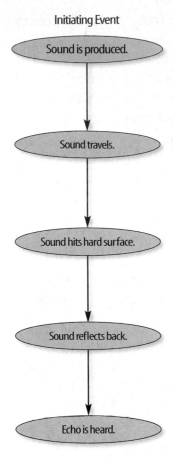

Figure 4 Events-chain concept maps show the order of steps in a process or event. This concept map shows how a sound makes an echo.

Cycle Map A specific type of events chain is a cycle map. It is used when the series of events do not produce a final outcome, but instead relate back to the beginning event, such as in **Figure 5.** Therefore, the cycle repeats itself.

To make a cycle map, first decide what event is the beginning event. This is also called the initiating event. Then list the next events in the order that they occur, with the last event relating back to the initiating event. Words can be written between the events that describe what happens from one event to the next. The number of events in a cycle map can vary, but usually contain three or more events.

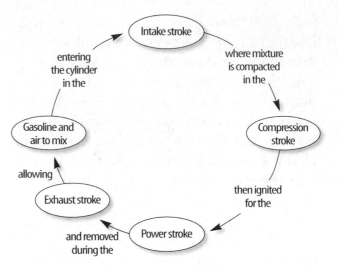

Figure 5 A cycle map shows events that occur in a cycle.

Spider Map A type of concept map that you can use for brainstorming is the spider map. When you have a central idea, you might find that you have a jumble of ideas that relate to it but are not necessarily clearly related to each other. The spider map on sound in **Figure 6** shows that if you write these ideas outside the main concept, then you can begin to separate and group unrelated terms so they become more useful.

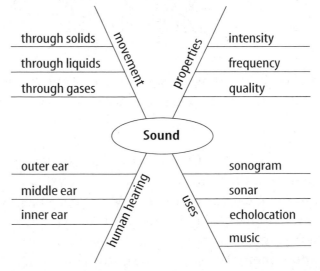

Figure 6 A spider map allows you to list ideas that relate to a central topic but not necessarily to one another.

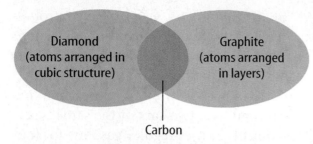

Figure 7 This Venn diagram compares and contrasts two substances made from carbon.

Venn Diagram To illustrate how two subjects compare and contrast you can use a Venn diagram. You can see the characteristics that the subjects have in common and those that they do not, shown in **Figure 7.**

To create a Venn diagram, draw two overlapping ovals that that are big enough to write in. List the characteristics unique to one subject in one oval, and the characteristics of the other subject in the other oval. The characteristics in common are listed in the overlapping section.

Make and Use Tables One way to organize information so it is easier to understand is to use a table. Tables can contain numbers, words, or both.

To make a table, list the items to be compared in the first column and the characteristics to be compared in the first row. The title should clearly indicate the content of the table, and the column or row heads should be clear. Notice that in **Table 1** the units are included.

Table 1 Recyclables Collected During Week			
Day of Week	**Paper (kg)**	**Aluminum (kg)**	**Glass (kg)**
Monday	5.0	4.0	12.0
Wednesday	4.0	1.0	10.0
Friday	2.5	2.0	10.0

Make a Model One way to help you better understand the parts of a structure, the way a process works, or to show things too large or small for viewing is to make a model. For example, an atomic model made of a plastic-ball nucleus and pipe-cleaner electron shells can help you visualize how the parts of an atom relate to each other. Other types of models can by devised on a computer or represented by equations.

Form a Hypothesis

A possible explanation based on previous knowledge and observations is called a hypothesis. After researching gasoline types and recalling previous experiences in your family's car you form a hypothesis—our car runs more efficiently because we use premium gasoline. To be valid, a hypothesis has to be something you can test by using an investigation.

Predict When you apply a hypothesis to a specific situation, you predict something about that situation. A prediction makes a statement in advance, based on prior observation, experience, or scientific reasoning. People use predictions to make everyday decisions. Scientists test predictions by performing investigations. Based on previous observations and experiences, you might form a prediction that cars are more efficient with premium gasoline. The prediction can be tested in an investigation.

Design an Experiment A scientist needs to make many decisions before beginning an investigation. Some of these include: how to carry out the investigation, what steps to follow, how to record the data, and how the investigation will answer the question. It also is important to address any safety concerns.

Test the Hypothesis

Now that you have formed your hypothesis, you need to test it. Using an investigation, you will make observations and collect data, or information. This data might either support or not support your hypothesis. Scientists collect and organize data as numbers and descriptions.

Follow a Procedure In order to know what materials to use, as well as how and in what order to use them, you must follow a procedure. **Figure 8** shows a procedure you might follow to test your hypothesis.

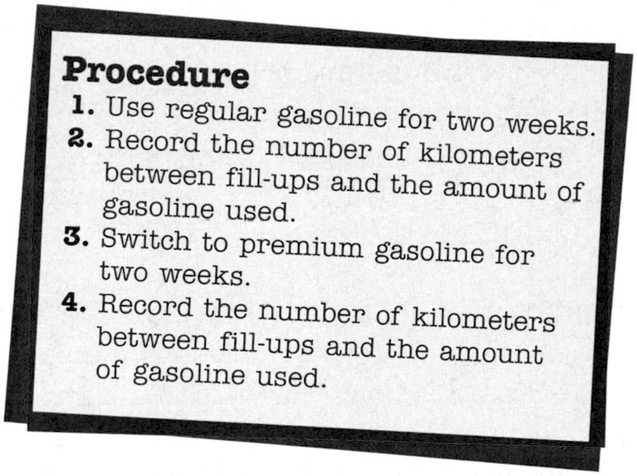

Procedure

1. Use regular gasoline for two weeks.
2. Record the number of kilometers between fill-ups and the amount of gasoline used.
3. Switch to premium gasoline for two weeks.
4. Record the number of kilometers between fill-ups and the amount of gasoline used.

Figure 8 A procedure tells you what to do step by step.

Identify and Manipulate Variables and Controls In any experiment, it is important to keep everything the same except for the item you are testing. The one factor you change is called the independent variable. The change that results is the dependent variable. Make sure you have only one independent variable, to assure yourself of the cause of the changes you observe in the dependent variable. For example, in your gasoline experiment the type of fuel is the independent variable. The dependent variable is the efficiency.

Many experiments also have a control—an individual instance or experimental subject for which the independent variable is not changed. You can then compare the test results to the control results. To design a control you can have two cars of the same type. The control car uses regular gasoline for four weeks. After you are done with the test, you can compare the experimental results to the control results.

Collect Data

Whether you are carrying out an investigation or a short observational experiment, you will collect data, as shown in **Figure 9.** Scientists collect data as numbers and descriptions and organize it in specific ways.

Observe Scientists observe items and events, then record what they see. When they use only words to describe an observation, it is called qualitative data. Scientists' observations also can describe how much there is of something. These observations use numbers, as well as words, in the description and are called quantitative data. For example, if a sample of the element gold is described as being "shiny and very dense" the data are qualitative. Quantitative data on this sample of gold might include "a mass of 30 g and a density of 19.3 g/cm^3."

Figure 9 Collecting data is one way to gather information directly.

Figure 10 Record data neatly and clearly so it is easy to understand.

When you make observations you should examine the entire object or situation first, and then look carefully for details. It is important to record observations accurately and completely. Always record your notes immediately as you make them, so you do not miss details or make a mistake when recording results from memory. Never put unidentified observations on scraps of paper. Instead they should be recorded in a notebook, like the one in **Figure 10.** Write your data neatly so you can easily read it later. At each point in the experiment, record your observations and label them. That way, you will not have to determine what the figures mean when you look at your notes later. Set up any tables that you will need to use ahead of time, so you can record any observations right away. Remember to avoid bias when collecting data by not including personal thoughts when you record observations. Record only what you observe.

Estimate Scientific work also involves estimating. To estimate is to make a judgment about the size or the number of something without measuring or counting. This is important when the number or size of an object or population is too large or too difficult to accurately count or measure.

Sample Scientists may use a sample or a portion of the total number as a type of estimation. To sample is to take a small, representative portion of the objects or organisms of a population for research. By making careful observations or manipulating variables within that portion of the group, information is discovered and conclusions are drawn that might apply to the whole population. A poorly chosen sample can be unrepresentative of the whole. If you were trying to determine the rainfall in an area, it would not be best to take a rainfall sample from under a tree.

Measure You use measurements everyday. Scientists also take measurements when collecting data. When taking measurements, it is important to know how to use measuring tools properly. Accuracy also is important.

Length To measure length, the distance between two points, scientists use meters. Smaller measurements might be measured in centimeters or millimeters.

Length is measured using a metric ruler or meter stick. When using a metric ruler, line up the 0-cm mark with the end of the object being measured and read the number of the unit where the object ends. Look at the metric ruler shown in **Figure 11.** The centimeter lines are the long, numbered lines, and the shorter lines are millimeter lines. In this instance, the length would be 4.50 cm.

Figure 11 This metric ruler has centimeter and millimeter divisions.

Mass The SI unit for mass is the kilogram (kg). Scientists can measure mass using units formed by adding metric prefixes to the unit gram (g), such as milligram (mg). To measure mass, you might use a triple-beam balance similar to the one shown in **Figure 12.** The balance has a pan on one side and a set of beams on the other side. Each beam has a rider that slides on the beam.

When using a triple-beam balance, place an object on the pan. Slide the largest rider along its beam until the pointer drops below zero. Then move it back one notch. Repeat the process for each rider proceeding from the larger to smaller until the pointer swings an equal distance above and below the zero point. Sum the masses on each beam to find the mass of the object. Move all riders back to zero when finished.

Instead of putting materials directly on the balance, scientists often take a tare of a container. A tare is the mass of a container into which objects or substances are placed for measuring their masses. To mass objects or substances, find the mass of a clean container. Remove the container from the pan, and place the object or substances in the container. Find the mass of the container with the materials in it. Subtract the mass of the empty container from the mass of the filled container to find the mass of the materials you are using.

Figure 12 A triple-beam balance is used to determine the mass of an object.

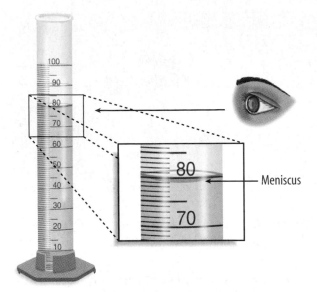

Figure 13 Graduated cylinders measure liquid volume.

Liquid Volume To measure liquids, the unit used is the liter. When a smaller unit is needed, scientists might use a milliliter. Because a milliliter takes up the volume of a cube measuring 1 cm on each side it also can be called a cubic centimeter (cm^3 = cm × cm × cm).

You can use beakers and graduated cylinders to measure liquid volume. A graduated cylinder, shown in **Figure 13,** is marked from bottom to top in milliliters. In lab, you might use a 10-mL graduated cylinder or a 100-mL graduated cylinder. When measuring liquids, notice that the liquid has a curved surface. Look at the surface at eye level, and measure the bottom of the curve. This is called the meniscus. The graduated cylinder in **Figure 13** contains 79.0 mL, or 79.0 cm^3, of a liquid.

Temperature Scientists often measure temperature using the Celsius scale. Pure water has a freezing point of 0°C and boiling point of 100°C. The unit of measurement is degrees Celsius. Two other scales often used are the Fahrenheit and Kelvin scales.

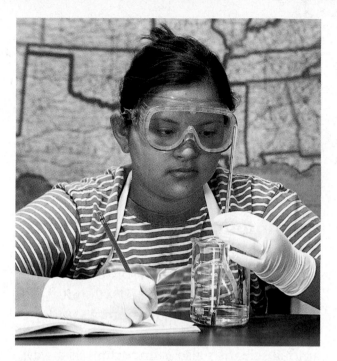

Figure 14 A thermometer measures the temperature of an object.

Scientists use a thermometer to measure temperature. Most thermometers in a laboratory are glass tubes with a bulb at the bottom end containing a liquid such as colored alcohol. The liquid rises or falls with a change in temperature. To read a glass thermometer like the thermometer in **Figure 14,** rotate it slowly until a red line appears. Read the temperature where the red line ends.

Form Operational Definitions An operational definition defines an object by how it functions, works, or behaves. For example, when you are playing hide and seek and a tree is home base, you have created an operational definition for a tree.

Objects can have more than one operational definition. For example, a ruler can be defined as a tool that measures the length of an object (how it is used). It can also be a tool with a series of marks used as a standard when measuring (how it works).

Analyze the Data

To determine the meaning of your observations and investigation results, you will need to look for patterns in the data. Then you must think critically to determine what the data mean. Scientists use several approaches when they analyze the data they have collected and recorded. Each approach is useful for identifying specific patterns.

Interpret Data The word *interpret* means "to explain the meaning of something." When analyzing data from an experiement, try to find out what the data show. Identify the control group and the test group to see whether or not changes in the independent variable have had an effect. Look for differences in the dependent variable between the control and test groups.

Classify Sorting objects or events into groups based on common features is called classifying. When classifying, first observe the objects or events to be classified. Then select one feature that is shared by some members in the group, but not by all. Place those members that share that feature in a subgroup. You can classify members into smaller and smaller subgroups based on characteristics. Remember that when you classify, you are grouping objects or events for a purpose. Keep your purpose in mind as you select the features to form groups and subgroups.

Compare and Contrast Observations can be analyzed by noting the similarities and differences between two more objects or events that you observe. When you look at objects or events to see how they are similar, you are comparing them. Contrasting is looking for differences in objects or events.

Recognize Cause and Effect A cause is a reason for an action or condition. The effect is that action or condition. When two events happen together, it is not necessarily true that one event caused the other. Scientists must design a controlled investigation to recognize the exact cause and effect.

Draw Conclusions

When scientists have analyzed the data they collected, they proceed to draw conclusions about the data. These conclusions are sometimes stated in words similar to the hypothesis that you formed earlier. They may confirm a hypothesis, or lead you to a new hypothesis.

Infer Scientists often make inferences based on their observations. An inference is an attempt to explain observations or to indicate a cause. An inference is not a fact, but a logical conclusion that needs further investigation. For example, you may infer that a fire has caused smoke. Until you investigate, however, you do not know for sure.

Apply When you draw a conclusion, you must apply those conclusions to determine whether the data supports the hypothesis. If your data do not support your hypothesis, it does not mean that the hypothesis is wrong. It means only that the result of the investigation did not support the hypothesis. Maybe the experiment needs to be redesigned, or some of the initial observations on which the hypothesis was based were incomplete or biased. Perhaps more observation or research is needed to refine your hypothesis. A successful investigation does not always come out the way you originally predicted.

Avoid Bias Sometimes a scientific investigation involves making judgments. When you make a judgment, you form an opinion. It is important to be honest and not to allow any expectations of results to bias your judgments. This is important throughout the entire investigation, from researching to collecting data to drawing conclusions.

Communicate

The communication of ideas is an important part of the work of scientists. A discovery that is not reported will not advance the scientific community's understanding or knowledge. Communication among scientists also is important as a way of improving their investigations.

Scientists communicate in many ways, from writing articles in journals and magazines that explain their investigations and experiments, to announcing important discoveries on television and radio. Scientists also share ideas with colleagues on the Internet or present them as lectures, like the student is doing in **Figure 15.**

Figure 15 A student communicates to his peers about his investigation.

SAFETY SYMBOLS		HAZARD	EXAMPLES	PRECAUTION	REMEDY
DISPOSAL		Special disposal procedures need to be followed.	certain chemicals, living organisms	Do not dispose of these materials in the sink or trash can.	Dispose of wastes as directed by your teacher.
BIOLOGICAL		Organisms or other biological materials that might be harmful to humans	bacteria, fungi, blood, unpreserved tissues, plant materials	Avoid skin contact with these materials. Wear mask or gloves.	Notify your teacher if you suspect contact with material. Wash hands thoroughly.
EXTREME TEMPERATURE		Objects that can burn skin by being too cold or too hot	boiling liquids, hot plates, dry ice, liquid nitrogen	Use proper protection when handling.	Go to your teacher for first aid.
SHARP OBJECT		Use of tools or glassware that can easily puncture or slice skin	razor blades, pins, scalpels, pointed tools, dissecting probes, broken glass	Practice common-sense behavior and follow guidelines for use of the tool.	Go to your teacher for first aid.
FUME		Possible danger to respiratory tract from fumes	ammonia, acetone, nail polish remover, heated sulfur, moth balls	Make sure there is good ventilation. Never smell fumes directly. Wear a mask.	Leave foul area and notify your teacher immediately.
ELECTRICAL		Possible danger from electrical shock or burn	improper grounding, liquid spills, short circuits, exposed wires	Double-check setup with teacher. Check condition of wires and apparatus.	Do not attempt to fix electrical problems. Notify your teacher immediately.
IRRITANT		Substances that can irritate the skin or mucous membranes of the respiratory tract	pollen, moth balls, steel wool, fiberglass, potassium permanganate	Wear dust mask and gloves. Practice extra care when handling these materials.	Go to your teacher for first aid.
CHEMICAL		Chemicals can react with and destroy tissue and other materials	bleaches such as hydrogen peroxide; acids such as sulfuric acid, hydrochloric acid; bases such as ammonia, sodium hydroxide	Wear goggles, gloves, and an apron.	Immediately flush the affected area with water and notify your teacher.
TOXIC		Substance may be poisonous if touched, inhaled, or swallowed.	mercury, many metal compounds, iodine, poinsettia plant parts	Follow your teacher's instructions.	Always wash hands thoroughly after use. Go to your teacher for first aid.
FLAMMABLE		Flammable chemicals may be ignited by open flame, spark, or exposed heat.	alcohol, kerosene, potassium permanganate	Avoid open flames and heat when using flammable chemicals.	Notify your teacher immediately. Use fire safety equipment if applicable.
OPEN FLAME		Open flame in use, may cause fire.	hair, clothing, paper, synthetic materials	Tie back hair and loose clothing. Follow teacher's instruction on lighting and extinguishing flames.	Notify your teacher immediately. Use fire safety equipment if applicable.

 Eye Safety
Proper eye protection should be worn at all times by anyone performing or observing science activities.

 Clothing Protection
This symbol appears when substances could stain or burn clothing.

 Animal Safety
This symbol appears when safety of animals and students must be ensured.

 Handwashing
After the lab, wash hands with soap and water before removing goggles.

Safety in the Science Laboratory

The science laboratory is a safe place to work if you follow standard safety procedures. Being responsible for your own safety helps to make the entire laboratory a safer place for everyone. When performing any lab, read and apply the caution statements and safety symbol listed at the beginning of the lab.

General Safety Rules

1. Obtain your teacher's permission to begin all investigations and use laboratory equipment.

2. Study the procedure. Ask your teacher any questions. Be sure you understand safety symbols shown on the page.

3. Notify your teacher about allergies or other health conditions which can affect your participation in a lab.

4. Learn and follow use and safety procedures for your equipment. If unsure, ask your teacher.

5. Never eat, drink, chew gum, apply cosmetics, or do any personal grooming in the lab. Never use lab glassware as food or drink containers. Keep your hands away from your face and mouth.

6. Know the location and proper use of the safety shower, eye wash, fire blanket, and fire alarm.

Prevent Accidents

1. Use the safety equipment provided to you. Goggles and a safety apron should be worn during investigations.

2. Do NOT use hair spray, mousse, or other flammable hair products. Tie back long hair and tie down loose clothing.

3. Do NOT wear sandals or other open-toed shoes in the lab.

4. Remove jewelry on hands and wrists. Loose jewelry, such as chains and long necklaces, should be removed to prevent them from getting caught in equipment.

5. Do not taste any substances or draw any material into a tube with your mouth.

6. Proper behavior is expected in the lab. Practical jokes and fooling around can lead to accidents and injury.

7. Keep your work area uncluttered.

Laboratory Work

1. Collect and carry all equipment and materials to your work area before beginning a lab.

2. Remain in your own work area unless given permission by your teacher to leave it.

3. Always slant test tubes away from yourself and others when heating them, adding substances to them, or rinsing them.

4. If instructed to smell a substance in a container, hold the container a short distance away and fan vapors towards your nose.

5. Do NOT substitute other chemicals/substances for those in the materials list unless instructed to do so by your teacher.

6. Do NOT take any materials or chemicals outside of the laboratory.

7. Stay out of storage areas unless instructed to be there and supervised by your teacher.

Laboratory Cleanup

1. Turn off all burners, water, and gas, and disconnect all electrical devices.

2. Clean all pieces of equipment and return all materials to their proper places.

3. Dispose of chemicals and other materials as directed by your teacher. Place broken glass and solid substances in the proper containers. Never discard materials in the sink.

4. Clean your work area.

5. Wash your hands with soap and water thoroughly BEFORE removing your goggles.

Emergencies

1. Report any fire, electrical shock, glassware breakage, spill, or injury, no matter how small, to your teacher immediately. Follow his or her instructions.

2. If your clothing should catch fire, STOP, DROP, and ROLL. If possible, smother it with the fire blanket or get under a safety shower. NEVER RUN.

3. If a fire should occur, turn off all gas and leave the room according to established procedures.

4. In most instances, your teacher will clean up spills. Do NOT attempt to clean up spills unless you are given permission and instructions to do so.

5. If chemicals come into contact with your eyes or skin, notify your teacher immediately. Use the eyewash or flush your skin or eyes with large quantities of water.

6. The fire extinguisher and first-aid kit should only be used by your teacher unless it is an extreme emergency and you have been given permission.

7. If someone is injured or becomes ill, only a professional medical provider or someone certified in first aid should perform first-aid procedures.

① Testing Horoscopes

Time Required 45 minutes

Materials
- Horoscopes can be found in many magazines and newspapers.
- Students can white out zodiac signs and birth dates with correction fluid, but caution them to be thorough to prevent cheating.

Safety Precaution
Students should not interview strangers.

Teaching Strategies
- Encourage students to collect a large sample of data to ensure accurate results.
- Challenge students to establish experimental controls that prevent cheating.

Conclude and Apply
1. Answers will vary but should be about 8 percent.
2. 8.3%

Extra Try at Home Labs

EXTRA Labs

From Your Kitchen, Junk Drawer, or Yard

① Testing Horoscopes

Real-World Question
How can horoscopes be tested scientifically?

Possible Materials
- horoscope from previous week
- scissors
- transparent tape
- white paper
- correction fluid

Procedure
1. Obtain a horoscope from last week and cut out the predictions for each sign. Do not cut out the zodiac signs or birth dates accompanying each prediction.
2. As you cut out a horoscope prediction, write the correct zodiac sign on the back of each prediction.
3. Develop a code for the predictions to allow you to identify them. Keep your code list in your Science Journal.
4. Scramble your predictions and tape them to a sheet of white paper. Write each prediction's code above it.
5. Ask your friends and family members to read all the predictions and choose the one that best matched their life events from the previous week. Interview at least 20 people.

Conclude and Apply
1. Calculate the percentage of people who chose the correct sign.
2. Calculate the chances of a person choosing their correct sign randomly.

② Disappearing Water?

Real-World Question
How much difference does the type of measuring equipment make?

Possible Materials
- scale
- water
- measuring cups of different sizes
- measuring spoons (1 tsp = 5 mL, 1 tbsp = 15 mL)

Procedure
1. Measure out 83 mL of water using one of the measuring devices. Transfer this amount of water to the other measuring devices.
2. Record the readings for each measuring device for the same amount of water. Do they all give the same reading, or does it seem like the amount of water changed?
3. Remember, 1 mL of water weighs 1 g. Use the scale to find out what the true amount of water is in the container.
4. Repeat steps 1–3 for different amounts of water. Try 50 mL, 128 mL, and 12 mL.

Conclude and Apply
1. Which measuring device was the most accurate? The least?
2. Which measuring device was the most precise? The least?
3. What problem came up when you had to use the small devices several times to get up to a larger amount of water?

Adult supervision required for all labs.

These labs are available at ips.msscience.com.

② Disappearing Water?

Time Required one class period

Materials Use graduated cylinders and beakers of various sizes if available.

Teaching Strategy Encourage students to try measuring first with the large glassware, and transferring it down to smaller glassware, and then to try measuring first with the smaller glassware and transferring up to larger glassware. They should notice right away that the smaller glassware gives more precise readings.

Conclude and Apply
1. The smallest measuring spoon should be the most accurate and the largest measuring cup the least. This may vary depending on the quality of glassware available.
2. The smallest measuring spoon should be the most precise and the largest measuring cup the least. This may vary depending on the quality of glassware available.
3. reader error

❸ Comparing Atom Sizes

❶ Real-World Question
How do the sizes of different types of atoms compare?

Possible Materials
- metric ruler or meterstick
- 1-m length of white paper
- transparent or masking tape
- colored pencils

❷ Procedure
1. Tape a 1-m sheet of paper on the floor.
2. Use a scale of 1 mm: 1 picometer for measuring and drawing the relative diameters of all the atoms.
3. Study the chart of atomic sizes.
4. Use your scale to measure the relative size of a hydrogen atom on the sheet of paper. Use a red pencil to draw the relative diameter of a hydrogen atom on your paper.

5. Use your scale to measure the relative sizes of an oxygen atom, iron atom, gold atom, and francium atom. Use four other colored pencils to draw the relative diameters of these atoms on the paper.
6. Compare the relative sizes of these different atoms.

Atomic Sizes (picometers)	
Element	Diameter
Hydrogen	50
Oxygen	146
Iron	248
Gold	288
Francium	540

❸ Conclude and Apply
1. Research the length of a picometer.
2. Using your scale, list the diameters of the atoms that you drew on your paper.

❸ Comparing Atom Sizes

Time Required 25 minutes

Safety Precaution Caution students to handle the metersticks with care.

Teaching Strategies
- Instruct students to start measuring the relative diameters at one end of the paper.
- If necessary, remind students that these measurements are relative diameters not the actual diameters of atoms.

Conclude and Apply
1. 1×10^{-12} m
2. hydrogen: 7.4 cm; oxygen: 14.6 cm; iron: 24.8 cm; gold: 28.8 cm; and francium: 54.0 cm

❹ Microscopic Crystals

❶ Real-World Question
What do crystalline and non-crystalline solids look like under a magnifying lens?

Possible Materials
- salt or sugar
- pepper
- magnifying lens
- paper
- bowl
- spoon
- measuring cup

❷ Procedure
1. Pour 10 mL of salt into a bowl and grind the salt into small, powdery pieces with the back of the spoon.
2. Sprinkle a few grains of salt from the bowl onto a piece of paper and view the salt grains with the magnifying lens.
3. Clean out the bowl.
4. Pour 10 mL of pepper into the bowl and grind it into powder with the spoon.
5. Sprinkle a few grains of pepper from the bowl onto the paper and view the grains with the magnifying lens.

❸ Conclude and Apply
1. Compare the difference between the salt and pepper grains under the magnifying lens.
2. Describe what a crystal is.

Adult supervision required for all labs.

EXTRA TRY AT HOME LABS 683

Time Required 20 minutes

Materials Students can also view sugar crystals under the magnifying lens. The crystals will be seen more clearly under lower powers of magnification.

Safety Precaution Caution students not to eat or drink anything in science class.

Teaching Strategy Have students view crystals of different sizes under the microscope to observe the consistency of their crystalline structure.

❹ Microscopic Crystals

Conclude and Apply
1. Salt grains will be cube-shaped crystals. The pepper grains will have an irregular, non-repeating structure.
2. A crystal is a solid with its particles arranged in a repeating, three-dimensional pattern.

5 Colorful Liquids

Time Required 30 minutes

Materials Students can also experiment with different shampoos.

Safety Precaution Caution students not to eat or drink anything during science class.

Teaching Strategies
- Make a demonstration for this lab using a 2,000-mL graduated cylinder.
- Explain that the drops of food coloring do not burst in the oil because the dye (which is made of water) is not soluble with oil. Once the drops break through the surface tension between the oil and water, they will dissolve in the water. If time allows, let students watch this happen.

Conclude and Apply
1. Being denser than oil, the drops fell through the oil and sat at the bottom of the oil layer. Once the drops broke through the oil-water boundary, they burst and dissolved in the water layer.
2. The syrup, alcohol, and water would dissolve into each other and form one layer. The oil would form a top layer.

5 Colorful Liquids

Real-World Question
How can the property of density be used to make a rainbow of liquids?

Possible Materials
- measuring cups (2)
- maple syrup or corn syrup
- water
- cooking oil
- food coloring
- rubbing alcohol

Procedure
1. Pour 25 mL of syrup into one measuring cup.
2. Slowly pour 25 mL of water down the sides of the same measuring cup so that the water sits on top of the syrup.
3. Slowly pour 25 mL of cooking oil down the sides of the same measuring cup so that the oil sits on top of the water.
4. Put several drops of blue food coloring into the oil and observe them for 5 minutes.
5. Slowly pour 25 mL of rubbing alcohol down the sides of the same measuring cup so that the alcohol sits on top of the oil.
6. Put several drops of red food coloring into the alcohol.

Conclude and Apply
1. Describe what happened to the drops of blue food coloring.
2. Infer what would happen if you poured the liquids into the cylinder in the reverse order.

6 Human Bonding

Real-World Question
How can humans model atoms bonding together?

Possible Materials
- family members or friends
- sheets of blank paper
- markers
- large safety pins
- large colored rubber bands

Procedure
1. Draw a large electron dot diagram of an element you choose. Have other activity participants do that too.
2. Pin the diagram to your shirt.
3. How many electrons does your element have? Gather that many rubber bands.
4. Place about half of the rubber bands on one wrist and half on the other.
5. Form bonds by finding someone who has the number of rubber bands you need to total eight. Try to form as many different compounds with different elements as you can. (You may need two or three of another element's atoms to make a compound.) Record the compounds you make in your Science Journal. Label each compound as ionic or covalent.

Conclude and Apply
1. Which elements don't form any bonds?
2. Which elements form four bonds?

These labs are available at ips.msscience.com.

6 Human Bonding

Time Required one class period

Safety Precaution Use a large open space, and remove any obstacle that could cause injury.

Teaching Strategies
- To avoid having students feel left out, do not assign the noble gases. Be one of the noble gases yourself. Assign extra halogens.
- Try to assign carbon and silicon to especially flexible students.

Conclude and Apply
1. the noble gases
2. carbon and silicon

⑦ Mini Fireworks

Real-World Question
Where do the colors in fireworks come from?

Possible Materials 🔥 🔲 🥽 🧤 ⚠️
- candle
- lighter
- wooden chopsticks (or a fork or tongs)
- penny
- water in an old cup
- steel wool

Procedure
1. Light the candle.
2. Use the chopsticks to get a firm grip on the penny.
3. Hold the penny in the flame until you observe a change. *(Hint: this experiment is more fun in the bathroom with the lights off!)*
4. Drop the penny in the water when you are finished and plunge the burning end of the chopsticks or hot part of the fork into the water as well.
5. Repeat the procedure using steel wool.

Conclude and Apply
1. What color did you see?
2. Infer why copper and iron are used in fireworks.
3. Research what other elements are used in fireworks.

⑧ A Good Mix?

Real-World Question
What liquids will dissolve in water?

Possible Materials 🥽 🧤 ⚠️
- cooking oil
- water
- apple or grape juice
- rubbing alcohol
- spoon
- glass
- measuring cup

Procedure
1. Pour 100 mL of water into a large glass.
2. Pour 100 mL of apple juice into the glass and stir the water and juice together. Observe your mixture to determine whether juice is soluble in water.
3. Empty and rinse out your glass.
4. Pour 100 mL of water and 100 mL of cooking oil into the glass and stir them together. Observe your mixture to determine whether oil is soluble in water.
5. Empty and rinse out your glass.
6. Pour 100 mL of water and 100 mL of rubbing alcohol into the glass and stir them together. Observe your mixture to determine whether alcohol is soluble in water.

Conclude and Apply
1. List the liquid(s) that are soluble in water.
2. List the liquid(s) that are not soluble in water.
3. Infer why some liquids are soluble in water and others are not.

Adult supervision required for all labs.

---

⑦ Mini Fireworks

Time Required 15 minutes

Materials The chopsticks will be unusable after this lab. The cup also may be damaged.

Safety Precaution Clear away all flammable materials from the experiment area.

Teaching Strategy If students cannot keep a firm grip on the penny with the chopsticks, wire or tape them together while away from the flame.

Conclude and Apply
1. copper—green, iron—red
2. because they make attractive colors
3. cobalt, vanadium, chlorine, nickel, and more

⑧ A Good Mix?

Time Required 20 minutes

Materials
- Orange, grapefruit, tomato, and other juices will also dissolve in water.
- Olive, peanut, and other oils are also insoluble in water.
- Students can also test various types of sodas, which are soluble in water.
- Students will need dish soap to rinse the oil from beakers.

Safety Precaution Warn students not to drink anything during science lab.

Teaching Strategy Students can complete this lab at home by using equal volumes of water and each liquid.

Conclude and Apply
1. juices and rubbing alcohol
2. cooking oil
3. Like dissolves like. Water, juices, and alcohols are all polar, but oils are nonpolar.

Liquid Lab

Time Required 45 minutes

Materials 70% isopropyl alcohol can be used for this lab.

Teaching Strategies
- Explain to the class that rubbing alcohol is also called isopropyl alcohol.
- Liquids with a low viscosity will pour quickly.

Physical Properties

	Water	Rubbing Alcohol
Color	Clear	Clear
Odor	None	Strong
Viscosity	Low	Low
Density	> Ice	< Ice
Solubility with Oil	No	No

Conclude and Apply
1. Both are clear in color, have a low viscosity, and will not mix with oil. Alcohol has a strong odor and is less dense than ice. Water has no odor and has a density greater than ice.
2. The liquids would dissolve into each other.

Liquid Lab

Real-World Question
How do the properties of water and rubbing alcohol compare?

Possible Materials
- water
- rubbing alcohol
- vegetable oil
- glasses (2)
- ice cubes (2)
- measuring cup
- spoon

Procedure
1. Copy the Physical Properties chart into your Science Journal.
2. Slowly pour 200 mL of water into one glass and observe the viscosity of water. Slowly pour 200 mL of rubbing alcohol into a second glass and observe the viscosity of rubbing alcohol. Record your observations in your chart.
3. Observe the color and odor of both liquids and record your observations in your chart.

Physical Properties

	Water	Rubbing Alcohol
Color		
Odor		
Viscosity		
Density		
Solubility with oil		

4. Drop an ice cube into each glass. Comment on the density of each liquid in your chart.
5. Pour 50 mL of vegetable oil into each glass and stir. Record your observations in your chart.

Conclude and Apply
1. Compare the properties of water and isopropyl alcohol.
2. Infer what would happen if water and isopropyl alcohol were mixed together.

Measuring Momentum

Real-World Question
How much momentum do rolling balls have?

Possible Materials
- meterstick
- orange cones or tape
- scale
- stopwatch
- bucket
- bowling ball
- plastic baseball
- golf ball
- tennis ball
- calculator

Procedure
1. Use a balance to measure the masses of the tennis ball, golf ball, and plastic baseball. Convert their masses from grams to kilograms.
2. Find the weight of the bowling ball in pounds. The weight should be written on the ball. Divide the ball's weight by 2.2 to calculate its mass in kilograms.
3. Go outside and measure a 10-m distance on a blacktop or concrete surface. Mark the distance with orange cones or tape.
4. Have a partner roll each ball the 10-m distance. Measure the time it takes each ball to roll 10 m.
5. Use the formula: velocity $= \frac{\text{distance}}{\text{time}}$ to calculate each ball's velocity.

Conclude and Apply
1. Calculate the momentum of each ball.
2. Infer why the momentums of the balls differed so greatly.

Adult supervision required for all labs.

These labs are available at ips.mssience.com.

Measuring Momentum

Time Required 40 minutes

Materials
- Students can transport the bowling balls in heavy-duty 5-gallon construction buckets.
- You might have to help students find the weights of the bowling balls.

Safety Precautions
- Caution students not to throw or drop the bowling balls.
- Students should use the metersticks with care.

Teaching Strategies
- Students should roll each ball so that it does not bounce.
- Instruct students to use the formula: momentum = mass × velocity to calculate each ball's momentum.

Conclude and Apply
1. Answers will vary, but all answers should have the units kg m/s.
2. The masses of balls varied greatly.

11 Friction in Traffic

◉ Real-World Question

How do the various kinds of friction affect the operation of vehicles?

Possible Materials

- erasers taken from the ends of pencils (4)
- needles (2)
- small match box
- toy car

◉ Procedure

1. Build a match box car with the materials listed, or use a toy car.
2. Invent ways to demonstrate the effects of static friction, sliding friction, and rolling friction on the car. Think of hills, ice or rain conditions, graveled roads and paved roads, etc.
3. Make drawings of how friction is acting on the car, or how the car uses friction to work.

◉ Conclude and Apply

1. In what ways are static, sliding, and rolling friction helpful to drivers?
2. In what ways are static, sliding, and rolling friction unfavorable to car safety and operation?
3. Explain what your experiment taught you about driving in icy conditions.

12 Submersible Egg

◉ Real-World Question

How can you make an egg float and sink again?

Possible Materials

- egg
- 10 mL (2 teaspoons) of salt
- measuring spoons
- water
- glass (250–300 mL)
- spoon
- marking pen

◉ Procedure

1. Put 150 mL of water in the glass.
2. Gently use a marking pen to write an X on one side of the egg.
3. Put the egg in the glass. Record your observations.
4. Use the spoon to remove the egg. Add 1 mL (1/4 teaspoon) of salt and swirl or stir to dissolve. Put the egg back in. Record your observations.
5. Repeat step 4 until you have used all the salt. Remember to make observations at each step.

◉ Conclude and Apply

1. How could you resink the egg? Try your idea. Did it work?
2. The egg always floats with the same point or side down. Why do you think this is?
3. How does your answer to question 2 relate to real-world applications?

---

11 Friction in Traffic

Time Required one to one-and-a-half hours, including building the car

Materials

- You will need to make ice the night before.
- For an icy hill, you could use a cookie sheet full of ice, soap, or a sprinkling of cornstarch. Use books to elevate it.
- Students could make a heavier truck by using two match boxes and filling the boxes with small stones.

Teaching Strategies

- Introduce how to draw force diagrams. Combining this lab with force drawings can help students understand the types of friction.
- You can introduce the idea that heavier objects are acted upon more by forces.

Conclude and Apply

1. Static friction helps a car park on a hill. Sliding friction helps it stop by braking. Rolling friction is necessary for the wheels to move. Other answers are possible.
2. The engine needs to work hard to overcome static friction. If there's not enough sliding friction, cars crash (like on wet and/or icy roads). Too much of all three kinds of friction decrease fuel economy. Other answers are possible.
3. Answers will vary.

---

12 Submersible Egg

Time Required one class period

Safety Precaution Make sure students wash their hands after handling the egg.

Teaching Strategies

- You may tell students to begin with 4 mL of salt to speed up the process.
- The egg begins to rise between 6 and 7 mL of salt. If students are careful around this point, they may see the egg hover halfway.

Conclude and Apply

1. Add more water. If students add the water slowly, they will be able to see the egg slowly sink down and hover halfway on the way to the bottom.
2. There is an air sac in the egg. It is lighter than the rest of the egg, so that side of the egg (usually the wide end) always rises to the top.
3. Answers will vary. One answer is that a submarine has compressed gas that is used to fill air chambers to get the sub to the surface.

The Heat is On

Time Required ten minutes

Materials
- Use an incandescent, not fluorescent, lightbulb.
- The lightbulbs should not be turned on before the lab.
- Black cloth can be used instead of the paper.

Safety Precaution
Warn students never to touch a lightbulb even if it is not lit.

Teaching Strategies
- Have students lay the sheet of paper in direct sunlight first, complete the other parts of the lab, and then return to the paper after ten minutes.
- Extend the lab by using thermometers.

Conclude and Apply
1. solar energy to heat energy
2. kinetic energy (energy of motion) to heat energy
3. electrical energy to heat energy

The Heat is On

Real-World Question
How can different types of energy be transformed into thermal energy?

Possible Materials
- lamp
- incandescent light bulb
- black construction paper or cloth

Procedure
1. Feel the temperature of a black sheet of paper. Lay the paper in direct sunlight, wait 10 min, and observe how it feels.
2. Rub the palms of your hands together quickly for 10 s and observe how they feel.
3. Switch on a lamp that has a bare light bulb. *Without touching the lightbulb,* cup your hand 2 cm above the bulb for 30 s and observe what you feel.

Conclude and Apply
1. Infer the type of energy transformation that happened on the paper.
2. Infer the type of energy transformation that happened between the palms of your hands.
3. Infer the type of energy transformation that happened to the lightbulb.

Simple Machines

Real-World Question
What types of simple machines are found in a toolbox?

Possible Materials
- box of tools

Procedure
1. Obtain a box of tools and lay all the tools and other hardware from the box on a table.
2. Carefully examine all the tools and hardware, and separate all the items that are a type of inclined plane.
3. Carefully examine all the tools and hardware, and separate all the items that are a type of lever.
4. Identify and separate all the items that are a wheel and axle.
5. Identify any pulleys in the toolbox.
6. Identify any tools that are a combination of two or more simple machines.

Conclude and Apply
1. List all the tools you found that were a type of inclined plane, lever, wheel and axle, or pulley.
2. List all the tools that were a combination of two or more simple machines.
3. Infer how a hammer could be used as both a first class lever and a third class lever.

Adult supervision required for all labs.

These labs are available at ips.msscience.com.

Simple Machines

Time Required 40 minutes

Safety Precaution Caution students to handle sharp tools with care.

Teaching Strategy To help students match each tool with a type of simple machine, instruct them to think about how each is used.

Conclude and Apply
1. Answers will vary. Wedge (inclined plane): utility knife, putty knife, doorstop, nail. Screw (inclined plane): screw, flashlight top, clamp, nut and bolt. Lever: hammer, pliers, wrench. Wheel and axle: clamp, faucet, doorknob, screwdriver. Pulley: window blind pulley.
2. Answers will vary. A clamp is a combination of a screw and wheel and axle. A wrench is screw, wheel and axle, and a lever.
3. A hammer is a first class lever when its claw is used to remove a nail and a third class lever when using it to hammer a nail.

15 Estimate Temperature

▶ Real-World Question
How can we learn to estimate temperatures?

Possible Materials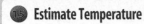
- thermometer
- water
- bowl
- ice

▶ Procedure
1. If you have a dual-scale weather thermometer, you can learn twice as much by trying to do your estimation in degrees Fahrenheit and Celsius each time.
2. Fill a bowl with ice water. Submerge your fingers in the water and estimate the water temperature.
3. Place the thermometer in the bowl and observe the temperature.
4. Place a bowl of warm water in direct sunlight for 20 min. Submerge your fingers in the water and estimate the water temperature.
5. Place the thermometer in the bowl and observe the temperature.
6. Place the thermometer outside in a location where you can see it each day.
7. Each day for a month, step outside and estimate the temperature. Check the accuracy of your estimates with the thermometer. Record the weather conditions as well.

▶ Conclude and Apply
1. Describe how well you can estimate air temperatures after estimating the temperature each day for a month. Did the cloudiness of the day affect your estimation skills?
2. Infer why understanding the Celsius scale might be helpful to you in the future.

16 Exploding Bag

▶ Real-World Question
What happens when a bag pops?

Possible Materials
- paper bag or plastic produce bag

▶ Procedure
1. Obtain a paper lunch bag. Smooth out the bag on a flat surface if it has any wrinkles.
2. Hold the neck of the bag and blow air into it until it is completely filled. The sides of the bag should be stretched out completely.
3. Twist the neck of the bag tightly to prevent air from escaping.
4. Pop the paper bag between your palms and observe what happens.
5. Examine the bag after you pop it. Observe any changes in the bag.

▶ Conclude and Apply
1. Describe what happened when you popped the bag.
2. Infer why this happened to the bag.

Adult supervision required for all labs.

Extra Try at Home Labs

15 Estimate Temperature

Time Required 20 minutes set up time, plus three minutes to observe and record each day for a month

Materials Encourage students to estimate air temperature before they observe temperatures on display.

Safety Precautions
- Caution students not to touch the glass of a broken thermometer.
- Use nonmercury thermometers.

Teaching Strategy It is easier for students to learn the Celsius scale by experiencing and comparing temperatures to the scale (Fahrenheit) they probably already know. If most students do not have dual scale thermometers at home, you can set one up outside the school and have students check it as they come to school each day.

Conclude and Apply
1. Answers will vary.
2. Students will use the Celsius scale during future science classes, science careers, and travel to other countries.

16 Exploding Bag

Time Required five minutes

Materials Paper lunchbags or thin plastic produce bags work well.

Safety Precaution Caution the students not to pop the bags near other people.

Teaching Strategy Instruct students that the bags must be fully inflated, and they must pop the bags quickly to produce a loud sound.

Conclude and Apply
1. If done correctly, a loud popping sound escaped the bag as the bag tore open.
2. Compressed air in the bag created a force that split the bag allowing compressional sound waves to escape.

Seeing Sound

Time Required 15 minutes

Materials A stringed musical instrument could be used in place of the rubber-band bow.

Safety Precaution Use caution with scissors and rubber bands.

Teaching Strategy The hanging kernels of puffed rice closest to the vibrating string or rubber band will move the most, but none will make large movements. The movement will die off quickly. The test should be done with the string vibrating in different directions relative to the puffed rice to find a vibration direction that creates the largest visible effect.

Conclude and Apply

1. When the rubber band is plucked and it makes a sound, the kernels of puffed rice vibrate back and forth with the sound. This means that the rubber band is making the air vibrate and the air is making the puffed rice vibrate. Kernels farthest away from the rubber band vibrate the least, which shows that the sound compression waves become weaker as they travel farther from the rubber band.

Seeing Sound

Real-World Question
Is it possible to see sound waves?

Possible Materials
- scissors
- rubber band
- twigs, curved and stiff
- sewing thread
- puffed-rice cereal
- clothing hanger

Procedure
1. Make a rubber-band bow as follows: Cut the rubber band at one point. Tie the rubber band around opposite ends of the twig so that it looks like an archery bow. Make sure the rubber band is tight like a guitar string.
2. Cut about 10 pieces of thread to equal lengths, 10 to 15 cm long.
3. With each piece of thread, tie one end around a kernel of puffed rice and the other end around the bottom of a clothing hanger. Space the hanging kernels about 1 cm apart.
4. Hook the clothing hanger over something so that the threads and cereal hang freely.
5. Hold the rubber-band bow so that the rubber band is just underneath the central hanging kernels. Pluck the rubber band, being careful not to touch the kernels. Write down your observations.

Conclude and Apply
1. Explain how this experiment relates to the fact that sound travels through air using compression waves.

Black Light

Real-World Question
How do you know that ultraviolet waves exist?

Possible Materials
- normal lamp with a white lightbulb
- ultraviolet light source (a black light)
- white paper
- laundry detergent
- glow-in-the-dark plastic toy
- a variety of rocks and minerals
- a variety of flowers and plants
- a variety of household cleaners
- different colors and materials of clothing

Procedure
1. Dab a small amount of laundry detergent on some white paper and place it somewhere to dry.
2. Place the black light in a dark room and turn it on.
3. Write down what the detergent looks like under a normal lamp. Then, place the paper under the black light. Write down what you see.
4. Place other items under the different lights and write down what you see.

Conclude and Apply
1. Describe the difference between the way things look under normal light and the way they look under ultraviolet light.
2. Explain how you know from this experiment that ultraviolet waves exist.

Adult supervision required for all labs.

These labs are available at ips.msscience.com.

Black Light

Time Required 15 minutes

Materials Some students have black lights at home.

Safety Precautions
- Rinse immediately if a cleaner gets on skin.
- Caution students not to look directly at the black light.

Teaching Strategy Have the students keep a lab record and research how things absorb ultraviolet light and emit visible light.

Conclude and Apply
1. Things look normal under white light. Under black light, some things glow different colors or do not glow.
2. Materials respond the same to normal light, but not all glow under black light. There is a type of electromagnetic wave coming from the black light. The black light is an ultraviolet wave source.

⑲ Light in Liquids

❓ Real-World Question

What happens to light when it passes through different liquids found in your kitchen?

Possible Materials 🔲 📺 📃

- flashlight
- glass
- orange juice
- water
- milk
- maple syrup
- white vinegar
- red vinegar
- honey
- molasses
- milk
- fruit juice
- powdered drink mix
- salad dressing
- salsa

⚙ Procedure

1. Fill a glass with water and darken the room. Shine the beam of a flashlight through the glass and observe how much of the light passes through the water.
2. Identify water as an opaque, translucent, or transparent substance.

3. Repeat steps 1–2 to test a wide variety of other liquids found in your kitchen. Use the original containers when you can, but remove any labels from containers that block the light beam.

❓ Conclude and Apply

1. Identify all the opaque liquids you tested.
2. Identify all the translucent liquids you tested.
3. Identify all the transparent liquids you tested.

⑳ Bending Water

❓ Real-World Question

How can a plastic rod bend water without touching it?

Possible Materials 🔲 📃

- plastic rod
- plastic clothes hanger
- 100% wool clothing
- water faucet

⚙ Procedure

1. Turn on a faucet until a narrow, smooth stream of water is flowing out of it. The stream of water cannot be too wide, and it cannot flow in a broken pattern.

2. Vigorously rub a plastic rod on a piece of 100% wool clothing for about 15 s.
3. Immediately hold the rod near the center of the stream of water. Move the rod close to the stream. Do not touch the water.
4. Observe what happens to the water.

❓ Conclude and Apply

1. Describe how the plastic rod affected the stream of water.
2. Explain why the plastic rod affected the water.

Extra Try at Home Labs *(side tab)*

⑲ Light in Liquids

Time Required 30 minutes

Materials

- A flashlight with a narrow beam works best for this lab.
- If you are using the original containers, remove the labels from them.
- Only glass or very clear plastic containers will work for this lab.

Safety Precautions

- Caution students never to eat or drink anything during science class.
- Caution students not to shine a flashlight beam into anyone's eyes.
- Caution students to handle the glass containers carefully and to never touch broken glass.

Teaching Strategy For an in-class lab, students can fill large test tubes with test liquids and focus a narrow beam of light from a small, pocket flashlight through the liquids.

Conclude and Apply

1. Answers will vary but may include orange juice, molasses, salsa, and many salad dressings.
2. Answers will vary but may include milk, red vinegar, maple syrup, and honey.
3. Answers will vary but may include water, white vinegar, drink mix, and apple juice.

⑳ Bending Water

Time Required ten minutes

Materials

- Smooth plastic coat hangers and rubber rods also work well for this lab.
- Be certain students use 100% wool fabric. Wool mixed with other fabrics will not work as well.

Teaching Strategies

- Instruct students to completely fold the wool fabric over the plastic rod before rubbing it.
- To see the water bending, students should look at the bottom portion of the water stream as the rod approaches it.

Conclude and Apply

1. The stream of water will bend and move toward the rod.
2. The rod becomes negatively charged from the wool fabric and attracts the positive ends of the water molecules, causing the stream to bend.

Testing Magnets

Time Required 15 minutes

Materials Students should use metric rulers with edges that begin with zero centimeters.

Safety Precaution Caution students to handle the pins with care.

Teaching Strategies
- Review with students that each centimeter equals ten millimeters.
- Each student should hold the rulers so that magnets are against the edge of the ruler but still directly over the pin.

Conclude and Apply
1. Answers will vary, but weak kitchen magnets need to be 1–4 mm away from the pin. Stronger magnets can be 1 cm or more away from the pin.
2. Weak magnets should only hold one or two sheets of paper, but stronger magnets can keep several sheets of paper attached to a refrigerator.

21 Testing Magnets

Real-World Question
How do the strengths of kitchen magnets compare?

Possible Materials
- several kitchen magnets
- metric ruler
- small pin or paper clip

Procedure
1. Place a small pin or paper clip on a flat, nonmetallic surface such as a wooden table.

2. Holding your metric ruler vertically, place it next to the pin with the 0 cm mark on the tabletop.
3. Hold a kitchen magnet at the 10 cm mark on the ruler.
4. Slowly lower the magnet toward the pin. At the point where the pin is attracted to the magnet, measure the height of the magnet from the table. Record the height in your Science Journal.
5. Repeat steps 2–4 to test your other kitchen magnets.

Conclude and Apply
1. Describe the results of your experiment.
2. Infer how the kitchen magnets should be used based on the results of your experiment.

22 Pattern Counting

Real-World Question
What pattern is used to count in binary?

Procedure
1. Study the pattern used for counting in 4-bit binary.
2. Describe the pattern in your own words.
3. To test your understanding of the pattern, close the book and write the counting pattern from 0–15 by using your notes.

Conclude and Apply
1. Can this pattern continue past 15? Explain.
2. Develop a pattern to count to 32.

Decimal Number	Binary Number	Decimal Number	Binary Number
0	0000	8	1000
1	0001	9	1001
2	0010	10	1010
3	0011	11	1011
4	0100	12	1100
5	0101	13	1101
6	0110	14	1110
7	0111	15	1111

Adult supervision required for all labs.

These labs are available at ips.msscience.com.

22 Pattern Counting

Time Required one class period

Teaching Strategies
- Have students study the pattern individually and write down their answers. Then have them work in groups and discuss their thoughts.

- You could make a quiz game with two teams and test the students' knowledge of binary.
- There are many online resources about binary counting. You could make a research project of having them research hexadecimal and octadecimal counting.

Conclude and Apply
1. No. All of the combinations of four digits have already been used.
2. Any reasonable system should be accepted.

Computer Skills

People who study science rely on computers, like the one in **Figure 16,** to record and store data and to analyze results from investigations. Whether you work in a laboratory or just need to write a lab report with tables, good computer skills are a necessity.

Using the computer comes with responsibility. Issues of ownership, security, and privacy can arise. Remember, if you did not author the information you are using, you must provide a source for your information. Also, anything on a computer can be accessed by others. Do not put anything on the computer that you would not want everyone to know. To add more security to your work, use a password.

Use a Word Processing Program

A computer program that allows you to type your information, change it as many times as you need to, and then print it out is called a word processing program. Word processing programs also can be used to make tables.

Figure 16 A computer will make reports neater and more professional looking.

Learn the Skill To start your word processing program, a blank document, sometimes called "Document 1," appears on the screen. To begin, start typing. To create a new document, click the *New* button on the standard tool bar. These tips will help you format the document.

- The program will automatically move to the next line; press *Enter* if you wish to start a new paragraph.
- Symbols, called non-printing characters, can be hidden by clicking the *Show/Hide* button on your toolbar.
- To insert text, move the cursor to the point where you want the insertion to go, click on the mouse once, and type the text.
- To move several lines of text, select the text and click the *Cut* button on your toolbar. Then position your cursor in the location that you want to move the cut text and click *Paste*. If you move to the wrong place, click *Undo*.
- The spell check feature does not catch words that are misspelled to look like other words, like "cold" instead of "gold." Always reread your document to catch all spelling mistakes.
- To learn about other word processing methods, read the user's manual or click on the *Help* button.
- You can integrate databases, graphics, and spreadsheets into documents by copying from another program and pasting it into your document, or by using desktop publishing (DTP). DTP software allows you to put text and graphics together to finish your document with a professional look. This software varies in how it is used and its capabilities.

Use a Database

A collection of facts stored in a computer and sorted into different fields is called a database. A database can be reorganized in any way that suits your needs.

Learn the Skill A computer program that allows you to create your own database is a database management system (DBMS). It allows you to add, delete, or change information. Take time to get to know the features of your database software.

- Determine what facts you would like to include and research to collect your information.
- Determine how you want to organize the information.
- Follow the instructions for your particular DBMS to set up fields. Then enter each item of data in the appropriate field.
- Follow the instructions to sort the information in order of importance.
- Evaluate the information in your database, and add, delete, or change as necessary.

Use the Internet

The Internet is a global network of computers where information is stored and shared. To use the Internet, like the students in **Figure 17,** you need a modem to connect your computer to a phone line and an Internet Service Provider account.

Learn the Skill To access internet sites and information, use a "Web browser," which lets you view and explore pages on the World Wide Web. Each page is its own site, and each site has its own address, called a URL. Once you have found a Web browser, follow these steps for a search (this also is how you search a database).

Figure 17 The Internet allows you to search a global network for a variety of information.

- Be as specific as possible. If you know you want to research "gold," don't type in "elements." Keep narrowing your search until you find what you want.
- Web sites that end in *.com* are commercial Web sites; *.org, .edu,* and *.gov* are non-profit, educational, or government Web sites.
- Electronic encyclopedias, almanacs, indexes, and catalogs will help locate and select relevant information.
- Develop a "home page" with relative ease. When developing a Web site, NEVER post pictures or disclose personal information such as location, names, or phone numbers. Your school or community usually can host your Web site. A basic understanding of HTML (hypertext mark-up language), the language of Web sites, is necessary. Software that creates HTML code is called authoring software, and can be downloaded free from many Web sites. This software allows text and pictures to be arranged as the software is writing the HTML code.

Use a Spreadsheet

A spreadsheet, shown in **Figure 18,** can perform mathematical functions with any data arranged in columns and rows. By entering a simple equation into a cell, the program can perform operations in specific cells, rows, or columns.

Learn the Skill Each column (vertical) is assigned a letter, and each row (horizontal) is assigned a number. Each point where a row and column intersect is called a cell, and is labeled according to where it is located— Column A, Row 1 (A1).

- Decide how to organize the data, and enter it in the correct row or column.
- Spreadsheets can use standard formulas or formulas can be customized to calculate cells.
- To make a change, click on a cell to make it activate, and enter the edited data or formula.
- Spreadsheets also can display your results in graphs. Choose the style of graph that best represents the data.

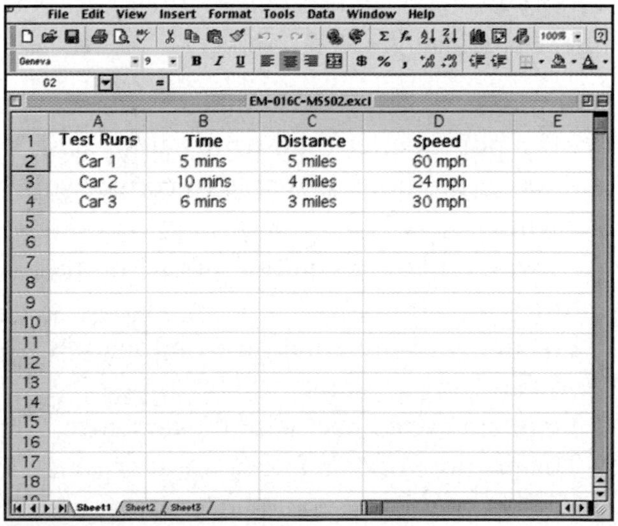

Figure 18 A spreadsheet allows you to perform mathematical operations on your data.

Use Graphics Software

Adding pictures, called graphics, to your documents is one way to make your documents more meaningful and exciting. This software adds, edits, and even constructs graphics. There is a variety of graphics software programs. The tools used for drawing can be a mouse, keyboard, or other specialized devices. Some graphics programs are simple. Others are complicated, called computer-aided design (CAD) software.

Learn the Skill It is important to have an understanding of the graphics software being used before starting. The better the software is understood, the better the results. The graphics can be placed in a word-processing document.

- Clip art can be found on a variety of internet sites, and on CDs. These images can be copied and pasted into your document.
- When beginning, try editing existing drawings, then work up to creating drawings.
- The images are made of tiny rectangles of color called pixels. Each pixel can be altered.
- Digital photography is another way to add images. The photographs in the memory of a digital camera can be downloaded into a computer, then edited and added to the document.
- Graphics software also can allow animation. The software allows drawings to have the appearance of movement by connecting basic drawings automatically. This is called in-betweening, or tweening.
- Remember to save often.

Presentation Skills

Develop Multimedia Presentations

Most presentations are more dynamic if they include diagrams, photographs, videos, or sound recordings, like the one shown in **Figure 19.** A multimedia presentation involves using stereos, overhead projectors, televisions, computers, and more.

Learn the Skill Decide the main points of your presentation, and what types of media would best illustrate those points.

- Make sure you know how to use the equipment you are working with.
- Practice the presentation using the equipment several times.
- Enlist the help of a classmate to push play or turn lights out for you. Be sure to practice your presentation with him or her.
- If possible, set up all of the equipment ahead of time, and make sure everything is working properly.

Figure 19 These students are engaging the audience using a variety of tools.

Computer Presentations

There are many different interactive computer programs that you can use to enhance your presentation. Most computers have a compact disc (CD) drive that can play both CDs and digital video discs (DVDs). Also, there is hardware to connect a regular CD, DVD, or VCR. These tools will enhance your presentation.

Another method of using the computer to aid in your presentation is to develop a slide show using a computer program. This can allow movement of visuals at the presenter's pace, and can allow for visuals to build on one another.

Learn the Skill In order to create multimedia presentations on a computer, you need to have certain tools. These may include traditional graphic tools and drawing programs, animation programs, and authoring systems that tie everything together. Your computer will tell you which tools it supports. The most important step is to learn about the tools that you will be using.

- Often, color and strong images will convey a point better than words alone. Use the best methods available to convey your point.
- As with other presentations, practice many times.
- Practice your presentation with the tools you and any assistants will be using.
- Maintain eye contact with the audience. The purpose of using the computer is not to prompt the presenter, but to help the audience understand the points of the presentation.

Math Review

Use Fractions

A fraction compares a part to a whole. In the fraction $\frac{2}{3}$, the 2 represents the part and is the numerator. The 3 represents the whole and is the denominator.

Reduce Fractions To reduce a fraction, you must find the largest factor that is common to both the numerator and the denominator, the greatest common factor (GCF). Divide both numbers by the GCF. The fraction has then been reduced, or it is in its simplest form.

Example Twelve of the 20 chemicals in the science lab are in powder form. What fraction of the chemicals used in the lab are in powder form?

Step 1 Write the fraction.

$$\frac{\text{part}}{\text{whole}} = \frac{12}{20}$$

Step 2 To find the GCF of the numerator and denominator, list all of the factors of each number.

Factors of 12: 1, 2, 3, 4, 6, 12 (the numbers that divide evenly into 12)

Factors of 20: 1, 2, 4, 5, 10, 20 (the numbers that divide evenly into 20)

Step 3 List the common factors.

1, 2, 4.

Step 4 Choose the greatest factor in the list.

The GCF of 12 and 20 is 4.

Step 5 Divide the numerator and denominator by the GCF.

$$\frac{12 \div 4}{20 \div 4} = \frac{3}{5}$$

In the lab, $\frac{3}{5}$ of the chemicals are in powder form.

Practice Problem At an amusement park, 66 of 90 rides have a height restriction. What fraction of the rides, in its simplest form, has a height restriction?

Add and Subtract Fractions To add or subtract fractions with the same denominator, add or subtract the numerators and write the sum or difference over the denominator. After finding the sum or difference, find the simplest form for your fraction.

Example 1 In the forest outside your house, $\frac{1}{8}$ of the animals are rabbits, $\frac{3}{8}$ are squirrels, and the remainder are birds and insects. How many are mammals?

Step 1 Add the numerators.

$$\frac{1}{8} + \frac{3}{8} = \frac{(1+3)}{8} = \frac{4}{8}$$

Step 2 Find the GCF.

$$\frac{4}{8} \quad (\text{GCF, 4})$$

Step 3 Divide the numerator and denominator by the GCF.

$$\frac{4}{4} = 1, \ \frac{8}{4} = 2$$

$\frac{1}{2}$ of the animals are mammals.

Example 2 If $\frac{7}{16}$ of the Earth is covered by freshwater, and $\frac{1}{16}$ of that is in glaciers, how much freshwater is not frozen?

Step 1 Subtract the numerators.

$$\frac{7}{16} - \frac{1}{16} = \frac{(7-1)}{16} = \frac{6}{16}$$

Step 2 Find the GCF.

$$\frac{6}{16} \quad (\text{GCF, 2})$$

Step 3 Divide the numerator and denominator by the GCF.

$$\frac{6}{2} = 3, \ \frac{16}{2} = 8$$

$\frac{3}{8}$ of the freshwater is not frozen.

Practice Problem A bicycle rider is going 15 km/h for $\frac{4}{9}$ of his ride, 10 km/h for $\frac{2}{9}$ of his ride, and 8 km/h for the remainder of the ride. How much of his ride is he going over 8 km/h?

Reduce Fractions

$$\frac{66 \div 6}{90 \div 6} = \frac{11}{15}$$

Add and Subtract Fractions

$$\frac{4}{9} + \frac{2}{9} = \frac{6}{9}$$

$$\frac{6 \div 3}{9 \div 3} = \frac{2}{3}$$

Math Skill Handbook

Unlike Denominators

Problem 1

$1 \times 5 = 5, 8 \times 5 = 40$

$1 \times 4 = 4, 10 \times 4 = 40$

$\frac{5}{40} + \frac{4}{40} = \frac{9}{40}$

Problem 2

If $\frac{7}{10}$ are involuntary, the remainder are voluntary.

$\frac{10}{10} - \frac{7}{10} = \frac{3}{10}$

Unlike Denominators To add or subtract fractions with unlike denominators, first find the least common denominator (LCD). This is the smallest number that is a common multiple of both denominators. Rename each fraction with the LCD, and then add or subtract. Find the simplest form if necessary.

Example 1 A chemist makes a paste that is $\frac{1}{2}$ table salt (NaCl), $\frac{1}{3}$ sugar ($C_6H_{12}O_6$), and the rest water (H_2O). How much of the paste is a solid?

Step 1 Find the LCD of the fractions.

$\frac{1}{2} + \frac{1}{3}$ (LCD, 6)

Step 2 Rename each numerator and each denominator with the LCD.

$1 \times 3 = 3, \quad 2 \times 3 = 6$

$1 \times 2 = 2, \quad 3 \times 2 = 6$

Step 3 Add the numerators.

$\frac{3}{6} + \frac{2}{6} = \frac{(3+2)}{6} = \frac{5}{6}$

$\frac{5}{6}$ of the paste is a solid.

Example 2 The average precipitation in Grand Junction, CO, is $\frac{7}{10}$ inch in November, and $\frac{3}{5}$ inch in December. What is the total average precipitation?

Step 1 Find the LCD of the fractions.

$\frac{7}{10} + \frac{3}{5}$ (LCD, 10)

Step 2 Rename each numerator and each denominator with the LCD.

$7 \times 1 = 7, \quad 10 \times 1 = 10$

$3 \times 2 = 6, \quad 5 \times 2 = 10$

Step 3 Add the numerators.

$\frac{7}{10} + \frac{6}{10} = \frac{(7+6)}{10} = \frac{13}{10}$

$\frac{13}{10}$ inches total precipitation, or $1\frac{3}{10}$ inches.

Practice Problem On an electric bill, about $\frac{1}{8}$ of the energy is from solar energy and about $\frac{1}{10}$ is from wind power. How much of the total bill is from solar energy and wind power combined?

Example 3 In your body, $\frac{7}{10}$ of your muscle contractions are involuntary (cardiac and smooth muscle tissue). Smooth muscle makes $\frac{3}{15}$ of your muscle contractions. How many of your muscle contractions are made by cardiac muscle?

Step 1 Find the LCD of the fractions.

$\frac{7}{10} - \frac{3}{15}$ (LCD, 30)

Step 2 Rename each numerator and each denominator with the LCD.

$7 \times 3 = 21, \quad 10 \times 3 = 30$

$3 \times 2 = 6, \quad 15 \times 2 = 30$

Step 3 Subtract the numerators.

$\frac{21}{30} - \frac{6}{30} = \frac{(21-6)}{30} = \frac{15}{30}$

Step 4 Find the GCF.

$\frac{15}{30}$ (GCF, 15)

$\frac{1}{2}$

$\frac{1}{2}$ of all muscle contractions are cardiac muscle.

Example 4 Tony wants to make cookies that call for $\frac{3}{4}$ of a cup of flour, but he only has $\frac{1}{3}$ of a cup. How much more flour does he need?

Step 1 Find the LCD of the fractions.

$\frac{3}{4} - \frac{1}{3}$ (LCD, 12)

Step 2 Rename each numerator and each denominator with the LCD.

$3 \times 3 = 9, \quad 4 \times 3 = 12$

$1 \times 4 = 4, \quad 3 \times 4 = 12$

Step 3 Subtract the numerators.

$\frac{9}{12} - \frac{4}{12} = \frac{(9-4)}{12} = \frac{5}{12}$

$\frac{5}{12}$ of a cup of flour.

Practice Problem Using the information provided to you in Example 3 above, determine how many muscle contractions are voluntary (skeletal muscle).

Multiply Fractions To multiply with fractions, multiply the numerators and multiply the denominators. Find the simplest form if necessary.

Example Multiply $\frac{3}{5}$ by $\frac{1}{3}$.

Step 1 Multiply the numerators and denominators.

$$\frac{3}{5} \times \frac{1}{3} = \frac{(3 \times 1)}{(5 \times 3)} = \frac{3}{15}$$

Step 2 Find the GCF.

$$\frac{3}{15} \quad (\text{GCF, 3})$$

Step 3 Divide the numerator and denominator by the GCF.

$$\frac{3}{3} = 1, \quad \frac{15}{3} = 5$$

$$\frac{1}{5}$$

$\frac{3}{5}$ multiplied by $\frac{1}{3}$ is $\frac{1}{5}$.

Practice Problem Multiply $\frac{3}{14}$ by $\frac{5}{16}$.

Find a Reciprocal Two numbers whose product is 1 are called multiplicative inverses, or reciprocals.

Example Find the reciprocal of $\frac{3}{8}$.

Step 1 Inverse the fraction by putting the denominator on top and the numerator on the bottom.

$$\frac{8}{3}$$

The reciprocal of $\frac{3}{8}$ is $\frac{8}{3}$.

Practice Problem Find the reciprocal of $\frac{4}{9}$.

Divide Fractions To divide one fraction by another fraction, multiply the dividend by the reciprocal of the divisor. Find the simplest form if necessary.

Example 1 Divide $\frac{1}{9}$ by $\frac{1}{3}$.

Step 1 Find the reciprocal of the divisor.

The reciprocal of $\frac{1}{3}$ is $\frac{3}{1}$.

Step 2 Multiply the dividend by the reciprocal of the divisor.

$$\frac{\frac{1}{9}}{\frac{1}{3}} = \frac{1}{9} \times \frac{3}{1} = \frac{(1 \times 3)}{(9 \times 1)} = \frac{3}{9}$$

Step 3 Find the GCF.

$$\frac{3}{9} \quad (\text{GCF, 3})$$

Step 4 Divide the numerator and denominator by the GCF.

$$\frac{3}{3} = 1, \quad \frac{9}{3} = 3$$

$$\frac{1}{3}$$

$\frac{1}{9}$ divided by $\frac{1}{3}$ is $\frac{1}{3}$.

Example 2 Divide $\frac{3}{5}$ by $\frac{1}{4}$.

Step 1 Find the reciprocal of the divisor.

The reciprocal of $\frac{1}{4}$ is $\frac{4}{1}$.

Step 2 Multiply the dividend by the reciprocal of the divisor.

$$\frac{\frac{3}{5}}{\frac{1}{4}} = \frac{3}{5} \times \frac{4}{1} = \frac{(3 \times 4)}{(5 \times 1)} = \frac{12}{5}$$

$\frac{3}{5}$ divided by $\frac{1}{4}$ is $\frac{12}{5}$ or $2\frac{2}{5}$.

Practice Problem Divide $\frac{3}{11}$ by $\frac{7}{10}$.

Multiply Fractions

$$\frac{3}{14} \times \frac{5}{16} = \frac{(3 \times 5)}{(14 \times 16)} = \frac{15}{224}$$

Find a Reciprocal

$$\frac{9}{4}$$

Divide Fractions

The reciprocal of $\frac{7}{10}$ is $\frac{10}{7}$.

$$\frac{3}{11} \times \frac{10}{7} = \frac{(3 \times 10)}{(11 \times 7)} = \frac{30}{77}$$

Math Skill Handbook

Math Skill Handbook

Use Ratios

$$\frac{100 \text{ cm}}{144 \text{ cm}} = \frac{100 \div 4}{144 \div 4} = \frac{25}{36}$$

25:36

Add or Subtract Decimals

$$\begin{array}{r} 1 \\ 1.245 \\ + \ 3.842 \\ \hline 5.087 \end{array}$$

Use Ratios

When you compare two numbers by division, you are using a ratio. Ratios can be written 3 to 5, 3:5, or $\frac{3}{5}$. Ratios, like fractions, also can be written in simplest form.

Ratios can represent probabilities, also called odds. This is a ratio that compares the number of ways a certain outcome occurs to the number of outcomes. For example, if you flip a coin 100 times, what are the odds that it will come up heads? There are two possible outcomes, heads or tails, so the odds of coming up heads are 50:100. Another way to say this is that 50 out of 100 times the coin will come up heads. In its simplest form, the ratio is 1:2.

Example 1 A chemical solution contains 40 g of salt and 64 g of baking soda. What is the ratio of salt to baking soda as a fraction in simplest form?

Step 1 Write the ratio as a fraction.
$$\frac{\text{salt}}{\text{baking soda}} = \frac{40}{64}$$

Step 2 Express the fraction in simplest form. The GCF of 40 and 64 is 8.
$$\frac{40}{64} = \frac{40 \div 8}{64 \div 8} = \frac{5}{8}$$

The ratio of salt to baking soda in the sample is 5:8.

Example 2 Sean rolls a 6-sided die 6 times. What are the odds that the side with a 3 will show?

Step 1 Write the ratio as a fraction.
$$\frac{\text{number of sides with a 3}}{\text{number of sides}} = \frac{1}{6}$$

Step 2 Multiply by the number of attempts.
$$\frac{1}{6} \times 6 \text{ attempts} = \frac{6}{6} \text{ attempts} = 1 \text{ attempt}$$

1 attempt out of 6 will show a 3.

Practice Problem Two metal rods measure 100 cm and 144 cm in length. What is the ratio of their lengths in simplest form?

Use Decimals

A fraction with a denominator that is a power of ten can be written as a decimal. For example, 0.27 means $\frac{27}{100}$. The decimal point separates the ones place from the tenths place.

Any fraction can be written as a decimal using division. For example, the fraction $\frac{5}{8}$ can be written as a decimal by dividing 5 by 8. Written as a decimal, it is 0.625.

Add or Subtract Decimals When adding and subtracting decimals, line up the decimal points before carrying out the operation.

Example 1 Find the sum of 47.68 and 7.80.

Step 1 Line up the decimal places when you write the numbers.
$$\begin{array}{r} 47.68 \\ + \ 7.80 \end{array}$$

Step 2 Add the decimals.
$$\begin{array}{r} 47.68 \\ + \ 7.80 \\ \hline 55.48 \end{array}$$

The sum of 47.68 and 7.80 is 55.48.

Example 2 Find the difference of 42.17 and 15.85.

Step 1 Line up the decimal places when you write the number.
$$\begin{array}{r} 42.17 \\ - \ 15.85 \end{array}$$

Step 2 Subtract the decimals.
$$\begin{array}{r} 42.17 \\ - \ 15.85 \\ \hline 26.32 \end{array}$$

The difference of 42.17 and 15.85 is 26.32.

Practice Problem Find the sum of 1.245 and 3.842.

Math Skill Handbook

Multiply Decimals To multiply decimals, multiply the numbers like any other number, ignoring the decimal point. Count the decimal places in each factor. The product will have the same number of decimal places as the sum of the decimal places in the factors.

Example Multiply 2.4 by 5.9.

Step 1 Multiply the factors like two whole numbers.
$24 \times 59 = 1416$

Step 2 Find the sum of the number of decimal places in the factors. Each factor has one decimal place, for a sum of two decimal places.

Step 3 The product will have two decimal places.
14.16

The product of 2.4 and 5.9 is 14.16.

Practice Problem Multiply 4.6 by 2.2.

Divide Decimals When dividing decimals, change the divisor to a whole number. To do this, multiply both the divisor and the dividend by the same power of ten. Then place the decimal point in the quotient directly above the decimal point in the dividend. Then divide as you do with whole numbers.

Example Divide 8.84 by 3.4.

Step 1 Multiply both factors by 10.
$3.4 \times 10 = 34, 8.84 \times 10 = 88.4$

Step 2 Divide 88.4 by 34.

$$
\begin{array}{r}
2.6 \\
34\overline{)88.4} \\
-68 \\
\hline
204 \\
-204 \\
\hline
0
\end{array}
$$

8.84 divided by 3.4 is 2.6.

Practice Problem Divide 75.6 by 3.6.

Use Proportions

An equation that shows that two ratios are equivalent is a proportion. The ratios $\frac{2}{4}$ and $\frac{5}{10}$ are equivalent, so they can be written as $\frac{2}{4} = \frac{5}{10}$. This equation is a proportion.

When two ratios form a proportion, the cross products are equal. To find the cross products in the proportion $\frac{2}{4} = \frac{5}{10}$, multiply the 2 and the 10, and the 4 and the 5. Therefore $2 \times 10 = 4 \times 5$, or $20 = 20$.

Because you know that both proportions are equal, you can use cross products to find a missing term in a proportion. This is known as solving the proportion.

Example The heights of a tree and a pole are proportional to the lengths of their shadows. The tree casts a shadow of 24 m when a 6-m pole casts a shadow of 4 m. What is the height of the tree?

Step 1 Write a proportion.
$$\frac{\text{height of tree}}{\text{height of pole}} = \frac{\text{length of tree's shadow}}{\text{length of pole's shadow}}$$

Step 2 Substitute the known values into the proportion. Let h represent the unknown value, the height of the tree.
$$\frac{h}{6} = \frac{24}{4}$$

Step 3 Find the cross products.
$$h \times 4 = 6 \times 24$$

Step 4 Simplify the equation.
$$4h = 144$$

Step 5 Divide each side by 4.
$$\frac{4h}{4} = \frac{144}{4}$$
$$h = 36$$

The height of the tree is 36 m.

Practice Problem The ratios of the weights of two objects on the Moon and on Earth are in proportion. A rock weighing 3 N on the Moon weighs 18 N on Earth. How much would a rock that weighs 5 N on the Moon weigh on Earth?

Multiply Decimals

Multiply 4.6 and 2.2 by 10.

$46 \times 22 = 1012$

Each factor had one decimal place.

10.12

Divide Decimals

Multiply both factors by 10.

Divide 756 by 36.

$$
\begin{array}{r}
21 \\
36\overline{)756} \\
72 \\
\hline
36 \\
36 \\
\hline
0
\end{array}
$$

Use Proportions

$$\frac{3}{18} = \frac{5}{w}$$

$$w \times 3 = 5 \times 18$$

$$\frac{3w}{3} = \frac{90}{3}$$

$$w = 30$$

Use Percentages

$$\frac{73}{365} = \frac{x}{100}$$

$$\frac{7300}{365} = \frac{365x}{365}$$

$$20\% = x$$

Solve One-Step Equations

$$h = gd$$

$$\frac{17.4}{12.3} = \frac{12.3d}{12.3}$$

$$1.41 = d$$

Use Percentages

The word *percent* means "out of one hundred." It is a ratio that compares a number to 100. Suppose you read that 77 percent of the Earth's surface is covered by water. That is the same as reading that the fraction of the Earth's surface covered by water is $\frac{77}{100}$. To express a fraction as a percent, first find the equivalent decimal for the fraction. Then, multiply the decimal by 100 and add the percent symbol.

Example Express $\frac{13}{20}$ as a percent.

Step 1 Find the equivalent decimal for the fraction.

$$\begin{array}{r} 0.65 \\ 20\overline{)13.00} \\ \underline{12\ 0} \\ 1\ 00 \\ \underline{1\ 00} \\ 0 \end{array}$$

Step 2 Rewrite the fraction $\frac{13}{20}$ as 0.65.

Step 3 Multiply 0.65 by 100 and add the % sign.
$$0.65 \times 100 = 65 = 65\%$$

So, $\frac{13}{20} = 65\%$.

This also can be solved as a proportion.

Example Express $\frac{13}{20}$ as a percent.

Step 1 Write a proportion.
$$\frac{13}{20} = \frac{x}{100}$$

Step 2 Find the cross products.
$$1300 = 20x$$

Step 3 Divide each side by 20.
$$\frac{1300}{20} = \frac{20x}{20}$$
$$65\% = x$$

Practice Problem In one year, 73 of 365 days were rainy in one city. What percent of the days in that city were rainy?

Solve One-Step Equations

A statement that two things are equal is an equation. For example, $A = B$ is an equation that states that A is equal to B.

An equation is solved when a variable is replaced with a value that makes both sides of the equation equal. To make both sides equal the inverse operation is used. Addition and subtraction are inverses, and multiplication and division are inverses.

Example 1 Solve the equation $x - 10 = 35$.

Step 1 Find the solution by adding 10 to each side of the equation.
$$x - 10 = 35$$
$$x - 10 + 10 = 35 + 10$$
$$x = 45$$

Step 2 Check the solution.
$$x - 10 = 35$$
$$45 - 10 = 35$$
$$35 = 35$$

Both sides of the equation are equal, so $x = 45$.

Example 2 In the formula $a = bc$, find the value of c if $a = 20$ and $b = 2$.

Step 1 Rearrange the formula so the unknown value is by itself on one side of the equation by dividing both sides by b.
$$a = bc$$
$$\frac{a}{b} = \frac{bc}{b}$$
$$\frac{a}{b} = c$$

Step 2 Replace the variables a and b with the values that are given.
$$\frac{a}{b} = c$$
$$\frac{20}{2} = c$$
$$10 = c$$

Step 3 Check the solution.
$$a = bc$$
$$20 = 2 \times 10$$
$$20 = 20$$

Both sides of the equation are equal, so $c = 10$ is the solution when $a = 20$ and $b = 2$.

Practice Problem In the formula $h = gd$, find the value of d if $g = 12.3$ and $h = 17.4$.

Math Skill Handbook

Use Statistics

The branch of mathematics that deals with collecting, analyzing, and presenting data is statistics. In statistics, there are three common ways to summarize data with a single number—the mean, the median, and the mode.

The **mean** of a set of data is the arithmetic average. It is found by adding the numbers in the data set and dividing by the number of items in the set.

The **median** is the middle number in a set of data when the data are arranged in numerical order. If there were an even number of data points, the median would be the mean of the two middle numbers.

The **mode** of a set of data is the number or item that appears most often.

Another number that often is used to describe a set of data is the range. The **range** is the difference between the largest number and the smallest number in a set of data.

A **frequency table** shows how many times each piece of data occurs, usually in a survey. **Table 2** below shows the results of a student survey on favorite color.

Table 2 Student Color Choice		
Color	**Tally**	**Frequency**
red	IIII	4
blue	IIII	5
black	II	2
green	III	3
purple	IIII II	7
yellow	IIII I	6

Based on the frequency table data, which color is the favorite?

Example The speeds (in m/s) for a race car during five different time trials are 39, 37, 44, 36, and 44.

To find the mean:

Step 1 Find the sum of the numbers.

$$39 + 37 + 44 + 36 + 44 = 200$$

Step 2 Divide the sum by the number of items, which is 5.

$$200 \div 5 = 40$$

The mean is 40 m/s.

To find the median:

Step 1 Arrange the measures from least to greatest.

36, 37, 39, 44, 44

Step 2 Determine the middle measure.

36, 37, <u>39</u>, 44, 44

The median is 39 m/s.

To find the mode:

Step 1 Group the numbers that are the same together.

44, 44, 36, 37, 39

Step 2 Determine the number that occurs most in the set.

<u>44, 44</u>, 36, 37, 39

The mode is 44 m/s.

To find the range:

Step 1 Arrange the measures from largest to smallest.

44, 44, 39, 37, 36

Step 2 Determine the largest and smallest measures in the set.

<u>44</u>, 44, 39, 37, <u>36</u>

Step 3 Find the difference between the largest and smallest measures.

$$44 - 36 = 8$$

The range is 8 m/s.

Practice Problem Find the mean, median, mode, and range for the data set 8, 4, 12, 8, 11, 14, 16.

Use Statistics

mean

$$8 + 4 + 12 + 8 + 11 + 14 + 16 = 73$$

$$73 \div 7 = 10.4$$

median

4, 8, 8, <u>11</u>, 12, 14, 16

mode

4, <u>8</u>, <u>8</u>, 11, 12, 14, 16

range

<u>4</u>, 8, 8, 11, 12, 14, <u>16</u>

$$16 - 4 = 12$$

Perimeter

Problem 1

$P = 2(18\,\text{m} + 7\,\text{m})$

$P = 2(25\,\text{m})$

$P = 50\,\text{m}$

Problem 2

$P = 1.6\,\text{cm} + 2.4\,\text{cm} + 2.4\,\text{cm}$

$P = 6.4\,\text{cm}$

Area of a Rectangle

$A = (4\,\text{m} \times 4\,\text{m})$

$A = 16\,\text{m}^2$

Area of a Triangle

$A = \frac{1}{2}(27\,\text{cm} \times 17\,\text{cm})$

$A = \frac{1}{2}(459\,\text{cm}^2)$

$A = 229.5\,\text{cm}^2$

Use Geometry

The branch of mathematics that deals with the measurement, properties, and relationships of points, lines, angles, surfaces, and solids is called geometry.

Perimeter The **perimeter** (P) is the distance around a geometric figure. To find the perimeter of a rectangle, add the length and width and multiply that sum by two, or $2(l + w)$. To find perimeters of irregular figures, add the length of the sides.

Example 1 Find the perimeter of a rectangle that is 3 m long and 5 m wide.

Step 1 You know that the perimeter is 2 times the sum of the width and length.

$P = 2(3\,\text{m} + 5\,\text{m})$

Step 2 Find the sum of the width and length.

$P = 2(8\,\text{m})$

Step 3 Multiply by 2.

$P = 16\,\text{m}$

The perimeter is 16 m.

Example 2 Find the perimeter of a shape with sides measuring 2 cm, 5 cm, 6 cm, 3 cm.

Step 1 You know that the perimeter is the sum of all the sides.

$P = 2 + 5 + 6 + 3$

Step 2 Find the sum of the sides.

$P = 2 + 5 + 6 + 3$

$P = 16$

The perimeter is 16 cm.

Practice Problem Find the perimeter of a rectangle with a length of 18 m and a width of 7 m.

Practice Problem Find the perimeter of a triangle measuring 1.6 cm by 2.4 cm by 2.4 cm.

Area of a Rectangle The **area** (A) is the number of square units needed to cover a surface. To find the area of a rectangle, multiply the length times the width, or $l \times w$. When finding area, the units also are multiplied. Area is given in square units.

Example Find the area of a rectangle with a length of 1 cm and a width of 10 cm.

Step 1 You know that the area is the length multiplied by the width.

$A = (1\,\text{cm} \times 10\,\text{cm})$

Step 2 Multiply the length by the width. Also multiply the units.

$A = 10\,\text{cm}^2$

The area is 10 cm^2.

Practice Problem Find the area of a square whose sides measure 4 m.

Area of a Triangle To find the area of a triangle, use the formula:

$$A = \frac{1}{2}(\text{base} \times \text{height})$$

The base of a triangle can be any of its sides. The height is the perpendicular distance from a base to the opposite endpoint, or vertex.

Example Find the area of a triangle with a base of 18 m and a height of 7 m.

Step 1 You know that the area is $\frac{1}{2}$ the base times the height.

$A = \frac{1}{2}(18\,\text{m} \times 7\,\text{m})$

Step 2 Multiply $\frac{1}{2}$ by the product of 18×7. Multiply the units.

$A = \frac{1}{2}(126\,\text{m}^2)$

$A = 63\,\text{m}^2$

The area is 63 m^2.

Practice Problem Find the area of a triangle with a base of 27 cm and a height of 17 cm.

Circumference of a Circle The **diameter** (*d*) of a circle is the distance across the circle through its center, and the **radius** (*r*) is the distance from the center to any point on the circle. The radius is half of the diameter. The distance around the circle is called the **circumference** (C). The formula for finding the circumference is:

$$C = 2\pi r \ \ or \ \ C = \pi d$$

The circumference divided by the diameter is always equal to 3.1415926... This nonterminating and nonrepeating number is represented by the Greek letter π (pi). An approximation often used for π is 3.14.

Example 1 Find the circumference of a circle with a radius of 3 m.

Step 1 You know the formula for the circumference is 2 times the radius times π.
$$C = 2\pi(3)$$

Step 2 Multiply 2 times the radius.
$$C = 6\pi$$

Step 3 Multiply by π.
$$C = 19 \text{ m}$$

The circumference is 19 m.

Example 2 Find the circumference of a circle with a diameter of 24.0 cm.

Step 1 You know the formula for the circumference is the diameter times π.
$$C = \pi(24.0)$$

Step 2 Multiply the diameter by π.
$$C = 75.4 \text{ cm}$$

The circumference is 75.4 cm.

Practice Problem Find the circumference of a circle with a radius of 19 cm.

Area of a Circle The formula for the area of a circle is:
$$A = \pi r^2$$

Example 1 Find the area of a circle with a radius of 4.0 cm.

Step 1 $A = \pi(4.0)^2$

Step 2 Find the square of the radius.
$$A = 16\pi$$

Step 3 Multiply the square of the radius by π.
$$A = 50 \text{ cm}^2$$

The area of the circle is 50 cm^2.

Example 2 Find the area of a circle with a radius of 225 m.

Step 1 $A = \pi(225)^2$

Step 2 Find the square of the radius.
$$A = 50625\pi$$

Step 3 Multiply the square of the radius by π.
$$A = 158962.5$$

The area of the circle is 158,962 m^2.

Example 3 Find the area of a circle whose diameter is 20.0 mm.

Step 1 You know the formula for the area of a circle is the square of the radius times π, and that the radius is half of the diameter.
$$A = \pi\left(\frac{20.0}{2}\right)^2$$

Step 2 Find the radius.
$$A = \pi(10.0)^2$$

Step 3 Find the square of the radius.
$$A = 100\pi$$

Step 4 Multiply the square of the radius by π.
$$A = 314 \text{ mm}^2$$

The area is 314 mm^2.

Practice Problem Find the area of a circle with a radius of 16 m.

Math Skill Handbook

Circumference of a Circle

$C = 2\pi r$

$C = 2\pi(19)$

$C = 38\pi$

$C = 119.3$

Area of a Circle

$A = \pi r^2$

$A = \pi(16 \text{ m})^2$

$A = \pi\, 256 \text{ m}^2$

$A = 803.8 \text{ m}^2$

Math Skill Handbook

Volume

Problem 1

$V = 8\,m \times 4\,m \times 4\,m$

$V = 128\,m^3$

Problem 2

$V = \pi r^2 \times height$

$V = \left[\pi\left(\frac{1}{2} \times 7\right)^2\right] \times 16$

$V = [\pi(3.5)^2] \times 16$

$V = [\pi(12.25)] \times 16$

$V = 38.46 \times 16$

$V = 615.36$

Volume The measure of space occupied by a solid is the **volume** (V). To find the volume of a rectangular solid multiply the length times width times height, or $V = l \times w \times h$. It is measured in cubic units, such as cubic centimeters (cm^3).

Example Find the volume of a rectangular solid with a length of 2.0 m, a width of 4.0 m, and a height of 3.0 m.

Step 1 You know the formula for volume is the length times the width times the height.

$V = 2.0\,m \times 4.0\,m \times 3.0\,m$

Step 2 Multiply the length times the width times the height.

$V = 24\,m^3$

The volume is 24 m³.

Practice Problem Find the volume of a rectangular solid that is 8 m long, 4 m wide, and 4 m high.

To find the volume of other solids, multiply the area of the base times the height.

Example 1 Find the volume of a solid that has a triangular base with a length of 8.0 m and a height of 7.0 m. The height of the entire solid is 15.0 m.

Step 1 You know that the base is a triangle, and the area of a triangle is $\frac{1}{2}$ the base times the height, and the volume is the area of the base times the height.

$V = \left[\frac{1}{2}(b \times h)\right] \times 15$

Step 2 Find the area of the base.

$V = \left[\frac{1}{2}(8 \times 7)\right] \times 15$

$V = \left(\frac{1}{2} \times 56\right) \times 15$

Step 3 Multiply the area of the base by the height of the solid.

$V = 28 \times 15$

$V = 420\,m^3$

The volume is 420 m³.

Example 2 Find the volume of a cylinder that has a base with a radius of 12.0 cm, and a height of 21.0 cm.

Step 1 You know that the base is a circle, and the area of a circle is the square of the radius times π, and the volume is the area of the base times the height.

$V = (\pi r^2) \times 21$

$V = (\pi 12^2) \times 21$

Step 2 Find the area of the base.

$V = 144\pi \times 21$

$V = 452 \times 21$

Step 3 Multiply the area of the base by the height of the solid.

$V = 9490\,cm^3$

The volume is 9490 cm³.

Example 3 Find the volume of a cylinder that has a diameter of 15 mm and a height of 4.8 mm.

Step 1 You know that the base is a circle with an area equal to the square of the radius times π. The radius is one-half the diameter. The volume is the area of the base times the height.

$V = (\pi r^2) \times 4.8$

$V = \left[\pi\left(\frac{1}{2} \times 15\right)^2\right] \times 4.8$

$V = (\pi 7.5^2) \times 4.8$

Step 2 Find the area of the base.

$V = 56.25\pi \times 4.8$

$V = 176.63 \times 4.8$

Step 3 Multiply the area of the base by the height of the solid.

$V = 847.8$

The volume is 847.8 mm³.

Practice Problem Find the volume of a cylinder with a diameter of 7 cm in the base and a height of 16 cm.

Science Applications

Measure in SI

The metric system of measurement was developed in 1795. A modern form of the metric system, called the International System (SI), was adopted in 1960 and provides the standard measurements that all scientists around the world can understand.

The SI system is convenient because unit sizes vary by powers of 10. Prefixes are used to name units. Look at **Table 3** for some common SI prefixes and their meanings.

Table 3 Common SI Prefixes			
Prefix	**Symbol**	**Meaning**	
kilo-	k	1,000	thousand
hecto-	h	100	hundred
deka-	da	10	ten
deci-	d	0.1	tenth
centi-	c	0.01	hundredth
milli-	m	0.001	thousandth

Example How many grams equal one kilogram?

Step 1 Find the prefix *kilo* in **Table 3.**

Step 2 Using **Table 3,** determine the meaning of *kilo*. According to the table, it means 1,000. When the prefix *kilo* is added to a unit, it means that there are 1,000 of the units in a "*kilo*unit."

Step 3 Apply the prefix to the units in the question. The units in the question are grams. There are 1,000 grams in a kilogram.

Practice Problem Is a milligram larger or smaller than a gram? How many of the smaller units equal one larger unit? What fraction of the larger unit does one smaller unit represent?

Dimensional Analysis

Convert SI Units In science, quantities such as length, mass, and time sometimes are measured using different units. A process called dimensional analysis can be used to change one unit of measure to another. This process involves multiplying your starting quantity and units by one or more conversion factors. A conversion factor is a ratio equal to one and can be made from any two equal quantities with different units. If 1,000 mL equal 1 L then two ratios can be made.

$$\frac{1,000 \text{ mL}}{1 \text{ L}} = \frac{1 \text{ L}}{1,000 \text{ mL}} = 1$$

One can covert between units in the SI system by using the equivalents in **Table 3** to make conversion factors.

Example 1 How many cm are in 4 m?

Step 1 Write conversion factors for the units given. From **Table 3,** you know that 100 cm = 1 m. The conversion factors are

$$\frac{100 \text{ cm}}{1 \text{ m}} \quad and \quad \frac{1 \text{ m}}{100 \text{ cm}}$$

Step 2 Decide which conversion factor to use. Select the factor that has the units you are converting from (m) in the denominator and the units you are converting to (cm) in the numerator.

$$\frac{100 \text{ cm}}{1 \text{ m}}$$

Step 3 Multiply the starting quantity and units by the conversion factor. Cancel the starting units with the units in the denominator. There are 400 cm in 4 m.

$$4 \text{ m} \times \frac{100 \text{ cm}}{1 \text{ m}} = 400 \text{ cm}$$

Practice Problem How many milligrams are in one kilogram? (Hint: You will need to use two conversion factors from **Table 3.**)

Measure in SI

smaller; 1000; one thousandth

Dimensional Analysis

$$x \text{ mg} = 1 \text{ kg} \times \frac{1000 \text{ g}}{1 \text{ kg}} \times \frac{1000 \text{ mg}}{1 \text{ g}} =$$

1,000,000 mg

1,000,000 mg = 1 kg

Math Skill Handbook

Convert Between Unit Systems

$$\frac{(1 \text{ in})^3}{(2.54 \text{ cm})^3}$$

$$= \frac{1 \text{ in} \times 1 \text{ in} \times 1 \text{ in}}{2.54 \text{ cm} \times 2.54 \text{ cm} \times 2.54 \text{ cm}}$$

$$= \frac{1 \text{ in}^3}{16.39 \text{ cm}^3}$$

Table 4 Unit System Equivalents

Type of Measurement	Equivalent
Length	1 in = 2.54 cm
	1 yd = 0.91 m
	1 mi = 1.61 km
Mass and Weight*	1 oz = 28.35 g
	1 lb = 0.45 kg
	1 ton (short) = 0.91 tonnes (metric tons)
	1 lb = 4.45 N
Volume	$1 \text{ in}^3 = 16.39 \text{ cm}^3$
	1 qt = 0.95 L
	1 gal = 3.78 L
Area	$1 \text{ in}^2 = 6.45 \text{ cm}^2$
	$1 \text{ yd}^2 = 0.83 \text{ m}^2$
	$1 \text{ mi}^2 = 2.59 \text{ km}^2$
	1 acre = 0.40 hectares
Temperature	$°C = \dfrac{(°F - 32)}{1.8}$
	$K = °C + 273$

*Weight is measured in standard Earth gravity.

Convert Between Unit Systems Table 4 gives a list of equivalents that can be used to convert between English and SI units.

Example If a meterstick has a length of 100 cm, how long is the meterstick in inches?

Step 1 Write the conversion factors for the units given. From **Table 4,** 1 in = 2.54 cm.

$$\frac{1 \text{ in}}{2.54 \text{ cm}} \quad and \quad \frac{2.54 \text{ cm}}{1 \text{ in}}$$

Step 2 Determine which conversion factor to use. You are converting from cm to in. Use the conversion factor with cm on the bottom.

$$\frac{1 \text{ in}}{2.54 \text{ cm}}$$

Step 3 Multiply the starting quantity and units by the conversion factor. Cancel the starting units with the units in the denominator. Round your answer based on the number of significant figures in the conversion factor.

$$100 \text{ cm} \times \frac{1 \text{ in}}{2.54 \text{ cm}} = 39.37 \text{ in}$$

The meterstick is 39.4 in long.

Practice Problem A book has a mass of 5 lbs. What is the mass of the book in kg?

Practice Problem Use the equivalent for in and cm (1 in = 2.54 cm) to show how $1 \text{ in}^3 = 16.39 \text{ cm}^3$.

Math Skill Handbook

Precision and Significant Digits

When you make a measurement, the value you record depends on the precision of the measuring instrument. This precision is represented by the number of significant digits recorded in the measurement. When counting the number of significant digits, all digits are counted except zeros at the end of a number with no decimal point such as 2,050, and zeros at the beginning of a decimal such as 0.03020. When adding or subtracting numbers with different precision, round the answer to the smallest number of decimal places of any number in the sum or difference. When multiplying or dividing, the answer is rounded to the smallest number of significant digits of any number being multiplied or divided.

Example The lengths 5.28 and 5.2 are measured in meters. Find the sum of these lengths and record your answer using the correct number of significant digits.

Step 1 Find the sum.

5.28 m	2 digits after the decimal
+ 5.2 m	1 digit after the decimal
10.48 m	

Step 2 Round to one digit after the decimal because the least number of digits after the decimal of the numbers being added is 1.

The sum is 10.5 m.

Practice Problem How many significant digits are in the measurement 7,071,301 m? How many significant digits are in the measurement 0.003010 g?

Practice Problem Multiply 5.28 and 5.2 using the rule for multiplying and dividing. Record the answer using the correct number of significant digits.

Scientific Notation

Many times numbers used in science are very small or very large. Because these numbers are difficult to work with scientists use scientific notation. To write numbers in scientific notation, move the decimal point until only one non-zero digit remains on the left. Then count the number of places you moved the decimal point and use that number as a power of ten. For example, the average distance from the Sun to Mars is 227,800,000,000 m. In scientific notation, this distance is 2.278×10^{11} m. Because you moved the decimal point to the left, the number is a positive power of ten.

The mass of an electron is about 0.000 000 000 000 000 000 000 000 000 000 911 kg. Expressed in scientific notation, this mass is 9.11×10^{-31} kg. Because the decimal point was moved to the right, the number is a negative power of ten.

Example Earth is 149,600,000 km from the Sun. Express this in scientific notation.

Step 1 Move the decimal point until one non-zero digit remains on the left.
1.496 000 00

Step 2 Count the number of decimal places you have moved. In this case, eight.

Step 3 Show that number as a power of ten, 10^8.

The Earth is 1.496×10^8 km from the Sun.

Practice Problem How many significant digits are in 149,600,000 km? How many significant digits are in 1.496×10^8 km?

Practice Problem Parts used in a high performance car must be measured to 7×10^{-6} m. Express this number as a decimal.

Practice Problem A CD is spinning at 539 revolutions per minute. Express this number in scientific notation.

Math Skill Handbook

Precision and Significant Digits

Problem 1
7; 4

Problem 2
$5.28 \times 5.2 = 27.456$

5.28 has 3 significant digits.

5.2 has 2 significant digits.

When multiplying and dividing, the answer is rounded to the smallest number of significant digits of the numbers being multiplied or divided—in this case, 2.

27.456 is rounded to 27.

Scientific Notation

Problem 1
4; 4

Problem 2
0.000007

Problem 3
5.39×10^2

Math Skill Handbook

Line Graph

x	y
3	52
6	72
9	83
12	86

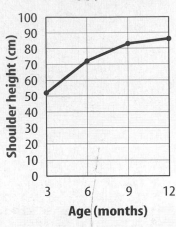

Make and Use Graphs

Data in tables can be displayed in a graph—a visual representation of data. Common graph types include line graphs, bar graphs, and circle graphs.

Line Graph A line graph shows a relationship between two variables that change continuously. The independent variable is changed and is plotted on the *x*-axis. The dependent variable is observed, and is plotted on the *y*-axis.

Example Draw a line graph of the data below from a cyclist in a long-distance race.

Table 5 Bicycle Race Data	
Time (h)	**Distance (km)**
0	0
1	8
2	16
3	24
4	32
5	40

Step 1 Determine the *x*-axis and *y*-axis variables. Time varies independently of distance and is plotted on the *x*-axis. Distance is dependent on time and is plotted on the *y*-axis.

Step 2 Determine the scale of each axis. The *x*-axis data ranges from 0 to 5. The *y*-axis data ranges from 0 to 40.

Step 3 Using graph paper, draw and label the axes. Include units in the labels.

Step 4 Draw a point at the intersection of the time value on the *x*-axis and corresponding distance value on the *y*-axis. Connect the points and label the graph with a title, as shown in **Figure 20.**

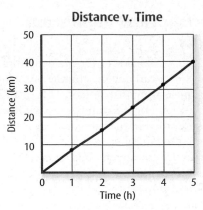

Figure 20 This line graph shows the relationship between distance and time during a bicycle ride.

Practice Problem A puppy's shoulder height is measured during the first year of her life. The following measurements were collected: (3 mo, 52 cm), (6 mo, 72 cm), (9 mo, 83 cm), (12 mo, 86 cm). Graph this data.

Find a Slope The slope of a straight line is the ratio of the vertical change, rise, to the horizontal change, run.

$$\text{Slope} = \frac{\text{vertical change (rise)}}{\text{horizontal change (run)}} = \frac{\text{change in } y}{\text{change in } x}$$

Example Find the slope of the graph in **Figure 20.**

Step 1 You know that the slope is the change in *y* divided by the change in *x*.
$$\text{Slope} = \frac{\text{change in } y}{\text{change in } x}$$

Step 2 Determine the data points you will be using. For a straight line, choose the two sets of points that are the farthest apart.
$$\text{Slope} = \frac{(40-0) \text{ km}}{(5-0) \text{ hr}}$$

Step 3 Find the change in *y* and *x*.
$$\text{Slope} = \frac{40 \text{ km}}{5 \text{h}}$$

Step 4 Divide the change in *y* by the change in *x*.
$$\text{Slope} = \frac{8 \text{ km}}{\text{h}}$$

The slope of the graph is 8 km/h.

Math Skill Handbook

Bar Graph To compare data that does not change continuously you might choose a bar graph. A bar graph uses bars to show the relationships between variables. The *x*-axis variable is divided into parts. The parts can be numbers such as years, or a category such as a type of animal. The *y*-axis is a number and increases continuously along the axis.

Example A recycling center collects 4.0 kg of aluminum on Monday, 1.0 kg on Wednesday, and 2.0 kg on Friday. Create a bar graph of this data.

Step 1 Select the *x*-axis and *y*-axis variables. The measured numbers (the masses of aluminum) should be placed on the *y*-axis. The variable divided into parts (collection days) is placed on the *x*-axis.

Step 2 Create a graph grid like you would for a line graph. Include labels and units.

Step 3 For each measured number, draw a vertical bar above the *x*-axis value up to the *y*-axis value. For the first data point, draw a vertical bar above Monday up to 4.0 kg.

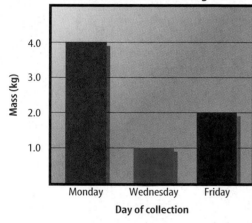

Aluminum Collected During Week

Practice Problem Draw a bar graph of the gases in air: 78% nitrogen, 21% oxygen, 1% other gases.

Circle Graph To display data as parts of a whole, you might use a circle graph. A circle graph is a circle divided into sections that represent the relative size of each piece of data. The entire circle represents 100%, half represents 50%, and so on.

Example Air is made up of 78% nitrogen, 21% oxygen, and 1% other gases. Display the composition of air in a circle graph.

Step 1 Multiply each percent by 360° and divide by 100 to find the angle of each section in the circle.

$$78\% \times \frac{360°}{100} = 280.8°$$

$$21\% \times \frac{360°}{100} = 75.6°$$

$$1\% \times \frac{360°}{100} = 3.6°$$

Step 2 Use a compass to draw a circle and to mark the center of the circle. Draw a straight line from the center to the edge of the circle.

Step 3 Use a protractor and the angles you calculated to divide the circle into parts. Place the center of the protractor over the center of the circle and line the base of the protractor over the straight line.

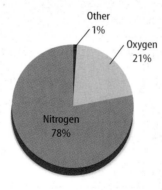

Practice Problem Draw a circle graph to represent the amount of aluminum collected during the week shown in the bar graph to the left.

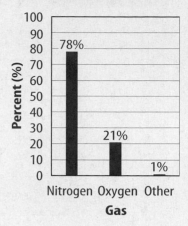

Bar Graph

Composition of Air

Circle Graph

The total amount of aluminum collected is:

$$4.0 \text{ kg} + 1.0 \text{ kg} + 2.0 \text{ kg} = 7.0 \text{ kg}$$

$$\frac{4.0 \text{ kg}}{7.0 \text{ kg}} = \frac{x}{360°}; \ x = 206°$$

$$\frac{1.0 \text{ kg}}{7.0 \text{ kg}} = \frac{x}{360°}; \ x = 51°$$

$$\frac{2.0 \text{ kg}}{7.0 \text{ kg}} = \frac{x}{360°}; \ x = 103°$$

PERIODIC TABLE OF THE ELEMENTS

Columns of elements are called groups. Elements in the same group have similar chemical properties.

Gas

Liquid

Solid

Synthetic

Element — Hydrogen
Atomic number — 1
Symbol — **H**
Atomic mass — 1.008

State of matter

The first three symbols tell you the state of matter of the element at room temperature. The fourth symbol identifies elements that are not present in significant amounts on Earth. Useful amounts are made synthetically.

1	2	3	4	5	6	7	8	9
1 Hydrogen 1 **H** 1.008								
2 Lithium 3 **Li** 6.941	Beryllium 4 **Be** 9.012							
3 Sodium 11 **Na** 22.990	Magnesium 12 **Mg** 24.305							
4 Potassium 19 **K** 39.098	Calcium 20 **Ca** 40.078	Scandium 21 **Sc** 44.956	Titanium 22 **Ti** 47.867	Vanadium 23 **V** 50.942	Chromium 24 **Cr** 51.996	Manganese 25 **Mn** 54.938	Iron 26 **Fe** 55.845	Cobalt 27 **Co** 58.933
5 Rubidium 37 **Rb** 85.468	Strontium 38 **Sr** 87.62	Yttrium 39 **Y** 88.906	Zirconium 40 **Zr** 91.224	Niobium 41 **Nb** 92.906	Molybdenum 42 **Mo** 95.94	Technetium 43 **Tc** (98)	Ruthenium 44 **Ru** 101.07	Rhodium 45 **Rh** 102.906
6 Cesium 55 **Cs** 132.905	Barium 56 **Ba** 137.327	Lanthanum 57 **La** 138.906	Hafnium 72 **Hf** 178.49	Tantalum 73 **Ta** 180.948	Tungsten 74 **W** 183.84	Rhenium 75 **Re** 186.207	Osmium 76 **Os** 190.23	Iridium 77 **Ir** 192.217
7 Francium 87 **Fr** (223)	Radium 88 **Ra** (226)	Actinium 89 **Ac** (227)	Rutherfordium 104 **Rf** (261)	Dubnium 105 **Db** (262)	Seaborgium 106 **Sg** (266)	Bohrium 107 **Bh** (264)	Hassium 108 **Hs** (277)	Meitnerium 109 **Mt** (268)

The number in parentheses is the mass number of the longest-lived isotope for that element.

Rows of elements are called periods. Atomic number increases across a period.

The arrow shows where these elements would fit into the periodic table. They are moved to the bottom of the table to save space.

Lanthanide series

Cerium 58 **Ce** 140.116	Praseodymium 59 **Pr** 140.908	Neodymium 60 **Nd** 144.24	Promethium 61 **Pm** (145)	Samarium 62 **Sm** 150.36

Actinide series

Thorium 90 **Th** 232.038	Protactinium 91 **Pa** 231.036	Uranium 92 **U** 238.029	Neptunium 93 **Np** (237)	Plutonium 94 **Pu** (244)

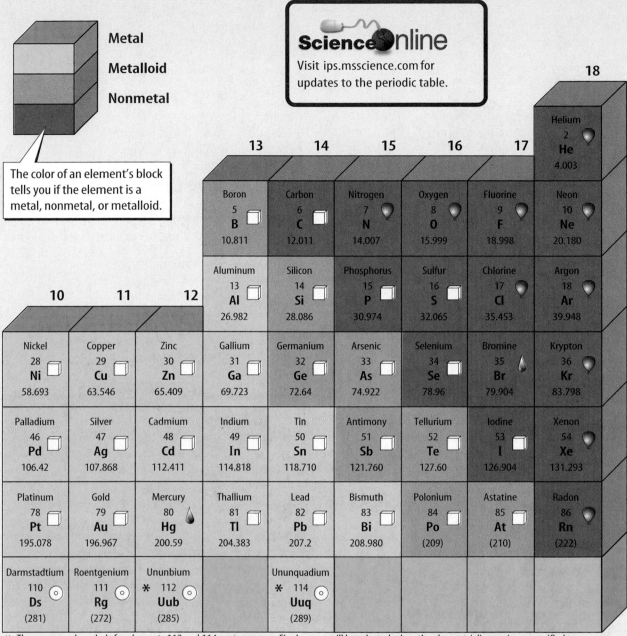

Metal

Metalloid

Nonmetal

The color of an element's block tells you if the element is a metal, nonmetal, or metalloid.

Science Online

Visit ips.msscience.com for updates to the periodic table.

			13	14	15	16	17	18
								Helium 2 He 4.003
			Boron 5 B 10.811	Carbon 6 C 12.011	Nitrogen 7 N 14.007	Oxygen 8 O 15.999	Fluorine 9 F 18.998	Neon 10 Ne 20.180
10	11	12	Aluminum 13 Al 26.982	Silicon 14 Si 28.086	Phosphorus 15 P 30.974	Sulfur 16 S 32.065	Chlorine 17 Cl 35.453	Argon 18 Ar 39.948
Nickel 28 Ni 58.693	Copper 29 Cu 63.546	Zinc 30 Zn 65.409	Gallium 31 Ga 69.723	Germanium 32 Ge 72.64	Arsenic 33 As 74.922	Selenium 34 Se 78.96	Bromine 35 Br 79.904	Krypton 36 Kr 83.798
Palladium 46 Pd 106.42	Silver 47 Ag 107.868	Cadmium 48 Cd 112.411	Indium 49 In 114.818	Tin 50 Sn 118.710	Antimony 51 Sb 121.760	Tellurium 52 Te 127.60	Iodine 53 I 126.904	Xenon 54 Xe 131.293
Platinum 78 Pt 195.078	Gold 79 Au 196.967	Mercury 80 Hg 200.59	Thallium 81 Tl 204.383	Lead 82 Pb 207.2	Bismuth 83 Bi 208.980	Polonium 84 Po (209)	Astatine 85 At (210)	Radon 86 Rn (222)
Darmstadtium 110 Ds (281)	Roentgenium 111 Rg (272)	Ununbium * 112 Uub (285)		Ununquadium * 114 Uuq (289)				

✷ The names and symbols for elements 112 and 114 are temporary. Final names will be selected when the elements' discoveries are verified.

Europium 63 Eu 151.964	Gadolinium 64 Gd 157.25	Terbium 65 Tb 158.925	Dysprosium 66 Dy 162.500	Holmium 67 Ho 164.930	Erbium 68 Er 167.259	Thulium 69 Tm 168.934	Ytterbium 70 Yb 173.04	Lutetium 71 Lu 174.967
Americium 95 Am (243)	Curium 96 Cm (247)	Berkelium 97 Bk (247)	Californium 98 Cf (251)	Einsteinium 99 Es (252)	Fermium 100 Fm (257)	Mendelevium 101 Md (258)	Nobelium 102 No (259)	Lawrencium 103 Lr (262)

Glossary/Glosario

Cómo usar el glosario en español:
1. Busca el término en inglés que desees encontrar.
2. El término en español, junto con la definición, se encuentran en la columna de la derecha.

Pronunciation Key

Use the following key to help you sound out words in the glossary.

a	back (BAK)	ew	food (FEWD)
ay	day (DAY)	yoo	pure (PYOOR)
ah	father (FAH thur)	yew	few (FYEW)
ow	flower (FLOW ur)	uh	comma (CAH muh)
ar	car (CAR)	u (1 con)	rub (RUB)
e	less (LES)	sh	shelf (SHELF)
ee	leaf (LEEF)	ch	nature (NAY chur)
ih	trip (TRIHP)	g	gift (GIHFT)
i (i 1 con 1 e)	idea (i DEE uh)	j	gem (JEM)
oh	go (GOH)	ing	sing (SING)
aw	soft (SAWFT)	zh	vision (VIH zhun)
or	orbit (OR buht)	k	cake (KAYK)
oy	coin (COYN)	s	seed, cent (SEED, SENT)
oo	foot (FOOT)	z	zone, raise (ZOHN, RAYZ)

English — A — Español

acceleration: equals the change in velocity divided by the time for the change to take place; occurs when an object speeds up, slows down, or turns. (p. 288)

aceleración: es igual al cambio de velocidad dividido por el tiempo que toma en realizarse dicho cambio; sucede cuando un objeto aumenta su velocidad, la disminuye o gira. (p. 288)

accuracy: compares a measurement to the true value. (p. 45)

exactitud: comparación de una medida con el valor real. (p. 45)

acid: substance that releases H^+ ions and produces hydronium ions when dissolved in water. (p. 232)

ácido: sustancia que libera iones H^+ y produce iones de hidronio al ser disuelta en agua. (p. 232)

activation energy: minimum amount of energy needed to start a chemical reaction. (p. 201)

energía de activación: cantidad mínima de energía necesaria para iniciar una reacción química. (p. 201)

alternating current (AC): electric current that changes its direction repeatedly. (p. 626)

corriente alterna (CA): corriente eléctrica que cambia de dirección repetidamente. (p. 626)

alternative resource: new renewable or inexhaustible energy source; includes solar energy, wind, and geothermal energy. (p. 391)

recurso alternativo: nueva fuente de energía renovable o inagotable; incluye energía solar, eólica y geotérmica. (p. 391)

amino acids: building blocks of proteins; contain both an amino group and a carboxyl acid group replacing hydrogens on the same carbon atom. (p. 259)

aminoácidos: bloques de construcción de las proteínas que contienen un grupo amino y un grupo ácido carboxilo reemplazando hidrógenos en el mismo átomo de carbono. (p. 259)

amino (uh ME noh) group: consists of one nitrogen atom covalently bonded to two hydrogen atoms; represented by the formula $-NH_2$. (p. 259)

grupo amino: consiste en un átomo de nitrógeno unido por enlaces covalentes a dos átomos de hidrógeno; se lo representa con la fórmula $-NH_2$. (p. 259)

amplitude: for a transverse wave, one half the distance between a crest and a trough. (p. 467)

amplitud: la mitad de la distancia entre la cresta y el valle en una onda transversal. (p. 467)

analog signal: a electronic signal that carries information and varies smoothly with time. (p. 642)

señal analógica: señal electrónica que conduce información y varía de manera uniforme con el tiempo. (p. 642)

aqueous (A kwee us): solution in which water is the solvent. (p. 224)

Archimedes' (ar kuh MEE deez) principle: states that the buoyant force on an object is equal to the weight of the fluid displaced by the object. (pp. 121, 351)

atom: a very small particle that makes up most kinds of matter and consists of smaller parts called protons, neutrons, and electrons. (p. 73)

atomic mass: average mass of an atom of an element; its unit of measure is the atomic mass unit (u), which is 1/12 the mass of a carbon-12 atom. (p. 84)

atomic number: number of protons in the nucleus of each atom of a given element; is the top number in the periodic table. (p. 83)

aurora: light display that occurs when charged particles trapped in the magnetosphere collide with Earth's atmosphere above the poles. (p. 625)

average speed: equals the total distance traveled divided by the total time taken to travel the distance. (p. 285)

acuoso: solución en la cual el agua es el solvente. (p. 224)

principio de Arquímedes: establece que la fuerza de empuje ejercida sobre un objeto es igual al peso del fluido desplazado por dicho objeto. (pp. 121, 351)

átomo: partícula muy pequeña que constituye la mayoría de los tipos de materia y que está formada por partes más pequeñas llamadas protones, neutrones y electrones. (p. 73)

masa atómica: masa promedio de un átomo de un elemento; su unidad de medida es la unidad de masa atómica (u), la cual es 1/12 de la masa de un átomo de carbono-12. (p. 84)

número atómico: número de protones en el núcleo de un átomo de determinado elemento; es el número superior en la tabla periódica. (p. 83)

aurora: despliegue de luz que se produce cuando partículas cargadas atrapadas en la magnetosfera chocan contra la atmósfera terrestre por encima de los polos. (p. 625)

velocidad promedio: es igual al total de la distancia recorrida dividida por el tiempo total necesario para recorrer dicha distancia. (p. 285)

B

balanced forces: two or more forces whose effects cancel each other out and do not change the motion of an object. (p. 311)

bar graph: a type of graph that uses bars of varying sizes to show the relationship among variables. (p. 58)

base: substance that accepts H^+ ions and produces hydroxide ions when dissolved in water. (p. 235)

Bernoulli's principle: states that when the speed of a fluid increases, the pressure exerted by the fluid decreases. (p. 359)

binary system: number system consisting of two digits, 0 and 1, that can be used by devices such as computers to store or use information. (p. 650)

buoyant force: upward force exerted on an object immersed in a fluid. (pp. 120, 348)

fuerzas balanceadas: dos o más fuerzas cuyos efectos se cancelan mutuamente sin cambiar el movimiento de un objeto. (p. 311)

gráfico de barras: tipo de gráfico que usa barras de diferentes tamaños para mostrar las diferencias entre las variables. (p. 58)

base: sustancia que acepta los iones H^+ y produce iones de hidróxido al ser disuelta en agua. (p. 235)

principio de Bernoulli: establece que cuando se incrementa la velocidad de un fluido, disminuye la presión ejercida por el mismo. (p. 359)

sistema binario: sistema numérico que consiste en dos dígitos, 0 y 1, que se puede usar con dispositivos como las computadoras para almacenar o usar información. (p. 650)

fuerza de empuje: fuerza ascendente ejercida sobre un objeto inmerso en un fluido. (pp. 120, 348)

C

carbohydrates: organic compounds containing only carbon, hydrogen, and oxygen; starches, cellulose, glycogen, sugars. (p. 264)

carbohidratos: compuestos orgánicos que sólo contienen carbono, hidrógeno y oxígeno; ejemplos son los almidones, la celulosa, el glucógeno y los azúcares. (p. 264)

carboxyl (car BOK sul) group: consists of one carbon atom, two oxygen atoms, and one hydrogen atom; represented by the formula —COOH. (p. 259)

carrier wave: radio waves broadcast by a radio or TV station at an assigned frequency that contains information used to produce pictures and sound. (p. 536)

catalyst: substance that speeds up a chemical reaction but is not used up itself or permanently changed. (p. 205)

center of mass: point in a object that moves as if all of the object's mass were concentrated at that point. (p. 322)

chemical bond: force that holds two atoms together. (p. 169)

chemical change: any change of a material into a new material with different properties. (p. 145)

chemical energy: energy stored in chemical bonds. (p. 377)

chemical equation: shorthand form for writing what reactants are used and what products are formed in a chemical reaction; sometimes shows whether energy is produced or absorbed. (p. 192)

chemical formula: combination of chemical symbols and numbers that indicates which elements and how many atoms of each element are present in a molecule. (p. 178)

chemical property: characteristic of something that permits its change to something new. (p. 139)

chemical reaction: process that produces chemical change, resulting in new substances that have properties different from those of the original substances. (p. 190)

cholesterol: a complex lipid that is present in foods that come from animals. (p. 269)

circle graph: a type of graph that shows the parts of a whole; sometimes called a pie graph, each piece of which represents a percentage of the total. (p. 58)

circuit: closed conducting loop in which electric current can flow continually. (p. 591)

compound: a substance produced when elements combine and whose properties are different from each of the elements in it. (pp. 87, 171)

compound machine: machine made up of a combination of two or more simple machines. (p. 417)

compressional wave: a type of mechanical wave in which matter in the medium moves forward and backward along the direction the wave travels. (p. 465)

grupo carboxilo: consiste en un átomo de carbono, dos de oxígeno y uno de hidrógeno; se lo representa con la fórmula —COOH. (p. 259)

ondas conductoras: ondas de radio emitidas por una estación de radio o televisión a una frecuencia asignada, las cuales contienen información utilizada para producir imágenes y sonido. (p. 536)

catalizador: sustancia que acelera una reacción química pero que ella misma ni se agota ni sufre cambios permanentes. (p. 205)

centro de masa: punto en un objeto que se mueve como si toda la masa del objeto estuviera concentrada en ese punto. (p. 322)

enlace químico: fuerza que mantiene a dos átomos unidos. (p. 169)

cambio químico: cualquier transformación de un material en otro nuevo con propiedades diferentes. (p. 145)

energía química: energía almacenada en enlaces químicos. (p. 377)

ecuación química: forma breve para representar los reactivos utilizados y los productos que se forman en una reacción química; algunas veces muestra si se produce o absorbe energía. (p. 192)

fórmula química: combinación de símbolos y números químicos que indican cuáles elementos y cuántos átomos de cada elemento están presentes en una molécula. (p. 178)

propiedad química: característica de algo que le permite su transformación en algo nuevo. (p. 139)

reacción química: proceso que produce cambios químicos que dan como resultado nuevas sustancias cuyas propiedades son diferentes a aquellas de las sustancias originales. (p. 190)

colesterol: lípido complejo presente en alimentos de origen animal. (p. 269)

gráfico circular: tipo de gráfico que muestra las partes de un todo; algunas veces se le llama gráfico de pastel en el que cada parte representa un porcentaje del total. (p. 58)

circuito: circuito conductor cerrado en el cual la energía puede fluir continuamente. (p. 591)

compuesto: sustancia resultante de la combinación de elementos cuyas propiedades son diferentes de los elementos que la componen. (pp. 87, 171)

máquina compuesta: máquina compuesta por la combinación de dos o más máquinas. (p. 417)

onda de compresión: tipo de onda mecánica en la que la materia en el medio se mueve hacia adelante y hacia atrás en dirección de la onda. (p. 465)

computer software: any list of instructions for a computer to follow that is stored in the computer's memory. (p. 653)

concave lens: lens that is thicker at its edges than in the middle. (p. 565)

concentration: describes how much solute is present in a solution compared to the amount of solvent. (pp. 203, 229)

condensation: change of matter from a gas to a liquid state. (p. 113)

conduction: transfer of thermal energy by direct contact; occurs when energy is transferred by collisions between particles. (p. 439)

conductor: material in which electrons can move or that transfers heat easily. (pp. 441, 588)

constant: variable that is not changed in an experiment. (p. 18)

controlled experiment: involves changing one factor and observing its effect on one thing while keeping all other things constant. (p. 18)

convection: transfer of thermal energy by the movement of particles from one place to another in a gas or liquid. (p. 440)

convex lens: lens that is thicker in the middle than at its edges. (p. 564)

covalent bond: chemical bond formed when atoms share electrons. (p. 173)

critical thinking: involves using knowledge and thinking skills to evaluate evidence and explanations. (p. 27)

software para computadoras: cualquier lista de instrucciones que debe realizar una computadora y que se almacena en la memoria de ésta. (p. 653)

lente cóncavo: lente que es más grueso en sus bordes que en el centro. (p. 565)

concentración: describe la cantidad de soluto presente en una solución, comparada con la cantidad de solvente. (pp. 203, 229)

condensación: cambio de estado de la materia de gas a líquido. (p. 113)

conducción: transferencia de energía térmica por contacto directo; se produce cuando la energía se transfiere mediante colisiones entre las partículas. (p. 439)

conductor: material en el cual los electrones se pueden mover o que transfiere calor fácilmente. (pp. 441, 588)

constante: variable que no cambia en un experimento. (p. 18)

experimento controlado: consiste en cambiar un factor y observar su efecto sobre algo mientras el resto de las cosas se mantiene constante. (p. 18)

convección: transferencia de energía térmica por el movimiento de partículas de un sitio a otro en un líquido o un gas. (p. 440)

lente convexo: lente que es más grueso en el centro que en sus bordes. (p. 564)

enlace covalente: enlace químico que se forma cuando los átomos comparten electrones. (p. 173)

pensamiento crítico: consiste en utilizar los conocimientos y habilidades del pensamiento para evaluar evidencias y explicaciones. (p. 27)

D

data: information gathered during an investigation; recorded in the form of descriptions, tables, graphs, or drawings. (p. 28)

density: physical property of matter that can be found by dividing the matter's mass by its volume. (pp. 121, 134, 352)

dependent variable: variable that changes as a result of a change in the independent variable. (p. 18)

diffraction: bending of waves around a barrier. (p. 475)

digital signal: electronic signal that varies information that does not vary smoothly with time, but changes in steps between certain values, and can be represented by a series of numbers. (p. 643)

datos: información recopilada durante una investigación y archivada en forma de descripciones, tablas, gráficas o planos. (p. 28)

densidad: propiedad física de la materia que se puede determinar dividiendo la masa de la materia por su volumen. (pp. 121, 134, 352)

variable dependiente: variable que cambia como resultado de un cambio en la variable independiente. (p. 18)

difracción: curvatura de las ondas alrededor de una barrera. (p. 475)

señal digital: señal electrónica que varía aquella información que no varía de manera uniforme con el tiempo, pero que cambia por grados entre ciertos valores y que puede ser representada por una serie de números. (p. 643)

diode: a solid-state component made from two layers of semiconductor material that allows electric current to flow in only one direction and is commonly used to change alternating current to direct current. (p. 646)

direct current (DC): electric current that flows only in one direction. (p. 627)

Doppler effect: change in the frequency of a sound wave that occurs when the sound source and the listener are in motion relative to each other. (p. 496)

diodo: componente de estado sólido conformado por dos capas de material semiconductor que permite el flujo de corriente eléctrica en una sola dirección y que comúnmente se utiliza para cambiar la corriente alterna a corriente directa. (p. 646)

corriente directa (CD): corriente eléctrica que fluye solamente en una dirección. (p. 627)

efecto Doppler: cambio en la frecuencia de una onda sonora que ocurre cuando la fuente de sonido y quien lo escucha están en movimiento relativo el uno del otro. (p. 496)

E

eardrum: membrane stretching across the ear canal that vibrates when sound waves reach the middle ear. (p. 508)

Earth science: study of Earth systems and systems in space, including weather and climate systems, and the study of nonliving things such as rocks, oceans, and planets. (p. 10)

echo: a reflected sound wave. (p. 495)

efficiency: equals the output work divided by the input work; expressed as a percentage. (p. 415)

electrical energy: energy carried by electric current. (p. 378)

electric current: the flow of electric charge, measured in amperes (A). (p. 591)

electric discharge: rapid movement of excess charge from one place to another. (p. 589)

electric field: surrounds every electric charge and exerts forces on other electric charges. (p. 587)

electric force: attractive or repulsive force exerted by all charged objects on each other. (p. 587)

electric power: rate at which electrical energy is converted into other forms of energy, measured in watts (W) or kilowatts (kW). (p. 600)

electromagnet: magnet created by wrapping a current-carrying wire around an iron core. (p. 621)

electromagnetic spectrum: range of electromagnetic waves, including radio waves, visible light, and X rays, with different frequencies and wavelengths. (p. 525)

electromagnetic waves: waves that can travel through matter or space; include radio waves, infrared waves, visible light waves, ultraviolet waves, X rays and gamma rays. (pp. 466, 520)

tímpano: membrana que se extiende a través del canal auditivo y que vibra cuando las ondas sonoras alcanzan el oído medio. (p. 508)

ciencias de la Tierra: estudio del sistema de la Tierra y de los sistemas en el espacio, incluyendo el clima y los sistemas climáticos y el estudio de los seres inanimados como las rocas, los océanos y los planetas. (p. 10)

eco: el reflejo de una onda sonora. (p. 495)

eficiencia: equivale al trabajo aplicado dividido el trabajo generado y se expresa en porcentaje. (p. 415)

energía eléctrica: energía transportada por corriente eléctrica. (p. 378)

corriente eléctrica: flujo de carga eléctrica, el cual se mide en amperios (A). (p. 591)

descarga eléctrica: movimiento rápido de carga excesiva de un lugar a otro. (p. 589)

campo eléctrico: campo que rodea a todas las cargas eléctricas y que ejerce fuerzas sobre otras cargas eléctricas. (p. 587)

fuerza eléctrica: fuerza de atracción o de repulsión que ejercen todos los objetos cargados entre ellos mismos. (p. 587)

potencia eléctrica: tasa a la cual la energía eléctrica se convierte en otras formas de energía, la cual se mide en vatios (W) o en kilovatios (kW). (p. 600)

electroimán: imán que se crea al enrollar un cable transportador de corriente alrededor de un centro de hierro. (p. 621)

espectro electromagnético: rango de ondas electromagnéticas, incluyendo las ondas de radio, luz visible, y rayos X, con diferentes frecuencias y longitudes de onda. (p. 525)

ondas electromagnéticas: ondas que pueden viajar a través de la materia o del espacio; incluyen ondas radiales, ondas infrarrojas, ondas de luz visible, ondas ultravioletas, rayos X y rayos gama. (pp. 466, 520)

electron: invisible, negatively charged particle located in a cloudlike formation that surrounds the nucleus of an atom. (p. 76)

electron cloud: area where negatively charged electrons, arranged in energy levels, travel around an atom's nucleus. (p. 162)

electron dot diagram: chemical symbol for an element, surrounded by as many dots as there are electrons in its outer energy level. (p. 168)

electronic signal: a changing electric current that is used to carry information; can be analog or digital. (p. 642)

element: natural or synthetic material that cannot be broken down into simpler materials by ordinary means; has unique properties and is generally classified as a metal, metalloid, or nonmetal. (p. 80)

endothermic (en duh THUR mihk) reaction: chemical reaction in which heat energy is absorbed. (p. 197)

energy: the ability to cause change. (p. 374)

energy level: the different positions for an electron in an atom. (p. 163)

enzyme: catalysts that are large protein molecules which speed up reactions needed for your cells to work properly. (p. 206)

estimation: method of making an educated guess at a measurement; using the size of something familiar to guess the size of a new object. (p. 43)

exothermic (ek soh THUR mihk) reaction: chemical reaction in which heat energy is released. (p. 197)

electrón: partícula invisible con carga negativa, localizada en una formación parecida a una nube que rodea el núcleo de un átomo. (p. 76)

nube de electrones: área en donde los electrones cargados negativamente se distribuyen en niveles de energía y se mueven alrededor del núcleo de un átomo. (p. 162)

diagrama de punto de electrones: símbolo químico para un elemento, rodeado de tantos puntos como electrones se encuentran en su nivel exterior de energía. (p. 168)

señal electrónica: corriente eléctrica dinámica que se usa para conducir información; puede ser analógica o digital. (p. 642)

elemento: material natural o sintético que no puede ser descompuesto fácilmente en materiales más simples por medios ordinarios; tiene propiedades únicas y generalmente es clasificado como metal, metaloide o no metal. (p. 80)

reacción endotérmica: reacción química en la cual se absorbe energía calórica. (p. 197)

energía: capacidad de producir cambios. (p. 374)

nivel de energía: las diferentes posiciones de un electrón en un átomo. (p. 163)

enzimas: catalizadores que son grandes moléculas de proteínas las cuales aceleran las reacciones necesarias para que las células trabajen en forma adecuada. (p. 206)

estimación: método para hacer una suposición fundamentada en una medida, usando el tamaño de algo conocido para suponer el tamaño de un nuevo objeto. (p. 43)

reacción exotérmica: reacción química en la cual se libera energía calórica. (p. 197)

F

fluid: a substance that has no definite shape and can flow. (p. 343)

focal length: distance along the optical axis from the center of a mirror or lens to the focal point. (p. 558)

focal point: point on the optical axis of a mirror or lens where rays traveling parallel to the optical axis pass through. (p. 558)

force: a push or a pull. (p. 310)

freezing: change of matter from a liquid state to a solid state. (p. 111)

frequency: number of wavelengths that pass a given point in one second; measured in hertz (Hz). (p. 469)

fluido: sustancia que no tiene forma definida y que puede fluir. (p. 343)

distancia focal: distancia a lo largo del eje óptico desde el centro de un espejo o lente hasta el punto focal. (p. 558)

punto focal: punto en el eje óptico de un espejo o lente por el cual atraviesan los rayos que viajan en paralelo al eje óptico. (p. 558)

fuerza: presión o tracción. (p. 310)

congelación: cambio de la materia de estado líquido a sólido. (p. 111)

frecuencia: número de longitudes de onda que pasan un punto determinado en un segundo; se mide en hertz (Hz). (p. 469)

friction: force that acts to oppose sliding between two surfaces that are touching. (p. 312)

fundamental frequency: lowest natural frequency that is produced by a vibrating object, such as a string or a column of air. (p. 503)

fricción: fuerza que actúa para oponerse al deslizamiento entre dos superficies que se tocan. (p. 312)

frecuencia fundamental: frecuencia natural más baja producida por un objeto que vibra, tal como una cuerda o una columna de aire. (p. 503)

G

gamma ray: highest-energy electromagnetic waves with the shortest wavelengths and highest frequencies. (p. 530)

gas: matter that does not have a definite shape or volume; has particles that move at high speeds in all directions. (p. 106)

generator: device that uses a magnetic field to turn kinetic energy into electrical energy. (pp. 384, 626)

Global Positioning System (GPS): uses satellites, ground-based stations, and portable units with receivers to locate objects on Earth. (p. 539)

graph: used to collect, organize, and summarize data in a visual way, making it easy to use and understand. (p. 57)

rayos gama: ondas electromagnéticas que poseen la mayor cantidad de energía y las cuales presentan las longitudes de onda más cortas y las frecuencias más altas. (p. 530)

gas: materia que no tiene ni forma ni volumen definidos; tiene partículas que se mueven a altas velocidades y en todas las direcciones. (p. 106)

generador: dispositivo que utiliza un campo magnético para convertir energía cinética en energía eléctrica. (pp. 384, 626)

Sistema de Posicionamiento Global (SPG): sistema que utiliza satélites, estaciones en tierra y unidades portátiles con receptores para ubicar objetos en la Tierra. (pp. 539)

gráfico: se usa para recolectar, organizar y resumir información en forma visual, facilitando su uso y comprensión. (p. 57)

H

heat: movement of thermal energy from a substance at a higher temperature to a substance at a lower temperature. (pp. 108, 438)

heat engine: device that converts thermal energy into mechanical energy. (p. 445)

heterogeneous mixture: type of mixture where the substances are not evenly mixed. (p. 219)

homogeneous mixture: type of mixture where two or more substances are evenly mixed on a molecular level but are not bonded together. (p. 220)

hydraulic system: uses a fluid to increase an applied force. (p. 357)

hydrocarbon: organic compound that has only carbon and hydrogen atoms. (p. 251)

hydronium ion: hydrogen ion combines with a water molecule to form a hydronium ion, H_3O^+. (p. 232)

hydroxyl (hi DROK sul) group: consists of an oxygen atom and a hydrogen atom joined by a covalent bond; represented by the formula $-OH$. (p. 258)

calor: movimiento de energía térmica de una sustancia que se encuentra a una alta temperatura hacia una sustancia a una baja temperatura. (pp. 108, 438)

motor de calor: motor que transforma la energía térmica en energía mecánica. (p. 445)

mezcla heterogénea: tipo de mezcla en la cual las sustancias no están mezcladas de manera uniforme. (p. 219)

mezcla homogénea: tipo de mezcla en la cual dos o más sustancias están mezcladas en de manera uniforme a nivel molecular pero no están enlazadas. (p. 220)

sistema hidráulico: usa un fluido para incrementar una fuerza aplicada. (p. 357)

hidrocarburo: compuesto orgánico que sólo contiene átomos de carbono e hidrógeno. (p. 251)

ion de hidronio: ion de hidrógeno combinado con una molécula de agua para formar un ion de hidronio, H_3O^+. (p. 232)

grupo hidroxilo: consiste en un átomo de oxígeno y un átomo de hidrógeno unidos por un enlace covalente; se lo representa con la fórmula $-OH$. (p. 258)

hypothesis: reasonable guess that can be tested and is based on what is known and what is observed. (p. 14)

hipótesis: suposición razonable que puede ser probada y que está basada en lo que se sabe y en lo que ha sido observado. (p. 14)

I

inclined plane: simple machine that is a flat surface, sloped surface, or ramp. (p. 417)

independent variable: variable that is changed in an experiment. (p. 18)

indicator: compound that changes color at different pH values when it reacts with acidic or basic solutions. (p. 238)

inertia: tendency of an object to resist a change in its motion. (p. 293)

inexhaustible resource: energy source that can't be used up by humans. (p. 391)

infer: to draw a conclusion based on observation. (p. 16)

infrared wave: electromagnetic waves with wavelengths between 1 mm and 0.7 millionths of a meter. (p. 527)

inhibitor: substance that slows down a chemical reaction, making the formation of a certain amount of product take longer. (p. 204)

input force: force exerted on a machine. (p. 412)

instantaneous speed: the speed of an object at one instant of time. (p. 285)

insulator: material in which electrons cannot move easily. (p. 588)

integrated circuit: circuit that can contain millions of interconnected transistors and diodes imprinted on a single small chip of semiconductor material. (p. 647)

interference: occurs when two or more waves combine and form a new wave when they overlap. (p. 477)

internal combustion engine: heat engine in which fuel is burned in a combustion chamber inside the engine. (p. 446)

ion (I ahn): atom that is positively or negatively charged because it has gained or lost electrons. (pp. 171, 584)

ionic bond: attraction that holds oppositely charged ions close together. (p. 171)

isomers (I suh murz): compounds with the same chemical formula but different structures and different physical and chemical properties. (p. 254)

plano inclinado: máquina simple que consiste en una superficie plana, inclinada, o una rampa. (p. 417)

variable independiente: variable que cambia en un experimento. (p. 18)

indicador: compuesto que cambia de color con diferentes valores de pH al reaccionar con soluciones ácidas o básicas. (p. 238)

inercia: tendencia de un objeto a resistirse a un cambio de movimiento. (p. 293)

recurso inagotable: fuente de energía que no puede ser agotada por los seres humanos. (p. 391)

deducción: sacar una conclusión con base en una observación. (p. 16)

ondas infrarrojas: ondas electromagnéticas con longitudes de onda entre un milímetro y 0.7 millonésimas de metro. (p. 527)

inhibidor: sustancia que reduce la velocidad de una reacción química, haciendo que la formación de una determinada cantidad de producto tarde más tiempo. (p. 204)

fuerza aplicada: fuerza que se ejerce sobre una máquina. (p. 412)

velocidad instantánea: la velocidad de un objeto en un instante de tiempo. (p. 285)

aislante: material en el cual los electrones no se pueden mover fácilmente. (p. 588)

circuito integrado: circuito que puede contener millones de transistores y diodos interconectados y fijados en un solo chip de tamaño reducido y hecho de material semiconductor. (p. 647)

interferencia: ocurre cuando dos o más ondas se combinan y al sobreponerse forman una nueva onda. (p. 477)

motor de combustión interna: motor de calor en el cual el combustible es quemado en una cámara de combustión dentro del motor. (p. 446)

ion: átomo cargado positiva o negativamente a que ha ganado o perdido electrónes. (pp. 171, 584)

enlace iónico: atracción que mantiene unidos a iones con cargas opuestas. (p. 171)

isómeros: compuestos que tienen la misma fórmula química pero diferentes estructuras y propiedades físicas y químicas. (p. 254)

isotopes (I suh tohps): two or more atoms of the same element that have different numbers of neutrons in their nuclei. (p. 83)

isótopos: dos o más átomos del mismo elemento que tienen diferente número de neutrones en su núcleo. (p. 83)

K

Kelvin (K): SI unit for temperature. (p. 54)
kilogram (kg): SI unit for mass. (p. 53)
kinetic energy: energy an object has due to its motion. (p. 375)

Kelvin (K): unidad del SI para temperatura. (p. 54)
kilogramo (kg): unidad del SI para masa. (p. 53)
energía cinética: energía que posee un objeto debido a su movimiento. (p. 375)

L

law of conservation of energy: states that energy can change its form but is never created or destroyed. (p. 380)

law of conservation of matter: states that matter is not created or destroyed but only changes its form. (p. 74)

law of conservation of momentum: states that the total momentum of objects that collide with each other is the same before and after the collision. (p. 295)

law of reflection: states that when a wave is reflected, the angle of incidence is equal to the angle of reflection. (p. 555)

lens: transparent object that has at least one curved surface that causes light to bend. (p. 563)

lever: simple machine consisting of a rigid rod or plank that pivots or rotates about a fixed point called the fulcrum. (p. 420)

life science: study of living systems and how they interact. (p. 9)

light ray: narrow beam of light traveling in a straight line. (p. 550)

line graph: a type of graph used to show the relationship between two variables that are numbers on an x-axis and a y-axis. (p. 57)

lipids: organic compound that contains the same elements as carbohydrates but in different proportions. (p. 267)

liquid: matter with a definite volume but no definite shape that can flow from one place to another. (p. 104)

loudness: the human perception of how much energy a sound wave carries. (p. 492)

ley de la conservación de la energía: establece que la energía puede cambiar de forma pero nunca puede ser creada ni destruida. (p. 380)

ley de la conservación de la materia: establece que la materia no se crea ni se destruye, solamente cambia de forma. (p. 74)

ley de conservación de momento: establece que el momento total de los objetos que chocan entre sí es el mismo antes y después de la colisión. (p. 295)

ley de la reflexión: establece que cuando se refleja una onda, el ángulo de incidencia es igual al ángulo de reflexión. (p. 555)

lente: objeto transparente que tiene por lo menos una superficie curva que hace cambiar la dirección de la luz. (p. 563)

palanca: máquina simple que consiste en una barra rígida que puede girar sobre un punto fijo llamado punto de apoyo. (p. 420)

ciencias de la vida: estudio de los sistemas vivos y de la forma como interactúan. (p. 9)

rayo de luz: haz estrecho de luz que viaja en línea recta. (p. 550)

gráfico lineal: tipo de gráfico usado para mostrar la relación entre dos variables que son números en un eje x y en un eje y. (p. 57)

lípidos: compuestos orgánicos que contienen los mismos elementos que los carbohidratos pero en proporciones diferentes. (p. 267)

líquido: materia con volumen definido pero no con forma definida que puede fluir de un sitio a otro. (p. 104)

intensidad: percepción humana de la cantidad de energía conducida por una onda sonora. (p. 492)

M

magnetic domain: group of atoms whose fields point in the same direction. (p. 616)

dominio magnético: grupo de átomos cuyos campos apuntan en la misma dirección. (p. 616)

magnetic field: surrounds a magnet and exerts a magnetic force on other magnets. (p. 615)

magnetosphere: region of space affected by Earth's magnetic field. (p. 617)

mass: amount of matter in an object. (pp. 53, 293)

mass number: sum of the number of protons and neutrons in the nucleus of an atom. (p. 83)

matter: anything that takes up space and has mass. (pp. 72, 102)

measurement: way to describe objects and events with numbers; for example, length, volume, mass, weight, and temperature. (p. 42)

mechanical advantage: number of times the input force is multiplied by a machine; equal to the output force divided by the input force. (p. 413)

mechanical wave: a type of wave that can travel only through matter. (p. 463)

medium: material through which a wave travels. (p. 551)

melting: change of matter from a solid state to a liquid state. (p. 109)

metal: element that is malleable, ductile, a good conductor of electricity, and generally has a shiny or metallic luster. (p. 84)

metallic bond: bond formed when metal atoms share their pooled electrons. (p. 172)

metalloid: element that has characteristics of both metals and nonmetals and is a solid at room temperature. (p. 85)

meter (m): SI unit for length. (p. 51)

microprocessor: integrated circuit that controls the flow of information between different parts of the computer; also called the central processing unit or CPU. (p. 655)

mixture: a combination of compounds and elements that has not formed a new substance and whose proportions can be changed without changing the mixture's identity. (p. 89)

model: any representation of an object or an event that is used as a tool for understanding the natural world; can communicate observations and ideas, test predictions, and save time, money, and lives. (p. 21)

molecule (MAH lih kewl): neutral particle formed when atoms share electrons. (p. 173)

momentum: a measure of how difficult it is to stop a moving object; equals the product of mass and velocity. (p. 294)

monomer: small, organic molecules that link together to form polymers. (p. 262)

motor: device that transforms electrical energy into kinetic energy. (p. 624)

campo magnético: campo que rodea a un imán y ejerce fuerza magnética sobre otros imanes. (p. 615)

magnetosfera: región del espacio afectada por el campo magnético de la Tierra. (p. 617)

masa: cantidad de materia en un objeto. (pp. 53, 293)

número de masa: suma del número de protones y neutrones en el núcleo de un átomo. (p. 83)

materia: cualquier cosa que ocupe espacio y tenga masa. (pp. 72, 102)

medida: forma para describir objetos y eventos con números; por ejemplo, longitud, volumen, masa, peso y temperatura. (p. 42)

ventaja mecánica: número de veces que la fuerza aplicada es multiplicada por una máquina; equivale a la fuerza producida dividida por la fuerza aplicada. (p. 413)

onda mecánica: tipo de onda que puede viajar únicamente a través de la materia. (p. 463)

medio: material a través del cual viaja una onda. (p. 551)

fusión: cambio de la materia de estado sólido a líquido. (p. 109)

metal: elemento maleable, dúctil y buen conductor de electricidad que generalmente tiene un lustre brillante o metálico. (p. 84)

enlace metálico: enlace que se forma cuando átomos metálicos comparten sus electrones agrupados. (p. 172)

metaloide: elemento que comparte características de los metales y de los no metales y es sólido a temperatura ambiente. (p. 85)

metro (m): unidad del SI para longitud. (p. 51)

microprocesador: circuito integrado que controla el flujo de información entre diferentes partes de una computadora; también se lo denomina la unidad central de procesamiento o CPU. (p. 655)

mezcla: combinación de compuestos y elementos que no han formado una nueva sustancia y cuyas proporciones pueden ser cambiadas sin que se pierda la identidad de la mezcla. (p. 89)

modelo: cualquier representación de un objeto o evento utilizada como herramienta para entender el mundo natural; puede comunicar observaciones e ideas, predicciones de las pruebas y ahorrar tiempo, dinero y salvar vidas. (p. 21)

molécula: partícula neutra que se forma cuando los átomos comparten electrones. (p. 173)

momento: medida de la dificultad para detener un objeto en movimiento; es igual al producto de la masa por la velocidad. (p. 294)

monómeros: moléculas orgánicas pequeñas que se unen entre sí para formar polímeros. (p. 262)

motor: dispositivo que transforma energía eléctrica en energía cinética. (p. 624)

natural frequencies: frequencies at which an object will vibrate when it is struck or disturbed. (p. 501)

net force: combination of all forces acting on an object. (p. 311)

neutralization (new truh luh ZAY shun): reaction in which an acid reacts with a base and forms water and a salt. (p. 238)

neutron: an uncharged particle located in the nucleus of an atom. (p. 78)

Newton's first law of motion: states that if the net force acting on an object is zero, the object will remain at rest or move in a straight line with a constant speed. (p. 312)

Newton's second law of motion: states that an object acted upon by a net force will accelerate in the direction of the force, and that the acceleration equals the net force divided by the object's mass. (p. 316)

Newton's third law of motion: states that forces always act in equal but opposite pairs. (p. 323)

nonmetals: elements that are usually gases or brittle solids and poor conductors of electricity and heat; are the basis of the chemicals of life. (p. 85)

nonrenewable resource: energy resource that is used up much faster than it can be replaced. (p. 388)

nuclear energy: energy contained in atomic nuclei. (p. 378)

nucleus (NEW klee us): positively charged, central part of an atom. (p. 77)

frecuencias naturales: frecuencias a las cuales un objeto vibrará cuando es golpeado o perturbado. (p. 501)

fuerza neta: la combinación de todas las fuerzas que actúan sobre un objeto. (p. 311)

neutralización: reacción en la cual un ácido reacciona con una base para formar agua y una sal. (p. 238)

neutrón: partícula sin carga localizada en el núcleo de un átomo (p. 78)

primera ley de movimiento de Newton: establece que si la fuerza neta que actúa sobre un objeto es igual a cero, el objeto se mantendrá en reposo o se moverá en línea recta a una velocidad constante. (p. 312)

segunda ley de movimiento de Newton: establece que si una fuerza neta se ejerce sobre un objeto, éste se acelerará en la dirección de la fuerza y la aceleración es igual a la fuerza neta dividida por la masa del objeto. (p. 316)

tercera ley de movimiento de Newton: establece que las fuerzas siempre actúan en pares iguales pero opuestos. (p. 323)

no metales: elementos que por lo general son gases o sólidos frágiles y malos conductores de electricidad y calor; son la base de los compuestos químicos biológicos. (p. 85)

recurso no renovable: recurso energético que se agota mucho más rápidamente de lo que puede ser reemplazado. (p. 388)

energía nuclear: energía contenida en los núcleos de los átomos. (p. 378)

núcleo: parte central con carga positiva del átomo. (p. 77)

Ohm's law: states that the current in a circuit equals the voltage divided by the resistance in the circuit. (p. 597)

organic compounds: most compounds that contain carbon. (p. 250)

output force: force exerted by a machine. (p. 412)

overtones: multiples of the fundamental frequency. (p. 503)

ley de Ohm: establece que la corriente en un circuito es igual al voltaje dividido por la resistencia en el circuito. (p. 597)

compuestos orgánicos: la mayoría de compuestos que contienen carbono. (p. 250)

fuerza generada: fuerza producida por una máquina. (p. 412)

armónicos: múltiplos de la frecuencia fundamental. (p. 503)

parallel circuit: circuit that has more than one path for electric current to follow. (p. 599)

circuito paralelo: circuito en el cual la corriente eléctrica puede seguir más de una trayectoria. (p. 599)

Pascal's principle: states that when a force is applied to a confined fluid, an increase in pressure is transmitted equally to all parts of the fluid. (pp. 122, 357)

pH: measure of how acidic or basic a solution is, ranging in a scale from 0 to 14. (p. 236)

photovoltaic: device that transforms radiant energy directly into electrical energy. (p. 392)

physical change: any change in the size, shape, form, or state of matter in which the matter's identity remains the same. (p. 143)

physical property: any characteristic of matter—such as color, shape, and taste—that can be detected by the senses without changing the identity of the matter. (p. 134)

physical science: study of matter, which is anything that takes up space and has mass, and the study of energy, which is the ability to cause change. (p. 10)

pitch: how high or low a sound is. (p. 494)

polar bond: bond resulting from the unequal sharing of electrons. (p. 174)

polymer: large molecule made up of small repeating units linked by covalent bonds to form a long chain. (p. 262)

polymerization: a chemical reaction in which monomers are bonded together. (p. 262)

potential energy: energy stored in an object due to its position. (p. 376)

power: rate at which work is done; equal to the work done divided by the time it takes to do the work; measured in watts (W). (p. 409)

precipitate: solid that comes back out of its solution because of a chemical reaction or physical change. (p. 220)

precision: describes how closely measurements are to each other and how carefully measurements were made. (p. 44)

pressure: amount of force applied per unit area on an object's surface; SI unit is the Pascal (Pa). (pp. 116, 340)

product: substance that forms as a result of a chemical reaction. (p. 192)

protein: biological polymer made up of amino acids; catalyzes many cell reactions and provides structural materials for many parts of the body. (p. 263)

proton: positively charged particle located in the nucleus of an atom and that is counted to identify the atomic number. (p. 77)

principio de Pascal: establece que cuando se ejerce una fuerza sobre un fluido encerrado, se transmite un incremento de presión uniforme a todas las partes del fluido. (pp. 122, 357)

pH: medida para saber qué tan básica o ácida es una solución, en una escala de 0 a 14. (p. 236)

fotovoltaico: dispositivo que transforma la energía radiante directamente en energía eléctrica. (p. 392)

cambio físico: cualquier cambio en el tamaño, apariencia, forma o estado de la materia, en el que la identidad de la materia permanece igual. (p. 143)

propiedad física: cualquier característica de la materia, como el color, apariencia o sabor, que puede ser detectada por los sentidos sin que cambie la identidad de la materia. (p. 134)

ciencias física: estudio de la materia, lo cual es todo lo que ocupe espacio y tenga masa, y el estudio de la energía, que es la habilidad de producir cambios. (p. 10)

altura: expresa qué tan alto o bajo es un sonido. (p. 494)

enlace polar: enlace que resulta de compartir electrones en forma desigual. (p. 174)

polímero: molécula grande formada por unidades pequeñas que se repiten y están unidas por enlaces covalentes para formar una cadena larga. (p. 262)

polimerización: reacción química en la que los monómeros se unen entre sí. (p. 262)

energía potencial: energía almacenada en un objeto debido a su posición. (p. 376)

potencia: velocidad a la que se realiza un trabajo y que equivale al trabajo realizado dividido por el tiempo que toma realizar el trabajo; se mide en vatios (W). (p. 409)

precipitado: sólido que se aísla de su solución mediante una reacción química o un cambio físico. (p. 220)

precisión: describe qué tan aproximada es una medida respecto a otra y qué tan cuidadosamente fueron hechas dichas medidas. (p. 44)

presión: cantidad de fuerza aplicada por unidad de área sobre la superficie de un objeto; la unidad internacional SI es el Pascal (Pa). (pp. 116, 340)

producto: sustancia que se forma como resultado de una reacción química. (p. 192)

proteína: polímero biológico formado por aminoácidos; cataliza numerosas reacciones celulares y conforma materiales estructurales para diversas partes del cuerpo. (p. 263)

protón: partícula cargada positivamente, localizada en el núcleo de un átomo y que se cuenta para identificar el número atómico. (p. 77)

pulley: simple machine made from a grooved wheel with a rope or cable wrapped around the groove. (p. 422)

polea: máquina simple que consiste en una rueda acanalada con una cuerda o cable que corre alrededor del canal. (p. 422)

R

radiant energy: energy carried by an electromagnetic wave. (pp. 377, 524)

energía radiante: energía conducida por una onda electromagnética. (pp. 377, 524)

radiation: transfer of energy by electromagnetic waves. (p. 439)

radiación: transferencia de energía mediante ondas electromagnéticas. (p. 439)

radio waves: lowest-frequency electromagnetic waves that have wavelengths greater than about 0.3 m and are used in most forms of telecommunications technology—such as TVs, telephones, and radios. (p. 526)

ondas de radio: ondas electromagnéticas con la menor frecuencia, las cuales poseen longitudes de onda mayores de unos 0.3 metros y son utilizadas en la mayoría de técnicas de telecomunicaciones, tales como televisores, teléfonos y radios. (p. 526)

random-access memory (RAM): temporary electronic memory within a computer. (p. 652)

memoria de acceso aleatorio (RAM): memoria electrónica temporal dentro de una computadora. (p. 652)

rate: a ratio of two different kinds of measurements; the amount of change of one measurement in a given amount of time. (p. 54)

tasa: relación de dos diferentes tipos de medidas; los cambios en una medida en un tiempo determinado. (p. 54)

rate of reaction: measure of how fast a chemical reaction occurs. (p. 202)

velocidad de reacción: medida de la rapidez con que se produce una reacción química. (p. 202)

reactant: substance that exists before a chemical reaction begins. (p. 192)

reactivo: sustancia que existe antes de que comience una reacción química. (p. 192)

reactivity: describes how easily something reacts with something else. (p. 140)

reactividad: describe la facilidad con la que dos cosas pueden reaccionar entre sí. (p. 140)

read-only memory (ROM): electronic memory that is permanently stored within a computer. (p. 652)

memoria de sólo lectura (ROM): memoria electrónica almacenada permanentemente dentro de una computadora. (p. 652)

reflecting telescope: uses a concave mirror to gather light from distant objects. (p. 569)

telescopio de reflexión: utiliza un espejo cóncavo para concentrar la luz proveniente de objetos lejanos. (p. 569)

reflection: occurs when a wave strikes an object or surface and bounces off. (p. 473)

reflexión: ocurre cuando una onda choca contra un objeto o superficie y rebota. (p. 473)

refracting telescope: uses two convex lenses to gather light and form an image of a distant object. (p. 568)

telescopio de refracción: utiliza dos lentes convexos para concentrar la luz y formar una imagen de un objeto lejano. (p. 568)

refraction: bending of a wave as it moves from one medium into another medium. (p. 474)

refracción: curvatura de una onda a medida que se mueve de un medio a otro. (p. 474)

renewable resource: energy resource that is replenished continually. (p. 390)

recurso renovable: recurso energético regenerado continuamente. (p. 390)

resistance: a measure of how difficult it is for electrons to flow in a material; unit is the ohm (Ω). (p. 594)

resistencia: medida de la dificultad que tienen los electrones para fluir en un material; se mide en ohmios (Ω). (p. 594)

resonance: occurs when an object is made to vibrate at its natural frequencies by absorbing energy from a sound wave or other object vibrating at this frequency. (p. 502)

resonancia: ocurre cuando se hace vibrar un objeto a sus frecuencias naturales mediante la absorción de energía de una onda sonora o de otro objeto que vibra a dicha frecuencia. (p. 502)

reverberation: repeated echoes of sounds. (p. 507)

reverberación: ecos repetidos de los sonidos. (p. 507)

S

salts: compounds made of a metal and a nonmetal that are formed along with water when acids and bases react with each other. (p. 142)

saturated: describes a solution that holds the total amount of solute that it can hold under given conditions. (p. 228)

saturated hydrocarbon: hydrocarbon, such as methane, with only single bonds. (p. 252)

science: way of learning more about the natural world that provides possible explanations to questions and involves using a collection of skills. (p. 6)

scientific law: a rule that describes a pattern in nature but does not try to explain why something happens. (p. 7)

scientific theory: a possible explanation for repeatedly observed patterns in nature supported by observations and results from many investigations. (p. 7)

screw: simple machine that is an inclined plane wrapped around a cylinder or post. (p. 419)

semiconductor: element, such as silicon, that is a poorer electrical conductor that a metal, but a better conductor than a nonmetal, and whose electrical conductivity can be changed by adding impurities. (p. 645)

series circuit: circuit that has only one path for electric current to follow. (p. 598)

SI: International System of Units, related by multiples of ten, designed to provided a worldwide standard of physical measurement. (p. 50)

simple machine: a machine that does work with only one movement; includes the inclined plane, wedge, screw, lever, wheel and axle, and pulley. (p. 417)

size-dependent properties: physical properties—such as volume and mass—that change when the size of the object changes. (p. 136)

size-independent properties: physical properties—such as density—that do not change when the size of the object changes. (p. 136)

solid: matter with a definite shape and volume; has tightly packed particles that move mainly by vibrating. (p. 103)

solubility (sahl yuh BIH luh tee): measure of how much solute can be dissolved in a certain amount of solvent. (p. 227)

solute: substance that dissolves and seems to disappear into another substance. (p. 220)

sales: compuestos formados por un metal y un no metal que se forman junto con agua cuando reaccionan ácidos y bases entre sí. (p. 142)

saturado: describe a una solución que retiene toda la cantidad de soluto que puede retener bajo determinadas condiciones. (p. 228)

hidrocarburo saturado: hidrocarburo, como el metano, que sólo presenta enlaces sencillos. (p. 252)

ciencia: mecanismo para aprender más acerca del mundo natural, que da respuestas posibles a los interrogantes e implica hacer uso de numerosas habilidades. (p. 6)

ley científica: regla que describe un modelo en la naturaleza pero que no intenta explicar por qué suceden las cosas. (p. 7)

teoría científica: posible explicación para patrones observados repetidamente en la naturaleza y apoyada en observaciones y resultados de muchas investigaciones. (p. 7)

tornillo: máquina simple que consiste en un plano inclinado envuelto en espiral alrededor de un cilindro o poste. (p. 419)

semiconductor: elemento, como el silicio, que no es tan buen conductor de electricidad como un metal, pero que es mejor conductor que un no metal y cuya conductividad eléctrica puede ser modificada al añadirle impurezas. (p. 645)

circuito en serie: circuito en el cual la corriente eléctrica sólo puede seguir una trayectoria. (p. 598)

SI: Sistema Internacional de Unidades, se ordena en múltiplos de diez, diseñados para suministrar un estándar de medidas físicas a nivel mundial. (p. 50)

máquina simple: máquina que ejecuta el trabajo con un solo movimiento; incluye el plano inclinado, la palanca, el tornillo, la rueda y el eje y la polea. (p. 417)

propiedades dependientes del tamaño: propiedades físicas, tales como volumen y masa, que cambian cuando se modifica el tamaño del objeto. (p. 136)

propiedades independientes del tamaño: propiedades físicas, tales como la densidad, que no cambian cuando se modifica el tamaño del objeto. (p. 136)

sólido: materia con forma y volumen definidos; tiene partículas fuertemente compactadas que se mueven principalmente por vibración. (p. 103)

solubilidad: medida de la cantidad de soluto que puede disolverse en cierta cantidad de solvente. (p. 227)

soluto: sustancia que se disuelve y parece desaparecer en otra sustancia. (p. 220)

solution: homogeneous mixture whose elements and/or compounds are evenly mixed at the molecular level but are not bonded together. (p. 220)

solvent: substance that dissolves the solute. (p. 220)

specific heat: amount of heat needed to raise the temperature of 1 kg of a substance by 1°C. (p. 442)

speed: equals the distance traveled divided by the time it takes to travel that distance. (p. 284)

starches: polymers of glucose monomers in which hundreds or thousands of glucose molecules are joined together. (p. 265)

state of matter: physical property that describes a substance as a solid, liquid, or gas. (p. 136)

static charge: imbalance of electric charge on an object. (p. 585)

substance: matter with a fixed composition whose identity can be changed by chemical processes but not by ordinary physical processes. (pp. 87, 218)

sugars: carbohydrates containing carbon atoms arranged in a ring. (p. 265)

surface tension: the uneven forces acting on the particles on the surface of a liquid. (p. 105)

system: collection of structures, cycles, and processes that relate to and interact with each other. (p. 8)

solución: mezcla homogénea cuyos elementos o compuestos están mezclados de manera uniforme a nivel molecular pero no se enlazan. (p. 220)

solvente: sustancia que disuelve al soluto. (p. 220)

calor específico: cantidad de calor necesario para elevar la temperatura de 1 kilogramo de una sustancia en 1 grado centígrado. (p. 442)

rapidez: equivale a dividir la distancia recorrida por el tiempo que toma recorrer dicha distancia. (p. 284)

almidones: polímeros de monómeros de la glucosa en los que cientos o miles de moléculas de glucosa están unidas entre sí. (p. 265)

estado de la materia: propiedad física que describe a una sustancia como sólido, líquido o gas. (p. 136)

carga estátlca: desequilibrio de la carga eléctrica en un objeto. (p. 585)

sustancia: materia que tiene una composición fija cuya identidad puede ser cambiada mediante procesos químicos pero no mediante procesos físicos corrientes. (pp. 87, 218)

azúcares: carbohidratos que contienen átomos de carbono dispuestos en un anillo. (p. 265)

tensión superficial: fuerzas desiguales que actúan sobre las partículas que se encuentran en la superficie de un líquido. (p. 105)

sistema: colección de estructuras, ciclos y procesos relacionados que interactúan entre sí. (p. 8)

T

table: presents information in rows and columns, making it easier to read and understand. (p. 57)

technology: use of science to help people in some way. (p. 11)

temperature: measure of the average kinetic energy of the individual particles of a substance. (pp. 108, 434)

thermal energy: the sum of the kinetic and potential energy of the particles in a material. (pp. 376, 437)

thermal pollution: increase in temperature of a natural body of water; caused by adding warmer water. (p. 443)

transformer: device used to increase or decrease the voltage of an alternating current. (p. 628)

transistor: a solid-state component made from three layers of semiconductor material that can amplify the strength of an electric signal or act as an electronic switch. (p. 647)

tabla: presentación de información en filas y columnas, facilitando la lectura y comprensión. (p. 57)

tecnología: uso de la ciencia para ayudar en alguna forma a las personas. (p. 11)

temperatura: medida de la energía cinética promedio de las partículas individuales de una sustancia. (pp. 108, 434)

energía térmica: la suma de la energía cinética y potencial de las partículas en un material. (pp. 376, 437)

polución térmica: incremento de la temperatura de una masa natural de agua producido al agregarle agua a mayor temperatura. (p. 443)

transformador: dispositivo utilizado para aumentar o disminuir el voltaje de una corriente alterna. (p. 628)

transistor: componente de estado sólido formado por tres capas de material semiconductor que puede amplificar la fuerza de una señal eléctrica o actuar a manera de interruptor electrónico. (p. 647)

transverse wave: a type of mechanical wave in which the wave energy causes matter in the medium to move up and down or back and forth at right angles to the direction the wave travels. (p. 464)

turbine: set of steam-powered fan blades that spins a generator at a power plant. (p. 384)

onda transversal: tipo de onda mecánica en el cual la energía de la onda hace que la materia en el medio se mueva hacia arriba y hacia abajo o hacia adelante y hacia atrás en ángulos rectos respecto a la dirección en que viaja la onda. (p. 464)

turbina: conjunto de aspas de ventilador impulsadas por vapor que hacen girar a un generador en una planta de energía eléctrica. (p. 384)

ultraviolet radiation: electromagnetic waves with wavelengths between about 0.4 millionths of a meter and 10 billionths of a meter; has frequencies and wavelengths between visible light and X rays. (p. 529)

unbalanced forces: two or more forces acting on an object that do not cancel, and cause the object to accelerate. (p. 311)

unsaturated hydrocarbon: hydrocarbon, such as ethylene, with one or more double or triple bonds. (p. 253)

radiación ultravioleta: ondas electromagnéticas con longitudes de onda entre aproximadamente 0.4 millonésimas de metro y 10 billonésimas de metro; tienen frecuencias y longitudes de onda entre aquellas de la luz visible y los rayos X. (p. 529)

fuerzas no balanceadas: dos o más fuerzas que actúan sobre un objeto sin anularse y que hacen que el objeto se acelere. (p. 311)

hidrocarburo insaturado: hidrocarburo, como el etileno, con uno o más enlaces dobles o triples. (p. 253)

vaporization: change of matter from a liquid state to a gas. (p. 112)

variable: factor that can be changed in an experiment. (p. 18)

velocity: speed and direction of a moving object. (p. 287)

viscosity: a liquid's resistance to flow. (p. 105)

visible light: electromagnetic waves with wavelengths between 0.4 and 0.7 millionths of a meter that can be seen with your eyes. (p. 528)

voltage: a measure of the amount of electrical potential energy an electron flowing in a circuit can gain; measured in volts (V). (p. 592)

volume: the amount of space an object occupies. (p. 52)

vaporización: cambio de estado de la materia de líquido a gas. (p. 112)

variable: factor que puede cambiar en un experimento. (p. 18)

velocidad: rapidez y dirección de un objeto en movimiento. (p. 287)

viscosidad: resistencia de un líquido al flujo. (p. 105)

luz visible: ondas electromagnéticas con longitudes de onda entre 0.4 y 0.7 millonésimas de metro y que pueden ser observadas a simple vista. (p. 528)

voltaje: medida de la cantidad de energía eléctrica potencial que puede adquirir un electrón que fluye en un circuito; se mide en voltios (V). (p. 592)

volumen: la cantidad de espacio que ocupa un objeto. (p. 52)

W

wave: rhythmic disturbance that carries energy but not matter. (p. 462)

wavelength: for a transverse wave, the distance between the tops of two adjacent crests or the bottoms of two adjacent troughs; for a compressional wave, the distance from the centers of adjacent rarefactions or adjacent compressions. (p. 468)

onda: alteración rítmica que transporta energía pero no materia. (p. 462)

longitud de onda: en una onda transversal, es la distancia entre las puntas de dos crestas adyacentes o entre dos depresiones adyacentes; en una onda de compresión es la distancia entre los centros de dos rarefacciones adyacentes o compresiones adyacentes. (p. 468)

wedge: simple machine consisting of an inclined plane that moves; can have one or two sloping sides. (p. 418)

weight: a measurement of force that depends on gravity; measured in newtons. (pp. 53, 317)

wheel and axle: simple machine made from two circular objects of different sizes that are attached and rotate together. (p. 420)

work: is done when a force exerted on an object causes that object to move some distance; equal to force times distance; measured in joules (J). (p. 406)

cuña: máquina simple que consiste en un plano inclinado que se mueve; puede tener uno o dos lados inclinados. (p. 418)

peso: medida de fuerza que depende de la gravedad y que se mide en Newtons. (pp. 53, 317)

rueda y eje: máquina simple compuesta por dos objetos circulares de diferentes tamaños que están interconectados y giran. (p. 420)

trabajo: se realiza cuando la fuerza ejercida sobre un objeto hace que el objeto se mueva determinada distancia; es igual a la fuerza multiplicada por la distancia y se mide en julios (J). (p. 406)

X

X ray: high-energy electromagnetic wave that is highly penetrating and can be used for medical diagnosis. (p. 530)

rayos X: ondas electromagnéticas de alta energía, las cuales son altamente penetrantes y pueden ser utilizadas para diagnósticos médicos. (p. 530)

Index

Index

Index

Index

Index

Index

Index

Magnification Key: Magnifications listed are the magnifications at which images were originally photographed.
LM–Light Microscope
SEM–Scanning Electron Microscope
TEM–Transmission Electron Microscope

Acknowledgments: Glencoe would like to acknowledge the artists and agencies who participated in illustrating this program: Absolute Science Illustration; Andrew Evansen; Argosy; Articulate Graphics; Craig Attebery represented by Frank & Jeff Lavaty; CHK America; John Edwards and Associates; Gagliano Graphics; Pedro Julio Gonzalez represented by Melissa Turk & The Artist Network; Robert Hynes represented by Mendola Ltd.; Morgan Cain & Associates; JTH Illustration; Laurie O'Keefe; Matthew Pippin represented by Beranbaum Artist's Representative; Precision Graphics; Publisher's Art; Rolin Graphics, Inc.; Wendy Smith represented by Melissa Turk & The Artist Network; Kevin Torline represented by Berendsen and Associates, Inc.; WILDlife ART; Phil Wilson represented by Cliff Knecht Artist Representative; Zoo Botanica.

Photo Credits

Cover Mark Gamba/CORBIS; **ii** Mark Gamba/CORBIS; **vii** Aaron Haupt; **viii** John Evans; **ix** (t)PhotoDisc, (b)John Evans; **x** (l)John Evans, (r)Geoff Butler; **xi** (l)John Evans, (r)PhotoDisc; **xii** PhotoDisc; **xiii** NASA; **xiv** (t)Brenda Tharp/Photo Researchers, (b)Charles Benes/FPG International; **xv** Sovfoto/Eastfoto/PictureQuest; **xvi** PhotoDisc; **xvii** (t)Tom McHugh/Photo Researchers, (b)Duomo; **xviii** (t)Gregory G. Dimijian/Photo Researchers, (b)Douglas Peebles/CORBIS; **xix** Bjorn Backe/Papilio/CORBIS; **xx** (l)Aaron Haupt, (r)Amanita Pictures; **xxi** Amanita Pictures; **xxii** Bobby Model/National Geographic Image Collection; **xxiv** Matt Meadows; **xxvi** Morrison Photography; **1** Glencoe; **2–3** (bkgd)Wolfgang Kaehler; **2** (l)PhotoDisc; **3** (t)PhotoDisc; **4–5** David Keaton/CORBIS; **6** (l)Jack Star/Photolink/PhotoDisc, (c)Rudi Von Briel, (r)Richard T. Nowitz/CORBIS; **8** Mary Kate Denny/PhotoEdit, Inc.; **9** Peter Veit/National Geographic Image Collection; **10** (tl)G. Brad Lewis/Stone/Getty Images, (bl)Roger Ball/The Stock Market/CORBIS, (br)Will & Deni McIntyre/Photo Researchers; **11** (t)AFP/CORBIS, (b)Reuters NewMedia, Inc./CORBIS; **13 14** Richard Hutchings; **15** Matt Meadows; **16** Icon Images; **17** Richard Hutchings/PhotoEdit, Inc./PictureQuest; **18** Rudi Von Briel; **19** Bob Daemmrich; **20** Glasheen Graphics/Index Stock; **21** (cw from top)David Young-Wolff/PhotoEdit, Inc., Donald C. Johnson/The Stock Market/CORBIS, John Bavosi/Science Photo Library/Photo Researchers, A. Ramey/PhotoEdit, Inc.; **22** CORBIS/PictureQuest; **23** Todd Gipstein/CORBIS; **24** (tl cl)Betty Pat Gatliff, (tr)Richard Nowitz/Words & Pictures/PictureQuest, (bl)Michael O'Brian/Mud Island, Inc., (br)Betty Pat Gatliff; **25** (l)Carol Anne Petrachenko/CORBIS, (c)Jim Sugar Photography/CORBIS, (r)Tom Wurl/Stock Boston/PictureQuest; **26** (l)Stock Montage, (r)North Wind Picture Archives; **27** Digital Art/CORBIS; **28** SuperStock; **29** (t)Lester V. Bergman/CORBIS, (b)Bob Handelman/Stone/Getty Images; **31** Amanita Pictures; **32** (t)Aaron Haupt, (b)Matt Meadows; **35** (t)Reuters/CORBIS, (bl)UPI/Bettmann/CORBIS, (br)TIME; **37** Tim Courlas; **38** Peter Veit/National Geographic Image Collection; **39** (l)Tim Courlas/Horizons, (c r)Aaron Haupt; **40–41** Buck Miller/SuperStock; **42** Paul Almasy/CORBIS; **43** AFP/CORBIS;

44 David Young-Wolff/PhotoEdit, Inc.; **45** (tr)The Purcell Team/CORBIS, (l)Lowell D. Franga, (br)Len Delessio/Index Stock; **46** Photo by Richard T. Nowitz, imaging by Janet Dell Russell Johnson; **47** Matt Meadows; **49** Mark Burnett; **51** Tom Prettyman/PhotoEdit, Inc.; **53** (tl)Michael Dalton/Fundamental Photographs, (cl)David Young-Wolff/PhotoEdit, Inc., (cr)Dennis Potokar/Photo Researchers, (br)Matt Meadows; **55** Michael Newman/PhotoEdit, Inc.; **57** John Cancalosi/Stock Boston; **60 61** Richard Hutchings; **62** (t)Fletcher & Baylis/Photo Researchers, (b)Charles O'Rear/CORBIS; **63** Mark Burnett; **64** Chuck Liddy/AP/Wide World Photos; **66** Michael Dalton/Fundamental Photographs; **68–69** (bkgd)Stephen Frisch/Stock Boston/PictureQuest; **68** (inset)CORBIS/PictureQuest; **70–71** Russell Dohrman/Index Stock; **71** Morrison Photography; **72** (l)Gary C. Will/Visuals Unlimited, (c)Mark Burnett/Stock Boston, (r)CORBIS; **74** Mark Burnett; **75** (l)Mark Burnett, (r)NASA; **76** Van Bucher/Photo Researchers; **80** Fermi National Accelerator Laboratory/Science Photo Library/Photo Researchers; **81** Tom Stewart/The Stock Market/CORBIS; **82** (br)New York Public Library, General Research Division, Astor, Lenox, and Tilden Foundations, (others)Bettmann/CORBIS; **84** Emmanuel Scorcelletti/Liaison Agency/Getty Images; **86** Doug Martin; **87** NASA; **88** Mark Burnett; **89** Klaus Guldbrandsen/Science Photo Library/Photo Researchers; **90** (tl)Mark Thayer, (tr)CORBIS, (bl)Kenneth Mengay/Liaison Agency/Getty Images, (bc)Arthur Hill/Visuals Unlimited, (br)RMIP/Richard Haynes; **90–91** (bkgd)KS Studios; **91** (inset)Mark Burnett; **92** (t)Mark Burnett, (b)Michael Newman/PhotoEdit, Inc.; **94** (tl)Robert Essel/The Stock Market/CORBIS, (tr)John Eastcott & Yva Momatiuk/DRK Photo, (cl)Ame Hodalic/CORBIS, (cr)Diaphor Agency/Index Stock, (br)TIME; **100–101** Roger Ressmeyer/CORBIS; **102** Layne Kennedy/CORBIS; **103** (t)Telegraph Colour Library/FPG/Getty Images, (b)Paul Silverman/Fundamental Photographs; **104** Bill Aron/PhotoEdit, Inc.; **105** (l)John Serrao/Photo Researchers, (r)H. Richard Johnston; **106** Tom Tracy/Photo Network/PictureQuest; **107** Annie Griffiths Belt/CORBIS; **108** Amanita Pictures; **109** (t)David Weintraub/Stock Boston, (b)James L. Amos/Peter Arnold, Inc.; **110** Dave King/DK Images; **111** Joseph Sohm/ChromoSohm, Inc./CORBIS; **112** Michael Dalton/Fundamental Photographs; **113** Swarthout & Associates/The Stock Market/CORBIS; **114** Tony Freeman/PhotoEdit, Inc.; **116** David Young-Wolff/PhotoEdit, Inc.; **117** (b)Richard Hutchings, (t)Joshua Ets-Hokin/PhotoDisc; **118** Robbie Jack/CORBIS; **120** A. Ramey/Stock Boston; **121** Mark Burnett; **122** (t)Tony Freeman/PhotoEdit, Inc., (b)Stephen Simpson/FPG/Getty Images; **124** (t)Lester Lefkowitz/The Stock Market/CORBIS, (b)Bob Daemmrich; **125** Bob Daemmrich; **126** Daniel Belknap; **127** (l)Andrew Ward/Life File/PhotoDisc, (r)NASA/TRACE; **129** Mark Burnett; **131** Joshua Ets-Hokin/PhotoDisc; **132–133** Daryl Benson/Masterfile; **134** Steven R. Krous/Stock Boston/PictureQuest; **135** Ryan McVay/PhotoDisc; **136** David W. Hamilton/Image Bank/Getty Images; **137** (t)Morrison Photography, (b)Jose Azel/Aurora/PictureQuest; **138** Morrison Photography; **139** (l)Aaron Haupt, (r)Arthur S. Aubry/PhotoDisc; **140** (tl bl)Morrison Photography, (br)Bob Daemmrich/Stock Boston; **141** Morrison Photography; **142** Aaron Haupt; **143** AFP/CORBIS; **144** (tl)Morrison Photography, (tr)Art Montes de Oca/FPG/Getty Images, (bl)Anthony Ise/PhotoDisc, (br)Novastock/Index Stock; **145** (l)John Maher/Stock Boston/PictureQuest, (c)Matt Meadows, (r)AP/Wide World Photos/Jim McKnight; **146** Morrison Photography;

147 (t)Charles Benes/FPG/Getty Images, (b)Brenda Tharp/ Photo Researchers; **148** Gerry Ellis/GLOBIO.org; **149 150 151** Morrison Photography; **152** (t)Morton Beebe, SF/CORBIS, (b)Will & Deni McIntyre/Photo Researchers; **153** (l)file photo, (r)courtesy Diamond International; **154** (tr)Michael Nelson/FPG/Getty Images, (others)Morrison Photography; **155** Amanita Pictures; **156** Rubberball Productions; **157** (l)Zefa Visual Media-Germany/Index Stock, (r)Bruce James/Getty Images; **158–159** (bkgd)PhotoDisc; **159** (inset)Stephen Frisch/Stock Boston/PictureQuest; **160–161** Christian Michel; **169** Laura Sifferlin; **170** (l)Lester V. Bergman/CORBIS, (r)Doug Martin; **175** Matt Meadows; **176** (tr cr)Kenneth Libbrecht/Caltech, (cl)Albert J. Copley/ Visuals Unlimited, (bl)E.R. Degginger/Color-Pic; **178** James L. Amos/Photo Researchers; **179 180 181** Aaron Haupt; **182** Fulcrum Publishing; **187** Matt Meadows; **188–189** Simon Fraser/Science Photo Library/Photo Researchers; **190** (l)Aaron Haupt, (r)Doug Martin; **191** (tl)Patricia Lanza, (tc)Jeff J. Daly/Visuals Unlimited, (tr)Susan T. McElhinney, (bl)Craig Fuji/Seattle Times, (br)Sovfoto/Eastfoto/ PictureQuest; **192** Amanita Pictures; **195** Sovfoto/Eastfoto/ PictureQuest; **197** Christopher Swann/Peter Arnold, Inc.; **198** (tl)Frank Balthis, (tr)Lois Ellen Frank/CORBIS, (b)Matt Meadows; **199** David Young-Wolff/PhotoEdit/PictureQuest; **200** (l)Amanita Pictures, (r)Richard Megna/Fundamental Photographs/Photo Researchers; **201** Victoria Arocho/AP/ Wide World Photos; **202** (t)Aaron Haupt, (bl)Kevin Schafer/ CORBIS, (br)Icon Images; **203** SuperStock; **204** (tl)Chris Arend/Alaska Stock Images/PictureQuest, (tr)Aaron Haupt, (b)Bryan F. Peterson/CORBIS; **205** courtesy General Motors; **206 207** Matt Meadows; **208** Amanita Pictures; **209** Bob Daemmrich; **210** (l)Tino Hammid Photography, (r)Joe Richard/UF News & Public Affairs; **211** David Young-Wolff/ PhotoEdit, Inc.; **214** Lester V. Bergman/CORBIS; **215** Peter Walton/Index Stock; **216–217** Joseph Sohm/ChromoSohm, Inc./CORBIS; **219** (l)Stephen W. Frisch/Stock Boston, (r)Doug Martin; **220** (t)HIRB/Index Stock, (b)Doug Martin; **221** Richard Hamilton/CORBIS; **222** John Evans; **223** (l)SuperStock, (r)Annie Griffiths/CORBIS; **226** John Evans; **228** Richard Nowitz/Phototake/PictureQuest; **230** Aaron Haupt; **231** KS Studios/Mullenix; **233** John Evans; **234** (l)Joe Sohm, Chromosohm/Stock Connection/ PictureQuest, (c)Andrew Popper/Phototake/PictureQuest, (r)A. Wolf/Explorer, Photo Researchers; **235** John Evans; **236** (tl tr)Elaine Shay, (tcl)Brent Turner/BLT Productions, (tcr)Matt Meadows, (bcr)Icon Images, (bl bcl)CORBIS, (br)StudiOhio; **240 241** KS Studios; **242** CORBIS; **244** Royalty-Free/CORBIS; **247** Stephen W. Frisch/Stock Boston; **248–249** Ariel Skelley/Masterfile; **250** (l)Michael Newman/PhotoEdit, Inc., (r)Richard Price/FPG/Getty Images; **252** (l)Tony Freeman/PhotoEdit, Inc., (r)Mark Burnett; **253** (l c)Mark Burnett, (r)Will & Deni McIntyre/ Photo Researchers; **254** Ted Horowitz/The Stock Market/ CORBIS; **257** (l)Gary A. Conner/PhotoEdit/PictureQuest, (r)Stephen Frisch/Stock Boston/PictureQuest; **259** (t)Kim Taylor/Bruce Coleman, Inc./PictureQuest, (b)John Sims/Tony Stone Images/Getty Images; **264** (t)Elaine Shay, (b)Mitch Hrdlicka/PhotoDisc; **265** (t)KS Studios, (b) Matt Meadows; **266 267** KS Studios; **268** (l)Don Farrall/PhotoDisc, (r)KS Studios; **269** Alfred Pasieka/Peter Arnold, Inc.; **270** (t)Geoff Butler, (b)Aaron Haupt; **271** Aaron Haupt; **272** (t)Waina Cheng/Bruce Coleman, Inc., (c)David Nunuk/Science Photo Library/Photo Researchers, (b)Lee Baltermoal/FPG/Getty Images; **273** Aaron Haupt; **277** Richard Hutchings; **278–279** (bkgd)Museum of the City of New York/CORBIS;

279 (l)Lee Snider/CORBIS, (r)Scott Camazine/Photo Researchers; **280–281** Brian Snyder/Reuters Newmedia Inc/Corbis; **282** Telegraph Colour Library/FPG/Getty Images; **283** Geoff Butler; **286** Richard Hutchings; **289** Runk/ Schoenberger from Grant Heilman; **291** Mark Doolittle/ Outside Images/Picturequest; **293** (l)Ed Bock/The Stock Market/CORBIS, (r)Will Hart/PhotoEdit, Inc.; **295** (t)Tom & DeeAnn McCarthy/The Stock Market/CORBIS, (bl)Jodi Jacobson/Peter Arnold, Inc., (br)Jules Frazier/PhotoDisc; **296** Mark Burnett; **298** Robert Brenner/PhotoEdit, Inc.; **299** Laura Sifferlin; **300 301** Icon Images; **302** Alexis Duclos/ Liaison/Getty Images; **303** (l r)Rudi Von Briel/PhotoEdit, Inc., (c)PhotoDisc; **307** (l)Jodi Jacobson/Peter Arnold, Inc., (r)Runk/Schoenberger from Grant Heilman; **308–309** Wendell Metzen/Index Stock; **309** Richard Hutchings; **310** (l)Globus Brothers Studios, NYC, (r)Stock Boston; **311** Bob Daemmrich; **312** (t)Beth Wald/ImageState, (b)David Madison; **313** Rhoda Sidney/Stock Boston/ PictureQuest; **315** (l)Myrleen Cate/PhotoEdit, Inc., (r)David Young-Wolff/PhotoEdit, Inc.; **316** Bob Daemmrich; **318** (t)Stone/Getty Images, (b)Myrleen Cate/PhotoEdit, Inc.; **320** David Madison; **322** Richard Megna/Fundamental Photographs; **323** Mary M. Steinbacher/PhotoEdit, Inc.; **324** (t)Betty Sederquist/Visuals Unlimited, (b)Jim Cummins/ FPG/Getty Images; **325** (tl)Denis Boulanger/Allsport, (tr)Donald Miralle/Allsport, (b)Tony Freeman/PhotoEdit/ PictureQuest; **326** (t)David Madison, (b)NASA; **328** NASA; **329** Richard Hutchings; **330 331** Mark Burnett; **332** (t)Tom Wright/CORBIS, (b)Didier Charre/Image Bank; **333** (tl)Philip Bailey/The Stock Market/CORBIS, (tr)Romilly Lockyer/Image Bank/Getty Images, (bl)Tony Freeman/ PhotoEdit, Inc.; **337** Betty Sederquist/Visuals Unlimited; **338–339** Hughes Martin/CORBIS; **339** Matt Meadows; **340** David Young-Wolff/PhotoEdit, Inc.; **342** Runk/ Schoenberger from Grant Heilman; **343** Dominic Oldershaw; **344** (t)Matt Meadows, (b)Tom Pantages; **346** (t)Bobby Model/National Geographic Image Collection, (cl)Richard Nowitz/National Geographic Image Collection, (cr)George Grall/National Geographic Image Collection, (bl)Ralph White/CORBIS, (br)CORBIS; **348** Ryan McVay/PhotoDisc; **349** CORBIS; **350** (t)Matt Meadows, (b)Vince Streano/Stone/ Getty Images; **351 353** Matt Meadows; **355** John Evans; **357** KS Studios; **358** Dominic Oldershaw; **361** (t)Michael Collier/Stock Boston, (bl)George Hall/CORBIS, (br)Dean Conger/CORBIS; **362** Steve McCutcheon/Visuals Unlimited; **363** Runk/Schoenberger from Grant Heilman; **364** AP/Wide World Photos/Ray Fairall; **365** (l)D.R. & T.L. Schrichte/Stone/ Getty Images, (r)CORBIS; **366** Matt Meadows; **369** Vince Streano/Stone/Getty Images; **370–371** (bkgd)Douglas Peebles/CORBIS; **371** (inset)Henry Ford Museum & Greenfield Village; **372–373** Chris Knapton/Science Photo Library/Photo Researchers; **373** Matt Meadows; **374** (l c)file photo, (r)Mark Burnett; **375** (t b)Bob Daemmrich, (c)Al Tielemans/Duomo; **376** KS Studios; **377** (l r)Bob Daemmrich, (b)Andrew McClenaghan/Science Photo Library/Photo Researchers; **378** Mark Burnett/Photo Researchers; **379** Lori Adamski Peek/Stone/Getty Images; **380** Richard Hutchings; **381** Ron Kimball/Ron Kimball Photography; **382** (t)Judy Lutz, (b)Lennart Nilsson; **384 386** KS Studios; **392** (t)Dr. Jeremy Burgess/Science Photo Library/Photo Researchers, (b)John Keating/Photo Researchers; **393** Geothermal Education Office; **394** Carsand-Mosher; **395** Billy Hustace/Stone/Getty Images; **396** SuperStock; **397** Roger Ressmeyer/CORBIS; **398** (tl)Reuters NewMedia, Inc./CORBIS, (tr)PhotoDisc,

(br)Dominic Oldershaw; **399** (l)Lowell Georgia/CORBIS, (r)Mark Richards/PhotoEdit, Inc.; **404–405** Rich Iwasaki/ Getty Images; **405** Mark Burnett; **406** Mary Kate Denny/ PhotoEdit, Inc.; **407** (t)Richard Hutchings, (b)Tony Freeman/ PhotoEdit, Inc.; **414** (l)David Young-Wolff/PhotoEdit, Inc., (r)Frank Siteman/Stock Boston; **417** Duomo; **418** Robert Brenner/PhotoEdit, Inc.; **419** (t)Tom McHugh/Photo Researchers, (b)Amanita Pictures; **420** Amanita Pictures; **421** (t)Dorling Kindersley, (bl br)Bob Daemmrich; **422** (l)Wernher Krutein/Liaison Agency/Getty Images, (r)Siegfried Layda/Stone/Getty Images; **424** Tony Freeman/ PhotoEdit, Inc.; **425** Aaron Haupt; **426** (t)Ed Kashi/CORBIS, (b)James Balog; **427** (l)Inc. Janeart/The Image Bank/Getty Images, (r)Ryan McVay/PhotoDisc; **431** (l)Comstock Images, (r)PhotoDisc; **432–433** Peter Walton/Index Stock; **434** John Evans; **435** (t)Nancy P. Alexander/Visuals Unlimited, (b)Morton & White; **437** Tom Stack & Assoc.; **438** Doug Martin; **439** Matt Meadows; **440** Jeremy Hoare/PhotoDisc; **441** Donnie Kamin/PhotoEdit, Inc.; **442** SuperStock; **443** Colin Raw/Stone/Getty Images; **444** Aaron Haupt; **445** PhotoDisc; **446** (l)Barbara Stitzer/PhotoEdit, Inc., (c)Doug Menuez/PhotoDisc, (r)Addison Geary/Stock Boston; **448** C. Squared Studios/PhotoDisc; **450 451** Morton & White; **452** (bkgd)Chip Simons/FPG/Getty Images, (inset) Joseph Sohm/CORBIS; **453** SuperStock; **456** John Evans; **457** Michael Newman/Photo Edit, Inc.; **458–459** (bkgd) Matthew Borkoski/Stock Boston/PictureQuest; **459** (inset)L. Fritz/H. Armstrong Roberts; **460–461** Douglas Peebles/ CORBIS; **462** (l)file photo, (r)David Young-Wolff/PhotoEdit, Inc.; **463** David Young-Wolff/PhotoEdit, Inc.; **464** Mark Thayer; **467** Steven Starr/Stock Boston; **472** Ken Frick; **473** Mark Burnett; **475** Ernst Haas/Stone/Getty Images; **476** Peter Beattie/Liaison Agency/Getty Images; **478** D. Boone/CORBIS; **479** Seth Resnick/Stock Boston; **480–481** John Evans; **482** (t)Roger Ressmeyer/CORBIS, (b)SuperStock; **486** Mark Burnett; **488–489** Tom Wagner/ CORBIS SABA; **493** (t)Joe Towers/The Stock Market/ CORBIS, (c)Bob Daemmrich/Stock Boston/PictureQuest, (b)Jean-Paul Thomas/Jacana Scientific Control/Photo Researchers; **496** NOAA; **499** Spencer Grant/PhotoEdit, Inc.; **500** Timothy Fuller; **504** Dilip Mehta/Contact Press Images/ PictureQuest; **505** (tl)CORBIS, (tr)Paul Seheult/Eye Ubiquitous/CORBIS, (b)Icon Images; **506** (t)William Whitehurst/The Stock Market/CORBIS, (b)G. Salter/Lebrecht Music Collection; **507** SuperStock; **508** (t)Geostock/ PhotoDisc, (b)SuperStock; **509** Fred E. Hossler/Visuals Unlimited; **510** (t)Will McIntyre/Photo Researchers, (b)Oliver Benn/Stone/Getty Images; **512** Douglas Whyte/The Stock Market/CORBIS; **513** (l)The Photo Works/Photo Researchers, (r)PhotoDisc; **515** C. Squared Studios/ PhotoDisc; **518–519** Maxine Hall/CORBIS; **520** (l)Bob Abraham/The Stock Market/CORBIS, (r)Jeff Greenberg/ Visuals Unlimited; **521** (l)David Young-Wolff/PhotoEdit, Inc., (r)NRSC, Ltd./Science Photo Library/Photo Researchers; **522** (t)Grantpix/Photo Researchers, (b)Richard Megna/ Fundamental Photographs; **524** Luke Dodd/Science Photo Library/Photo Researchers; **526** (t)Matt Meadows, (b)Jean Miele/The Stock Market/CORBIS; **528** (t)Gregory G. Dimijian/Photo Researchers, (b)Charlie Westerman/Liaison/ Getty Images; **529** Aaron Haupt; **531** (l)Matt Meadows, (r)Bob Daemmrich/The Image Works; **532** (tr)Phil Degginger/Color-Pic, (l)Phil Degginger/NASA/Color-Pic, (cr)Max Planck Institute for Radio Astronomy/Science Photo Library/Photo Researchers, (br)European Space Agency/ Science Photo Library/Photo Researchers;

533 (l)Harvard-Smithsonian Center for Astrophysics, (c)NASA/Science Photo Library/Photo Researchers, (r)European Space Agency; **534** Timothy Fuller; **539** Ken M. Johns/Photo Researchers; **540** (t)Michael Thomas/Stock South/PictureQuest, (b)Dominic Oldershaw; **541** Michael Thomas/Stock South/PictureQuest; **542** (bkgd)TIME, (t)Culver Pictures, (b)Hulton Archive/Getty Images; **543** (l)Macduff Everton/CORBIS, (r)NASA/Mark Marten/Photo Researchers; **547** Eric Kamp/Index Stock; **548–549** Chad Ehlers/Index Stock; **550** Dick Thomas/Visuals Unlimited; **551** John Evans; **552** (tl)Bob Woodward/The Stock Market/CORBIS, (tc)Ping Amranand/Pictor, (tr)SuperStock, (b)Runk/Schoenberger from Grant Heilman; **553** Mark Thayer; **556** (l)Susumu Nishinaga/Science Photo Library/Photo Researchers, (r)Matt Meadows; **558** (l)Matt Meadows, (r)Paul Silverman/Fundamental Photographs; **559** (l)Digital Stock, (r)Joseph Palmieri/Pictor; **561** Geoff Butler; **563** Richard Megna/Fundamental Photographs; **567** David Young-Wolff/PhotoEdit, Inc.; **568 569** Roger Ressmeyer/CORBIS; **572 573** Geoff Butler; **574** The Stapleton Collection/Bridgeman Art Library; **580–581** (bkgd)Richard Pasley/Stock Boston/PictureQuest; **580** (inset)Layne Kennedy/CORBIS; **581** (inset)Mark Burnett; **582–583** V.C.L./Getty Images; **585** (t)Richard Hutchings, (b)KS Studios; **588** Royalty Free/CORBIS; **590** J. Tinning/Photo Researchers; **593** Gary Rhijnsburger/ Masterfile; **598** Doug Martin; **599** (t)Doug Martin, (b)Geoff Butler; **601** Bonnie Freer/Photo Researchers; **603** Matt Meadows; **604 605** Richard Hutchings; **606** (bkgd)Tom & Pat Leeson/Photo Researchers, (inset)William Munoz/Photo Researchers; **610** J. Tinning/Photo Researchers; **611** Doug Martin; **612–613** James Leynse/CORBIS; **615** Richard Megna/Fundamental Photographs; **616** Amanita Pictures; **619** John Evans; **620** Amanita Pictures; **621** (l)Kodansha, (c)Manfred Kage/Peter Arnold, Inc., (r)Doug Martin; **625** Bjorn Backe/Papilio/CORBIS; **627** Norbert Schafer/The Stock Market/CORBIS; **629** AT&T Bell Labs/Science Photo Library/Photo Researchers; **630** (t)Science Photo Library/ Photo Researchers, (c)Fermilab/Science Photo Library/Photo Researchers, (b)SuperStock; **631** PhotoDisc; **632** (t)file photo, (b)Aaron Haupt; **633** Aaron Haupt; **634** John MacDonald; **635** (l)SIU/Peter Arnold, Inc., (r)Latent Image; **639** John Evans; **640–641** Andrew Syred/Science Photo Library/Photo Researchers; **642** Willie L. Hill, Jr./Stock Boston; **643** (l)Icon Images, (r)Doug Martin; **645** (l r)CMCD/PhotoDisc, (c)Russ Lappa; **646** Amanita Pictures; **647** (t)Amanita Pictures, (b)Charles Falco/Photo Researchers; **648** Charles Falco/Photo Researchers; **649** (l)Bettmann/CORBIS, (r)Icon Images; **652** (t)courtesy IBM/Florida State University, (b)Andrew Syred/Science Photo Library/Photo Researchers; **655** file photo; **656** Thomas Brummett/PhotoDisc; **658** (l)Dr. Dennis Kunkel/PhotoTake, NYC, (r)Aaron Haupt; **659** Timothy Fuller; **660** David Young-Wolff/PhotoEdit, Inc.; **661** Frank Cezus; **662** Tek Images/Science Photo Library/Photo Researchers; **663** (tr)Amanita Pictures, (l)Aaron Haupt, (br)Keith Brofsky/PhotoDisc; **667** Thomas Brummett/ PhotoDisc; **668** PhotoDisc; **670** Tom Pantages; **674** Michelle D. Bridwell/PhotoEdit, Inc.; **675** (t)Mark Burnett, (b)Dominic Oldershaw; **676** StudiOhio; **677** Timothy Fuller; **678** Aaron Haupt; **680** KS Studios; **681** Matt Meadows; **683** (t)Dominic Oldershaw, (b)Mark Burnett; **684** John Evans; **685** (t)Amanita Pictures, (b)John Evans; **686** Mark Burnett; **688** John Evans; **690** Mark Burnett; **691** Amanita Pictures; **692** Icon Images; **693** Amanita Pictures; **694** Bob Daemmrich; **696** Davis Barber/PhotoEdit, Inc.

PERIODIC TABLE OF THE ELEMENTS

Columns of elements are called groups. Elements in the same group have similar chemical properties.

Gas

Liquid

Solid

Synthetic

Element — Hydrogen
Atomic number — 1
Symbol — H
Atomic mass — 1.008

State of matter

The first three symbols tell you the state of matter of the element at room temperature. The fourth symbol identifies elements that are not present in significant amounts on Earth. Useful amounts are made synthetically.

1								
1 Hydrogen 1 **H** 1.008	**2**							
2 Lithium 3 **Li** 6.941	Beryllium 4 **Be** 9.012							
3 Sodium 11 **Na** 22.990	Magnesium 12 **Mg** 24.305	**3**	**4**	**5**	**6**	**7**	**8**	**9**
4 Potassium 19 **K** 39.098	Calcium 20 **Ca** 40.078	Scandium 21 **Sc** 44.956	Titanium 22 **Ti** 47.867	Vanadium 23 **V** 50.942	Chromium 24 **Cr** 51.996	Manganese 25 **Mn** 54.938	Iron 26 **Fe** 55.845	Cobalt 27 **Co** 58.933
5 Rubidium 37 **Rb** 85.468	Strontium 38 **Sr** 87.62	Yttrium 39 **Y** 88.906	Zirconium 40 **Zr** 91.224	Niobium 41 **Nb** 92.906	Molybdenum 42 **Mo** 95.94	Technetium 43 **Tc** (98)	Ruthenium 44 **Ru** 101.07	Rhodium 45 **Rh** 102.906
6 Cesium 55 **Cs** 132.905	Barium 56 **Ba** 137.327	Lanthanum 57 **La** 138.906	Hafnium 72 **Hf** 178.49	Tantalum 73 **Ta** 180.948	Tungsten 74 **W** 183.84	Rhenium 75 **Re** 186.207	Osmium 76 **Os** 190.23	Iridium 77 **Ir** 192.217
7 Francium 87 **Fr** (223)	Radium 88 **Ra** (226)	Actinium 89 **Ac** (227)	Rutherfordium 104 **Rf** (261)	Dubnium 105 **Db** (262)	Seaborgium 106 **Sg** (266)	Bohrium 107 **Bh** (264)	Hassium 108 **Hs** (277)	Meitnerium 109 **Mt** (268)

The number in parentheses is the mass number of the longest-lived isotope for that element.

Rows of elements are called periods. Atomic number increases across a period.

The arrow shows where these elements would fit into the periodic table. They are moved to the bottom of the table to save space.

Lanthanide series	Cerium 58 **Ce** 140.116	Praseodymium 59 **Pr** 140.908	Neodymium 60 **Nd** 144.24	Promethium 61 **Pm** (145)	Samarium 62 **Sm** 150.36
Actinide series	Thorium 90 **Th** 232.038	Protactinium 91 **Pa** 231.036	Uranium 92 **U** 238.029	Neptunium 93 **Np** (237)	Plutonium 94 **Pu** (244)